ISBN 978-1-330-87266-6
PIBN 10055340

1 MONTH OF
FREE
READING

at

www.ForgottenBooks.com

By purchasing this book you are eligible for one month membership to ForgottenBooks.com, giving you unlimited access to our entire collection of over 700,000 titles via our web site and mobile apps.

To claim your free month visit:

www.forgottenbooks.com/free55340

English
Français
Deutsche
Italiano
Español
Português

www.forgottenbooks.com

Mythology Photography **Fiction**
Fishing Christianity **Art** Cooking
Essays Buddhism Freemasonry
Medicine **Biology** Music **Ancient
Egypt** Evolution Carpentry Physics
Dance Geology **Mathematics** Fitness
Shakespeare **Folklore** Yoga Marketing
Confidence Immortality Biographies
Poetry **Psychology** Witchcraft
Electronics Chemistry History **Law**
Accounting **Philosophy** Anthropology
Alchemy Drama Quantum Mechanics
Atheism Sexual Health **Ancient History**
Entrepreneurship Languages Sport
Paleontology Needlework Islam
Metaphysics Investment Archaeology
Parenting Statistics Criminology
Motivational

HEORETICAL CHEMISTR

FROM THE STANDPOINT OF

AVOGADRO'S RULE & THERMODYNAMICS

BY

PROF. WALTER NERNST, PH.D.
OF THE UNIVERSITY OF BERLIN

REVISED IN ACCORDANCE WITH THE
SIXTH GERMAN EDITION
BY

H. T. TIZARD
MAGDALEN COLLEGE, OXFORD

MACMILLAN AND CO., LIMITED
ST. MARTIN'S STREET, LONDON
1911

First English Edition published in 1895.
Second Edition, 1904.
Third Edition, 1911.

TRANSLATOR'S PREFACE

THE present (third) English edition of Professor·Nernst's great work corresponds to the sixth German edition. It contains a detailed account of the author's new theorem in thermodynamics, a chapter on radioactivity, and a large amount of other new matter.

In preparing the new edition, I have revised and partly rewritten the old translation, incorporated the new matter, and made a few additions to the text here and there, at the suggestion of Professor Nernst, in order to bring the book up to as late a date as possible. These additions include an account of Nernst's recent work on specific heats at low temperatures; Perrin's researches on the Brownian movement; and a few of the latest applications of Nernst's new theorem.

H. T. TIZARD.

PREFACE TO THE FIRST GERMAN EDITION

THE following presentation of Theoretical Chemistry is a development of an "introduction" which I wrote two years ago for the *Handbuch der anorganischen Chemie*, edited by Dr. O. Dammer (vol. i. pp. 1-358). In keeping with the broader requirements of an independent text-book—not merely an introduction to a special work—it has been considerably rearranged and extended. The necessity for this was further made clear on consideration of the latest investigations, which, without causing any material change in the more recent theories, have nevertheless developed them to a surprising extent.

I believe that at present there has come a period of quiet but fruitful toil for the investigator of physical chemistry. The ideas are not only at hand, but they have attained a certain maturity. New theories of value are always fruitful, in that they are followed by a period of enthusiastic activity; thus at present we see the powers of investigation of many civilised nations occupied with rare unanimity in the hearty and successful development of the general system of theoretical chemistry.

At such times there is especial need of a statement of the guiding ideas, which shall give instruction to the student and advice to the investigator. As is well known, this need was completely satisfied in every respect by Ostwald's two excellent treatises, the short *Outlines* and the larger *Manual of General Chemistry* (*Lehrbuch der allgemeinen Chemie*), the latter of which has passed to a new edition.

Therefore I entertained serious doubts as to the advisability of a new work on the same subject from essentially the same point of view. But the saying that "When many come, much comes" seemed applicable, and my scruples were finally completely removed by the direct encouragement of Professor Ostwald in the preparation of this separate edition of the introduction to Dammer's *Handbuch*; and I was supported in this undertaking both by the editor, Dr. O. Dammer, and by the publisher, Mr. F. Enke, of that work.

In a treatise on theoretical chemistry, widely different chapters of physics and chemistry must, of course, find their place ; it must contain, in fact, all that the physicist must know of chemistry, and all that the chemist must know of physics, unless both are content to be specialists in their own science. The development of physical chemistry as a special branch of natural science means, therefore,—and I would lay particular emphasis on this—not so much the shaping of a new science, as the uniting of two sciences hitherto somewhat independent of each other. In the selection of the material with which physical and chemical investigation has provided us, I have been guided less by the aim to make this as complete as possible—a task to which I did not feel equal—as by the wish to describe in detail, only those experimental data which either possess universal importance, or show promise of attaining it ; only those hypotheses which have already proved themselves helpful ; and finally only those applications capable of being used systematically, whether their nature is that of calculation or of experiment. The latter aim necessitates the description and illustration of several important pieces of apparatus for the laboratory. I have attached great importance to the incidental description of some simple lecture experiments, which I have tested for several years in my capacity as teacher of physical chemistry. As I have sought to represent the science as it is at present, not the process of its evolution, —to give it in fact a form unobscured by the accidents of historical development—the historical element has necessarily been suppressed, and recent literature more particularly considered. I trust that this method of treatment will not be taken as implying any lack of respect for those remarkable men, who, by their work, laid the foundations upon which we build to-day.

In carrying out this plan, it continually became clearer to me that the theoretical treatment of chemical processes—the most important part of my task—depended firstly on the Rule of Avogadro, which seems to me an almost inexhaustible "horn of plenty" for the molecular theory ; and secondly on the Laws of Energy, which govern all natural processes. I considered that this view should be emphasised in the title of my book. . . .

W. N.

GÖTTINGEN, *April* 1893.

CONTENTS

INTRODUCTION TO SOME FUNDAMENTAL PRINCIPLES OF MODERN INVESTIGATION

BOOK I

THE UNIVERSAL PROPERTIES OF MATTER

CHAPTER I

THE GASEOUS STATE OF AGGREGATION

BOOK II

ATOM AND MOLECULE

CHAPTER I

ATOMIC THEORY

CHAPTER II

THE KINETIC THEORY OF THE MOLECULE

CHAPTER III

THE DETERMINATION OF THE MOLECULAR WEIGHT

CHAPTER IV

THE CONSTITUTION OF THE MOLECULE

CHAPTER V

PHYSICAL PROPERTIES AND MOLECULAR STRUCTURE

CHAPTER XI

RADIOACTIVITY

CHAPTER XII

COLLOIDAL SOLUTIONS

CHAPTER XIII

THE ABSOLUTE SIZE OF MOLECULES

BOOK III

THE TRANSFORMATION OF MATTER
(THE DOCTRINE OF AFFINITY, I)

CHAPTER I

THE LAW OF CHEMICAL MASS-ACTION

CHAPTER II

CHEMICAL STATICS—HOMOGENEOUS SYSTEMS

CHAPTER III

CHEMICAL STATICS—HETEROGENEOUS SYSTEMS

CHAPTER IV

CHEMICAL EQUILIBRIUM IN SALT SOLUTIONS

CHAPTER V

CHEMICAL KINETICS

BOOK IV

THE TRANSFORMATIONS OF ENERGY
(THE DOCTRINE OF AFFINITY, II)

CHAPTER I

THERMO-CHEMISTRY I

THE APPLICATIONS OF THE FIRST LAW OF HEAT

CHAPTER II

THERMO-CHEMISTRY II

TEMPERATURE AND COMPLETE CHEMICAL EQUILIBRIUM

CHAPTER III

THERMO-CHEMISTRY III

TEMPERATURE AND INCOMPLETE EQUILIBRIUM

CHAPTER IV

THERMO-CHEMISTRY IV

TEMPERATURE AND THE REACTION VELOCITY

CHAPTER V

THERMO-CHEMISTRY V

HEAT AND CHEMICAL ENERGY

CHAPTER VI

ELECTRO-CHEMISTRY I

GENERAL FACTS

CHAPTER VII

ELECTRO-CHEMISTRY II

THERMODYNAMIC THEORY

CHAPTER VIII

ELECTRO-CHEMISTRY III

OSMOTIC THEORY

CHAPTER IX

PHOTO-CHEMISTRY

INTRODUCTION

TO SOME FUNDAMENTAL PRINCIPLES OF MODERN INVESTIGATION

Empirical Facts and their Hypothetical Generalisation.—As the most common and immediate aim of physics and chemistry, we may propose to answer as thoroughly and as simply as possible, and for as many cases as possible, this question, viz. in a given system of limited dimensions, what events will take place, and what will be the condition of this system after the lapse of a definite time? For the solution of this problem it appears necessary, first of all, to realise and to trace out the history of that system whose future we would follow. With what success this problem is to be attacked depends upon the skill and the resources of the observer, and results will grow with the art of experimentation.

But the infinite variety of interesting systems occurring in nature on the one hand, and on the other the unlimited pains which human endeavour must take in a thorough investigation of any one changing system, would effectually deter the discouraged investigator from a systematic examination of natural phenomena, had he not another resource besides the direct impression of his senses. This resource is the theoretical value of conclusions drawn from different systems, and consists simply and solely in transferring to a second system, by means of analogy, observations already obtained from any given system. If we have studied the case of the falling of a heavy body at one point of the earth's surface, then it is at once possible to transfer some of the observed phenomena to other systems; for example, to the falling of a heavy body at other points of the earth's surface. The successful scrutiny of the student of nature reveals itself in finding out that which phenomena, apparently very diverse, have in common, and the results are the more brilliant as the parallelised phenomena appear at the outset more diverse.

B

The transference of observations from one case to another is naturally at first attended with uncertainty, but when it is repeatedly confirmed by experience, takes place with ever-increasing certainty, until it finally attains the position of an empirical law of nature. The discovery of such a law—as, for example, that which permits the calculation of the specific heat of solid compounds, from certain numerical coefficients of the elements, viz. the so-called atomic-heats—invariably indicates great and undoubted progress, as it embodies many empirical facts and allows the anticipation of many new ones previously unknown.

The history of the exact sciences teaches us that we may discover new laws of nature in two essentially different ways, one of which may be designated as the empirical, the other as the theoretical. In the first way we endeavour, by means of suitable observations, to collect abundant material, capable where possible of mathematical expression, concerning the occurrences between which we suspect a connection, and then to approach our end by combining (again purely empirically) the results so obtained ; in this way, for example, were found certain relations between the properties of the elements and their atomic weights. The second way, on the other hand, leads from a thorough conception of the nature of certain phenomena by means of pure speculative thought, to new knowledge, the correctness of which must then be tested by experiment ; thus, by kinetic considerations of the combination and dissociation of substances reacting on each other, the law of chemical mass action was discovered.

The first of these two methods, the empirical, can be proposed in all cases, and will invariably lead to definite results, after work which is indeed usually very tedious. The value of a law of nature so won will be mainly determined by its applicability, and our admiration for it will be the greater, the more numerous and varied are the phenomena concerning which it affords information. For these reasons the most brilliant example of an empirically derived law of nature is undoubtedly afforded by the doctrines of thermodynamics, which are applicable to every process occurring in nature, and therefore demand attention in the scientific investigation of each single natural phenomenon. On the other hand, to be sure, the comprehension of such a far-reaching law of nature will be the more difficult, and its treatment will require more practice, the more universal it is, and in the given cases the difficulties of a correct and complete application to a particular phenomenon are often so great that the successful transference of the general principles to a special case denotes an undoubted scientific advance, although the result so obtained, considered as an application of a more general law, offers really nothing new.

Although this purely inductive method has always had and will always have great significance for the advancement of the natural sciences, yet we undoubtedly penetrate more deeply into the nature of the phenomena under consideration when by means of the second way, *i.e.* on the ground of conclusions exhaustively arrived at and their subsequent theoretical extension, we arrive at a new law of nature; therefore this way must always be the more enticing. Obviously it is only by a proper choice of those conceptions which serve as a basis for our theoretical considerations that we can use this method successfully. But now the nature of the case often prevents us from submitting the truth of these fundamental conceptions to the direct test of experiment, so that the investigator who uses the method too rashly is in constant danger of being led astray by the *ignis fatuus* of unhappily chosen first principles.

Conceptions of this sort, incapable of direct proof by experiment, are called hypotheses: as, for instance, the assumption of a space-pervading luminiferous ether which, because of its imponderable mass, is imperceptible to our senses; or the assumption that all matter consists of very small but not infinitesimal particles, incapable of further subdivision, and, on account of their smallness, intangible to the senses. The introduction of these hypotheses, as above observed, has become necessary in order to obtain a deeper knowledge of natural phenomena, which in turn leads to new and legitimate results. These are accessible to experiment, and good results prove, not the correctness of the hypothesis itself indeed, but its utility; while a miscarriage shows beyond a doubt not only the unsuitableness, but also the incorrectness, of the conceptions from which we have started.

In suitable ways the hypothesis is a very important assistance to science; it has no self-interest at all, at least not for the student of the exact sciences, but must rather adduce proof for its own right of existence, like a bridge uniting known empirical facts with one another, or leading us to new ones. The advantage of a good hypothesis consists essentially in deepening and broadening our knowledge of natural phenomena, *i.e.* in doing the same as an empirical law of nature. That the human mind has turned with predilection at all times, though in different degrees, to the elaboration of hypotheses, is to be ascribed to the circumstance that the mental satisfaction afforded in finding a new law of nature is greater when it is inferred deductively from universal generalisations, than when inferred inductively from knowledge tediously acquired.

We may say then that the speculative activity of the investigator must be directed, not only to observation and measurement of phenomena, but to the discovery of the most general laws and the most useful hypotheses. When these theorems are put into words or formulæ others than the discoverer can take part in testing them; and any really sound new theorem brings the power of foretelling a whole sheaf of detail. "He who learns the law of phenomena gains not only learning, but the power of entering into the course of nature and of working on it further according to his will and need. He gains insight into the future course of these phenomena. He gains indeed faculties that in superstitious times were looked for in prophets and magicians " (Helmholtz, Goethe Lecture, 1892).

At present we possess some empirical laws and hypotheses which are of the widest application; which must be considered in the didactic treatment of every branch of natural science, and which demand very particular consideration in showing the present condition of theoretical chemistry. The law of the indestructibility of matter was first clearly demonstrated by chemical investigation. The law of the indestructibility of energy has called into being a special branch of chemistry, viz. thermochemistry; and the fruitfulness of the law of the convertibility of heat into external work has perhaps never had a more brilliant illustration than in its application to chemical processes. Finally, the atomic and molecular hypotheses appear to be indispensable for a comprehension of the nature of chemical compounds.

Range of Validity of a Law of Nature.—It has often been assumed in the past that any real law of nature must be absolutely true; at present this can no longer be accepted, at least everything points to the conclusion that there are no such laws at all, but that all so-called laws of nature are more or less exact, but never completely so, and that a limit can be reached in every case where the law entirely fails. To take one example, we have very decided grounds for believing that the second law of thermodynamics no longer holds when applied to very small masses of substances. It would be absurd, however, in this and similar cases, to deprive at once the principle in question of the rank of a law of nature; in fact, we can say that the question whether a law of nature is absolutely true or not, never arises; what we have to consider is the range of its validity.

This conception is not without importance for the question of the certainty of scientific progress altogether. It is common to speak of the inadequacy of human inquiry, simply because many a long-recognised law has had to undergo revision to meet the requirements of the progress of knowledge. If we consider the matter more closely, it is obvious that the law in question has retained its validity over a wide range, but that the limits of its applicability have been more sharply defined. It can even be said that since the development of the exact natural sciences, there is scarcely one law established by an investigator of the highest rank which has not preserved for all time a wide range of applicability, *i.e.* which has not remained a serviceable law of nature within certain limits. We cannot say, for example, that the electro-magnetic theory of light has completely overthrown the older optical theory put forward by Fresnel and others. On the contrary, now as formerly, an enormous range of phenomena can be adequately dealt with by the older theory. It is only in special cases that the latter fails; and further, there are many relations between optical and electrical phenomena which certainly exist, but of which the older theory takes no account. Hence the electro-magnetic theory implies a great advance, but by no means nullifies the successes of the older theory.

So scientific theories, far from dropping off like withered leaves in the course of time, appear to be endowed under certain restrictions with eternal life; every famous theoretical discovery of the day will doubtless undergo certain restrictions on future development, and yet remain for all time the essence of a certain sum of truths.

Measurement.—It must be the constant endeavour of the investigator to give his observations a quantitative form. A description of phenomena is usually unintelligible and misleading, repetition of observations is made greatly more difficult, when data as to the magnitudes concerned are not given.

The choice of units is arbitrary; various practical and historical accidents have led to the fundamental units of length, time, mass, and temperature. Similarly other quantities that arise in our growing knowledge of nature give occasion for new units, many of which are in use; for example, the "atmosphere," "candle-power," "horse-power," "calorie," etc.

It was consequently a great advance when Gauss (1832) and Weber (1852) showed in the case of magnetic and electric units that this arbitrariness could be, if not quite done away with, at least much restricted. Their method was to *use the laws of nature to define new units.*

Thus instead of comparing electric currents in any arbitrary way, and so restricting themselves to *relative* measurements, they made use of the electrodynamic action between currents to refer current strength to the fundamental units, and defined the unit current *absolutely* as such that two portions, each 1 cm. long, and at a great distance L apart on the same axis, exercise a force $1/L^2$. The unit of resistance thus follows immediately as that in which unit current produces in unit time an amount of heat equivalent to the unit of work; and electromotive force is defined by means of Ohm's law, so that the potential difference between the ends of a conductor of unit resistance is unity, when unit current flows through it.[1]

This method of referring new units to old, and comparing new quantities by reference to those previously known, is not free from arbitrariness; in the foregoing case, the unit of current might equally well be defined by means of elements of a different shape or position; or, as Gauss and Weber pointed out, electrostatic forces instead of electrodynamic might be made the basis of the system of measurement. Still the arbitrariness is much reduced by the principle of Gauss and Weber. But it is even more important that the absolute system does

[1] Further details in F. Kohlrausch, *Leitfaden der prakt. Physik, Anhang.*

away with the numerical factor in the expression of many laws of nature, so that they assume an extremely simple form; thus this system, like a good theorem, gives the physicist a quantity of detailed knowledge of the art of measurement, and of the most varied character.

The four fundamental units so far generally used, and mentioned above, are not necessary. Mass may be referred to length and time by means of Newton's law of gravitation (Maxwell): The gas equation $pv = RT$ may by putting $R = 1$ be used to define temperature in mechanical measure, as a quantity of energy. For various reasons such definitions are not convenient, at least at the present time, and it will be well to wait for the discovery of new laws of nature before reducing the number of fundamental units. The latter should of course be so chosen that they can be as accurately measured as possible; this condition is satisfied by length, mass, time, and temperature to a high degree, but not by energy, which for that reason is not acceptable as a fundamental unit.

The Indestructibility of Matter.—Numerous investigations have shown that neither by physical change of a substance, as, for example, by pressure, heating, magnetisation, etc., nor by chemical decomposition, does there occur a variation of its mass, as measured by the attraction of the earth (Lavoisier). Innumerable chemical analyses and syntheses speak for the correctness of this law; in spite of the mighty chemical processes occurring in the sun, its attraction of the planets remains unchanged—an extraordinarily sharp proof that in these processes the total mass of the sun itself remains unchanged.

The question whether the weight of a product of reaction is equal to that of the reacting bodies has lately been tested by H. Landolt, with great accuracy (*Zeitsch. f. phys. Chem* [1893], **12**. 1; *Sitzungsber. d. Preuss. Akad. d. Wissensch.*, 1908, p. 354). It appeared that in the 15 cases investigated the change of weight due to chemical reaction was at most a millionth part, probably much less, and in no case was greater than the probable error in weighing (0·03 mg.).

The Transmutability of Matter.—The properties of a substance vary with the external circumstances under which we study it; but, nevertheless, for a slight change of external conditions (especially of pressure and temperature) there corresponds only a slight change in the *physical* properties of a substance. On the other hand, if we bring together different substances, as, for example, sugar and water, or sulphur and iron, even when the same external conditions are maintained, there commonly occurs a deep-seated change in their properties, producing substances which on comparison with the original are very different in many respects. Thus it is possible for the same substance under the same external conditions to assume entirely different external properties: the substance is convertible into another.

But according to our experiments hitherto, the convertibility of matter is limited to certain conditions. The law of the indestructibility of matter furnishes the first limitation, viz. that in any event this change in physical property concerns only *identical masses* of the substances [*i.e.* that in the change there is neither gain nor loss of mass]. Further experience gained in this direction—the result of a vast amount of painstaking work of the chemical laboratory, from the attempts of the alchemists to change base metals into gold, to the wonderful syntheses performed by our organic chemists of the present—has brought the further knowledge that, in general, even identical masses of substances *essentially different* are not convertible into each other.

Simple and Compound Matter.—Innumerable investigations, which have had for their object, on the one hand, to reduce compound matter into simpler by chemical analysis, and, on the other hand, to bring together different substances to make a new one by chemical synthesis, have led to the conviction that, in decomposing the substances occurring in nature, one always comes to a number of substances incapable of further decomposition, the so-called elementary bodies or elements ; of these nearly eighty have been isolated. Every attempt at the further decomposition of these elementary bodies has thus far been fruitless ;[1] but from these elementary bodies can be made synthetically all the substances collectively known to us. Only those substances are convertible into each other which contain the same elements, and indeed each element in the same proportion.

The Indestructibility of Energy. (The first law of thermodynamics).—Many fruitless attempts to find a *perpetuum mobile*—*i.e.* a machine which of itself is able to perform external work continuously, and to an unlimited degree,—have finally led to the conviction that such a thing is impossible, and that the fundamental notion of making such a machine is in opposition to some law of nature. This law of nature is stated in the following way :—If any selected system is subjected to a reversible process, *i.e.* if any series of changes whatsoever occur so that it finally returns to its original condition, then the external work A, performed by the system during the reversible process, is proportional to the amount of heat, W, absorbed at the same time, *i.e.*

$$A = JW . \qquad . \qquad . \qquad . \qquad . \qquad (a)$$

The coefficient J, the mechanical equivalent of heat, is independent of the nature of the system selected, and its numerical value varies only with the

---

[1] The phenomena of radio-activity, which will be described later, point certainly to a spontaneous decomposition of certain elements which is outside the influence of the experimenter.

scale of measurement employed to express the amount of heat and external work.

If any system whatever is subjected to any desired changes, these are, in general, identified with the following changes in energy : firstly, a certain amount of heat is either absorbed or given out ; secondly, a certain amount of external work is either performed by the system or is performed against it ; thirdly, the internal energy of the system will either diminish or increase. In general in any event the diminution of the internal energy U must be equal to the external work A accomplished by the system, minus the amount of heat Q absorbed ; *i.e.* the following relation exists—

$$U = A - Q \qquad . \quad . \quad . \quad . \qquad (b)$$

In this equation all the quantities must be expressed in terms of the same unit of energy, *e.g.* heat must be put into work-units.

Of course each of these three quantities may be negative ; thus when a development of heat occurs Q is negative, when an increase of internal energy occurs U is negative, and when there occurs an introduction of external work A is negative. When the system considered consists of reactive substances, and the change is a chemical decomposition, then Q signifies the heat of reaction, U the change of the substances' internal energy occasioned by the decomposition, and A is the external work performed by the reaction in overcoming the external pressure, and, as above, is positive when the reaction is accompanied by an increase of volume of the system, but negative when accompanied by a diminution of volume. When, as often happens, the external work is negligibly small, U is equal to the heat evolved in the reaction.

If we bring a system that has suffered any change back to its original state, the work done by the system is, according to equation (*a*), equal to the heat supplied. Hence by (*b*) U must be zero, or the system possesses the same content of energy as before the change ; *the energy contained at any moment is therefore completely determined by the state of the system at that moment.*

U must therefore be a single valued function of the variables characterising the system ; and dU be capable of being put in the form of a complete differential. If, for example, the only external work done is against an external pressure, the system is in general completely defined by the temperature T and volume v, and we may put

$$dU = \frac{\partial U}{\partial v} dv + \frac{\partial U}{\partial T} dT.$$

As already stated, equation (*b*) is applicable to every occurrence ; for it is the direct analytical expression of the law of the *conservation of energy*. A change of the energy content of a system can occur in very many ways,—partly by a simple change of temperature, partly by isothermic changes of condition, and partly by the two together. In the first case, the change of energy is measured by the product of the heat capacity of the system and the change of temperature; in the second case, by a certain quantity of energy which can usually be determined easily and exactly (as the latent heat, heat of reaction, and the like, + the external work); the third case, finally, can always be referred to the first two cases, as the following consideration shows :— .

Let a system suffer any desired change, and at the same time let its temperature change from T to T + t. Now, let us think of this process as conducted in the two following ways: in the first way, the process is completed at constant temperature T, whereby the change of energy amounts to U_T, and then the system is warmed to T + t, whereby it needs the introduction of Kt calories, if K denotes the heat capacity of the system after it has suffered the change; in the second way, the system is warmed at once from T to T + t, whereby it needs an introduction of $K_0 t$ calories of heat, if K_0 denotes the initial heat capacity, and after this the process is finished which is associated with a change of energy amounting to U_{T+t}. The heating takes place without any performance of external work; for example, if the system be a gas, it is heated at constant volume. In both ways, we pass from the same initial to the same final condition; then, according to the law of the conservation of energy, the changes of energy in both cases must be equal : in the first case, the diminution of total energy amounts to $U_T - Kt$, in the second to $U_{T+t} - K_0 t$, and therefore we have the following equation—

$$U_T - Kt = U_{T+t} - K_0 t,$$

or

$$K_0 - K = \frac{U_{T+t} - U_T}{t}.$$

The right-hand expression is the increase in the energy change per degree rise of temperature, and for small temperature differences may be written $\frac{dU}{dT}$; *this, according to the above law, is equal to the difference between the thermal capacities of the system before and after the change.* If, for example, we consider the process of fusion, the proposition given above declares that the heat of fusion of one gram of a solid substance increases as much for every degree of temperature elevation as the specific heat c_0, of the *fused* substance, is greater than that c of the *solid*.

If a homogeneous substance be heated through dT, at constant pressure, the heat required is $c_p dT$, where c_p means the thermal capacity at constant pressure; the process may, however, be conducted in this way : raise the temperature through dT at constant volume, with absorption of heat $c_v dT$ (c_v = thermal capacity at constant volume), then allow it to expand isothermally by the amount dv, for which the quantity $-\dfrac{\partial U}{\partial v}dv + pdv$ will be required. Put dv equal to the expansion that would be caused by rise of temperature dT at constant pressure, and we arrive in each case at the same final, from the same initial state, so that the quantities of heat absorbed must be the same—

$$c_p dT = c_v dT + \left(p - \frac{\partial U}{\partial v}\right)dv,$$

or

$$c_p - c_v = \left(p - \frac{\partial U}{\partial v}\right)\frac{\partial v}{\partial T}.$$

The law of the conservation of energy, above all other laws, has introduced a new epoch of investigation of nature ; it was clearly stated for the first time by Julius Robert Mayer (1842), but was first recognised in its full significance, and applied systematically to the most various phenomena, by Hermann von Helmholtz, in his paper " On the Conservation of Force," 1847.[1] It received its first quantitative confirmation by the fundamental investigation of Joule (1850) on the conversion of work into heat, which in turn led to the determination of the mechanical equivalent of heat.

The share taken by these investigators in the common work is well characterised by Mach (*Prinzipien der Wärmetheorie*, Leipzig, 1896, p. 268) : " The need for the principle was strikingly brought out by Mayer, who pointed out its applicability to all subjects. To Helmholtz is due the complete critical working out in detail, and the connection to results already arrived at. Finally, Joule introduced the new method and conception, in the most exemplary manner, into the region of quantitative experiment."

Measurement of Energy.—Since we shall have much to do with energy, some special remarks on its measurement may be in place here. The absolute system gives as unit the work that is done in moving the point of application of unit force through 1 cm. But unit force, called the dyne, is that which in one second gives to one gram unit velocity (1 cm./sec. called " cel" from celeritas) ; it is, moreover, nearly the weight of a milligram (more exactly $\dfrac{1}{980\cdot6}$ gm. in middle latitudes). The corresponding unit of work is called the " erg " (ἔργον), and is of course equal to the kinetic energy $\left(\dfrac{m}{2}v^2\right)$ of two grams moving with a speed of 1 cel.

This unit of work is often inconveniently small, and for a long time past other units, suited to particular purposes, have been in use. The " kilogram-metre " is used in technology, *i.e.* the work done in lifting one kilogram through one metre, the unit of length being here taken as the metre, and that of force as the weight of a kilo. But as

---

[1] Ostwald's *Klassiker*, No. 1. Leipzig, 1889. *Über die Erhaltung der Kraft.*

work can be done in increasing a volume against pressure, or causing electricity to flow against a difference of potential, units of work are suggested for such cases in the form of products of pressure by volume, and quantity of electricity by potential. If, as is customary in scientific calculations, the C.G.S. system is adhered to, *the unit of work is of course always the same*; but if, as we shall occasionally do for clearness, the conventional measures are used, the work unit will of course be different in different cases.

The *unit of heat* is determined in principle by the law of conservation of energy as being equivalent to the unit of work. But here also for practical reasons the reduction is often avoided, and a special heat unit, in closer connection with the methods of measurement, adopted; as such we shall always use the *gram calorie* (cal.), *i.e.* the heat required to raise one gram of water through $1°$ on the *air thermometer scale*.[1] But as the specific heat of water is appreciably variable, it is necessary to complete this definition by stating the temperature of the water. Now, by far the most calorimetric measurements, especially in thermochemistry, are made by observing the rise of temperature produced in water at room temperature by the heat to be measured; so that it is best for our purposes to choose as unit *that quantity of heat which will raise one gram of water at $15°$ through $1°$ Cels.* ; and between $15°$ and $20°$ the specific heat of water may for most purposes be regarded as constant.

Besides the calorie given above, there are also the so-called "*mean calorie*," *i.e.* $\frac{1}{100}$ of the quantity of heat which is necessary to warm 1 g. of water from $0°$ to $100°$; the so-called "*zero-calorie*," *i.e.* the quantity of heat which is necessary to raise 1 g. of water from $0°$ to $1°$; and also a number of other calories which refer to temperatures arbitrarily or casually chosen.

The change in the specific heat of water with the temperature has recently been satisfactorily determined, and as we are frequently compelled, in making use of calorimetric measurements by different investigators, to reduce their observations to the same unit, the latest values obtained for the specific heat of water are put together in the following table. In the first column are the results of Rowland, who carried out at different temperatures the experiments of Joule on the conversion of friction into heat; in the second column the figures of Bartoli and Stracciati,[2] obtained by the method of mixing; in the third those of Lüdin,[3] by the same method; in the fourth those of Callendar and Barnes,[4] by a continuous electric

---

[1] For reduction of a Jena glass mercury thermometer to the air scale, see Wiebe, *Z. f. analyt. Chem.* **30**. 1 ; *Chem. Centralbl.*, 1891, **1**. 249 ; *Z. f. Instrumentenk.* **10**. 233, 435 (1890). [2] *Calore specifico dell' aqua.* Catania, 1892.
[3] *Dissertation*, Zürich, 1895 ; see also a critical discussion by J. Pernet, *Vierteljahrsschrift der nat. Ges. Zurich*, **41**, Jubelband II. 1896.
[4] Brit. Ass. Rep. Dover, 1899, p. 642 ; *Z. f. Instrumentenk.* **20**. 276 (1900) ; *Phil. Trans.* **199**. 149 (1902).

calorimeter ; in the fifth those of Dieterici,[1] obtained by the use of an ice calorimeter.

	I.	II.	III.	IV.	V.
0°	...	1·0080	1·0051	1·0080	1·0088
5°	1·0054	1·0046	1·0027	1·0050	1·0050
10°	1·0019	1·0018	1·0010	1·0020	1·0021
15°	1·0000	1·0000	1·0000	1·0000	1·0000
20°	0·9979	0·9994	0·9994	0·9986	0·9987
25°	0·9972	0·9997	0·9993	[0·9977	0·9983
30°	0·9969	1·0000	0·9996	0·9972	0·9984
35°	0·9981	...	1·0003	0·9971	0·9985

The zero-calorie is 1·008 times the usual calorie ; the value of the mean calorie is 1·005 according to Lüdin, 1·0013 according to Dieterici, and 0·9997 according to Behn.[2]

For the mechanical equivalent of the usual calorie at latitude 45°, Pernet (l.c.) reckons 42,555 gram centimetres from the experiments of Joule, 42,547 from Rowland, and 42,637 from Miculescu ; E. H. Griffiths, on the one hand, Schuster and Gannon on the other, found by measurements of electrically developed heat practically the same value, 42,730 ; as the most probable value we shall adopt 42,720, following the example of Warburg,[3] and Waidner and Mallory.[4] The meaning of this number is that if in latitude 45° a gram be allowed to fall through 42,720 centimetres the kinetic energy acquired converted into heat would suffice to raise the temperature of a gram of water at 15° by 1° on the air thermometer scale.

In the absolute system of measurement the value of the ordinary calorie is

$$42,720 \times 980·6 = 41,890,000 \text{ ergs.}$$

(980·6 = acceleration of gravity in latitude 45°), or 41·89 million ergs. = 4·189 Joules.

Sometimes the kilogram-calorie, which is 1000 times the gram-calorie, is used instead of the latter : its mechanical equivalent is 427 metre kilograms. The two units are distinguished by the names "large" and "small calorie" respectively ; *in the following the former will be denoted Cal., the latter cal.*

Very often, and in calculations which are of especial importance for the chemist, the problem is given to express, in units of heat, the work performed in overcoming the pressure on a definite volume. For example, in a cylinder with a movable piston of a cross-section of 1 sq. dcm., on which the atmosphere presses with a pressure of one

[1] *Ann. d. Phys.* [4], **16**. 593 (1905).   [2] *Ann. d. Phys.* [4], **16**. 653 (1905).
[3] See *Die Wärmeeinheit.* Leipzig, 1900 (Barth).
[4] *Zeitschr. f. Instrumentenkunde*, 1900, p. 59 ; *Phys. Rev.* **8**. 193 (1899).

atmosphere, let the piston be raised 1 dcm. so that the atmospheric pressure will be forced back from the space of a litre. This unit of work, after the analogy of the "metre kilogram," we appropriately call a "litre-atmosphere." The pressure of an atmosphere on a sq. cm., as is known, is 1·0333 kg. = 76 × 13·596 gr., and on a sq. dcm. 103·33 kg. ; the work performed in raising the piston is as great as though 103·33 kg. were raised 1 dcm., or as though 1 g. were raised 1,033,300 cm. Therefore the work sought, in calorimetric units, is

$$1 \text{ Litre-atmosphere} = \frac{1,033,300}{42,720} = 24\cdot19 \text{ g.-cal.}$$

Equations of Motion of a Particle.—Some remarks on this point will be inserted here, partly to elucidate further the law of conservation of energy, partly because we shall later have to do repeatedly with the movement of particles. If a particle of mass m, under the influence of a force X, move in a direction which may be defined as that of the axis of x in a system of co-ordinates, and if t is the time, then by the fundamental laws of dynamics

$$m\frac{d^2x}{dt^2} = X \qquad . \qquad . \qquad . \qquad . \qquad (1)$$

(or mass × acceleration = effective force). Multiplying (1) by the identity

$$\frac{dx}{dt}dt = dx,$$

and remembering that

$$m\frac{dx}{dt}\frac{d^2x}{dt^2}dt = d\left[\frac{m}{2}\left(\frac{dx}{dt}\right)^2\right],$$

and finally replacing the velocity $\frac{dx}{dt}$ by the symbol v, we have

$$d\left(\frac{m}{2}v^2\right) = Xdx \qquad . \qquad . \qquad . \qquad . \qquad (2)$$

or in words : the increase in kinetic energy of the particle during any element of time is equal to the work performed by the force.

If the particle is travelling in the direction s which at the moment considered makes with the axes of a rectangular co-ordinate system the angles a, β, γ, then

$$\cos a = \frac{dx}{ds}, \quad \cos \beta = \frac{dy}{ds}, \quad \cos \gamma = \frac{dz}{ds}.$$

If forces X, Y, Z act along the axes, the force T exerted on the point is

$$X \cos a + Y \cos \beta + Z \cos \gamma,$$

and equation (1) becomes in this case

$$m\frac{d^2s}{dt^2} = X\frac{dx}{ds} + Y\frac{dy}{ds} + Z\frac{dz}{ds},$$

or, by a similar transformation to that previously used,

$$d\left(\frac{m}{2}v^2\right) = Xdx + Ydy + Zdz,$$

in which the velocity

$$v = \frac{ds}{dt}.$$

If we have a system of any number of particles acted on by no external forces, the work done depends only on the forces between the particles; and if the right-hand expression is a complete differential, its integral is called the *potential*, and in this case the work is done exclusively at the cost of the potential energy. Then the increase of kinetic energy is equal to the decrease of potential energy, or the total energy of the system is constant (law of conservation of energy in mechanical systems).

If the particle suffers friction in its course, equation (1) requires a limitation. The friction is to be regarded as a force acting in the direction opposite to that of the motion of the particle at the moment, and in many cases is proportional to the velocity v. Hence there acts on the particle the force X – kv, where k is the opposing force for unit velocity. Then (1) becomes

$$m\frac{d^2x}{dt^2} = X - kv \quad . \qquad . \qquad . \qquad . \qquad (3)$$

and (2) becomes

$$d\left(\frac{m}{2}v^2\right) = (X - kv)dx \qquad . \qquad . \qquad . \qquad (4)$$

When X is constant, v must obviously increase if X>kv, and decrease in the contrary case, so that in both cases X – kv approaches zero, and v approaches the limit

$$v_0 = \frac{X}{k} . \qquad . \qquad . \qquad . \qquad . \qquad (5)$$

After a certain (often immeasurably short) time the velocity is equal to the force divided by the frictional resistance; consequently in the case of movement under sufficiently great friction it is not, as in pure dynamics, the acceleration, but the velocity that is proportional to the applied force.

Writing (4) in the form

$$d\left(\frac{m}{2}v^2\right) + kvdx = Xdx,$$

we see that the work spent by the (internal or external) forces, Xdx, goes partly to produce kinetic energy, partly to do work against friction. The larger the latter portion is compared to the former, the more nearly true is the very simple equation (5).

Writing (5) in the form

$$kv_0 = X,$$

multiplying by dx and integrating from 0 to x and 0 to t we get

$$\int kv_0 dx = \int kv_0^2 dt = \int X dx,$$

or

$$kv_0^2 t = Xx \qquad . \qquad . \qquad . \qquad . \qquad (6)$$

But Xx is the work done on the particle in time t; this frictional heat is equal to the product of resistance (k), velocity squared, and time. The resemblance of (5) to Ohm's law and (6) to that of Joule is obvious.

To calculate the time after which (5) may be regarded as true, we will write (3) in the form

$$\frac{dv}{X - kv} = \frac{dt}{m}$$

and integrate

$$-\frac{1}{k} \log (X - kv) = \frac{t}{m} + \text{const.}$$

But for $t = o$

$$-\frac{1}{k} \log X = \text{const.}$$

whence

$$v = \frac{X}{k}\left(1 - e^{-\frac{m}{k}t}\right) \qquad . \qquad . \qquad . \qquad . \qquad (7)$$

The expression in brackets increases rapidly with time towards the limit 1, i.e. (7) passes over into (5); and the more rapidly the larger the friction k and the smaller the mass m.

The Convertibility of Energy. (The second law of the mechanical theory of heat).—While the law of the conservation of energy furnishes us with the quantitative relations which must necessarily be satisfied in changing into each other the various forms of energy, as external work, heat, internal energy, etc., the so-called "second law of the mechanical theory of heat" teaches us the limitations of the *convertibility* of the different forms of energy. It may be expressed qualitatively in the following way : *External work and kinetic energy of moving bodies may be transformed into one another completely and in many ways, and can also be converted into heat* (most simply by employing the external work to set heavy masses in motion, which is then destroyed by friction—as by applying brakes to a railway train—with production of heat) ; but conversely, *the reverse change of heat into work is only possible under certain conditions.* (Principle of Carnot and Clausius.) The train of thought which has led to a clearing up of the question how far the different forms of energy are interconvertible, and to the supposition that a law of nature determines the limits, is essentially as follows :—As fruitless as have been the endeavours of innumerable inventors to construct a machine which should be able to do work continually without ever needing an expenditure of force to keep the machine in motion, so brilliant is the knowledge which explains this miscarriage by a law of nature. On the ground which was richly fertilised by the ruined fancies of unlucky inventors, grew up like a tree of knowledge the law of the indestructibility of energy, the golden fruit of which was plucked by Mayer and Helmholtz. *Yet, in the judgment of some inventors who are completely permeated with the accuracy of this law, it is by no means regarded as impossible to construct a machine which should be able to furnish work as desired and free of cost.* According to this law, external work and heat are equivalent to each other—both are manifested forms of energy. But energy in the form of heat is in abundance, so that all we need is a contrivance to use up the energy of the surroundings by employing it in the form of external work to drive our engines. Such an apparatus, for example, might be sunk in a great water reservoir, whose enormous energy-content could be changed into useful work; it would, for example, make the steam-engines of our ocean steamers unnecessary, and would keep the screw of a ship in motion as long as desired, and at the cost of the immeasurable store of heat in the sea. Such an apparatus would be in certain respects a *perpetuum mobile*, and yet not contradict the first law of thermodynamics, since, acting according to this law, it would extract the heat of its environment and give it back again as external work, which, after its expenditure, according to rule (in the above case, as a result of the friction of the ship and screw) would be again changed back into heat, to enter on the cycle anew.

Unfortunately such an apparatus, which would make coal worthless as a source of energy, appears to be a chimera, exactly as was the *perpetuum mobile* of the inventor of the eighteenth century; at least many fruitless attempts have made this more than probable. Thus, as we sum up the numerous abortive endeavours, we come, in a way exactly analogous to that which led to the knowledge of the first law of thermodynamics, to the proposition *that an apparatus which could continually change the heat of its environment into external work is in contradiction to a law of nature, and therefore an impossibility.* Although, by recognising this law, the human spirit of invention may be poorer by one problem, yet natural investigation is compensated for it by a principle of almost unlimited application.

This result—in itself of an entirely *negative* character—can, with the help of other considerations and some empirical facts, be employed in working out the quantitative relations which restrict the convertibility of energy, and which we understand under the name of the *Second Law of Thermodynamics.*

The fundamental considerations which led to this law were stated with great clearness by Carnot[1] as far back as 1824, before the law of conservation of energy was precisely understood; but to bring the

---

[1] *Réflexions sur la puissance motrice du feu.* Paris, 1824. German translation, Ostwald's *Klassiker*, No. 37. Leipzig, 1892.

second law into the form of a universally applicable and fruitful law of nature, and to give it exact mathematical expression, was the undying work of Clausius (1850).[1] In the following a brief deduction of the fundamental formulæ will be given.

The earliest applications were technical, but to bring the result of experience into the form of a universal physical principle we may say :—

I. *Every process which takes place in a given system by itself*, i.e. *without application of energy in any form, can, when properly used, yield a finite amount of work.*

By process is meant a change in the system by which it passes from an initial state to a different final state. If application of energy from without is not excluded, a system can naturally yield an indefinite amount of work, *e.g.* an electromotor supplied with sufficient current may be regarded, at least in principle, as an inexhaustible source of work.

We may ask now what is the best use, *i.e.* how the process may be made to give the maximum amount of work. For this it is obviously necessary that the apparatus used to gain the work must be technically efficient, so that loss of external work due to secondary defects (friction and similar causes, leakage of a piston in a cylinder during expansion or compression of gases, faults of insulation in electrical circuits, loss of heat in thermal machines, etc.) is avoided ; secondly, the change must be so conducted that force and resistance are almost equal at every stage of the process. If the resistance is made smaller, the process will go in one sense ; if greater, in the opposite ; and as all losses are avoided, as much work is gained in the one case as is absorbed in reversing it. In such cases the process is called *reversible* ; we shall find cases in which this ideal limiting state can, at least in principle, be approached. We shall assume that this is, in general, possible, and postulate that—

II. *A process yields the maximum amount of work when it is conducted reversibly.*

We may easily see that I. and II. are identical with the law that no arrangement is possible by which work shall be continuously performed at the expense of the surrounding heat. According to I., since a process can yield only a finite amount of work, such an arrangement must be a periodically acting machine, which, after a certain time, returns to its initial state ; according to II., such a machine at the best (ideally perfect construction), after a complete period, has absorbed no external work, but has also yielded none, because, working reversibly in order to avoid losses, the work given out during the outward process must be equal to that taken in in the return.

---

[1] " Über die bewegende Kraft der Warme " (*Pogg. Ann.* **79.** 369 and 500) ; Ostwald's *Klassiker*, No. 99. Leipzig, 1898. The separate papers from 1850 on were collected by Clausius in his book, *Mechanische Wärmetheorie.* Braunschweig, 1876.

Examples of self-acting processes in the sense of I. are: the falling of a stone to earth, mixing of two liquids or gases, solution and diffusion of solids in a solvent, and all the numberless chemical reactions that take place of their own accord. The problem of calculating for each case the maximum work obtainable, *i.e.* when the process is conducted reversibly according to II., is of the highest importance, and its solution, in particular instances, has led to most fruitful discoveries.

When bodies at different temperatures are put in contact, a transfer of heat from higher to lower temperature occurs. This process, as is well known, takes place of itself, for no work need be done to make it go; from I. it follows that it is possible to gain external work by means of this interchange of heat, and, on the other hand, that work is required to reverse it, *i.e.* to transfer heat from the cold to the hot body.

Clausius stated the last result as a separate principle, "that heat cannot of itself, *i.e.* without compensation by means of external energy, pass from a colder to a hotter body." But this principle is obviously only a case of a much more general law.

We shall now, in order to elucidate these general discussions, apply them to two specially important cases: firstly, to *isothermal processes*; secondly, to *processes consisting essentially in transfer of heat* (equalisation of temperature differences).

1. Isothermal Process.—Suppose the system undergoing a change to be throughout at the same temperature, and to be immersed in an indefinitely large bath at the same temperature; further, that all processes are conducted so slowly that any heat evolved is given up to the bath, and any required ·is absorbed from it, without appreciable temperature differences being set up. The system is then clearly not isolated, for it is in thermal connection with the bath; but if we treat the system and the bath together as a new isolated system, then the preceding considerations are directly applicable.[1] Also let it be possible to conduct the processes in question reversibly.

The last condition is essential. Moreover, the problem of conducting a process isothermally and reversibly has not by any means been solved in all cases in which it appears possible. The expansion of a gas or evaporation of a liquid can be performed in this manner easily by means of a cylinder and piston. Certain voltaic cells, such as the Daniell, can be used isothermally and reversibly by combining them with a well-constructed, *i.e.* efficient, electromotor; if the cell works it causes the motor to rotate and so does external work; if the motor be reversed by application of the same amount of work from

---

[1] Strictly, the system + heat bath must fall in temperature in proportion to the external work done, according to the First law; but if the capacity of the bath is great enough, the fall of temperature is negligibly small.

without, it causes a current to flow through the cell in the opposite sense, which reverses the chemical process that produced the original current. But in other cases such arrangements are not known; thus, it is not yet possible to conduct isothermally and reversibly the combustion of many organic compounds, or the radiation of a phosphorescent body.

Let A be the external work that a process in a given system is capable of doing, by means of an arrangement working isothermally and reversibly. Imagine now another arrangement, which, under the same conditions, but by a different mechanism, performs an amount of work A' *while the same system passes through the same change*; and to fix the ideas let A>A'. Then, by combining the two, we can construct an arrangement of this kind; by the first machine, we allow the process to take place with production of external work A; by the second, we reverse it, with expenditure of work A'. The system has then passed through an isothermal and reversible cyclic process, leaving it in its initial state; this may be repeated any number of times, and each time a net amount of work

$$A - A',$$

is performed. *This would be a machine capable of yielding an indefinite amount of work at the expense of the heat bath, i.e.* a machine whose existence we have already denied. We conclude, therefore, that A' cannot be different from A or

$$A = A' \quad . \quad \quad . \quad \quad . \quad \quad . \quad \quad (c)$$

In words, this equation, of which we shall make repeated use, states that—

III. *The external work that can be done by a given process when most efficiently used is independent of the arrangement by which this "maximal external work" is obtained*; or, more briefly, *the work done in an isothermal, reversible, cyclic process is zero.*

During such a cyclic process, certain quantities of heat are, in general, given to, and taken from, the heat bath; according to the law of conservation of energy the sum of these must be zero.

2. Transfer of Heat.—The calculation of the work that can be done by the passage of heat from higher to lower temperature is of great importance; we can easily solve the problem for a simple case— a cyclic process performed with a perfect gas—since here the quantities of energy involved are known from the laws of gases.

Let there be two reservoirs, at different temperatures, say in the form of large masses of water, which we can draw on for supplies of heat. For simplicity of calculation we will suppose the two temperatures to differ only infinitesimally, and that they are (on the absolute scale) T and T + dT. We have then to think out a mechanism by which heat may be withdrawn reversibly, and so with the greatest useful effect, from the second reservoir (at $T + dT$), and given to the first at T.

For this purpose we take a cylinder, closed by a movable piston and containing a certain quantity of an ideal gas—say one gram-molecule (32 g. of oxygen or 28 g. of nitrogen, etc.). The apparatus is put in contact with reservoir I., *i.e.* immersed in the large vessel of water at T, and the gas, originally occupying a volume v_1, compressed to v_2. Work is thus spent to the amount

$$A = RT \ln \frac{v_1}{v_2},$$

where R is the gas constant,

$$R = \frac{p_0 v_0}{273}$$

(p_0 and v_0 the pressure and volume at the temperature of melting ice). The heat Q required for this, measured in the same unit as A, is

$$Q = RT \ln \frac{v_1}{v_2},$$

given to the first reservoir. Now the cylinder is brought in contact with reservoir II. so that it is warmed to $T + dT$; the heat thus absorbed is KdT, where K is the thermal capacity of the cylinder and its contents. During the heating the volume v_2 is to be kept constant, so that no external work is done. Now, on allowing the gas to expand from v_2 to v_1, we gain the external work

$$A + dA = R(T + dT) \ln \frac{v_1}{v_2},$$

and withdraw from reservoir II. the equivalent quantity of heat

$$Q + dQ = R(T + dT) \ln \frac{v_1}{v_2}.$$

Finally, we put the apparatus in contact with the colder bath, and keeping its volume constant at v_1, allow it to give up the quantity KdT of heat, and so fall to T. It is then in the initial state again.

The sum of the work done by the gas in the cycle is

$$dA = RdT \ln \frac{v_1}{v_2},$$

and at the same time the quantity of heat

$$Q + KdT$$

is carried from reservoir II. to I., and has consequently fallen in temperature from $T + dT$ to T, whilst the quantity of heat $dQ = dA$ is converted into useful work. KdT is an infinitesimal quantity that may be neglected by comparison with Q.

If the thermal capacity of the cylinder and its contents were zero, instead of Q + KdT only Q of heat would have been transferred from T + dT to T, and this arrangement would increase the useful effect, it is true, but only by an infinitesimal percentage. Hence we may say, without appreciable error, that the quantity Q of heat has fallen from T + dT to T during the cyclic process; comparing this with the work done we find

$$dA = Q\frac{dT}{T} \qquad . \qquad . \qquad . \qquad . \qquad (d)$$

i.e. of the quantity Q of heat transferred from reservoir II. *to* I., *the part* $Q\frac{dT}{T}$ *is turned into external work.*

We can now easily show that this result, though derived from a special case, is *perfectly general.* Assume that some other reversible cyclic process exists, by which the quantity Q' of heat falling from T + dT to T accomplishes dA' of work. Then we may combine this with the former process, choosing the quantity of gas so that in it also Q' of heat suffers the temperature change. Now let the two systems each pass through a cycle, in opposite senses, so that the temperature of the quantity Q' of heat falls in the one by dT but rises in the other by the same amount, and the thermal transport is thus neutralised; then there can be no external work done, otherwise we should have constructed a machine capable of converting heat into work indefinitely, *i.e.* we must have

$$dA' = Q'\frac{dT}{T} \qquad . \qquad . \qquad . \qquad . \qquad (d')$$

Hence—

IV. *If a process consists merely in transfer of heat, and a quantity Q be carried from one body at temperature* T +dT *to another at* T, *the work that can be accomplished is* $Q\frac{dT}{T}$ *in whatever way this work is obtained, provided it is a reversible way.*

There are few laws so fruitful as that contained in (*d*) or (*d'*), which represents the quantitative expression of the convertibility of heat into work, and in particular, has been applied with great success to chemical processes.

It will be worth while to remark further on the meaning of the quantity dA (or dA'). It must not be supposed that in the equation

$$dA = Q\frac{dT}{T} \quad \text{or} \quad \frac{dA}{dT} = \frac{Q}{T}$$

dA is the work done in raising the temperature of the system by dT. This is not the case, for we have particularly carried out the cyclic process in such a way that no work is associated with the rise of temperature. Rather dA is the *excess* of work spent in reversing at $T + dT$ the same process that has been performed at T, so that $\dfrac{dA}{dT}$ is the temperature coefficient of the availability of the process for work.

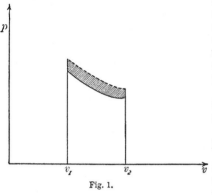

Fig. 1.

We should obtain a wrong value for dA if a gain or loss of work were associated with the warming or cooling of the system, and so a change in its availability for work took place, of a secondary character with regard to the present argument.

Clapeyron's graphical method is very instructive in this matter. The work done in an expansion $\displaystyle\int_{v_1}^{v_2} p\,dv$ is expressed in the figure by the area between the curve $p = f(v)$, the two ordinates, and the axis of abscissæ.

When the temperature is raised this curve is changed to

$$p = f(v) + \frac{\partial f(v)}{\partial T}dT,$$

and we thus obtain a neighbouring line (dotted in the figure). Then clearly the shaded portion expresses dA. If in any case other than expansion the work is given by $\displaystyle\int_{w_1}^{w_2} \Re\,dw$, then $\Re$ must be used as ordinate, w as abscissa.

All results so far known in thermodynamics can be deduced by means of cyclic processes ; the laws to be stated in the four following sections contain nothing essentially new, they are merely another way of expressing the relations already dealt with in this section. This must be expressly stated, as many authors take results which have already been firmly established by cyclic processes, and re-establish them by application of the entropy principle, or use of thermodynamic potential, free energy, and so on, and then not only talk learnedly of a "stricter foundation," but also seem to find favour thereby in the eyes of others. From a pædagogic point of view a certain value may be attached to such "stricter proofs," but usually the only thing that is proved is that the author has studied the work of his predecessors with intelligence. There is no independent scientific value to be attributed to such discussions.

Which method is to be preferred—the explicit discussion of a cyclic process, or its abstraction in the theory of functions—is a pure matter of taste ; it should be remarked, however, that while the prophets *ex eventu* of thermodynamics, with one accord, prefer the thermodynamic functions, investigators who happened to prefer the careful working out of new results to the mathematical polishing up of old ones have all used the original method of Carnot and Clausius, obviously because the consideration of an (at any rate in principle) experimentally realisable cyclic process offers more protection against error.

Still, any one who wishes to go deeper into the problems of the theory of heat may be recommended to a careful study of thermodynamic functions, especially in the admirably clear exposition of M. Planck (*Thermodynamik*, Leipzig, 1897).[1]

Summary of the Two Laws.—The results arrived at in the foregoing section may be summarised as follows :—

1. Every natural process can, by the most advantageous use, yield a definite amount of work, and by the expenditure of the same amount of work, it is theoretically possible to reverse the process; here by " process " we mean any change of a system that can occur without application of work from without.

2. If the process takes place isothermally, the maximal work A depends only on the initial and final states, and not on the path between.

3. If the process consists in an *equalisation of temperature* by which a quantity of heat Q falls from the absolute temperature T + dT to T, it is capable, whatever the nature of the system, of the work

$$dA = Q\frac{dT}{T}$$

as a maximum. (A and Q in the same units.)

Now, the first law gives the relation (p. 8)

$$U = A - Q.$$

Eliminating Q from the two last equations, we have

$$dA = (A - U)\frac{dT}{T},$$

or $$A - U = T\frac{dA}{dT}$$ . . . . (e)

Here A is the maximum work of an *isothermal* process (compare equation (c), p. 19) at temperature T, U the simultaneous decrease in the energy of the system A – U (called Q in the foregoing); or the heat withdrawn from the surroundings during the process, to which the old term "*latent heat*" may conveniently be given.

Hence, according to (e), the excess of the maximal work of an isothermal process over the decrease in total energy, or the latent heat of the process, is equal to the absolute temperature multiplied by the temperature coefficient of the maximal work (the capacity for work).

[1] English translation by Ogg (London, 1903).—TR.

This is the most intelligible statement of the second law, because it contains only quantities with a direct physical meaning; for the change in total energy is always simply measurable by allowing the process to take place, without production of work, in a calorimeter. The maximal work is more difficult to measure, because for that the process must be conducted reversibly; but in many cases this quantity also can be directly recorded (*e.g.* by a Watt indicator, or a Siemens electrodynamometer), so that there can scarcely be any great difficulty in making its meaning clear in new instances. The above form of the law is especially to be preferred in application to chemical and electrochemical reactions.

Remembering, further, that the juxtaposition of A and U implies that both [1] these quantities are independent of the path, and therefore completely defined by the initial and final states, and further, that A – U is the latent heat of the system, equation (*e*) may be regarded as including both fundamental laws.

When the work done by the process consists merely in overcoming a pressure during an expansion of the system, we can put A in the form

$$A = \int_{v_1}^{v_2} p dv,$$

where v_1, v_2 are the initial and final volumes respectively. Frequently the pressure remains constant during this change (evaporation, fusion, dissociation of a solid, etc.) and then

$$A = (v_2 - v_1)p \; ; \quad dA = (v_2 - v_1)dp,$$

and

$$A - U = Q = (v_2 - v_1)T\frac{dp}{dT},$$

where Q is the heat absorbed during the expansion from v_2 to v_1.

When p varies during the expansion (evaporation of a mixture, expansion of a gas or liquid, etc.), we may regard it as constant during an infinitesimal expansion $v_2 - v_1 = dv$, and obtain from the last equation

$$dQ = T\frac{dp}{dT}dv.$$

Here it is to be noted that dp is the increase of pressure at constant volume, but dQ means the heat absorbed when at constant temperature the volume of the system increases by dv (and external work is done). This is indicated by the symbols

$$\left(\frac{dQ}{dv}\right)_T = T\left(\frac{dp}{dT}\right)_v \quad \text{or} \quad \frac{\partial Q}{\partial v} = T\frac{\partial p}{\partial T}.$$

Analytical Formulation of the Maximal Work.

—The greatest difficulty in applying the fundamental equation (*e*) lies in

---

[1] U is so by the First law (p. 8).

obtaining an analytical expression for the maximal work; for there are few cases in which A and $\frac{dA}{dT}$ can be measured by direct experiment, and otherwise the quantities must be determined by values characteristic of the initial and final states, and these values differentiated with respect to temperature, under the condition that during the temperature change no external work is done.

The following considerations are important for the choice of variables to express the initial and final states of a system. As a matter of fact, in most cases the number of these variables reduces to one. The quantity A of work can in general be decomposed into two factors, such as force × distance, pressure × volume, thermodynamic potential × mass, electric potential × quantity of electricity, and so on, of which the first is in general a temperature function, but the second can be made independent of temperature; the latter should therefore, with the temperature, be chosen as independent variable for expressing A.

This remark needs elucidation. Let A_0 be the expression characterising the initial state, F the final; then

$$A = F - A_0 \quad . \quad . \quad . \quad . \quad . \quad (1)$$

Let A_0 and F differ only infinitesimally, so that A becomes the differential dA. If we can find a variable to the changes of which dA is proportional, we may put

$$dA = \Re d\mathfrak{w} \text{ (T const.)} \quad . \quad . \quad . \quad (2)$$

in which the factor $\Re$ is equal to the (partial) differential coefficient of A with respect to $\mathfrak{w}$, and A itself, when $\Re$ is known as a function of $\mathfrak{w}$, can be arrived at by an integration from the initial to the final state

$$A = \int_{\mathfrak{w}_2}^{\mathfrak{w}_1} \Re d\mathfrak{w}.$$

The simplest case is when a force X acts at a point; if the point of application moves through the element dx

$$dA = X dx,$$

i.e. for small displacements the changes of A and x are proportional. Now the analysis (2) appears to be always possible, so that by analogy we may call $\Re$ the *force* and $d\mathfrak{w}$ an *element of path*.

If, then, the system has several ways of doing work,

$$dA = \Re_1 d\mathfrak{w}_1 + \Re_2 d\mathfrak{w}_2 + \dots \text{ (T const.)} \quad (3)$$

and $\Re_1$, $\Re_2$ are the partial differential coefficients of A with respect to $\mathfrak{w}_1$, $\mathfrak{w}_2$, etc. Thus the differential of A with respect to volume is pressure, with respect to quantity of electricity is electromotive force, etc. So that, in general, $\frac{\partial A}{\partial \mathfrak{w}}$ is the force with which the system suffers a certain change;

but as we shall be concerned almost exclusively with changes involving great
friction, by analogy with (5) (p. 14), the velocity of the corresponding change
is equal to the quotient of force by friction.   As the latter depends
essentially on the particular system, thermodynamics gives no information
with respect to it.

The evaluation of $\dfrac{dA}{dT}$, the temperature coefficient of the maximal work,
is now easy.   After the value of

$$A = F - A_0$$

is arrived at by integration, we have to differentiate A partially with respect
to T; and since according to equation (3), when $\mathfrak{w}$ is constant no work is
done, the condition (p. 22) that no work should accompany rise of
temperature is necessarily satisfied.

Again, supposing F and A_0 to differ only infinitesimally, the maximal
work becomes

$$\mathfrak{R}_1 d\mathfrak{w}_1 + \mathfrak{R}_2 d\mathfrak{w}_2 + \ \ldots$$

where the quantities $d\mathfrak{w}$ represent small, but definite changes.   Applying
the fundamental equation (e) to the process so defined, we have

$$\mathfrak{R}_1 d\mathfrak{w}_1 + \mathfrak{R}_2 d\mathfrak{w}_2 + \ \ldots \ - dU = T\left(\frac{\partial \mathfrak{R}_1}{dT} d\mathfrak{w}_1 + \frac{\partial \mathfrak{R}_2}{\partial T} d\mathfrak{w}_2 + \ \ldots \ \right)$$

or

$$\Sigma\left(\mathfrak{R} - T\frac{\partial \mathfrak{R}}{\partial T}\right) d\mathfrak{w} = dU,$$

in which, therefore, dU is the change of total energy due to the displace-
ments $d\mathfrak{w}$.   The equation on p. 24 is a particular case of this ($\mathfrak{R} = p$, $\mathfrak{w} = v$).

There is a relation between the values of $\mathfrak{R}$ that we will develop in the
case of two kinds of external work ; let

$$dA = \mathfrak{R}_1 d\mathfrak{w}_1 + \mathfrak{R}_2 d\mathfrak{w}_2 \qquad \text{(T const.)}$$

Since dA in this equation is a complete differential (independent of the
" path ") we must have

$$\frac{\partial^2 A}{\partial \mathfrak{w}_1 \partial \mathfrak{w}_2} = \frac{\partial^2 A}{\partial \mathfrak{w}_2 \partial \mathfrak{w}_1},$$

i.e.

$$\frac{\partial \mathfrak{R}_1}{\partial \mathfrak{w}_2} = \frac{\partial \mathfrak{R}_2}{\partial \mathfrak{w}_1},$$

a relation which in its applications coincides with equation (c) of p. 19.   The
generalisation for more than two variables is obvious, but has so far hardly
found any application.

Finally, it may be remarked that the assumption of reversibility is
implicitly made in all equations (such as (3)) which express the external
work by means of variables, and do not contain the time.

Free Energy.—The quantity A expresses that part of the energy
change involved in any process that can be turned without limitation

into external work, kinetic energy, etc.—*a fortiori* into heat—and is therefore in every respect free. Helmholtz [1] gave to this the name "*change of free energy*," and to A – U, *i.e.* the difference between the changes of free and total energy, the name "*change of bound energy*."

Only the *changes* of free or total energy have physical meaning. The *absolute value* of these quantities is unknown, and without interest for us, since probably it does not influence the course of surrounding phenomena. In the same way, we speak only of relative movements of the bodies surrounding us, since their absolute velocities are unknown and, so far as we know, indifferent. Thus, writing $\mathfrak{U}$ for the absolute value of the total energy, and A for the free energy, we measure (calorimetrically)

$$. U = \mathfrak{U}_2 - \mathfrak{U}_1,$$

and (*e.g.* by a Watt's indicator)

$$A = \mathfrak{A}_2 - \mathfrak{A}_1,$$

but the actual values of $\mathfrak{U}$ and $\mathfrak{A}$ escape us. We may, however, count U and A from a fixed initial condition, and speak of them as the "total" and "free" energy; then (*e*) would be expressed in words as: *the difference between the free and total energy* (also described as the *bound energy*) *is equal to the absolute temperature multiplied by the temperature coefficient of the free energy.*

According to the first law the total energy remains constant in a system isolated from communication of energy; according to the second law the same would be true of the free energy in a system at constant temperature in which all the processes were reversible. In reality it always decreases, for this ideal limiting case can never be strictly realised, but friction and similar processes constantly convert free into bound energy.

Clausius introduced a function which is useful for many purposes, viz. the *entropy*—

$$\mathfrak{S} = \frac{\mathfrak{U} - \mathfrak{A}}{T},$$

i.e. the difference between free and total energy divided by the absolute temperature. This is especially useful in dealing with *adiabatic* processes (*i.e.* when no heat is taken in or given out). Clausius showed that this function is increased by all irreversible processes that occur in an isolated system, so that the second law may be put in the form of the *principle of the increase of entropy*. This conception is not, however, more general than that of the decrease of free energy; the former principle is directly applicable only to systems of constant energy content, the latter only to systems at constant temperature; but as from each we may deduce the impossibility

---

[1] *Sitzber. d. Berl. Akad.*, 2nd Feb. 1882; *Ges. Abh.* **2.** 958. See also Massieu, *Journ. de phys.* **6.** 216 (1877), and W. Gibb's *Trans. Connecticut Acad.* **3.** 1875-78. German translation by Ostwald, Leipzig, 1892.

of the engine described on p. 16, each of these special principles may be separately regarded as the most complete expression of the second law.

The combination of

$$\mathfrak{S} = \frac{\mathfrak{U} - \mathfrak{A}}{T} \text{ and } \mathfrak{U} - \mathfrak{A} = - T\frac{d\mathfrak{A}}{dT}$$

gives

$$\mathfrak{S} = - \frac{d\mathfrak{A}}{dT},$$

i.e. the entropy is the negative temperature coefficient of the free energy. We shall henceforth always work with the intelligible notion of the maximal work (free energy), and not with its negative temperature coefficient (entropy); moreover, as Helmholtz pointed out, it is preferable to use the integral function (free energy) rather than its differential (entropy), because $\mathfrak{U}$ can be determined from equation (e), and $\mathfrak{S}$ can easily be expressed in terms of $\mathfrak{A}$ by the preceding equation.

Conditions of Thermodynamic Equilibrium.—Finally, it may be remarked, the fundamental equations yield an easy test whether a system is in equilibrium or not. It was noticed above that for a reversible process force and resistance must be equal; if one slightly exceeds the other, a change takes place in one or the other sense. Hence follows that—

A system is in equilibrium at every phase of a reversible process; and for a system to be in equilibrium it is sufficient that the conditions should be so chosen that only reversible processes are possible.[1]

Thus, a mixture of chemically indifferent gases in a closed vessel is in equilibrium if the temperature and composition are the same throughout, for otherwise the irreversible processes of diffusion and thermal conduction will occur. Further, there is the condition that the containing vessel shall not burst under the pressure of the gas, for that would introduce a new irreversible process, and so on.

Since no system is in equilibrium in which there are temperature differences, we may confine ourselves to considering isothermal systems; and as further on bringing a system at uniform temperature into a sufficiently large bath at the same temperature, no existing equilibrium is destroyed nor any new equilibrium created it is sufficient to consider isothermal processes. But as by p. 27, if all changes are accompanied by an increase of A, irreversible processes are excluded, we find that—

A system at constant temperature is in equilibrium when its free energy is a minimum.

The analytical condition is

$$\delta\mathfrak{A} = 0 \qquad (T \text{ const.}) \qquad . \qquad . \qquad . \qquad (1)$$

---

[1] Conversion of potential into kinetic energy is an irreversible process in all systems in nature, since friction is never entirely absent.

Since the entropy is increased by all irreversible processes in an isolated system (p. 27), we find the corresponding condition that in a system of constant energy all changes involve an increase of the entropy $\mathfrak{S}$, or that $\mathfrak{S}$ is a maximum

$$\delta\mathfrak{S} = 0 \qquad (\text{U const.}) \qquad . \qquad . \qquad . \qquad . \qquad (2)$$

The two equations of equilibrium (1) and (2) are, however, identical, for whether the equilibrium of a system is disturbed by change of temperature, or by introduction of heat, comes to the same thing.

Physical Mixtures and Chemical Compounds.—Closely connected with the empirical laws given above, which form at once the basis of physics as well as of chemistry, there is another law which leads us at once more into the region of chemistry. Many different elements can unite in many ways so as to form new *homogeneous* substances, *i.e.* such as are everywhere alike, and when examined with the most powerful microscope, present the same properties at all points. Experience teaches us that in all cases the properties of compound substances vary more or less with the composition, but that in no case does composition alone determine the properties. Thus "knall-gas," water vapour, liquid water, and ice, are all substances having the same composition, but having very different properties even when compared under the same external conditions of temperature and pressure.

The thorough study of the relations of compound substances, and their dependence upon the composition, has led to their division into two classes. By the mixture of two gaseous elements, as of hydrogen and iodine vapour, for example, we can obtain, according to the conditions, two very different gaseous mixtures, each of which appears homogeneous in all physical and chemical respects, but which yet offer marked chemical differences. In one mixture we can easily recognise the properties of each particular element: the iodine vapour by its colour, and the hydrogen by its enormous diffusibility through porous partitions. In the other mixture many properties of both components are totally changed; the colour of the iodine vapour has vanished, and we seek in vain for the characteristic diffusibility of hydrogen. Further, the two mixtures behave characteristically on condensation to the liquid or solid form: from the first, by cooling or by suitable compression, there is at once separated from the gas mixture solid iodine, a substance of entirely different composition from the gas remaining uncondensed; from the second mixture, by similar treatment, we obtain a homogeneous liquid of the same composition as the uncondensed gas.

We call the first of these gaseous aggregates, a *physical mixture*; the second, a *chemical compound* of hydrogen and iodine (hydriodic acid); and we are forced to conclude that the union of the two gases is much more intimate in the second case than in the first.

We make the same distinction in the union of different compound substances with each other, or with elements ; here we often meet with homogeneous aggregates which can be liquefied, evaporated, solidified, recrystallised, etc., without change of composition, and whose properties are in many respects totally different from those of their respective components ; these, beyond all doubt, can be designated chemical compounds. Other aggregates of this kind change their composition very easily by condensation, volatilisation, etc., their particular components can be reobtained in many ways without difficulty, and in the mass we can recognise many properties possessed by the components when separated. These complexes, with all certainty, are affirmed to be only physical mixtures.

Further, as a rule, the formation of chemical compounds is attended with much more considerable changes of volume and energy, than simple union to a physical mixture ; moreover, the external work which we must apply in order to separate the components of the mixture, is much greater in the first case than in the last. All this means that the union of the components in the first case is incomparably more intimate than in the second.

Nevertheless, the distinctions between physical mixtures and chemical compounds are only of degree, and we find in nature all gradations between these extremes. Thus we are inclined to speak of the solution of a salt in water as a physical mixture, on account of the ease with which the components can be separated from each other ; thus we can remove pure water from the solution both by evaporation and by freezing ; and, on the other hand, we can extract the pure salt without difficulty by crystallisation. At the same time, many properties of salts may be changed in a pronounced way by the process of solution : this is well shown, for example, on dissolving in water anhydrous copper sulphate, a white substance which in solution assumes an intense blue colour. These and other phenomena suggest emphatically that there is a chemical process associated with solution. On the other hand, in the union of various substances to form a new homogeneous complex, which for good reasons is to be regarded as a chemical compound, we find that certain properties of the components are unchanged. Thus, for example, in the union of iodine and mercury to form mercuric iodide, we find that the heat capacity of the newly-formed complex is almost exactly the same as before the union ; thus the specific heat of each element remains unchanged in the compound.

The Law of Constant and Multiple Proportions.—The quantitative investigation of the amounts in which the different elements are present, has led to a much sharper distinction between physical mixtures and chemical compounds : we can vary the composition of the former within wide limits, but the composition of the latter is constant in whatever way they be prepared. John Dalton (1808) found a wonderfully simple law to express the relative quantities according to which the particular elements are contained in compounds of constant composition; this is called the *law of constant and multiple proportions.* It states that one can find for every particular element, a certain number which we will· designate the *combining weight,* which is the standard unit for the quantity of the element entering into *all its various compounds. The quantities of the various elements in their respective compounds are either in the exact ratios of their combining weights, or else in simple multiples of these.*

This law is the foundation of chemical investigation; thus innumerable analyses, and also especially the determinations of the combining weights of the elements, conducted in the most various ways and with the greatest possible care, show that this law holds good with practically absolute exactness for the union of the elements in all compounds which are shown to be genuine chemical compounds.

The Molecular Hypothesis.—Although it appears entirely feasible to construct a methodical chemical system on the basis of the empirical laws of the exchange of matter and energy as given above, in which the empirical data can be comprehensively arranged, yet there has been added to these empirical laws a hypothesis concerning the constitution of material aggregates, which, although advanced in ancient times, was first shown to be advantageous for a deeper and clearer conception of chemical processes by Dalton and Wollaston at the beginning of the last century, and since then has remained the guiding principle of Chemistry and Physics. In the light of this hypothesis, a material aggregate does not fill, continuously and in all points, the gross space occupied by it; but is composed of particles of very small, but yet of *finite* dimensions, situated more or less distantly from each other, and called the *molecules* of matter. The fact that matter appears to fill space continuously, that the gaps between the separate molecules escape us, and that these, as such, are inaccessible to our immediate knowledge, much more to our unbiassed senses, all this is easily explained by the smallness of the molecule, and by our inability to grasp such tiny dimensions.

Whether the molecular hypothesis can be reconciled with the actual facts, or whether it merely owes its origin to our existing inability at present to come at a deeper knowledge of natural phenomena from any other view—whether, perchance, the further building up of the doctrine of energy will lead to another and a clearer conception of matter, this is not the place nor the time to discuss. As a matter of fact—and this is the most important and only decisive test—the molecular hypothesis, more than any other theoretical speculation, has given powerful and· varied assistance to every branch of natural science, and to chemistry in particular. Therefore, in the following presentation of theoretical chemistry, the molecular hypothesis will receive special consideration, and also in some cases it will be introduced where, perhaps, one can advance as far without it as with it, but where by the introduction of molecular conceptions the demonstration gains in interest and brevity of expression. Even to our day, the further extension of the molecular hypothesis has borne remarkably great and unexpectedly fine fruit for the positive enrichment of our science; therefore why should we not ever strive to make our conception of the molecule more tangible, and at the same time provide our eyes with increasingly powerful microscopes for the consideration of this molecular world?

The Atom and the Molecule.—The first great result of the assumption of a discrete distribution of matter in space, was the simple and clear explanation of the law of constant and multiple proportions, by its discoverer Dalton, through which the hypothesis, by one effort of modern science, arose like a phœnix from the ashes of the old Greek philosophy.

The formation of a chemical compound from its elements, in the light of the molecular hypothesis, may be most easily conceived in this way, viz., that the smallest parts of the element enter into the molecules of the compound. Therefore these molecules must be divisible, and such a separation takes place when a compound decomposes into its elements. Thus we reach the assumption that a molecule does not continuously fill the space appropriated by it, but is an aggregate of discrete particles arranged in its total space. These particles we call "*atoms.*" These atoms, by the union of which molecules are made, are all alike if they belong to the molecule of an element, but different if they belong to the molecule of a chemical compound. Only in the first case [*i.e.* of an element] can it happen that a molecule may consist of a single atom. The force which binds the atoms in molecular union, we call the *chemical affinity* of the atom. To the action of this force we must primarily ascribe the fact that the properties of the atom vary so much according to the molecular compound to which they belong, and that their properties in the compounds are commonly so different from their properties in the free state.

Many experimental facts support the obvious assumption that the atoms of one and the same element are equally heavy, and that the molecules of a uniform chemical compound have the same composition. Then plainly the relative weights with which the elements enter into a compound must be those according to which the atoms enter into the molecule; and as a definite number of atoms always unite to form a molecule of a compound, so will the composition of this molecule always be definite. Further, since molecules of all kinds of compounds always contain a whole number of atoms, and usually not many, therefore *the relative weights with which the elements enter into union to form the different compounds, must be either in the same ratios as the atomic weights, or simple multiples of these.* Experiment confirms these demands of the atomic theory to the greatest degree : the last statement contains the law of constant and multiple proportions, but it is an essential extension of this empirical statement, in that the combining weights, which are only obtained by experiment, are given a more obvious meaning. In the light of the atomic theory, the combining weights and the atomic weights must obviously stand in simple ratios to each other ; the latter, however, cannot be ascertained with certainty without further experimental data. The discussion (Book II.) of atomic weight determinations will explain how the present values for, the relative atomic weights (assumed accurate within the limits of error) have been arrived at.

The Table of the Elements.—Since we cannot obtain the absolute atomic weights from the stoichiometric combining ratios, but only the relative figures, a unit must be chosen. Dalton took the atomic weight of hydrogen as unit, as it was the smallest of all the elements. But as the exact determination of the relative combining weights of the other elements compared with hydrogen, offers experimental difficulties, and furthermore, as most combining weights of the elements are determined from oxygen compounds, Berzelius made the atomic weight of oxygen the basis, and placed it at 100, in order to have no atomic weight less than unity. Recently there has been a return to Dalton's unit for many reasons ; but there still exists the disadvantage that the ratio in which hydrogen and oxygen unite to form water has not yet been determined with satisfactory exactness (at the most to one part in a thousand) ; and therefore, after every new determination of this ratio there must follow a recalculation of all the atomic weights. How unsatisfactory it is to work with atomic weights of fluctuating value is obvious. The fact that it is so very hard to obtain pure hydrogen, and to weigh it with satisfactory accuracy, explains the great difficulty of a sharp determination of its combining weight. Therefore from different sources a proposal has been made by way of compromise, which is now practically universally accepted. The ratio of the atomic weights of hydrogen and oxygen is nearly 1 : 16 ; if then we assume the atomic weight of oxygen as the normal, and not 1, but

$$O = 16 \cdot 000,$$

then the atomic weight of hydrogen will be nearly but not exactly 1, and we unite the advantages of the units chosen by both Dalton and Berzelius ; thus we are entirely relieved from the necessity of changing the atomic weight of all the other elements, after every more exact determination of the composition of water.

In the following table the elements are arranged in alphabetical order with their symbols and their atomic weights according to the International Atomic Weight Commission.[1]

[1] *Journ. Chem. Soc.* **97.** 1865 (1910).

Substance.	Symbol.		Substance.	Symbol.	
Aluminium . .	Al	27·1	Neodymium . .	Nd	144·3
Antimony . .	Sb	120·2	Neon . . .	Ne	20·2
Argon . . .	A	39·88	Nickel . . .	Ni	58·68
Arsenic . .	As	74·96	Niobium . .	Nb	93·5
Barium . . .	Ba	137·37	Nitrogen . . .	N	14·01
Beryllium . .	Be	9·1	Osmium . .	Os	190·9
Bismuth . . .	Bi	208·0	Oxygen . . .	O	**16·00**
Boron . . .	B	11·0	Palladium . .	Pd	106·7
Bromine . . .	Br	79·92	Phosphorus . .	P	31·04
Cadmium . .	Cd	112·4	Platinum . . .	Pt	195·2
Cæsium . . .	Cs	132·81	Potassium . .	K	39·10
Calcium . . .	Ca	40·09	Praseodymium .	Pr	140·6
Carbon . . .	C	12·00	Radium . .	Ra	226·4
Cerium . . .	Ce	140·25	Rhodium . . .	Rh	102·9
Chlorine . . .	Cl	35·46	Rubidium . .	Rb	85·45
Chromium . .	Cr	52·0	Ruthenium . .	Ru	101·7
Cobalt . . .	Co	58·97	Samarium . .	Sm	150·4
Copper . . .	Cu	63·57	Scandium . .	Sc	44·1
Dysprosium .	Dy	162·5	Selenium . . .	Se	79·2
Erbium . . .	Er	167·4	Silicon . . .	Si	28·3
Europium . .	Eu	152·0	Silver . . .	Ag	107·88
Fluorine . . .	F	19·0	Sodium . . .	Na	23·00
Gadolinium . .	Gd	157·3	Strontium . .	Sr	87·63
Gallium . . .	Ga	69·9	Sulphur . . .	S	32·07
Germanium . .	Ge	72·5	Tantalum . .	Ta	181
Gold . . .	Au	197·2	Tellurium . .	Te	127·5
Helium . . .	He	3·99	Terbium . . .	Tb	159·2
Hydrogen . .	H	1·008	Thallium . .	Tl	204·0
Indium . . .	In	114·8	Thorium . . .	Th	232·0
Iodine . . .	I	126·92	Thulium . . .	Tm	168·5
Iridium . . .	Ir	193·1	Tin	Sn	119·0
Iron . . .	Fe	55·85	Titanium . .	Ti	48·1
Krypton . . .	Kr	82·9	Tungsten . .	W	184·0
Lanthanum . .	La	139·0	Uranium . . .	U	238·5
Lead . . .	Pb	207·10	Vanadium . .	V	51·06
Lithium . . .	Li	6·94	Xenon . . .	X	130·2
Magnesium . .	Mg	24·32	Ytterbium . .	Yb	172·0
Manganese . .	Mn	54·93	Yttrium . . .	Y	89·0
Mercury . . .	Hg	200·0	Zinc. . . .	Zn	65·37
Molybdenum . .	Mo	96·0	Zirconium . .	Zr	90·6

Classification of Natural Processes.—Natural changes have long been grouped into physical and chemical; in the former the composition of matter usually plays an unimportant part, whereas in the latter it is the chief object of consideration. From the point of view of molecular theory a physical process is one in which the molecules remain intact, a chemical process, one in which their composition is altered. This classification has real value, as is shown by the extremely wide separation of physics and chemistry, not only in teaching, but in methods of research : a fact that is all the more striking as both sciences deal with the same fundamental problem, in reducing to the simplest rules the complicated phenomena of the external world.

That, however, a separation of the two sciences cannot be advantageous in the long-run, appears to enjoy general recognition at the present time when physicists and chemists are busily engaged in cultivating together the common ground of their sciences.

But since thermodynamic laws appear to be applicable to all the phenomena of the external world, the question arises, whether processes occurring in nature cannot be classified according to their thermodynamic properties. As a matter of fact, a consideration of our fundamental formula (p. 23)

$$A - U = T\frac{dA}{dT}$$

draws attention at once to the following special cases :—

1· $U = A$; *the changes in free and total energy are equal.* Then the temperature coefficient of A and therefore also of U is zero, *i.e. temperature does not influence the phenomenon in question,* at least not as regards its thermodynamic properties. Conversely, if the last condition is fulfilled $A = U$. This behaviour is shown by all systems in which only gravitational, electric, and magnetic forces act ; these can be described by means of a function (the potential) which is independent of temperature. Also in most chemical processes A and U are approximately equal (see Book IV. Chapter V.).

2. $U = 0$, so that $A = T\frac{dA}{dT}$, or A *is proportional to the absolute temperature.* The expansion of a perfect gas and mixture of dilute solutions are instances of this behaviour, in which the influence of temperature comes out the most clearly (gas thermometer).

3. $A = 0$, and therefore $U = -T\frac{dA}{dT}$.

This condition can only occur at a single point of temperature ; but A *can be small in comparison with* U *over a considerable range of temperature.* As then the percentage variation of A must be large, the *influence of temperature must be very marked* in such cases (evaporation, fusion, dissociation, *i.e.* all properly " physico-chemical " phenomena).

Case 3 is of course not so strikingly simple, and does not bring to life such important hypotheses as Case 1, which introduced forces of attraction into science, and Case 2, which was decisive for the development of the molecular theory.

The case $U = 0$ and $A = 0$ would not be a process in the thermodynamic sense. Such cases, however, exist and are of importance (movement of a mass at right angles to the direction of gravity, passage of one optical isomer into the other, etc.), so it appears that though thermodynamics suggests important points in the classification of phenomena, it is too narrow [1] to cover the whole.

The Principle of Arrangement.—As we have thus obtained a general glimpse in this introductory sketch, a few words may here be added to explain the division of the material to be considered in the following pages. It is to be treated in a series of four books. In the *first* we will consider the *universal properties of matter*, devoting ourselves almost exclusively to the basis of facts experimentally verified from all sides ; the doctrine of energy will also here do useful service, inasmuch as it will not only throw light upon the empirical data, but also very often will broaden and deepen the results of observations. The *second* book is devoted essentially to developing the *molecular hypothesis*, and, accordingly, more than the first, which is on the whole physical, leads us into the region of questions characteristically chemical ; here will be specially considered the relations between chemical composition and physical behaviour.

As we shall have studied the systems thus considered, in the light respectively of their *properties* of matter or of energy, we will then direct our main attention to the *changes* which they undergo under the action of chemical forces, and the *conditions* under which these forces find themselves in equilibrium. The last two books are, accordingly, devoted to the *doctrine of affinity*, and, according to the twofold nature of chemical decompositions, which alter on the one hand properties of matter, on the other properties of energy, we will consider in the *third* book the *transformations of matter*, in the *fourth* the *transformations of energy*.

---

[1] This of course is due to the fact that the two laws of thermodynamics are insufficient as an explanation of nature (*e.g.*, they take no account of the course of phenomena in time) ; unlike the molecular theory, in which such a limitation has not so far been shown to exist.

BOOK I

THE UNIVERSAL PROPERTIES OF MATTER

CHAPTER I

THE GASEOUS STATE OF AGGREGATION

The Universal Properties of Gases.—Matter occurring in the gaseous state has the property of completely filling all available space, and, if not acted upon by any external force, as gravity for example, of filling it at all points with equal density. The gas particles are easily movable against each other, and this very small internal friction makes it easy to give a gaseous mass, at constantly maintained volume, any desired form without noticeable expenditure of work. For the vessel in which the gas is kept, by its shape and capacity, determines the form and density of the enclosed gas.

But a change of volume, and the associated change in density, calls for an important expenditure of work. Now, since gases have the tendency to occupy the greatest amount of space possible, or, in other words, as a result of this tendency, to exert a pressure on the walls of the enclosing vessel, therefore by diminishing their volume external work must be performed, and by an increase of their volume external work is gained.

In their reciprocal relations gases are characterised by unlimited reciprocal permeability : one can mix with each other gases most dissimilar in composition, in all proportions, and for this there is needed no expenditure of external work ; but it is rather a process which takes place " of its own accord," and therefore it can perform external work when properly employed.

A further characteristic, at least under the conditions commonly employed for working with gases, is the *very slight density* exhibited by matter in the gaseous state ; thus 1 c.cm: of atmospheric air, under atmospheric pressure at 0°, weighs only 0·001293 times as much as 1 c.cm. of water. But this is not an essential characteristic of the gaseous condition, since under certain conditions, by raising the external pressure, we can bring a gas to any desired density ; but by reason of the great tenuity of matter, which we meet with in the case of gases not too strongly compressed, there results a very pronounced simplicity of the laws which control both their physical and their chemical relations,—laws, moreover, which are of fundamental significance in the development of our conceptions of matter and of energy, and also for our conceptions of chemical processes. As we shall make continual use of these gas laws, they will be enumerated below, and in a form suited for subsequent application ; in a later section reference will be made to the changes which these laws experience in the case of gases compressed to a great density.

The Laws of Gases.—1. *The pressure* p, *and the volume* v, *at constant temperature, are inversely proportional to each other, i.e.* pv = a *constant* (law of Boyle and Mariotte). If we bring successively into the space of one liter, 1, 2, 3, . . . to n grams of oxygen, then we obtain 1, 2, 3, . . . to n-fold pressure respectively ; every gram of oxygen presses as much on the enclosing vessel as though it were there alone. We can express this result thus :—the pressure of· a gas is proportional to its concentration, provided its temperature be constant.

2. *As a result of a rise in temperature, the pressure of a gas at constant volume (or, what is identical in the light of the first law, the volume of a gas at constant pressure) increases by an amount which is independent of the nature of the gas and of the initial temperature,* the increase of pressure corresponding to a rise of $1°$ C. being $\frac{1}{273}$ $[= 0.003663]$ of that pressure which the gas exerts at the same volume at $0°$. Accordingly, at the temperature $t°$, if p_0 and v_0 denote respectively the pressure and volume at $0°$, then the pressure which the gas exerts at the constant volume v_0, is

$$P = p_0\left(1 + \frac{t}{273}\right) = p_0(1 + 0.003663t) ;$$

and the volume which the gas would assume, at constant pressure p_0, would be (law of Gay-Lussac)

$$V = v_0(1 + 0.003663t).$$

When pressure and volume both change during the heating, if at $t°$ they amount respectively to p and v, then, according to the first law,

$$p = P\frac{v_0}{v} \quad \text{and} \quad v = V\frac{p_0}{p} ;$$

and if by one of these equations we eliminate P and V in the equations given above, we obtain

$$pv = p_0 v_0(1 + 0.003663t),$$

and if we reckon from $-273°$ instead of from $0°$, we obtain

$$pv = \frac{p_0 v_0}{273}T,$$

in which $T = 273° + t°$, and its factor is a constant for any given quantity of gas.

3. *When different gases unite chemically, the volumes of the reacting gases, measured of course under similar conditions, bear simple ratios to each other, and the volume of the resulting compound, if gaseous, also stands in a simple ratio to the volumes of its components* (law of Gay-Lussac).

4. *The total pressure exerted by a gas mixture on the walls of a vessel, is equal to the sum of the pressures which each gas singly would exert* (Dalton's law).

The laws given above are the immediate expression of experiment; as to their universal validity, it can at once be shown that they are not absolutely correct, but that they suffer variations (at most very slight), which, however, increase, the greater the pressure and the lower the temperature. Moreover, they are not free from great exceptions, inasmuch as there are gases, as for example nitrogen dioxide, iodine vapour, etc., which at elevated temperatures certainly cannot be compressed proportionally to the external pressure, and which do not expand in proportion to their distance from the absolute zero. But in all these cases it has been shown, as we shall see by the laws of dissociation, that the change of volume or temperature is accompanied by a chemical decomposition, and that if we take this influence into consideration, the laws of gases preserve their full validity, at least with variations of small amount.

The Hypothesis of Avogadro.—To explain the fact that the union of gases always occurs according to very simple proportions by volume, Avogadro (1811) advanced a hypothesis which, after much opposition, has come to be recognised as an important foundation of molecular physics, as well as of all chemical investigation. *According to this hypothesis, all gases under the same conditions of temperature and pressure, in unit volume, have the same number of molecules.* Thus the densities of gases, measured under the same external conditions, have the same ratios to each other as their molecular weights.

Naturally this hypothesis can no more be absolutely proved than the molecular hypothesis; but it appears at the outset very plausible, as it explains in the simplest way the validity of the third law of gases. Further, the numerous results which have been obtained in consequence of its application, are telling witnesses in its favour; molecular weights inferred from investigations of a purely chemical character, are commonly in surprising accord with those reckoned from the vapour density of gases. The kinetic theory of gases, as will be further shown in detail, leads, in an entirely independent way, to the same assumption. The usefulness of the hypothesis is further clearly brought out by the fact that, as will be shown in the theory of solutions, it can be applied to the case of substances occurring in very dilute solution, and has proved itself here to be of an adaptability hitherto unforeseen. Finally, a fact which speaks convincingly in favour of the hypothesis, is that it has been very successful in a case which was formerly supposed to be a noted exception, viz., abnormal vapour densities, as will be explained in the description of the dissociation phenomena of gases.

By the help of Avogadro's rule, the laws of gases [1] can be summed up in the following form :—

If we take a gram-molecule of the various gases into consideration, *i.e.* the molecular weight expressed in grams, as for example 2g. H_2, 32g. O_2, 18g. H_2O, etc., then for any mass of gas there exists the following simple relation between p, v, and the temperature T, counting from $-273°$:

$$pv = \frac{p_0 v_0}{273}T = RT,$$

in which the factor R *is only conditioned by the unit of measure chosen, but is independent of the chemical composition of the gases in question.*

According to measurements of the density of various gases the pressure which a gram-molecule, or *mol* (as it is now called) of a gas at 0° would exercise is $22·412$ atmospheres, *i.e.* $22·412 \times 760$ mm. of mercury at 0° measured at sea-level and latitude 45°, when the gas occupies one litre. Hence

$$pv = \frac{22·412T}{273} = 0·08207T.$$

The numerical factor occurring in this equation,—an equation which finds abundant application in the most varied calculations,—is probably determined with great accuracy. In the following we shall use the round value $0·0821$.

The following observations serve for calculating the gas constant. According to the measurements of Regnault, Joly, Leduc, and Rayleigh, the densities of the following gases at 0° and 760 mm. at sea-level and 45° latitude are : [2]—

---

[1] According to Guldberg (1867 ; cf. Ostwald's *Klassiker*, No. 139, p. 6) and Horstman, *Berl. Ber.* **14**. 1243 (1881).

[2] For the gravity correction see Landolt and Bornstein, *Physikalische-chemische Tabellen*, 3rd ed. p. 17, table 5 ff.

Gas.	M.	Density.	p_0.
Hydrogen . . .	2·016	$89·88 \times 10^{-6}$	22·43
Oxygen	32·00	1429·1 ,,	22·39
Nitrogen . . .	28·02	1250·7 ,,	22·40
Nitric oxide . . .	30·01	1342·65 ,,	22·35
Carbon monoxide .	28·00	1250·7 ,,	22·44
Nitrous oxide. . .	44·02	1970·6 ,,	22·34
Methane. . . .	16·04	714·64 ,,	22·44
Ammonia . . .	17·07	762·1 ,,	22·39

Of course only such gases are available for calculating R as follow the laws of gases closely, and in particular have the normal coefficient of expansion.

Dividing 1000 times the density (*i.e.* mass of a litre) by the molecular weight M we obtain the numbers given under p_0, *i.e.* pressure in atmospheres of a mol contained in one litre.   As at latitude 45° the acceleration of gravity is 980·6 and the density of mercury at 0° is 13·596, the atmosphere is

$$76 \times 980·6 \times 13·596 = 1,013,250 \text{ absolute units.}$$

The densities of the first three gases have been measured with remarkable agreement by a number of experimentalists [1] (Regnault, Joly, Leduc, Rayleigh, Morley, etc.), the rest are from the observations of Regnault.   The mean of the first three values for p_0 is 22·41, of the others 22·40.   We shall adopt the value 22·412.[2]   In a similar way D. Berthelot arrives at the number − 273·09° as the most probable value of the zero point on the absolute temperature scale.

The density of atmospheric nitrogen (containing argon) is $1257·1 \times 10^{-6}$ from which $p_0 = 22·29$.   The difference between this value and 22·41 would have been sufficient—if there had been more trust in the gas laws—to indicate an impurity in the nitrogen, and so lead to the discovery of argon.

If n mols of different gases are under the pressure P, and if they fill the volume V at temperature T, then, of course, in the sense of Dalton's law

$$PV = nRT.$$

The counting of the temperature from − 273·09° or roundly − 273° is called the *absolute temperature scale*, and T the *absolute temperature*.   If we regard the gas equation as available even for very small values of T (and whether this is allowable or not is of course irrelevant in its practical application), we arrive at the result that a gas cooled to − 273° Celsius would exert no pressure on the walls of the containing vessel ; this point is called the "absolute zero."

The formula given above, by means of the mechanical theory of

[1] See Lord Rayleigh, *Chem. News,* **67**. 183, 198, 211 (1893).
[2] D. Berthelot, *Zeitschr. für Elektrochem.* **10**. 621-29 (1904) ; cf. also Book II. Chapter III.   Section "Calculation of Atomic Weights."

heat, is applicable to several of the most diverse processes; thus the gas law is employed to ascertain the convertibility of heat into external work (p. 20). The gas equation is implicitly contained in all thermodynamical formulæ, in which the "absolute temperature" almost always plays an important part. Scarcely any empirical law of nature has as yet been applied to such an extent as the law expressed by this gas equation.

The Content of Energy of a Gas.—If one connects two vessels containing gas at different pressures, so that an equalisation of pressure between the vessels takes place, but with no performance of external work, *then in this process heat will be neither developed nor absorbed* (Gay-Lussac, Joule, Thomson); the same result is obtained if a vessel is exhausted by an air-pump.

This result, expressed most simply in the language of thermodynamics, states that *the content of energy of a gas is independent of its volume.*

If two vessels which contain two different gases are put in communication with each other, these gases begin at once to diffuse into each other, and the final condition consists in a complete equalisation of the difference in composition. In this process also, *i.e.* in the mixing of two gases, neither development nor absorption of heat is observed, provided, of course, that no chemical action takes place. *The content of energy of a gas mixture is accordingly equal to the sum of the energy-contents of the ingredients.*

These laws are of fundamental importance for the thermodynamics of gases; they are, like the laws mentioned above, available only in the case of ideal gases, and become the more inexact the lower the temperature and the higher the pressure of the gas in question.

The Specific Heat of Gases.—Experience has shown that the quantity of heat which must be imparted to a definite quantity (by weight) of a gas, in order to raise its temperature $1°$, varies accordingly as the heating takes place at constant *pressure*, or at constant *volume*; in the first case the increase in temperature causes an increase in volume, in the second an increase in pressure, to the amount of $\frac{1}{273}$ of the values which these magnitudes possess at $0°$—according to the gas laws.

Accordingly we must distinguish between the specific heat of a gas at constant *pressure* and that at constant *volume*. Regarding the experimental determination, the simplest way to measure the specific heat at constant pressure is by a process patterned after the method of mixture, which consists in leading the warmed gas through a spiral calorimeter tube which is surrounded with water, and so determining the quantity of heat which is given out by the cooling. Delaroche and Bérard first worked with this method (1811); then, more extensively, Regnault (1853), and E. Wiedemann (1876), who considered especially the influence of temperature on the specific heat of gases; Lussana[1] has recently thoroughly investigated the influence of pressure. Further experiments are in progress at the Physikalisch-technische Reichsanstalt (Holborn).

For the direct determination of the specific heat at constant volume, the gas must be enclosed in a vessel, warmed to a measured temperature, and then cooled by dipping it in a calorimeter; an exact determination is easily prevented by the fact that the heat capacity of the vessel must be subtracted from that of the system in order to obtain that of the contained gas, and the heat capacity of the vessel is much greater than that of the contained gas.[2] But with the aid of thermodynamics we can, on the one hand, derive without difficulty a simple formula which allows the calculation of the specific heat at constant volume from that at constant pressure, and on the other we will be led to certain experimental methods which show how the ratio of the two specific heats may be determined.

Instead of the specific heat itself, *i.e.* the heat capacity of 1 g., we will commonly work with the heat capacity of 1 g.-mol, the so-called "molecular heat." If c_p and c_v denote respectively the specific heats of a gas of mol wt. M, at constant pressure and constant volume, then the two molecular heats are respectively

$$C_p = Mc_p \quad \text{and} \quad C_v = Mc_v,$$

and between these two exists the relation

$$C_p - C_v = 1\cdot985 \text{ cal.}$$

as will be shown below.

The Specific Heat of Gases at Very High Temperatures.—

A number of French investigators have recently succeeded in determining the specific heats of gases *at very high temperatures* with quite a considerable degree of accuracy. Mallard and Le Chatelier[3] exploded a gas mixture of known composition in a closed iron cylinder, and determined the *maximal pressure* developed thereby: this last measurement was performed at first with a Bourdon's manometer, which recorded its data by means of a needle on an evenly rotating cylinder. Later these same investigators employed "the crushing manometer" constructed by Sarreau and Vieille,[4] on which the pressure was measured by the permanent deformation of a small, solid, copper cylinder placed between an anvil face and a piston on which the

---

[1] Lussana, *Nuov. Cim.* [3], **36.** 5, 70, 130 (1894).

[2] But Joly (*Proc. R. S. Lond.* **55.** 390, 1894) showed that for sufficiently condensed gases this difficulty could be overcome.

[3] *Compt. rend.* **93.** 1014, 1076 (1881), in detail in *Recherches expérimentales, etc.*, Paris, 1883 (Dunod), and *Ann. des mines,* 1883.

[4] *Compt. rend.* **95.** 26 (1882).

pressure to be determined acted; also here the time occupied in developing the pressure was determined by means of a needle and a rotating cylinder. From the observed maximal pressure of the explosion we can calculate the maximal temperature, and since the heat developed by the explosion is known from the thermochemical data, we obtain at once the *heat capacity* of the gas mixture. A correction must be made to account for the heat given off to the walls of the explosion bomb, which on account of the quick occurrence of the explosion is inconsiderable; this correction can be calculated from the velocity of cooling observed by the decrease of pressure after the explosion, or it can be determined quite accurately in an experimental way by the use of receiving vessels of varying size.

From the fact that the maximal pressure of an exploding gas mixture, for example, "knall gas," when mixed with equal volumes of nitrogen, or oxygen, or hydrogen, or carbon monoxide, is diminished to the same extent, it follows *that these gases possess the same heat capacity up to the maximal temperature of explosion*, i.e. *up to* 2700°. This assumes that these gases have the same coefficient of expansion up to these temperatures, which can scarcely be doubted after the measurements of V. Meyer and Langer.[1]

These results have been confirmed as well as extended in several ways by Vieille,[2] and also by Berthelot and Vieille.[3] After it was established that nitrogen and carbon monoxide had the same molecular heats, the specific heats of the two gases could be calculated from the observed maximal pressure of an explosion of a mixture of cyanogen and oxygen

$$C_2N_2 + O_2 = N_2 + 2CO$$

and the heat evolved by this reaction. Finally, from further researches which were conducted with an excess of nitrogen, a linear formula available up to 4500°, for the molecular heat of N_2, H_2, O_2, and CO at constant volume, could be established.

This formula shows that the molecular heat of the permanent gases increases not inconsiderably with the temperature.

Later Mallard and Le Chatelier[4] used in a very similar way the maximal pressures of various explosives, as observed by Sarreau and Vieille, to calculate the specific heats of gases, and also obtained the result that the molecular heats of the permanent gases increase strongly at high temperatures.

Finally, A. Langen[5] has repeated on a larger scale the determinations of the maximal pressure of explosions of gas mixtures. The pressure charges are graphically recorded by means of a piston

---

[1] *Pyrochem. Unterss.* Brunswick, 1885.
[2] *Compt. rend.* **96.** 1358 (1883).   [3] *Ibid.* **98.** 545, 601, 770, 852 (1884).
[4] *Wied. Beibl.* **14.** 364 (1890).
[5] Compare the investigations by E. Meyer, published by the Verein deutscher Ingenieure, vol. viii. (1903); the monograph contains a very complete historical account.

indicator. Excluding the more uncertain measurements, when the maximum temperature of the explosion rose considerably over $2000°$, he finds a weaker increase of the specific heats than the investigators mentioned above. He gives for the mean molecular heat at constant volume :

Carbon dioxide	.	.	.	$6·7 + 0·0026t$
Water vapour	.	.	.	$5·9 + 0·00215t$
Diatomic gases	.	.	.	$4·8 + 0·0006t$

But gases with high molecular weight (halogens) depart from the last formula ; for instance, Mathias Pier [1] found by the explosion method, for the mean molecular heat of chlorine—$5·71 + 0·0005t$.

By the method of mixing, Holborn [2] finds between $0°$ and $1400°$ for molecular heats at constant pressure

Carbon dioxide .	.	.	$8·84 + 0·00326t - 0·00000079t^2$
Water vapour (between $100°$ and $1400°$)	.		$8·45 - 0·000302t + 0·00000079t^2$
Permanent, diatomic gases	.	.	$6·59 + 0·0005t$

If we subtract $1·985$ from the last value, we obtain the molecular heats at constant volume ; comparison with Langen values shows plainly that there is a source of error in the explosion method. As we shall see in Book IV. Chapter IV., extraordinarily strong compression waves and correspondingly strong movements are produced in an exploded gas mixture ; if the energy of these movements is not quite inconsiderable, as may be assumed, too small maximal pressures must be found by the explosion method, and therefore too low temperatures and too high specific heats.

Le Chatelier (*Zeitschr. phys. Chem.*, **1.** 456, 1887) has expressed the increase with temperature in molecular heats at constant pressure of poly-atomic gases by the formula

$$C_p = 6·5 + aT.$$

The coefficient a was found by him to be the greater the more complex the molecule.

Modern observations have shown this formula to be no longer tenable ; it can no longer be assumed that molecular heats of all gases converge to the number $6·5$ at absolute zero. The author has proposed the formula

$$C_p = 3·5 + n . 1·5 + aT.$$

n signifies the number of atoms in the gaseous molecules. This expression appears to agree satisfactorily with present measurements, and at the same time takes into account the condition that C_p for monatomic gases (where $a = o$) has the value $5·0$, as required by the kinetic theory (Book II. Chapter II).

The Thermodynamics of Gases : First Law.—As we have thus in the preceding sections familiarised ourselves with the most

---

[1] *Zeitschr. phys. Chem.* **62.** 385 (1908).
[2] Holborn and Henning, *Drude's Ann.* **23.** 809 (1907).

important *empirical facts*, to a knowledge of which we have been led by the experimental study of the behaviour of gases, we will now consider them from the standpoint of thermodynamics, which will both strengthen and extend them. It must be emphasised here that the results so obtained are not inferior in accuracy to the empirical facts on which they are based.

The law of the conservation of energy (p. 8), insists that the change in total energy which a system experiences through any event, is independent of the way by which it passes from the one to the other condition. Let us consider 1 mol of any gas enclosed in a vessel of volume v, which can be brought into communication with a second vessel of volume v'; and let us imagine that this system passes in the two following ways from the same initial to the same final condition. In the first way, the mol of gas, which originally occupies the volume v, is warmed 1° in temperature, and then a communication established between the two vessels. In the second way, communication is established at once between the two vessels, and then the gas, which now occupies the volume v + v', is warmed 1°. In neither case is the flowing over of the gas from the full to the empty vessel accompanied by any change of energy—either the performance of external work, or the development of heat—since the content of energy of a gas is independent of its volume (see p. 42); and in both cases the change of energy consists solely in the amount of heat which must be introduced to raise the temperature of the gas 1°. But in both cases the quantity of heat is equal to the molecular heat of the gas at constant volume, and the only difference is that in the first way the gas is warmed at the volume v, in the second at the volume v + v'. The two quantities of heat must be equal to each other, *i.e. the molecular heat, and of course the specific heat also, of a gas at constant volume, is independent of the volume at which the warming occurs.*

If 1 mol of an ideal gas is changed from the vol. v to that of v + v' by connecting a vessel of volume v which holds the g.-mol with an empty vessel of volume v', then there occurs no change in the total energy; but, as in the case of every automatic process, there is a decrease of the free energy, and it can therefore be used to do external work. The only question is to find a mechanism which will yield the maximal work, as is necessary for the application of the second law.

Such a mechanism is easy to find in this case: a cylinder closed at one end by a strong head, and shut at the other by a movable airtight piston, will satisfy the demands. When we raise the piston the enclosed gas does work because it presses on the piston from within; when we lower it we must overcome the gas pressure. If the cylinder is only capable of sufficient expansion we can bring the enclosed gas to any desired volume; and that by means of this apparatus we really obtain the *maximal* work capable of being obtained in the expansion, we may know by the fact that in a compression we must apply the same amount of work which we obtain in the corresponding dilation. Thus the mechanism described is "reversible."

. When a gas expands without performing external work no thermal effect is observed; but if, by the apparatus above described, e.g., the expansive force of a gas is used to do external work, then the gas must lose the equivalent amount of energy; and conversely, if the gas is compressed it must absorb an amount of energy equal to the work of compression. Therefore, by the application of the law of the conservation of energy to the ideal gas, we obtain the result, that *a gas when expanding absorbs heat equivalent to the external work it performs, and when being compressed evolves heat equivalent to the external work spent on it.*

Let us now imagine 1 mol of a gas, enclosed in the cylinder above described, to be warmed 1° by the addition of heat; in general, the pressure exerted by the gas, as well as the volume occupied by the gas, will vary with the temperature; the amount of heat necessary for a definite elevation of temperature will, therefore, also vary according to the manner in which these values change, as is shown both by experiment and by a consideration of some conclusions from the law of the consérvation of energy. Most easily considered are the two following limiting cases :—Firstly, we will add to 1 g.-mol of a gas the amount of heat C_p, required to raise it 1° in temperature, the warming being so conducted that the *pressure* remains constant : or, Secondly, we will add to 1 g.-mol of a gas the amount of heat C_v required to raise it 1°, the warming being so conducted 'that the *volume* remains constant. These quantities of heat, C_p and C_v, as already observed, are called respectively the *molecular heat at constant pressure* and the *molecular heat at constant volume*; by division by the mol wt. of the gas in question, we obtain respectively the *specific heat at constant pressure* and the *specific heat at constant volume.*

In order to obtain the relation between these two specific heats, on the one hand we heat the mol of gas, whose volume is v, through 1° at constant pressure; this requires C_p g.-cal. But since the gas expands during the heating, and, indeed, overcomes the constant pressure p which is weighting it down, so at the same time external work will be performed, which is found by the product of the pressure and the increase of volume; and since the former is p, and the latter is $\frac{v}{T}$, it amounts to $\frac{pv}{T}$. If, on the other hand, we heat the gas at constant volume, there occurs no performance of external work, and it requires only the addition of C_v g.-cal.

Now, according to the law of the conservation of energy,

$$C_p - \frac{pv}{T} = C_v,$$

or if we combine with it the gas equation (p. 40),

$$pv = RT,$$

we get

$$C_p - R = C_v.$$

If the molecular heat is expressed in cal. the constant R must be also so expressed.

Now, if we express p in atmospheres and v in litres, then

$$pv = 0\cdot0821T,$$

and therefore

$$R = 0\cdot0821 \frac{\text{litre-atmospheres}}{\text{degrees Celsius}}.$$

The left side of the equation, which represents the product of pressure and volume, is a quantity of energy which we estimate according to the method given above in litre-atmospheres (p. 13); in order to transform it to g.-cal. we remember that

$$1 \text{ litre-atmosphere} = 24\cdot19 \text{ g.-cal.},$$

and then

$$pv = 0\cdot0821 \times 24\cdot19T = 1\cdot985T,$$

and consequently

$$R = 1\cdot985 \frac{\text{cal.}}{\text{degrees Celsius}}.$$

The difference of the two molecular heats, therefore, amounts to

$$C_p - C_v = 1\cdot985 \frac{\text{cal.}}{\text{degrees Cel.}},$$

and the difference of the specific heats will be

$$c_p - c_v = \frac{1\cdot985}{M}.$$

Since, for the calculation of litre-atm. in g.-cal. the mechanical equivalent of heat must be known, so conversely this equivalent of heat can be determined from the difference between these two specific heats of a gas. As is well known, this is the way used by Mayer in 1842.

The relation between C_p and C_v can also be derived from the equation of p. 10—

$$C_p - C_v = \left(p - \frac{\partial U}{\partial v}\right)\frac{\partial v}{\partial T}.$$

If we apply this to one mol of gas, and remember that here

$$\frac{\partial U}{\partial v} = 0, \quad v = \frac{RT}{p}, \quad \frac{\partial v}{\partial T} = \frac{R}{p},$$

it follows that

$$C_p - C_v = R.$$

The Ratio of the Specific Heats of a Gas.—The application of the first law of thermodynamics to the ideal gas has led further to two very important experimental methods, which make possible a fairly exact determination of the quotient

$$k = \frac{C_p}{C_v} = \frac{c_p}{c_v}.$$

1. THE METHOD OF CLÉMENT AND DESORMES.—In a large glass globe is enclosed the gas to be investigated under the pressure P_1, which is made a little greater than the atmospheric pressure P. The globe is opened for an instant so that the pressure in the interior of the vessel sinks to that of the atmosphere, and then is closed again as quickly as possible. In consequence of the expansion the gas has somewhat cooled ; heat will therefore flow in from without, and consequently the pressure in the interior of the vessel will increase a little over that of the atmospheric pressure, to the value P_2.

We develop the formula for the case when P_1 (and therefore of course P_2 also) is only very slightly different from P, so that if we make

$$P_1 = P + p_1,$$
$$P_2 = P + p_2,$$

then p_1 and p_2 are very small in comparison with P, a proviso which must be realised in practical experiment.

If V is the volume of the globe, then on opening it at atmospheric pressure P, the volume $V \times \dfrac{p_1 - p_2}{P}$ escapes, and accordingly performs the work $V(p_1 - p_2)$ against the atmospheric pressure. This amount of work corresponds to the cooling of the gas in consequence of the outflow : on the assumption that, at the moment of the outflow, the quantity of heat introduced to the gas from without is vanishingly small, or, as we say, that the dilation occurs "adiabatically," then the amount of undercooling, by which the gas sinks below the temperature of the experiment T, can be calculated from the equation

$$\frac{t}{T} = \frac{p_2}{P},$$

since, in consequence of the subsequent reheating from $T - t$ to T, which was caused by the heat coming in from without after closing the vessel, the pressure of the gas increased from P to $P + p_2$. This reheating took place at constant volume ; and as there were contained in the vessel

$$n = \frac{PV}{RT} \text{ g.-mol (p. 41),}$$

so accordingly there was introduced

$$t\frac{PV}{RT}C_v = \frac{p_2 V}{R}C_v \text{ cal.,}$$

which must correspond to the work performed by the gas, and calculated above [viz. $V(p_1 - p_2)$] ; hence, if we express this in calorimetric units, we have

E

$$p_1 - p_2 = \frac{p_2}{R}C_v.$$

This equation will serve for the experimental determination of C_v; if we multiply it by the equation developed above on p. 48, viz.

$$C_p - C_v = R,$$

we shall have

$$k = \frac{C_p}{C_v} = \frac{p_1}{p_1 - p_2}.$$

In consequence of the unavoidable fact that, during the outflow, the undercooled gas extracts heat from the walls of the vessel, the value found for t, and accordingly that for p_2, and also that for k, will come out too small. These sources of error can be, however, reduced to a minimum by operating with as large a globe, and as small differences of pressure, as possible. In this or in a slightly modified way Röntgen (1870) found for dry air k = 1·4053, Lummer and Pringsheim (1894) k = 1·4015, Maneuvrier and Fournier (1896) k = 1·395.

2. THE METHOD OF THE VELOCITY OF SOUND WAVES (Dulong, Kundt).—According to a formula first developed by Laplace, the velocity, u, of transmission of a wave is given by the following equation :

$$u = \sqrt{\frac{p}{d}k},$$

where d is the density of the gas in question. The ratio of the velocity of sound u_1 and u_2 in two gases with the densities d_1 and d_2, when measured under the same conditions of pressure and temperature, is therefore

$$\frac{u_1}{u_2} = \sqrt{\frac{k_1 d_2}{k_2 d_1}},$$

or if we replace the densities of these gases by their respective mol weights (M_1 and M_2),

$$\frac{u_1}{u_2} = \sqrt{\frac{k_1 M_2}{k_2 M_1}}. \quad (1)$$

Now the ratio of two wave velocities is capable of exact measurement by a method given by Kundt.[2] If the clamped glass rod, G

Fig. 2.

(see Fig. 2), be rubbed with a slightly moistened cloth till it sounds its longitudinal tones, the air contained within the glass tube will be thrown into stationary waves which can be rendered visible to the

[1] Since pressure and density are proportional, the velocity is independent of pressure ; in the above formula, therefore, only equality of temperature is assumed.
[2] *Pogg. Ann.* **127.** 497 (1866) ; **135.** 337, and 527 (1868).

eye and easily measurable by the introduction of fine dust (as cork-powder, precipitated silica, etc.). By adjusting the stop E, which closes the end of the tube, the point at which the stationary waves are most sharply defined can be easily found. The distance l between two nodes is proportional to the velocity of sound in the gas.

The ratio for the specific heat of any desired gas, of mol wt. M, is thus obtained by comparison with the similarly determined value for atmospheric air (viz. 1·400), from the equation

$$k = 1\cdot400 \; \frac{M.l_1^2}{29\cdot01_2^2},$$

when l_1 and l_2 are the node intervals for the gas in question and for air respectively, measured under the same conditions of temperature and pressure; instead of $\frac{M}{29\cdot0}$, we may write the vapour density.

We will return later to the results obtained experimentally by these methods (Book II. Chapter II.).

The Thermodynamics of Gases: Second Law.—The application of the second law of thermodynamics will in this case teach us nothing new, since we actually derived the quantitative side of this law from the relations of an ideal gas to pressure and temperature, after learning that experiments conducted in any special system could be at once generalised. At the same time it is instructive to reverse our steps and convince ourselves how the general equation

$$A - U = T\frac{dA}{dT}$$

is to be manipulated in this case.

The process which we will consider will be the flowing over of a gas from a full to an empty space, and let the volume of 1 mol increase from v_1 to v_2: the change of total energy is equal to zero (p. 42).

$$U = 0.$$

The maximal external work to be obtained in this process, a knowledge of which is essential for many purposes, is easily found; for, according to the considerations put forward on p. 46, it is equal to the work required for the compression of 1 mol at constant temperature, from v_2 to v_1.

If we diminish the volume v of a gas, at pressure p, by an amount dv, then the work pdv must be done; if we diminish the volume v_2 of 1 mol of a gas to v_1, then accordingly the work $\int_{v_1}^{v_2} pdv$ must be done; remembering that $pv = RT$, we have

$$A = \int_{v_1}^{v_2} pdv = RT\int_{v_1}^{v_2}\frac{dv}{v} = RT \ln \frac{v_2}{v_1},$$

in which ln denotes the natural logarithm. If the pressure of 1 g.-mol, at the volumes v_1 and v_2 respectively, amounts to p_1 and p_2, then according to the law of Boyle and Mariotte

$$\frac{v_2}{v_1} = \frac{p_1}{p_2},$$

and therefore

$$A = RT \ln \frac{p_1}{p_2}.$$

The maximal external work to be obtained by the increase in volume of 1 g.-mol of an ideal gas from v_1 to v_2, or, as we have already defined it, the diminution of free energy associated with this process, is, accordingly—

1. Only dependent on the ratio of the initial and final volumes or pressures respectively, but is independent of their absolute magnitudes.
2 Proportional to the absolute temperature.
3. Equally great for different gases.

Of course n times the work is necessary for the compression of n molecules. If we choose, as unit of work, that which will be spent when the pressure of one atm. works during an increase in volume of one litre, then according to the above (p. 40),

$$A = 0{\cdot}0821T \ln \frac{v_2}{v_1} = 0{\cdot}0821T \ln \frac{p_1}{p_2} \text{ litre-atm.}$$

On the other hand, if we choose, as the unit of work, as is more customary, the work performed when 1 g. is raised 1 cm., against the earth's attraction, then it must be noticed that the pressure of one atmosphere, i.e. of a column of mercury 76 cm. high, amounts per sq. dcm. to

$$100 \times 76 \times 13{\cdot}596 = 103,330 \text{ g. in weight,}$$

and that therefore, when this pressure weighs down the volume of a litre, and thus works against the force mentioned above through a distance of 10 cm., then A assumes the value

$$A = 84,800T \ln \frac{v_2}{v_1} \text{ cm.g.}$$

Finally, in order to obtain A in our practical scale of energy, viz. the cal., we must divide this last expression by the mechanical equivalent of heat:

$$A = \frac{84,800}{42,720} T \ln \frac{v_2}{v_1} = 1{\cdot}985T \ln \frac{v_2}{v_1} \text{ g.-cal.}$$

Now, observing that

$$U = 0 ; \quad A = RT \ln \frac{v_2}{v_1}; \quad \text{and} \quad \frac{dA}{dT} = R \ln \frac{v_2}{v_1},$$

then the equation of the second law of thermodynamics

$$A - U = T\frac{dA}{dT}$$

becomes in this case an identity.

The Behaviour of Gases at Higher Pressures.—When we work with strongly-compressed gases, then the laws which we have thus far studied can be applied only with precaution; and at high pressures, and therefore at great densities, they lose their value entirely. Low concentration, the dissemination of gaseous material throughout a relatively great volume, is, in fact, the essential condition for the simple and regular behaviour of the ideal gas.

The compressibility of highly-condensed gases has been investigated by Natterer, Regnault, Cailletet, Andrews, and with special thoroughness in more recent times by Amagat. As the behaviour of strongly-compressed gases has given occasion to some remarkable investigations on the molecular theory, it will be considered more thoroughly in the second book. Here will be given a series of observations by Amagat[1] on nitrogen at $22°$, as follows :—

p in Atm.	pv.	p in Atm.	pv.
1·00	1·0000	126·90	1·0015
27·29	0·9894	168·81	1·0255
46·50	0·9876	208·64	1·0520
62·03	0·9858	251·13	1·0815
73·00	0·9868	290·93	1·1218
80·58	0·9875	332·04	1·1625
90·98	0·9893	373·30	1·2070
109·17	0·9940	430·77	1·2696

The compressibility is at first much greater than required by the Boyle-Mariotte law, reaches a maximum, then decreases considerably, and at about 124 atm. pv regains and passes its normal initial value. This behaviour is general.

The *thermodynamic treatment* of highly-compressed gases offers corresponding complications. If we consider again the expansion of 1 mol of a gas from v_1 to v_2, it must be at once observed in the application of the equation

$$A - U = T\frac{dA}{dT} \quad . \qquad . \qquad . \qquad . \qquad (1)$$

that U, the heat developed by expansion without the expenditure of external work, is no longer equal to zero, but has a value by no means inconsiderable, and, after the analogy of the heat of evaporation, it is usually negative. A is again given by the integral

$$A = \int_{v_1}^{v_2} p\,dv \quad . \qquad . \qquad . \qquad . \qquad (2)$$

[1] *Ann. chim. phys.* [5], **19.** 345 (1880).

to calculate which, p must be determined as a function of v in any given case by experiment. Finally, the first law of thermodynamics gives for change of U with the temperature (p. 9),

$$\frac{dU}{dT} = C_{v_1} - C_{v_2}. \qquad . \qquad . \qquad . \qquad . \qquad (3)$$

in which C_v denotes the molecular heat at volume v. The differentiation of the equation (1), or also direct application of the equation developed on p. 24, gives

$$\frac{\partial Q}{\partial v} = T\frac{\partial p}{\partial T} \qquad . \qquad . \qquad . \qquad . \qquad . \qquad (4)$$

in which $Q = A - U$, and denotes the heat absorbed in isothermal expansion with expenditure of work. Equation (3) can also be written in the form

$$\frac{\partial^2 U}{\partial T \partial v} = -\frac{\partial C_v}{\partial v} \qquad . \qquad . \qquad . \qquad . \qquad (3a)$$

assuming $v_2 - v_1$ to be very small. Now

$$\frac{\partial Q}{\partial v} = \frac{\partial(A - U)}{\partial v} = p - \frac{\partial U}{\partial v},$$

or combined with (4)

$$\frac{\partial U}{\partial v} = p - T\frac{\partial p}{\partial T} \qquad . \qquad . \qquad . \qquad . \qquad (5)$$

and this differentiated for T gives

$$\frac{\partial^2 U}{\partial v \partial T} = -T\frac{\partial^2 p}{\partial T^2}$$

or with the aid of (3a)

$$\frac{\partial C_v}{\partial v} = T\frac{\partial^2 p}{\partial T^2} \qquad . \qquad . \qquad . \qquad . \qquad (6)$$

Finally, the equation of p. 10

$$C_p - C_v = \left(p - \frac{\partial U}{\partial v}\right)\frac{\partial v}{\partial T}$$

in combination with (5) yields

$$C_p - C_v = T\frac{\partial p}{\partial T} \cdot \frac{\partial v}{\partial T} \qquad . \qquad . \qquad . \qquad . \qquad (7)$$

Although hitherto, applications of these equations have been advanced [1] only in a disjointed way, nevertheless it cannot be doubted that they are of great value in proving and extending investigations conducted on highly-compressed gases. Moreover, it should be emphasised that *these equations also hold good for the compression of homogeneous bodies, whether liquid or solid.*

---

[1] Compare, for example, Margules, *Wiener Sitzungsber.* **97**. 1385 (1888), and especially Amagat, *J. de phys.* [3], **5**. 114 (1896).

CHAPTER II

The General Properties of Liquids.—If we diminish the available volume of a definite amount of a simple gas by increasing the external pressure, the pressure exerted by the gas on the surrounding walls increases continually with the diminution of volume; if the temperature is low enough, there suddenly comes a point at which, by diminishing the volume, the pressure experiences no increase, but remains constant. At the same time it is observed that the material contained in the vessel, although of the same composition at all points, is present in two forms, distinguished by density, refractive index, etc. The substance has passed from the gaseous state of aggregation to a *much greater state of condensation.* The capacity of the substance to exist at the same time in two different forms depends on definite conditions of temperature and external pressure; for every temperature there is a certain pressure, the so-called "vapour pressure" (also called the vapour tension, maximal pressure, etc.), at which the gas and the more condensed form can exist side by side, or, as is said, *exist in equilibrium with each other.* If we diminish this external pressure, the whole mass goes over into the gaseous state; if we increase the pressure, it goes over to the condensed condition. If all the gas is condensed at constant pressure, then a further increase of pressure causes, qualitatively, the same phenomena as before the beginning of condensation. A gradually diminishing volume corresponds to an increase of the opposing pressure; only now the same percentage increase of pressure brings about a much smaller diminution in volume than before the condensation.

Now it is possible, according to the nature of the gas, by means of the experimental method described above, to condense the substance into two essentially different forms; if removed from the influence of external forces, especially gravity, it appears either in the spherical form or else crystallised in geometrical forms; in the first case the substance is called a *liquid*, in the latter a *solid.* Matter in the liquid state, like that in the gaseous state, has a relatively easy mobility of its particles, though the work performed by this reciprocal mobility, which is measured by the "internal friction," and appears in the form of heat, is always much greater in the liquid state than in the gaseous. It is not to be assumed that the common property of the gaseous and liquid states, as contrasted with the solid, is the lack of a tendency to assume a definite shape; for a liquid when left to itself, as when suspended in another liquid of the same density, and so removed from the action of gravity, by virtue of those inherent forces, which we will presently consider under "surface tension," takes the sharply-defined form of a sphere.

The special properties of the solid state will be dealt with in the following chapter.

Surface Tension.—The characteristic tendency of substances in the liquid state, when left to themselves, to take a spherical form, to reduce the free surface to a minimum under all circumstances, can be clearly explained by the method of Young (1804), by assuming that certain characteristic forces are active in the free surface of liquids. The superficial layer behaves like a tightly-drawn elastic skin which strives to contract. The force exerting itself normal to a section 1 cm. in length of the surface, is called the surface tension. A strip of the superficial layer of water of 1 cm. in breadth, for example, exerts a contracting force equal to 0·082 g. weight. Contrary to the behaviour of an elastic skin, this force, of course, is unchanged with unchanging temperature, despite an increase or decrease of the surface.

The absolute value of the superficial tension can be directly measured in several ways; if, *e.g.*, a moistened cylindrical tube of radius v is dipped vertically into the surface of a liquid, then the superficial tension works in the section cut off, and in a direction at right angles to the tube, with the force : length of the section × superficial tension = $2\pi v\gamma$, if we denote the latter by γ; this force will raise the liquid in the tube to such a height that it is exactly compensated by the action of gravity; hence

$$2\pi v\gamma = v^2\pi \mathrm{bs},$$

where h is the height of the liquid, and s its specific gravity, and therefore the right side of the equation represents the weight of the liquid raised. Therefore the surface tension, expressed in magnitudes which can be easily determined, is

$$\gamma = \frac{1}{2}\,h v s.$$

Vapour Pressure and the Heat of Vaporisation.—If we bring a simple liquid into a vacuum, evaporation takes place at once, till the pressure of the gas formed has reached a definite maximal value, namely, the corresponding vapour pressure. This pressure increases with the temperature, and usually very rapidly. In the presence of another, but an indifferent gas, evaporation takes place till now the *partial pressure* of the resulting vapour is equal to the vapour pressure (law of Dalton).

The passage from the liquid to the gaseous state, under the pressure of the saturated vapour, is attended with very important changes of energy : firstly, external work is performed; secondly, heat is absorbed from without.

Let there be enclosed in a cylinder with a movable air-tight piston a simple liquid, the vapour of which has the same composition as the liquid itself; and let the vapour pressure which it exerts at the (absolute) temperature T in question amount to p. Now we will raise the piston so far that 1 g.-mol of the substance goes over to the state of a gas; if this amount as a liquid occupied the space v', but as a gas under the pressure p, the volume v, then the external work performed in its evaporation is $p(v - v')$. When p is not too great, we can, firstly, consider v' as a very small, negligible fraction of v ; and, secondly, we can apply the gas equation in the form $pv = RT$, where, as usual, the volume is reckoned in litres and the pressure in atmospheres. The external work which can be gained by the evaporation of 1 g.-mol of any selected liquid under these conditions, amounts therefore to $0.0821T$ litre-atmospheres or $1.985T$ g.-cal. (p. 48) ; *it is independent of the nature of the liquid, and is proportional to the absolute temperature.*

Secondly, the evaporation of 1 g.-mol is associated with the absorption of heat. That quantity of heat which is identified with the evaporation of 1 g. of a substance is called the *heat of vaporisation* ; and that identified with the evaporation of 1 g.-mol of a substance is called the *molecular heat of vaporisation*. It varies with the substance ; its dependence on temperature can be calculated, on thermochemical principles (p. 9), from the difference of the specific heats of the liquid and of the saturated vapour, in the following way.

According to what has been said above, the diminution U of total energy in the evaporation of 1 g.-mol is equal to the external work performed RT, minus the heat absorbed, *i.e.* the *molecular heat of vaporisation* λ ; accordingly, if we assume that we can calculate the external work from the gaseous laws,

$$U = RT - \lambda,$$

and

$$\frac{dU}{dT} = R - \frac{d\lambda}{dT} = Mc - C_v,$$

where C_v is the molecular heat of the vapour at constant volume, and Mc the heat capacity of 1 g.-mol of the liquid. If, according to p. 48, we make $C_p - C_v = R$, we have

$$\frac{d\lambda}{dT} = C_v + R - Mc = C_p - Mc,$$

or if l denotes the ordinary heat of vaporisation,

$$\frac{dl}{dT} = c_p - c \qquad . \qquad . \qquad . \qquad . \qquad (1)$$

Now, in all cases hitherto investigated, the specific heat of a substance is greater in the liquid than in the gaseous state ; therefore *the heat of vaporisation always decreases as the temperature increases.*

The specific heat of liquid benzene was found by Regnault to be 0·436 between 21° and 71° ; that of benzene vapour at the mean temperature (46°) can be calculated, according to p. 45, as

$$\frac{6·5 + (273 + 46) \times 0·051}{78} = 0·292,$$

so that

$$c_p - c = -0·144.$$

Actually Griffiths and Marshall[1] found for the heat of evaporation of benzene between 20° and 50°

$$l = 107·05 - 0·158t ;$$

the difference between 0·144 and 0·158 lies within the limits of experimental error. The specific heat of liquid water at 100° is 1·01, that of water vapour (at constant pressure) 0·46, whence the latent heat ought to fall off by $1·01 - 0·46 = 0·55$ per degree, whilst Henning[2] found the decrease to be 0·63 between 90° and 100°. It should be remarked that water vapour deviates from the laws of gases appreciably on account of polymerisation (formation of double molecules).

The second law of thermodynamics gives an important connection between the heat of vaporisation and the change of vapour pressure with the temperature : in the same way in which we considered the flowing of a gas into an empty space (p. 51), we will now apply to the evaporation of 1 g.-mol of a liquid in a vacuum, the equation

$$A - U = T\frac{dA}{dT} ;$$

the volume, which is at the disposal of the evaporating liquid, we will choose as equal to the difference between the specific volumes of the saturated vapour V and of the liquid V' ; then we have

$$A = p(V - V') ; \quad \frac{dA}{dT} = \frac{dp}{dT}(V - V') ; \quad U = p(V - V') - l,$$

and accordingly

$$l = T\frac{dp}{dT}(V - V') \qquad . \qquad . \qquad . \qquad (2)$$

[1] *Phil Mag.* [5], **41.** 1 (1896).
[2] *Ann. d. Phys.* [4], **21.** 849 (1906).

an equation first developed by Clausius, and also given by the immediate application of the equation on p. 24.

Henning (*loc. cit.*) found the heat of vaporisation of water at 100° to be 538·7 cal.

The vapour pressure of water at 99·5° is 746·52, at 100·5° is 773·69 mm. (Wiebe, *Tafeln über die Spannkraft des Wasserdampfes*, Braunschweig, 1903); hence[1] at 100°

$$\frac{dp}{dt} = 773 \cdot 69 - 746 \cdot 52 = 27 \cdot 17 \text{mm.} = 0 \cdot 03570 \text{ atm.}$$

The specific volume V of saturated water vapour[2] at 100° amounts to 1·674 litres (Knoblauch, Linde, and Klebe, *Mitteil. über Forschungsarb. aus dem Gebiete des Ingenieurwesens*, vol. 21, p. 53, 1905), somewhat greater than that calculated from the theoretical vapour density of water (0·633 instead of 0·622 compared with air); the specific volume V′ of liquid water is 0·001 litre; therefore we find

$$V - V' = 1 \cdot 673 \text{ litres,}$$

and

$$1 = 373 \ . \ 0 \cdot 03570 \ . \ 1 \cdot 673 = 22 \cdot 29 \text{ litre-atm.,}$$

or

$$1 = 22 \cdot 29 \times 24 \cdot 19 = 539 \cdot 12 \text{ g.-cal.,}$$

a result in satisfactory agreement with observation (538·7).

As in the example given above, one can very often neglect V′ in comparison with V, and can calculate V with satisfactory accuracy from the laws of gases. The volume v of 1 g.-mol of saturated vapour amounts to

$$v = MV = \frac{RT}{p},$$

and therefore

$$1M = \lambda = \frac{RT^2}{p} \frac{dp}{dT},$$

or transformed and expressed, like R, in g.-cal. (p. 48),

$$\lambda = 1 \cdot 985 T^2 \frac{d \ln p}{dT} \text{g.-cal.} \qquad . \qquad . \qquad . \qquad (3)$$

a formula well suited for practical applications.

Within small temperature limits $T_2 - T_1$ we can regard λ as constant; then equation (3) suitably transformed

$$d \ln p = \frac{\lambda}{1 \cdot 985} \cdot \frac{dT}{T^2}$$

---

[1] On determining differential coefficients in such cases see Nernst and Schönflies, *Einleitung in die math. Behandl. der Naturw.*, 4th edit., München, 1904, p. 286 ff.

[2] Wüllner and Grotrian, *Wied. Ann.* **11**. 545 (1880).

can be integrated over this interval, giving

$$\lambda = \frac{1 \cdot 985 T_1 T_2}{T_2 - T_1} \ln \frac{p_2}{p_1},$$

in which p_1, p_2 are the vapour pressures at T_1, T_2. Introducing common logarithms

$$\lambda = 1 \cdot 985 \times 2 \cdot 303 \frac{T_1 T_2}{T_2 - T_1} \log \frac{p_2}{p_1}.$$

For benzene, Kahlbaum and v. Wirkner (*Dampfspannkraftmessungen*, **2**. 17, Basel, 1897) found, in good agreement with the earlier measurements of Regnault and Young,

$$T_1 = 273 + 20 \qquad p_1 = 75 \cdot 0 \text{ mm.}$$
$$T_2 = 273 + 30 \qquad p_2 = 118 \cdot 0 \text{ mm.}$$

whence the molecular latent heat λ is calculated at 7990 cal., whilst at the mean temperature $(273 + 25)$ the measurements referred to on p. 60 give $(C_6 H_6 = 78)$

$$(107 \cdot 05 - 0 \cdot 158 \times 25)78 = 8040.$$

For the temperatures

$$T_1 = 273 + 70 \qquad p_1 = 546 \cdot 5$$
$$T_2 = 273 + 80 \qquad p_2 = 750 \cdot 0,$$

whence $\lambda = 7640$ and the observed value is 7426. The appreciable difference in this case is due to benzene vapour being more dense at these pressures than accords with the gaseous laws.

The Form of the Vapour Pressure Curve.—The question, how the vapour pressure of a liquid changes with the temperature, or, in other words, what is the form of the *vapour pressure curve*, has been the subject of much experimental and theoretical investigation. At first the purely empirical result was found that the vapour pressure increases with the temperature, and indeed very rapidly, and accordingly the vapour pressure curve is convex downwards and highly bent ; its upper extremity is found at the critical point (see below) ; *its lower extremity in all probability is not found till the absolute zero*, where gases cease to be capable of existence, and the corresponding vapour pressure becomes zero. If the vapour pressures are chosen as abscissæ, and the corresponding temperatures as ordinates, the *curve of boiling-points* of the liquid is obtained.

There have been a very great number of researches to find out a universal law which should express the dependence of the temperature of boiling on the external pressure, with satisfactory accuracy. Theoretically, indeed, this problem was solved to a certain degree by Clausius in the formula derived above—

$$l = T \frac{dp}{dT} (V - V') ;$$

for, by means of this formula, the change of the boiling-point with the external pressure can be strictly calculated, and doubtless also with the greatest accuracy, if the heat of vaporisation, and the specific volumes of the liquid and of its saturated vapour in their dependence on the temperature, are known, and further if the volume of the vapour can be calculated from temperature and pressure (by means of a suitable equation of condition).

Thus, if the vapour pressure p_0 at some one temperature is known, we can calculate the value of V belonging to it, and thence $\dfrac{dp}{dt}$ by the above equation.   For a temperature higher by the small amount Δt, the vapour pressure is $p_0 + \Delta t \left(\dfrac{dp}{dt}\right)_{p=p_0}$, whence we may find V again, and so on.   It is therefore possible to calculate the vapour pressure curve by successive steps.

If the gaseous laws are applicable to the vapour (p. 59)

$$\lambda = Rt^2 \frac{d \ln p}{dT} \quad . \qquad . \qquad . \qquad . \qquad . \qquad (1)$$

and, by p. 57,

$$\frac{d\lambda}{dT} = C_p - C \quad . \qquad . \qquad . \qquad . \qquad . \qquad (2)$$

where C_p is the molecular heat of the vapour at constant pressure, and C the molecular heat of the liquid ; we can then integrate this over an interval of temperature such that C_p and C can be regarded as constant, $i.e.$ λ is a linear function of the temperature

$$\lambda = \lambda_0 - (C - C_p)T \quad . \qquad . \qquad . \qquad . \qquad (3)$$

(1) and (3) give

$$\frac{d \ln p}{dT} = \frac{\lambda_0}{RT^2} - \frac{C - C_p}{RT},$$

from which, by integration, .

$$\log p = -\frac{\lambda_0}{RT} - \frac{C - C_p}{R} \log T + \text{const.},$$

or

$$p = Ae^{-\frac{B}{T}} T^{-\frac{C-C_p}{R}},$$

where A and B are two constants that can be calculated by means of two pairs of values of p and T.   This equation is suitable over intervals of temperature that are not too great and are well removed from the critical point.[1]   For calculation over larger intervals of temperature C and C_p must of course be treated as functions of the temperature.

Comparison of the vapour pressure curves of different substances has led to results of importance that are very convenient in applica-

---

[1] For an application see Hertz, *Wied. Ann.* **17.** 193 (1882) ; *Ges. Abh.* **1.** 215.

tion. Dalton[1] pointed out such a relation, and by reckoning the *boiling-point from the absolute, instead of from the conventional, zero,* more striking regularities have been discovered.

As was shown in numerous examples by Ramsay and Young,[2] whose extended observations on the evaporation of liquids gave important information on many points, the ratio of the boiling-points of two substances *chemically related* is nearly constant when measured at equal pressures and absolute temperatures, *i.e.* reckoned from $-273°$; in the comparison of substances chemically different this ratio changes with the temperature.

In the following table, the figures of which are taken from the measurements of Schumann,[3] are given the absolute boiling-points with the corresponding pressures, for a number of esters, *i.e.* substances of closely-related composition :—

Substance.	T_1 760 mm.	T_2 200 mm.	$\dfrac{T_1}{T_2}$.
Methyl formate . . .	305·3	273·7	1·115
Methyl acetate . . .	330·5	296·5	1·115
Methyl propionate . . .	352·9	316·7	1·114
Methyl butyrate . . .	375·3	336·9	1·114
Methyl valerate . . .	389·7	350·2	1·113
Ethyl formate	327·4	293·1	1·117
Ethyl acetate	350·1	314·4	1·114
Ethyl propionate . . .	371·3	333·7	1·113
Ethyl butyrate . . .	392·9	352·2	1·116
Ethyl valerate . . .	407·3	365·3	1·115
Propyl formate . . .	354·0	318·0	1·113
Propyl acetate	373·8	336·1	1·112
Propyl propionate . . .	395·2	355·0	1·113
Propyl butyrate . . .	415·7	374·2	1·111
Propyl valerate . . .	428·9	385·6	1·112

According to the rule of Ramsay and Young, the ratio of the boiling-points in the vertical columns for any two substances must be equal ; the quotient $\dfrac{T_1}{T_2}$ must therefore be almost constant for all cases, as is in fact strikingly shown in the last column.

Other relations are found on comparing the boiling-point curves of two substances of unlike chemical composition, as, for example, mercury and water. In the following table are given some boiling-points, on the absolute scale, corresponding to the pressure p :—

---

[1] See also Dühring, *Wied. Ann.* **11**. 163 (1880) ; **52**. 556 (1894) ; and a criticism on Dühring's rule by Kahlbaum and v. Wirkner, *Ber.* **27**. 3366 (1894).
[2] *Phil. Mag.* [5], **20**. 515 ; **21**. 33, 135 ; **22**. 32 ; and *Zeitschr. phys. Chem.* **1**. 249 (1887), and S. Young, *Phil. Mag.* [5], **34**. 510 (1892) ; Groshans, *Wied. Ann.* **6**. 127 (1879).
[3] *Wied. Ann.* **12**. 58 (1881).

p.	T. Hg.	T. H_2O.	Ratio.
34·4	495·15	304·5	1·6262
157·15	553·2	334·2	1·6553
760·83	631·68	373·03	1·6934
2904·5	721·0	415·36	1·7359

The ratio of any two boiling-points at equal pressures is here by no means constant, but increases with the temperature; but if the increase of this ratio is divided by the corresponding rise of the boiling-point of water, we find for the three intervals of the preceding table, 0·00098; 0·00098; 0·00100; i.e. the ratio of the absolute boiling-points corresponding to the same pressures increases *linearly with the temperature*. The absolute boiling-point T of mercury for any desired pressure can therefore be calculated from the absolute boiling-point T_0 of water at the same pressure, from the equation

$$T = 1·6934 T_0 + 0·00098(T_0 - 373);$$

in this $1·6934 = \dfrac{T}{T_0}$, when $T_0 = 373$, and the vapour pressure is equal to one atmosphere.

The Boiling-Point.—Vapour is constantly ascending from the surface of a liquid except when the partial pressure of the vapour is greater than, or equal to, the tension of the liquid; in the former case a reverse condensation takes place; while only in the latter case can there be an equilibrium between vapour and liquid. Its surface is always acted upon by a pressure, which, according to Dalton's law, is equal to the sum of the partial pressures of the vapour and of the other gases present. If the liquid is heated so high that its vapour pressure begins to overcome the external pressure, then vapour bubbles begin to form in its interior, and the phenomenon of *boiling* is observed. The *lowest* temperature at which a liquid can remain *steadily* boiling is called the *boiling-point* corresponding to that particular pressure. That corresponding to the normal pressure of 760 mm. is called the *normal boiling-point*, or simply the *boiling-point*; its experimental determination is so simple and so common that we may dispense with a thorough treatment of it, but attention should be called to some important corrections.

Thus, it should be noticed that the boiling-point, measured at the prevailing atmospheric pressure, must be reduced to the normal pressure. The change dT, which the boiling-point experiences by a variation of the pressure amounting to dp, can be calculated theoretically from the formula of Clausius (p. 58):

$$dT = T\frac{V - V'}{1}dp;$$

but since the heat of evaporation 1 is as a rule unknown, it is proposed to introduce a method recently given by Crafts,[1] which is based on the law of boiling-points found by Ramsay and Young (p. 62), namely, that the absolute boiling-points, corresponding to the same pressures, of two substances chemically related, stand *in a constant relation*. In the following table are given the changes of boiling-point, divided by the absolute boiling-point of the respective substances at normal pressure ; the changes refer to a change in pressure of 1 mm. of mercury, calculated from the change of boiling-point which the substances experience in varying the pressure from 720 to 740 mm.

Water	.	. 0·000100	Carbon disulphide	.	. 0·000129
Ethyl alcohol .	.	. 0·000096	Ethylene bromide	.	. 0·000118
Propyl alcohol .	.	. 0·000096	Benzene .	.	. 0·000122
Amyl alcohol .	.	. 0·000101	Chlor-benzene .	.	. 0·000122
Methyl oxalate.	.	. 0·000111	m-Xylene .	.	. 0·000124
Methyl salicylate	.	. 0·000125	Brom-benzene .	.	. 0·000123
Phthalic acid anhydride	.	0·000119	Oil of turpentine	.	. 0·000131
Phenol .	.	. 0·000109	Naphthalene	.	. 0·000121
Aniline .	.	. 0·000113	Diphenyl-methane	.	. 0·000125
Acetone .	.	. 0·000117	Brom-naphthalene	.	. 0·000119
Benzophenone .	.	. 0·000111	Anthracene	.	. 0·000110
Sulfobenzide .	.	. 0·000104	Triphenyl-methane	.	. 0·000110
Anthraquinone	.	. 0·000115	Mercury .	.	. 0·000122

If the boiling-point of a substance is determined at a pressure removed from the normal, it may be approximately corrected by the addition of the absolute temperature 273, and then selecting that substance *most closely resembling it* from the preceding list : the corresponding factor is multiplied by the absolute boiling temperature, by which is obtained the correction which must be applied to the observed variation per mm. from the normal pressure.

The Critical Phenomena.—If a liquid is heated in contact with its saturated vapour, the density of the saturated vapour increases very quickly, since the vapour tension rises rapidly with the temperature. But the density of the liquid, which is expanding in consequence of the rise in temperature, is, conversely, continually diminishing. The question arises, does there exist a point at which the densities of the liquid and of the saturated vapour may be equal to each other ? The study of this question led to the discovery of the *critical phenomena*, which have assumed great significance in our conceptions of the nature of the liquid state.

As was discovered by Cagniard de la Tour,[2] and later thoroughly investigated by Andrews,[3] the following phenomena are observed when a gas is compressed, or a liquid heated in an enclosed vessel. If a gas, *e.g.* carbon dioxide, is compressed, then, at a suitably high pressure and low temperature, the contents, originally homogeneous,

[1] *Ber.* **20.** 709 (1887).
[2] *Ann. chim. phys.* [2], **21.** 121, 178 ; **22.** 411 (1821).
[3] *Trans. Roy. Soc.* **159.** 583 (1869).

separate into two parts with a dividing surface sharply defined ; or in other words, it is partially liquefied. The pressure at which this happens is, of course, the corresponding maximal pressure of the separated liquid, and it increases very considerably with the temperature. The question arises whether liquefaction can occur at all temperatures if the pressure is high enough,—a question which has been decided in the *negative* by the work of the investigators just mentioned. Thus, for example, carbon dioxide is convertible into a liquid by the application of a pressure of 70 atmospheres below $30 \cdot 9°$; but above that temperature the pressure can be increased at will, without the gas losing its homogeneity, and without liquefaction taking place.

When, on the other hand, a glass tube filled with liquid and gaseous carbon dioxide is heated, evaporation takes place gradually because the vapour pressure of the liquid increases faster, with a rise of temperature, than the pressure of the gaseous part. But at $30 \cdot 90°$, when the vapour pressure has reached 70 atmospheres, all the liquid evaporates, the meniscus which separated the liquid from the gas, and which had already begun to flatten out, vanishes at this temperature, and the contents of the tube are completely homogeneous. On cooling, a fog appears at the same temperature, and quickly gathers as a liquid in the lower part.

These very important phenomena are called "critical." That temperature, above which the liquid ceases to be capable of existence, is called the "*critical temperature*" (or the "absolute boiling-point"); the vapour pressure of the liquid at this point is called the "*critical pressure*," and its specific volume the "*critical volume.*" These three magnitudes are the characteristic *critical* data for every simple liquid, and, as will be shown in Chapter II. of the second book, they are typical of the entire relations between gases and liquids.

The critical phenomena make it possible to change a liquid into a gas *in one continuous process*, *i.e.* without its losing its homogeneity, by partial evaporation during the process, and the reverse. The liquid is heated above its critical temperature, care being taken to keep the external pressure always greater than the vapour pressure, and finally greater than the critical pressure ; if the volume is then allowed to increase, the originally liquid mass remains homogeneous, however much it is diluted ; it has been converted continuously into the gaseous state. In order to convert a gas continuously into a liquid, its temperature must be raised above the critical point, while the pressure is kept below that required for condensation ; then it must be compressed above its critical pressure, and cooled below its critical temperature, the external pressure being always kept greater than the corresponding maximal pressure of the liquid ; if now the volume is increased, the originally gaseous mass loses its homogeneity, gives off vapour, and is to be regarded as a liquid.

F

The term "absolute boiling-point" was proposed by Mendelejeff;[1] but since we ordinarily understand that to be the boiling-point of a liquid reckoned from − 273°, it might lead to confusion, and therefore the expression "critical temperature" is preferable, and particularly so as it is now universally accepted.

The results of the measurement of critical data, for which we are indebted to Cagniard, Andrews, Pawlewski, Dewar, and others, and recently to Ramsay and Young especially, are given very fully in Landolt-Börnstein's tables. I will only mention here a simple lecture experiment, which I consider very instructive for the demonstration of critical phenomena. A small glass tube with thick walls, partially filled with liquid sulphur dioxide, is placed in a larger test-tube which contains paraffin. If this is heated from the side in an inclined position, with a Bunsen burner, so that the upper part of the inner little tube is heated above the critical temperature of sulphur dioxide (155·4°), while the lower part, surrounded by unmelted paraffin, remains considerably cooler, then the meniscus vanishes. Under these conditions we have without doubt *gaseous* sulphur dioxide in the upper part of the little inner tube, and *liquid* in the lower part, *yet one sees nowhere a parting surface.* Thus this shows how liquid and gas can pass into each other continuously, in the circuit over the critical point. When carrying out this experiment, it is wise to protect oneself from the danger of an explosion, by a thick plate of glass.

If the liquid is not quite pure the vapour will in general have a somewhat different composition, and as owing to slowness of diffusion the state of equilibrium is only very gradually reached, the meniscus will disappear on heating at a different temperature to that at which it appears on cooling, unless the operations are very carefully conducted. Some investigators, in recent times, have been so deceived by this that they doubted the existence of a well-defined critical point. The careful experiments of Ramsay,[2] Young,[3] and Villard[4] have, however, put this beyond question.

---

[1] *Lieb. Ann.* **119.** 1 (1861).
[2] *Zeitschr. phys. Chem.* **14.** 486 (1894).   [3] *Trans. Chem. Soc.*, 1897, p. 446.
[4] *Ann. chim. phys.* [7], **10.** 387 (1897).

CHAPTER III

THE SOLID STATE OF AGGREGATION [1]

General Properties of Solid Bodies.—If we condense a substance occurring in the gaseous state, at a sufficiently low temperature,—*i.e.* below its fusing-point,—or if we cool a liquid substance to its solidifying-point,—then the matter appears in the solid state. This, in common with the liquid, and in contrast to the gaseous state, has the property, that *a change of volume* by a pressure from all sides is resisted by an extraordinarily great force. But it is characteristic of the solid state alone, that *a change of form* without compression is resisted by the so-called *elastic forces*. Work, which appears again as heat, must be expended indeed in a change of form of gases and liquids, in consequence of their internal friction. But in the case of solids, it happens that a relative distortion (not too great) of the particles places the system in a state of tension which corresponds to a considerable amount of potential energy. When the action of the deforming force ceases, then the body resumes again its original form.

Melting-Point and Pressure.—In the same way that at a given temperature a substance can coexist in both the liquid and gaseous states, only at a certain definite external pressure, so a solid substance can exist in equilibrium with its molten product, only at very definitely related values of pressure and temperature. We find the quantitative distinction, that while the boiling-point varies very much with the external pressure, the melting-point varies very little; so that for practical purposes the variation can usually be disregarded, and for a long time it was not observed.

This was established by William Thomson in 1850 for water, after James Thomson had previously predicted it theoretically. The process of melting can be treated thermodynamically, similarly to that of vaporisation.

The maximal work to be obtained by the fusion of 1 g. of a solid substance, is of course equal to the product of the increase of volume

---

[1] In the preparation of the crystallographic part of this chapter I have enjoyed the valuable co-operation of Dr. Pockels.

V – V' (when V is the specific volume of the liquid, and V' that of the solid substance), and the pressure p, at which both states are in equilibrium ; then will

$$A = p(V - V'), \quad \text{and} \quad dA = dp(V - V').$$

The diminution of total energy U is equal to the work performed A, minus the heat absorbed r, the so-called heat of fusion, *i.e.*

$$U = p(V - V') - r,$$

the change of which with the temperature (p. 9), neglecting the insignificant external work, is

$$-\frac{dU}{dT} = \frac{dr}{dT} = c' - c''$$

when c' and c'' denote respectively the specific heats of the substance in the liquid and solid states. The specific heat of ice is 0·5 ; that of water 1·00 ; therefore the heat of fusion of ice increases per degree of rise in temperature, by an amount equal to 1·00 – 0·5 = 0·5 g.-cal.

The equation,

$$A - U = T\frac{dA}{dT}$$

in this case assumes the form,

$$p(V - V') + r - p(V - V') = T(V - V')\frac{dp}{dT},$$

or

$$r = T(V - V')\frac{dp}{dT},$$

as is also given by the direct application of the equation on p. 24 ; when transformed the equation becomes:

$$\frac{dT}{dp} = \frac{T(V - V')}{r}.$$

An increase of pressure corresponds to a positive value of dT, *i.e.* a rise of the melting-point, if V – V' is positive, *i.e.* when the change to the liquid state is accompanied by an increase of volume ; on the other hand, it corresponds to a fall of the melting-point when the body contracts in melting, as is the case with ice.

Carrying out the calculation for water, at T = 273° ; V = 0·001 ; and V' = 0·001091 litre ; the heat of fusion r = 79·3 cal., then the work is equal to

$$r = \frac{79·3}{24·19} \text{ litre-atmospheres,}$$

and therefore

$$\frac{dT}{dp} = -0·0076°,$$

i.e. an increase of an atmosphere in the external pressure corresponds to a lowering of the melting-point of water, of about $0.0076°$. William Thomson (1851) showed that, as a matter of fact, by raising the external pressure about 8.1 and 16.8 atmospheres, the temperature of melting ice sank from $0°$ to $-0.059°$ and $-0.129°$ respectively, while these calculated from the formula given above, should be $-0.061°$ and $-0.127°$ respectively.

On the other hand, that the melting-point is raised by applying external pressure, in the case of substances which melt with increase of volume, was first shown by Bunsen (1857) for spermaceti and paraffin. Recently Batelli[1] and Demerliac[2] has found Thomson's formula to be well established for a number of organic compounds. Further, L. E. O. de Visser[3] has succeeded in measuring with great accuracy the change in melting-point with the pressure, *for acetic acid*; since he did not, as was done before, determine the melting-point corresponding to a definite pressure, but the pressure corresponding to a definite temperature. The simple apparatus used by de Visser, and which he named a *Manocryometer*, consisted of a large inverted thick-walled thermometer, its capillary tube being bent upwards, and then horizontally (Fig. 3). According to the temperature of the

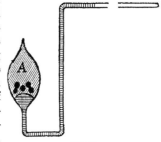

Fig. 3.

surrounding bath, it would assume that pressure at which the substance in A, partly liquid, partly solid, would find itself in equilibrium; the capillary tube filled with mercury served as a closed manometer with which to measure this pressure. The direct measurements of de Visser showed that

$$\frac{dT}{dp} = 0.02435°.$$

The heat of fusion was found to be 46.42 g.-cal., the fusing-point T, $273° + 16.6 = 289.6°$, and the increase of volume $V - V' = 0.0001595$ litre, whence

$$\frac{dT}{dp} = 0.0242°;$$

the agreement is excellent.

Recently the effect of pressure has been studied over a very wide range by G. Tammann.[4] The curve of fusion for benzene was traced to pressures of more than 3000 atms.; the heat of fusion was determined directly and shown to be constant within the experimental error of 1% between 1 and 1200 atms. The volume change $V - V'$

[1] *Atti del R. Ist. Ven.* [3], **3.** (1886).   [2] *Compt. rend.* **124.** 75 (1897).
[3] Dissertation, Utrecht, 1892; ref. *Zeitschr. physik. Chem.* **9.** 767 (1892).
[4] *Ann. d. Phys.* **3.** 161 (1900).

was also measured as a function of pressure along the curve of fusion. The following table gives the results ; the pressure p is in kg/sq. cm. ; V – V' in c.c. per gram of substance :—

t.	p.	V – V'.	r.
5·43	1	0·1307	29·2
10·12	161	0·1272	30·0
20·13	533	0·1118	29·6
29·59	925	0·1053	30·9
42·06	1455	0·0919	30·6
55·02	2040	0·0770	29·0
66·00	2620	0·0738	30·6
76·96	3250	0·0693	31·8

To calculate r from the foregoing formula the empirical equation

$$p = 34 \cdot 4(T - 5 \cdot 43) + 0 \cdot 150(T - 5 \cdot 43)^2$$

was obtained from the observations, $\frac{dp}{dT}$ deduced and then r calculated for the different temperatures. The heat of fusion appeared constant, in harmony with the result of direct measurement ; the mean calculated value was 30·0, the mean of the calorimetric observations 30·4.

The fact that V – V' falls off rapidly while r remains constant seems to be general, and indicates that the two quantities do not vanish at the same point.

The Vapour Pressure of Solid Substances.—As in the case of liquids, so also for every solid substance, at a given temperature, there is a correspondingly definite vapour pressure, although, indeed, in most cases it is so extraordinarily small as to escape a direct measurement. The vaporisation of a solid substance is called *sublimation*. Sublimation, like evaporation, takes place gradually from a solid substance in contact with the free atmosphere under all conditions, but it is especially rapid if the *sublimation pressure* exceeds that of the atmosphere. If this point, comparable with the boiling-point of the liquid substance, lies below the melting-point, then when the substance is heated in the open air it will sublime without melting. It is only by heating the substance in a closed vessel that it is possible to heat the substance to the melting-point, and thus to accomplish its liquefaction. But ordinarily the sublimation pressure of solid substances at the melting-point is much smaller than the atmospheric pressure.

The "*heat of sublimation*," *i.e.* the quantity of heat absorbed in the vaporisation of 1 g. of the solid substance, can be calculated from the change of vapour pressure with the temperature $\frac{dp}{dT}$, and from the specific volumes V and V' of the vapour and substance respectively, in the same way that was used for the calculation of the heat of vaporisation (p. 58), since the considerations there advanced hold good whether a solid or a liquid substance is evaporated ; accordingly

$$s = T\frac{dp}{dT}(V - V').$$

On account of the smallness of the vapour pressure of the solid substance, V' can be neglected in comparison with V.

At the melting-point, the heat of sublimation is equal to the heat of fusion + the heat of vaporisation of the melted substance, *i.e.*

$$s = r + l = T\frac{dp}{dT}V ;$$

and further for the vaporisation, the following equation holds good :—

$$l = T\frac{dP}{dT}V,$$

if by P we denote the vapour pressure of the liquid substance in the neighbourhood of the melting-point. Subtracting these two equations we get

$$r = TV\left(\frac{dp}{dT} - \frac{dP}{dT}\right).$$

The expression in brackets obviously depends on the angle which the pressure curves of the substance in the solid and the liquid states make with each other at the melting-point. But now the vapour pressures of the two states must be *equal* at the melting-point, because it is the point at which the solid and liquid states of the substance are in equilibrium with each other. Otherwise there would occur an isothermal distillation process which would cease only with the disappearance of that state with the greater vapour pressure, *i.e.* the two states of

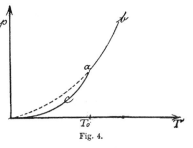

Fig. 4.

aggregation would not be in equilibrium. Therefore the pressure curves *intersect* at the melting-point, as is shown in Fig. 4. The dotted line is the pressure curve of the *under-cooled* liquid substance, and is the continuation of the pressure curve of the liquid. Probably the two curves would intersect asymptotically at abs. zero,[1] if one could under-cool a liquid so far. The preceding formula, which was developed by W. Thomson (1851), and also again independently by Kirchhoff (1858), was later experimentally proved by Ramsay and

[1] There is no evidence in favour of the view, often expressed, that there is a temperature below which solids and liquids do not evaporate at all.

Young (1884) for benzene, and by W. Fischer (1886) for water; also recently by Ferche (1891) for benzene.

From the latter's measurements[1] are taken the following numbers. In accordance with theory, the pressure of solid and liquid benzene at the melting-point (5·6°) had the *same* value (35·5 mm. Hg.). Measurement gave

$$\frac{dp}{dT} - \frac{dP}{dT} = 2·428 - 1·905 = 0·523.$$

On the other hand, this value can be calculated from the formula given above. The heat of fusion r was found to be 30·18 cal. $= \dfrac{30·18}{24·19}$ litre-atmospheres.

Further, according to the laws of gases

$$TV = \frac{0·0821(273 + 5·6)^2 . 760}{35·5 . 78}$$

(78 = molecular weight of benzene).

Hence

$$\frac{dp}{dT} - \frac{dP}{dT} = \frac{30·18 . 35·5 . 78}{24·19(273 + 5·6)^2 . 0·0821} \text{ (reduced to mm. Hg.)}$$
$$= 0·543$$

a result in satisfactory accord with experiment.

The Crystallised State.—Most solid substances separate by condensation from the gaseous state, or by congealing from a state of fusion, or by precipitation from solutions, in regular polyhedral forms, in case unfavourable circumstances do not interfere with their normal formation, *i.e.* they *crystallise*. All the physical properties have the closest connection with the external form; both the external form and the physical properties are conditioned by the *structure* of the particular body. Thus a *crystal* can be defined as a *homogeneous body, in which the different physical properties conduct themselves differently, in the different directions radiating from one of its points.*

The proviso of *homogeneity*, which is always tacitly assumed in the following sketch, declares that the physical properties depend *only on the direction, not on any particular portion,* of the crystal, and accordingly they are the same for all *parallel directions.* Only in a few cases are physical properties different in parallel, but opposite, directions. It is well to notice that this definition of a crystal does not consider the geometrical form of the limiting surface; this latter is the most obvious external sign of the crystallised condition, but it occurs only when the formation is undisturbed.

Crystallised (anisotropic) bodies are contrasted with the *amorphous* (isotropic), in which all directions are alike respecting the physical properties. Amorphous bodies are probably, as a rule, in a more or less unstable condition. (See the final paragraph of this chapter.)

[1] *Wied. Ann.* **44.** 265 (1891).

If two or more directions radiating from one point of a crystal are *equivalent*, we say that the crystal possesses *symmetry*. The symmetry of a crystal, as regards the different physical properties, varies according to the nature of the physical process considered. Experience has shown that the lowest grade of symmetry is always shown in the processes of *growth* and *disintegration* of crystals, especially in the *external polyhedral form* attending undisturbed growth. Therefore the latter, which lends itself easily to observation, is especially suited for the characterisation and classification of crystals. We will consider next, on this basis, the laws which regulate the *forms* of crystals.

The Fundamentals of Geometrical Crystallography.—As is known, normally-formed crystals are bounded by flat planes, which make *convex polyhedra* (*i.e.* such polyhedra as are cut by any straight line in only two points at most). It follows from the definition of a crystal as a *homogeneous* body, that planes having the same direction are equivalent. It must be noticed that in a plane the two sides are to be distinguished, and therefore two planes of the bounding surface can be similarly directed only when the direction of their *external* normals are coincident. Therefore it must always be borne in mind that, in studying the form of a crystal, the bounding planes can always be imagined to be moved at will parallel with themselves.

The first fundamental *law* of geometrical crystallography is the "*law of the constancy of interfacial angles*" (discovered by Steno in 1669); this declares that *the inclination of two definite crystal planes to each other, for the same substance, and measured at the same temperature, is constant, and independent of the size and development of the planes.*

The abundant data obtained in crystal measurement by means of the reflection goniometer, have taught us that this law has only an *approximate* value, for not infrequently on good crystals of the same chemically pure substance, which have apparently formed under the same conditions, and even on the same crystal, the corresponding angle is liable to variations of over $0.5°$.

By the term "*zone*" is understood a set of planes which intersect with *parallel edges*; the common direction of the latter is called the "zonal axis." A zone is fixed by any two of its planes. Conversely, if it is known that a crystal plane lies in two known zones, it is completely determined, for it is parallel to the two zonal axes, viz. two straight lines, which intersect. Experience has led to the following law, formulated by F. E. Neumann (1826), which is called the "*law of zones*," and which is the *characteristic fundamental law of crystallography*: *all planes which can occur on a crystal are related to each other in zones*; or, in other words: *from any four planes, no three of which lie in one zone, all possible crystal planes can be derived by means of zones.*

According to this there might be an unlimited number of bounding planes on a crystal; but by no means can every arbitrary geometrical plane be a face of a crystal. We must mention two other forms of the law which will make this point clearer. It must be considered that the law of zones insists on the zone relation only for all *possible* crystal faces. The planes then actually occurring on a single crystal need not necessarily stand in complete zone relation to each other.

In order to state properly, *i.e.* by numbers, the position of a face of a crystal, it can be compared with any system of co-ordinates fixed relatively to the crystal. It is usual to select as the co-ordinate planes (on grounds to be explained below), any three crystal faces not lying in the same zone (such faces, for example, as are remarkable for their prevailing occurrence, or as cleavage planes), and to correspond to the co-ordinate axes, three crystal edges, viz. the lines of inter-section of the three planes, OX, OY, and OZ in Fig. 5. In general this system of co-ordinates will be *oblique angled*. Then the position of any given fourth crystal plane (E_1, E_2, E_3), is determined by the length of the intersections OE_1, OE_2, and OE_3, which it makes on the co-ordinate axes; if a, b, and c respectively are these lengths, the equation of the plane is $\frac{x}{a} + \frac{y}{b} + \frac{z}{c} = 1$. As only the *direction* of the face is in question, we are only concerned with the *ratios* of a : b : c, which remain constant if the plane is moved parallel to itself. Usually one selects as *units*, the axial intersections a, b, and c, of any face (the unit plane), which does not lie in the same zone with two of the co-ordinate planes (fundamental planes); and by means of these units, the intersections of all other faces are expressed. These "axis units" a, b, and c, are usually unequal, and stand in irrational proportions to each other. Now if ma, nb, and pc are the axial intersections (parameters) of any fifth face of a crystal (H_1, H_2, H_3, Fig. 5), the three numbers h, k, l, which are proportional to $^1/_m$, $^1/_n$, $^1/_p$, respectively, are called the *indices* of this latter plane, and so, after establishing the fundamental planes and the unit planes, the direction of any other will be determined by the ratios of these three numbers

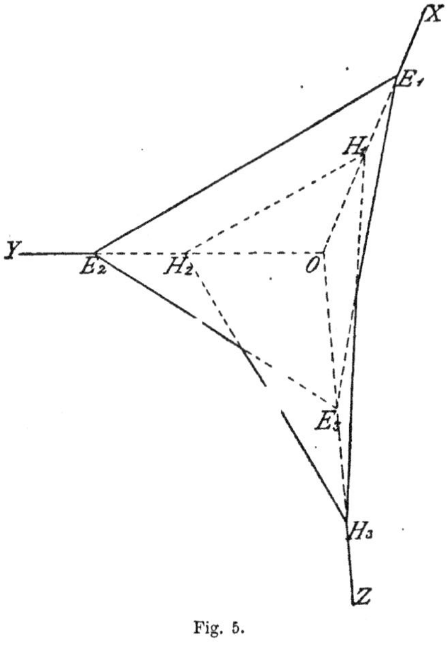

Fig. 5.

h, k, l. Now it can be easily shown that the law of zones leads to the conclusion that *the ratios of the indices of all possible bounding planes occurring on a crystal are rational numbers.* This *law of the rationality of indices*, the principle of which was first advanced by Hauy in 1781, of course holds good for any arbitrary choice of fundamental planes and unit planes, provided that these are crystal faces. The arbitrary common factor to h, k, l is so chosen that h, k, l shall be the smallest possible *whole* numbers; in the case of a plane which is parallel to one or two co-ordinate axes, one or two indices respectively will be equal to zero. It is to be observed that the indices are, in almost all cases, the *lowest whole* numbers (usually 0, 1, 2, 3, 4, etc.), and from this the law of the rationality of indices derives its significance; for if they were indeed irrational, one could always express the indices in sufficiently large whole numbers with an accuracy corresponding to that of the angle measurements.

The calculations of the indices from the angle measurements usually give at first irrational proportions. But according to the preceding empirical law, one is seldom left in doubt as to which whole numbers are to be regarded as the true indices; for those whole numbers are selected whose ratios are nearest to the irrational values. In general, for the determination of the indices of a face, it is necessary to measure two angles (see the paragraph on "The Determination of Crystal Symmetry," p. 90); but if one zone is known in which the plane lies, then the measurement of only *one* angle is necessary; and if two zones are known in which the plane lies, then the indices are fully given without the measurement of any angle.

Since this last case occurs very frequently in the determination of crystals, the course to be pursued will be explained more fully. For this purpose we must first consider the method of determining the *direction of the edges.* From any four crystal edges (*three fundamental edges* and *one unit edge*), all other possible ones can be developed, in accordance with the law of zones, by finding out successively the lines of intersection of the planes which connect two zones already known. Now if a, β, γ are the co-ordinates of a point of the unit edge, referred to the fundamental edges, and if $a\xi$, $\beta\eta$, and $\gamma\zeta$ are the co-ordinates of a point of any fifth crystal edge, then it follows from the preceding law that the ratios $\xi : \eta : \zeta$ are rational. We call ξ, η, ζ the *indices* of the edge or zone, and designate this latter by the symbol $[\xi, \eta, \zeta]$. Now if we select for the fundamental edges the intersection lines of the fundamental planes, and for the unit edge the resultant from the axial units a, b, c, so that $a : \beta : \gamma = a : b : c$, then to express the relation that a plane h, k, l passes through an edge $[\xi, \eta, \zeta]$, or lies in a zone $[\xi, \eta, \zeta]$, we have the equation

$$h\xi + k\eta + l\zeta = 0.$$

It is evident from this how the indices of a plane lying in two given zones, or how those of the intersection edge of two given planes, can be calculated from the solution of two linear equations, and also at the same time how the law of the rationality of indices follows from the law of zones.

A third method of expressing the fundamental law of crystallography, due to Gauss (1831), is the *law of the rationality of compound ratios*; this declares that between four crystal planes lying in one zone, or between four crystal edges lying in one plane, there exists such a connection that their compound ratio is rational. By the compound ratio of four such straight lines or planes a, β, γ, δ, is meant the following quotients of the sines of their included angles, viz.—

$$\frac{\sin (a \cdot \gamma)}{\sin (\beta \cdot \gamma)} : \frac{\sin (a \cdot \delta)}{\sin (\beta \cdot \delta)}.$$

That this quotient must be rational for the planes and edges of a *crystal*, is easily shown by the fundamental principles of projective geometry according to the law of zones, or according to that of the rationality of indices. In consequence of this relation, if we know three planes in a zone, or three edges in a plane, then all the planes or edges possible for the crystal, lying in this zone or plane, are completely determined. Since the compound ratio of four planes lying in a zone can be expressed by their indices, we obtain formulae which are of fundamental importance for the calculation of crystals, since they give the solution of the two following problems :—1. If we know the indices of four planes of a zone, and also two of the six angles between these planes, to calculate the other four angles ; 2. If we know the angles between four planes of a zone, and the indices of three of them, to find the indices of the fourth plane.[1]

In order to describe the geometrical form of a crystal it is clear from the preceding statements that one must specify as follows :— 1. The three angles between the fundamental edges or between the fundamental planes ; 2. The relative lengths of the units of the axes ; 3. The indices of the planes (or edges) occurring on the crystal. The quantities given under 1 and 2, which are the so-called axial units or the geometrical constants of the crystal, are, in general, characteristic for the crystallised substance in question (compare the last sections in this chapter, p. 80 ff.). The choice of these, as already observed, is to a certain extent arbitrary. At the same time, we must consider not only the fundamental law of crystallography, but also the relations of the crystal regarding its *symmetry* (see below).

As Hauy first observed, in its limitation the *symmetry* of crystals holds good to the extent that the differently directed planes on a well-developed crystal, which are regularly related to each other, are always of equal value and physical behaviour (as shown by the glance, striation, etc.). The relations of symmetry can be established much

---

[1] Compare Th. Liebisch, *Geometrische Krystallographie*, chap. iv., Leipzig, 1881.

more certainly by angle measurements; for the angles between two
pairs of equivalent planes must of course be identical.   If the symmetry were clearly expressed in the external form of the crystal polyhedron, we must suppose all equivalent planes to be moved parallel,
each with itself, till they are all at the same distance from a fixed
point in the interior of the crystal.   This ideal geometrical shaping,
which occurs in nature only in very favourable cases, must always be
presupposed in the study of the symmetry of a crystal polyhedron.
Let it be noticed here for subsequent use, that the related set of
equivalent faces is called a *crystal form* in distinction from a *combination*, which latter is a crystal polyhedron made up of dissimilar
planes.   It is not necessary for a simple crystal form to be a closed
polyhedron; but it can consist merely, for example, of a pair of
parallel planes, or even of one single plane.

The Classification of Crystals according to Symmetry.—We
now turn to the more detailed study of the properties of the symmetry
that a crystal polyhedron can have.

Symmetry can be determined by the occurrence of the three
following kinds of *elements of symmetry*: 1. A centre of symmetry; 2.
One or more axes of symmetry; 3. One or more planes of symmetry.
These symmetral elements have the following meaning in crystal
structure and geometrical form.

A Centre of Symmetry occurs when every two opposite directions
are equivalent.   In that case the crystal polyhedron is bounded by
pairs of parallel planes which, in ideal construction, are at an equal
distance from a fixed [interior] point.

An Axis of Symmetry is such, that by a rotation through a certain
fraction of $360°$ about this axis, every direction is transferred to an
equivalent one, and the crystal polyhedron again coincides with itself.
If $\frac{1}{n} \cdot 360°$ is the smallest angle of rotation needed, then the axis is
described as n-fold.   According as its two opposite directions are
congruent or not, this axis is said to be "*two-sided*" [bi-lateral], or
"*one-sided*" [hemimorphic].   Three sorts of "one-sided" [hemimorphic]
axes are to be distinguished according as the groups of faces lying
about their ends are enantiomorphic directly, or only after a rotation,
or as they are wholly different; in the latter case, the axis of symmetry
is styled "*polar*."   From the fundamental laws of crystallography it
follows also, among other deductions, that an axis of symmetry is
always a possible crystal edge, and the plane normal to it a possible
crystal face; and further, that only 2-, 3-, 4-, and 6-fold axes are
possible.

A Plane of symmetry is one in reference to which the two equivalent
directions lie, like an object and its reflected image, and by this plane
the crystal polyhedron is divided into two equal halves resembling

each other as object and image. A plane of symmetry must obviously always be parallel to some possible crystal face.

When several of the symmetral elements occur in certain combinations with each other, then the occurrence of certain other symmetral elements is conditioned thereby. Those symmetral elements which condition the others are styled "*generative.*" An important example of this is the law, that a centre of symmetry, a plane of symmetry, and an even-fold axis of symmetry normal to the latter, constitute a set of elements such, that any two condition the third absolutely.

Simple forms which cannot be brought into coincidence with their reflected image, and which therefore possess neither a centre of symmetry nor a plane of symmetry, are said, after Marbach, to be "turned back on themselves." Such a crystal form and its reflected image are styled *enantiomorphic* (Naumann), and are distinguished as right and left forms.

As such forms are of considerable theoretical interest in stereo-

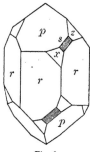

Fig. 6.

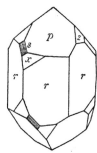

Fig. 7.

chemistry, drawings are here given of two enantiomorphically similar, but not congruent quartz crystals.[1]

From the different possible combinations of the generative symmetral elements, there comes about *the division of crystallised substances into thirty-two groups,*[2] which will be considered below. Of these groups, each of which is characterised by special symmetral elements, those are included in one *crystal system* which can be referred to *the same system of crystallographic axes.* By a *system of crystallographic axes* is meant such a system of co-ordinate axes as shall, on the one hand, satisfy the law of the rationality of indices, *i.e.* such axes as are

[1] From Bodlander, *Lehrbuch d. Chemie,* p. 427, Stuttgart, 1896.

[2] This was developed by J. F. C. Hessel, 1830; A. Bravais, 1850; A. Gadolin, 1867; P. Curie, 1884; B. Minnegerode, 1886; a thorough presentation is given in Th. Liebisch's *Physikalische Krystallographie,* pp. 3-50, Leipzig, 1891; also in the work of A. Schoenfliess, *Krystallsysteme und Krystallstruktur,* Leipzig, 1891. [For a brief but clear presentation of this somewhat difficult subject, see chapter ix., "Deduction of all Theoretically Possible Classes of Crystal Forms" in *Elements of Crystallography,* 3rd edit., by G. H. Williams, New York (1892).—Tr.]

parallel to possible crystal edges ; and, on the other hand, such as
express the symmetral behaviour of the crystal, in that this crystal
is always brought to coincide with itself by all those operations which
transfer a direction over to an equivalent one.   In reference to such
a system of axes, all equivalent faces receive indices which differ from
each other only in their order of succession and their sign.   Therefore
one can concisely designate *a simple crystal form*, by a statement of the
indices of any one of its planes (such indices are enclosed in round
brackets to distinguish them from the symbols of particular faces).
(For the numerous other symbols of crystal forms, which have been
introduced, see the text-books of Crystallography.)

Before we proceed to the enumeration of the thirty-two groups, and of
the crystal forms belonging to each, we must call to mind certain geometrical
relations which exist between the simple forms of the groups belonging
to the same system.   The symmetral elements of the groups of lower
symmetry of every system, form a part of the symmetral elements of the
groups of highest symmetry of the same system ; hence from the simple
forms of the latter groups (*holohedral*), we can geometrically derive all the
other groups by causing one-half, or three-fourths, or seven-eighths of the
planes of the holohedral forms to disappear, according to well-defined laws.
The forms so obtained are called respectively *hemihedral, tetartohedral,
ogdohedral*, and those which have *one* polar axis of symmetry *hemimorphic*.
It must be noticed that not all the simple forms of the hemihedral and
tetartohedral groups are geometrically different from the corresponding
holohedral forms ; thus, for example, the hexahedron [cube] and the
dodecahedron appear in all the groups of the regular system.   But the
lower symmetry of such crystals can always be recognised by their physical
behaviour, and especially by the position and shape of the *etched figures*
on their faces.   The notation of the hemihedral forms is accomplished by
prefixing certain Greek letters, as (κ, π, γ, τ, ρ), before the symbols of the
holohedral forms from which they are derivable ; in the case of tetartohedral
forms, two such letters are prefixed, since these forms can be developed by
the combined application of two sorts of hemihedrism.   The correlated
complementary forms of the hemihedral and tetartohedral groups respectively, corresponding to the holohedral forms, which are always physically
different, but only geometrically different when they are enantiomorphic,
receive symbols, which differ only by sign or position of the indices.   In the
accompanying abstract of the thirty-two groups, the following abbreviated
symbols will be used for the symmetral elements :

C, for a centre of symmetry ;

for m equivalent, n-fold, two-sided axes of symmetry, mL_n (in which the
   opposite directions are both counted, so that m at least is equal to 2) ;

for m equivalent, one-sided axes, and their opposites, mL_n and ml_n,
   $mL_n{}^*$ and $ml_n{}^*$, and $m\bar{L}_n$ and $m\bar{l}_n$ respectively, accordingly as they
   are one-sided of the first variety, or of the second variety, or polar ;
   and, finally,

for a plane of symmetry which is normal to no axis of symmetry, P ;
   and for one which is normal to an n-fold axis, P_n.

Unequal axes of symmetry or planes of symmetry of the same sort will be distinguished by accents. Of the simple crystal forms of the groups of lower symmetry, only those will be mentioned which differ geometrically from the corresponding holohedral forms. Further, the forms of the hemimorphic groups will not be especially mentioned, since it is clear that they can be derived from the holohedral forms by allowing the planes grouped about one end of the polar axis to disappear. Those groups of which no examples are known, will be given in brackets without stating the forms; in the other cases there will be instanced a number of the most important minerals and artificially-prepared substances belonging to them.

I. Regular System

Crystallographic system of axes; three equal axes at right angles to each other (parallel to the edges of the hexahedron [or cube]).

1. Holohedrism. C ; $6L_4$, $8L_3$, $12L_2$; $3P_4$, $6P_2$.

Hexakis-octahedron (hkl) $h > k > 1$; triakis-octahedron (hhl); icosi-tetrahedron (hll); tetrakis-hexahedron (hk0); octahedron (111); rhombic-dodecahedron (110); hexahedron (100).

Examples: P, Si, Fe, Pb, Cu, Ag, Hg, Au, Pt; PbS, Ag_2S; As_2O_3, Sb_2O_3; NaCl, AgCl, AgBr, CaF_2, K_2PtCl_6; Fe_3O_4; $MgAl_2O_4$, and the other spinels: garnet, analcite, perofskite, sodalite, etc.

2. Tetrahedral Hemihedrism. $6L_2$, $4\bar{L}_3$, $4\bar{l}_3$; 6P.

Hexakis-tetrahedron, κ(hkl); deltoid-dodecahedron, κ(hhl); triakis-tetrahedron, κ (hll); tetrahedron, κ(111).

Examples: Diamond; ZnS as zinc-blende; tetrahedrite; boracite; helvite.

3. Plagiohedral Hemihedrism. $6L_4$, $8L_3$, $12L_2$.
Pentagonal ikosa-tetrahedron, γ(hkl).
Examples: Cu_2O; KCl, $(NH_4)Cl$.

4. Pentagonal Hemihedrism. C ; $6L_2$, $4L_3^*$, $4l_3^*$; $3P_2$.
Dyakis-dodecahedron, π(hkl); pentagonal dodecahedron π(hk0).
Examples: FeS_2 (as iron pyrites), $CoAs_2$, etc.; SnI_4; the Alums.

5 Tetartohedrism. $6L_2$, $4\bar{L}_3$, $4\bar{l}_3$.
Tetrahedral pentagonal dodecahedron, $\kappa\pi$(hkl) ; the other forms as in 2, excepting (hk0), which appears as the pentagonal dodecahedra.
Examples: $NaClO_3$, $NaBrO_3$, $Ba(NO_3)_2$, $Sr(NO_3)_2$, $Pb(NO_3)_2$; $Na_3SbS_4 + 9H_2O$; $NaUO_2(C_2H_3O_2)_3$.

II. Hexagonal System

System of crystallographic axes; one principal [vertical] axis, and three others [lateral] normal to it: these are equal to each other, and intersect each other at an angle of 120°. Each plane has four indices, i, h, k, l, three of which, referring to the lateral axes, are related thus $-i + h + k = 0$.

6. Holohedrism. C ; $2L_6$, $6L_2$, $6L_2'$; P_6, $3P_2$, $3P_2'$.

Dihexagonal pyramids (ihkl), $i > h$, $-k = \bar{k} = i + h$; hexagonal pyramids, 1st order (i0il), and 2nd order (i.i.2i.l); dihexagonal prisms (ihk0);

hexagonal prism, 1st order ($10\bar{1}0$), and 2nd order ($11\bar{2}0$); basal plane (0001).

Examples: Beryl, Milarite.

7. Hemimorphic Hemihedrism. $\bar{L}_6$, $\bar{l}_6$; 3P, 3P'.

Examples: ZnO; ZnS (as Wurtzite), CdS (Greenockite); AgI_2.

8. Trapezohedral Hemihedrism. $2L_6$, $6L_2$, $6L_2'$.

Examples: d. lead antimonyl tartrate $+ KNO_3$; d. barium-antimonyl tartrate $+ KNO_3$.

9. Pyramidal Hemihedrism. C; L_6, l_6; P_6.

Hexagonal pyramids, 3rd order, π(ihkl); hexagonal prisms, 3rd order, π(ihk0).

Examples: $Ca_5Cl(PO_4)_3$, $Pb_5Cl(PO_4)_3$, $Pb_5Cl(AsO_4)_3$, $Pb_5Cl(VdO_4)_3$.

10. First Hemimorphic Tetartohedrism. L_6, l_6.

Examples: Nephelin $KLiSO_4$; d·$Sr(SbO)_2(C_4H_4O_6)_2$ and d·$Pb(SbO)_2$ $(C_4H_4O_6)_2$.

[11. Sphenoidal Hemihedrism. $2L_3$, $3\bar{L}_2$, $3\bar{l}_2$; P_3, 3P.]
[12. Sphenoidal Tetartohedrism. L_3, l_3; P_3.]
13. Rhombohedral Hemihedrism. C; $2L_3$, $3L_2$, $3l_2$; $3P_2$.

Skalenohedron, ρ(ihkl), rhombohedron, ρ(i0il).

Examples: P, Te, As, Sb, Bi, Mg, Pd, Os; H_2O, Al_2O_3, Fe_2O_3, Cr_2O_3, $Mg(OH)_2$; $NaNO_3$, $CaCO_3$ (as calcite), $MgCO_3$, $FeCO_3$, $ZnCO_3$, $MnCO_3$; eudialite, chabazite, etc.

14. Second Hemimorphic Tetartohedrism (Hemimorphism of Group 13). $\bar{L}_3$, $\bar{l}_3$; 3P.

Examples: $KBrO_3$, $Ag_6Sb_2S_6$ and $Ag_6As_2S_6$ (ruby silver), tourmaline; $NaLiSO_4$; tolyl-phenyl-ketone, $C_{14}H_{13}O$.

15. Trapezohedral Tetartohedrism. $2L_3$, $3L_2$, $3l_2$.

Trigonal trapezohedron, $\rho\tau$(ihkl); rhombohedron (1st variety), $\rho\tau$(i0il); trigonal pyramids, $\rho\tau$(i.i.2i.l); ditrigonal prisms, $\rho\tau$(ihk0), trigonal prisms $\rho\tau$($11\bar{2}0$).

Examples: SiO_2 (as quartz); HgS; $K_2S_2O_6$, $PbS_2O_6 + 4H_2O$, SrS_2O_6 $+ 4H_2O$, $CaS_2O_6 + 4H_2O$; benzil $C_{14}H_{10}O_2$, matico-stearoptene, $C_{10}H_{16}O$.

16. Rhombohedral Tetartohedrism. C; L_3^*, l_3^*.

Rhombohedron, 3rd order, $\rho\tau$(ihkl), 1st order, $\rho\tau$(i0il), and 2nd order, $\rho\pi$(i.i.2i.l); hexagonal prisms, 3rd order, $\rho\tau$(ihk0).

Examples: $CaMg(CO_3)_2$ (dolomite), titaniferous iron; H_2CuSiO_4, Zn_2SiO_4, Be_2SiO_4.

17. Ogdohedrism. $\bar{L}_3$, $\bar{l}_3$. Hemimorphism of 15 or 16.

Example: $NaIO_4 + 3H_2O$.

III. Tetragonal System

System of crystallographic axes; one chief [vertical] axis to which the third index refers, and two equal lateral side axes at right angles to it and to each other.

18. Holohedrism. C; $2L_4$, $4L_2$, $4L_2'$; P_4, $2P_2$, $2P_2'$.

Di-tetragonal pyramids (hkl), tetragonal pyramids, 1st order (hhl), and

G

2nd order (h0l); di-tetragonal prisms (hk0), tetragonal prisms, 1st order (110), and 2nd order (100); basal plane (001).

Examples: B, Sn; SnO_2, TiO_2 (rutile and anatase), $ZrSiO_4$; Hg_2Cl_2, HgI_2, $Hg(CN)_2$; $MgPt(CN)_6 + 7H_2O$; $NiSO_4 + 6H_2O$; KH_2PO_4, $(NH_4)H_2PO_4$, $Pb_2Cl_2CO_3$; vesuvianite, melilite, gehlenite, apophyllite.

19. Hemimorphic Hemihedrism. $\bar{L}_4$, $\bar{l}_4$; 2P, 2P'.

Example: Iodo-succinimide. $C_4H_4O_2NI$; Pentaerythrite $C_5H_{12}O_4$.

20. Trapezohedral Hemihedrism. $2L_4$, $4L_2$, $4L_2'$.

Tetragonal Trapezohedron, τ(hkl).

Examples: Guanidine carbonate, Strychnine sulphate, $NiSO_4 + 6H_2O$.

21. Pyramidal Hemihedrism. C; L_4, l_4; P_4.

Tetragonal pyramids, 3rd order, π(hkl), and prisms, 3rd order, π(hk0).

Example: $CaWO_4$, $PbMoO_4$; scapolite; erythrite, $C_4H_{10}O_4$.

22. Hemimorphic Tetartohedrism. $\bar{L}_4$, $\bar{l}_4$.

Example: $d \cdot Ba(SbO)_2(C_4H_4O_6)_2 + H_2O$.

23. Sphenoidal Hemihedrism. $2L_2$, $4L_2$; 2P.

Tetragonal di-sphenoid, κ(hkl), and sphenoid, κ(hhl).

Examples: $CuFeS_2$ (copper pyrites); CH_4N_2O (urea); KH_2PO_4.

[24. Sphenoidal Tetartohedrism. L_2^*, l_2^*.]

IV. Orthorhombic System

System of crystallographic axes; three unequal axes at right angles to each other.

25. Holohedrism. C; $2L_2$, $2L_2'$, $2L_2''$; P_2, P_2', P_2''.

Orthorhombic pyramids (hkl); prisms (hk0), (h0k), and (0hk); pairs of planes (pinacoids) (100), (010), and (001) the basal plane.

The great majority of minerals, and especially also of artificially-prepared substances, crystallise partly in this group and partly in group 28.

Some examples are: S, I, $HgCl_2$, HgI_2; FeS_2 (marcasite), Cu_2S; Sb_2S_3; TiO_2 (brookite); $BaCO_3$, $CaCO_3$ (aragonite), $SrCO_3$, $PbCO_3$; KNO_3, $AgNO_3$; $CaSO_4$, $BaSO_4$, $SrSO_4$, $PbSO_4$; K_2SO_4; Mg_2SiO_4, Fe_2SiO_4; topaz, andalusite; $MgSiO_3$.

26. Hemimorphism. $\bar{L}_2$, $\bar{l}_2$; P, P'.

Examples: $Zn_2(HO)_2SiO_3$, $Mg(NH_4)PO_4 + 6H_2O$; resorcin, $C_6H_6O_2$, tri-phenyl-methane $(C_6H_5)_3CH$.

27. Hemihedrism. $2L_2$, $2L_2'$, $2L_2''$.

Orthorhombic sphenoid, κ(hkl).

Examples: $MgSO_4 + 7H_2O$, $ZnSO_4 + 7H_2O$; $d \cdot K(SbO)C_4H_4O_6$, $KHC_4H_4O_6$, $KNaC_4H_4O_6 + 4H_2O$, $NH_4NaC_4H_4O_6 + 4H_2O$, $C_3H_8O_3$, asparagine, mycose, etc.

V. Monoclinic System

System of crystallographic axes; two inclined axes, and another (ortho-axis) normal to the plane of the first two; the middle index refers to this ortho-axis: all three axes are unequal.

28. Holohedrism. C, L_2; l_2; P_2.

Prisms (hkl), (hk0), (0kl): pairs of planes in the zone of the ortho-axis (h0l) ; especially orthopinacoid (100), and basal plane (001) ; clinopinacoid (010).

Examples very numerous; among others: S (two modifications), Se ; AsS ; As_2O_3 ; Sb_2O_3 ; $NaCl + 2H_2O$; $KClO_3$; $Na_2CO_3 + 10H_2O$; $BaCa(CO_3)_2$; $(CuCO_3)_2 + H_2CuO_2$; $Na_2SO_4 + 10H_2O$; $CaSO_4 + 2H_2O$ (selenite), $(FeSO_4 + 7H_2O$; $MgK_2(SO_4)_2 + 6H_2O$; and its isomorph, $CaNa_2(SO_4)_2$; $PbCrO_4$; $(MnFe)WO_4$ (wolframite) ; $Fe_4(PO_4)_2 + 8H_2O$; $Na_2B_4O_7 + 10H_2O$; $CaSiO_3$ (wollastonite) ; augite, hornblende, euclase, epidote, orthite, datholite, orthoclase, mica, titanite, heulandite, harmotome, etc. ; most organic substances, as oxalic acid, potassium binoxalate, salicylic acid, naphthalene, anthracene.

29. Hemimorphism. $\bar{L}_2, \bar{I}_2$.
Examples : Tartaric acid, quercite, cane sugar, milk sugar, etc.
30. Hemihedrism. P. Example : skolezite.

VI. Triclinic System

System of crystallographic axes ; three obliquely inclined, unequal axes.
31. Holohedrism. C.
All the simple forms are only pairs of [parallel] planes.
Examples : $B(OH)_3$; $CuSO_4 + 5H_2O$, $K_2Cr_2O_7$, $CaS_2O_3 + 6H_2O$; $MnSiO_3$, Al_2SiO_5 (disthene), axinite, microcline, albite and anorthite, racemic acid, $C_4H_6O_6 + 2H_2O$.
32. Hemihedrism. No element of symmetry.
Example : d. monostrontium tartrate, $Sr(HC_4H_4O_6)_2 + 2H_2O$.

One can also deduce these thirty-two groups, without assuming the law of the rationality of indices, by starting with the conception of homogeneity. This method of treatment is considered in the " theories of crystal structure,"[1] which rest on molecular conceptions, and according to which there occurs an arrangement of the molecules of a crystal about its centre of gravity *in a regular system of points.* All the possible regular *point-systems* can be developed by the interpenetration of congruent, parallelopipedal *space-gratings*, of which there are fourteen varieties ; and according to their symmetry, the point-systems arrange themselves in the well-known thirty-two groups. This theory leads also, in an obvious way, to the law of the rationality of indices, by regarding the faces of a crystal as *net-planes* of the point-system.

Twinning and Growths of Crystals.—We must now consider those regular· growths called *twins*, [threelings, fourlings, etc.], which consist respectively of two or more individuals, and which allow the production of forms of apparently higher symmetry than corresponds to their crystal structure. These growths can, as a rule, be recognised

---

[1] Frankenheim, 1835 ; Bravais, 1850 ; Camille Jordan, 1868 ; Sohncke, 1876 ; Fedorow, 1890 ; and with special thoroughness in Schoenfliess' *Krystallsysteme und Krystallstruktur*. Leipzig, 1891.

by the presence of re-entrant angles, which never occur on simple crystal individuals, or else by a varying behaviour of different parts of the same face.

We distinguish between twins with parallel axes and those with axes which are not parallel. The former are growths of two *hemihedral* (or tetartohedral) forms respectively which bear the same relative position to each other as in the [theoretical] derivation from their holohedral (or hemihedral) forms. They are called *complementary twins*. Examples are the interpenetration of two pentagonal dodecahedra of iron pyrites, or the intergrowths of right- and left-handed quartz crystals. For the second class of twins [viz. with axes not parallel], which are by far the more common, the regularity is that the two crystal individuals lie symmetrically with reference either to one of their *possible faces or one of their edges*. In the case of those twins which are symmetrical to a plane, this plane is called the *twinning plane*; in the case of those twins which are symmetrical with reference to a straight line, the plane normal to this line is the *twinning plane*; the line normal to this plane is the *twinning axis*; in crystals which are centrally symmetric it is a symmetric axis of twinning. The two twinning individuals may either penetrate each other (interpenetration twins), or they may touch each other along a plane (contact twins); and, as is often the case, it is not necessary that this plane should be the twinning plane.

Repeated twinning growths frequently occur in parallel planes; in this case the alternating individuals (often as thin sheets), occur in parallel arrangement; in this way arise the *twinning lamellæ*, for instance, of calcite, aragonite, and especially of the triclinic feldspars (polysynthetic twinning). Twins or fourlings may show forms which apparently belong to crystal systems of a higher symmetry than that possessed by the single individuals; important illustrations are the pseudohexagonal prisms (or pyramids) of orthorhombic aragonite and witherite; also the crystals of chrysoberyl, harmotome, and phillipsite; such forms are called *pseudo-symmetric* or *mimetic*.

It is worthy of notice that twinning growth may occur not only in the original building-up of a crystal, but also in a secondary way from external pressure; calcite is a remarkable example of this.

The *growth of crystals, i.e.* the relative development of the different faces, is very variable and often irregular, so that equivalent faces often have a very different size; these are distortions. The conditions controlling these distortions are not well understood. P. Curie (1885) and others have suggested as a controlling factor a certain "surface energy," analogous to that on the surface of liquids, which would be different for the unequal planes of the same crystal; but except for the observation that larger crystals grow at the expense of smaller ones, when placed in the same saturated solution, this hypothesis has led to hardly any results in harmony with experiment.

The solubility of a crystal is not the same in all directions. This can be shown by treating the surfaces for a short time with a solvent. Regularly bounded marks are thus formed (*Aetzfiguren*) whose arrangement shows the same symmetry as the ideally developed crystal, and often offers the only means of determining the crystallographic group.[1] Of two dissimilar faces of the same crystal, one may show the greater solubility in one solvent, the other in another. This may explain the varying *habitus* of crystals of the same substances, *e.g.* sodium chloride, which usually crystallises in cubes, comes down with octahedral faces from a solution containing urea.

The Physical Properties of Crystals.—In the case of all physical properties which are directed quantities, there appears in crystals a dependence on direction which, in the elementary laws of the processes in question, is expressed by a number of constants characteristic for each crystal. As already stated, the symmetry, which in the behaviour of a crystal appears correlated with some physical action, is always the same as that of its geometrical form, or higher; and the division into groups which one obtains by a classification based on any physical property is always in harmony with the classification previously developed from the crystalline form. In the following section we will consider the physical properties particularly in their relations to symmetry; and we will consider the physical laws themselves only in so far as they are of especial importance for the determination of crystallographic symmetry. For more details reference must be made to the text-books of physics; and here special mention should be made of Liebisch's *Grundriss der physikalischen Krystallographie*.

The physical properties of crystals may be divided into two groups, according as they possess a higher or lower symmetry. But the symmetry of the physical properties is never lower than that shown by the processes of growth and solution. Higher symmetry is shown by all those physical properties whose elementary laws in crystals can be expressed by an ellipsoid (for which, therefore, regular crystals behave as isotropic); lower symmetry by those for which this is not possible.

To the first class belong *thermal expansion* and *compression by equal pressure from all sides*; the *conduction* of *heat* and *electricity*, *dielectric* and *magnetic polarisation*, and finally the *thermo-electric phenomena*. The significance of the ellipsoid in these cases is essentially as follows :—

In thermal expansion an imaginary sphere in the inner part of the crystal is distorted to an ellipsoid, the principal axes of which are proportional to $1 + \lambda_1 t$, $1 + \lambda_2 t$, $1 + \lambda_3 t$; where λ_1, λ_2, and λ_3 respectively are the principal coefficients of expansion, and t is the amount of the

---

[1] Liebisch, *Grundriss der physikalischen Krystallographie*, p. 43, Leipzig, 1896.

change of temperature. If this *ellipsoid of dilatation* is given for a definite temperature interval t, then one can calculate the changes of the dimensions and of the angles of the crystal.

In the case of the phenomena of conduction, suppose that at a point of a crystal (of unlimited extension), there is a source of heat or of electricity; then the surfaces of equal temperature (or potential respectively) will be similar and similarly arranged ellipsoids, the principal axes of which are proportional to the square roots of the principal conductivities.

Finally, the relations between the intensity and the direction of di-electric polarisation (or of the magnetic polarisation) of a crystal, in a homogeneous field, on the one hand, and the direction of the lines of force on the other hand, can be shown by the aid of an ellipsoid, whose principal semi-axes are the square roots of the reciprocals of the principal di-electric coefficients (or magnetic constants respectively). Similarly, an ellipsoid serves to show the connection between thermo-electric force and the direction of the greatest fall in temperature.

Inasmuch as six magnitudes must be determined in order to fix the directions and lengths of the principal axes of an ellipsoid of un-equal axes, so processes of this sort, in the most general cases, depend on *six* physical constants, the values of which will vary with the temperature (and the pressure). Thus, from the consideration of each of the physical properties enumerated above, we can classify crystals into the five following groups :—

I. Regular System : the ellipsoid is a sphere; no distinction from the behaviour of amorphous bodies. 1 constant.

II. Hexagonal and Tetragonal Systems : the ellipsoid is one of rotation, where the chief crystallographic axis is the axis of rotation; the length of this axis and of the equatorial semi-diameter are alone to be determined; therefore 2 constants. For every physical property one can make two subdivisions of this class, according as the ellipsoid of rotation is oblate or prolate.

III. Orthorhombic System : the ellipsoid has three unequal axes having a fixed direction, but of variable lengths ; these are the crystallographic axes. 3 constants.

IV. Monoclinic System : one of the three unequal axes of the ellipsoid coincides with the ortho-axis ; the directions of the two others vary. 4 constants.

V. Triclinic System : all three axes of the ellipsoid vary in length and direction. 6 constants.

In relation to the properties considered here, the crystals of group I. are *isotropic*, those of group II. have *one axis of isotropy*, those of groups III., IV., and V. have *no axis of isotropy*.

The Optical Properties of Crystals.—A somewhat greater multiplicity of the relations of symmetry appears in the *optical pro-*

perties of crystals.   Here also, as will be seen below, the behaviour of the great majority of *transparent* crystals can be explained by the aid of an ellipsoid, but there are two groups of transparent crystals, viz. the " optically active," for which the ellipsoid is not suitable ; and when the crystals absorb light the relations are very complicated. The latter subject we must pass by with a reference to P. Drude's [1] work, only it should be observed that an absorbing crystal has always twice as many optical constants as a [perfectly] transparent one of the same symmetry.

The division of crystals, then, according to their optical behaviour, is as follows :—

A. Optically Isotropic Crystals

I. *Singly refracting* : regular system.— The wave-surface is a sphere. 1 constant. (Very often regular crystals also show weak, irregular double refraction ; this belongs to the so-called " optical anomalies," the cause of which, though certainly of a secondary nature, has not been satisfactorily explained.)

II. *Having the power of rotation* [rotary polarisation].—A part of the crystals of group 5 belong here.   The wave-surface consists of two concentric spheres.   2 constants.

B. Optically Anisotropic Crystals with One Axis of Isotropy

III. *Optically Uni - axial without Rotatory Power* (hexagonal and tetragonal system).—The wave-surface (Huyghens's) consists of an ellipsoid of rotation (the rotation axis of which coincides with the chief crystallographic axis), and of a sphere which touches the former at the poles.   The optically uni-axial crystals are subdivided into positive and negative varieties, according as the ellipsoid of rotation is prolate or oblate. 2 constants.

IV. *Optically Uni-axial with Rotatory Power* (groups 15, 17, and 20).— The wave-surface consists of two rotation-surfaces, one differing but little from an ellipsoid, and the other but little from a sphere.   3 constants.

C. Optically Anisotropic Crystals without Axis of Isotropy

The wave-surface (Fresnel's) is in all cases a surface of the fourth degree, with three twofold axes of symmetry at right angles to each other. It is cut by its planes of symmetry in a circle and in an ellipse, and has two pairs of singular tangential planes touching it in circles.   The normals to these tangential planes are *the optic axes*.   Distinctions arise here if we take into consideration the crystallographic orientation of the optic axes of symmetry, and their connection with the temperature and with the wavelength of light.   There are the three following classes :—

V. *Optically Bi-axial Crystals of. the Orthorhombic System.* — Fixed

[1] *Wied. Ann.* **40.** 665 (1890).

directions of the optic axes of symmetry, coinciding with the crystallographic axes. 3 constants.

VI. *Optically Bi-axial Crystals of the Monoclinic System.*—Only one optical axis of symmetry is fixed, viz. that having the same direction as the ortho-axis. 4 constants.

VII. *Optically Bi-axial Crystals of the Triclinic System.*—All three of the optic axes of symmetry have variable positions. 6 constants.

The law of double refraction in inactive anisotropic crystals, or those of categories III., V., VI., and VII., can be easily developed in the following way with the help of the so-called "*index-ellipsoid.*" Its semi-axes coincide in direction with the optic axes of symmetry, and their values can be easily derived from the three or two chief indices of refraction as follows.

One obtains the velocity of transmission, and the polarising directions of those plane waves which advance in a given direction, by passing, through the middle point of the index ellipsoid, a plane normal to this direction, and then determining the principal axes of the resulting elliptical section. These axes are the polarising directions sought, and their reciprocals are the velocities of transmission, compared with these in air as unity; here it is to be observed that the velocity of transmission of every wave is determined by that ellipse axis which is at right angles to the plane of polarisation. The two directions for which the ellipse section is a circle, when the polarisation direction is indefinite and the two wave velocities are equal to each other, are the *optic axes.* On this method is based the derivation of many phenomena of double refraction, which cannot be entered into here, but which will be found thoroughly presented, for example, in Liebisch's *Physikalische Krystallographie.*

Optical activity is superimposed on ordinary double refraction, in the case of crystals of category IV.; this leads to the result that in the direction of the axis of isotropy there occurs *circular polarisation,* but *elliptic polarisation* in all other directions inclined to it. An analogous superposition of optical activity on ordinary double refraction, might occur in the case of those optically *bi-axial* substances which have crystal forms "turned back upon themselves"; but such instances have not been recognised hitherto, perhaps because the circular polarisation may be obscured by the double refraction, in all directions highly inclined to the optic axis. Optical activity is theoretically possible in all groups having neither centre nor plane of symmetry, *i.e.* apart from those mentioned, in the groups 3, 8, 10, 22, 24, 27, 29, and 32. Experience shows that in the case of crystals "turned back upon themselves," it does *not* follow conversely that there must be circular polarisation; instances of this are found in the regular tetartohedral nitrates of Pb, Ba, and Sr. It is worthy of remark that those (organic) substances which are optically active in solution always crystallise in the inverted forms (Pasteur, 1848); but most crystals with circular polarisation (for example $NaClO_3$, $NaBrO_3$) give *inactive* solutions. Optical activity in both crystallised and dissolved states is shown only by a few organic compounds such as strychnine sulphate, rubidium tartrate, etc.[1]

The Physical Properties of Lower Symmetry.—The most

---

[1] See H. Traube, *Jahrb. f. Mineralogie,* 1896, p. 788.

important property by which all regular crystals are distinguished from amorphous substances is *elasticity*. According to the theory of elasticity, the potential energy of unit volume of a deformed homogeneous crystal is a quadratic function of the moduli of deformation (as named by Kirchhoff); the coefficients occurring here are the so-called *elasticity constants* of the crystals, provided that the crystallographic axes are chosen as the co-ordinate axes. As Minnegerode[1] first showed, according to the symmetry of their behaviour respecting elasticity, the following nine classes of crystals are to be distinguished :—

(a) Regular system; groups 1–5, with 3 elasticity constants.

(b) Hexagonal system; groups 6–12, with 5 elasticity constants.

(c) Hexagonal system; groups 13–15, with 6 elasticity constants.

(d) Hexagonal system; groups 16 and 17, with 7 elasticity constants.

(e) Tetragonal system; groups 18, 19, 20, and 23, with 6 elasticity constants.

(f) Tetragonal system; groups 21, 22, and 24, with 7 elasticity constants.

(g) Orthorhombic system; groups 25–27, with 9 elasticity constants.

(h) Monoclinic system; groups 28–30, with 13 elasticity constants.

(i) Triclinic system; groups 31 and 32, with 21 elasticity constants.

That no more groups occur is due to the fact that the elastic pressure, as well as the amount of deformation, are magnitudes *centrally* symmetric. The elastic symmetry is expressed with especial clearness in the dependence of the *coefficient of elongation* (*i.e.* the elongation effected by the pull 1, in the direction of this pull) upon the direction. This relation can be shown by means of a closed surface, by plotting through a fixed point each pull-direction corresponding to the co-efficients of elongation. Similarly the *torsion coefficient* of a circular cylinder can be represented as a function of the crystallographic orientation of the axis of the cylinder. (Reference should be made to the numerous researches of W. Voigt, a summary of which is given in Liebisch's book, chap. ix., and especially to the account in § 7 of Voigt's *Kristallphysik*, Leipzig, 1898). It is especially worthy of mention that, in the case of the groups of the hexagonal system, under (b) in the preceding classification, the elasticity is the same in all directions, having the same inclination to the principal axis. This does not hold good for the other groups of the hexagonal system, nor for those of the tetragonal system. Moreover, there are very remarkable variations of the co-efficients of elongation and of torsion respectively, in different directions, as appears from the observations on calcite, dolomite, tourmaline, and barite, for example.

[1] Minnegerode, *Gött. Nachr.*, 1884.

The properties associated with cohesion, as *cleavage* and *hardness*, in respect to which the regular crystals also seem to be anisotropic, have not as yet yielded to mathematical treatment.

A physical process, which *is not centrally symmetrical*, and which therefore leads to an entirely different classification of crystals, is that of *electrical excitement by elastic or thermal deformation* (piezo-electricity and pyro-electricity). As long as one considers only homogeneous deformation, these phenomena can only occur on crystals *without a centre of symmetry*. Pyro-electric excitement by uniform heating or cooling is particularly characteristic of the groups having a characteristic polar axis of symmetry, viz. 7, 10, 14, 17, 19, 22, 27, and 29 (groups 30 and 32 have not been observed as yet); this property, therefore, is a good sign whereby to recognise these groups, apart from their crystalline form and etched figures. Remarkable examples are tourmaline, calamine, struvite, cane-sugar, and tartaric-acid; also quartz, in which the three side-axes, and boracite, in which the four threefold axes are polar, can take electrical charges only by *uneven* heating or cooling, with + and − alternately on the ends of the polar axes.

The Determination of the Crystallographic Symmetry.— In the study of transparent crystals optical tests should be first applied. It should first be determined, by a polarisation apparatus for parallel light, or by a microscope fitted with polarising and analysing nicols, whether the crystal is optically isotropic (singly refracting or circularly polarising), or doubly refracting; and in the latter case, how the directions of extinction are orientated with reference to the bounding crystal faces : (these extinction directions are the directions which must be parallel to the polarising planes of the crossed nicols, when the crystal appears dark, and they are therefore the polarisation planes of the waves transmitted in the direction of observation).

Next follows an examination in converging polarised light (with the Nörremberg's apparatus, or, in the case of small objects, with a microscope fitted for converging light), when the light is passed through crystal sections with parallel planes, which are either naturally suited for this, or artificially prepared, by grinding or splitting. Usually it will be advantageous and save polishing, if one immerses the crystal in a liquid having nearly the same refractive index. The following is a description of the characteristic interference phenomena which one first observes in homogeneous light; it will be noticed whether the crystal is optically uni-axial or bi-axial, and in the latter case how the optic axes lie. In the case of uni-axial crystals, in plates cut perpendicularly to the optic axis, between crossed nicols one sees a series of concentric circles, alternately light and dark, which are intersected by two dark bands which are at right angles to each other; in plates cut parallel to the axis the rings become equilateral hyperbolas; a section, cut from a crystal in any other direction, shows

excentric systems of ellipses or hyperbolas according to its inclination
to the optic axis.   In the case of crystals optically bi-axial, in sections
normal to the *"first middle line"* (*i.e.* the line bisecting the acute angle
of the optic axes), when the angle is not too great, one sees a system
of *lemniscates* which are crossed by two dark bands at right angles
to each other, or by two equal dark hyperbolic brushes, according
as the plane of the axes coincides with the principal section of one
nicol (normal position), or as it makes an angle of 45° with it (diagonal
position).   With sections normal to "the second middle line" (*i.e.* the
line bisecting the obtuse angle of the optic axes), or parallel to the
plane of the optic axes, there are seen systems of concentric hyperbolas
which are exactly symmetrical in the latter case, but not so in the former.
Finally, it is to be noticed that sections normal to one axis of a bi-axial
crystal show an interference figure consisting of almost circular curves
which are crossed by *one* dark band.   Interference curves are visible in
white light, but only in sufficiently thin sections, or such as are nearly
normal to one optic axis ; the symmetry of the distribution of colour
observed in the normal or diagonal position of the plate, and which
depends on the position of the middle lines of each particular colour,
allows one to determine whether the crystal system is orthorhombic,
monoclinic, or triclinic.   (We distinguish in the case of monoclinic
crystals three varieties of the "dispersion of the optic axes of symmetry" : 1, inclined dispersion when the optic axes lie in the plane
of symmetry ; 2, horizontal, and 3, crossed dispersion when the plane
of the optic axes is at right angles to the plane of symmetry, and the
first and second middle lines respectively lie parallel to this latter
plane.

After the study of these optical phenomena has enabled a fairly
accurate conclusion to be drawn on the nature of the symmetry of the
crystal under examination,—which may be of great value when dealing
with complex combinations with irregular development of planes,—
the angles are measured by means of a reflection goniometer, a perspective
sketch having been previously made to show, as far as possible, the
arrangement of the particular planes, each of which is marked with a
letter.

The angular measurements will enable the symmetry of the
geometrical form to be more accurately determined because equal
angles lie between similar planes) ; and, further, will serve to determine
the elements of the axes (*i.e.* the geometrical constants) of the crystal.
In the case of monoclinic and triclinic crystals, the choice of fundamental planes is purely arbitrary (for the former, 100 and 001, and
also for the latter 010), but one can give to any fourth plane not
lying in a zone of any two of the first planes, arbitrary indices, for
example 111, and can calculate from the inclination to the fundamental
planes, directly or indirectly obtained, the axial units a : b : c.   (The
angles between the axes are already known by establishing the

fundamental planes.) To determine the indices of the other crystal planes, one needs at most two angles, measured from different zones ; but it is the custom to have more, if possible, in order to have a control of the calculated elements of the axes and indices.

If the occurrence of the faces gives rise to doubts to which group of the system a crystal belongs, we must proceed to study the etched figures, the pyro-electric properties, etc. Finally, after the symmetry and geometrical constants have been determined, further tests should be made of the characteristic physical properties, especially the character (*i.e.* whether positive or negative), and the strength of the double refraction must be determined ; in the case of crystals optically bi-axial, *the angle between the optic axes* ; and in monoclinic and triclinic crystals, the *orientation of the optic axes of symmetry* must be determined for the different colours ; also, when it is possible, one must measure the principal indices of refraction by the method of total reflection, or by the prism method, and eventually one must study the absorption phenomena (pleochroism).

Polymorphism.—Although, in general, each substance occurs in a definite crystallographic symmetry and form, which is characteristic for itself, yet many instances occur where *the same substance exhibits different crystal forms.* The appearance of one and the same substance (having not only identical composition, but also identical constitution) in two or more crystal forms, *i.e.* forms with different symmetries, and also with different elements of the axes, is called *dimorphism* or *polymorphism.* This phenomenon was first recognised by E. Mitscherlich, in the salt $NaH_2PO_4 + H_2O$ (1821), and in sulphur (1823). The different kinds of crystals of a polymorphous substance are to be regarded as *different modifications* analogous to the different states of aggregation ; they are therefore called *physical isomers*, in contrast to *chemical isomers.*

The following are among the important examples of polymorphic substances. For the particular group to which each modification belongs, see the preceding summary of the thirty-two groups.

C, S, Se, Sn ; Cu_2S, ZnS, HgS, FeS_2 ; As_2O_3, Sb_2O_3, SiO_2 (quartz and tridymite), TiO_2 ; AgI, HgI_2 ; $CaCO_3$, KNO_3, $NaClO_3$, $KClO_3$, NH_4NO_3 ; K_2SO_4, $NiSO_4 + 6H_2O$, $MgSO_4 + 7H_2O$, $FeSO_4 + 7H_2O$, $NaH_2PO_4 + H_2O$, boracite, Al_2SiO_5 (andalusite, disthene, and sillimanite), the humite group, zoisite and epidote, leucite, potassium feldspar ; also many organic compounds as chlor-m-di-nitro-benzene, chlor-o-di-nitro-benzene, benzo-phenone, β-di-brom-propionic acid, mono-chlor-acetic acid, mono-nitro-tetra-brom-benzene, benzoïn, carbon, tri-chloride, hydroquinone, malon-amide, m-nitro-para-acet-toluide.

Polymorphism (unlike chemical isomerism) is restricted to the solid state ; on sublimation, polymorphic modifications yield the same vapour ; on solution, the same liquid, just as the vapour from ice or water is identical, and the solution of ice or water in alcohol gives an identical aqueous alcohol.

But the vapour pressure (and solubility) of two polymorphic modifications is, in general, different; hence, in general, two polymorphic forms are not in equilibrium together, for vapour would pass from the form with the higher to that with the lower pressure, and the one would grow at the cost of the other. Equilibrium can occur only at the temperature at which the vapour pressure of the two forms is the same, *i.e.* at the point of intersection of the two vapour pressure curves, just as (p. 71) coexistence of the solid and liquid states depends on equality of vapour pressure.

The point at which the two modifications coexist is called the *transition temperature*; above that, only one, below it only the other form is stable, just as below 0° water freezes, and above 0° ice melts. But an important difference is that solids cannot be heated above their melting-point without melting, whereas most polymorphs can be kept for some time above their transition temperature before being entirely converted, and some even show no tendency to be converted. Thus, calcite and aragonite can exist together through a wide range of temperature, and others, such as diamond and graphite, have not so far been converted by mere change of temperature. The transition is usually facilitated by contact with substance that has been already converted, just as the solidification of an undercooled liquid is brought about by contact with the frozen substance.[1]

The energy of two modifications is usually considerably different, as with the solid and liquid states; the evolution of heat in passing from one into the other is called the *heat of transition*.

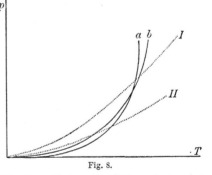

Fig. 8.

These relations can best be studied with the aid of Fig. 8 which, like Fig. 4 (p. 71), shows the vapour pressure curves of the different modifications. The point of intersection of curves a and b which represent the polymorphic forms A and B is the transition point, for there the vapour pressure of both is the same. Below that point A has the smaller vapour pressure, and is stable; above, the conditions are reversed, and B is stable.

The melting-point of each modification is at the intersection with the vapour pressure curve of the liquid. Two cases are possible.[2]

[1] See "Synopsis of Literature and Researches," by W. Schwarz, "Umkehrbare Umwandlungen polymorpher Körper," *Preisschrift der phil. Fakultät*, Gottingen, 1892.
[2] Ostwalt, *Allg. Chem.* 1st ed. **1.** 695 (1885) ; 2nd ed. **1.** 948 (1891).

Either the latter curve cuts a and b above the transition point (I, Fig. 8) or below (II). Only in the former case is the transition point actually attainable; in the latter, both modifications would melt first. Sulphur is an example of the first case; rhombic sulphur on heating to 95·6 passes over into the monoclinic form, and the latter on cooling reverts to rhombic. Benzophenone is an instance of the second; two modifications with different melting-points are known, and, as appears from Fig. 8, that with the higher melting-point must be the more stable. In this case, then, it is not possible to pass from either modification to the other by mere heating or cooling; the unstable modification has to be prepared by crystallisation from suitably under-cooled liquid.[1]

Amorphous State.—On cooling a homogeneous liquid sufficiently, it acquires, in general, the property of crystallising; at points of its interior nuclei arise which grow more or less fast, and eventually cause the whole liquid to become crystalline. A liquid can therefore be *undercooled* (*i.e.* cooled below the melting-point) the more easily the fewer the nuclei in it and the more slowly they grow.

If a liquid were suddenly cooled to the absolute zero the facility for crystallising would not occur; for then molecular movement would cease, and the favourable collisions of molecules (Book II. Chapter II.) needed for the formation of a crystal nucleus would be wanting; nor could a nucleus grow, since the velocity of crystallisation must vanish too. It appears, then, that at the absolute zero the state of under-cooled liquid must be practically stable; it is further obvious that, with the cessation of molecular movement, the easy mobility of the parts of a liquid must cease too, whereas its isotropy must remain (in contrast with the crystalline state).

Numerous observations show that such a state is possible for many substances at the ordinary and even higher temperatures, *i.e.* great undercooling can be relatively stable; this condition has long been called *amorphous*[2] (in opposition to crystalline).

The characteristics of the amorphous state follow from what we have said; externally it has the properties of a solid, owing to great viscosity and considerable rigidity, produced by strong mutual action of the molecules. An amorphous body differs from a crystal, however, in its complete isotropy and absence of a melting-point; on heating, it passes continuously from the amorphous to the usual liquid state, as its properties show steady change with rise of temperature, and no breaks anywhere.

Since amorphous bodies (such as glasses) show rigidity, it would follow from this hypothesis that ordinary liquids, and even gases, must also, though

[1] K. Schaum, "Arten der Isomerie," *Habilitationsschrift*, Marburg, 1897.
[2] This view of the amorphous state is developed and discussed by G. Tammann, *Schmelzen und Kristallisieren*, Leipzig, 1903 (Ambrosius-Barth).

to a very slight extent; so far, this has not been proved, possibly owing to the extreme smallness of the property.

Quartz, silicates (glasses), and many metallic oxides, are good examples of the amorphous state. Amorphous precipitates, difficult to wash and apt to bring down impurities with them, are frequent in chemical work and disadvantageous.

Sometimes crystallisation of amorphous bodies cannot be observed within ordinary limits of time; sometimes it occurs slowly, as in the devitrification of glass; occasionally with almost explosive violence. Tammann (*loc. cit.*) quotes a good example of this in. Grove's discovery (1855) of explosive antimony. This metal is deposited in amorphous form (always containing some chloride) by electrolysis from solutions of antimonious chloride; on passing over into the crystalline state an evolution of 21 calories per gram occurs. If a part of the antimony be heated to 100° – 160°, rapid crystallisation takes place, and this, on account of the heat developed, is propagated like an explosive wave.

CHAPTER IV

THE PHYSICAL MIXTURE

General Observations.—In the preceding chapters we have considered chiefly the behaviour of substances having a simple chemical composition : in the following chapter will be considered the most important properties of the *physical mixture*. By the term *physical mixture* we mean a *complex of different substances, which is at all points homogeneous, both in a physical and a chemical sense*. According to the state of aggregation we must distinguish between gaseous, liquid, and solid mixtures ; in special cases we call them gas-mixtures, solutions, isomorphous mixtures, alloys, and the like.

The physical mixture must not be confounded with the coarse mechanical admixtures of solid or liquid substances, as powders, emulsions, and the like, the various ingredients of which can be separated from each other without much difficulty, as by detection with the microscope, separation by gravity, by washing out, etc. They originate by the mutual molecular intermingling of the various substances of which they are composed, and the separation of their components is for the most part associated with the expenditure of a very considerable degree of work, a knowledge of which is of the very greatest importance. In terms of the molecular hypothesis, physical mixtures differ from chemically simple substances, in that the latter consist of the same kind of molecules, while the former consist of different kinds of molecules.

The gases alone possess collectively the property of unlimited miscibility. The solvent power of different liquids for each other, and also of liquids for solids, is much more limited ; and still more rarely are crystallised substances able to form mixed crystals in all proportions.

Gas Mixtures.—As would be expected, the most simple relations are found in the case of mixtures arising from the mutual interpenetration (diffusion) of different gases. In those cases where there is no chemical action associated with the intermingling, the properties of each particular gas remain unchanged in the mixture, *i.e.* each gas conducts itself as though the others were not present ; the pressure exerted upon the containing walls, the capacity of absorbing and refracting light, the solubility in any selected solvent, the specific heat, etc., all of these properties experience no change in the intermixture. Thus we can predict the [physical] properties of a gas mixture of known composition, if we have previously determined the properties of each particular ingredient.   This can be regarded as characteristic of ideal gases.   As all the laws of gases are only approximate rules, exact measurement will probably bring to light small deviations from the rules given above.   At least it has already been shown that the pressure exerted by a gas mixture does not strictly obey the law of the sum of their pressures.

If two gases are mixed by allowing them to diffuse into each other at constant volume, there occurs no development of heat, and also no expenditure of external work ; consequently *the total energy* [U], remains unchanged in this process.   But since the mixing of two gases takes place automatically, it is obvious that the process, rightly directed, can perform external work ; the *maximum* of external work is obtained, as always, when the process is conducted *reversibly*.

Now, as a matter of fact, a very simple mechanism may be contrived to work in the desired way : it depends upon a property possessed by certain partition walls, *of being permeable for certain substances, but not for others* ; partitions of this sort are called " *semipermeable* "; they have recently proved of immense service in the advance of both theory and experiment.   Let there be n_1 g.-mol of a gas in the division I. of a cylinder (Fig. 9), the volume of which is v_1, and in division II., the volume of which is v_2, n_2 g.-mol of another gas. During the process the system is

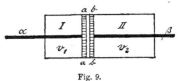

Fig. 9.

maintained at the constant temperature T.   In the cylinder are two closely-fitting, movable pistons a and b ; let piston a be permeable for the *first* gas, but not for the second ; and, conversely, piston b should give free passage for the *second* gas, but not for the first.   Two piston rods, α and β, which pierce the two air-tight cylinder heads, serve to carry the motion of the contents to the outside.   At first the pistons should be pushed up close to each other ; then the first gas will exert a pressure on piston b, but not on a, since it can freely pass through the latter ; and conversely for a similar reason, the second gas, by virtue of its expansive force, will tend to move only the piston a.   If we offer no resistance to the piston rods, this pressure action will cause the pistons to move to the ends of the cylinder, as is shown in Fig. 10 ; at the same time there has occurred the *intermingling* of the two gases.   If, conversely, we press in the two piston rods, the first gas will offer resistance only to

H

the movement of piston b, and the second gas only to the movement of piston a; if we push back the pistons to their original positions, there occurs a *separation* of the gases, and, at the same time, we bring the two gases back to their original volumes. The process is thus completely reversible.

Now the work which can be obtained by the intermingling is easily calculated: during the expansion each gas presses with its

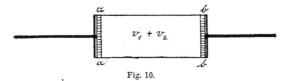

Fig. 10.

actual partial pressure on the piston opposing its passage, and accordingly performs exactly the same work, *as though the other gas were not present.* Since the n_1 molecules of the first gas expand from v_1 to $v_1 + v_2$, the work performed by them according to p. 51 is

$$A_1 = n_1 RT \ln \frac{v_1 + v_2}{v_1},$$

and for the second gas the work is

$$A_2 = n_2 RT \ln \frac{v_1 + v_2}{v_2},$$

and for the sum of the two

$$A = A_1 + A_2 = RT \left(n_1 \ln \frac{v_1 + v_2}{v_1} + n_2 \ln \frac{v_1 + v_2}{v_2} \right). \qquad (I.).$$

This formula was first developed by Lord Rayleigh,[1] but afterwards independently and more thoroughly by Boltzmann.[2] Of course, if the system were not maintained at constant temperature, it would be cooled during the performance of the work, since there results no heat from the simple intermingling of the gases; under these circumstances, the equivalent quantity of heat would be absorbed from the environment, exactly as in the expansion or compression of a single gas.

From the equation (p. 23), viz.—

$$A - U = T \frac{dA}{dT},$$

since in our case U is equal to zero (p. 51), it follows that

$$A = T \frac{dA}{dT},$$

or integrated

$$\ln A = \ln T + C,$$

[1] *Phil. Mag.* **49.** 311 (1875).   [2] *Wiener Sitzungsber.*, 1878, II. p. 733.

in which C denotes an unknown constant; from this it follows that

$$A = cT,$$

in which c denotes a new constant.

Thermodynamics confirms, therefore, the correctness of the result given above, inasmuch as it requires a ratio between A and the absolute temperature, which, in fact, coincides with the ' formula obtained by the method described.

Though the derivation given above is extremely clear, yet it must not be overlooked that *it cannot be used in demonstration* until it has been proved that the semi-permeable walls used in the process *can be realised* in actual cases: thermodynamic considerations must not be developed by fictitious cyclic processes, but only by those which are possible in nature, if they are to attain to the rank of scientific proof, and not merely to that of arbitrary speculation. I would emphasise this the more, because hitherto the question of the practicability of the process in question has been disposed of rather too easily. Now, as "semi-permeable partitions" have played a very important part in many lines of research in recent times, and as their introduction has simplified calculation, a few words will be offered concerning their legitimate use in thermodynamic conclusions.

For certain cases there are undoubtedly partitions having the quality desired; thus, palladium foil at high temperatures possesses the property of allowing hydrogen to pass through easily, but of hindering other gases. A gas very soluble in water can easily diffuse through a membrane moistened with water, while a gas which is soluble with difficulty in water cannot so diffuse. Thus if a piece of moist pig's bladder is tied over the mouth of a funnel, which is fixed with the mouth upwards, and with the tip in connection with a mercury manometer, and then ammonia gas is led under a jar held inverted over the funnel, a rise in pressure of a tenth of an atmosphere at once takes place, caused by the partial pressure of the diffused ammonia.[1] Thus the experiment shown in Figures 9 and 10 can be realised when we are dealing with the mixture of ammonia and hydrogen. At the same time it becomes probable in the highest degree that the formula (I.), obtained on p. 98, holds good universally, since it is strictly proved for one case, and it can hardly be assumed that a law of nature of that kind is dependent, so to speak, upon the casual question whether we possess the desired partition or not for all special cases.

. Another still more striking argument is that other cyclic processes have been devised by which the intermingling can be conducted isothermally and reversibly, and which lead to the same final result, as was thoroughly shown by Boltzmann in 1878. A cyclic process of this sort can be represented in a much simplified form, as it seems to me. Let us suppose that we have a solvent which easily dissolves one of two gases which are to be mixed, but the other with great difficulty. Thus water, for example, is a solvent having the desired properties for the gas pair, nitrogen and hydrogen sulphide, and still better for nitrogen and hydrogen chloride.

Suppose we are to consider the separation of hydrogen chloride and

---

[1] This is recommended as a simple lecture experiment.

nitrogen : we first bring the mixture of gases to a large volume V, and then connect it with a large volume of a water solution of hydrogen chloride, choosing such a concentration for the latter that the partial pressure of its hydrochloric acid is equal to the partial pressure of this gas in the gas mixture of volume V. Then if we bring the gas mixture and the hydrochloric acid solution into contact with each other, hydrogen chloride will neither enter nor leave the solution. Now we will compress the gas mixture, which is in constant contact with the solution, to a volume which is very small in comparison with the original volume V ; during this the hydrogen chloride will practically go completely into solution. Then we will separate the nitrogen, which remains behind in a state of almost complete purity, from the solution, and then will liberate from the solution the amount of hydrogen chloride dissolved ; thus the desired separation has been effected. If we neglect the vapour tension of the water, which can be done without doubt if we work at low temperatures, especially as the water vapour mixed with the two gases may be almost completely removed by compression, and if we also neglect the nitrogen dissolved in the solution, then it can be easily proved that the work expended in the separation of the gases is given by formula (I.).

If we select a solvent in which the solubility of nitrogen cannot be neglected, but in which the solubility of the two gases is very different, we can effect the separation of the two gases isothermally and reversibly by the repeated application of a cyclic process similar to the one just described, *i.e.* by " fractionation of the solution " ; and, without carrying out the calculation, we can conclude from the second law of thermodynamics, that the work to be applied can be calculated from formula (I.), since its efficiency has been already proved for the mixture of nitrogen and hydrogen chloride.

Now we can take any pair of gases, and can find some suitable solvent which will dissolve the two gases in different degrees, for otherwise they would be chemically identical ; and thus a cyclic process can always be realised which can be calculated by formula (I.). *This formula therefore holds good universally, and hence it is shown at the same time that it is permissible to work with semi-permeable partitions in all cases concerning the mingling or the separation of two gases which are chemically different.*

The Physical Properties of Liquid Mixtures.—The relations of liquid and solid mixtures are more complicated than those of gases. The mixing of solids and liquids is usually accompanied by a change in the properties of the single components. The volume of the mixture of two liquids is in general different from the sum of the volumes of the individual ingredients, since the mixing is accompanied by a contraction or expansion, which is, however, usually not very considerable ; the colour, refractive index, specific heat, etc., of the mixture are also slightly different from that which would be calculated from the same properties of the ingredients, under the assumption that they remained unchanged on mixing. But one commonly obtains results at least approximately coincident by calculating, on this assumption, the properties of a physical mixture from those of the ingredients.

In accordance with a proposal of Ostwald, we will call properties of this sort *additive*; the essential idea will be best made clear by examples.

Many liquids can unite with each other, as also many solid bodies with liquids, to form homogeneous liquid aggregates, the volumes of which are very nearly equal to the sums of the volumes of the respective ingredients. If we denote the volume of the mixture by V, and the volumes of the particular ingredients by V_1, V_2, etc., then it is approximately true that

$$V = V_1 + V_2 + \ldots$$

Let the weights of the particular ingredients be m_1, m_2, etc.; let us denote the volume of the unit of mass of the mixture, the so-called "specific volume," by v, and the respective volumes of the particular ingredients by v_1, v_2, etc.; then the preceding equation becomes

$$v(m_1 + m_2 + \ldots) = v_1 m_1 + v_2 m_2 + \ldots,$$

or

$$v = v_1 \frac{m_1}{m_1 + m_2 +} + v_2 \frac{m_2}{m_1 + m_2 +} + \ldots$$

The specific volume of the mixture can therefore be calculated from the specific volumes of the particular ingredients, by the so-called "partnership" calculation, viz. as though each particular ingredient entered the mixture with the specific volume which it had in the free state. The specific volume under these circumstances is an additive property. For purely algebraic reasons it follows, of course, that the specific gravity, which is the reciprocal of the specific volume, cannot be an additive property;[1] and this example teaches that it is often only necessary to effect an algebraic transformation of values determined experimentally, to meet with much simpler relations.

The *heat capacity* of a liquid mixture is likewise as a rule equal to the sum of the heat capacities of the ingredients. If we denote by c the specific heat of a mixture containing m_1 g. of one ingredient of a specific heat c_1 and m_2 g. of another ingredient of a specific heat c_2, then according to the preceding law

$$c(m_1 + m_2) = c_1 m_1 + c_2 m_2 ;$$

but since $\frac{100 m_1}{m_1 + m_2}$ is the weight per cent p of the first component, we obtain, as the formula to calculate c—

$$c = c_1 \frac{p}{100} + c_2 \frac{100 - p}{100}.$$

As a matter of fact, in the case of particular mixtures, as, for example, chloroform and carbon disulphide, this calculation proves

---

[1] That is not, if as above the calculation is performed according to per cent by weight; but it will be additive if calculated according to per cent by volume.

very good, the differences between the observed and the calculated values being less than one per cent ; but in other cases, as in the mixture of acetic acid and water, the results are only approximate. Indeed, we find in the case of a mixture of alcohol and water, that the real specific heat is greater than it should be according to the preceding formula ; thus a mixture of equal parts does not have a mean of the specific heats,

$$\frac{1 \cdot 000 + 0 \cdot 612}{2} = 0 \cdot 806,$$ but the specific heat is $0 \cdot 910$.

Mixtures of salt and water have as a rule a considerably smaller heat capacity than the sum of the ingredients, and sometimes even smaller than what should correspond to the amount of water contained in the mixture (Thomsen, 1871 ; Marignac, 1873). In the case of solutions not too concentrated, one can estimate the heat capacity as nearly equal to that of the contained water, a very important rule for practical thermochemistry.

The *optical relations* of mixtures have been investigated with especial thoroughness ; these will be dealt with in the next paragraph. It need only be noticed here that except in one case, exact research has always brought to light differences, exceeding the limits of error, between the results of observation and those calculated on the assumption of a simple additive relation. From all that we know up to date, in the case of liquid and solid mixtures, there is only one strictly additive property, that of *mass*, which of course, both in a simple mixture and in the case of a chemical compound, must remain unchanged, according to the law of the indestructibility of matter.

There can be no doubt that the deviations observed in the simple additive relations of liquids will some day be of great significance in determining the nature of the force concerned in the mixing of two liquids, and of the kind of mutual action occurring. That commonly, and especially in the use of water in particular as a solvent, there occurs a *chemical action, i.e.* the formation of new molecules or the splitting of those previously existing, and that the reactions in question are incomplete (see Book II. Chapter II.) can hardly be doubted, but hitherto it has been impossible to prove this with certainty. Perhaps this much may be maintained, that when the properties of the mixture differ very considerably from the mean value a chemical action is probable ; and that in such mixtures there is a certain parallelism between the variations attending their different properties ; at least in those mixtures where we find a strong contraction, *i.e.* where the specific volumes are not simply additive, the specific heat seems also to be considerably removed from the mean value. But the fact on the other side, that certain compounds, which are undoubtedly chemical, show properties having an additive character, warns us not to be premature in drawing conclusions like the above. (See Book II. Chapter V.)

The Optical Behaviour of Mixtures.—The *specific refractive power* of a mixture, by which is meant the quotient of the refractive index minus one, divided by the density $[i.e. \dfrac{n-1}{d}]$, can be determined from the corresponding values of the particular components in exactly the same way as the specific volume ; and as Landolt[1] has shown, the calculated value of the specific refractive power of the mixture coincides so well with that determined experimentally, that we can, conversely, usually determine with great certainty the composition of a mixture from its optical behaviour. This example shows how sometimes a skilful combination of two physical properties (in the preceding case the refractive index and the specific gravity), leads to simple and universal relations.

If we denote by n the refractive power of a mixture, measured for any selected line of the solar spectrum, and if the specific gravity of the mixture is d, and it contains p per cent by weight of one ingredient and $100 - p$ of the other ; and moreover, if the corresponding values for these ingredients when pure are n_1 and d_1 and n_2 and d_2 respectively ; then the specific refractive power of the mixture can be calculated by the formula

$$\frac{n-1}{d} = \frac{n_1-1}{d_1} \frac{p}{.100} + \frac{n_2-1}{d_2} \frac{100-p}{100}.$$

As an example of the accuracy with which this formula corresponds to observations there is given the following series of measurements of mixtures of ethylene bromide and propyl alcohol, for the temperature $18.07°$ and the sodium line.[2]

THE REFRACTIVE POWERS OF MIXTURES OF ETHYLENE BROMIDE
AND PROPYL ALCOHOL.

Ethylene Bromide per cent (p).	Sp. Gr.	Refraction Coefficient.	Calc.—Obs.	
			Diff. I.	Diff. II.
0	0·80659	1·386161	0·00000	0·00000
10·0084	0·86081	1·391892	+ 32·	– 1
20·9516	0·92908	1·399136	+ 66	– 3
29·8351	0·99300	1·405958	+ 95	– 5
40·7320	1·08453	1·415815	+ 128	– 12
49·9484	1·17623	1·425748	+ 155	– 18
60·0940	1·29695	1·439013	+ 171	– 34
70·0123	1·44175	1·455063	+ 180	– 46
80·0893	1·62640	1·475796	+ 169	– 57
90·1912	1·86652	1·503227	+ 116	– 59
100	2·18300	1·540399	0·00000	0·00000

[1] *Lieb. Ann.* Suppl. **4.** 1 (1865). Also compare Gladstone and Dale, *Phil. Trans.*, 1858, p. 887.

[2] Schütt, *Zeitschr. phys. Chem.* **9.** 349-377 (1892). For an extended form of the law of mixtures, from the introduction of a new constant, compare Pulfrich, *ib.* **4.** 161 (1889), and Buchkremer, *ib.* **6.** 161 (1890).

In the fourth column are given the differences between calculation and observation, which are obtained when the values of n are
calculated according to the preceding formula, from the experimentally
determined values of p, n_1, n_2, d_1, d_2, and d. The differences all lie
on the same side, and almost reach two units of the third decimal
place, thus being a hundredfold greater than the errors of observation,
which can be assigned as $\pm\, 0\cdot000082$. We conclude from this example
that the law of mixtures just described by no means represents a strict
law of nature, but yet that as an approximate rule can frequently find
practical application.

Now it has been investigated whether another function of the
refractive power may be better suited to represent the phenomena,
and in fact H. A. Lorentz and L. Lorentz (1880), guided by certain
theoretical considerations, found that the expression $\dfrac{n_2 - 1}{n_2 + 2} \cdot \dfrac{1}{d}$ is more
accurate than the expression $\dfrac{n - 1}{d}$, although it is not so simple. In
the last column of the preceding table are given the differences between
calculation and observation, which are obtained by solving the value of
n from p, n_1, n_2, d_1, d_2 and d, by the formula

$$\frac{n^2 - 1}{n_2 + 2} \cdot \frac{1}{d} = \frac{n_1{}^2 - 1}{n_1{}^2 + 2} \cdot \frac{p}{100d_1} + \frac{n_2{}^2 - 1}{n_2{}^2 + 2} \cdot \frac{100 - p}{100d_2} \; ;$$

as a matter of fact the result so obtained coincides much better with
experiment.

These results have a certain practical interest to this extent; by
means of the law of mixtures,

$$R = R_1 \frac{p}{100} + R_2 \frac{100 - p}{100},$$

in which the *specific refraction* R denotes either $\dfrac{n - 1}{d}$, or $\dfrac{n_2 - 1}{n_2 + 2} \cdot \dfrac{1}{d}$,
*we can calculate the specific refraction of one ingredient from that of a
mixture, provided the composition of the mixture and the refraction of the other
ingredients are known.* Although this method of calculation may give only
approximate results, it is of great value for the question of the relation
between specific refraction and chemical composition, for by its means we
can deduce the specific refraction of a substance which cannot be obtained
pure in the liquid condition, but only in the presence of a solvent.

Finally, it has been attempted to obtain results harmonising better
with experiment, by introducing into the formula for the rule of
mixtures certain constants suitably chosen for each particular case;
thus, for example, instead of $\dfrac{n_2 - 1}{n_2 + 2} \cdot \dfrac{1}{d}$, let $R = \dfrac{n_2 - 1}{n_2 + C} \cdot \dfrac{1}{d}$. But however useful such an equation may be as an exact interpolation formula
in special cases, it would only be of general interest when from the

deviations from simple additive relations given by the numerical value of these constants a deeper insight could be obtained into the nature of the mixture under investigation.

One-sided Properties.—In the study of the relations of mixtures those physical properties are especially important which belong to only one compound of a mixture; if, for example, we mix a coloured with an uncoloured substance, or one optically active with one optically inactive, we can obviously decide with certainty whether a change of property occurs by such a mixture or not; and therefore in such cases we would have the best chance of arriving at a general standpoint. If, for example, we find that the refractive power of a mixture is the same as that calculated on the supposition of a simple additive relation, then it is certainly probable, but by no means strictly proved, that the specific refractive power of each component in the free state remains unchanged in the mixture, since it is possible that the property of one component might have increased to the same degree to which that of another has diminished. But if, for example, the specific rotatory power of an active substance in the mixture is exactly the same as in the free state, then the conclusion is unavoidable that every molecule rotates as strongly in the mixture as in the free state. In fact, "one-sided properties" of this sort, as they are called, are of the greatest importance in the investigation of solutions; besides the rotation and the absorption of light, there should be mentioned particularly the electrical conductivity and the osmotic pressure of dissolved substances.

An investigation of the optical properties just referred to has shown that the absorption of light is often greatly altered by intermixture with colourless liquids; as a rule, but not always, the absorption bands of a dissolved substance are displaced the more toward the red end the greater the refractive power of the solvent. (Kundt's rule.)[1] Also, as a rule, the optical rotation of active molecules is greatly influenced by the presence of inactive molecules; and this influence, which may consist in a strengthening or a weakening of the rotary power, varies with the quantity of the inactive substance added;[2] general regularities have not as yet been found. We may fairly assume that every important influence of this sort in mixtures may be ascribed to the formation of new molecular groupings by incomplete reactions.

The Vaporisation of Mixtures.—One property of liquid mixtures, which changes with the proportions of the ingredients in a much more complicated way than those hitherto described, is their *vapour*

---

[1] Compare P. Stenger, *Wied. Ann.* **33.** 577 (1888).

[2] For further particulars see Landolt, *Optisches Drehungsvermögen organischer Substanzen*, Brunswick, 1898, p. 146 ff.

pressure. The vapour emitted by a mixture will in general have the same components as the liquid remaining behind : the ingredients exert therefore *partial pressures*, the sum of which is the vapour pressure of the mixture. Sometimes, of course, the volatility of one ingredient is so very small that its pressure can be neglected ; thus the vapour pressure of water solutions of salts is simply equal to the pressure of the water vapour in equilibrium with the solution.

The following law holds good universally, and is of fundamental importance : *the partial pressure of each component of a mixture is always smaller than its vapour pressure in the free state (liquid or solid) at the same temperature.* If this were not the case the vapour of the component whose partial pressure was greater than in the pure state would be supersaturated ; it would deposit from the vapour, and we should thus have spontaneous separation of the mixture. But this would mean that a self-acting process—the formation of a mixture—was reversed without any compensation, and this is not possible (see also below on the thermodynamic treatment of liquid mixtures). In the following chapters we shall see that the vapour pressures of dilute solutions follow very simple laws.

On the basis of the law given above we may predict the following behaviour of mixtures of *two liquids which dissolve each other in all proportions* : If we add to a liquid A a small quantity of another liquid B, then on the one hand the vapour pressure of A will be diminished, and on the other hand the total vapour pressure of the resulting solution will be increased by the circumstance that the quantity of B dissolved also gives out vapour ; moreover, the partial pressure of B in the vapour existing in equilibrium with the resulting solution will be so much greater as *the coefficient of solubility* of the vapour of B in the liquid A is smaller. According as the first or second action of the added liquid preponderates, the vapour pressure of the solution will be smaller or greater than that of A. Of course the same holds good for the solution arising from the addition of a slight quantity of A to B, which likewise, according to circumstances, can have a smaller or a greater vapour pressure than the liquid B in the pure state. But now since the properties of mixtures must always vary with the composition, we must distinguish the three following characteristic cases when considering the dependence of the vapour pressure upon the varying proportions of the two liquids :—

I. The vapour of A is *easily soluble* in B, and that of B in A. Then a slight addition of A to B, as also of B to A, will cause the vapour pressure of the resulting solution to fall. If we start with the pure solvent A (the vapour pressure of which at the temperature employed amounts to p_1), and add in succession small but increasing quantities of B, then the vapour pressure will at first diminish, will reach a *minimum*, then will begin to increase, and, finally, on the addition of large quantities of B will approach the vapour pressure p_2, that of the pure solvent B.

II. The vapour of A is only *slightly soluble* in B, as well as that of B in A.   Then the addition of a slight amount of A to B, as well as that of B to A, will cause the vapour pressure of the resulting solution to increase.   By the gradual addition of B to A the vapour pressure of the solution will at first become greater than p_1, will then reach a *maximum*, and, finally, by the addition of a great excess of B, will sink and approximate the value p_2.

III. The vapour of the first liquid is easily soluble in the second, but that of the second is soluble with difficulty in the first.   Then by the addition of a slight quantity of B to A the vapour pressure of the resulting solution will be slightly smaller ; by the addition of a small quantity of A to B it will be slightly greater than that of the pure solvent. Now if the vapour pressure p_1 of A is greater than p_2 of B, then by the successive additions of B to A the vapour pressure of the solution will fall, passing continuously without maximum or minimum from p_1 to p_2 (III.a).   But we can imagine a case where the first addition of B to A would raise the vapour pressure, but that of A to B diminish it ; then by the gradual addition of B to A the vapour pressure would at first increase, reach a maximum, then decrease till it became smaller than p_2, pass a minimum, and finally, with the great excess of B, would approach the vapour pressure p_2 (III.b).

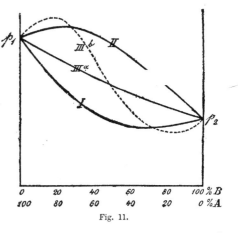

Fig. 11.

These various relations have been explained by the excellent theoretical and practical work of Konowalow ;[1] the curve tracings (Fig. 11) will assist the general statement.   The abscissæ are the varying proportions of the mixture in percentages of B ; the ordinates are their varying vapour pressures.   Case I. illustrates mixtures of formic acid and water from the measurements of Konowalow ; Case II., of water and propyl alcohol from the same source ; Case III.a, from the same, experimentally proven for ethyl or methyl alcohol and water.   The dotted line curve illustrating Case III.b, so far as I know, has not been realised.[2]

[1] *Wied. Ann.* **14**. 34 (1881).
[2] Ostwald has shown (*Lehrb. d. allg. Chem.* 2nd ed., II., **2**. 642 (1899) that this case is only possible for dissociating vapours ; a very clear account of the evaporation of mixtures, including some new matter, is given (p. 617 ff.) in that work.

The Theory of Fractional Distillation.—We can now easily perceive what must be the relations in the isothermal evaporation of a solution, which we can imagine to be effected by the raising of a piston in a cylinder containing the solution. In general the vapour of the solution will have a different composition from that of the solution itself, and therefore as a result of the evaporation, the composition and, at the same time, the vapour pressure of the solution will vary. *Now the change in composition of the mixture must be such that its vapour pressure is diminished by the evaporation.* If this were not the case, but if the pressure increased on raising the piston, and decreased on lowering it, a stable equilibrium between the pressure on the piston from the vapour and that exerted from without would be impossible. The evaporation proceeds in such a way that the more volatile ingredients evaporate first. Thus in Case I. the mixture must remain behind with a minimal vapour pressure; in Case II., one of the two solvents, according to the relative proportions of the original solution; in Case III.^{a}, since we neglect the Case III.^{b}, which is not as yet realised (and may be unrealisable ?), after a sufficiently long evaporation, that solvent with the smaller vapour pressure remains behind.

In practical laboratory work one does not as a rule boil and distil the mixture at constant temperature, but nearly always at constant pressure, that of the atmosphere. Since, as a rule, the vapour has a different composition from the remaining solution, we possess in this operation one of the most important and convenient methods of separating substances. Of course the separation will never be complete by one distillation, but may usually be carried to a high degree by interrupting the process and separating the parts which pass over at the successive temperatures ("fractional distillation"), and by suitable repetition of the operation. From the law that a change of composition of the solution must result in decreasing the vapour pressure, it follows in this case that *the boiling-point must rise during the distillation.* We can now easily see that, in Case I., we will finally obtain, as the least volatile *residue*, the mixture with the minimal vapour pressure, while the product of the fractional distillation, if this is repeated often enough, will be *one* of the pure solvents; and that component will form the ultimate distillate, which was present originally in a larger proportion than that required by the mixture of minimum vapour pressure. In Case II., on the other hand, one obtains, as the final *distillate*, a *mixture* corresponding to the maximum of vapour pressure, and as the less volatile *residue*, that one of the pure solvents which was present in excess. Only in Case III.^{a} is it possible to effect a complete separation of the two ingredients of the mixture by repeating the operation sufficiently.

It is thus possible to obtain, under certain definite conditions, which will be discussed later, *mixtures having constant boiling-points*:

such mixtures, as, for example, the aqueous solution of hydrochloric acid which distils at constant boiling-point, have occasionally been wrongly considered chemical compounds (hydrates), since their chief characteristic was the property of being unchanged by distillation. Apart from the fact that this property of a mixture is due to the, so to speak, casual coincidence that the partial pressures of the two ingredients of the mixture stand in such relations that the vapour emitted has the same composition as the mixture itself, it must also be remembered that the relative proportions of the ingredients change with the pressure at which the distillation is conducted, which is not the case with genuine chemical compounds.

A quantitative theory of fractional distillation, which, however, is only applicable to Case III.ᵃ, is given by Barrell, Thomas, and Young (*Phil. Mag.* [5], **37**. 8 (1894)); it rests on an assumption justified by the experiments of F. D. Brown (*Trans. Chem. Soc.*, 1879, p. 550; 1880, pp. 49, 304; 1881, p. 517), that the ratio of the components passing off in vapour at any moment is proportional to the ratio of the components in the boiling liquid. Thus if x and y are the masses of the components in the liquid, the quantities dx and dy passing off as vapour satisfy the condition

$$\frac{dx}{dy} = c\,\frac{x}{y},$$

where c is a constant factor depending on the nature of the liquids. See also their researches on the separation of ternary mixtures by distillation.

The Thermodynamic Treatment of Liquid Mixtures.—In the preparation of a mixture, a certain amount, Q, of heat will usually be developed or absorbed. The external work performed, which is measured by the product of the external pressure and the change of volume, has a negligible value, so that we can make the diminution of the internal energy U, as a result of the mixing, equal to the heat of mixture Q; this can be experimentally determined by means of a very simple calorimetric measurement; hence

$$U = Q.$$

If there are x mol of the second component to 1 mol of the first, then Q is a function of x, *i.e.*

$$U = Q(x);$$

this can sometimes be expressed by a simple formula; thus the development of heat observed on mixing 1 mol of H_2SO_4 with x mol of water was found by J. Thomsen[1] to be very accurately expressed by the formula,

$$Q(x) = \frac{17,860x}{x + 1\cdot 8}.$$

[1] *Thermochem. Untersuchungen*, Bd. III. 34.

The variation of the heat of mixture with the temperature is given by the difference between the heat capacities of the components and of the mixture : if K_0 denotes the heat capacity of the components before the mixture, and K that of the liquid resulting from their mixture, then we have

$$\frac{dU}{dT} = \frac{dQ}{dT} = K_0 - K.$$

This equation shows that only when

$$\frac{dQ}{dT} = 0 \text{ can } K = K_0 \text{ ;}$$

i.e. it leads to the necessary and sufficient condition for the specific heat of the mixture to be capable of being calculated additively from that of the components (p. 101).

Very much harder, but very much more important, is the determination of the diminution of *free energy* associated with the intermixture ; to calculate this we must find some way to accomplish the intermixture isothermally and reversibly ; if it is possible to find several methods of this sort, then all must give the same result, a law which will give particularly valuable results in the discussion of dilute solutions. Now as a matter of fact the process of mixing two liquids, which takes place spontaneously when the liquids are brought into contact (provided they are mutually soluble), can be conducted isothermally and reversibly in very many ways, namely by *isothermal distillation* (Kirchhoff), by *electrical transference* (Helmholtz), by *osmose* (van't Hoff), by *selective solubility*, and the like. But since these methods for the most part first found practical application in the case of dilute solutions, which will be thoroughly treated in the following chapter, there will be given here only a short description of the method which is most universal and most important, namely that of *mixture by means of isothermal distillation.*

We will take, as the basis of our considerations, the mixture formed by mixing 1 mol of the first component with x mols of the second, and we will also assume that the gas laws are applicable both to the vapours emitted by the mixture, and also to the vapour emitted by each component. If necessary, the formulæ can be easily generalised for the case that another equation of condition—an equation of dissociation, or the van der Waals' equation, for example—holds good for the vapour.

Now let us imagine two semi-permeable partitions, brought into the space over the mixture, one of which is permeable by the vapour of the first, the other by that of the second ingredient. The vapour emitted by the mixture contains both ingredients ; let p be the pressure of the first ingredient of the saturated vapour standing in equilibrium with the liquid mixture, at the absolute temperature T ;

and let P be the pressure of the second ingredient; then, according to Dalton's law, $P + p$ is the maximal pressure of the mixture. Let the two ingredients in the pure state have the pressure p_0 and P_0 respectively at the same temperature.

Now let us imagine the following process to take place:—We will allow 1 g.-mol of the first component, in the pure liquid state, to evaporate to saturated vapour; the work thus obtained will be—

$$p_0 v_0 = RT \;;$$

then let it expand till the pressure p_0 shall have fallen to p, whereby the work performed by the gas will be—

$$RT \ln \frac{p_0}{p} \;;$$

finally, bring it into contact with the membrane which is permeable by it and compress it; in consequence of this, it passes through the membrane and is condensed in the mixture; if this condensation is performed under constant pressure p, the external work, $pv = RT$, is necessary.

In order to realise the condition that the composition of the mixture, and hence that the value of p, shall not change during this condensation, we cause x mol of the second ingredient to evaporate at the same time; thus we obtain the work,

$$x P_0 V_0 = xRT \;;$$

and if we let this expand from the pressure P_0 to P, there is performed the work,

$$x RT \ln \frac{P_0}{P} \;; \;$$

we then condense it simultaneously with 1 g.-mol of the first ingredient by forcing it through the second semi-permeable partition. The two vapours meet in the space enclosed by the two semi-permeable membranes with the pressures P and p. Thus we have it always completely in our power to send through the partitions such quantities that there will condense a mixture having the composition just described; and if we do this, 1 g.-mol of the first ingredient condenses under the constant pressure p, and x g.-mol of the second under the constant pressure P; as just stated, the external work needed to condense the first is RT, and for the second

$$xPV = xRT.$$

Hence in the transference of 1 mol of the first component to the mixture the external work

$$RT + RT \ln \frac{p_0}{p} - RT = RT \ln \frac{p_0}{p}$$

is performed by the system, and in the transference of x g.-mol of the second ingredient the work

$$xRT + xRT \ln \frac{P_0}{P} - xRT = xRT \ln \frac{P_0}{P}$$

is performed; the sum of the work is therefore

$$RT\left(\ln \frac{P_0}{p} + x \text{ in } \ln \frac{P_0}{P}\right).$$

Now, since the processes above described can all be completed reversibly and isothermally, the last expression corresponds to the maximal external work or the diminution of free energy A. The latter, which may be suitably designated by A (x), thus becomes

$$A(x) = RT\left(\ln \frac{P_0}{p} + x \ln \frac{P_0}{P}\right), . \qquad . \qquad . \qquad (1)$$

and therefore

$$\frac{dA(x)}{dT} = R\left(\ln \frac{P_0}{p} + x \ln \frac{P_0}{P}\right) + RT\frac{d}{dT}\left(\ln \frac{P_0}{p} + x \ln \frac{P_0}{P}\right).$$

Introducing this into the formula (p. 23),

$$A - U = T\frac{dA}{dT} ;$$

and remembering that U = Q(x) (p. 109), we have

$$Q(x) = -RT^2\frac{d}{dT}\left(\ln \frac{P_0}{p} + x \ln \frac{P_0}{P}\right). \qquad . \qquad . \qquad (2)$$

This formula affords the calculation of the heat of mixture of two liquids from the temperature coefficients of their vapour pressures and that of their mixture and the pressure of the vapour emitted by the mixture.

A(x) can also be found by allowing x g.-mol of the second ingredient to distil over into 1 g.-mol of the first liquid ingredient; then the vapour pressure of the second ingredient in the mixture rises from 0 to P, and the work obtained thereby is given by the integral,

$$A(x) = RT\int_0^x \ln \frac{P_0}{P}dx \qquad . \qquad . \qquad . \qquad (3)$$

in the evaluation of which P must be known as a function of x. ✔

A(x) can be similarly found by allowing 1 mol of the first liquid to distil over into x mols of the second, thus

$$A(x) = RT\int_0^1 \ln \frac{P_0}{\pi}d\nu.$$

To evaluate this integral we must know the partial pressure π of the first component as a function of the number of mols. ν which mix with x mols. of the second ingredient.

From (1) and (3) we obtain

$$\ln \frac{p_0}{p} + x \ln \frac{P_0}{P} = \int_0^x \ln \frac{P_0}{P} dx.$$

Introducing this into (2), we obtain

$$Q(x) = - RT^2 \frac{d}{dT} \int_0^x \ln \frac{P_0}{P} dx,$$

or, differentiated for x,

$$\frac{\partial Q(x)}{\partial x} = - RT^2 \frac{\partial \ln \frac{P_0}{P}}{\partial T}.$$

This last equation, which can be easily derived directly by considering the isothermal distillation of one component into a large quantity of the mixture, was first derived by Kirchhoff,[1] and is a special case of the preceding generalisation; it was applied by him to the calculation of Regnault's vapour-pressure curve, for mixtures of water and sulphuric acid, the heat of mixture of which is known (p. 109); the calculation gives a fairly satisfactory result.

The physical significance of $\frac{\partial Q(x)}{\partial x}$ is given by the development of heat observed on the addition, for example, of 1 mol. of water to a very large quantity of a mixture having the composition of $H_2SO_4 + xH_2O$. Now, if we try to calculate this quantity of heat from Regnault's vapour pressures of such a mixture, and from those of pure water, we obtain results widely differing from the truth.[2] This is due to the fact that small variations in the value of P—the measurement of which, by the way, is very difficult—change the results of the calculation very greatly; this is also the reason why hitherto a successful quantitative application of Kirchhoff's formula to the calculation of the heat of dilution has been made impossible by the difficulty of measuring the vapour pressures of mixtures with sufficient accuracy. But it can be at any rate qualitatively inferred from Tammann's[3] measurements that, in accordance with Kirchhoff's formulæ, in those cases where addition of water develops heat (as H_2SO_4, $CaCl_2$, and the like), i.e. where

$$\frac{\partial Q}{\partial x} > 0,$$

[1] Pogg. Ann. 104. (1856); Ges. Abh. p. 492.
[2] Compare R. von Helmholtz, Wied. Ann. 27. 542 (1886).
[3] Mem. d. Petersburger Akad. 35. No. 9 (1887).

the value of $\dfrac{P_0}{P}$, and accordingly $\dfrac{P_0 - P}{P}$ also, the so-called "*relative*

lowering of the vapour pressure," decreases with increasing temperature; but that these values increase with increasing temperature when addition of water causes an absorption of heat.

The above formulæ show, as was first pointed out in the second edition of this book, that the composition of the vapour can be calculated when the vapour-pressure curves of the components (solid or liquid) are known, and the partial pressure of one component as a function of the composition of the liquid. A number of other deductions will be found in Duhem, "Solutions and Mixtures," *Trav. et Mém. des facultés de Lille*, Nos. 12 and 13 (1894); also M. Margules, *Wien. Ber.* **104**. 1243 (1895), who calculated examples. See also Lehfeldt, *Phil. Mag.* [5], **40**. 397 (1895), and Dolezalek, *Z. phys. Chem.* **26**. 321 (1898).

On differentiating (1) and (3) we get from (1)

$$\frac{dA}{dx} = RT\left(-\frac{d \ln p}{dx} + \ln P_0 - x\frac{d \ln P}{dx} - \ln P \right),$$

from (3)

$$\frac{dA}{dx} = RT \ln P_0 - RT \ln P,$$

whence follows at once the differential equation given by Duhem (*loc. cit.*)—

$$\frac{d \ln p}{dx} + x\frac{d \ln P}{dx} = 0.$$

For applications of this equation see Gahl, *Zeitschr. phys. Chem.* **33**. 178 (1900); and Zawidzki, *ibid.* **35**. 129 (1900).

The Critical Point of Mixtures.—In the warming of mixtures there are observed the same characteristic phenomena which we have called "critical" (p. 64). Of the critical data of mixtures, only the temperature has been measured to any great extent; the results have shown [1] that the critical temperature t, of a solution containing n per cent by weight of one liquid having the critical temperature t_1, and 100 – n per cent by weight of another liquid having the critical temperature t_2, can be calculated by the mixing rule,

$$t = \frac{nt_1 + (100 - n)t_2}{100}.$$

This formula can also be used conversely to calculate the critical temperature of one ingredient, provided that of the mixture and also that of the other ingredient be known.

G. C. Schmidt [2] has found the preceding rule very well established for a number of mixtures, which places the *critical point on the list of the additive properties*; the variations between calculation and experiment

[1] Pawlewski, *B.B.* **16**. 2633 (1883).   [2] *Lieb. Ann.* **266**. 266 (1891).

never amount to more than 4°, and as they lie irregularly on both sides of the mean, it is possible that they may be explained as due, at least in part, to the uncertainty of observation.

Kuenen[1] has recently found that the critical temperatures of certain mixtures, as of ethane and nitrous oxide, sometimes lie considerably below that of the components.

Isomorphous Mixtures.—The capacity of two crystallised substances for uniting to form a homogeneous mixed crystal, is observed quite rarely, although this property is not so exclusively limited to substances related chemically and crystallographically (*i.e.* substances possessing the same properties of symmetry and almost the same geometrical constants), as was formerly supposed; but since it has been found that pairs like albite and anorthite, ferric chloride and ammonium chloride, tetramethyl-ammonium iodide and chrysoidine hydrochloride, etc., are able to form mixed crystals, substances therefore in which one seeks in vain for any analogy of composition and constitution,[2] no doubt can be entertained that further investigation will considerably increase the list of such instances. (Compare the section on Isomorphism, Book II. Chapter I.)

It is undeniable that such solid mixtures are to be classified with liquid mixtures in many respects, just as certain liquids, as for example water and alcohol, are miscible in all proportions, while others are of limited miscibility, as for example water and ether, which are able to dissolve each other only slightly; so we also find substances which can crystallise together in all proportions, as for example the alums, and also other substances where gaps exist in the series of mixtures, as for example the sulphate and the selenate of beryllium.

Very often two salts can crystallise together in molecular proportions when they have otherwise only a partial, and sometimes hardly any recognisable miscibility in each other; this "*double salt*" forms a particular point in the gap exhibited by the series of mixtures. An analogy to this in many respects is found in certain pairs of liquids which dissolve each other only to a limited degree, and which at the same time are able to form a homogeneous molecular mixture in the shape of a chemical compound. Thus, for example, amylene, C_5H_{10}, and water, H_2O, are almost mutually insoluble towards each other; yet they are able to unite with each other in molecular proportions to form amyl alcohol, $C_5H_{10} + H_2O = C_5H_{12}O$, and thus this substance appears as a particular point in the gap exhibited by the series of mixtures of amylene and water. But, of course, the question whether the kind of chemical union in the two cases is not essentially different cannot be determined by this analogy.

Moreover, the property of water of uniting in molecular proportions

[1] *Phil. Mag.* **40.** 173 (1895).
[2] See especially the work of O. Lehmann, *Molekular-physik.*, Bd. I. and II.

with many substances, as *water of crystallisation*,—a property, by the way, not limited to water alone, as is shown by *alcohol of crystallisation, benzene of crystallisation*, etc.,—may be compared with the formation of double salts.

Of course, the relations of crystallised mixtures are more complicated than those of liquid mixtures, since the crystal form is a new factor of considerable significance.   Following a classification given by Retgers,[1] I give here a list of the different cases observed in the mutual miscibility of two crystalline substances.

1. The two substances form a complete series of mixtures, *i.e.* it is possible to make mixed crystals of them in every desired proportion ; pure isomorphism.   Example : $ZnSO_4 \cdot 7H_2O$ and $MgSO_4 \cdot 7H_2O$.

2. On account of slight differences in the crystal angles or in the molecular volume, the two substances can intermix only to a limited degree ; this case also is usually called pure isomorphism.   Examples : $KClO_3$ and $TlClO_3$, $BaCl_2 \cdot 2H_2O$ and $SrCl_2 \cdot 2H_2O$.

3. The different substances have forms more or less different, but mix with each other in considerable quantities ; the gap in the series of mixtures is relatively small.   Example : $NaClO_3$ regular and $AgClO_3$ quadratic.

4. Intermixture occurs only to a very slight extent, and can be recognised only by micro-chemical reactions on fragments free from inclusions ; the gap in the series is relatively very large.   Example : KNO_3 and $NaNO_3$.

Cases 3 and 4 are instances of *Iso-di-morphism* ; this is the phenomenon where both of the two different substances occur in two crystal modifications which are isomorphous in pairs.   Very often the two modifications are not both known in the free state, but one may be known in the form of an isomorphous mixture.   Thus in such mixtures as are instanced in 3 and 4, that substance which is in excess forces its crystal form in some degree upon the other substance.

5. There occurs an isolated double salt standing in the middle of the series, which crystallises differently from the end members, and does not mix with either of the simple salts ; the gap between the end members is usually very great.   The recognition of this case is of great importance, since by a superficial examination of the double salt, and especially if it resembled one of the end members, one would easily mistake it for an isomorphous mixture, and the phenomenon as one of pure isomorphism.

(Example : Calcite and magnesite which crystallise in molecular proportions, as dolomite.)

6. The two substances do not mix with each other appreciably.

In order to decide the degree of miscibility by a practical case, according to Retgers, one should prepare a number of solutions holding each ingredient in greatly varying proportions, and by evaporation

---

[1] *Zeitschr. phys. Chem.* **5.** 461 (1890).

of the solvent obtain crystals which should then be investigated. In order to obtain a product as homogeneous as possible, it is best to use a large quantity of solvent, and to study only the crystals which separate first. For the more the composition of the solution changes with the separation of the earlier portions, the greater is the danger of the formation of heterogeneous products.

Hereafter by an "*isomorphous mixture*" will be understood a mixed crystal, the composition of which is capable of a constant change within certain limits large or small; every member of a complete or incomplete series of mixtures is thus an isomorphous mixture, but not the isolated double salt.

The Physical Properties of Mixed Crystals.—The analogies between a liquid and a solid mixture extend thus far, that in both cases many properties of the mixture are additive, *i.e.* they can be calculated from the properties of the particular ingredients according to the so-called "partnership" calculation (p. 101).

This holds good especially for the volume of mixed crystals, which is frequently equal to the sum of the volumes of the ingredients in the free state ; in other words, *in the intermixture of two crystals there is observed neither contraction nor dilation.* As an example, there is given below a table of the specific volumes of mixed crystals of potassium and ammonium sulphates, by Retgers,[1] to whom we are indebted for these very exact measurements.

Composition.		Spec. Volume.		Difference.
$(NH_4)_2SO_4$.	K_2SO_4.	Obs.	Calc.	
0	100	0·3751	(0·3751)	...
5·45	94·55	0·3885	0·3855	+ 0·0030
8·33	91·67	0·3879	0·3906	− 0·0027
15·03	84·97	0·4042	0·4037	+ 0·0005
18·45	81·55	0·4080	0·4098	− 0·0018
20·55	79·45	0·4112	0·4138	− 0·0026
26·47	73·53	0·4270	0·4250	+ 0·0020
29·30	70·70	0·4305	0·4307	− 0·0002
42·67	57·33	0·4572	0·4556	+ 0·0016
65·35	34·65	0·4990	0·4988	+ 0·0002
83·37	16·63	0·5311	0·5324	− 0·0013
100	0	0·5637	(0·5637)	...

Although the law given above, as far as known, holds good and with great exactness for the case of isomorphous mixtures, yet a modification is necessary in the case of *iso-di-morphous mixtures.* Thus the sulphates of magnesium and iron, $MgSO_4 \cdot 7H_2O$, and $FeSO_4 \cdot 7H_2O$,

[1] *Zeitschr. phys. Chem.* **3.** 497 (1889) ; see also **3.** 289 ; **4.** 189 ; **5.** 436 ; **6.** 193 (1890) ; **8.** 6 (1892).

the first being orthorhombic, the second being monoclinic, are able to form orthorhombic and monoclinic mixed crystals, and yet are miscible to only a limited degree, since mixed crystals containing more than 54 per cent, and less than 81·22 per cent of magnesium sulphate cannot be obtained, at least at ordinary temperatures ; and, moreover, the mixed crystals having the magnesium sulphate in excess are orthorhombic, and those having the iron salt in excess are monoclinic. If the specific volumes of the mixed crystals are calculated from those of the two salts in the pure state (Fe 0·5269, Mg 0·5963), one-sided deviations are met with ; but if the specific volume of the iron salt in the orthorhombic crystals is taken as 0·5333, and that of the mono-clinic crystals as 0·5269, and similarly the volume of the magnesium salt in the monoclinic crystals as 0·5914, and in the orthorhombic crystals as 0·5963, the deviations vanish almost completely. It is very probable that the two values assumed above represent respectively the specific volume of theoretical orthorhombic iron, and of the mono-clinic magnesium salts which have not yet been produced in the free state. *Probably in general every salt in iso-di-morphous mixtures possesses a specific volume more or less different from that in the free state* ; this is in harmony with the fact that di-morphous modifications in the free state have different specific gravities.

It follows from the observations of Dufet (1878), Fock (1880), Bodländer (1882) and others that the optical properties of mixed crystals are emphatically additive ; but of course the crystal structure is attended with certain complications.[1]

Fusion and Solidification of Mixtures.—Investigation of the laws regulating the solidification of liquid mixtures is of much practical importance, on account of the method of fractional crystallisation that is so often used. The theory of this phenomenon cannot be developed so far as that of fractional distillation, at present, and also experimental study is still much needed. Still the leading principles are well established and will be given here.

When a mixture freezes the solid deposited may be homogeneous, *i.e.* it may be a single component of the liquid, or an isomorphous mixture ; or else more than one solid may separate at the same time ; thus from an aqueous solution either ice, salt, or hydrate may crystallise out, or more than one of these may appear together. In this lies a complication that is absent in evaporation, for gases are always homo-geneous.

We will take first the simple case that *one component separates out in the pure state* ; then we have the simple rule that the *solidifying point of such a mixture is always lower than that of the separated substance in the pure state.*

The proof of this follows from the consideration (p. 106) that the

[1] See especially F. Pockel's *Jahrb. f. Mineral.* **8.** 117 (1892).

vapour pressure of a substance in a mixture is always less than in the pure state; the melting-point, being the intersection of the vapour-pressure curves of solid and liquid (pp. 71 and 93), is accordingly always lowered.

Numerous examples of this rule are to be found. Salt solutions freeze (*i.e.* deposit ice) at a lower temperature than pure water; on the other hand, if they deposit salt, it is at a temperature below the melting-point of the salt, so that we may look on the crystallisation of a dissolved salt as freezing at a temperature very much lowered by addition of water. Phenol liquefies, when wet, much below its proper melting-point (42°); this too may be simply regarded as a lowering of melting-point due to mixture with water. Again the fusibility of alloys is a well-known and technically important fact of the same order; iron rich in carbon melts at a lower temperature than when containing little; and the alloys of Rose, Wood, Lipowitz, etc., are striking instances of how greatly the components of a mixture can lower each other's melting-point. Similarly, mixtures of salts, of fatty acids, and so on, are noticeable for their low melting-point. The latter case was fully investigated by Heintz.[1]

It will appear in the following chapter that the lowering of the melting-point of dilute solutions follows very simple laws.

It is essentially different when an isomorphous mixture or a chemical compound in molecular proportions (hydrate, double salt, substance with alcohol of crystallisation, benzene of crystallisation, etc.) separates from a mixture; then the melting-point of the mixture may, according to circumstances, lie higher or lower than that of the pure substances. For example, the melting-point of naphthalene is raised by addition of β-naphthol, and accordingly pure naphthalene does not freeze out from the liquid, but an isomorphous mixture.[2] It is noteworthy that under these circumstances the freezing-point of a liquid, like the boiling-point, may be either raised or lowered. If the solid mixture separating out changes continuously in composition with change in that of the liquid, the freezing-point varies continuously from that of one component to that of the other. This case is rare; often there is a sudden change in the composition of the solid owing to replacement of one component by the other, or by a compound in molecular proportions (*e.g.* a new hydrate); for instances see the work of Vignon[3] and Miolati.[4]

In one case we find the phenomenon of *continuous change in the solid deposit as the composition of the liquid is continuously changed*; then the freezing-point curve is continuous, showing no sudden changes of slope. This happens in the case of *mixtures of isomorphous and at*

[1] *Pogg. Ann.* **92.** 588 (1854).
[2] Van't Hoff, *Zeitschr. f. phys. Chem.* **5.** 388 (1890); Van Bijlert, *ibid.* **8.** 343 (1891).
[3] *Bull. Soc. Chim.* [3], **7.** 387, 656 (1892).
[4] *Zeitschr. phys. Chem.* **9.** 649 (1892).

the same time chemically similar materials. Küster[1] was the first to observe this case, and found that the *melting-point could be calculated from the composition by the simple rule of mixtures.* The agreement between observed and calculated melting-points is better when the composition is expressed in molecular percentage (mols. in 100 mols. of mixture) than in percentage by weight. It is necessary, in order that this rule be true, that the composition of the frozen part should be the same as that of the liquid; this can be tested by seeing whether the melting-point is independent of the quantity melted or not. Only if the temperature does not change during the fusion, is the rule true. When there is much difference in composition between the liquid and the frozen mass, the melting-points differ considerably from the values calculated by the (linear) rule. The regular behaviour is well shown by mixtures of hexachlor-α-keto-γ-R-pentene (C_5Cl_6O) and pentachlor-monobrom-α-keto-γ-R-pentene (C_5Cl_5BrO) (Küster).

Molecular per-centage of C_5Cl_5BrO.	Freezing-point.	
	Obs.	Calc.
0·00	87·50	...
5·29	87·99	88·04
8·65	88·30	88·38
25·32	89·85	90·09
42·26	91·61	91·81
71·33	94·59	94·78
90·45	96·67	96·74
98·00	97·49	97·50
100·00	97·71	...

Often, however, more than one solid separates from the liquid; in this case it is not at present possible to give a rule for the position of the melting-point, but experience seems to show that it may lie above or below those of the components. In general the composition of the remaining liquid is altered by the separation; and whatever the composition of the solid that separates, the change must always be in such a direction that the *melting-point of the remaining liquid is lowered.* This is the analogue of the law that during distillation the temperature always rises (p. 108). If, then, a mixture be repeatedly fractionally crystallised, a liquid will eventually be reached with minimum freezing-point; if this is frozen, the solid separating must have the same composition, otherwise we should obtain a liquid of still lower freezing-point. Conversely, the solid has a melting-point that is constant, *i.e.* independent of the amount melted. Such a substance was called by Guthrie,[2] who discovered these relations, an *eutectic mixture*; it melts

[1] *Zeitschr. phys. Chem.* **5.** 601 (1890); **8.** 577 (1891).
[2] *Phil. Mag.* [5], **17.** 462 (1884).

and freezes like a chemically simple substance, and is comparable with the mixture of constant boiling-point mentioned on p. 108; there are no grounds for assuming that it is a chemical compound, nor does experiment point in that direction.

Thus Guthrie found that a mixture of 46·86 per cent lead nitrate and 53·14 per cent potassium nitrate melts at 207°, and that by altering these proportions in either sense a higher melting-point is obtained. The following table gives the melting-point t of eutectic compounds of bismuth containing p per cent of the metal alloyed with bismuth :—

	p.	t.
Lead	44·42	122·7
Tin	53·30	133·
Cadmium . . .	40·81	144
Zinc	7·15	248

In the same way, by repeated partial freezing, eutectic mixtures of more than two components can be obtained, e.g. the mixture

Bi 47·75, Pb 18·39, Cd 13·31, Sn 20·00 per cent

melts at 71°, the .lowest melting-point known of any alloy except those containing alkali metals and the amalgams.

"Cryohydrates" are also examples of eutectic mixtures. When a salt solution is cooled it first deposits ice, and so becomes more concentrated; hence on cooling further a point must be reached when the salt in solution has become saturated, then a mechanical mixture of ice and salt will come down, and necessarily in the same proportions as they occur in the liquid. This temperature is at the intersection of the curve of saturation with the curve of lowering of freezing-point; the solution freezes completely and at constant temperature, as if it were a single substance. It was at one time supposed to be such, and described as *cryohydrate.*

The temperature at which the solution freezes as a whole, to form a mechanical mixture, is also the *lowest* that can be obtained by mixing ice and salt. Thus, according to Guthrie,[1] ice and NaCl give − 22°, ice and NaI − 30°; the cryohydric temperature is clearly lower the more the salt lowers the freezing-point of water and the more soluble it is. The temperature can be still further reduced by using more than one salt simultaneously; Mazotto[2] investigated the case of water, NH_4Cl and $NaNO_3$, and found the cryohydric point at − 31°·5.

Apparently the solid that deposits from eutectic mixtures arrived at in this way consists always of a mechanical mixture of two or more substances; there are, however, cases, as mentioned above, in which a

[1] *Ibid.* [4], **16**. 446 ; [5], **2**. 211 ; **6**. 35, 105.   [2] *Beibl.* **15**. 323 (1891).

liquid mixture freezes to a *single homogeneous substance* (double salt, hydrate, etc.). If the composition of such a mixture be altered, then, unlike an eutectic (*i.e.* easy melting) mixture, the freezing-point is lowered; therefore the mixture is one of maximum melting point, and may be described as *dystectic*. Thus Roozeboom [1] found that a mixture of composition $FeCl_3 + 12H_2O$ freezes constantly at $37°$ to a solid hydrate; if the composition is varied, within certain limits, whether by addition of $FeCl_3$ or of water, a mixture of lower freezing-point is obtained.

From what has been said it may be seen that the different kinds of mixtures that we have distinguished must show characteristic differences when allowed to solidify gradually. Both eutectic and dystectic mixtures, like simple substances, solidify at one temperature. When the solid separating out *changes in composition continuously* with the change in the residual liquid, the fall of temperature, on cooling, will be made *slower* as soon as the separation begins, and the latent heat comes into play; this condition lasts until, after a longer or shorter interval of temperature, the whole has become solid. In cases in which this condition is not satisfied, but new substances appear, twice or more, in the solid deposit, the fall of temperature will be made slower each time, a phenomenon noticed in 1830 by Rudberg ("repeated melting-point"). Further, the course of the cooling may be influenced by phenomena of undercooling, and by subsequent gradual allotropic modification of solid deposits.[2]

Finally, this difference may be noted between the behaviour of a simple substance and a mechanical mixture. A simple substance always melts at the same temperature, and it is not possible to keep it solid even for a short time at a higher temperature. It is otherwise with a mixture; a finely powdered mixture of two metals can often be kept a long time at a temperature above the melting-point of the alloy that would result from it. Thus in a mixture, melting-point and freezing-point are not identical, as they are for a single substance.

On the other hand, even a rough mixture will sometimes liquefy at a temperature below the melting-point of either pure substance. Thus if a mixture of tin and lead be kept for some hours at $200°$ it liquefies, although the melting-point of tin is $230°$ and lead $325°$; and a mixture of 1 part Cd, 1 part Sn, 2 parts Pb, 4 parts Bi (Wood's metal), all the components of which melt above $200°$, can be liquefied by keeping for some hours or days in a water-bath, under slight pressure (Hallock); [3] a mixture of sodium acetate and potassium nitrate melts when kept for some hours at $100°$, though the melting-point of the components is above $300°$ (Spring).[4]

The Thermodynamics of Isomorphous Mixtures. — The

[1] *Zeitschr. phys. Chem.* **10.** 477 (1892).
[2] See Ostwald, *Lehrb. d. allg. Chem.*, 2nd ed., **1.** 1023 (1891).
[3] *Zeitschr. phys. Chem.* **2.** 378 (1888.)   [4] *Ibid.* 536.

observations which we have advanced above (p. 109) concerning liquid mixtures, from the standpoint of energy, can be applied directly to solid mixtures, in their essential principles. With the union of two crystals to form a new homogeneous mixed crystal, there is usually associated a certain diminution of the *total energy* U, which may also be described here as the heat of mixing. To ascertain the diminution of free energy associated with the mixing, we must find some method of making the mixed crystals reversibly and isothermally. Strictly speaking, we could employ here the same methods which were successfully used in the case of liquid mixtures, namely, isothermal distillation or direct sublimation, and we should thus arrive at the same formulæ as in the preceding case. But, since the vapour pressure of crystals is far too small for us to hope to measure, we must devise some other way: there is such a method in *isothermal solution* and *crystallisation*. By distilling over sufficient water into the two ingredients, isothermally and reversibly, we can bring the crystals isothermally and reversibly into solution. Then we mix the two solutions. This is a process which can be conducted isothermally and reversibly, as we shall see in the theory of dilute solutions (next chapter). Now, if we withdraw both ingredients from the resulting solution by the isothermal distillation of water, we can obtain the mixed crystal. If we know the conditions of solubility of the mixed crystal and its ingredients, as well as the vapour pressure of their respective solutions, the calculation of the maximal work obtained by mixing and the application of the second law of thermodynamics present no difficulty. Of course, instead of water, we can select any other solvent, where we get the same maximal work. The condition for the identity of this work leads to certain conditions of solubility for the different solvents that have recently been tested and verified by E. Sommerfeldt.[1] It appears that the maximal work is of the same order of magnitude as in the case of liquid mixtures, and, therefore, there can be no doubt that the isomorphous mixtures arise by mutual molecular penetration, and not by a variable superposition of very thin lamellæ, as is sometimes supposed.

The analogy between liquid and isomorphous mixtures is also borne out by the fact that just as the maximal pressure, and the composition of the vapour emitted by the liquid mixture, vary steadily with the relative quantities of the ingredients, so also do the concentration and the composition of the saturated solution of the mixed crystals vary steadily with the relative quantities of the ingredients. In the third book we shall return again to this subject.

Adsorption.—Charcoal shaken with an iodine solution or placed in an atmosphere of iodine vapour condenses appreciable amounts of

[1] *Neues Jahrb. f. Mineral.*, 1900, vol. ii.

iodine on its surface; this is known as "adsorption." The quantity adsorbed increases with the partial pressure (gas or osmotic) of the iodine. A definite state of equilibrium is set up; this was shown among others by Chappius,[1] who found that a definite amount of charcoal took up a quantity of carbon dioxide that depends only on the pressure of that gas. The adsorption of dissolved substances by solids has been studied especially by Bemmelen.[2] The thermodynamics of the subject will not be discussed here; but it may be remarked that the heat of adsorption may be calculated from the influence of temperature on equilibrium.

Lagergren[3] has lately put forward remarkable experiments and views on the phenomena of adsorption in aqueous solutions. Here it is probable that the most important influence is the formation of an aqueous layer on the surface of the adsorbing powder, and that this is in a highly compressed state owing to cohesive forces. The heat evolved by wetting insoluble powders would, according to this view, be due to the strong compression of the adsorbed water.

If foreign substances are present in the water their solubility in adsorbed water may be greater or less than in ordinary water; greater if the solubility increases with pressure, and *vice versa*. Hence the dissolved substance will be concentrated or diluted in the water film, *i.e.* positive or negative adsorption will occur. Lagergren actually demonstrated negative adsorption, *e.g.* when sodium chloride solution is shaken with charcoal its concentration is raised. The data so far collected seem to support this view.

[1] *Wied. Ann.* **12.** 161 (1881).
[2] *Zeitschr. phys. Chem.* **18.** 331 (1895); *Zeitschr. anorg. Chem.* **13.** 233 (1896); see also G. C. Schmidt, *Zeitschr. phys. Chem.* **15.** 56 (1894); Georgewics u. Löwy, *Wien. Akad.* **104.** (1895); Walker and Appleyard, *J. Chem. Soc.* **69.** 1334 (1896).
[3] *Bihang till K. Sv. Vet. Akad. Handl.*, Band **24.** Afd. II. Nos. 4 and 5 (1898).

CHAPTER V

General Remarks.—One class of liquid and solid mixtures which has attracted great attention in recent investigations, because their behaviour is very simple in many respects, is that of *dilute solutions*, *i.e.* mixtures containing one component greatly in excess of the others. This component is called the "solvent"; the other, or others, the "dissolved substances."

A close study of the relations of dilute solutions is justified on several grounds. In the first place, the laws of thermodynamics have been applied here with especially good results, which are simple and obvious, and which in their turn clear up old principles, and throw light on new subjects. The method proposed by van't Hoff for the study of solutions can be regarded as typical for the treatment of questions like this. Also, the study of dilute solutions attracts great practical interest from the consideration that most chemical processes which the analyst uses, and also those which claim attention in animal and plant physiology, take place in dilute water solutions. Finally, although most of the results here obtained were obtained independently of the molecular hypothesis, yet the study of the properties of dilute solutions has led to a development of our conceptions regarding molecules, which presents this subject in an entirely new phase (see Book II. Chapter VII.).

The investigations on this subject had for a starting-point the attempt to answer this question : *What is the maximal work to be obtained by the addition of a pure solvent to a solution ?* After methods of solving the problem were found, the experimental work gave general results of an unexpected nature, the very simplicity of which required a theoretical explanation ; it lay close at hand, and consisted in an extension of the rule of Avogadro which was previously unexpected.

Osmotic Pressure.—In order to answer the question, What is the maximal work capable of being obtained by mixing a dilute solution with a pure solvent? we may propose the same way as that employed by us above (p. 109), where we met a similar problem concerning the mixing of two liquids; the same formulæ developed there can be transferred without further change to this case, if we cause the pure solvent to distil over isothermally into the solution. We will return to this a little later, but will next consider a simpler and plainer apparatus which permits the mixing and the separating to be conducted isothermally and reversibly. The fortunate use of this apparatus was the artifice by means of which van't Hoff (1885) discovered the laws prevailing here almost by one stroke; this artifice, moreover, has already advantageously served us in a similar question (p. 97).

Let us imagine, for example, a sugar solution covered with pure water; as is well known, such a system at once suffers a change, since the sugar begins to wander from the lower to the upper part, i.e. from places having a higher to those having a lower concentration; this diffusion process, as this phenomenon is called, does not cease till the concentration has become the same in all parts of the solution. Now let us imagine the solution to be separated from the layer of water above it by a so-called "semi-permeable" partition, i.e. such a partition as allows free passage to the water, but not to the dissolved sugar; it must happen, of course, that the sugar will exert a *pressure* on the partition, which opposes its endeavour to fill the whole solution. If the partition is movable in a cylinder, as shown in Fig. 12, in which L is the solution and W the layer of water above, which are separated by the partition just described, then we have the desired apparatus to conduct the mixing isothermally and reversibly. When the piston is pressed downwards the sugar in L is compressed, and the water passes over from L to W; on the other hand, if the piston is raised, water passes from W to L, and the sugar solution is correspondingly diluted. But from the fact that the sugar will wander up into the pure water by means of diffusion, if we imagine the piston to be removed, it necessarily follows that there will be exerted a pressure on the piston in the direction of the arrow; and the greater this pressure is, so much greater, of course, is the work which the dissolved sugar can perform in its expansion, i.e. as it takes up new solvent material through the "semi-permeable" partition; the amount of this work can be calculated from the product of the pressure and the volume through which the piston is displaced.

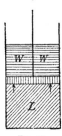

Fig. 12.

We will call the pressure measured by such an apparatus "*the osmotic pressure of solution.*" The analogy with the pressure exerted by a gas on its enclosing walls is at once obvious. If we imagine the solvent to be removed, and the space L to be filled with a gas, and the space W to be made vacuous, then we have obviously an entirely analogous experimental arrangement, since the ordinary gas pressure is acting, instead of the osmotic pressure.   Moreover, the molecules of a dissolved substance, just the same as the molecules of a gas, have the tendency to occupy *the greatest possible space*; and just as the molecules of a gas can be removed from each other to any desired distance by expansion, so the same is true of the tendency of the molecules of a dissolved substance, provided that we constantly add more pure solvent.

The Direct Measurement of the Osmotic Pressure.—The question now arises, whether we are able to realise the conditions of the experiment just described, whether we can construct partitions having the desired properties.   Now, as a matter of fact, such is really the case; the semi-permeable partitions do occur in nature ready formed, and can also be artificially prepared, at least in certain cases.   According to the researches of M. Traube,[1] *the membranes of precipitation*, which are formed on the surface separating a solution of cupric sulphate from one of potassium ferro-cyanide, and which consist of cupric ferro-cyanide, do possess the property of being permeable for water, but not for many substances soluble in water, as cane-sugar, for example.   Therefore when Pfeffer[2] dipped, into a weak solution of potassium ferro-cyanide, a porous jar filled with a solution of sugar containing a little copper sulphate, and fitted with an upright tube, there was formed at once on the interior of the porous jar a precipitated membrane.   By means of this the outward passage of the sugar molecules through the cell wall is hindered, but not so the inward passage of the water.   As a result there follows the pressure action on the semi-permeable membrane, as above described, but the membrane cannot yield since it is fastened to the resistant porous cell; therefore, according to the principle of action and reaction, there will be exerted on the solution an impulse which will tend to drive it away from the membrane.   This impulse will cause water to flow in and the solution to rise in the upright tube; if the upright tube be long enough, the opposing hydrostatic pressure will increase till it stops the further inflow of water.   Of course after the equilibrium is established, this opposing hydrostatic pressure is equal to the osmotic pressure of the solution.   But since the pressure amounts to several atmospheres, as we will see later, Pfeffer used, instead of an open manometer, a closed mercury manometer, and thus, besides having the advantage of a quicker adjustment, he also succeeded in avoiding the influx of large quantities of water and the associated changes of concentration which are difficult to control.

If one uses the cupric ferro-cyanide membrane, it must be noticed that it is permeable for many soluble substances, such as saltpetre,

---

[1] *Archiv f. Anatomie und Physiologie*, 1867, p. 87.
[2] *Osmotische Untersuchungen.* Leipzig, 1877.

hydrochloric acid, and many colouring substances, and therefore does
not satisfy the desired conditions for these substances.   As would be
expected, the osmotic pressure in such cases is too small.   The fact
that other investigators, in repeating the experiments of Pfeffer, did
not give sufficient attention to this point, although Pfeffer clearly
recognised and emphasised its significance, makes a large number of
measurements useless in the consideration of the theory of osmotic
pressure.   Some other precipitated membranes,
such as zinc ferro-cyanide, tannic acid sizing, etc.,
likewise find application.

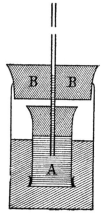

The efficiency of a semi-permeable membrane
used by myself [1] depends on the principle of *selective solubility* ; thus, for example, ether can diffuse
into water since it is partially soluble in water ;
but a substance dissolved in ether, and which is
also insoluble in water, cannot so diffuse into
water.   In order to give stability to the separating membrane, just as Pfeffer arranged the membrane of cupric ferro-cyanide in a porous cell, so I
arranged the water in contact with a plant or
animal membrane.   By means of the simple
apparatus shown in Fig. 13, the efficiency of an
osmotic cell can be very easily demonstrated—

Fig. 13.

for lectures, for example.   A is a glass tube (for
example, a piece cut from a test tube) with a piece of pig's bladder,
moistened with lukewarm water, tied over the lower end ; it is closed
at the upper end with a well-fitting cork, provided with one hole
bored through.   After filling the cell A completely, with ether
containing a considerable amount of benzene, the opening in the cork
is closed with a narrow upright tube which fits tight ; the cell is then
dipped into a wider glass filled with ether.   The cork B, which is not
air-tight, serves both to hinder the evaporation of the outer ether, and
also to hold the cell in place.   Both the solution and the solvent must
be previously saturated with water, in order that the solvent action of
the ether may not destroy the skin of water in the partition membrane.
Also, it is well to add a colouring substance which is insoluble in
water, to the ether in the inner cell, so that the action of the experiment will be visible, and one can also be thus assured that the
membrane is tight.   In order to prevent the membrane from bulging
out, it is rested upon a small tripod covered with wire gauze.   After
the cell has been left to itself for some time, one will notice the rising
of the ether column from the osmotic pressure of the benzene ; this
usually amounts in an hour to more than a decimetre.

A very elegant optical method for the discovery of solutions
having the same osmotic pressure, *i.e.* the so-called *is-osmotic solutions*,

[1] Nernst, *Zeitschr. phys. Chem.* **6.** 37 (1890).

is described by Tammann,[1] who placed a drop of a solution of potassium ferro-cyanide in a solution of copper sulphate. The drop is at once surrounded with a membrane of precipitation ; accordingly as the osmotic pressure is greater in the inner or the outer solution, the cell will expand or contract, with the inflow or outflow of water. Tammann observed the osmotic stream produced by the changes of concentration by means of a so-called " schlieren " apparatus. When the striæ disappear, the osmotic pressure is the same outside and inside. If foreign substances are added to both solutions producing the membrane, which do not themselves diffuse through the membrane, then their osmotic action can be compared. These phenomena can be beautifully demonstrated. If a drop of a strong solution of potassium ferro-cyanide is added by means of a capillary pipette to a moderately strong solution of copper sulphate, it can be seen with the naked eye how striæ of a concentrated solution of copper sulphate flow downwards from the cell ; this is a proof that the inner solution continually extracts water from the outer one. This very instructive phenomenon can be shown on the lantern to a large audience.

Semi-permeable partitions and the associated action of the osmotic pressure play a very important rôle in the economy of living nature, and it should be emphasised that the investigations in plant physiology, and, among others, those of Traube, of de Vries, and especially of Pfeffer, made possible the more detailed study of osmotic pressure, the laws of which form the basis of the modern theory of solutions. Thus the living protoplasmic layer, which entirely surrounds the surface of the cell-sap of plants, is very permeable for the solvent, water, but is an almost completely impermeable membrane[2] for the substances dissolved in the cell-sap, such as glucose, calcium, and potassium malates, etc., as well as some inorganic salts. If, therefore, some plant cells, taken for example from the leafy part of *Tradescantia discolor*, are sprinkled with a water solution having a greater osmotic pressure than that exerted by the substances dissolved in the cell-sap in the protoplasts, then the latter will contract, *i.e.* *plasmolysis* is said to occur : if, on the other hand, a smaller osmotic pressure exists in the outer solution, then the protoplasmic sheath expands as far as the cell wall permits. Thus, by means of microscopic observation, one can prepare solutions of selected substances which are *is-osmotic* (iso-tonic) with the cell-sap. Osmotic action can also be recognised in the red blood corpuscles,[3] and in bacteria cells,[4] and nerve cells,[5] all of which can be applied to the study of osmotic solutions. Of course

---

[1] *Wied. Ann.* **34.** 229 (1888).

[2] See especially the treatise written for those who are not professional botanists by de Vries, *Zeitschr. phys. Chem.* **2.** 414 (1888).

[3] Hamburger, *Zeitschr. phys. Chem.* **6.** 319 (1890). See also Löb, *ibid.* **14.** 424 (1894) ; Köppe, *ibid.* **16.** 261 ; **17.** 552 (1895) ; Hedin, **17.** 164 ; **21.** 272 (1896).

[4] Wladimiroff, *Zeitschr. phys. Chem.* **7.** 524 (1891).

[5] See Tammann, *Zeitschr. phys. Chem.* **8.** 685 (1891).

these methods are useless when the dissolved substances either exert a specific poisonous action on the protoplasmic sheath of the cells in question, or else diffuse through them. It is not without interest to observe that the pressure in animal and plant cells under the most diverse conditions, amounts to from four to five atmospheres; and that sometimes it is even four times as great in those protoplasts which serve as the storehouse of dissolved substances held in reserve; examples of the latter are the cell contents of beets, and also the cells of bacteria.

In concluding this sketch, I give the measurements obtained by Pfeffer of the osmotic pressure in a water solution of cane sugar, which was the substance most thoroughly investigated by him. The cupric ferro-cyanide membrane used by Pfeffer satisfied most completely the conditions of *impermeability* for this substance.

OSMOTIC PRESSURE OF A ONE PER CENT WATER SOLUTION OF CANE SUGAR AT DIFFERENT TEMPERATURES

t.	Pressure.		Diff.
	Obs.	Calc.	
6·8	0·664 Atm.	0·665 Atm.	+ 0·001
13·7	0·691 ,,	0·681 ,,	− 0·010
14·2	0·671 ,,	0·682 ,,	+ 0·011
15·5	0·684 ,,	0·686 ,,	+ 0·002
22·0	0·721 ,,	0·701 ,,	− 0·020
32·0	0·716 ,,	0·725 ,,	+ 0·009
36·0	0·746 ,,	0·735 ,,	− 0·011

The figures in the third column are calculated from the formula

$$P = 0·649(1 + 0·00367t) \text{ atm.,}$$

which is well suited to express the results of the investigation, as is shown by the smallness and irregularity of the differences given in the last column. The measurements arranged *for varying concentration* can be calculated with similarly good results from the formula

$$P = n \cdot 0·649(1 + 0·00367t),$$

in which n denotes the per cent strength of the solution, *i.e.* the number of g. sugar in 100 g. of the solution; thus the pressure of a 4 per cent solution, measured at 13·7°, amounted to 2·74 atm., while according to the preceding formula it should be 2·73 atm. It is obvious that the pressures involved are of considerable magnitude.

H. N. Morse and J. C. W. Frazer (*American Chem. Journal*, **36.** 1, 37. 324, 1907) have recently succeeded in measuring the osmotic pressures of sugar solutions up to very high pressures. The following table contains their results, and also the pressures calculated according to van't Hoff's theory (see below), which agree when a normal solution is taken as containing 1 mol sugar to 1000 grams water, *i.e.* 1 litre at 4 per cent, instead of 1 mol sugar to 1 litre solution.

Concentration of the Solution.	Temp.	Pressure in Obs. Atm.	Theoretical Gas Pressure.	Diff.
0·05	20·5	1·25	1·21	+ 0·04
0·1	18·5	2·44	2·40	+ 0·04
0·2	21·5	4·80	4·85	− 0·05
0·3	19·4	7·23	7·22	+ 0·01
0·5	20	12·08	12·07	+ 0·01
0·8	17·5	19·07	19·14	− 0·07
0·9	20·2	21·80	21·74	+ 0·06
1·0	22·5	24·34	24·34	0·00

The osmotic pressure is of course independent of the nature of the semi-permeable membrane; if the membrane is more or less permeable by the solute, too low values for the pressure are obtained. Selective solubility, as mentioned above (p. 128), probably plays a large part in the mechanism of osmose; other complications can, however, interfere (see the detailed study by G. Flurin, *Chemical Action of the Membrane*, Grenoble, 1907). When the membrane is simply a second solvent, only slightly miscible with the first, osmose can be entirely referred to diffusion phenomena when the law of relative lowering of solubility (see below) is properly taken into account; for a discussion of this see Nernst, *Zeitschr. phys. Chem.* **6.** 37 (1890). [See also Berkeley and Hartley (*Phil. Trans.* **206.** 481; **209.** 177).]

Indirect Methods for the Measurement of Osmotic Pressure.

—In most cases the direct measurement of osmotic pressures is attended by very great experimental difficulties, which depend upon the successful accomplishment of making a semi-permeable membrane of sufficient stability and osmotic activity. Fortunately the measurement in almost all cases can be easily and certainly obtained by *indirect methods.*

The indirect methods all depend on the measurement of the expenditure of work which is necessary to separate the dissolved substance from the solvent. Now, according to what was said above, since the osmotic pressure is a direct measure of this expenditure of work, it is evident that if we know one we also know the other.

Of the many methods which can be employed for the reversible separation of solvent and dissolved substance, we will consider the following:—

1. Separation by evaporation.
2. Separation by selected solubility.
3. Separation by crystallisation.

But since each of these methods can be used in a double sense, *i.e.* we can remove either the *solvent* or the *dissolved substance* from the solution, we have the six following methods for the indirect measurement of osmotic pressure :—

A. The Separation of the Pure Solvent from the Solution

1. Separation by Evaporation.—We can see at once without further remark, that the partial pressure of the solvent above a solution must always be less than that over the pure solvent, at the same temperature. For if a solution and a solvent, at the same temperature, were separated only by a semi-permeable membrane, then the solution would add to itself at the expense of the solvent. If we assume that the partial pressure of the saturated vapour of the solvent is greater over the solution, then there must necessarily occur a process of isothermal distillation, whereby some of the solvent would be forced back from the solution to the pure solvent. In that case we would have a perpetually automatic cyclic process, *i.e.* a *perpetuum mobile*, which would perform work at the expense of the heat of the environment, which is contrary to the second law of thermodynamics (p. 16).

In what follows we will limit ourselves to solutions of non-volatile substances, *i.e.* solutions the vapour pressure of which is equal to the partial pressure of the solvent, as described above. The diminution of pressure experienced by a solvent, on dissolving a small quantity of a foreign substance, is obtained as follows : [1]

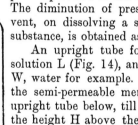

Fig. 14.

An upright tube for osmotic action holds the solution L (Fig. 14), and is dipped into the solvent W, water for example. Water will enter through the semi-permeable membrane A, which closes the upright tube below, till the liquid has mounted to the height H above the outer level, corresponding to the osmotic pressure prevailing in the solution. The whole system must be closed air-tight, and must be maintained at the same temperature at all points, reckoned in absolute temperature T. Then between the vapour pressure p of the water, and the vapour pressure p' of the solution, there must exist the relation that p', increased by the vapour column of the height H acting on W, must be equal to p. This relation merely states that the system is in equilibrium. For if we assume that p' is greater than that corresponding to this relation, then water would constantly distil over from the upright tube into W, to be again transported by osmotic pressure into L ; in short,

[1] See Gouy and Chaperon, *Ann. chim. phys.* [6], **13**. 124 (1888) ; and Arrhenius, *Zeitschr. phys. Chem.* **3**. 115 (1889).

the water would constantly traverse a cyclic process, *i.e.* the system would represent a *perpetuum mobile*, which would be able to perform any desired amount of external work at the expense of the heat of the environment, and the existence of which would contradict the second law of thermodynamics.

Also, conversely, if p' were smaller than would correspond to the preceding relation, then water would distil over from W into the upright tube, would pass below from L into W, and again around in this reverse cycle. Equilibrium, therefore, can exist only when the excess of pressure of p over p' is compensated by the hydrostatic pressure of a vapour column, equal in height to the difference between the levels.

The pressure of this vapour column can be easily calculated. If we denote the molecular weight of the solvent by M_0, then from the gas formula, $pv = 0.0821T$, we obtain the specific weight of the vapour, compared with that of water as unity, and since there are M_0g. of the vapour in v litres, the weight of one c.c. in g. amounts to

$$\frac{M_0}{1000v} = \frac{M_0 p}{0.0821T \cdot 1000}.$$

Instead of p we can introduce p', since their difference can be neglected if the solution is very dilute. In the same way we can neglect the fact that, strictly speaking, the density of the vapour column varies along the upright tube, and express the hydrostatic pressure simply by the formula

$$\frac{HM_0 p'}{0.0821T \cdot 1000 \cdot 76\sigma} \text{ atm.,}$$

where H is measured in cm., and σ denotes the specific gravity of mercury. The osmotic pressure of the solution corresponds to the pressure of the elevated column of liquid H. Therefore between H, and the osmotic pressure P expressed in atmospheres, there exists the relation

$$P = \frac{HS}{76\sigma},$$

where S denotes the specific gravity of the solution, or also that of the slightly differing solvent.

If we eliminate H in the expression for the hydrostatic pressure of the vapour column, by introducing

$$\frac{P76\sigma}{S}$$

for H, then we obtain the following expression for the relation of p and p' (developed as above from the conditions of equilibrium), viz.

$$p = p' + \frac{PM_0 p'}{1000S \cdot 0.0821T},$$

and thus obtain the expression sought for the osmotic pressure, viz.

$$P = \frac{p - p'}{p'} \frac{0 \cdot 0821 T \cdot 1000 S}{M_0} \text{ atm.} \qquad . \qquad . \qquad (1)$$

which was found by van't Hoff (1886),[1] by a method not differing in principle from the preceding.

The vapour pressure of a solution containing 2·47 g. of ethyl benzoate to 100 g. of benzene was found to be 742·60 mm. at 80°, while that of pure benzene at the same temperature amounted to 751·86 mm.;[2] the molecular weight M of benzene is 78; its specific weight at the preceding temperature is 0·8149; therefore the osmotic pressure of the aforesaid solution is calculated to be

$$P = \frac{9 \cdot 26}{742 \cdot 6} \frac{0 \cdot 0821 \cdot (273 + 80) \cdot 814 \cdot 9}{78} = 3 \cdot 78 \text{ atm.}$$

The simple yet obvious derivation given above for the fundamental relation between osmotic pressure and vapour tension is not quite strict, because it assumes that $p - p'$ is only a small fraction (say the hundredth part) of p, a condition satisfied only in the case of very dilute solutions. We obtain a more exact formula in the following way.

By means of the apparatus figured on p. 126 (Fig. 12), we remove a small quantity of the solvent from the solution. The expenditure of work necessary for this amounts to Pdv, in which dv is the volume through which the piston is lowered. Let the quantity of solvent removed from the solution be dx g.-mol. Now we can also remove the same quantity of solvent from the solution by means of isothermal distillation, and denoting by p and p' the respective vapour tensions of the pure solvent, and of the solution at the temperature T, the expenditure of work necessary, according to the equations on p. 111, is

$$dx RT \ln \frac{p}{p'}.$$

Now since the work must be the same in these two isothermal and reversible ways, it follows that

$$P = \frac{dx}{dv} RT \ln \frac{p}{p'} \ . \qquad . \qquad . \qquad . \qquad (2)$$

Now as the addition of dx mols of the pure solvent to a sufficiently dilute solution produces neither contraction nor dilution, dv is obviously equal to dx mols, i.e. it follows that

$$dv = \frac{M_0}{S} dx \qquad . \qquad . \qquad . \qquad . \qquad (3)$$

[1] van't Hoff, "Lois de l'équilibre chimique dans l'état dilué ou dissous." Stockholm, 1886. An abstract of this is to be found in Zeitschr. phys. Chem. 1. 481 (1887).
[2] Beckmann, Zeitschr. phys. Chem. 6. 439 (1890).

From (2) and (3) we find

$$P = \frac{S}{M_0} \, RT \ln \frac{p}{p'} \qquad . \qquad . \qquad . \qquad . \qquad (4)$$

In order to obtain P in atmospheres, we must express the volume of 1 mol of the solvent in litres, and must write $0\cdot0821$ for R, when it follows that

$$P = \frac{0\cdot0821T \; 1000S}{M_0} \ln \frac{p}{p'} \, atm. \qquad . \qquad . \qquad (5)$$

For $\ln \frac{p}{p'}$ in equation (5) we may write

$$\ln \left(1 + \frac{p - p'}{p'} \right) = \frac{p - p'}{p'},$$

if $\frac{p - p'}{p'}$ is very small, cf. with 1. Equation (5) gives with the former data for the pressure of ethyl benzoate in benzene

$$P = 3\cdot76 \text{ atms.,}$$

while the less exact formula gives $3\cdot78$ atm.

It is recommended in practice to determine the *boiling-point* instead of the vapour pressure. Instead of the lowering of the vapour pressure $p - p'$, one can measure much more simply and accurately the *elevation of the boiling-point* produced by the addition of soluble substances. If the determination is conducted at the atmospheric pressure B, then the vapour pressure of the solution at its boiling point will be $p' = B$. The vapour pressure p of the pure solvent at the same temperature is B, increased by the amount by which it rises from the temperature of the boiling solvent to that of the solution; this can be obtained from the vapour-pressure tables of Regnault and others with satisfactory accuracy for most available solvents.

For *small elevations of the boiling-point t*, we can calculate p, by means of the formula of Clausius (p. 58):

$$\frac{d \ln p}{dT} = \frac{\lambda}{RT^2}.$$

When the temperature interval is small, λ may be considered constant; integration then gives

$$\ln p = -\frac{\lambda}{RT} + \text{const.}$$

Now, at the boiling-point T_0 of the pure solvent, we have

$$\ln B = -\frac{\lambda}{RT_0} + \text{const.,}$$

and therefore

$$\ln \frac{p}{p'} = \ln \frac{p}{B} = \frac{\lambda}{R} \left[\frac{1}{T_0} - \frac{1}{T} \right].$$

This, introduced into formula (4), gives

$$P = \frac{\lambda}{M_0} ST \left[\frac{1}{T_0} - \frac{1}{T} \right].$$

This, simplified, becomes

$$P = \frac{Slt}{T} \text{ or } P = \frac{1000S.1}{24.19} \cdot \frac{t}{T_0} \text{ atm. .   . } \quad (6)$$

where

$$1 = \frac{\lambda}{M_0}$$

denotes the heat of evaporation of 1 g. of the solvent, 24·19 is the factor to reduce cal. to litre atmospheres (p. 13) ; and $t = T - T_0$ denotes the elevation of the boiling-point of the solution. As before S denotes the specific gravity of the solvent. The factor 1000 is again introduced because we must express the volume of 1 mol of the solvent in litres in order to obtain p in atmospheres. This formula does not depend on the condition that the vapour of the solvent must follow the laws of gases ; but, on the other hand, it takes no account of the slight change of the heat of vaporisation with the temperature ; yet it can be used for elevations of boiling-point of $5° - 10°$, within 1 per cent of the correct value of the osmotic pressure prevailing at the temperature $T_0 + t$.

Thus the elevation experienced by the boiling-point of benzene, on the addition of 2·47 g. of ethyl benzoate to 100 g. of the solvent, is 0·403°. If, according to p. 58, we put the heat of vaporisation of benzene at 80° as equal to 94·4 cal., it follows that

$$P = \frac{814.9 \, . \, 94.4}{24.19} \cdot \frac{0.403}{(273 + 80)} = 3.63 \text{ atm.}$$

The difference, as compared with the value 3·76 found on p. 135, can be explained by the fact that in the first calculation we assumed that the gas laws hold for benzene vapour, which is not quite accurate (see also p. 60).

The osmotic pressure of *a water solution* at the boiling-point $100 + t°$ is accordingly

$$P = \frac{0.959 \, . \, 536.4}{24.19} \cdot \frac{t}{273 + 100},$$

or $$P = 57.0t \text{ atm.}$$

2. Separation by Selected Solubility.—The far-reaching analogy which exists between the process of solution and that of evaporation, and to which repeated reference must be made, is also shown in the fact that just as the vapour pressure of a solvent A is depressed by the addition of a foreign substance B, so also the solubility of A in a second solvent is diminished by the addition of a foreign substance B ; and the two phenomena follow the same laws. Thus, if we mix together two liquids, as ether and water, which are only slightly

soluble in each other, and if we denote by L the solubility of pure
ether in water at the temperature T, and by L′ the solubility in water
of ether containing a foreign substance at the same temperature, then
L′ must always be smaller than L ; and the osmotic pressure P of the
foreign substance dissolved in the ether is given by the relation

$$P = \frac{L - L'}{L'} \frac{0.0819T \cdot 1000S}{M_0} \text{ atm.} \qquad . \qquad . \qquad (7)$$

where, as above, S and M denote respectively the specific gravity
and the molecular weight of the ether ; this relation is completely
analogous to the relation between the lowering of vapour pressure and
osmotic pressure, equation (5).[1]

The proof of equation (7) is most easily arrived at from the observation
that the solubility of ether in water must be the same as that of ether
vapour.   But as the latter, according to Henry's law, must have a solubility
proportional to its partial pressure,

$$L : L' = p : p',$$

and therefore equation (7) is a necessary consequence of (1).

3. **Separation by Crystallising (Freezing Out).**—From the law
that solutions of various substances in the same solvent are is-
osmotic when they have the same vapour pressure, it follows directly
that the same osmotic pressure must prevail in solutions of the solvent
which have the same *freezing-point*.   For as the freezing-point is that
temperature[2] at which the solid solvent (ice) and the solution are
capable of existing together, it must also be the point at which the
curves of the vapour pressures of
the solution and of the solid solvent cut each other, *i.e. where both
have the same vapour pressure.*   For
if we suppose, for example, that
the vapour pressure of ice and
that of the water solution were
different at the freezing-point,
then a process of isothermal distillation would begin, by which
equilibrium would be disturbed ;
equilibrium can only be stable
when the vapour of the solvent
over the solution and the solid is of

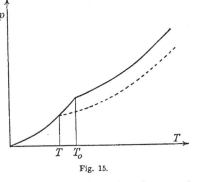

Fig. 15.

the same density.   Solutions of equal freezing-point have therefore equal
vapour pressures, namely, that of the separated ice, and are isotonic.
    These relations are shown in Fig. 15, in which, as in Fig. 4, the

[1] Nernst, *Zeitschr. phys. Chem.* 6. 16 (1890).
[2] It is assumed in all this argument that pure solvent crystallises out of the solution,
as is usually the case.   But see "Solid Solutions," p. 161.

vapour pressure curves of solid and liquid are shown, but also—dotted —the vapour pressure curve of the solution. The latter must lie below the curve for the solvent, according to the foregoing argument; hence its intersection T, with the curve for the solid, must lie below T_0. $T_0 - T = t$ is the lowering of the freezing-point.

The relation existing between the lowering of the freezing-point and of the osmotic pressure of a solution is found by combining the equation for the molecular heat of sublimation σ (p. 58) with that for the heat of vaporisation λ (p. 71), viz.

$$\sigma = RT^2\frac{d \ln p'}{dT}, \quad \text{and} \quad \lambda = RT^2\frac{d \ln p}{dT}; \qquad . \qquad . \qquad (8)$$

in which p' denotes the vapour pressure of the *solidified* solvent, equivalent to that of the solution according to the aforesaid law, and p denotes the vapour pressure of the pure (undercooled) *liquid* solvent, both values being referred to the freezing-point of the solution: by integration we obtain

$$\ln p' = -\frac{\sigma}{RT} + C'; \quad \ln p = -\frac{\lambda}{RT} + C.$$

Now, according to p. 71, at the freezing-point of the pure solvent, the temperature of which is T_0, the vapour pressures of the solid and of the liquid solvent are the same, *i.e.* at T_0 we have $p' = p = p_0$, and therefore

$$\ln p_0 = -\frac{\sigma}{RT_0} + C'; \quad \ln p_0 = -\frac{\lambda}{RT_0} + C.$$

If we eliminate the integration constants C' and C respectively, by the subtraction of the equations standing under each other in the same column we obtain

$$\ln \frac{p'}{p_0} = -\frac{\sigma}{R}\left[\frac{1}{T} - \frac{1}{T_0}\right]; \quad \ln \frac{p}{p_0} = -\frac{\lambda}{R}\left[\frac{1}{T} - \frac{1}{T_0}\right];$$

and by the subtraction of these last two equations we obtain

$$\ln\frac{p}{p'} = \frac{\sigma - \lambda}{R}\left[\frac{1}{T} - \frac{1}{T_0}\right]; \qquad . \qquad . \qquad . \qquad (9)$$

thus we obtain a formula which affords us the relation between the lowering of the vapour pressure and of the freezing-point of a solution, as well as *the molecular heat of fusion*, $\sigma - \lambda$, of the solution; this was found by Guldberg[1] as early as 1870; R here amounts to 1·985 if we express the heat of fusion in g.-cal.

In formula (4), p. 135, putting $\rho = \sigma - \lambda$ we have

$$P = \frac{\rho}{M_0}St\left[\frac{1}{T} - \frac{1}{T_0}\right],$$

[1] *Compt. rend.* **70.** 1349 (1870).

or simply as in equation (6), p. 136,

$$P = \frac{Swt}{T_0} \text{ or } P = \frac{1000 \, S \, . \, w}{24 \cdot 19} \frac{t}{T_0} \text{ atm.} \quad . \quad . \quad (10)$$

In this formula w denotes $\frac{\sigma - \lambda}{M}$, the heat of fusion of 1 g. of the solvent expressed in g.-cal. ; T_0 is the fusing-point; S is its specific gravity ; and t denotes $T_0 - T$, the lowering of the freezing-point.

Thus by the addition of 2·47 g. of ethyl benzoate to 100 g. of benzene, the freezing-point, 5·5°, of the solvent is lowered about 0·840° : its heat of fusion amounts to 30·08 g.-cal., and its specific gravity at the freezing-point is 0·8875. The osmotic pressure of the solution is thus

$$P = \frac{887 \cdot 5 \, . \, 30 \cdot 08}{24 \cdot 19} \cdot \frac{0 \cdot 840}{273 + 5 \cdot 5} = 3 \cdot 329.$$

For water we have

$$\frac{1000 S \, . \, w}{24 \cdot 19 T_0} = \frac{1000 \times 79 \cdot 6}{24 \cdot 19 \times 273} = 12 \cdot 05,$$

and therefore the pressure of a water solution freezing at $T_0 - t$ is $P = 12 \cdot 05 \, t$ atm.

According to the very accordant measurements of Abegg[1] ; Ponsot[2] ; and Raoult[3] ; the freezing-point of a 1 per cent sugar solution is about $- 0 \cdot 0546°$. Its osmotic pressure is therefore 0·657 atms., in good agreement with Pfeffer's direct measurement of 0·649.

Moreover, we observe from the preceding formula that the thousandth part of a degree of temperature, a quantity quite difficult to measure, corresponds to a pressure of 0·012 atm., i.e. about 9·1 mm. of mercury ; this latter value could be determined to one part per cent, provided one had a semi-permeable membrane sufficiently sure and rapid in its action.

On account of the simplicity of determining the lowering of the freezing-point, in practice the method above described finds application almost always, in preference to the measurement of the osmotic pressure : its experimental treatment will be considered in the chapter on the determination of the molecular weight.

B. The Separation of the Dissolved Substance from the Solution

1. Separation by Evaporation.—We will consider two solutions of the same substance in the same solvent, of very nearly the same degree of concentration. Let P be the osmotic pressure of the substance dissolved in solution I. ; let p be its vapour pressure over the solution ; let V be the volume of the solution containing 1 mol of the substance dissolved ; and let v be the volume assumed by the mol in the gaseous state at the pressure p. Let the corresponding magnitudes in solution II. be $P + dP$, $p + dp$, $V - dV$, and $v - dv$,

---

[1] *Zeitschr. phys. Chem.* **20.** 221 (1896).   [2] *Bull. Soc. Chim.* [3], **17.** 395 (1897).
[3] *Zeitschr. phys. Chem.* **27.** 617 (1898).

respectively. We will now conduct the following cyclic process at the constant temperature T. We will first set free from solution I., 1. mol of the dissolved substance, whereby the work PV will be performed *against* the osmotic pressure, and the work pv *by* the vapour pressure p. Then we will compress the g.-mol now existing in the gaseous state from v to v − dv, whereby there will be performed the work pdv. Next we will bring the mol into solution II., whereby there must be applied the work (p + dp) (v − dv) *against* the gas pressure, and the osmotic pressure *performs* the work (P + dp) (V − dV). Finally, we bring the mol from solution II. back again to solution I., whereby the osmotic pressure expends the work Pdv, and then all is reduced to the original condition.

Now, since the sum of the work *expended on* the system, diminished by the work *performed by* the system, in a reversible, isothermal, cyclic process must be equal to zero, we have the equation

$$PV - pv + pdv + (p + dp)(v - dv) - (P + dP)(V - dV) - PdV = 0,$$

or simplifying it and neglecting the small magnitudes of the second order,

$$vdp = VdP \qquad . \qquad . \qquad . \qquad . \qquad (11)$$

2. Separation by Selective Solubility.—We bring together two liquids which are only slightly soluble in each other, as, for example, carbon disulphide and water; we then dissolve a third substance, as iodine, which is divided between the two solvents. We will denote by P_1 and V_1, the osmotic pressure and the volume respectively, assumed by 1 g.-mol of the dissolved substance in one solvent, and by P_2 and V_2, the corresponding values in the second solvent. Then by means of a cyclic process completely analogous to that just described above, we can at once derive the relation

$$V_1 dP_1 = V_2 dP_2 . \qquad . \qquad . \qquad . \qquad (12)$$

3. Separation by Crystallisation.—The method employed altogether most frequently in practice to separate a dissolved substance from its solution, consists in crystallising it out from its saturated solution, by means of a suitable change of temperature.

This process reminds us of the condensation of a substance from its saturated vapour, and we also easily see that the analogy between the processes of solution and of vaporisation is not merely external, but that it is really deep-seated. For if we vaporise a solid or a liquid body, its molecules are driven by an expansive force, called the " vapour pressure," into a space where they arrive under a certain pressure, viz. the pressure of the saturated vapour for the temperature in question. The conditions are similar when a solid goes into solution; in this case also the molecules are driven by a certain expansive force, called the *solution pressure*, into a space where they attain a definite pressure, viz. *the osmotic pressure* of the saturated solution.

We have developed thermodynamically on p. 58 a formula of Clausius, giving a simple relation between the change of vapour pressure with temperature, the increase of volume from vaporisation, and the heat of vaporisation. In a precisely similar way, by effecting the solution of a substance—instead of its vaporisation into a vacuum —and by making the process reversible by means of a semi-permeable partition, we can derive a relation between the change of "solution pressure" with the temperature, the increase of volume from solution, and the heat of solution of a solid substance : thus we obtain directly

$$Q = T\frac{dP}{dT}(V - v').$$

Here Q denotes the amount of *heat absorbed* when 1 mol of a solid substance goes into saturated solution, at the constant osmotic pressure P, and the temperature T; v' denotes the volume occupied by 1 mol of the substance before going into solution, and V the volume assumed by 1 mol of the same substance in the saturated solution (van't Hoff).[1]

If the substance going into solution is a liquid, there arises a complication from the solution of the solvent itself in this substance ; but this can be overcome by easy calculation.

The Law of Osmotic Pressure.—The laws of osmotic pressure must of course deal with the questions how the osmotic pressure depends on (1) the volume of the solution, *i.e.* the concentration, (2) the temperature, (3) the nature of the substance dissolved, (4) the nature of the solvent. The answer to these questions, which of course can be obtained only by experiment, *i.e.* by the direct or indirect measurement of the osmotic pressure in the most numerous and various conditions possible, is very simple, and has led to the following remarkable result, that *the osmotic pressure is independent of the nature of the solvent, and in general obeys the laws of gases* (van't Hoff). The various proofs requisite for establishing this law will be given in the following sections.

Osmotic Pressure and Concentration.—Pfeffer found that the pressure of solutions of cane sugar was proportional to the concentration (p. 130) ; the rules, according to which the lowering of vapour tension (law of Wüllner), and the lowering of the freezing-point (law of Blagden), vary proportionally with the concentration of the dissolved substances, have long been known, and in the light of the formulæ developed on pages 134 and 139 must mean that the same

[1] See also van Deventer and van der Stadt, *Zeitschr. phys. Chem.* **9.** 43 (1891).

holds good for the osmotic pressure. If we denote by c the number of mols dissolved per litre, then

$$P = c \times \text{const.} ;$$

and we notice that

$$c = \frac{1}{V},$$

if V denotes the volume of the solution containing 1 mol of the dissolved substance; then

$$PV = \text{constant} ;$$

i.e. the Boyle-Mariotte law holds good for the osmotic pressure.

Osmotic Pressure and Temperature.—Pfeffer's measurements of the pressure of solutions of cane sugar can be well represented by the formula

$$P = 0\cdot649(1 + 0\cdot00367t).$$

But the temperature coefficient $0\cdot00367$ is the same as that of gases, *i.e. the osmotic pressure is proportional to the absolute temperature.* This result is confirmed by a simple law which was discovered by Babo as early as 1848, and which has been verified repeatedly by experiment in recent times; viz. *that the relative lowering of the vapour pressure,* $\frac{p - p'}{p}$ *of a dilute solution, and also the quotient,* $\frac{p}{p'}$, *is independent of the temperature.* For if we observe in the equation

$$P = \frac{0\cdot0821 \; T \; 1000 \; S}{M_0} \ln \frac{p}{p'}$$

that S is inversely proportional to the volume V of the quantity of solvent containing a definite amount of the dissolved substance, say 1 mol, and if we also notice that, according to Babo's law, the expression

$$\frac{0\cdot0821}{M_0} \ln \frac{p}{p'}$$

is independent of the temperature, then it also follows in this way that

$$PV = T \times \text{const.} ;$$

i.e. the law of Gay-Lussac holds good for the osmotic pressure.

This law will later be established more rigorously by thermodynamic considerations; but remark should here be made that the numerous determinations of the elevation of the boiling-point and of the lowering of the freezing-point of dilute solutions, have all shown that the osmotic pressure of solutions of similar dilutions at these two points referred to the same *spatial* concentration,[1] have

---

[1] Such a reduction is necessary, since the expansion of the solution from heat increases the volume of the subtance dissolved.

the same ratio as the absolute temperatures of the boiling-point and melting-point.

Osmotic Pressure and the Heat of Dilution.—When more solvent is added to a dilute solution, *there is no heat developed, neither is external work performed.* The total energy remains unchanged in this process. If the operation is conducted in such a way that external work is obtained at the same time, then the solution must cool itself an equivalent amount, exactly as was the case with gases (p. 46). And if, on the other hand, one compresses the solution by the osmotic apparatus figured on p. 126 (Fig. 12), then the work applied will reappear as heat, according to the law of the conservation of energy. We may express this law by saying that the content of energy of a dissolved substance is independent of the volume of the solution.

If we displace an osmotic piston through the volume v, and apply the equation (*e*) on p. 23, viz.

$$A - U = T\frac{dA}{dT},$$

then since

$$U = 0,$$

the maximal work

$$A = T\frac{dA}{dT},$$

or integrated, we have

$$A = T \times \text{const.} ;$$

i.e. A is proportional to the absolute temperature. Now $A = Pv$, when v is the volume of 1 mol; then the osmotic pressure must also be proportional to the absolute temperature. We found this latter law established by experience. Now we see that the necessary and sufficient condition for its validity is that the *heat of dilution is equal to zero* (van't Hoff, 1885).

Quite generally, in the case of concentrated, and sometimes also in the case of dilute solutions, where the process of dilution is associated with the formation of new molecular complexes, or with the decomposition of those already occurring, the heat of dilution may have a positive or a negative value. In such cases, observation shows no ratio between the osmotic pressure and the absolute temperature (see section on ideal concentrated solutions).

The Osmotic Pressure and the Nature of the Substance dissolved.—In 1883, on the basis of a very extended series of observations, Raoult advanced the theorem that by dissolving equi-molecular quantities of the most various substances in the same solvent, its . freezing-point is lowered the same amount. Soon after, 1887, he showed that the same holds good for the lowering of the vapour pressure, and therefore of course for the raising of the boiling-point.

But solutions having the same freezing-point and the same vapour pressure, have the same osmotic pressure; and thus the rules of Raoult can be condensed into the statement that *solutions having the same osmotic pressure can be obtained by dissolving equi-molecular quantities of the most various substances in the same solvent.*

Osmotic Pressure and Gas Pressure.—It has been shown in the preceding sections on the basis of many experimental results, that the osmotic pressure of dissolved substances depends on the volume and on the temperature, in the same way that the gas pressure does; further, that in both cases the amount of pressure is determined by the number of molecules, dissolved or gaseous, contained in unit volume; and, finally, that the analogy between the behaviour of dissolved and gaseous substances finds expression in the theorem, that in both cases the content of energy at constant temperature is independent of the volume occupied. Now it is but a step to identify the absolute osmotic pressure, with the gas pressure which would be observed under similar relations.

From the observations conducted by Pfeffer on water solutions of cane sugar, and satisfying the formula (p. 130), viz.

$$P = n \; 0.649(1 + 0.00367t) \text{ atm.,}$$

the pressure of 1 per cent solution at $0°$ is estimated to be 0.649 atm. The volume of a 100 g.-solution at $0°$ is 99.7 c.c., and the volume, therefore, containing 1 mol of cane sugar $(C_{12}H_{22}O_{11} = 342)$, is 342×99.7 c.c. $= 34.1$ litres. But the pressure in a volume v, containing 1 mol of a gas, as calculated from the gas laws (p. 40), is

$$p = \frac{Rt}{v} = \frac{0.0821 \cdot 273}{34.1} = 0.657 \text{ atm.}$$

This value coincides in a striking way with that found directly (viz. 0.649 atm.); *i.e. the osmotic pressure is exactly the same as the gas pressure which would be observed if the solvent were removed, and the dissolved substance were left filling the same space in the gaseous state at the same temperature.*

Thus the same equation of condition holds good for the dissolved cane sugar, as for a gas, viz.

$$PV = RT = 0.0821 \text{ T litre-atm.,} \qquad . \qquad . \qquad (13)$$

where P denotes the osmotic pressure of a solution containing 1 mol of the substance dissolved in V litres, and measured in atmospheres, at the absolute temperature T.

It has been proved by numerous indirect measurements of the osmotic pressure, that this result has a universal value. We will next proceed to discuss a purely empirical law discovered by Raoult,[1] according to which *the relative lowering of vapour pressure experienced by a*

[1] Raoult, *Zeitschr. phys. Chem.* **2**. 353 (1888).

solvent on dissolving a foreign substance is equal to the quotient obtained by dividing the number of dissolved molecules n, *by the number of molecules* N, *of the solvent.* This law, especially well established for dilute ethereal solutions, leads to the relation

$$\frac{p - p'}{p'} = \frac{n}{N}. \qquad . \qquad . \qquad . \qquad . \qquad (14)$$

If we introduce this value for the *relative* vapour pressure, in the formula (1) on p. 134, we obtain

$$P = \frac{n}{N} \frac{0 \cdot 0821 \ T \times 1000 \ S}{M_0}.$$

But NM_0 denotes the number of grams of the solvent containing n mols of the dissolved substance, and $\frac{NM_0}{1000S}$ denotes the volume of this in litres, because S denotes the sp. gr. of the solvent; and therefore it follows that

$$\frac{NM_0}{n \ 1000 \ S} = V$$

is the volume of the solution in litres, containing 1 mol; and thus again we obtain the equation of condition

$$P = \frac{0 \cdot 0821T}{V}, \quad \text{or } PV = 0 \cdot 0821T \text{ litre-atm.}$$

The analogous law for the lowering of solubility has been proved by researches with various solvents [1]: *the relative lowering of solubility is equal to the number of molecules of the dissolved substance divided by the number of molecules of the solvent,* i.e.

$$\frac{L - L'}{L'} = \frac{n}{N}.$$

If we introduce this equation into the relation given on p. 137 which connects the lowering of the solubility with the osmotic pressure, we again obtain precisely as above, the equation

$$PV = RT = 0 \cdot 0821T.$$

Finally, this relation is proved by measurements of osmotic pressure conducted according to the method of freezing. In particular Blagden (1788), Rüdorff (1861), and Coppet (1871) studied the lowering of the freezing-point experienced by water from dissolving salts, but without arriving at any simple laws of general applicability. The reason of this, as will be shown later, is that on account of the electrolytic dissociation of salts in water, the relations are much more complicated, and therefore the laws are much more obscure than in the use of other dissolved or solvent materials. Therefore, as soon as Raoult turned his attention particularly to the study of the substances of

[1] Nernst, *Zeitschr. phys. Chem.* **6.** 19 (1890).

organic chemistry, he discovered the validity of the following remarkable law, which is supported by very numerous observations : *if one dissolves in any selected solvent equimolecular quantities of any selected substances, the freezing-point is lowered the same amount in all cases.*

If we denote the lowering of the freezing-point occasioned by the addition of m grams of the dissolved substance to 100 g. of the solvent, by t, then by combining the proposition of Raoult with the law of Blagden (p. 141), we have

$$t = E \frac{m}{M}, \qquad \cdots \qquad (15)$$

where M. denotes the molecular weight of the dissolved substance ; *i.e. the lowering of the freezing-point is proportional to the molecular content of dissolved substance.* The factor E is independent of the particular substance dissolved, but varies with the solvent used. Raoult called this factor E the "*molecular lowering of the freezing-point*" of the solvent in question. Its physical meaning is simply that it represents the lowering of the freezing-point which would be observed on dissolving 1 mol of any selected substance in 100 g. of a solvent, if solutions of such concentrations obeyed the law that the ratio between the molecular content and the freezing-point remains constant, which is only strictly true in dilute solutions.

Compare Raoult's rule with equation (10), p. 139,

$$P = \frac{Swt}{T_0},$$

which gives the relation between osmotic pressure and lowering of freezing-point ; multiply both sides by V, *i.e.* the volume of solution that contains 1 mol of dissolved substance, then the gas equation (13) gives at the freezing-point T_0

$$PV = RT_0 = \frac{SVwt}{T_0}.$$

Now SV is the mass of solvent in which 1 mol. of dissolved substance is found ; but as there are m grams, *i.e.* $\frac{m}{M}$ mols, for 100 g. solvent, we must have

$$SV = \frac{100M}{m}.$$

Hence

$$RT_0 = \frac{100Mwt}{mT_0},$$

or

$$t = \frac{RT_0^2}{100w} \cdot \frac{m}{M}. \qquad \cdots \qquad (16)$$

Equations (15) and (16) become identical when

$$E = \frac{RT_0^2}{100w}. \qquad \cdots \qquad (17)$$

Thus Raoult's empirical molecular lowering of the freezing-point is calculated in equation (17), *from the gas constant* (R), *the absolute melting-point* (T_0), *and the heat of fusion* (w) *of the solvent* (van 't Hoff, 1885).

If w is expressed in calories, R must be in the same unit, *i.e.* is 1·985 (p. 48). For water we have

$$T_0 = 273 \; ; \quad w = 79 \cdot 3 \text{ cal.}$$

Hence
$$E = \frac{1 \cdot 985 \times 273^2}{7930} = 18 \cdot 6,$$

whilst the latest determinations on very dilute solutions give (p. 139) as the most probable value
$$E = 18 \cdot 4.$$

The following table gives for a number of solvents the molecular lowering of the freezing-point as observed and as calculated according to van 't Hoff:—

Solvent.	E [1] observed.	E calc.	$T_0 - 273$.	w. [2]
Water	18·4	18·6	0°	79·3
Nitrogen dioxide .	41	43–47	− 10°	32–37
Formic acid	27·7	28·4	8·5°	55·6
Acetic acid	39	38·8	16·7°	43·2
Stearic acid	44	48	64°	47·6
Lauric acid	44	45·2	43·4°	43·7
Palmitic acid . . .	44	55	55°	39·2
Capric acid	47	...	27°	...
Phenyl-propionic acid . .	88	...	48·5°	...
Stearin	51	...	55·6°	...
Ethylene-dibromide . .	118	119	7·9°	13
Chloral alcoholate . .	78	...	46·2°	...
Benzene	49	51	5·5°	30
Diphenyl	82	84	70·2°	28·5
Diphenyl-methane . .	67	...	26°	...
Naphthalene . . .	71	69·4	80°	35·5
Phenol	74	76	39°	25
p-Mono-brom-phenol . .	107	...	63°	...
p-Cresol	74	73	34°	26
Thymol	83	85	48·2°	27·5
Anethol	62	...	20·1°	...
Benzo-phenone . . .	95	96	48°	21·5
Urethane	50	50	48·7°	41
Methyl carbamate . .	44	...	50°	...
Acetoxime	55	...	59·4°	...
Azo-benzene . . .	82	82	66°	27·9
Nitro-benzene . . .	70·7	69·5	5·3°	22·3
p-Toluidine . . .	52	49	42·5°	39
Diphenyl-amine . .	88	88·8	54°	24
Naphthyl-amine . .	78	81·2	50·1°	25·6

[1] From the measurements of Raoult, *Ann. chim.* [5], **28.** [6], **11.** ; Beckmann, *Zeitschr. phys. Chem.* **2.** 715 ; Eykman, *ib.* **3.** 113 and 203, **4.** 497 ; Ramsay, *ib.* **5.** 222.

[2] w, the heat of fusion, from the measurements of Berthelot, Pettersson, Eykman, Battelli, Bruner, and others. See especially Stillmann and Swain, *Zeitschr. phys. Chem.* **29.** 705 (1899).

At first Raoult suspected that the relation between the molecular lowering of the freezing-point and the molecular weight of the various solvents was a simple one, represented by the equation $E = 0.62M_0$. This was not supported by further observations. It was van 't Hoff who first showed how the value of E could be calculated from the melting-point and the heat of fusion of the solvent.

The Law of Absorption of Henry and Dalton.—It has long been known that there is a simple relation between the vapour pressure of a substance in solution and the concentration. It is usually formulated thus : *gases dissolve in any selected solvent in the direct ratio of their pressure* (Henry's Law of Absorption, 1803). The proof of the law was mainly confined to measurements of the solubility of permanent gases, and was shown to be extremely accurate. The law, of course, holds good in a similar way for dissolved liquids, and thus, to take an example, the partial pressure of alcohol in the vapour over its dilute water solution is proportional to its concentration in water.

In the sense of Henry's law there must exist between the vapour pressure p, and the osmotic pressure P, of the dissolved substance, a ratio which can be expressed by the equation

$$\frac{dp}{p} = \frac{dP}{P} \; ;$$

if we compare these with the equation developed on page 140, viz.

$$vdp = VdP,$$

it follows that

$$pv = PV,$$

i.e. we again obtain

$$PV = RT.$$

Thus for all gases or vapours which dissolve in any selected solvent proportionally to their pressure, i.e. *for those which obey Henry's law of absorption, their osmotic pressure is equal to the corresponding gas pressure.*[1] From the —so far as is known—high accuracy of the law of absorption it may be concluded that the osmotic pressure follows the laws of gases with equal accuracy. The exactness of the law of absorption offers the simplest, and also the most exact experimental proof, that the dissolved substance exerts the same pressure on a semi-permeable partition that it would exert on an ordinary partition, were it a gas at the same temperature and concentration.

As Dalton discovered in 1807, each gas in a gas mixture dissolves in accordance with its own partial pressure ; and this can only mean that each of the dissolved gases exerts the same osmotic pressure that it would if it were alone ; *i.e.* the same simple law of summation, as found by Dalton for gases, also holds good for the osmotic pressure of a solution of several substances ; and therefore the total lowering of

---

[1] van 't Hoff, *l.c.*

the freezing-point occasioned by two dissolved substances in the same solution is equal to the sum of the lowerings which each would occasion were it alone ; the same holds good also for the lowering of the vapour pressure, and of the solubility, provided, of course, that no chemical action occurs which would effect a change in the number of the molecules.   •

The Nature of the Solvent.—The question how the nature of the solvent influences the osmotic pressure of the dissolved substance, is at once ,settled by the fact that, as it is identical with the gas pressure, there is no dependence at all between the osmotic pressure and the nature of the solvent.

A direct proof is afforded by investigation *of the partition of a substance between two solvents*; in analogy to Henry's law it is found that the concentrations in the two solvents are proportional, just as in the partition between gas-space and solvent ; thus, for example, if one mixes together carbon disulphide, water, and iodine, then the ratio of the concentration of the iodine in the carbon disulphide, to that in the water, at a temperature of 15°, is 410, regardless of the quantity of iodine used.

If we introduce this relation into the-equation (p. 140), $V_1dP_1 = V_2dP_2$, then by a method exactly similar to that given in the preceding section, we obtain the result

$$P_1V_1 = P_2V_2 ;$$

i.e. under the same spatial concentration the osmotic pressure is the same in the two solutions. We must conclude, therefore, that by dissolving the same quantity of iodine in a litre of water as in a litre of carbon disulphide, we obtain the same osmotic pressure in the two solutions.

It is, of course, assumed in this that the dissolved substance has the same molecular weight in the two solvents : otherwise the osmotic pressure of equally concentrated solution would be different (*e.g.* if double molecules are formed in one solvent—as by acetic acid in benzene,—whilst in another, such as water, the molecular weight is normal). If the molecular weight is not the same, the ratio of partition is not constant (Book III. Chapter III.).

The earliest experiments on partition between two solvents are due to Berthelot and Jungfleisch (*Ann. chim. phys.* [4], **26**. 396, 1872) ; as they investigated many substances that did not satisfy the above condition, Berthelot concluded that the partition coefficients vary with concentration even in dilute solution. I showed in 1891 that constancy of the partition coefficient is associated with similarity of molecular condition of the dissolved substance in the two solvents (*Zeitschr. phys. Chem.* **8**. 110, 1891).

Since for a given concentration, osmotic pressure is independent of the nature of the solvent, it follows that it is not altered by compression of the solvent, provided that no change of molecular state is produced. This result may be easily proved thermodynamically.

Molecular State of Bodies in Solution.—The results of the preceding paragraphs all support the empirical law that the osmotic pressure of a dissolved substance is equal to the gas pressure which could be observed manometrically if the solvent were removed and the dissolved substance left in gaseous form occupying the same space.

• From this follows a practical application of the methods for measuring osmotic pressures that is of great importance. If the osmotic pressure of a substance—not too concentrated—in any solvent is measured, the corresponding gas pressure is known, and all the data are at hand for determining the vapour density, and so by Avogadro's law the molecular weight. We have thus methods of finding the molecular weight of substances whose vapour density it is difficult or impossible to measure, because they only evaporate at high temperature or not at all without dissociation. Moreover, it is to the advantage of these methods, that with a proper choice of solvent the osmotic pressure is usually more convenient to measure in this way than the vapour density.

It must be observed, however, that determination of molecular weight by osmotic pressure is purely empirical. It is only a result of experience that the osmotic pressure is equal to the pressure that the dissolved substance would exert as a gas in the same space if the solvent were removed. It is, moreover, indifferent whether the experiment can be realised or not, *i.e.* whether the dissolved substance is capable of existing as a gas under the given conditions ; it is true that we can calculate the vapour pressure under given conditions of any chemically well-defined substance by means of Avogadro's law, and conversely, when we know the vapour pressure (corresponding to the osmotic pressure), we can calculate the molecular weight. But the calculation has no other basis than the equality that is often observed between gas and osmotic pressure ; no assumption can be made beforehand as to the molecular state of the substance in solution.

The remarkable relation between osmotic pressure and molecular weight, however, demands a theoretical explanation ; and the explanation evidently must turn on the molecular state of the substance in solution. Hypothesis must, of course, come in here, because everything about the molecular state is hypothetical, and rests on the hypothetical assumption of a discrete arrangement of matter in space. The choice met with in establishing a suitable hypothesis is not often more easily made, however, than in this case.

The knowledge that dissolved substances follow the laws of gases leads by analogy to the conclusion that the molecular state of a dissolved substance is like that of a gas ; or in other words, that Avogadro's law applies to the former. Thus we arrive at the following hypothesis :—

Is-osmotic solutions contain the same number of molecules of dissolved substance in a given volume, at a given temperature, and the number is the same as in an equal volume of a perfect gas at the same temperature and pressure (van 't Hoff).

It is often stated that *experiment* shows the osmotic pressure to follow the laws of gases, namely, those of Boyle, Gay-Lussac, and Avogadro ; this is an error in principle and must be especially guarded against. Only the two first are the expression of experimental facts. Avogadro's rule is equally hypothetical for solutions and gases, and one can hardly see how this can be altered by experimental facts.

Osmotic Pressure and Hydro-diffusion.—Reference has already been made to the well-known phenomenon that substances in solution, when left to themselves, wander from places of a higher to those of a lower concentration, and this leads to the conclusion that external work can be developed by diluting a solution.   The osmotic pressure, which we have come to regard as a most convenient help in calculation to express the value of this work numerically, must also be regarded as exerting a great influence in the phenomenon just described ; this is generally known as "*hydro-diffusion,*" or simply as "*diffusion*" ; it plays a very important rôle in many processes of sub-organic structures in nature, but especially in plant and animal organisms.

This was first discovered in its general signification by Parrot (1815), but Graham[1] first made it the object of a thorough investigation which was mainly confined to aqueous solutions.   It was shown that the coefficient of diffusion varies with the nature of the substance dissolved, and in all cases increases strongly with increasing temperature. Later investigations showed that a simple law may be formulated for the process of diffusion, which is completely analogous to that advanced by Fourier for the conduction of heat.   This states that the mechanical force which drives the dissolved substances from places of higher to those of a lower temperature, and, therefore, also the velocity with which the dissolved substance wanders in the solvent, is proportional to *the concentration gradient.*.   It is this fundamental law which makes possible a complete mathematical description of the process of diffusion, as was first suspected by Berthollet,[2] but later and independently restated by Fick,[3] who subjected it to a thorough theoretical and experimental proof.   In the sense of the preceding law, the quantity of salt dS, which passes in the time dz, through the cross-section q of a diffusion cylinder, when c is the concentration of the whole cross-section at the point x, and c + dc at the point x + dx, is given by the equation :

$$dS = -Dq\frac{dc}{dx}d_z ;$$

D denotes a constant peculiar to the particular substance dissolved, and

[1] *Lieb. Ann.* **77.** 56 and 129 (1851) ; **80.** 197 (1851).
[2] *Essai de statique chimique.* Paris, 1883. Part I. chap. iv.
[3] *Pogg. Ann.* **94.** 59 (1855).

called the "*diffusion coefficient.*" Fick's law has nothing to say concerning the nature of the mechanical force. Moreover, later and thorough investigations of this have led to the result that it can claim to hold good only approximately, since the coefficient of diffusion in general varies more or less with the concentration.

The author [1] has sought to develop the theory of the phenomena of diffusion, on the basis of the modern theory of solution. Thus, for example, we will consider the diffusion of cane sugar in water : if we pour a layer of pure water over a solution of cane sugar, the dissolved sugar at once begins to pass from points of higher to those of lower concentration, and this process does not cease till the differences of concentration are completely equalised. This obviously concerns the action of the same expansive force which we have learned to call the osmotic pressure ; the process is completely analogous to the equalisation of differences in density, developed by any cause whatever, in gases; and, moreover, under corresponding conditions the active forces are of the same magnitude. But, on the other hand, equalisation of density comes about very quickly in gases, while the substances dissolved in a liquid move very slowly. *The reason for this is to be found in the fact that gas molecules in their movement meet with only very slight resistant friction, which, however, in the case of liquids is enormous.*

The efficiency of the law of Fick is shown by the fact, that *the driving force occasioned by differences of pressure, is proportional to the steepness of the concentration gradient.* But since we can calculate the absolute value of the force from the law of osmotic pressure, and since we can measure directly the velocity of diffusion, it is possible to calculate on the absolute scale the resistant friction experienced by the dissolved substance in its movement through the solvent. By carrying out the corresponding calculation (see Book II. Chapter VII.) for the resistant friction K, we obtain the formula

$$K = \frac{1 \cdot 99}{D} \times 10^9 (1 + 0 \cdot 00367t) \; ;$$

where D denotes the coefficient of diffusion measured for the temperature t. Thus, for example, K for cane sugar at 9°, where $D = 0 \cdot 312$, is calculated to be $6 \cdot 7 \times 10^9$ kg. in weight ; *i.e.* it requires this enormous force to drive 1 mol of cane sugar ($= 342$ g.) through the solvent (water) with a velocity of 1 cm. per second : this enormous value finds its explanation in *the smallness of the molecules.*

Osmosis by Isothermal Distillation.

A very interesting experiment made by Magnus (1827) has recently been brought into notice again by Askenasy,[2] who carried it out in the

---

[1] Nernst, *Zeitschr. phys. Chem.* **2.** 613 (1888).

[2] E. Askenasy, " Beiträge zur Erklärung des Saftsteigens," *Verhandl. des naturh. med. Vereins zu Heidelberg,* **5.** (1896).

following form. A glass tube is widened to a funnel at one end and closed there by a layer of gypsum ; it is filled full of water and placed with the gypsum plate uppermost and its lower end dipping in a dish of mercury. The water used may conveniently be saturated with gypsum to avoid solution of the plate. The water evaporates slowly through the layer of gypsum—the process can be hastened by leading dry air over the plate. As the evaporation proceeds the mercury rises in the tube and may reach a height considerably exceeding that of the barometer at the time.

In a recorded experiment the mercury rose in fifteen hours to 89·3 cms., the barometer being at 75·3 ; it then touched the gypsum layer and so closed the experiment. The diameter of the tube was 3·3 mm. and evaporation took place in free air.

Usually the end of the experiment was caused by formation of an air bubble under the gypsum, which consequently dried ; then the mercury gradually fell again.

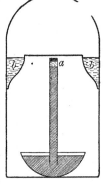

Equilibrium was apparently not reached in these experiments : a simple thermodynamic argument will show what the equilibrium should be. Clearly evaporation will go on till it is stopped by the tension of the mercury column, and the tension will be greater the drier the air over the gypsum layer.

For definiteness consider the following arrangement (Fig. 16) :—At a is a thin layer of pure water, under it mercury, over it a thin partition which has the property of being impermeable for gaseous,

Fig. 16.

but permeable for liquid water. This property is possessed by Askenasy's moist gypsum through the pores of which water passes easily, though it is air-tight even for moderately high pressures.[1] Let the pressure above the gypsum be p', which may be that of a solution bb ; the vapour pressure of the pure solvent being p. To determine equilibrium apply the law (p. 27), that at constant temperature variations in the neighbourhood of equilibrium must be reversible. If dx mols of water are distilled from the funnel to the solution, the system loses free energy to the extent $dx\, RT \ln \dfrac{p}{p'}$; at the same time mercury is raised through the height H and so free (potential) energy is stored up to the extent $H\dfrac{gM\sigma}{S}dx$, where g is the acceleration of gravity, M the molecular weight of the solvent, S its density, and that of mercury σ, so that $\dfrac{M\sigma}{S}dx$ is the mass of mercury lifted. Since the

---

[1] The same property would be possessed by any solid partition that can dissolve water.

process is reversible, *i.e.* involves no loss in power to do work of the system (free energy), these quantities of work must be equal, or

$$dx\ RT \ln \frac{p}{p'} = H \frac{gM\sigma}{S} dx,$$

or the pressure P of the mercury column is

$$P = H\sigma g = \frac{S}{M} RT \ln \frac{p}{p'},$$

in other words, it is simply equal to the osmotic pressure of the solution in bb (p. 135).[1]

Conversely, measurements of the rise in the tube—which, it is seen, is quite large—would be a means of determining osmotic pressure, or lowering of vapour pressure.

Osmotic Pressure in Mixture.—If for 1 mol of dissolved substance there are ν mols of a simple solvent, then according to p. 145, we have

$$\frac{1}{\nu} = \ln \frac{p}{p'}, \text{ or } 1 = \nu \ln \frac{p}{p'}, \qquad . \qquad . \qquad . \qquad (1)$$

where p is the vapour pressure of the solvent, p' that of the solution.

If a substance occurs in a mixture of several solvents, a formula may be found on the very reasonable assumption that the osmotic pressure of a substance (in normal molecular state) being independent of the solvent, follows the gaseous laws in mixed solvents also. It may be shown thermodynamically that if there be ν_1, ν_2 mols of the solvents containing 1 mol of dissolved substances, p_1, p_2 their vapour pressures, p'_1, p'_2 the same after addition of the dissolved substance,[2]

$$1 = \nu_1 \ln \frac{p_1}{p_1} + \nu_2 \ln \frac{p_2}{p_2}, \ldots \qquad . \qquad . \qquad (2)$$

Formula (2), which is a generalisation of the Raoult-van 't Hoff formula (1), was satisfactorily verified by Roloff,[3] so one may conclude that the osmotic pressure follows the gas laws in mixtures also.

It is interesting to note that Roloff found some of the terms in the summand (2) may be negative. Thus when KCl is dissolved in a mixture of water and acetic acid the vapour pressure of the acid is raised ; $p_2' > p_2$, and consequently the corresponding logarithm is negative.

General Remarks on the Theory of Osmotic Pressure.—It is remarkable, and, I may say, inexplicable, how often we find the statement in modern literature that osmotic pressure is only of secondary importance for the theory of solutions.

[1] An elementary proof analogous to that of p. 132 ff, is given by Reinganum, *Wied. Ann.* **59.** 764 (1896).
[2] Nernst, *Zeitschr. phys. Chem.* **11.** 1 (1893).   [3] *Ibid.* 17.

It is of course admitted that the laws of lowering vapour pressure, freezing point, etc., and in fact all questions of physical and chemical *equilibrium*, may be treated thermodynamically without the introduction of osmotic pressure. Whether the thermodynamic method is as clear and convincing as van 't Hoff's treatment is another question; in this connection the strength of the generalisation of Avogadro's rule by the analogy between gaseous and osmotic pressure may well be pointed out. But when it comes to explaining hydro-diffusion, an essentially dynamic phenomenon, the theory of osmotic pressure is indispensable; and as, when a doubt exists, we should always choose as our theoretical basis that conception which allows the *most complete and extensive treatment*, so every rational *general* theory of dilute solutions should, in my opinion, start from the conception of osmotic pressure.

Osmotic Pressure at High Concentrations

The osmotic pressure reaches considerable amounts even for moderate concentrations; in a solution of 1 mol (*e.g.* 46 grams of alcohol) in a litre it is 22·4 atmospheres at the freezing-point, according to the laws of gases (p. 40). As there is no prospect of making semi-permeable partitions capable of standing this or higher pressures, we are driven to indirect means of measurement for the osmotic pressure of concentrated solutions.[1]

The calculation of this quantity gives the work needed to separate the two components of the mixture—as a concentrated solution may be called—a problem already considered in a general way on p. 109. The following calculations form therefore a special application of the principles developed there, but with the aid of the experience we have gained in the consideration of a special class of mixtures, viz. dilute solutions.

It was found on p. 135, equation (4), by means of isothermal distillation, that

$$P = \frac{S}{M_0} RT \ln \frac{p}{p'},$$

or

$$P \frac{M_0}{S} = RT \ln \frac{p}{p'},$$

in the latter form the left-hand side stands for the osmotic work, the right-hand that done in isothermal distillation; equality of the two follows, in all cases, from the second law as expressed in equation (c) of p. 19.

Now the expression *for the work in isothermal distillation* holds good for any range of concentration, provided only the vapour of the

[1] Berkeley and Hartley, *Phil. Trans.* **206.** 481 (1906), have, however, succeeded in preparing semi-permeable membranes capable of standing pressures of over 100 atmospheres.—TR.

solvent follows the laws of gases and the difference between the specific volumes of the solution and solvent can be neglected in comparison with that of the saturated vapour. The latter condition is practically always satisfied, and if the former is not, a correction can easily be applied to the calculation if the characteristic equation of the vapour is known.

The osmotic work, on the other hand, is also equal to the osmotic pressure multiplied by the volume through which the semi-permeable piston must be lowered to press out 1 mol of solvent for solutions of any concentration; this volume, however, is not necessarily equal to that of the expelled solvent, as is the case in dilute solutions. That is only the case when on adding a small amount of solvent to the mixture the volume of the latter is increased by the volume of the solvent added, i.e. if the mixture occurs without contraction or expansion. Still this assumption is usually permissible even for strong solutions.

E.g. if 2 grams of water are added to 100 g. of a 50 per cent sugar solution we get a $\frac{50}{1\cdot02} = 49\cdot02$ per cent solution; the density of the former at $17\cdot5°$ is $1\cdot2320$ S, of the latter $1\cdot2275$ S where S is the density of water at the same temperature. The change of volume is therefore

$$\frac{100 + 2}{1\cdot2275 \text{ S}} - \frac{100}{1\cdot2329 \text{ S}} = \frac{1\cdot987}{\text{S}},$$

whilst $\frac{2}{\text{S}}$ is what it would be if there were no contraction. Calculation of a number of such cases shows that equation (3), p. 134,

$$dv = \frac{M_0}{S}dx,$$

may be applied even to 20 to 30 per cent solutions with an error of less than 1 per cent. Moreover, the circumstance that a compressed solution (inside the osmotic cell) is mixed with an uncompressed solvent, matters little, for the compressibility of liquids is always minute. In what follows we shall, to avoid complication, assume the liquid to be incompressible, though that is of course not the case.

If Π be the osmotic work for a solution of any concentration, we have

$$\Pi = P\frac{M}{S}(1 + \epsilon) \qquad . \qquad . \qquad . \qquad (1)$$

in which ϵ is the relative increase in volume due to mixture of a mol of solvent with a large quantity of solution (under pressure P)—consequently a mostly negligible amount. Further

$$\Pi = RT \ln \frac{p}{p'} \qquad . \qquad . \qquad . \qquad (2)$$

with the restrictions already mentioned, which are of no practical consequence.

According to the second law (equation e, p. 23)

$$\Pi - q = T\frac{d\Pi}{dT} \quad . \qquad . \qquad . \qquad . \qquad (3)$$

in which q is the heat evolved on adding a mol of solvent to a large quantity of solution. From (2) and (3) follows the relation already given on p. 113,

$$q = -RT^2\frac{\partial \ln \frac{p}{p'}}{\partial T}. \qquad . \qquad . \qquad . \qquad (4)$$

The meaning of q as $\dfrac{\partial Q(x)}{\partial x}$ has been referred to. If $q = 0$, $\ln \dfrac{p}{p'}$ is independent of T, so that according to (2) Π is proportional to T even for concentrated solutions.

The osmotic work may also be calculated from the freezing-point of strong solutions without much difficulty.

To integrate equation 8, p. 138, more exactly, we put, according to p. 61,

$$\lambda = \lambda_0 - (C_1 - C_p)T \quad . \qquad . \qquad . \qquad . \qquad (5)$$

and the heat of sublimation

$$\sigma = \sigma_0 - (C_2 - C_p)T \quad . \qquad . \qquad . \qquad . \qquad (6)$$

where C_1, C_2 are the molecular heats of the liquid and solid solvent. The integrals become (p. 61)

$$\ln p = -\frac{\lambda_0}{RT} - \frac{C_1 - C_p}{R}\ln T + K_1 \quad . \qquad . \qquad . \qquad (7)$$

$$\ln p' = -\frac{\sigma_0}{RT} - \frac{C_2 - C_p}{R}\ln T + K_2. \qquad . \qquad . \qquad (8)$$

To determine the integration constants K_1, K_2 we have (p. 138) that at T_0

$$p' = p = p_0,$$

and therefore

$$\ln p_0 = -\frac{\lambda_0}{RT_0} - \frac{C_1 - C_p}{R}\ln T_0 + T_1 \quad . \qquad . \qquad . \qquad (9)$$

$$\ln p_0 = -\frac{\sigma_0}{RT_0} - \frac{C_2 - C_p}{R}\ln T_0 + K_2 \quad . \qquad . \qquad . \qquad (10)$$

$(7) - (8) - (9) + (10)$ gives

$$\ln \frac{p}{p'} = \frac{\sigma_0 - \lambda_0}{R}\left[\frac{1}{T} - \frac{1}{T_0}\right] + \frac{C_1 - C_2}{R}\ln \frac{T_0}{T}. \qquad . \qquad (11)$$

If we put $t = T_0 - T$ and develop in series

$$\ln \frac{T_0}{T} = \ln \left(1 + \frac{t}{T}\right) = \frac{t}{T} - \frac{t^2}{2T^2} + \frac{t^3}{3T^3} \cdots$$

retaining only three terms, (11) becomes

$$\ln \frac{p}{p'} = \frac{t}{R}\left[\frac{\sigma_0 - \lambda_0 + (C_1 - C_2)T_0}{T_0 T} - \frac{C_1 - C_2}{2}\frac{t}{T^2} + \frac{C_1 - C_2}{3}\frac{t^2}{T^3}\right]. \qquad (12)$$

Now

$$\sigma_0 - \lambda_0 + (C_1 - C_2)T_0 = \rho,$$

where ρ is the heat of fusion at the melting-point of the solution; hence (12) becomes

$$\ln \frac{p}{p'} = \frac{t}{R}\left[\frac{\rho}{T_0 T} - \frac{C_1 - C_2}{2}\frac{t}{T^2} + \frac{C_1 - C_2}{3}\frac{t^2}{T^3}\right] \qquad . \qquad . \qquad (13)$$

and the osmotic work at temperature T, the freezing-point of the solution is

$$\Pi = RT \ln \frac{p}{p'} = t\left[\frac{\rho}{T_0} - \frac{C_1 - C_2}{2}\frac{t}{T} + \frac{C_1 - C_2}{3}\frac{t^2}{T^2}\right]. \qquad . \qquad (14)$$

If we require the osmotic work, not at the variable freezing-point of the solution, but always at the same temperature, say the freezing-point of the pure solvent T_0, we must integrate equation (4) and get

$$\ln \frac{p}{p'} = \frac{q}{RT} + \text{const.,} \qquad . \qquad . \qquad . \qquad . \qquad (15)$$

for as we are only concerned with a small correction, q may be regarded as constant with sufficient accuracy.

Then for T_0 (15) becomes

$$\left(\ln \frac{p}{p'}\right)_{T_0} = \frac{q}{RT_0} + \text{const.} \qquad . \qquad . \qquad . \qquad (16)$$

$(13) - (15) + (16)$ gives

$$\left(\ln \frac{p}{p'}\right)_{T_0} = \frac{t}{R}\left[\frac{\rho - q}{T_0 T} - \frac{C_1 - C_2}{2}\frac{t}{T^2} + \frac{C_1 - C_2}{3}\frac{t^2}{T^3}\right];$$

and the osmotic work at temperature T_0

$$\Pi_0 = RT_0\left(\ln \frac{p}{p'}\right)_{T_0} = t\left[\frac{\rho - q}{T} - \frac{C_1 - C_2}{2}\frac{T_0 t}{T^2} + \frac{C_1 - C_2}{3}\frac{T_0 t^2}{T^3}\right]. \qquad (17)$$

This formula was obtained by Dieterici (*Wied. Ann.* **52.** 263, 1894), who also showed by examples that (2) and (17) give values for the osmotic work in satisfactory agreement. The formula was also given independently by Th. Ewan (*Zeitschr. phys. Chem.* **14.** 409, 1894), who in integrating (4) paid attention to the variation of q with temperature; the correction term thus obtained, however—involving the specific heats of solution and solvent—is almost always negligible. To show the usefulness of equation (17) we will take the case of some potassium chloride solutions, whose vapour pressures (Dieterici, *Wied. Ann.* **42.** 513, 1891; **50.** 47, 1893) and freezing-points (Roloff, *Zeitschr. phys. Chem.* **18.** 572, 1895) have been accurately measured. In the following table m signifies the number of grams to 100 grams solvent, t the lowering of freezing-point, q the heat of dilution, p' the vapour pressure of the solution at 0°; p that of pure water at the same temperature is 4·620 mm. :—

m.	t.	g.	p'.	Π_0.	
				calc.$_1$.	calc.$_2$.
0	0	0	4·620	...	...
3·72	1·667	− 1·63	4·546	8·80	8·72
7·45	3·284	− 5·96	4·472	17·55	17·62
14·90	6·53	− 19·5	4·326	35·18	35·60
22·35	9·69	− 34·3	4·190	52·64	52·96

Under calc.$_1$ are given the values derived from equation (17), assuming that

$$T_0 = 273 \qquad \rho = 18 \times 80 \cdot 3 = 1445 \qquad C_2 - C_1 = 18 \times 0 \cdot 475 = 8 \cdot 55.$$

Under calc.$_2$ are the values derived from equation (2) assuming that

$$R = 1 \cdot 985.$$

In both cases we obtain the osmotic work in ordinary calories; the agreement is very satisfactory.

Ideal Concentrated Solutions.—It is natural to compare the change in total with that in free energy, or in other words, the heat of reaction with the osmotic work, in concentrated solutions.

If a mol of water be taken from a solution I. to II., then the heat evolved is

$$\left(\frac{\partial Q(n)}{\partial n}\right)_{n=n_2} - \left(\frac{\partial Q(n)}{\partial n}\right)_{n=n_1} \qquad \cdot \qquad \cdot \qquad \cdot \qquad (1)$$

if there are n_1 mols. of water to one of salt in solution I. and n_2 in II.

The osmotic work according to equation (2), p. 156, is

$$\Pi = RT \ln \frac{p_1}{p_2} \qquad \cdot \qquad \cdot \qquad \cdot \qquad \cdot \qquad (2)$$

where p_1 and p_2 are the vapour pressures of the two solutions.

Comparison shows that there are concentrated solutions for which these two quantities differ very little from each other, and as we shall see that such solutions have in many ways a remarkably simple behaviour, it is convenient to describe them as "ideal concentrated solutions." [1]

For example, take solutions of sulphuric acid containing respectively 29·2 mols and 4·76 mols of H_2O for one of H_2SO_4. The heat of dilution can be found from the equation of p. 109.

$$Q(n) = \frac{17,860n}{n + 1 \cdot 8}, \qquad \frac{\partial Q(n)}{\partial n} = \frac{32,150}{(n + 1 \cdot 8)^2}$$

Hence for (1) we get

$$747 \cdot 0 - 33 \cdot 5 = 713 \cdot 5 \text{ cal.}$$

and from (2)

[1] W. Nernst, *Wied. Ann.* **53.** 57 (1894).

$$\Pi = 1 \cdot 985 \times 273 \ \ln \frac{4 \cdot 284}{1 \cdot 206} = 688 \cdot 5 \text{ cal.}$$

taking the vapour pressures (at 0°) as $p_1 = 4 \cdot 284$, $p_2 = 1 \cdot 206$ nm. (Dieterici);[1] the results agree within the limits of error of measurement.

In the following table the same calculation is made for a number of solutions :—

n.	p.	$1252 \log_{10} \frac{p_1}{p_2}$	$\frac{\partial Q(n)}{\partial n}$.	$\left(\frac{\partial Q(n)}{\partial n}\right)_{n=n_2} - \left(\frac{\partial Q(n)}{\partial n}\right)_{n=n_1}$.
∞	4·620		0	
91·6	4·535	10·1	3·96	3·96
29·2	4·284	31·0	33·48	29·5
14·66	3·664	85·2 .	118·6	85·1
9·93	2·952	117·6	235·5	116·9
5·89	1·679	307·1	544·0	308·5
4·76	1·206	180·6	746·0	202·0
2·40	0·164	1080·0	1828·0	1082·0

In the third column is the osmotic work, in the last the corresponding development of heat, both quantities relating to the pair of solutions between which they are placed. The comparison shows that for $n = 91 \cdot 6$ even the region of ideal concentrated solutions is reached; the agreement between that point and $n = 2 \cdot 40$ is striking— the deviations are so irregular that they are probably due for the greater part to error of measurement.[2]

Just as in ideal dilute solutions the lowering of vapour pressure and change of boiling and freezing-points can be calculated from the osmotic pressure, and consequently also from the rise in boiling-point or fall in freezing-point, so here in ideal concentrated solutions the same things can be deduced from the *heat of dilution*. The relations are simple in both limiting cases, because in the fundamental equation

$$A - U = T \frac{dA}{dT}$$

one of the terms vanishes—in ideal dilute solutions U, in ideal concentrated solutions $\frac{dA}{dT}$. (See also p. 35.)

If now the identical equations

$$\frac{dA}{dT} = 0 \text{ and } A = U$$

---

[1] *Wied. Ann.* **50.** 47 (1893).
[2] The new numbers of Dieterici agree a good deal better than the earlier ones of Regnault used in my original paper.

are to hold not merely at a singular point, but over a considerable range of temperature we must also have

$$\frac{dU}{dT} = 0,$$

i.e. the heat of dilution of an ideal concentrated solution is independent of temperature.

Thus

$$H_2SO_4 . 4H_2O + 5H_2O = H_2SO_4 . 9H_2O$$

gives 2559 cal.; the thermal capacity before mixture is according to Thomsen

$H_2SO_4 + 4H_2O$	92·7
$5H_2O$	90
	182·7 cal.

and after

$$H_2SO_4 . 9H_2O \qquad 182·0 \text{ cal.}$$

The difference (0·7 cal.) is according to p. 9 the change of heat of dilution per degree of temperature; so the heat of dilution 2550 cals. varies only 3 parts in 1000 per degree.

According to measurements made up to the present, which however are still very few in number, those solutions with *considerable* heat of dilution behave as ideal concentrated solutions.

Calculations similar to those we have just carried out for the isothermal distillation of one component (H_2O), can of course also be carried out for the second component (H_2SO_4). According to the above considerations the vapour pressure of the water must decrease quicker with increase of concentration the greater is the heat of dilution. This is confirmed by many examples.

Solid Solutions.—We have already seen (p. 115) that these solid mixtures, which are not merely mechanically formed, but result from mutual molecular interpenetration of the components, can be compared with liquid mixtures in many respects. The supposition is thus at once forced upon us, that the behaviour of a solid mixture, like that of a liquid mixture, would be very simple in the case where one of its components is present in great excess, *i.e.* where we are considering a "*dilute solid solution.*"

Experiment shows that this supposition is fulfilled; at least van't Hoff[1] has endeavoured to show that we may venture to speak of the *osmotic pressure of substances existing in solid solution,* which is analogous to that of the liquid solution, and obeys the same laws.

To be sure there is no opportunity of measuring this directly by means of a semi-permeable partition, since the chance of its realisation in a solidified system is as good as impossible; but it is to be hoped

[1] *Zeitschr. phys. Chem.* **5.** 322 (1890).

M

that we may obtain measurements of these enormous pressures by indirect methods. Indeed, the property of substances dissolved in solidified systems, of *spreading through the solid by diffusion*, certainly speaks clearly and beyond all doubt in favour of the existence of an inherent expansive force, which can be regarded as comparable to the osmotic pressure.

Various facts point to diffusion in solids. Hydrogen dissolved in platinum and palladium gradually spreads through the whole metal, as has long been known. A very clear case of this was observed by Bellati and Lussana,[1] who showed in many ways that nascent hydrogen is capable of penetrating iron comparatively easily at ordinary temperatures. *E.g.* a barometer was closed at the top by an iron plate, and by cementing a glass ring on this, an electrolytic cell was made in which hydrogen was generated at the iron plate ; the mercury at once fell by diffusion of the hydrogen through the plate into the barometric vacuum. Carbon finds its way into hot iron, and can even pass through a porcelain crucible. Further, Roberts-Austen[2] observed that gold diffuses through lead at 251° (75° below the melting-point of the latter), and even to a perceptible extent at atmospheric temperature in the course of a few years. According to experiments by Spring (1886), solid barium sulphate and sodium-carbonate react to the extent of reaching a state of equilibrium, which appears hardly possible without molecular interpenetration.

Again the fact that many substances conduct electrolytically indicates the possibility of diffusion in solids, for, as we shall see later, ionic transport and diffusion are intimately connected.

It must, however, be remarked that there are other cases that do not show the slightest trace of diffusion in the solid state. Thus in petrography sharply bounded portions are sometimes found in a homogeneous crystal that show different colouring to the rest ; here no appreciable equalisation by diffusion has taken place in thousands of years, although the colouring matter must be regarded as in a state of solid solution. If osmotic pressure can be assumed in such cases the dissolved molecules must encounter quite extraordinary resistance to displacement in their solvent.

When a liquid solution is brought to its freezing-point, the solvent separates as a rule in the pure state, as is well known ; the Raoult-van 't Hoff formulae hold good for this case. But in some cases there are observed considerably smaller lowerings of the freezing-point, than those calculated from the molecular proportions of the dissolved substance, according to the preceding formulae ; usually this is explained by polymerisation of the dissolved substance. But there are cases in which such an explanation is highly improbable or even quite inadmissible, and then it appears that a mixture of solid solvent and

[1] *Atti R. Ist. Veneto* [7], **1.** 1173 (1890) ; abstract *Zeitschr. phys. Chem.* **7.** 229 (1891).   [2] *Proc. Roy. Soc. Lond.* **67.** 101 (1900).

dissolved substances crystallises out in place of the pure solvent—the hypothesis originally put forward by van't Hoff (*l.c.*).

It is easy to see that in such cases the lowering of the freezing-point must be too small. According to the considerations of p. 118 the freezing-point of a mixture must sink continuously, only becoming constant when the part crystallising out has the same composition as that remaining liquid. Thus if the solid separating out contains more of the dissolved substances than the residual liquid the latter is diluted by freezing, *i.e.* the freezing-point must, in this case, rise with increasing concentration; if, on the other hand, the frozen-out solid is less rich in the dissolved material than the residual liquid, the freezing-point must fall with increase of concentration; but clearly not so fast as when the pure solvent crystallises out, *i.e.* the lowering of freezing-point is lessened.

If, after van't Hoff, we apply the notion of osmotic pressure to solid solutions, the vapour pressure of the solid solvent must be reduced by the taking up of dissolved substance. If the vapour pressures of solid and liquid solvent are lowered to the same extent by the addition of dissolved substance the freezing-point must obviously remain unaltered, since this point is characterised by equality of vapour pressure in the two states of aggregation. The freezing-point must rise if the vapour pressure of the solid is more affected than that of the liquid, fall in the contrary case. These relations can be easily followed by means of Fig. 15, p. 137, if the vapour pressure of the solid solution be introduced by a line lying below and parallel to the curve of vapour pressure of the pure solid solvent.

It is found in fact that some abnormally small freezing-point depressions are produced by co-crystallisation of dissolved material. Thus, according to van Bijlert,[1] a solid solution freezes out of solutions of thiophene in benzene; its composition is, according to Beckmann,[2] practically 0·42 times the concentration in the liquid, whatever the strength of the solution; there is thus a constant ratio of partition of thiophene between the liquid and solid solvent. Solution of antimony in tin and β-naphthol in naphthalene raises the melting-point, and van Bijlert found that the crystals contain a larger percentage of the dissolved substance than the liquid, in accordance with the above theory. Beckmann and Stock[3] found that iodine, which gives abnormally small depressions in benzene, is shared between solid and liquid solvent in an approximately constant ratio, like thiophene. Ferrantini and Garelli[4] have made extensive investigations on co-crystallisation of dissolved substances, especially of cyclic-organic compounds; see further the work of Bruni[5] and his pupils.

[1] *Zeitschr. phys. Chem.* **8**. 343 (1891).   [2] *Ibid.* **22**. 609 (1897).
[3] *Ibid.* **17**. 107 (1895).
[4] *Zeitschr. phys. Chem.* **13**. 7 (1894), communicated by Ciamician; see also Garelli, *Gazz. chim.* **23**. 354; **24**. 229 (1894).
[5] Published in the recent volumes of *Gazz. chim.*

Observations made up to the present, though rather disconnected, appear to show that the osmotic pressure of dilute solid solutions can also be calculated according to the gas laws (see also Book II. Chapter III. paragraph "Molecular weight of solid substances").

It should be added that Kuster (*Zeitschr. phys. Chem.* **17.** 367, 1895) maintains the very reasonable view that a distinction should be made between solid solutions and isomorphous mixtures. Only in the former is diffusion of a dissolved substance possible, according to this view, while in the latter the molecules of the added material form part of the crystalline structure and are held in fixed positions of equilibrium by the forces that produce orientation of the crystal molecules. Again an opinion of Bodländer should be noted, that in the formation of solid solutions, *e.g.* separation of iodine with crystallising benzene, absorption phenomena play an important part (see for this and the theory of solid solutions generally, Bodlander, *Neues Jahrbuch für Mineralogie*, Beilage-Band, **12.** 25, 1898).

BOOK II

ATOM AND MOLECULE

CHAPTER I

ATOMIC THEORY

Combining Weight and Atomic Weight.—The question whether a well-defined chemical substance is an element or a compound of several different elements, and in the latter case to what extent each element is contained in unit weight of the substance, is a purely experimental problem, which can be answered in any given case with great certainty and exactness by means of analytical chemical methods, without recourse to theoretical speculation. The elementary analysis of a compound is included among the commonest operations of a chemical laboratory, and a description of the purely chemical methods of such an investigation does not lie in the province of this treatise.

The question as to the relative number of atoms in the molecule of a compound is, however, entirely different. To answer this question, besides knowing the combining weights, which may be obtained directly from experiment, we must also know the *relative weights of the atoms* which make up the compound considered : this can be learned only by the aid of theoretical speculation, and even then not with absolute certainty, but only with more or less probability. From the principles of the atomic theory stated on p. 31, it follows that the atomic weights and the combining weights are related to each other in the *simple ratios* of rational numbers ; but the values of these numerical ratios remain undetermined. But, if one obtains the same results by very different methods, the probability is very great that theoretical considerations will lead to safe conclusions. The question of the relative weights of the atoms has been established with such certainty that its general correctness is at present no longer called in question ; it is therefore very instructive to study the different ways which have finally led us, in spite of many errors, to the same desired result.

If we wish to explain empirical facts by an hypothesis, as here, for instance, where we make use of the atomic hypothesis to throw light on the laws of definite and multiple proportions, it should be remembered that that method of explanation is to be chosen which is the *simplest.* This should only be given up when later discoveries force us to adopt more complicated conceptions. Dalton (1808)[1] proceeded in this way when he arranged the first table of atomic weights.[2] In the case of those compounds which consist of only two elements, it is simplest to assume that the same number of atoms of the two elements have united to form the compound, so that *e.g.* carbon monoxide contains the same number of atoms of oxygen as of carbon, and that water contains the same number of atoms of oxygen as of hydrogen, etc. In this way Dalton tried to learn the relative atomic weights of the most important elements, and proceeding in the same way, to establish the number of atoms in compounds consisting of more than two elements, and thus to obtain a consistent system of the atomic weights.

But this method was by no means free from arbitrary assumption ; for the same logic that regarded carbon monoxide as composed of an equal number of atoms of oxygen and carbon, would regard carbon dioxide as containing twice as many atoms of oxygen as of carbon ; and, on the other hand, if Dalton had regarded carbon dioxide as containing the same number of atoms of carbon and oxygen, then carbonic oxide must contain twice as many atoms of carbon as of oxygen. Thus there was an opportunity for choice in selecting the atomic weight. That the choice in the preceding case was the right one was purely a matter of chance. We need to consult other experimental facts, and their meaning on the basis of a more extended development of the atomic hypothesis, in order to obtain a system of the atomic weights free from arbitrariness.

For an historical judgment of the fruitfulness of atomistic conceptions it is of interest to note that Dalton did not invent the atomic theory as a subsequent explanation of the laws of constant and multiple proportions, as was formerly thought ; on the contrary, he was led by considerations of molecular theory to the discovery of the fundamental laws of chemistry (see Roscoe and Harden, *Dalton's Atomic Theory*).

The Rule of Avogadro.—The necessary experimental facts were found in Gay-Lussac's law, according to which the volumes of those gases which combine with each other stand in simple ratios to each other, and also to the volumes of the resulting compounds, if gaseous. The theoretical interpretation of this law, in the light of the atomic hypothesis, was given by the hypothesis of Avogadro (1811), according to

[1] Ostwald's *Klassiker*, No. 3. Leipzig, 1889.
[2] The first table was arranged in 1804. See Thomson, *History of Chemistry*, vol. ii. p. 289.—TR.

which all gases, whether simple or compound, contain the same number of molecules in the same unit of space (p. 39). After a method was found for determining the relative weight of the *molecules* by measuring the vapour densities, it was easily possible, by applying the principle of the simplest explanation, to obtain constant determinations of the *atomic weights* of all those elements which formed a sufficient number of volatile compounds. If the molecules of a compound are really produced by the union of a small number of the atoms of each particular element, then it may be safely assumed that among a large number of molecules, whose molecular weights can be determined from their vapour density, some molecules will occur containing only *one atom* of the element in question. Thus we arrive at the conclusion *that the smallest relative quantity of an element which can enter into the molecule of a compound, corresponds to the atomic weight.* But even if only a few compounds of an element are investigated, and it is found, for example, that the quantity of that element present in a mol of the first compound is a, in the second $3a$, in the third $4a$, then there can be hardly any doubt that a is the atomic weight of the element. In practice, as other tests are not wanting, a few vapour-pressure measurements suffice, and the atomic weight is taken as that weight which, multiplied by whole numbers, as small as possible, gives the amount present in each molecule. To be sure in this way, strictly speaking, one can arrive only at the upper limit of the atomic weight; but with the investigation of a large number of compounds, the probability that one is not dealing with a multiple of the atomic weight, but with the desired value itself, becomes very great. Thus it was found that a gram molecule of the numerous chlorine compounds contained either at least 35·4 g. of chlorine, or an *exact multiple* of this, and similarly in the case of many other elements.

After determining the relative atomic weights, the vapour density determination of an element shows the number of atoms contained in its molecule. The fact that the molecule was found to consist of one atom in the case of only a few elements, *i.e.* the atomic and molecular weights are identical with each other, could only give rise to passing doubts; the further development of the doctrine of valence soon showed that similar, as well as dissimilar, atoms can unite firmly with each other by means of chemical forces.

The Law of Dulong and Petit.—Another empirical fact, the true theoretical significance of which is still unknown, is the relation between the atomic weight and the specific heat of an element in the solid state; this was discovered by Dulong and Petit in 1818. The product of the atomic weight by the specific heat is called the *atomic heat*; by this is to be understood the amount of heat expressed in g.-cal., which must be added to 1 gram atom of an element in order to raise its temperature 1°. The law may then be simply stated thus:

The atomic heat of elements in the solid state of aggregation is approximately constant, and amounts to about 6·4.

● This law is not strictly exact, for some of the elements having atomic weights smaller than 35, have atomic heats considerably removed from the mean. H. F. Weber in 1875 showed, in the case of the most marked exceptions, viz. boron (2·6), carbon (2 to 2·8, according to the modification), and silicon (about 4), that the atomic heats of these elements increase strongly with increasing temperature, and approach the values necessitated by the Dulong-Petit law.[1] Beryllium, which is also an exception (its atomic heat being 3·71), shows a fairly strong increase of the atomic heat with rising temperature according to the measurements of Nilson and Pettersson (1880). The law finds its most exact application in the case of the metals, where it holds good even for those of low atomic weight, as lithium, magnesium,[2] etc. Thus it takes about the same amount of heat (6·6 cal.) to raise the temperature of 1 g. atom of lithium (7·03), 1°, as to raise 1 g. atom of uranium (239), 1°. This clearly shows that we have here to do with a very remarkable regularity.[3]

Accordingly, by measuring the specific heat of a new element, we have a simple and a perfectly sure method for the determination of its atomic weight, provided that special attention is given to certain points : firstly, the specific heat must be measured at different temperatures in order to make sure that it does not vary too much with the temperature ; secondly, the determination must not be made too close to the melting-point ; and, finally, the atomic weight of the element in question must not be too small.

Thus recently [4] an investigation of the specific heat of the element germanium, discovered by Winkler, gave the atomic heat of 5·6, which speaks in favour of the atomic weight 72·3, assumed for the element.

It is very remarkable, and also of great assistance in determining the atomic weight, that the *constancy of the atomic heat also holds good for compounds existing in the solid state.* By means of the painstaking work of F. Neumann (1831), of Regnault (1840), and especially of Kopp,[5] who in his classic work on the specific heat of solid salts brought the subject practically to a conclusion, the existence of extensive and surprising regularities has been firmly established. According to these, the specific heat of solid substances is a pronounced *additive property* (p. 101) ; *the molecular heat of a solid compound (i.e. the*

---

[1] Moisson and Gautier confirmed this result for boron (*Ann. chim. phys.* [7], **7.** 568, 1896).

[2] See specially Waterman, "Specific Heats of Metals," *Phys. Rev.* **4.** 161, 1896.

[3] For a very clear summary of this subject in English, see M. M. P. Muir, *Prin. of Chem.* 2nd edit. pp. 49-67, Cambridge (1889) ; Remsen, *Theoret. Chem.* 4th edit. pp. 65-75 ; and Lothar Meyer, *Mod. Theories of Chem.*, trans. by Bedson and Williams, pp. 63-95, London and New York (1888).—TR.

[4] Nilson and Pettersson, *Zeitschr. phys. Chem.* **1.** 34 (1878).

[5] *Lieb. Ann.* Supplement, **3.** 1 and 289 (1864).

product of the specific heat and the molecular weight) is equal to the sum of the atomic heats of the elements contained.

The atomic heats have the following values : for C, 1·8 ; H, 2·3 ; B, 2·7 ; Be, 3·7 ; Si, 3·8 ; O, 4·0 ; P, 5·4 ; S, 5·4 ; Ge, 5·5 ; and for the other elements approximately 6·4.

Thus, for example, the specific heat of solid water, *i.e.* ice, amounts to 0·474, and the molecular heat therefore is $18 \times 0·474 = 8·5$; while the molecular heat calculated from the figures given above for the formula H_2O, is

$$\overline{2 \times 2·3} + 4 = 8·6.$$

The specific heat of calcium carbonate, $CaCO_3$, is 0·203, corresponding to a molecular heat of 20·4, while that calculated according to Kopp's law is

$$6·4 + 1·8 + \overline{3 \times 4} = 20·2.$$

Conversely, if the specific heat is calculated from this value by dividing by the molecular weight, 0·201 is obtained instead of 0·203 ; and similar coincidences are found in hundreds of other cases investigated, although small errors are sometimes found which exceed the errors of observation

Thus we find that the atomic heats of the elements, calculated from the specific heats of their compounds, coincide with the atomic heats of the elements in the free state, in so far as these can be studied in the solid state. It may therefore be concluded, with great certainty, that chlorine in the solid state has the specific heat

$$\frac{6·4}{35·5} = 0·180,$$

and thus obeys the Dulong-Petit law. Thus, in general, it is possible to calculate the atomic heats from the specific heats of solid compounds.

Kopp's law is of value in atomic weight determinations, because by it the atomic heat of elements can be deduced from the specific heat of their solid compounds.

It will be useful to illustrate this point by an example. Analysis of corrosive sublimate shows it to contain 100 gr. mercury to 35 gr. (1 gr. atom) of chlorine. The specific heat according to Regnault is 0·069. The molecular heat according to possible formulae would be—

Molecular Weight.	Molecular Heat Observations.	Calc.
$HgCl = 100 + 35$	$135 \times 0·069 = 9·3$	12·8
$HgCl_2 = 200 + 70$	$270 \times 0·069 = 18·6$	19·2
$HgCl_3 = 300 + 105$	$405 \times 0·069 = 28·0$	25·6

Only the triatomic formula $HgCl_2$ gives a molecular heat (according to

Kopp's law) in accordance with the facts : the atomic weight of mercury must therefore be 200.   Such a calculation does not give any information as to molecular weight, for if the formulae were $(HgCl_2)_n$ both observed and calculated molecular heats would be n times as great, and the agreement would still hold.

The specific heat of liquids is obviously of a more complicated character, at any rate no simple results have so far been arrived at. That of gases, which is sometimes of high importance in atomic weight determinations, will be dealt with in the next chapter.   We will only remark here that the specific heat of monatomic gases is 3·0, i.e. about half that of solid atoms according to Dulong and Petit's law.

Influence of the Temperature on Atomic Heats.—It has already been mentioned that the atomic heats of certain elements (carbon, silicon, etc.) increase very greatly with the temperature. Recent measurements have extended this result, and have shown that temperature nearly always has a considerable influence on atomic heats.   It has also been found that there is a very pronounced decrease in atomic heats at low temperatures ; the following table contains a few mean atomic heats between – 188° (liquid air) and room temperature :—

ATOMIC HEATS BETWEEN – 188° AND + 18°.

Element.	Atomic Heat.	Observer.	Element.	Atomic Heat.	Observer.
Aluminium	4·5	Tilden [1]	Cobalt	4·9	Tilden
,,	4·8	Behn [2]	Copper	5·1	Behn
Antimony	5·7	Behn	Nickel	5·1	Behn
Lead	6·1	Behn	Oxygen	2·8	N. and L.
Bromine ($PbBr_2$)	5·9	N. and L. [3]	Sulphur	4·1	Dewar [4]
Chlorine ($PbCl_2$)	4·9	N. and L.	Selenium	5·2	Dewar
Iron	4·8	Behn	Zinc	5·5	Behn
Iodine	6·2	N. and L.	Hydrogen	1·5	N. and L.

The numbers for oxygen and hydrogen are calculated by means of Kopp's law from the molecular heats of kieselguhr, grape sugar, anthraquinone, and ice.

Dewar (l.c.) has found that the atomic heat of carbon is extra-ordinarily small at very low temperatures :—

	18° to −78°	− 78° to −188°	− 188° to −252·5°
Diamond	0·95	0·23	0·052
Graphite	1·61	0·72	0·160

[1] Phil. Trans. **201**. 37 (1903).
[2] Wied. Ann. **66**. 237 (1898) ; Drudes Ann. **1**. 257 (1900).
[3] Nernst and Lowenstein (in progress).
[4] Proc. Roy. Soc. A, **76**. 325 (1905).

On the other hand atomic heats rise considerably with the temperature :—

Element.	Temperature.	Atomic Heat.	Observer.
Lead	310	7·6	Stücker [1]
Iron	500	9·8	Pionchon [2]
,,	525	12·1	Stücker
Magnesium	525	9·7	Stücker
Nickel	1000	9·5	Pionchon

Under these circumstances the rule of Dulong and Petit seems to possess only an accidental character, and in any case all theoretical speculations on the number 6 for atomic heats must be at present disregarded (compare the following chapter, paragraph : " Kinetic theory of the solid state ").

[During the past year a number of measurements of atomic heats at low temperatures have been made by Nernst and his collaborators. Two new forms of calorimeters have been introduced. The one consists of a block of copper, pierced longitudinally by a cavity which receives the warmed or cooled substance, and contained in a Dewar vessel to ensure heat isolation. The thermal conductivity of the block is great enough for the temperature to be the same all over, and the temperature is measured by means of a series of thermelements contained in small glass tubes, which are fixed into the copper block by means of Wood's alloy. The Dewar vessel is placed in a constant temperature bath, generally composed of ice or solid carbon dioxide.

The substances to be examined are contained in a small silver vessel, which is warmed (or cooled) to the desired temperature, and then dropped through a glass tube into the calorimeter. The temperature of the block is generally altered 2 to 3 degrees, which corresponds to a deviation of forty to sixty divisions of the millivoltmeter. In this way the specific heats can be measured with ease and rapidity to within a few parts per thousand.

The apparatus must of course be standardised by means of a substance whose specific heat is known. For this purpose, water is used at high temperatures, lead at low.

The second instrument is specially designed to measure specific heats at one particular temperature, instead of the mean specific heat over a wide range of temperature. The principle is simple : the substance under examination itself serves as a calorimeter, and its temperature is raised a few degrees by passing a known quantity of electricity through a platinum wire embedded in it. The rise in temperature is estimated by measuring the resistance of the same platinum wire, before and after the heating.

---

[1] *Wied. Beibl.* **30.** 151 (1906).
[2] Landolt-Börnstein tables (1905).

The substance must of course be placed in a vacuum, on the completeness of which the success of the experiment depends. With ordinary care an accuracy of 1 per cent can be easily attained.

The specific heat measurements were originally carried out for the purpose of examining and developing the new theorem in thermodynamics (see Book IV.). They have, however, a peculiar interest of their own. Einstein (*Ann. d. Phys.* [4], **22.** 184) has developed a very remarkable theory of the specific heats of crystallised bodies, and there can be no doubt that his theory is applicable to all solid bodies whose molecules cannot move freely, *i.e.* can only oscillate about fixed points. He arrives at the following expression for atomic heats :—

$$C = 3 \ R \ \frac{e^{-\frac{a}{T}} \left(\frac{a}{T}\right)^2}{\left(e^{-\frac{a}{T}} - 1\right)^2}$$

where R is the gas constant, and a, the only unknown constant, can be determined under certain conditions by optical measurements.

According to this formula, atomic heats are very small at very low temperatures, then increase rapidly at first, slowly afterwards, with rise of temperature, finally attaining a maximum given by

$$C = 3 \ R = 6 \ \text{(about)}$$

which is the constant of Dulong and Petit's law. In the case of lead, the maximum is already reached at the temperature of liquid air ; but for diamond it is not attained below 1000°. Quantitatively the formula only gives approximate results ; Magnus and Lindemann have added the empirical term $+ bT^{\frac{3}{2}}$; and the formula so corrected gives results in close accord with experiment, as the following table for silver will show :—

ATOMIC HEATS OF SILVER

$a = 162$ $b = 4 \cdot 8 \times 10^{-5}$

T	c (Calc.)	c (Obs.)	Observer.
64	3·61	3·72	Nernst
84	4·44	4·43	,,
86	4·50	4·40	,,
200	5·78	5·73	,,
208	5·81	5·92	,,
291-87	5·60	5·60	Behn
291-194	5·92	5·87	,,
373-288	6·13	6·08	Bartoli and Stracciate
780-290	6·51	6·46	Magnus
887-290	6·61	6·64	,,

For further details and experiments see Nernst, " Sur les chaleurs spécifiques aux basses températures," *Bulletin des séances de la Société française de Physique*, from which the above short account has been mainly taken.—Tr.]

Isomorphism.—The relation, discovered by Mitscherlich (1820), between atomic weight and isomorphism, affords another independent way of determining the atomic weight. Taken alone, it is indeed insufficient, but as an accessory it is of the greatest importance, and has repeatedly furnished practical results.

The following points may be cited as the most important characteristics of isomorphism :—

1. This term primarily denotes *identity of crystal form*, which must show complete coincidence of the properties of symmetry, and approximate coincidence of geometrical constants.

2. The property of forming *mixed crystals* in any selected proportion, at least within certain limits.

3. The property of *mutual overgrowth*, *i.e.* a crystal of one substance (as a nucleus) increases in size in a solution of the other substance.

Ostwald (*Zeitschr. phys. Chem.* **22.** 330, 1897) has proposed as a test of isomorphism the ability of a crystal to remove supersaturation of a solution and so act as nucleus for its crystallisation. This noteworthy criterion seems to be a combination of 2 and 3 ; but it will not be further considered here, as experimental tests of it are wanting, and that is precisely what is needed for any application in the study of isomorphism—at present an entirely empirical region.

There are a great number of analogous isomorphous compounds known where different elements are exchanged in proportion to their atomic weights, and thus far no clear example has been found where the exchange implies any inconsistency of the accepted atomic weights.[1]

On the other hand we can by no means conclude that if the substitution of one element by another alters the crystal form, the exchange has necessarily *not* taken place in the proportion of their atomic weights.

The following table contains the isomorphous series of elements, according to Arzruni.[2] The elements (or radicals) in a series can appear isomorphically in their analogous compounds, often in the ratio of their atomic weights (without change of crystalline form, and with little change in the geometric constants) ; the elements separated by a semicolon show isomorphism only in a few compounds. Regularly crystallising compounds are but little suited for showing isomorphism even when they have the same habitus.

---

[1] It should be noticed that the exchange of one element for another occurs not only in accordance with the ratio of their accepted atomic weights, but also the substituting element must assume the *valence* of the element substituted ; thus in the thallium alums, thallium has the valence of a monad, imitating the monad valence of K, Na, etc.; in short, it is a *thallous*, not a *thallic* compound.—Tr.

[2] " Relations between Crystalline Form and Chemical Composition." Braunschweig, 1893. In vol. i. of Graham Otto, *Lehrbuch d. Chemie.*

ISOMORPHIC SERIES

I. H(?), K, Rb, Cs, NH_4, Tl; Na, Li; Ag.

Example :—

Tl_2SO_4	rhombic	$a : b : c =$	$0\cdot5539 : 1 : 0\cdot7319$
$(NH_4)_2SO_4$	,,	,,	$0\cdot5643 : 1 : 0\cdot7310$
Rb_2SO_4	,,	,,	$0\cdot5723 : 1 : 0\cdot7522$
K_2SO_4	,,	,,	$0\cdot5727 : 1 : 0\cdot7464$
Cs_2SO_4	,,	,,	$0\cdot5805 : 1 : 0\cdot7400$
$KHSO_4$	,,	,,	$0\cdot5806 : 1 : 0\cdot7489$
NH_4HSO_4	,,	,,	$0\cdot6126 : 1 : 0\cdot7436$
Ag_2SO_4	,,	,,	$0\cdot5713 : 1 : 1\cdot2382$
Na_2SO_4	,,	,,	$0\cdot5914 : 1 : 1\cdot2492$

II. Be, Zn, Cd, Mg, Mn, Fe, Os, Ru, Ni, Pd, Co, Pt, Cu, Ca.

Example : $CoPtCl_6 . 6H_2O$, $FePtCl_6 . 6H_2O$, etc.

III. Ca, Sr, Ba, Pb.

Example : $CaCO_3$, $SrCO_3$, $BaCO_3$, $PbCO_3$.

IV. La, Ce, Di, Y, Er.

Example : $Di_2(SO_4)_3 . 8H_2O$, etc.

V. Al, Fe, Cr, Co, Mn, Ir, Rh, Ga, In, Ti.

Example : Cr_2O_3, Al_2O_3, Fe_2O_3, Ti_2O_3.

VI. Cu, Hg, Pb, Ag, Au.

VII. Si, Ti, Ge, Zr, Sn, Pb, Th, Mo, Mn, U, Ru, Rh, Ir, Os, Pd, Pt, Te.

Example : K_2PtCl_4, K_2PdCl_4.

VIII. N, P, V, As, Sb, Bi.

Example : As_2S_3, Sb_2S_3, Bi_2S_3.

IX. Nb, Ta.

X. S, Se, Cr, Mn, Mo, Wo; Te(?), As, Sb.

XI. F, Cl, Br, I; Mn : CN.

The elements B, Sc, C, O cannot be classified.

Usually isomorphism appears the more readily the more complex the compound; obviously because, as Kopp (1863) remarked, the dissimilar influence of the element on the crystalline form is over-powered by the influence of the remaining components. Thus the usual potassium and sodium salts are not isomorphous, but such complicated compounds as the alums $K_2Al_2(SO_4)_4 . 24H_2O$ and $Na_2Al_2(SO_4)_4 . 24H_2O$ are.

Mitscherlich discovered isomorphism from the four following salts crystallising in the tetragonal system, viz. H_2KPO_4, H_2KAsO_4, $H_2(NH_4)PO_4$, $H_2(NH_4)AsO_4$, and also from corundum and hematite.

Some of the best known series of isomorphous substances are the alums; $CaCO_3$ (as aragonite), $BaCO_3$, $SrCO_3$, and $PbCO_3$ (ortho-rhombic); $BaSO_4$, $SrSO_4$, $PbSO_4$ (in the same forms); $MgSO_4 . 7H_2O$,

$ZnSO_4 . 7H_2O$, $NiSO_4 . 7H_2O$ (orthorhombic hemihedral). An excellent classification has been given by H. Topsoë.[1]

It should also be noticed that elements and radicals may be mutually isomorphous, as for instance K and NH_4.

There is no doubt that isomorphism expresses a very remarkable law, but on further consideration, and especially on a careful examination of the abundant observations [2] made in this department, certain misgivings arise.

The condition of "approximate coincidence" of geometrical constants at once brings up the question: Where shall we draw the line between identity and difference of crystal form? Or if, as this is not possible, the decisive criterion for legitimate isomorphism is taken to be the capacity for mixed crystals the same difficulty at once arises, for we have already seen that there are all conceivable gradations in the mutual miscibility of solid substances (p. 115). When we come finally to the third indication of isomorphism, namely the property of overgrowth, it has been observed that substances which do not possess the slightest chemical or crystallographic analogy, exhibit this property; and therefore, on this ground, its value as a criterion of isomorphism has been criticised by Retgers.[3]

It is extremely likely that no criterion will ever be found which will enable us to answer decisively in all cases whether isomorphism is present or not; we should therefore confine our attention to the investigation of the *degree of isomorphism*, since the discussion of such vague and idle questions as whether isomorphism is shown in any given case or not, is not a subject for deliberate investigation. The only question at issue is: What are the properties suitable for adoption as standard for the *degree of isomorphism*?

Of all the properties of a crystal, its *form* is very important and very striking to the eye; but that is no reason for conceding to it a significance in precedence to the density, elasticity, optical constants, etc. That the first relations studied were those between crystal form and chemical composition, was obviously because this property obtruded itself upon the observer; their discovery was an undoubted acquisition, even though it could not always be retained as a rule without an exception; but to elevate that discovery to the grade of a guiding principle, would amount to voluntarily assuming the fetters of an historical accident.

The analogy between two crystals is shown more clearly in their *miscibility* than in their crystal form, and thus the statement appears to be completely established, as Retgers so strongly emphasised in his

---

[1] *Tidskrift f. Fysik og Chemi*, **8**. 5, 193, 321 (1869), and **9**. 225 (1870); see also the monograph on "Isomorphism," by Arzruni, referred to above.

[2] It is especially recommended to read the work of Retgers already cited on p. 116. A résumé may be found in the *Jahrbuch für Min.* (1891), **1**. 132, and in the *Chem. Centralbl.* (1891-1892).

[3] *Zeitschr. phys. Chem.* **5**. 460 (1890).

investigations, that though a more or less complete similarity of form is not without interest, yet the whole problem appears to centre about the question of miscibility. The various grades of miscibility, according to Retgers, may be represented as follows :—

1. Miscibility in all degrees, a rather rare case. The physical properties—as well as the crystal form—vary gradually and evenly, in the series of mixtures, and are decidedly additive.

2. Limited miscibility, without the formation of double salts ; the physical properties of the mixed crystals are emphatically additive, *i.e.* they can be calculated from those of the two substances when pure.

3. Limited miscibility, without double salt formation ; the physical properties of the mixed crystals are additive here also, but in calculating the properties of the series of mixtures, it is necessary to ascribe properties to the end member on one side of a gap, which are different from those of the end member on the other side, and moreover properties different from those which actually occur, *e.g. another crystal form. Sometimes there is a labile (unstable) form for one end member which conducts itself in the free state as though it were produced by intermixture with the mixed crystal, the properties of which have been transported beyond the gap by extrapolation ; the so-called iso-di-morphism or iso-poly-morphism.*

4. Limited miscibility, with double salt formation, such that it indicates an important *chemical contrast* ; the properties of the double salt are more or less different from those calculated from its end members.

5. The last degree ; no marked miscibility, either with or without double salt formation.

Thus in the series of mixtures of ammonium and potassium sulphates, the specific volumes of the mixed crystals, which can be produced in every desired proportion, can be calculated quite accurately from the specific volumes of the end members, as was shown on p. 117 ; this pair of salts would be included under the first class just enumerated. The sulphates of iron and magnesium, which form an iso-di-morphous mixture, are doubtless to be referred to class 3.

It is obvious that a sharp line can be drawn at least between classes 1 and 2 ; the question as to the existence of a gap in the series of mixtures can be decided definitely by experiment, provided we possess a solvent common for both of the crystals to be mixed. On this basis we might attempt to obtain miscibility in all proportions, as the decisive criterion of isomorphism. But this would amount to emphasising isomorphism as one particular phenomenon, and would be also unsuitable, because many crystals showing only a limited miscibility can, in all probability, be made miscible in all proportions by changing the temperature ; just as many liquids, as water and phenol, which show limited miscibility at certain temperatures, at others dissolve each other in all proportions.

The study of mixtures is doubtless to be preferred to the narrow study of the crystal form, as shown by many of the cases observed by Retgers. "Thus if we were shown a prism of KNO_3, a rhombohedron of $NaNO_3$, a tabular crystal of $KClO_3$, and a cube of $NaClO_3$, the chemical composition of all four of these being unknown, no one would suppose that they were substances chemically analogous. But that this is the case is shown beyond a doubt by their crystallising together."

On the other hand, certain cases suggest caution, because the property of forming mixed crystals does not belong exclusively to substances which are chemically analogous ; experience has shown that ammonium chloride has the peculiar property of uniting, to a certain extent, with substances which are entirely different chemically ;[1] solid benzene and iodine can crystallise together (p. 164), etc.

In conclusion, let me define what I think to be the present state of the question of isomorphism :—

The property of forming solid molecular mixtures is a very common property of solid substances ; but in general, in most cases, mixed crystals can be prepared only up to certain limits, which are the points of mutual saturation. Every solid substance may contain traces, at least, of another substance, and thus there is formed a solid solution (p. 161), even though very dilute. The concentration may be excessively small as *e.g.* when the solid substance is a metal and the dissolved substance is a non-metal, or *vice versa*, and though it may be much greater in the preceding case, which deals with the solution of a solid salt in a salt, yet it is usually small enough to escape notice. *The degree of miscibility grows with increasing chemical relationship*, so that the property of forming mixed crystals, within broad limits or in all proportions, finally appears in the case of substances which are completely analogous chemically. But in the case of complete miscibility, all the properties of the mixed crystal, including the crystal *form*, must be regular functions of the composition, exactly as in the cases of liquids and gases ; but since a gradual, regular coincidence of crystalline form is capable of being experimentally realised, only when the two pure crystallising substances have *an original similarity* of form, it therefore follows, as a special case of the above more general rule, that the rule of Mitscherlich is true, viz. that chemically analogous substances usually have similar crystal forms.

If the series of mixtures shows a gap, the crystal forms of the end members may be very different from each other, although the chemical analogy is very complete ; but since each crystal on the one side of the gap is forced to adapt itself to the other crystal respectively, the very fact of a great extension of the series of mixture indicates that each crystal shows this tendency ; as a matter of

[1] Lehmann, *Zeitschr. f. Krystall.* **8**. 438 (1883) ; Retgers, *Zeitschr. phys. Chem.* **9**. 385 (1892).

fact, it is often observed that one crystal, even when in a perfectly pure state, may assume a labile form of the other (iso-di-morphism or iso-poly-morphism).

Isomorphism is therefore hidden, so to speak, behind the rule that *miscibility varies directly with increasing chemical relationship*; it is a rule moreover which, in the case of liquids, is expressed in the statement that closely related substances dissolve each other in all proportions. Now, other things being equal, since a solid mixture is formed with greater difficulty than a liquid one, and especially so since the crystal form here exerts a limiting influence, much greater demands are made upon chemical analogy in the case of solids than in the case of liquids.

The Periodic System of the Elements.[1]—In addition to the facts already described, by means of which the tables of the atomic weights can be completed with a large degree of confidence, there now appears a strong support in the shape of the so-called "natural" or "periodic" system of the elements; this unites certain relations between the atomic weights and the physical properties which have been long suspected, into a complete, well-rounded system, and broadens our knowledge in many respects. The fact alone that most of these regularities would disappear only by a radical change of the atomic weights, makes it appear that no attempts of that kind will be made within the immediate future.

As early as 1829 Doebereiner called attention to the fact that there are certain triads of elements which show close analogies in their physical properties and certain regularities in their atomic weights. The following table shows series of such similar triad groups, the atomic weights of which exhibit *differences which are fairly constant*:—

	Atomic Weights.	Diff.
Lithium . . .	7·03	16·02
Sodium . . .	23·05	16·1
Potassium . . .	39·15	
Calcium . . .	40·10	47·5
Strontium . . .	87·6	49·8
Barium . . .	137·4	
Sulphur . . .	32·06	47·14
Selenium . . .	79·2	48·4
Tellurium . . .	127·6	
Chloride . . .	35·45	44·51
Bromine . . .	79·96	46·01
Iodine . . .	126·97	

[1] In the preparation of this section use was made of Lothar Meyer's *Grundzüge der theoretischen Chemie.* Leipzig, 1890.

n the other hand, in the following table we find triad groups
ated elements having *only slightly different atomic weights* :—

Iron .	.	.	.	.	.	55·9
Cobalt .	.	.	.	.	.	59·0
Nickel .	.	.	.	.	.	58·7
Ruthenium	.	.	.	.	.	101·7
Rhodium	.	.	.	.	.	103·0
Palladium	.	.	.	.	.	106·5
Osmium	.	.	.	.	.	191·0
Iridium	.	.	.	.	.	193·0
Platinum	.	.	.	.	.	194·8

ttempts were not wanting to advance farther along the line of
regularities. But the thorough generalisation and consequent
tion of this did not come till there appeared a simple classifica-
f the elements in the works of Mendelejeff and of Lothar Meyer
) ; these two by slightly different ways arrived at the same con-
, viz. that the properties of the chemical elements are periodic
ons of their atomic weights ; this will appear in detail from the
ing arrangement :—

[TABLE

0.	I.	II.	III.	IV.	V.	VI.	VII.	VIII.		
He 4	Li 7·03	Be 9·1	B 11·0	C 12·00	N 14·0	O 16·00	F 19·0			
Ne 20	Na 23·05	Mg 24·36	Al 27·1	Si 28·4	P 31·0	S 32·06	Cl 35·45			
A 39·9	K 39·15	Ca 40·1	Sc 44·1	Ti 48·1	V 51·2	Cr 52·1	Mn 55·0	Fe 55·9	Co 59·0	Ni 58·7
...	Cu 63·6	Zn 65·4	Ga 70	Ge 72·5	As 75	Se 79·2	Br 79·96			
Kr 81·8	Rb 85·5	Sr 87·6	Y 89·0	Zr 90·6	Nb 94	Mo 96·0	...	Ru 101·7	Rh 103·0	Pd 106·5
...	Ag 107·93	Cd 112·4	In 115	Sn 119·0	Sb 120·2	Te 127·6	I 127			
X 128	Cs 133	Ba 137·4	La 138·9	Ce 140·2		...	...			
...	...		Yb 173·0		Ta 181	W 184	...	Os 191	Ir 193·0	Pt 194·8
...	Au 197·2	Hg 200·0	Tl 204·1	Pb 206·9	Bi 208·0	...	...			

In column 0 are the new elements discovered in the atmosphere (the so-called "noble" gases); they were of course unknown to Meyer and Mendelejeff, and have only recently been introduced into the periodic system by Ramsay. We shall return to this column later; for the present it will be left out of consideration.

In each of the first two periods (horizontal rows) are seven elements, the respective members of which in the same column are very similar. In the four following rows we find some similarity of the elements in the same column; but we find the greatest similarity by comparing alternate elements, e.g. K with Rb, Cu with Ag, Zn with Cd, Br with I, etc. The seventh and eighth rows are very incomplete; but perhaps elements as yet not much investigated will be found to follow in after Ce. The elements of the ninth row, as far as known, accord well with the corresponding members of the sixth.

The elements in the eighth column, including the iron and platinum groups, occupy an exceptional position: the atomic weights of each group of three stand nearer together than most of the elements in the horizontal rows, and a similar statement may be made of their properties. The three triad groups together play the part each of an element, but at the same time of elements which do not fit well into the preceding scheme. This arrangement shows very clearly, as Mendelejeff emphasised, the relation between their respective *chemical values*, as compared with oxygen, and their atomic weights, as the following table of the oxides instead of the elements still further illustrates :—

I.	II.	III.	IV.	V.	VI.	VII.	VIII.
Li_2O	Be_2O_2	B_2O_3	C_2O_4	N_2O_5		Cl_2O_7	
Na_2O	Mg_2O_2	Al_2O_3	Si_2O_4	P_2O_5	S_2O_6	Mn_2O_7	
K_2O	Ca_2O_2	Sc_2O_3	Ti_2O_4	V_2O_5	Cr_2O_6	Br_2O_7	
Cu_2O	Zn_2O_2	Ga_2O_3	Ge_2O_4	As_2O_5	Se_2O_6	...	Ru_2O_3
Rb_2O	Sr_2O_2	Y_2O_3	Zr_2O_4	Nb_2O_5	Mo_2O_6	I_2O_7	
Ag_2O	Cd_2O_2	In_2O_3	Sn_2O_4	Sb_2O_5	Te_2O_6	...	Os_2O_8
Cs_2O	Ba_2O_2	La_2O_3	Ce_2O_4	Ta_2O_5	W_2O_6	...	
Au_2O	Hg_2O_2	Tl_2O_3	Pb_2O_4	Bi_2O_5	U_2O_6		

But in spite of this regularity we must take warning not to follow it blindly; for, as is well known, many elements form other oxides than will fit into the preceding table, and also some elements, which do not fit into this table, are omitted.

The elements discovered by Ramsay—helium, argon, etc.—are completely neutral in chemical behaviour; Ramsay therefore arranges them in a new column, as having the valency zero. The atomic weights (only approximately known) harmonise with this view, as may be seen from the table, p. 180;

actually these elements form a transition between the strongly positive and strongly negative univalent elements, being themselves neutral on account of their chemical indifference ; the following table given by Ramsay illustrates these points :—

H	He	Li	Be
1	4	7	9
F	Ne	Na	Mg
19	20	23	24
Cl	A	K	Ca
35	40	39	40
Br	Kr	Rb	Sr
80	82	85	88
I	X	Cs	Ba
127	128	133	137

Remembering that hydrogen according to its physical properties is throughout of a metalloid character, and also in many compounds, such as the hydrocarbons, stands much nearer chemically to the halogens than to the univalent metals, its position at the head of the univalent metalloids is not without reason. A certain number, at any rate, of the elements are satisfactorily arranged, then, in the above order (see Ramsay, *Ber. deutsch. chem. Ges.* **13**. 311 (1898), and *Modern Chemistry*, London, 1900, p. 50).

Staigmüller's (*Z. phys. Chem.* **39**. 243, 1902) similar arrangement of the elements is given on p. 184 ; the noble gases are introduced in it in the same way as in Ramsay's. Various difficulties of the old arrangement are thus avoided ; the elements in the last vertical column occur naturally ; the metalloids are separated from the metals by the heavy line ; moreover, C, B, Si, may very well be looked upon as metals, and in this way the grouping gains in simplicity of outline. By a slight rearrangement, already made in this table, the analogy is clearly brought out between the three triads, Fe, Ru, Os ; Co, Rh, Ir ; Ni, Pd, Pt (see the remarkable observations of H. Biltz, *Ber. chem. Ges.* **35**. 562, 1902).

In a similar way A. Werner (*Ber. chem. Ges.* **38**. 914, 1905) arranges the elements in a series of pairs of periods, containing a constantly increasing number of elements (see table, p. 185). The first period, which should contain three elements, is unknown ; the second contains the three elements H ; an unknown element, the prototype of the metalloids, which should stand over F, Cl, etc. ; and He. The next two periods, of eight elements each, begin with Li and Na respectively, and include the elements up to Ne and A ; between Li and Be, Na and Mg, is a large free space. The fifth and sixth periods contain 18 members : there is a gap under Mn. The last two periods contain may gaps ; in the last but one there are only 24 of the 33 elements known (see table). The last period contains only Ra, Laα, Th, U, Ac, Pbα, Biα, Teα, *i.e.* radio-active and mostly hypothetical elements. The mean increase of atomic weight between two neighbouring elements rises with the atomic weight. In the Li period it is 1·85, in the Na period 2·4, in the K period 2·47, in the Rb period 2·5 ; if it is still smaller in the H period, say 1·5, an element must be missing. If it is 2·56 for the last period, it follows that the period should contain 33 elements. Every pair of periods has more elements by a multiple of five than the preceding pair. The properties of the elements yet to be discovered must be between those of the elements between which they are respectively placed.

It should be mentioned that Newlands, as far back as 1864, attempted to arrange the elements systematically according to their atomic weights; for further history of the periodic system see K. Seubert, *Z. anorg. Chem.* **9.** 334 (1895). On the didactic value of the periodic system, see Lothar Meyer (*Ber. deutsch. chem. Ges.* **26.** 1230, 1893).

Regularities of the Atomic Weight Numbers.—It is very remarkable that the atomic weights of a number of elements, especially those of low atomic weight, approximate closely to whole numbers; a hypothesis put forward on the strength of this by Prout (1815), that they are exact multiples of the atomic weight of hydrogen, is certainly false; but the fact remains that many elements nearly satisfy the hypothesis in a way that cannot possibly be accidental.

Rydberg (1886) undertook to follow out these unmistakable regularities, and in a recent very thorough study (*Z. anorg. Chem.* **14.** 66, 1897) has brought to light a whole series of striking rules that will doubtless be of meaning in the future development of the periodic system. The atomic weights P can be put in the form $P = N + D$, where N is a whole number and D is a quantity always small compared with N and for the elements of low atomic weight, small compared with unity. If M be a whole number—Rydberg calls it the ordinal number of the element—elements of odd M have odd valency and odd values of $N = 2M + 1$; elements of even M have even valency and even values of $N = 2M$. The values of D, which can be pretty accurately determined in view of the above rules, form a *pronounced periodic function of the atomic weight.* From this follows the suggestion that in studies on the periodic system either N or perhaps better M should be taken as the independent variable instead of the atomic weight. Adopting this principle the difficulty disappears that is due to the newly determined atomic weight of tellurium (127·6 instead of 125). According to the views hitherto adopted, tellurium (127·6) would come after iodine—in a quite hopeless position; according to Rydberg, it should stay in its natural place with $M = 60$, $N = 120$, $D = 7·6$, the last value being more satisfactory than $D = 5$, as compared with the values of D for neighbouring elements. Where the curve showing the relation of any property E to M passes through a maximum or minimum, the value of E of course varies little with M, and as such maxima and minima occur in about the same place for the most varied properties, elements arise with little difference in character ("twin elements," according to R. Lorenz, who has worked out a number of rules for these, *Zeitschr. anorg. Chem.* **12.** 329; **14.** 103, 1897).

For further observations on regularity in atomic weights see Jul. Thomsen (*Bull. Acad. Danemark,* Dec. 14, 1894), and M. Töpler (*Ges. Isis Dresden,* 1896, Abh. 4).

Physical Properties of the Elements.—Some physical properties also stand in more or less definite relation to the atomic weights. A superficial consideration shows at once that the metallic

F 19	Cl 35·5	Br 80·0	J 126·9		
O 16	S 32·1	Se 79·2	Te 127		
N 14	P 31·0	As 75	Sb 120		Bi 208
		Ge 72	Sn 119		Pb 206·9
		Ga 70	In 114		Tl 204·1
		Zn 65·4	Cd 112		Hg 200·3
		Cu 63·6	Ag 107·9		Au 197·2
		Co 59	Pd 106		Pt 195
		Ni 58·7	Rh 103		Ir 193
		Fe 56	Ru 102		Os 191
		Mn 55·0			
		Cr 52·1	Mo 96·0		W 184
		V 51·2	Nb 94		Ta 183
C ·12	Si 28·4	Ti 48·1	Zr 90·6	Ce 140·2	
B 11	Al 27·1	Sc 44·1	Y 89	La 139	Yb 173
Be 9·1	Mg 24·4	Ca 40·1	Sr 87·6	Ba 137·4	
Li 7	Na 23	K 39·1	Rb 85·5	Cs 133	
He 4	Ne 20	A 40	Kr 82	X 128	

																									Be 9·1	B 11	C 12	N 14·01	O 16	Fl 19	Ne 20
																									Mg 24·4	Al 27·1	Si 28·4	P 31	S 32	Cl 35·5	A 40
Ca 80																Sc 44	Ti 48	V 51·2	Cr 52	Mn 55	Fe 55·9	Co 59	Ni 58·7	Cu 63·6	Zn 65·4	Ga 70	Ge 72	As 75	Se 79·1		
Sr 87·6																Y 89	Zr 90·7	Nb 94	Mo 96	..	Ru 101·7	Rh 103	Pd 106	Ag 108	Cd 112	In 114	Sn 118	Sb 120	Te 127·6	I 127	Xe 128
Ba 137·4	La 133	Ce 140	Nd 143·6	Pr 140	..	..	Sa 150	Eu 152	Gd 156	Tb 160	Ho 162	Er 166	..	Tu 171	Yb 173	..	..	Ta 181	W 184	..	Os 191	Ir 193	Pt 195	Au 197	Hg 200	Tl 204	Pb 207	Bi 208	..	..	..
Ra 225	Laα ?	Th 232	..	..	..	..	..	U 239·5	..	..	..	..	..	Ac ?	..	..	..	..	..	..	..	..	..	..	..	..	Pbα ?	Biα ?	Teα ?	..	..

elements (except the last series) are collected in the outer vertical columns only, while the metalloids are in the middle. The atomic volume, *i.e.* volume of 1 gram-atom of the element in the solid state, also comes clearly in its relation to atomic weight, as appears from Fig. 17 (L. Meyer, 1870).

Melting-points behave in the same way, as may be seen in the following table.

Melting-point of Elements on the Absolute Scale (from − 273°)—(*n.g.* not melted, *s.h.* very high, *s.n.* very low, *üb.* over, *u.* under, *h.a.* higher than, *n.a.* lower than, *r.* red, *f.* colourless).

MELTING-POINTS OF THE ELEMENTS IN ABSOLUTE TEMPERATURE
(*i.e.* FROM − 273°).

0.	I.	II.	III.	IV.	V.	VI.	VII.	VIII.		
	H 14									
He a. 6	Li 459	Be n.a. Ag	B n.g.	C n.g.	N 62·5	O 28	F 50			
Ne ·.n.	Na 371	Mg 924	Al 930	Si 1703	P r. 903 f. 317	S 388	Cl 171			
A 85	K 336	Ca 1043	Sc ?	Ti üb. 2570	V 1953	Cr 1788	Mn 1520	Fe 1818	Co 1778	1/
	Cu 1357	Zn 692	Ga 303	Ge 1200 ?	As at red heat	Se 490	Br 266			
Kr 104	Rb 312	Sr h.a. Ca	Y ?	Zr h.a. Si	Nb 2223	Mo 2373	...	Ru h.a. 2220	Rh h.a. Pt.	
	Ag 1234	Cd 595	In 428	Sn 505	Sb 904	Te 723	I 386			
Xe 133	Cs 300	Ba 1123	La 1083 Ce 896	...	...	...	...	...	...	
	...	...	...	...	Ta 2573	W h.a. 3070	...	Os 2770	Ir 2470	2
	Au 1337	Hg 234	Tl 575	Pb 600	Bi 541	...	...			
	...	...	...	Th ?	...	U s.h.	...			

If the atomic weights are taken as abscissæ and melting-points as ordinates of a curve, the regularity comes out more clearly ; the curve is wave-shaped, with maxima in the fourth or fifth columns. The curve of atomic volumes in Fig. 17 has a similar course, and comparison of the two shows that all the *gaseous and easily fusible (liquid below red heat) are on the rising branches and maximal points of the volume curve ; while the elements that are melted with difficulty, or are not fusible at all with the means now available, are on the descending branches and at the minima.* Comparing the elements in each vertical series, *i.e.* each natural family, the melting-point is usually found to rise with increasing atomic weight ; but the alkalis Li, Na, K, Rb, the group Zn, Cd, Hg, and probably the alkaline earths, Be, Mg, Ca, Sr, behave in the opposite manner.

The compressibility of solid elements is also a pronounced periodic function of the atomic weight, as T. W. Richards[1] has shown in a detailed investigation ; in general the compressibility is greater, the greater the atomic volume, so that the curve of compressibilities (*l.c.* p. 197) is very similar to Fig. 17.

Borchers has recently shown (*Äquivalent- Volum- und Atomgewicht*, Knapp, Halle a. S., 1905) that some regularities become more distinct when the volume of a gram equivalent is substituted for atomic volume.

Of other physical properties that have a more or less marked periodic character, we may note crystalline form (see the Isomorphous Series, p. 174), which has clear relations to the vertical columns of the periodic system (see also G. Linck, *Zeitschr. phys. Chem.* **19.** 193 (1896), Ortloff, *ibid.* 201), extensibility, thermal expansion, conductivity for heat and electricity, heat of formation of oxides and chlorides, magnetic and diamagnetic properties, refraction equivalents (see, on these properties, Lothar Meyer, *Modern Theories of Chemistry*, 1883, p. 144 ff.), " Hardness of the Free Elements " (Rydberg, *Zeitschr. phys. Chem.* **33.** 353, 1900), " Change of Volume on Fusion " (M. Töpler, *Wied. Ann.* **53.** 343, 1894), " Viscosity of Salts in Aqueous Solution " (Jul. Wagner, *Zeitschr. phys. Chem.* **5.** 49, 1890), " Colour of Ions " (Carey Lea, *Sill. Am. Journ.* [3], **49.** 357, 1895), " Ionic Mobility " (Bredig, *Zeitschr. phys. Chem.* **13.** 289, 1894), etc. The relations between emission of light and atomic weight are dealt with in the last section of this chapter.

Attempts to find quantitative relations in this region have so far proved almost without result. It is, however, possible that so far properties have always been compared under arbitrary conditions of temperature and pressure, and that exact laws are not to be expected thus ; if, too, the elements have much more power of existing in several modifications than we know at present, this would introduce another factor of arbitrariness, as the comparison is made between the modifications that happen to be known to us. Thus we find the most marked regularity in the solid state, which offers the safest basis of comparison, as the density of solids varies but little with temperature, pressure, or even with change of molecular condition.

Isomorphism of the Elements.—The crystal forms of most elements are unknown, because they are difficult to obtain as well-defined crystals. On the other hand, the question whether two

[1] *Zeitschr. phys. Chem.* **61.** 183 (1908).

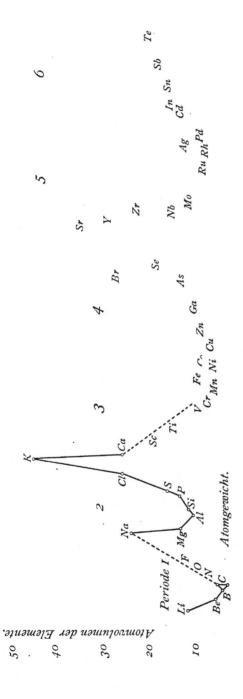

particular metals form mixed crystals with each other, *i.e.* are isomorphous (p. 173), can usually be settled with certainty. (For the methods employed, see Book IV. Chapter II. paragraph "Thermal Analysis.")

Tammann[1] has collected and discussed our knowledge of this phenomenon. It appears that, in general, elements of a natural group of the periodic system, and also such elements which are not far removed from each other in Staigmüller's arrangement (p. 184), can often form continuous series of mixed crystals with each other. At the same time, elements far removed from each other can sometimes form mixed crystals, especially when they are chemically similar, and have high melting-points.

Tammann puts forward the suggestion that elements, which form mixed crystals, could be built up in a similar way; in this connection it is significant that such elements show similar spectra (see below).

Significance of the Periodic System in the Table of Atomic Weights.—At first the establishment of the periodic system was regarded as a discovery of the highest importance, and far-reaching conclusions as to the unity of matter were expected from it; more recently a disparaging view has been taken of these noticeable, but unfruitful, regularities. One now often finds them underrated, which is intelligible enough, since this region, which especially needs scientific tact for its development, has become the playground of dilettante speculations, and has fallen into much discredit. It is all the more satisfactory that an intelligent and thorough investigation of this subject of fundamental importance in theoretical chemistry has begun anew.

The periodic system is of especial importance in settling atomic weights. Although the rules so far known do not possess—any of them—completely convincing validity, between them they give a striking proof that the choice of atomic weights underlying them is a happy one, and constitute a valuable indication in studying new or little known elements. It is usually possible to find the place of a new element in the periodic system by the analogies it shows to better known ones. Thus it was long doubtful whether beryllium had atomic weight $9 \cdot 08 = 2 \times 4 \cdot 54$ or $13 \cdot 62 = 3 \times 4 \cdot 54$; but only the former value fitted without strain into the periodic system, and since Nilson and Pettersson measured the vapour pressure of beryllium chloride and showed it to have, most probably, the formula $BeCl_2$, the lower atomic weight has been considered alone admissible. On the other hand, obvious gaps in the system lead to searches after new elements; scandium, gallium, and germanium, discovered since the establishment of the periodic system, have fitted in in this way. In such cases the chemical behaviour and some of the physical properties of

[1] *Zeitschr. anorg. Chem.* **53.** 446 (1907).

still unknown elements can be predicted—Mendelejeff did so for the metals just mentioned ; this must be regarded as a second *practical* consequence of knowing the relations between the atomic weights' of the elements and their properties. The periodic system, as may be seen from this, is of the greatest service to chemists as a mnemonic help in dealing with the huge mass of data in their science.

Besides the reasons mentioned above, there are other grounds for accepting the usual atomic weights as correct. The numerous recent measurements of molecular weight in solution have never led to contradiction with those values ; again dissociation has been shown to occur in many of the polyatomic gases, but never in those regarded as monatomic by the usual molecular theory.

The Spectra of the Elements.—At the end of this chapter we are forced to the question, in what way may we hope best to obtain a deeper insight into the nature and more intimate behaviour of these atoms, the relative magnitude of which we have already learned to determine by a number of distinct and safe methods. As far as we can judge at present, of all the physical properties, the consideration of the *spectra of the elements* offers altogether the best way to attack this problem.

An attempt to consider the phenomena of spectrum analysis, with even partial thoroughness, is of course beyond the limits of our task, which is to consider only those investigations which have served as a broader standpoint for the theoretical treatment of chemistry. But although spectrum analysis has been a great practical help in chemistry, and especially by its aid in the discovery of new elements, yet the hopes entertained of a theoretical explanation remain thus far unfulfilled. For this reason this section will give only a short summary concerning the emission spectra of the elements. Concerning the absorption spectra of organic compounds, another important class of spectrum phenomena, some reference will be made in a later chapter.

Irrespective of the so-called *phenomena of " luminescence,"* by which, after a proposal made by E. Wiedemann,[1] there is understood the property of certain substances of becoming luminous at *low temperatures,* from external conditions, as illumination (photo-luminescence), electric discharge (electro-luminescence of gases), chemical processes (chemico-luminescence), crystallisation (crystallo-luminescence), gentle heating (thermo-luminescence), etc. ; the normal development of light, *i.e.* light produced by the *heat movement of molecules,* and which we will consider exclusively in this section, is due to the *high temperature* of the substance emitting the light. According to Draper's law,[2] all solid and liquid substances radiate light of shorter wave-lengths

[1] *Wied. Ann.* **34**. 449 (1888).
[2] See the article by Pringsheim, *Zeitschr. f. wissenschaftl. Photographic,* **1**. 391 (1903).

with increasing temperature, and at about 525° they all begin to glow with a dark red light, then become bright red, and finally "white hot." If one observes this gradual increase in glow with a spectroscope, there appears at first the red end of the spectrum, which gradually stretches over to the violet end with increasing temperature. Thus all solid and liquid substances give *continuous spectra*; but the erbium and didymium earths give continuous spectra crossed by certain bright lines.

The glowing gases conduct themselves in a different, but a characteristic, way. These give out only, or at least mostly, *rays of a definite wave-length*; and therefore they give spectra, which consist of single bright bands sharply separated. According to the number and breadth of these bright bands, they are called *band-spectra* or simple *line-spectra*. Emission spectrum analysis, the introduction of which into science was the immortal work of Bunsen and Kirchhoff, and whose first-fruit was the discovery of several new elements, is based on this fact, viz. that under certain conditions of temperature and pressure every gas gives a definite, and, to a large degree, a characteristic spectrum. Therefore, in order to examine a substance by spectrum analysis,[1] it is necessary to bring it into the state of a glowing gas. For easily volatile substances, such as the salts of the alkalies, the flame of a Bunsen burner is sufficient; for substances volatile with great difficulty, one uses, according to the circumstances, the oxy-hydrogen blow-pipe, the electric spark, or the electric arc. As is well known, the production of monochromatic light, which is necessary for so many optical investigations, depends upon the selected rays emitted by incandescent gases. It should, however, also be pointed out that gases under high pressures can give continuous spectra. Thus, according to Frankland (1868), hydrogen, *e.g.* when burnt in oxygen under a pressure of twenty atmospheres, gives a continuous spectrum.

It cannot be doubted that each molecular species, whether representing isolated atoms or chemical compounds, has its own characteristic spectrum; but the question as to which particular molecular species corresponds to an observed spectrum, can be very rarely answered with certainty. The difficulties which are met are mainly due to the determination of the molecular condition of an incandescent gas; this is usually very much complicated at high temperatures where the capacity of the substance for reaction is apparently very much increased, and certainly is totally changed, and doubtless *the spectrum observed where a compound or even an element is volatilised, consists of the superimposed spectra belonging to different molecular species.* The dissociation phenomena, which, from all that is known, occur more

---

[1] For spectral analysis, see especially the review by Kayser in Winkelmann's *Handbuch der Physik*, Breslau, 1894, vol. ii. pp. 390-450. Of later work may be mentioned the extensive collection of references by Landauer, *Spektralanalyse*, Braunschweig, 1896.

often at high temperatures than under ordinary conditions, play an especially important *rôle*.[1] It is certain in many cases that the volatilised substance, by reaction with the gases of the flame or with atmospheric air, forms new molecular species, and although only very slight quantities of these may be present, yet such is the great sensitiveness of the spectroscope, that these may be sufficient to produce clearly recognisable lines. We have good reason for assuming that *single atoms give line spectra, and atomic complexes give band spectra.*

Regularities in the Distribution of the Spectral Lines of the Elements.

—Inasmuch as there is scarcely any reason to doubt that there is the most intimate dependence of emission spectra upon the configuration and state of vibration of the molecule and atom of a luminous substance, it requires only a glance at the laws (by which, on the one hand, the lines of the same substance arrange themselves in the spectrum, and by which, on the other hand, the arrangement varies with the substance), to hope that very soon, perhaps, we shall have further disclosures concerning the behaviour and the condition of movement of the atom. Although at present we are far removed from a thorough knowledge of the laws concerning the subject, yet already a beginning has been made which is worthy of attention, and which spurs us on to a continued search for the goal.

The most important result thus far obtained is in the calculation of the lines of the *first hydrogen spectrum* so-called, which is obtained by a Geissler's tube, for example, in which the pressure must not be too small. The peculiarly simple structure of this spectrum gives hydrogen a place apart from all the other elements; this is also clearly borne out by its position in the periodic system. As Balmer[2] discovered, the wave-length λ of each line can be calculated very accurately from the simple formula

$$\lambda^{-1} = A(1 - 4m^{-2}), \quad \text{or} \quad \lambda = \frac{1}{A} \cdot \frac{m^2}{m^2 - 4},$$

in which λ^{-1} denotes the vibration number; the successive numbers 3, 4, 5, etc., are to be substituted for m. By substituting in this formula the value 3647·20 of the constant $\frac{1}{A}$, for the calculated values corresponding to m, the following wave-lengths are obtained :—

---

[1] For example, water vapour above 3000° contains H_2O, H_2 O_2, H_2O_2, O_3, and probably also H and O in perceptible quantity. See Book IV. Chapters III. IV. V.

[2] *Wied. Ann.* **25**. 18 (1885).

THE HYDROGEN SPECTRUM

Line.	m	Calculated.	Observed.	Difference.
Hα	3	6564·96	6564·97	0·0
Hβ	4	4862·93	4862·93	0·0
Hγ	5	4341·90	4342·00	+ 0·1
Hδ	6	4103·10	4103·11	0·0
Hε	7	3971·40	3971·40	0·0
Hζ	8	3890·30	3890·30	0·0
Hη	9	3836·70	3836·80	+ 0·1
Hθ	10	3799·20	3799·20	0·0
Hι	11	3771·90	3771·90	0·0
Hκ	12	3751·40	3751·30	– 0·1
Hλ	13	3735·60	3735·30	– 0·3
Hμ	14	3723·20	3722·80	– 0·4
Hν	15	3713·20	3712·90	– 0·3

The wave-lengths in the "observed" column are taken from the latest measurements by Ames,[1] and are expressed in ten-millionths of a millimetre ; the correspondence between the wave-lengths observed and those calculated from Balmer's formula is very remarkable.

The preceding formula does not apply at all to the so-called *second hydrogen spectrum*. This consists of very numerous fine lines and appears to correspond to a lower temperature ; it is suspected that the two spectra belong to two different molecular conditions of hydrogen. It is possible that the discovery of further regular cases of this sort may be rendered difficult from the fact that the production of the spectra of other elements is due to the superimposition of spectra belonging to several different molecular conditions, and that their separation does not take place automatically, as in the case of hydrogen, where we obtain the first spectrum by itself.

Concerning the *relations which should exist between the spectra of allied elements*, it has been shown by Lecoq de Boisbaudran that the spectra of the alkali metals are displaced towards the red end of the spectrum with increasing atomic weight. Recently Kayser and Runge [2] volatilised a number of metals by means of the electric arc, and photographed their spectra by means of a Rowland concave grating ; the wave-lengths of the lines were exactly determined to within a hundred-millionth of a millimetre. They showed that the lines may be fairly well calculated by means of the formula

$$\lambda^{-1} = A - Bm^{-2} - Cm^{-4} ;$$

this formula is a generalisation of Balmer's formula ; yet although it

[1] *Phil. Mag.* [5], **30**. (1890) ; see also Cornu, *Journ. de phys.* [2], **5**. 341.
[2] *Wied. Ann.* **41**. 302 (1890), 43, 385 (1891), more completely in *Abh. d. Berl. Akad.*, 1890, 1891, 1892 ; collection of results on p. 200 of the section of Winkelmann's handbook quoted above. Rydberg put forward similar views independently of Kayser and Runge. See *Svenska Akad. Handl.* **23**. (1889-1891) ; *Wied. Ann.* **50**. 629 (1893) ; *Astrophysical Journal*, **6**. 233 (1897).

has two more constants than the other, the observations of the metals are not attended with the same degree of success as was the case with hydrogen. Moreover, it is not possible to obtain the spectrum of a metal by one formula like this; but it must be resolved into a number of series in order to calculate the values of the constants A, B, C.

Now it happens that for the elements of Mendelejeff's first group, the series (of which each element has several) consists not of lines, but of pairs of lines. Kayser and Runge distinguish the following series:—

1. The Principal Series: their pairs are the strongest lines of the spectrum, and are easily reversible, *i.e.* they appear dark when the vapour has a sufficient density.

2. The First Subordinate Series: strong but very hazy pairs of lines; they have a constant vibration difference.

3. The Second Subordinate Series: weaker pairs of lines, but better defined, with a constant vibration difference, as in 2.

The first pair of the principal series has also this same vibration difference: this difference is the most important spectroscopic constant of the element in question, and, as will appear in a moment, it seems to stand in a definite relation to the respective atomic weight. The principal series appears to be found only in the case of the alkali metals; the spectra of all other metals seem to consist only of secondary series; no series are found in the spectrum of barium; the spectrum of lithium seems to consist of only simple lines.

The elements that belong to the same vertical column of · the periodic system show an obvious similarity in the construction of their spectra. This is established at any rate for the first two groups and a part of the third; in the others it is as yet little known. These three groups can each be divided into two parts that show special chemical analogy; thus we have I. Li, Na, K, Rb, Cs; II. Cu, Ag; III. Mg, Ca, Sr; IV. Zn, Cd, Hg; V. Al, In, Tl. The relations inside each of these groups are particularly close, as may be seen from the following table. Within each group the spectrum is displaced towards the red by increase in atomic weight; but in passing from one group to the next, strongly towards the blue. The rules that hold are best seen from the numbers in the accompanying table, which give the constants A, B, C (multiplied by 10^8) for the first line of each pair or triplet in the subsidiary series:—

	Allied Series.			Allied Series.			ν	$\dfrac{\nu}{a^2}$
	A.	B.	C.	A.	B.	C.		
Li	28,587	109,625	1,847	28,667	122,391	231,700	...	...
Na	24,475	110,065	4,148	24,549	120,726	197,891	17	325
K	21,991	114,450	111,146	22,021	119,363	62,506	57	381
Rb	20,939	121,193	134,616	...	...	...	234	322
Cs	19,743	122,869	305,824	...	...	...	545	309
Cu	31,592	131,150	1,085,060	31,592	124,809	440,582	249	622
Ag	30,712	130,621	1,093,823	30,696	123,788	394,303	921	794
Mg	39,796	130,398	1,432,090	39,837	125,471	518,781	41	713
Ca	33,919	123,547	961,696	34,041	120,398	346,067	102	638
Sr	31,031	122,328	837,473	...	...	...	394	517
Zn	42,945	131,641	1,236,125	42,955	126,919	532,850	386	918
Cd	40,755	128,635	1,289,619	40,797	126,146	555,137	1159	929
Hg	40,159	127,484	1,252,695	40,218	126,361	613,268	4633	1161
Al	48,308	156,662	2,505,331	48,245	127,527	687,819	112	1534
In	44,515	139,308	1,311,032	44,535	126,766	643,584	2213	1721
Tl	41,542	132,293	1,265,223	41,506	122,617	790,683	7795	1879

These numbers show that A falls off with increase of atomic weight within each series—A being the frequency for $m = \infty$ or limiting frequency; *each series, therefore, is pushed towards the red end by increasing atomic weight.*

B and C are nearly the same for the lines of a pair or triplet belonging to the same series. The B values vary but little—especially those of the second series.

The constant difference between pairs (or the first two lines of triplets) in both series is given under the heading ν; in the last column this quantity is divided by the square of the atomic weight a. Within each of the five groups this quotient is *roughly constant, i.e.* the width of the pairs and triplets, measured in frequency of vibration, is approximately proportional to the square of the atomic weight within each group.

Series of subsidiary character have also been found in the spectra of oxygen and sulphur. The lines of the series are triplets.

There are likewise found in *the band spectra of the metalloids* certain regularities which are partially related to the preceding. Thus Deslandres[1] found that the distribution of the bands can be expressed by the formula

$$\lambda^{-1} = A + Bm^2 ;$$

when again " m " denotes the vibration number, and A and B

[1] *C.R.* **104.** 972 (1887); **106.** 842 (1888); **110.** 748 (1890); **112.** 661 (1891); *Ann. chim. phys.* [6], **14.** 5 (1888); *Journ. de phys.* [2], **10.** 276 (1890).

constants which are characteristic for the respective series of the element in question, λ denotes the wave-length of some *characteristic* line of the band which serves as its representative; thus the distribution of lines within any one band is given by the formula

$$\lambda^{-1} = a + bm^2,$$

where again "a" and "h" are constants. By making $m = 0$, we obtain the fundamental vibration of the' band, *i.e.* the line which, as stated above, was chosen by Deslandres to represent the band. This last rule requires that each of the bands belonging to the same series of an element shall show a manifest similarity as regards the number of their maxima and minima of brightness, and also as to their relative distances and arrangement; while the former rule requires just what was found to appear in the case of the line-spectra of the metals.[1]

As is obvious from what has preceded, the following law holds good, viz. *the farther we advance toward the violet (more refrangible) end of the spectrum, the closer do the lines approach each other*, so that the line-spectrum prevails almost exclusively at the ultra-violet end.

According to Riecke,[2] the difference between line and band spectra is that in the former the frequencies in the series form a simple progression, like those of a string or an organ pipe; the waves are therefore due to atomic or molecular vibrations similar to those of *linear systems*; while the vibrations of molecules producing band spectra are determined by three independent conditions, and are thus analogous to the vibrations of *bodies possessing extension in space*.

Reinganum[3] has pointed out that the relations of the constant A to the atomic volume are still more pronounced than those to the atomic weight a; in every vertical column of the periodic system, A is smaller the greater the atomic volume. An important criterion for the solution of the question, which series in the spectra of different elements correspond to each other, is the behaviour of the lines in question to the Zeeman effect.[4]

---

[1] Kayser and Runge found that carbon obeyed these rules approximately. (*Abhandl. d. Berl. Akad.*, 1899).

[2] *Lehrbuch d. Physik*, 3 edit. Bd. I. pp. 558 and 560 (1905).

[3] *Physik. Zeitschr.* **5.** 302 (1904).

[4] See Runge, *Ber. d. physik. Ges.* **5.** 313 (1904).

CHAPTER II

General Observations.—In the preceding chapter we have considered the properties of atoms; in this and the following chapter we will endeavour to obtain a mental picture of the molecular structures which are formed by the union of atoms. It cannot be denied that we depart from simple experiment at the outset: it would certainly be possible to construct a system of theoretical chemistry without speculations of this kind, and under the safe guidance of thermodynamics, but only in a very troublesome and unsatisfactory way, by which much important knowledge would remain hidden. "It is certainly an advantage that the laws of thermodynamics contain truths which cannot be shaken, since they do not rest upon any hypothesis of the constitution of substances. But if we therefore refrain from a more detailed investigation into the nature of substances, for fear of leaving the region of indisputable truths, we wilfully ignore a path leading to new truths." [1]

There are two very different ways which have led to conceptions of the molecular world.

On the one hand, an endeavour was made to derive many properties of molecules, and at the same time the properties of the substances formed from them, on purely mechanical principles. This was originally a purely deductive method; but afterwards, the necessity of bringing the properties of the substance into closer connection with those of the molecules led to a development of the method by inductive reasoning, as is common in all sciences. We regard it as the greatest result of this method of investigation, that it makes the nature of heat intelligible by means of simple kinetic conceptions.

On the other hand, the study of the innumerable carbon compounds led to thorough conceptions regarding the arrangement of the atoms in the molecule. The conjectures which at first were vague, soon assumed tangible form, and supported the work of investigators

---

[1] Van der Waals, *Kontinuität*, etc., p. 119. Leipzig, 1881.

so effectively that the fears that the hypotheses involved were too daring, became groundless in view of the undeniable results to which the hypotheses led : in this way arose *structural chemistry* and its consequence, stereo-chemistry.

In this chapter we will consider only the more physical side of the molecular theory, and on account of the limited space only the more important subjects will be noted. It should be noticed, as a matter of historical interest, that as early as 1740 Daniel Bernoulli developed conceptions regarding the behaviour of gases which were essentially identical with the views now universally entertained ; but it was not till 1845 that J.·J. Waterson presented before the London Royal Society a paper containing a very happy and complete development of the kinetic theory of gases. Unfortunately the paper at that time was not printed, and its publication was accomplished only lately by Lord Rayleigh,[1] who found it in the archives. Thus it happened that Kroenig in 1856, and Clausius in 1857, independently developed essentially the same views. After the fundamental ideas were thus clearly established, Clausius, Maxwell, Boltzmann, O. E. Meyer, van der Waals and others participated in the further development of the theory.

For the literature see O. E. Meyer, *Kinetic Theory of Gases*, in which weight is laid on simplicity of presentation and experimental proof; and especially Boltzmann, *Gas Theory*, i. and ii. (Leipzig, 1895-1898), which aims rather at the most exact working out of the fundamental hypotheses ; also the remarkable work of Clausius, *Mechanical Theory of Heat*, iii. (Braunschweig, 1889-1891), which unfortunately was never finished.

The Kinetic Theory of Gases.—This theory represents the first successful attempt to explain a number of the material properties of substance, by means of simple and clear assumptions on the nature of the molecule. The theory starts out by assuming that the molecule of a gas is indeed very small, but yet has *a certain finite extension*, so that the space occupied by the molecule itself, or by its sphere of activity, is very small as compared with the volume occupied by the gas as a whole. The molecules are separated by distances which are very *large* in comparison with their own size, and therefore exert no marked influence on each other. Only when they come very close to one another do *colliding* forces appear, and these at once cause them to separate ; or, in other words, the molecules conduct themselves on collision like *absolutely elastic* bodies.

Let us consider the path of any selected molecule ; this will continue to move with a certain *uniform* velocity, since it is not subject to the action of any force, until it collides with another molecule. After rebounding from this, it will, as a rule, move with a uniform velocity, but *changed* in direction and magnitude, till there follows

[1] *Phil. Trans.* **183**. 1 (1892).

another collision, etc. The path of a molecule will be a *zigzag*, the separate parts of which will be traversed with a velocity varying about a certain mean value. Thus the length of the "free path," *i.e.* the path traversed without colliding with any other molecule, is constantly subject to change; but when the external conditions are maintained constant, it varies about a definite mean value, viz. the "mean free path."

The *mean kinetic energy of the motion of translation* of any particular molecule amounts to $\frac{m}{2}u^2$ if "m" denotes its mass and "u" its mean velocity. But besides the energy of the motion, the molecule has a certain *internal* energy which is given by the kinetic energy both of the rotatory motion of the molecule, and also of the vibration of the atoms composing the molecule. The internal energy of a molecule is also assumed to be by no means constant, but to vary, in the course of time, about a certain mean value.

That pressure under which an enclosed volume of gas stands, and which it conversely exerts on the walls of the enclosing vessel, can be at once calculated from these assumptions without knowing anything more. It is caused by the blows of the molecules on the walls of the vessel as they strike and bound back from it; and it is obvious that, other things being equal, the number of these blows is proportional to the quantity of the molecules in unit volume, *i.e.* to the density of the gas. But this only amounts to saying that the pressure exerted by an enclosed quantity of gas must be inversely proportional to the space occupied by it, *which explains the Boyle-Mariotte law* (p. 38).

In order to calculate the pressure quantitatively, let us suppose a cube, the content of which represents unit volume, and the sides of which therefore represent unit area, to contain any selected quantity of a simple gas; let the mass of one molecule of the gas be "m," and the number of molecules be N; then the *density* of the gas will be represented by the equation

$$mN = \rho.$$

The mean square-velocity u^2 of the molecule determines the pressure exerted, as is easily seen; for both the force and the frequency of the blows of the gas molecules depend upon it. A molecule striking in a direction normal to a cube face will be thrown back in a reverse direction, but with the same velocity, and its momentum therefore changes sign; the total change in momentum caused by the collision being

$$2mu.$$

Now if we denote the number of molecules striking the cube wall in unit time by ν, then the pressure exerted on unit of surface amounts to

$$p = 2mu\nu.$$

In order to calculate ν, let us imagine the irregular movement of the molecules to be arranged in order, for an instant; and during this time, let them all move in the same direction, at right angles to one of the sides of the cube, and with the mean velocity u; then during this moment the number of molecules which will bound back from the wall, provided the external conditions remain constant, will be

$$Nu,$$

and it is obvious that during this time this wall only will be subjected to the total pressure exerted by the gas. But, as a matter of fact, this total pressure distributes itself between the six cube faces in the movements actually taking place; then in reality we shall obtain [1]

$$\nu = \frac{Nu}{6},$$

and the pressure sought therefore will be

$$p = \frac{1}{3}Nmu^2 = \frac{1}{3}\rho u^2.$$

From this equation we can calculate the mean velocity u for all sorts of gases. For example, let us consider a quantity of hydrogen enclosed in 1 c.c. at 0° and under atmospheric pressure; the weight of this amounts to 0·00008988 g. and the pressure exerted by this upon 1 sq. cm. amounts to 1033·3 g. weight, or 1033·3 × 980·6 absolute units (980·6 = gravity acceleration).

Thus the value of u is found to be

$$u_0 = \sqrt{\frac{3 \times 1033 \cdot 3 \times 980 \cdot 6}{0 \cdot 00008988}} = 183,900\frac{cm.}{sec}.$$

According to this the hydrogen molecules move with a velocity which averages about the enormous mean value of 1·84 kilometres per second. Since, according to Avogadro's rule, ρ is proportional to the molecular weight M, we can find the velocity for other gases by the formula

$$u_0 = 183,900\sqrt{\frac{2 \cdot 016}{M}}\frac{cm.}{sec.} = \frac{261,100}{\sqrt{M}}.$$

We observe that u·is independent of the pressure; but u increases with increasing temperature; and since p is proportional to the absolute temperature, then $\frac{m}{2}u^2$, *the mean kinetic energy of the translatory motion, is proportional to the absolute temperature; and conversely the mean kinetic energy of the molecules of a gas is a measure of the temperature.*

The Rule of Avogadro.—Let us compare two different gases at the same temperature and pressure; and let us denote by N_1, m_1, and

[1] This conclusion can really be based upon more satisfactory reasoning (p. 207 of the above-quoted work of Boltzmann).

u_1 the number of molecules in unit volume, their mass, and their mean velocity respectively for one gas, and similar values for the other gas by N_2, m_2, and u_2 respectively; then the common pressure p of both gases, by the formula (p. 200), must amount to

$$p = \frac{1}{3}N_1 m_1 u_1{}^2 = \frac{1}{3}N_2 m_2 u_2{}^2 \qquad . \qquad . \qquad . \qquad (1)$$

Now, experiment shows that by mixing different gases at the same temperature and pressure, there occurs no change of pressure or temperature; the different molecular species preserve their kinetic energy unchanged after the mixture. We might make the very improbable assumption that one kind of molecule gains as much kinetic energy as the other loses, on mixture; but even this assumption is contradicted by experience, for each gas in a mixture exerts (*e.g.* on a semipermeable partition) the same pressure as if the others were not there, and that would not be possible if the addition of another gas affected its kinetic energy. Hence the mean kinetic energy of the two kinds of molecules after mixing is $\frac{1}{2}m_1 u_1{}^2$ or $\frac{1}{2}m_2 u_2{}^2$ respectively. But as the two gases are in thermal equilibrium they must have the same mean kinetic energy, else, according to the laws of collision of elastic spheres, an interchange of energy would occur. Therefore we find that

$$\frac{1}{2}m_1 u_1{}^2 = \frac{1}{2}m_2 u_2{}^2 \qquad . \qquad . \qquad . \qquad . \qquad (2)$$

and accordingly from (1) and (2)

$$N_1 = N_2 \qquad . \qquad . \qquad . \qquad . \qquad (3)$$

That is, unit volumes of all the different gases, at the same temperature and pressure, contain the same number of molecules; or the molecular weights of gases have the same ratio to each other as their densities. Thus the law of Avogadro follows from the standpoint of the kinetic theory, a result of fundamental importance for physical chemistry, since its conclusions are largely based on Avogadro's law.

The Ratio of the Specific Heats.—As already pointed out, the heat content of 1 g.-mol. of a gas having the molecular weight M, consists of the energy of the progressive motion of the molecule $\left(= \frac{M}{2}u^2 \right)$, plus the energy of the internal movements of the molecule. If we denote the increase of the internal energy per degree of temperature by E, then the specific molecular heat at constant volume C_v (see p. 48) will be

$$J C_v = \frac{1}{2}M\frac{u^2}{T} + E;$$

and the specific molecular heat at constant pressure will be

$$JC_p = \frac{1}{2}M\frac{u^2}{T} + E + \frac{1}{3}M\frac{u^2}{T},$$

in which

$$\frac{1}{3}M\frac{u^2}{T} = \frac{pv}{T}$$

refers to the external work performed ; J is the mechanical equivalent of heat ; the ratio of the two specific heats is given by the equation

$$\frac{C_p}{C_v} = k = \frac{\frac{5}{6}M\frac{u^2}{T} + E}{\frac{1}{2}M\frac{u^2}{T} + E}.$$

Inasmuch as E, from necessity, has a positive value, k must always be less than $\frac{5}{3} = 1\cdot667$; and k approaches this limiting value only when E is very small. If, on the other hand, E becomes very great, then k approaches the value 1. These anticipations are most perfectly established by experiment, as the following table shows :—

	k			k
Mercury	1·666		Chloroform	1·10
Oxygen	1·404		Methyl ether	1·113
Nitrogen	1·410		Ethyl ether	1·029
Ammonia	1·30			

In only one case, viz. that of mercury, in which k was measured by Kundt and Warburg [1] by the "dust figure" method (p. 50), does the ratio of the specific heats reach its upper limit ; but mercury is a monatomic gas, and it was therefore to be expected a priori that, in this case, the internal kinetic energy would have an infinitesimal value compared with the energy of progression. This brilliant coincidence between anticipation and experiment is one of the most beautiful results of the kinetic theory of gases.

In case of the other gases studied, k is always smaller than 1·667, and in general it falls below this upper limit, i.e. the internal energy is larger as compared with the external energy, just in proportion as the number of atoms in the molecule increases ; and this is in accord with the theoretical explanation, that as a molecule becomes more complicated, a greater fraction of the heat introduced will be used in increasing the kinetic energy of the atoms in the molecule : thus in the case of ethyl ether, the relative difference between the specific heats is very small in comparison with their absolute magnitudes.

The molecular heat at constant volume may thus be calculated for monatomic gases, for which $E = 0$, in absolute measure ; it is

---

[1] Pogg. Ann. **157**. 353 (1876).

$$C_v = \frac{M}{2} \frac{u^2}{T}. \quad \text{But } u^2 = \frac{(261,100)^2 T}{273 \times M}, \text{ therefore}$$

$$C_v = \frac{(261,100)^2}{2 \times 273} \text{ absolute units}$$

$$= \frac{(261,100)^2}{2 \times 273 \times 41.89 \times 10^6} = 2.981 \text{ cal.}$$

Direct measurement of $C_p/C_v = 1.666$ for mercury vapour, together with the relation $C_p - C_v = 1.985$ (p. 48), gives $C_v = 2.980$. The remarkable agreement of these numbers is, of course, only another version of the test of theory already given. Lord Rayleigh, it is well known, found the ratio of the specific heats 1.667 for the newly discovered gaseous elements, helium, argon, etc., from which, by analogy with mercury, they were concluded to be monatomic. This is in accord with their position in the periodic system (p. 180).

The Mean Length of the Free Path.—The kinetic theory of the gaseous state has in a similar way led to a clearer conception concerning a number of other properties of gases, and in particular has thrown light upon the *properties of diffusion, internal friction, and conduction of heat.* All of these properties can be explained by the backward and forward motion of the gas molecules; these motions cause the impinging layers of gases of different composition to mingle with each other (ordinary diffusion); they also bring about the equalisation of the different velocities of the various gas molecules (internal friction), and thus effect the exchange of kinetic energy (conduction of heat). These three properties appear to be very closely related; we may define the first as the diffusion of matter, the second as the diffusion of momentum, and the third as the diffusion of kinetic energy (heat).[1]

Each one of these three processes has a very close dependence upon the "mean free path," L, of the molecule, which, according to Clausius, is calculated to be

$$L = \frac{\lambda^3}{\frac{4}{3} \pi s^2},$$

where we denote by λ the mean distance of the supposedly spherical molecules; by λ^3, the cube which in cross-section contains a molecule; and by s, the distance of the centres of gravity of two molecules on collision, *i.e.* when at the nearest approach that they can make to each other. The free path is inversely proportional to the number of molecules in unit volume, *i.e.* it is inversely proportional to the density of the gas. In deriving this formula, it is presupposed that s is small compared with L, and also that the same (mean) velocity of progressive motion is to be ascribed to the molecules. If we do not make this

---

[1] See Maxwell, *Theory of Heat*, chap. xxii.

last assumption, then in the preceding formula, according to Maxwell, in establishing his law of distribution, we obtain $\sqrt{2}$ instead of $\frac{4}{3}$; (*i.e.* 1·41 instead of 1·33).

The first determination of a mean free path was made by Maxwell (1860), who obtained for the value of η, *i.e.* the internal friction of a gas, the equation

$$\eta = \frac{L\rho\frac{12}{13}u}{\pi},$$

where ρ denotes the density, and $\frac{12}{13}u$ denotes the mean velocity cal-culated from the law of distribution. Later, the mean free path was calculated from the conductivity of heat (Maxwell and Clausius), and from the diffusion of gases (Maxwell and Stefan), and in all cases the values found by these different methods coincided with each other, at least approximately.

Thus O. E. Meyer [1] calculated these values at 20°, and 760 mm. pressure, for the following substances :

		L
Hydrogen	. . . . .	0·000185 mm.
Methane	. . . . .	0·000085 ,,
Carbon monoxide	. . . . .	0·000098 ,,
Carbon dioxide	. . . . .	0·000068 ,,
Ammonia	. . . . .	0·000074 ,,

The Maxwell law of distribution is this : out of N molecules of a gas, the number whose velocity lies between v and v + dv at any moment is

$$4\sqrt{\frac{27}{8}}\frac{Nv^2}{u^2}e^{-\frac{3v^2}{2u^2}}dv;$$

where u is the molecular velocity already calculated (p. 200), and thus expresses the velocity corresponding to the mean kinetic energy of the molecules. The chief fault of this law is that its complexity makes it almost impossible to carry out extensive numerical calculations based on kinetic concepts.

Thus the theory of neither thermal conduction nor diffusion can be regarded as complete. The only certainty is that the coefficient of heat conduction K takes in the kinetic theory a form

$$K = \kappa\eta c_v,$$

where κ is a numerical factor (probably depending on the ratio of the specific heats), and c_v is the specific heat of the gas. This relation is proved by Schleiermacher (*Wied. Ann.* **36**. 1889, p. 346).

The following remarkable result is due to Maxwell. L being inversely proportional to the density of the gas, the viscosity η, and consequently the

---

[1] *Kinetische Theorie der Gase*, Breslau, 1877, p. 142.

thermal conductivity K, is independent of the density. Unlikely as this appears at first sight it is fully confirmed by experience. No one who grasps the order of these thoughtful conclusions and their exact experimental confirmation would decide to give up the kinetic theory until some other self-contained theory of the phenomena appears.

For two gases of equal molecular weight and equal viscosity the coefficient of diffusion is found to be

$$D = \frac{\eta}{\rho};$$

e.g. CO_2 and NO_2 gave 0.089, whilst the calculated value from $\eta = 0.000160$ and $\rho = 0.00195$ is 0.082. The general theoretical treatment of gaseous diffusion involves great difficulties (see the above-mentioned work of Boltzmann quoted on p. 198).

Kinetic Theory and Heat.—The preceding developments of the kinetic theory have led to an extremely simple conception of the nature of heat. The heat content of a body, in whatever state of aggregation, is given by the total kinetic energy of its molecules; the kinetic energy is made up of the energy of motion of the molecules (or rather of their centres of gravity) and of their internal energy; the latter includes both the energy of rotation of the whole molecule, and especially also the energy of vibration of the atoms composing the molecule. The external energy of all substances, whether gaseous or otherwise, increases with the temperature; at absolute zero $(-273°)$ the motion of the molecules ceases—the material undergoes the "heat death." The irregular motion of molecules, which corresponds to the heat-content of a substance, does not therefore differ in principle from the regular motion of a body; for example, from a motion where all the molecules of a body are displaced with the same velocity and in the same direction through space, the body thus being moved as a whole.

From a purely practical point of view, however, there is a very great difference—for example, when we wish to apply the kinetic energy of a substance in regular or irregular motion to the production of work. For imagine kinetic energy to be supplied in two ways to a given body: first in the form of regular motion, when the body as a whole will receive a certain definite velocity of progression or rotation; and secondly in the form of irregular motion (heat), when the separate molecules of the body are given velocities of progression and rotation which differ in magnitude and direction, or, in other words, when the temperature is raised a certain amount dependent on the specific heat. It is not difficult to convert the first kind of energy into work, or to apply it to heat another body; up to the present, however, it has been found quite impossible to convert the total energy of the irregular motion into a given amount of work, to transform it, for example, completely into the energy of progressive motion of another body. This could be, of course, easily accomplished by a being able to take away from each separate molecule its energy of motion, just as we can take away the energy of motion of a sufficiently large body, although not from molecules which are imperceptible to our senses. If we cool the original body by means of suitable intermediate substances, and thus remove the imparted heat, we can at any rate partly convert the latter into energy of progressive motion. In this way the kinetic theory gives us a clear idea of the mutual convertibility of heat and external work, and just as the first law of the mechanical theory of heat, namely, the indestructibility of matter and equivalence of heat and work, follows at once from the kinetic conception of heat as kinetic energy, so the marked difference (in the present state of experimental art) between the values of kinetic energy of regular (microscopic) and irregular (molecular) motion leads to the law of limited convertibility of heat into external work—*i.e.* the second law of the mechanical theory of heat.

The second law was derived from kinetic conceptions by Boltzmann (see his book, mentioned on p. 198). It is extremely important to notice that by this means we can arrive at a fairly clear form of the entropy function mentioned on p. 27. Boltzmann showed, namely, that the *entropy of a gas is proportional to the logarithm of the probability of its condition.* Every isolated system naturally tends towards the most probable condition, and hence in every spontaneously occurring and irreversible change, the system will pass from a condition of small, to one of higher, probability. Boltzmann's law shows clearly that entropy must increase in every irreversible process (p. 27).

In recent times the kinetic theory has received strong support from the detailed investigations of the so-called Brownian movement. In the year 1827, the English botanist Brown (*Edin. Phil. Jour.* **5.** 358 (1828), *Phil. Mag.* **4.** 101 (1828), **6.** 161 (1829)) found that very small particles suspended in a liquid are subject to peculiar vibratory movements. This phenomenon was afterwards observed by a number of investigators; Zsigmondy showed that it was common to all colloidal solutions (chap. xii.); he observed further that when the particles were extremely small (with diameters less than about 4 μ), they undergo besides the vibratory a translatory motion, which is more pronounced the smaller the particle. The cause of the phenomenon was for a long time not understood, although different authors had supposed it to depend on the heat motion of the molecules. An exact kinetic theory was first developed by Einstein in 1905 (*Ann. d. Physik.* [4], **17.** 549 (1905); **19.** 289 (1906); more simply in *Zeitschr. f. Elektrochem,* **14.** 235 (1908)); this enabled the phenomenon to be quantitatively examined, and its causes to be definitely determined. The results of the theory were tested in various ways; Svedberg, for example (*Zeitschr. f. Elektrochem,* **12.** 853 (1906)), investigated the connection between the amplitude of the suspended particles and the viscosity of the solvent; Seddig (*Physik. Zeitschr.* **9.** 465 (1908)) determined the influence of the temperature on the magnitude of the amplitudes: by using values found by other methods for the absolute size of molecules (chap. xiii.) a satisfactory agreement with experiment was obtained. It can therefore be taken as proved that the Brownian movement is caused directly by the heat motion of the molecules. From this point of view, we must assume that a particle suspended in a liquid receives impulses on all sides from the rapidly moving molecules of the liquid.

According to the theory of probability, the resultant of all these forces will not in general be zero; the particle will therefore be set in motion, and the smaller it is, the fewer molecules will hit it simultaneously, and therefore the less will be the probability that the resultant of the forces is zero; hence the smaller the particle, the more lively is its motion.

The Brownian movement gives us, therefore, to a certain extent, a rough picture of molecular motion; we cannot follow the motion of a single molecule of the liquid, but we get an idea of the combined action of a large, but certainly *finite*, number of these molecules.

The Brownian movement gives us a possible way of converting heat into work, in contradiction to the second law; for invisible irregular motion is changed into visible regular motion. Of course we can only talk of regular motion when we consider only one, or at any rate very few suspended particles; when this number exceeds a certain amount, the motion is altogether as irregular as that of the molecules themselves. But it is of interest to note that the Brownian movement indicates the lower limit of the validity of the second law, which loses its importance (for sufficiently short times) even in spaces large enough to be easily comprehended by our senses with the help of optical instruments.

There is still another way by which we have recently obtained ocular demonstration of the irregular movement of molecules. On the basis of Maxwell's law of distribution, we must assume that different points in a gas are at different temperatures (velocity of molecules), have different densities, etc., provided that a sufficiently small space is under consideration. These irregularities can only be demonstrated under special conditions, namely, in the neighbourhood of the critical point (*cf*. p. 64) (*v. Smoluchowski, Ann. d. Phys.* [4], **25**. 205 (1908)). In a gas, for example, which is under its critical pressure, and at a temperature only slightly above its critical temperature, there will be small spaces in which the temperature will be so far under the mean value, that the critical point is reached, and local liquefaction takes place. This partial liquefaction at a point just above the critical point is shown by cloud formation, or opalescence, and has, in fact, been long observed by different investigators. Conversely, when a liquid is warmed to the critical point, it becomes turbid just before the meniscus vanishes, for, owing to the irregular velocities of the liquid molecules, the conditions for the gaseous state become realised at isolated points.

In the face of these *ocular* confirmations of the kinetic theory of the molecular world, we may well acknowledge that the theory begins to lose its hypothetical character.

The Behaviour of Gases at Higher Pressures.

—When we reduce a gas, by the application of great pressure, to a density comparable to that of the liquid state, the gases repudiate the gas laws entirely (as was shown on p. 53), and we are met with the important problem of accounting for the necessary modifications in the latter. This was studied with extraordinary success by van der Waals;[1] his theoretical explanation of the deviations, shown by strongly compressed gases, from the Boyle-Mariotte law, has given in a surprising way an indication of the nature of the liquid state.

The accepted view of the kinetic gas theory serves as the guiding idea. In ascribing the pressure exerted by the gas on the walls to the bombardment of the molecules in their backward and forward movement, two assumptions were made : firstly, that the whole space of the enclosing vessels is utilised by the moving molecules, or, in other words, the volume actually occupied by the molecules is very small in comparison with the whole volume ; and secondly, that the molecules exert no very great reciprocal action on each other. · These two assumptions, of course, would be realised at a great attenuation of a gas, and they would become less exact the nearer the molecules were brought together. Thus it is necessary to introduce the influence of these two factors into the gas equation

$$pv = RT.$$

We must, under all circumstances, hold fast to the assumption that the kinetic energy of the translatory motion of the molecule is proportional to the absolute temperature, and is independent of the particular nature of the molecule in question. Then a spatial extension of the molecules will cause a contraction of their "play space," and they will strike the wall *so much the oftener*. In consequence of this, the pressure exerted will be *greater* than that calculated from the gas formula, and, indeed, the pressure will be increased in the same ratio that the mean free path is shortened from the spatial extension of the molecules. In this way van der Waals found that, as a result of the increase of the volume of the molecule, the pressure would apparently increase in the ratio $\dfrac{v}{v-b}$; where "b," the so-called "volume correction," is *fourfold as large as the volume of the molecules.* Apparently "b" diminishes somewhat when the molecules are very close to each other ; but the important question of the rate of decrease needs further study.

Moreover, there are attracting and repelling forces active between the molecules as they approach each other in compression. From the experimental fact, discovered by Joule and Thomson (1854), that strongly compressed gases are noticeably cooled by expansion which takes place without doing work against external pressure, it is to be inferred that the expansion performs work against the action of molecular forces, *i.e. the molecules attract each other.* Therefore we must ascribe a certain *cohesion* to gases also, and this will be the more noticeable the greater their density. Regarding the mode of action

---

[1] *Kontinuität der gasförmigen und flüssigen Zustandes.* German trans. by F. Roth. Leipzig, 1881 ; 2nd ed., Leipzig, 1899.

of this molecular attraction, many facts lead in common to the conception that *these forces are active only when the molecules are very near each other*, and that they quickly vanish on their separation from each other.   The fact that the gas molecules do *not* agglomerate into one mass in spite of their attraction, and of their being separated by only empty space, must be ascribed to the heat motion which resists a diminution of volume, and acts like a repulsive force.   Thus likewise the moon, though attracted to the earth, does not fall upon it, because its centrifugal force, resulting from its circular motion, resists the attraction, and exactly compensates it, at least in finite time.

A molecule in the interior of a gas mass experiences, on the whole, no attractive force, because the molecules are distributed around it in homogeneous density, while a molecule existing in the surface is attracted inwards.   This attraction acts against the momentum of the blow with which the molecules strike the wall : *thus from the molecular attraction there results a diminution of the pressure acting outwards.* Without a knowledge of the law governing the decrease of molecular attraction with distance, we may make the following remarks on the relation between this diminution of pressure and the density of the gas.

If we consider a part of the surface, then the force attracting it inwards will be proportional to the number of molecules in the interior, *i.e.* to the density of the gas ; but, on the other hand, this force is also proportional to the number of molecules existing in the part of the surface considered, and this also increases with the density ; hence the *attraction sought varies directly with the square of the density, or inversely with the square of the volume of the gas mass.*   If we denote by p_0 the pressure of the gas, corresponding to its density and the kinetic energy of its molecules, and by p the effective pressure of the gas mass as actually measured by the manometer, then we have—

$$p_0 - p = K = \frac{a}{v^2},$$

where " a " denotes a constant which refers to the molecular attraction of the gas, and where K denotes the molecular pressure.

The Equation of van der Waals.—If we introduce into the gas equation (p. 40), in place of the volume occupied by the gas mass, the volume corrected for the space actually occupied by the molecules, and instead of the pressure actually exerted by the gas mass, the pressure which would exist if there were no molecular attraction, then the equation assumes the form

$$\left(p + \frac{a}{v^2}\right)(v - b) = RT.$$

This is van der Waals' *characteristic equation*, which also applies to

P

the liquid state, as will appear in considering the kinetic theory of liquids.

Now the formula given above with three constants shows, in a remarkable way, the dependence of any given gas mass upon the pressure, volume, and temperature. If we consider the case where a gas is compressed at constant temperature, experiment shows that Boyle's law holds good for large volumes ; and, as a matter of fact, for large values of the volume v, both the corrections are infinitesimally small. As we pass over to conditions of greater pressure, gases in general are compressed more easily than they should be to correspond with Boyle's law ; this is explained on the supposition that in compression the molecules are drawn more closely together by their attractive force, which thus tends to aid the action of external pressure. At very great compression, on the other hand, gases resist a diminution of volume more strongly than they should to correspond with Boyle's law ; the reason for this is, on the one hand, that, with a slight change of volume, the quantity $\frac{a}{v^2}$ increases very slowly ; and, on the other hand, the "volume correction," which acts in the sense just considered, begins to be an important factor, and becomes more so the nearer " v " approaches " b " by compression.

Amagat found (p. 53), in a series of gases (nitrogen, methane, ethylene, and carbon dioxide), that the product pv, instead of remaining constant as it should, according to Boyle's law, at first began to decrease, and afterwards increased very strongly : this is very well explained by the formula of van der Waals.

A picture of the degree of quantitative coincidence is shown in the following table, in which are given the values of pv as calculated by Baynes [1] for ethylene according to the formula

$$\left(p + \frac{0.00786}{v^2}\right)(v - 0.0024) = 0.0037(272.5 + t),$$

and the corresponding values of pv observed by Amagat :—

TABLE FOR ETHYLENE

v	1000 pv		p	1000 pv	
	Obs.	Calc.		Obs.	Calc.
31·58	914	895	133·26	520	520
45·80	781	782	176·01	643	642
72·86	416	387	233·58	807	805
84·16	399	392	282·21	941	940
94·53	413	413	329·14	1067	1067
110·47	454	456	398·71	1248	1254

[1] van der Waals, *l.c.* 101.

The pressures are estimated in atmospheres; the measurements are referred to t = 20°.

But hydrogen, which Regnault called a "more than perfect gas" (*gaz plus que parfait*), shows at the very first that, at ordinary temperatures,[1] it resists compression more than corresponds to Boyle's law, at least in the region thus far covered by experiment; thus if $p = 2\cdot21$ and $p_1 = 4\cdot431$ m. of mercury pressure, we obtain

$$\frac{pv}{p_1v_1} = 0\cdot9986.$$

It follows from this that even at these low pressures the volume correction of this gas is of greater influence than the molecular attraction. If one assumes "a" to be infinitesimally small, then from the preceding figures "b" is calculated to be $0\cdot00065$. It must therefore be inferred from van der Waals' interpretation of the volume correction, that at 0°, and under 1 m. pressure of mercury, the molecules of hydrogen, as a matter of fact, occupy only $\dfrac{0\cdot00065}{4} = 0\cdot00016$ of the apparent volume. We must therefore conclude that, even under the greatest pressures possible, hydrogen could not be compressed so as to occupy less space than $\frac{1}{7000}$th of what it occupies at 0° and under 1 m. pressure.

Finally, it must be emphasised that the van der Waals' formula may claim to hold good *only when the gas experiences no change in its molecular condition as its volume changes*; for the theory advanced above provides that the molecules, even under the highest degrees of condensation, must remain single individuals, and not unite to form larger groups. It cannot be stated *a priori* whether or not this occurs in particular cases, but the accuracy of the formula makes this very probable. Deviations of this sort from Boyle's law, which are shown by certain gases, are to be ascribed to the polymerisation of the molecules in the case of an increase, or to dissociation in case of a decrease, of pressure; such deviations, which can reach a value of quite a different order of magnitude, cannot of course be explained by van der Waals' equation of condition. The explanation of this will be found in the laws of dissociation, in the third and fourth books.

If we consider the dependence of the pressure, at constant volume, upon the temperature, then by applying the equation of condition to two temperatures, T_1 and T_2, there is obtained

$$\left(p_1 + \frac{a}{v^2}\right)(v - b) = RT_1,$$

---

[1] Wroblewski found that at very low temperatures even hydrogen began to show evidence of a diminution of the value of pv.— *Wiener Monatshefte*, **9.** 1067 (1888).

and

$$\left(p_2 + \frac{a}{v^2}\right)(v - b) = RT_2 ;$$

and by subtraction there is obtained

$$\frac{p_2 - p_1}{T_2 - T_1} = \frac{R}{v - b}.$$

Since there are no quantities on the right side of the equation which change with the temperature, the increase of the pressure also for highly compressed gases is proportional to the increase of the temperature; and, indeed, the pressure increases more rapidly than in the case of the ideal gases, *i.e.* more than $\frac{1}{T}$ per degree, since instead of $\frac{R}{v}$ as in the case of ideal gases, we have here $\frac{R}{v - b}$. This is also substantiated by experiment, and proves, therefore, that neither a nor b change very much with the temperature. It is of course assumed that there is no change of molecular condition associated with the temperature.

It was noticed in the third edition of this book that van der Waals' equation can be reduced to apply to perfect gases, and used to obtain an exact value of the gas constant R (see also Leduc, *C.R.* **124**. 285, 1897). This has been done meanwhile by Guye and Friedrich (*Arch. scien. phys. nat.* **9**. 505, 1900) as follows. For $p = 1$ atm. and $T = 273$, van der Waals' equation becomes

$$\left(1 + \frac{a}{v_0{}^2}\right)(v_0 - b) = R . 273,$$

where v_0 is the volume of a mol of gas under normal conditions, whilst the equation

$$p_0 V_0 = RT$$

gives the volume V_0 of an ideal gas under normal conditions. Hence

$$V_0 = v_0\left(1 + \frac{a}{v_0{}^2}\right)\left(1 - \frac{b}{v_0}\right),$$

or, accurately enough,

$$V_0 = v_0\left(1 - \frac{b}{v_0} + \frac{a}{v_0{}^2}\right).$$

In this way the above authors found for V_0 the value 22·41, while D. Berthelot (cf. p. 41) found similarly 22·412.

The Kinetic Theory of Liquids.—The views advanced by van der Waals to explain the behaviour of gases under great pressure lead to some very remarkable conclusions respecting the liquid condition. It has been already inferred from the critical phenomena which make it possible to transform the two states into each other without interruption (p. 65), that the molecular condition in the two is not very different; and, in fact, the following considerations lead also to this same conclusion.

According to the original hypothesis advanced for the case of ideal gases, the mean kinetic energy of the translatory motion of the molecule (in distinction from the kinetic energy contained in their atoms), is proportional to their absolute temperature, but independent of their nature; this hypothesis can now be also applied to gases of any desired density; we will next consider the consequences resulting from assuming that it also holds good *for liquids*.

In the light of this hypothesis, we come at once to the view that on account of the great velocity of the molecular movement (p. 200), and the very close approximation brought about by the condensation of the gas, the molecules must collide with each other very often, and therefore must exist under a very great partial pressure. But there results from this very active movement a tendency of the individual molecules to separate from each other; this tendency manifests itself unmistakably, not only in the vapour pressure, but also in the resulting property of liquids of filling a space completely with their molecules by way of evaporation; but it seems very small in comparison with the enormous expansive force of gases compressed gradually into liquids. The further question therefore at once arises, what hinders the liquid molecules, on account of their active movement, from separating from each other explosively? or, in other words, how is the enormous partial pressure held in check?

An answer to this question may be found by the assumption of an attractive force between the molecules which it was found necessary to introduce in explaining the behaviour of gases at high pressures. It was shown (p. 209) that this force of attraction vanished [*i.e.* was counterbalanced] in the case of molecules existing in the interior, and manifested itself only in the case of molecules at or near the bounding surface, inasmuch as the force gave a resultant perpendicular to the surface. Now the resultant directly counteracts the expansive force resulting from the heat motion of the molecules, and thus appears suited to hold this in equilibrium. In general a molecule coming from within, to the free surface, will be held back by the molecular attraction, and so will be retained within the liquid mass. Only those molecules which by chance reach the free surface with a very great velocity will be able to free themselves from the control of the molecular forces, and thus *to evaporate*. If there is a free space above a liquid this will always become filled with its molecules, but it must be noticed that the pressure of the evaporated molecules in the gaseous state cannot pass a certain maximal limit. For, conversely, those molecules in the gaseous state, which approach too near the surface of the liquid, will at once be drawn in by the molecular attraction; and thus there results a continual exchange between the liquid and gaseous parts of the system.

Obviously the pressure of the gaseous molecules can only go on increasing till the number of molecules striking upon and retained by unit area of the surface in unit time, is the same as the number of molecules passing from the liquid to the gaseous part of the system through the bounding surface; it is also easily seen that this maximal pressure must be independent of the relative amounts of the gas and liquid, and therefore corresponds in every respect to the *saturation pressure* of the liquid (Clausius, 1857).

Only those molecules can evaporate from the liquid which have a kinetic energy greater than the mean, since only these can overcome the molecular attraction. The mean kinetic energy of the liquid molecules must therefore be *diminished* by evaporation ; that is to say, the evaporation is attended with an absorption of heat, which of course is in accord with experiment.

Moreover, the phenomena exhibited by the surface tension of liquids (p. 56) can be ascribed to molecular attraction. In order to bring a molecule from the interior part into the free surface, work must be expended against the attractive force : it follows directly from this that a force must be overcome in order to produce a free surface, namely, the surface tension, and that the free surface of a liquid tends to reduce itself to a minimum.

The way to obtain quantitative results from the preceding considerations is obvious. The following formula of van der Waals

$$\left(p + \frac{a}{v^2}\right)(v - b) = RT$$

holds good both for a simple homogeneous gas and for a simple homogeneous liquid. In both cases a refers to the molecular attraction ; b refers here to the correction to be made for the total volume of the liquid, resulting from the contracted "play space" of the molecules. Now the constants a and b can be determined from the behaviour of gases under high pressure, and thus the theory leads to the surprising result, that from the behaviour of the gas as a gas we can quantitatively derive its behaviour when it is condensed into a homogeneous liquid.

Let us test the requirements of the preceding law by some special practical example. Thus van der Waals, from the compressibility of gaseous carbon dioxide, calculated the value of a to be $0 \cdot 00874$, and b, $0 \cdot 0023$, when the atmospheric pressure is the unit of pressure, and the unit of volume is the volume containing 1 g. of a gas at $0°$ and under 1 atm. pressure. We then have $\frac{1}{M}$ mol of gas and

$$\left(p + \frac{0 \cdot 00874}{v^2}\right)(v - 0 \cdot 0023) = \frac{R}{M}T.$$

If we make p and v both equal to one, then T will equal 273, and there follows for $\frac{R}{M}$ the equation

$$273\frac{b}{M} = (1 + 0.00874)(1 - 0.0023) = 1.00646,$$

and we thus obtain for the equation of condition of carbonic acid,

$$\left(p + \frac{0.00874}{v^2}\right)(v - 0.0023) = 1.00646\ \frac{273 + t}{2.3},$$

where t denotes the temperature on the ordinary Celsius scale. This formula represents very satisfactorily the observations made by Regnault and Andrews on the compression of gaseous carbon dioxide. Let us also see whether the formula represents the behaviour of liquid carbon dioxide.

For this purpose we will calculate a series of isothermals for different temperatures, putting the above equation into the more convenient form

$$p = \frac{1.00646}{v - 0.0023} \cdot \frac{273 + t}{273} - \frac{0.00874}{v^2},$$

and substituting various values of v, whilst t is kept the same. Thus for t = − 1.8 we get

v	p	v	p
0.1	9.37	0.008	38.8
0.05	17.47	0.005	20.9
0.015	39.9	0.004	42.0
0.01	42.6	0.003	457.0

Here p at first increases with decrease of v, reaches a maximum (for about v = 0.01), decreases, and finally increases rapidly.

For this purpose we will plot the curves, corresponding to the definite temperatures t, on a system of co-ordinates where the abscissæ represent volumes, and the ordinates represent the corresponding pressures. These curves are the so-called "isotherms," and are shown in Fig. 18. On studying these we are impressed by the fact that above 32.5° only one pressure corresponds to one volume, i.e. the latter is determined unequivocally by the former. *But below this temperature, within the limits of a pressure interval* (which is marked by a heavy curve for the isotherm of 13.1°), *for the same particular pressure there correspond three different volumes.* At first glance this would appear to be absurd. But we know that at these vapour pressures, and only at these pressures, the same substance is capable of occupying two different volumes, one as a homogeneous gas, and the other as a homogeneous liquid; but what is indicated by the third? Of course to suggest the volume of the substance in the solid state is out of the question. The van der Waals' formula does not consider this.

The matter will become clearer by considering this in the light of experiment.   The behaviour of gaseous and liquid carbon dioxide was studied very exactly by Andrews for those temperatures the isotherms of which are plotted.   Let us consider, for instance, the isotherm corresponding to 13·1°.   Andrews found, by beginning with small pressures and large volumes, that the gaseous carbon dioxide could be condensed to volume v_0 and pressure p_0, corresponding exactly to the path of the curve.   The constants a and b, as in the van der Waals' formula, were so determined as to make the compressibility of the

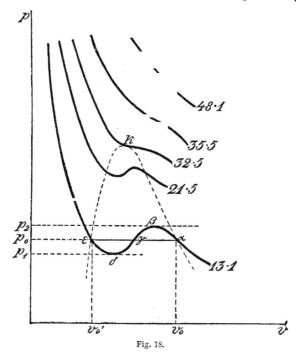

Fig. 18.

gas coincide as well as possible with the calculation.   That these constants may, as a matter of fact, be so chosen has been previously shown (p. 210).   But when the pressure was made greater than p_0, the diminution of volume did not correspond to the pressure of the advancing curve a β γ δ ϵ, but there occurred a partial liquefaction, corresponding to the vapour pressure of carbon dioxide at 13·1°.   The pressure remained constant until the volume of the saturated vapour had fallen from v_0 to the volume of the liquid v_0', i.e. until the whole of the substance was condensed.

After this any further diminution of volume was attended by an increase of pressure, and a very great increase too, as must be the case from the magnitudes of the coefficients of compression of liquids.

Beyond ϵ, Andrews found the path as given by the rest of the curve ; beyond ϵ, the figures of the formula go hand in hand with those of observation, and the rapid ascent of this part of the curve, as compared with that part before a, is due to the fact that liquid carbon dioxide is much less compressible than the gaseous form.

The formula rejects only the part of the curve from a to ϵ. Instead of passing from the first point to the second by the serpentine path a β γ δ ϵ, investigation shows that the substance passes from the condition at a to that at ϵ by the direct line. The formula does not hold good here. The substance from a to ϵ is not homogeneous ; it is part gas and part liquid. The formula is applicable to both gaseous and liquid forms, but it insists that each shall be homogeneous. The process of gradual liquefaction is such that the adequacy of the formula must be temporarily interrupted, and it is interrupted.

The question now arises whether it is possible to realise the portion of the curve a β γ δ ϵ, $i.e.$ whether it is possible to change a gas into a liquid isothermally and continuously. A glance shows this to be improbable ; for in the part of the curve β γ δ, an increase of pressure would be attended with an increase of volume, and conversely a decrease of pressure with a decrease of volume ; thus the substance would appear to be in an unstable form, the realisation of which is impossible.

But the first portions of the curves a-β and δ-ϵ can at any rate be realised. These portions represent respectively the conditions of supersaturated vapour and of over-heated liquid. In the first case, the pressure is in fact greater than p_0, and the volume less than v_0 ; and there can be no doubt that the conditions of a vapour after saturation represent a continuance of those before saturation. Thus the fact that the advance of a sound wave in a saturated vapour gives no evidence of interruption, shows conclusively that the vapour conducts itself in a normal way in the compression associated with supersaturation. On the other hand, the part of the curve ϵ-δ expresses the capacity of a liquid for existing in a labile condition under a lower pressure than that corresponding to the vapour pressure of the respective temperature, as shown by many observations.

The further study of the curves plotted in Fig. 18 shows also that the three volumes (at which carbon dioxide can exist at the temperature in question, and designated by the points a γ ϵ, for the temperature $13 \cdot 1°$), approach each other with increasing temperature, and finally at the isotherm corresponding to $32 \cdot 5°$ coincide in the point k. If we connect the points corresponding to a and ϵ, for the other isotherms ($i.e.$ the points where liquefaction begins and ends with increasing pressure), we obtain the dotted siphoidal (*bergförmige*) curve shown in the figure. The isotherm of $32 \cdot 5$ is tangential to this at the point k. The serpentine curve a β γ δ ϵ here is crowded together into a point ; the physical interpretation of this obviously is that the specific volume of the liquid carbon dioxide is the same as that of the gaseous carbon dioxide condensed to this vapour pressure. Here, and here only, is it possible to convert the gas into a liquid continuously and iso-thermally, and the reverse ; k corresponds to the critical point of carbon dioxide (p. 65).

We thus arrive at the conclusion, that by the aid of the con-stants a and b, of van der Waals' formula, all the critical data can be obtained. For this purpose we need only to plot a few isotherms until we arrive at the clearly marked k, where the curve portions α, β, γ, δ, ϵ are crowded together in one point of inflection.

We can obtain the same result more simply and easily by the analytical discussion of the van der Waals' formula,

$$\left(p + \frac{a}{v^2}\right)(v - b) = RT ;$$

or solved for v :

$$v^3 - \left\{b + \frac{RT}{p}\right\}v^2 + \frac{a}{p}v - \frac{ab}{p} = 0.$$

The equation is of the third degree for v. Then if the three roots are x_1, x_2, and x_3, we will have, as is well known,

$$(v - x_1)(v - x_2)(v - x_3) = 0.$$

The roots may be real and imaginary. Of course only the first have any physical significance. Since the product of the three $(v - x)$ values is real, then either two or none of the roots can be imaginary, because it is only by the product of two imaginary quantities that a real quantity can result. Therefore for one value of p at a given temperature there are either one or three values of v. This is seen at once from an inspection of Fig. 18 on p. 216. Thus above 32·5°, in general, for one value of p there is only one value of v. For lower temperatures, as at 13·1°, for example, in general the case is similar, and it is only in the interval from p_1 to p_2 that there may be three values of v for one of p.

The critical point k sought is that where the three real roots become equal to each other, i.e. if ϕ_0 denotes the critical volume, it must follow that

$$x_1 = x_2 = x_3 = \phi_0 ;$$

and it follows also that

$$(v - \phi_0)^3 = v^3 - \left\{b + \frac{R\theta_0}{\pi_0}\right\}v^2 + \frac{a}{\pi_0}v - \frac{ab}{\pi_0}.$$

In this equation π_0 denotes the critical pressure, and θ_0 the critical temperature. And since the coefficients of the different powers of v must be equal, we obtain the following equations :—

$$\phi_0{}^3 = \frac{ab}{\pi_0},$$

$$3\phi_0{}^2 = \frac{a}{\pi_0},$$

$$3\phi_0 = b + \frac{R\theta_0}{\pi_0}.$$

These, when simplified, give

$$\phi_0 = 3b \; ; \quad \pi_0 = \frac{a}{27b^2} \; ; \quad \theta_0 = \frac{8}{27}\frac{a}{bR}.$$

Thus the constants a and b in the equation given above determine the critical volume ϕ_0, the critical pressure π_0, and the critical temperature θ_0, and in this way are found the co-ordinates and the point k of the curve tracing, and also the particular isotherm in which k falls.

The critical temperature of carbon dioxide was calculated from the values for "a" and "b," assumed above, to be $273° + 32·5°$; while Andrews, by direct observation, found $273° + 30·9°$. The critical pressure was calculated to be 61 atm., while Andrews found 70 atm. by observation; and the theoretical critical volume was $0·0069$, while Andrews observed $0·0066$.[1]

Of course conversely, "a" and "b" can be calculated from the critical data, a fact of great importance in practical work. Thus the fact that the critical data can be calculated so approximately by the deviations of gases from Boyle's law, harmonises with the remarkable fruitfulness of van der Waals' theory, as already mentioned.

By calculating the molecular volume $\frac{b}{4}$ from the critical data, there is obtained this simple result, viz. that at their respective boiling-points and at atmospheric pressure *the molecules of the most various liquids, such as water, ether, carbon disulphide, benzene, chlor-ethane, ethyl acetate, sulphur dioxide,* etc., *occupy a space very nearly* $0·3$ *times the total apparent volume.* (See Chapter V., Molecular Volumes.)

Finally, let us calculate the superficial molecular tension K, which resists the expansive force resulting from the heat motion of the molecules; and from the preceding, we have

$$K = \frac{a}{v^2}.$$

Liquid carbon dioxide at $21·5°$ takes up about $0·003$ of the volume occupied by the substance as a gas at $0°$ under atmospheric pressure. From this K is calculated to be 970 atm., and this value indicates the enormous forces of pressure which are met here. These pressure forces have thus far eluded a direct determination.

The Reduced Equation of Condition.—The combination of the general equation of condition, viz.—

---

[1] Guye and Friedrich give a valuable collection of numerical data on critical pressures and temperatures (*Arch. sci. phys. nat.* **9.** 505 (1900); reference in *Zeitschr. phys. chem.* **37.** 380, 1901).

$$\left(p + \frac{a}{v^2}\right)(v - b) = RT,$$

with relations derived as above, between the critical data of a substance on the one hand, and the constants "a" and "b" on the other hand, has led to a very simple result. By introducing into the equation of condition the following values derived on p. 219, viz.—

$$a = 3\pi_0\phi_0{}^2,$$

$$b = \frac{\phi_0}{3}, \quad \text{and}$$

$$R = \frac{8}{3}\frac{\pi_0\phi_0}{\theta_0};$$

then instead of the constants a, b, and R, there appear the critical data, thus

$$\left(p + \frac{3\pi_0\phi_0{}^2}{v^2}\right)\left(v - \frac{\phi_0}{3}\right) = \frac{8}{3}\pi_0\phi_0\frac{T}{\theta_0}.$$

By dividing the left and right side of the equation by $\frac{\pi_0\phi_0}{3}$, we obtain

$$\left(\frac{p}{\pi_0} + \frac{3\phi_0{}^2}{v^2}\right)\left(3\frac{v}{\phi_0} - 1\right) = 8\frac{T}{\theta_0}.$$

Now if we make, as follows :—

$$\pi = \frac{p}{\pi_0}; \quad \phi = \frac{v}{\phi_0}; \quad \theta = \frac{T}{\theta_0},$$

we obtain

$$\left(\pi + \frac{3}{\phi^2}\right)(3\phi - 1) = 8\theta.$$

That is, by expressing the pressure, volume, and temperature respectively in fractions of the critical pressure, volume, and temperature, the equation of condition assumes the same form for all substances.

If one plots the values of π and ϕ for a definite value of θ in a system of co-ordinates, where the abscissæ represent values of ϕ, and the ordinates values of π, isotherms are obtained similar in form to those plotted in Fig. 18 (p. 216), and which will hold good for all substances. Thus, for example, for $\theta = 1$, when $\pi = 1$ and $\phi = 1$, this isotherm passes through the critical point.

The pressure divided by the critical pressure we will call the *reduced pressure*, in accordance with van der Waals; and also the respective quotients of the volume by the critical volume, and of the temperature by the critical temperature, we will call the *reduced volume* and the *reduced temperature*. Such reduced pressures, volumes, and temperatures, when identical are better called *corresponding* for short, and we may speak of two substances whose pressures, volumes, and temperatures "correspond" in the sense of what precedes, as being in a *corresponding state.*

It is not at all easy to form a conception of the *boldness* of this equation, which claims to express the general behaviour of all homogeneous liquid and gaseous substances, as regards their changes in pressure, temperature, and volume (excepting of course where these changes result in a chemical reaction, such as polymerisation, or dissociation). Therefore it will be useful to follow out some application of this equation which will serve at the same time as an illustration and a proof.

Application of the Theory of Corresponding States.—If we solve the following equation :—

$$\left(\pi + \frac{3}{\phi^2}\right)(3\phi - 1) = 8\theta,$$

for ϕ, we shall obtain

$$\phi = f(\pi, \ \theta),$$

in which the function f is the same for all substances. By raising the temperature from θ_1 to θ_2, the expansion produced at constant pressure π will amount to

$$\phi_2 - \phi_1 = f(\pi, \ \theta_2) - f(\pi, \ \theta_1).$$

Dividing both sides of the equation by

$$\phi_1 = f(\pi, \ \theta_1),$$

and observing that

$$\phi = \frac{v}{\phi_0},$$

we obtain

$$\frac{v_2 - v_1}{v_1} = \frac{f(\pi, \ \theta_2) - f(\pi, \ \theta_1)}{f(\pi, \ \theta_1)}.$$

Here v_1 and v_2 denote the specific volumes of the fluid according to the ordinary standards, and therefore the fractional expansion, experienced by the substance on raising the temperature, is equal to the quotient given, viz.—

$$\frac{v_2 - v_1}{v_1}.$$

The right side of the equation is independent of the special nature of the substance, and therefore the left must be so also ; *i.e. the fractional expansion, experienced by the most diverse liquids or gases, will be the same when they are heated, at a constant corresponding pressure, from one corresponding temperature to another.*

By means of this relation we can calculate the specific volume of any selected liquid at all temperatures, if its critical temperature, and also if its specific volume at some one temperature are known, inasmuch as we can compare it with any other liquid which is already well investigated. Such a liquid, for example, is fluor-benzene, the specific volumes of which have been measured up to its critical point ($\theta = 560°$).

Thus the specific volume of ethyl ether at $10°$ above the freezing-point of ice is $1\cdot3794$; suppose that we wish to calculate its value at $33\cdot8°$. For this purpose we calculate the two absolute temperatures, expressed in fractions of the critical temperature ($467\cdot4°$) :

$$\theta_1 = \frac{273 + 10}{467\cdot4} = 0\cdot6055,$$

and

$$\theta_2 = \frac{273 + 33\cdot8°}{467\cdot4} = 0\cdot6564.$$

The specific volumes of fluor-benzene at the temperatures θ_1 and θ_2, *i.e.* at the absolute temperatures

$$T_1 = 560\ \theta_1 = 339\cdot1,$$

and

$$T_2 = 560\ \theta_2 = 367\cdot6,$$

are $1\cdot0339$ and $1\cdot0741$ (p. 227), in absolute units ; the relative increase in volume of fluor-benzene, in consequence of a rise in temperature from $339\cdot1°$ to $367\cdot6°$ (abs.), amounts therefore to

$$\frac{1\cdot0741 - 1\cdot0339}{1\cdot0339} = 0\cdot0389.$$

Now this is the required increase of the volume of ether, and therefore its specific volume at $33\cdot8°$ amounts to

$$1\cdot3794 \times 1\cdot0389 = 1\cdot4331,$$

which is very close to the value as determined by experiment, $1\cdot4351$.

All the preceding specific volumes are measured at atmospheric pressure, which, strictly speaking, does not give the same reduced or corresponding pressure ; since the critical pressure of fluor-benzene is about 20 per cent greater than that of ether, then in the calculation the specific volume of the former should be measured at $1\cdot2$ atmospheric pressure ; but this is insignificant in view of the very slight compressibility of liquids. In general, in this sort of calculation of liquid volumes, *the atmospheric pressure can be regarded as one which is corresponding for all liquids.*

In a precisely similar way we derive the result that the percentage diminution of volume experienced by the most diverse substances, whether liquid or gaseous, is the same when one corresponding pressure is raised to another, the corresponding temperature remaining constant.

The coefficient of compression (*i.e.* the diminution of volume of one c.c. resulting from raising the external pressure one atmosphere) for ether amounts to $0 \cdot 00011$ at $0°$.   Now, according to the preceding law, the coefficient of compression for all liquids, at corresponding temperatures, must be inversely proportional to the critical pressure. Thus, the compression coefficient for chloroform, for instance, is calculated to be

$$0 \cdot 00011 \frac{36}{55} = 0 \cdot 000072,$$

55 and 36 atm. being the critical pressure for chloroform and for ether respectively.   This refers to the value of chloroform at a temperature of about $40°$, corresponding with that of ether at a temperature of $0°$, since the absolute critical temperature of ether, increased by about one-seventh of its amount, gives that of chloroform.   Observations at this temperature gave about $0 \cdot 000076$.

Amagat has given (*C.R.* **123**. 30, 83, 1896) a particularly clear test of the law of corresponding states.   If isothermals of two substances are drawn in such a way as to take for units of volume and pressure the critical values, the two series of curves must fit, *i.e.* in combination they must look as if they belonged to one substance : no two such reduced isothermals can cut, however close they may lie.   Without knowing the critical values, this can be tested by drawing the isothermals in the usual manner (not reduced) and seeing if it is possible to alter the scale so as to bring the isothermals to form a series without intersection.   Amagat accomplished the change of scale by projecting one diagram on the other with (nearly) parallel light ; the diagram to be projected was at the same time turned round one or other axis in order to alter the relative proportions of ordinates and abscissæ ; by a combination of the two changes, any derived change of scale could be arrived at.

C. Raveau (*J. de phys.* [3], **6**. 432, 1897) reached the same object by an even simpler and more ingenious means.   He plotted the logarithms of the volumes and pressures as co-ordinates ; now the unit of pressure or volume can be altered by merely adding a constant quantity to the logarithm ; it must therefore be possible to make the two diagrams fit by merely displacing one relatively to the other.

Amagat and Raveau both find a remarkably close fit between the diagrams of various substances [C_2H_4, CO_2, $(C_2H_5)_2O$, air], *i.e.* a striking confirmation of the theory of corresponding states.

To test further how far the special form of the function f $(\pi, \phi, \theta) = 0$, given by van der Waals, is applicable, Raveau drew a diagram of isothermals, using the logarithms of p and v from that equation.   It appeared that this diagram would not fit those for carbon dioxide and acetylene without intersections extending to somewhat widely separated isothermals. This shows—in harmony with the preceding—that van der Waals' formula is only an approximation to the truth ; it naturally deviates more from the truth the smaller v, and consequently the greater the correction terms $\frac{a}{v^2}$ and $\frac{b}{v}$.

It was remarked by Meslin (*C.R.* **116**. 135, 1893) that the theorem of corresponding states must be true for any characteristic equation that contains only as many constants as there are determining quantities (*i.e.* three-volume temperature and pressure), and which includes the critical point. For it is always possible to put the equation with three constants, a, b, R,

$$f(p, v, T, a, b, R) = 0$$

into the form

$$f(p, v, T, \pi_0, \phi_0, \delta_0) = 0,$$

as was done with van der Waals' equation on p. 221.

Since this equation must hold independently of the units adopted, and on the other hand it is not possible, without a fresh condition, to express one of the three determining quantities in terms of the other two, it follows that the equation must have the form

$$f\left(\frac{p}{\pi}, \frac{v}{\phi}, \frac{T}{\theta}\right) = 0 ;$$

hence the equation can contain nothing characteristic of the particular substance considered except the critical constants, *i.e.* can only contain numerical constants. For the conditions that such an equation must satisfy see Brillouin (*J. de phys.* [3], 2.·113, 1893).

The Coexistence of Liquid and Vapour.

—As has been repeatedly emphasised, both the original and the reduced equations of condition apply only to *homogeneous* substances, whether liquid or gaseous. They cease to hold true as soon as there occurs a partial evaporation or partial condensation of the liquid in question, and, therefore, the equation has nothing to say regarding the substance as soon as it has lost its homogeneity through evaporation or condensation ; such magnitudes as vapour pressure, boiling-point, volume of the saturated vapour, or of the liquid, lie beyond the region of its applicability.

If we consider an isotherm, such, for instance, as that plotted by van der Waals' equation for 13·1° in Fig. 18 (p. 216), we shall seek in vain for any marked point which indicates the beginning of liquefaction ; but we know this much from what precedes, viz. that for a vapour pressure p_0 there correspond three points of the curve, viz. a, γ, and ϵ. But, nevertheless, a simple thermodynamic law gives us the position of the straight line a-ϵ. Thus we can imagine a gas mass to be carried from a to ϵ by the path a-β-γ-δ-ϵ, and back again by the straight path ϵ-a to the original point. The sum of the work performed *by* the system and *upon* the system in this reversible and isothermal cyclic process must be equal to zero (p. 19). But since the former refers to the area bounded by a-β-γ and the straight line a-γ, and the latter to the area bounded by γ-δ-ϵ and the straight line γ-ϵ, *then these two areas must be equal to each other, and the line a-ϵ must be chosen so as to satisfy this condition* (Maxwell, 1875 ; Clausius, 1880). To be sure, we cannot regard this as a strict proof, since it is impossible to realise the cyclic process, but, nevertheless, the law appears very probable from this consideration. It should be again emphasised here that there has entered into the problem a purely thermodynamic element which is foreign to what was originally a *purely kinetic* theory.

The equality of the area embraced within the three straight lines av_0, vov_0', $v_0'\epsilon$, and the curve $\alpha\text{-}\beta\text{-}\gamma\text{-}\delta\text{-}\epsilon$, with the area embraced within the same three lines and the straight line $\alpha\text{-}\epsilon$, gives the following new relation, which is independent of the nature of the substance, viz.—

$$F(\pi, \theta, \phi_1, \phi_2) = 0,$$

in which π denotes the reduced vapour pressure, θ the reduced boiling-point, and ϕ_1 and ϕ_2 the reduced volumes of the liquid and the saturated vapour. This equation also, like that developed on p. 220, expresses a natural law of unusually wide application, since it requires that the nature of the function $F(\pi, \theta, \phi_1, \phi_2)$ shall be *the same for all substances.*

Although we can make no use of its special nature, we will briefly show this function because of its universal importance. The equality of the two areas just described requires that

$$\int_{v_0'}^{v_0} pdv = p_0(v_0 - v_0'),$$

or, by substituting in accordance with the equation of condition,

$$p = \frac{RT}{(v - b)} - \frac{a}{v^2},$$

we have, on integrating,

$$RT \ln\frac{v_0 - b}{v_0' - b} + \frac{a}{v_0} - \frac{a}{v_0'} = p_0(v_0 - v_0').$$

By dividing both sides by $\pi_0\phi_0$, and by substituting the values of "a" and "b" (p. 220) by the critical data, and introducing the reduced pressure, volume, and temperature, the preceding equation becomes

$$\left(\pi + \frac{3}{\phi_1\phi_2}\right)(\phi_2 - \phi_1) = \frac{8}{3}\theta \ln\frac{3\phi_2 - 1}{3\phi_1 - 1},$$

in which

$$\pi = \frac{p_0}{\pi_0}, \quad \phi_1 = \frac{v_0'}{\phi_0}, \quad \phi_2 = \frac{v_0}{\phi_0}, \quad \text{and } \theta = \frac{T}{\theta_0},$$

and denote respectively the corresponding values of the reduced condition, and by which the nature of the universal function mentioned above is explained.

Moreover, apart from establishing the equation,

$$F(\pi, \theta, \phi_1, \phi_2) = 0 \quad . \qquad . \qquad . \qquad . \qquad (1)$$

the universal equation of condition (p. 220) when applied to the case

Q

of a saturated vapour, and again to a vapour in equilibrium with a liquid, gives the two following new relations, viz.—

$$\left(\pi + \frac{3}{\phi_1^2}\right)(3\phi_1 - 1) = 8\theta \qquad . \qquad . \qquad . \qquad (2)$$

$$\left(\pi + \frac{3}{\phi_2^2}\right)(3\phi_2 - 1) = 8\theta \qquad . \qquad . \qquad . \qquad (3)$$

By eliminating π and ϕ_2 from equations (1) and (3), then π and ϕ_1, and finally ϕ_1 and ϕ_2, we obtain the three following equations, viz.—

$$\phi_1 = f_1(\theta),$$
$$\phi_2 = f_2(\theta),$$
$$\pi = f_3(\theta),$$

in which again the three functions $f_1(\theta)$, $f_2(\theta)$, and $f_3(\theta)$, are independent of the nature of the substance in question.

If we estimate the temperature in fractions of the critical temperature, then the specific volumes of the saturated vapours of all substances form a *constant temperature function*, provided that we estimate the volumes in fractions of the critical volumes, and that this holds good for both the volumes of liquids, and also for their vapour pressures.

We may formulate this law thus: at equally reduced boiling-points, the respective quotients, of the specific volume of the saturated vapour by the critical volume, of the specific volume of the liquid by the critical volume, and of the vapour pressure by the critical pressure, are identical for all substances.

Of course, according to this law, the reduced specific volumes of the vapour and liquid of the most diverse substances must be the same *when they are compared with each other at equal fractions of the critical pressure.*

The Demonstration by Young.—These laws have been subjected to a thorough test by S. Young.[1] Unfortunately, space does not permit us to give completely the material brought together in his work, which is an example of a problem subjected to complete theoretical and experimental treatment, and deserves the more attention because it has a fundamental and universal significance, as is illustrated by few problems in the whole extent of physics or chemistry.

The method proposed by Young consisted in the comparison of the specific volumes of different substances in the liquid state and the state of saturated vapour, as well as in the comparison of their vapour pressures, with the corresponding values afforded by a suitable "normal" substance in the "corresponding states." Fluor-benzene may be recommended as an example which has been very well studied. Below are given its complete data as an important basis for future calculations:—

[1] *Phil. Mag.* [5], **33.** 153 (1892).

FLUOR-BENZENE

Mol. Wt. = 95·8.

T	p ǀ	Mv$_0$	Mv$_0'$	Obs. vapour density Calc. ,, ,,
				...
272·27	20	...	91·47	...
289·3	50	...	93·20	
303·9	100	...	94·92	
320·25˙	200	...	96·80	
338·75	400	...	99·05	...
358·1	760	...	101·59	...
367·3	1,000	22,000	102·90	1·037
382·0	1,500	15,000	105·10	1·056
393·25	2,000	11,400	107·00	1·073
410·4	3,000	7,680	110·03	1·107
423·8	4,000	5,785	112·64	1·138
434·85	5,000	4,634	114·98	1·166
444·25	6,000	3,857	117·06	1·193
452·8	7,000	3,298	119·14	1·217
460·4	8,000	2,871	121·19	1·247
473·6	10,000	2,265	125·04	1·300
484·95	12,000	1,862	128·80	1·349
499·7	15,000	1,447	134·64	1·431
519·7	20,000	1,009	145·08	1·600
536·0	25,000	733	158·40	1·818
544·5	28,000	601	169·35	2·011
550·0	30,000	516	179·40	2·206
555·0	32,000	440	193·0	2·450
559·55	33,912	270·4	270·4	3·79

The vapour pressure p is expressed in millimetres, the molecular volumes of the saturated vapour Mv$_0$ and of the liquid Mv$_0'$ in c.c. The critical data of the substances investigated, measured partly by Young alone, and partly together with Ramsay, are given in the following table : [1]—

CRITICAL DATA

Substance.	Formula.	Mol. wt.	θ_0	π_0	ϕ_0
Fluor-benzene . .	C_6H_5F	95·8	559·55	33,912	2·822
Chlor-benzene . .	C_6H_5Cl	112·2	633·00	33,912	2·731
Brom-benzene . .	C_6H_5Br	156·6	670·00	33,912	2·059
Iodo-benzene . .	C_6H_5I	203·4	721·00	33,912	1·713
Benzene . . .	C_6H_6	77·84	561·50	36,395	3·293
Carbon tetrachloride	CCl_4	153·45	556·15	34,180	1·799
Stannic chloride .	$SnCl_4$	259·3	591·70	28,080	1·347
Ether . . .	$(C_2H_5)_2O$	73·84	467·40	27,060	3·801
Methyl alcohol .	CH_3OH	31·93	513·00	59,760	3·697
Ethyl alcohol .	C_2H_5OH	45·90	516·10	47,850	3·636
Propyl alcohol .	C_3H_7OH	59·87	536·70	38,120	3·634
Acetic acid . .	CH_3CO_2H	59·86	594·60	43,400	2·846

[1] *Phil. Mag.* [5], **34.** 505 (1892).

The critical volumes are not observed directly, but are extrapolated by the rule of Cailletet and Mathias;[1] according to this, the arithmetical mean between the densities of the liquid and of the saturated vapour diminishes linearly with the temperature. By the extrapolation of these mean values to the critical temperature we obtain the critical data.

The table on the following page contains an extract from the calculations of Young. The first three horizontal columns contain the comparison of the respective substances (given in column I.) with fluor-benzene at the *corresponding temperatures*, which are given under the horizontal column marked θ; the *absolute temperatures* of fluor-benzene are found in the horizontal column marked T; the second column (marked II.) contains the molecular volume of the saturated vapour of the substance divided by that of fluor-benzene; the third column (marked III.) contains the molecular volume of the substance in a liquid state divided by that of fluor-benzene; the fourth column (marked IV.) gives the vapour pressure of the substance divided by that of fluor-benzene; the sixth column (marked VI.) contains the boiling-points of the substance at the *reduced pressure* π, divided by that of fluor-benzene, referred to the same reduced pressure, while under p are given the actual vapour pressures of fluor-benzene.

[1] *C.R.* **102**. 1202 (1886).

[TABLE

TABLE OF COMPARISON

I.	II.	III.	IV.	V.	VI.
CH_3COOH	0·894, 8·818, 8·745, 0·681, 0·631.	0·6215, 0·6198, 0·6191, 0·6171, 0·6204, 0·6310	0·476, 0·708, 0·859, 1·008, 1·190, 1·280		1·1278, 1·1151, 1·1045, 1·0905, 1·0718, 1·0626
C_3H_7OH	2·678, 1·714, 1·216, 0·943, ...	·7748, 0·7661, 0·7633, 0·7711, ...	..., 0·323, 0·573, 0·810, 1·028, 1·124		1·0997, 1·0432, 1·0117, 0·9904, 0·9690, 0·9592
C_2H_5OH	2·076, 1·414, 1·028, 0·763, ...	0·5971, 0·5895, 0·5861, 0·5859, ...	..., 0·409, 0·681, 0·962, 1·253, 1·411		1·0494, 1·0061, 0·9801, 0·9577, 0·9347, 0·9223
CH_3OH	1·244, 0·945, 0·729, 0·572, ...	0·4136, 0·4087, 0·4048, 0·4047, ...	..., 0·678, 0·966, 1·259, 1·583, 1·762		1·0127, 0·9859, 0·9667, 0·9485, 0·9260, 0·9168
$(C_2H_5)_2O$	1·101, 1·083, 1·054, 1·030, ...	..., 1·0297, 1·0279, 1·0302, 1·0357, ...	..., 0·740, 0·761, 0·785, 0·804, 0·798		0·8411, 0·8394, 0·8370, 0·8343, 0·8353
$SnCl_4$	1·336, 1·316, 1·300, 1·262, ...	1·2657, 1·2744, 1·2775, 1·2797, 1·2913	0·706, 0·778, 0·805, 0·821, 0·828, 0·828		1·0679, 1·0633, 1·0667, 1·0585, 1·0574, 1·0575
CCl_4	0·828, 0·895, 0·938, 0·977, ...	..., 1·0273, 1·0280, 1·0257, 1·0281, ...	1·460, 1·206, 1·117, 1·066, 1·029, 1·008		0·9699, 0·9774, 0·9826, 0·9864, 0·9910, 0·9939
C_6H_6	0·842, 0·885, 0·923, 0·926, 0·940	0·9457, 0·9487, 0·9489, 0·9481, 0·9499, 0·9400	1·338, 1·200, 1·144, 1·114, 1·088, 1·073		0·9890, 0·9932, 0·9963, 0·9987, 1·0015, 1·0035
C_6H_5I	1·272, 1·298, ..., ..., ...	1·2761, 1·2782, 1·2777, ..., ..., ...	0·985, 0·998, 0·997, ..., ...		1·2302, 1·2889, 1·2890, ...
C_6H_5Br	1·174, 1·201, 1·189, ...	1·1802, 1·1805, 1·1793, 1·1824, ...	0·987, 0·998, 0·988, 1·007, ...		1·1985, 1·1980, 1·1988, 1·1965, ...
C_6H_5Cl	1·118, 1·150, 1·143, ...	1·1247, 1·1238, 1·1236, 1·1249, ...	0·998, 1·005, 0·993, 1·000, 1·007		1·1315, 1·1307, 1·1321, 1·1315, 1·1300, ...
C_6H_5F	1·000, ,, ,, ,,	1·000, ,, ,, ,, ,,	1·000, ,, ,, ,, ,,		1·000, ,, ,, ,, ,,
θ	0·656, 0·733, 0·822, 0·928, 1·000	0·486, 0·639, 0·733, 0·822, 0·928, 1·000	0·486, 0·939, 0·733, 0·822, 0·928, 1·000	π	0·0006, 0·0023, 0·0885, 0·2360, 0·5900, 1·0000
$\dfrac{T}{C_6H_5F}$	367·3, 410·4, 460·4, 519·7, 559·55	272·25, 358·1, 410·4, 460·4, 519·7, 559·55	272·25, 358·1, 410·4, 460·4, 519·7, 559·55	$\dfrac{p}{C_6H_5F}$	20, 760, 3,000, 8,000, 20,000, 33,912

Thus, for example, the molecular volume of the saturated vapour of alcohol at the absolute temperature $T (= 338\cdot75)$, is 45700 c.c., therefore, since the critical temperature of alcohol is $516\cdot1$, the reduced temperature is

$$\theta = \frac{338\cdot75}{516\cdot1} = 0\cdot656 \; ;$$

the corresponding temperature of fluor-benzene amounts to

$$T = 559\cdot55 \times \theta = 367\cdot3°.$$

In the table on p. 227 the molecular volume of the saturated vapour of fluor-benzene at this temperature is found to be 22,000 and thus the quotient is

$$\frac{45,700}{22,000} = 2\cdot076 \; ;$$

and this last number, as a matter of fact, is found in column II. (p. 229) under C_2H_5OH, corresponding to the value $\theta = 0\cdot656$.

It appears from a study of the preceding table, that the figures for the three halogen derivatives of benzene meet the demands of the theory as the comparison requires they should at *corresponding temperatures*, as shown by the constancy of the figures in the vertical rows ; but that the numbers for benzene, carbon tetrachloride, stannic chloride, and ether, given in the vertical rows of each particular column, are not constant as they should be, but regular deviations can be recognised; and that the deviations are much greater still in the case of acetic acid and the three alcohols ; and, further, that the requirements of the theory are well satisfied only in the case of *the molecular volume in the liquid state* (see column III.)

The comparison of the boiling-points at *corresponding pressures*, again, gives very good results, except in the case of the substances last mentioned.

Moreover, the fact that there is less variation in comparing the quotients of the boiling-points at *corresponding pressures*, than in comparing the quotients of the vapour pressure at *corresponding temperatures*, is easily explained as follows : since the pressures diminish in the ratio of $16,000 : 1$, when the reduced temperature θ sinks from 1 to $0\cdot5°$, the inexactness of the theory will be rendered more apparent by those quotients which are developed from the pressures, than by those developed from the temperatures.

By means of the equations on p. 219, the critical volume ϕ_0 is estimated to be

$$\phi_0 = \frac{3}{8} \frac{R\theta_0}{\pi_0},$$

if the gaseous laws held up to the critical point it would be $\dfrac{R\theta_0}{\pi_0}$.

Thus we find that the actual critical vapour density should for every substance equal $\frac{8}{3}$ of the theoretical, *i.e.* the density according to Avogadro's law.

This law holds good to a certain extent, as actually found by Young;[1] for omitting the alcohols and acetic acid, the critical vapour density (obtained from critical volumes given on p. 227) of all the substances investigated was the same multiple of the theoretical value; but it was not $\frac{8}{3}$ ($= 2\cdot67$), but about $3\cdot8$ times as great as the theoretical.

In general the ratio of the observed to the calculated vapour densities is very nearly the same at corresponding pressures (but not quite so exact at corresponding temperatures). These quotients are calculated for fluor-benzene on p. 227.

Young and Thomas[2] have studied, further, the behaviour of a series of esters. The reduced temperatures and volumes for these, as well as for the substances previously investigated, are given in the following table, for reduced pressure $0\cdot08846$:—

Substance.	Reduced Co-ordinates (p. 225).		
	θ	ϕ_1	ϕ_2
Methyl formate	0·7348	0·4007	29·4
Ethyl formate	0·7385	0·4004	29·6
Methyl acetate	0·7445	0·3992	30·2
Propyl formate	0·7430	0·4010	29·4
Ethyl acetate	0·7504	0·4006	30·3
Methyl propionate . . .	0·7485	0·4006	29·6
Propyl acetate	0·7541	0·3094	29·75
Ethyl propionate . . .	0·7540	0·3996	30·05
Methyl butyrate . . .	0·7522	0·4005	29·5
Methyl isobutyrate . . .	0·7502	0·4021	29·2
Methyl alcohol	0·7734	0·3949	34·2
Ethyl alcohol	0·7794	0·4047	32·1
Propyl alcohol	0·7736	0·4028	31·1
Acetic acid	0·7624	0·4106	25·5
Ethyl ether	0·7371	0·4044	28·2
Fluorbenzene	0·7334	0·4067	28·4
Chlorobenzene	0·7345	0·4046	28·65
Bromobenzene	0·7343	0·4041	·28·4
Iodobenzene	0·7337	0·4042	28·45
Benzene	0·7282	0·4053	28·2
Carbon tetrachloride . . .	0·7251	0·4072	27·4
Tin chloride	0·7357	0·4021	28·1

Within each group the theorem of corresponding states holds remarkably

[1] *Phil. Mag.* [5], **34.** 507 (1892).   [2] *Trans. Chem. Soc.*, 1893, p. 1191.

for the volume of the liquid ϕ_1, and fairly for the vapour volume ϕ_2, and temperature θ.

A comparison of the reduced co-ordinates for isopentane with those of benzene turned out quite in accord with the theorem.[1]

The special form of the characteristic equation developed on p. 225 for coexistence of liquid and vapour does not agree at all with the observations,[2] a further proof that van der Waals' special equation for matter in a highly compressed state is only true qualitatively.

Volume at Absolute Zero.—From the equation of van der Waals

$$\left(p + \frac{a}{v^2}\right)(v - b) = RT$$

we get for the volume at absolute zero the relation

$$v_0 = b = \frac{\phi_0}{3}.$$

The value of v_0 can be obtained, after Guldberg,[3] either by extrapolating the volume under constant pressure for the absolute zero, or the volume at constant temperature for infinite pressure. D. Berthelot calculated the same magnitude by means of Cailletet's and Mathias' straight line rule (p. 228), by simply producing this line to the absolute zero; as at this point the density of the saturated vapour is infinitely small, that of the liquid is double the mean value given by the above extrapolation.

The following table contains the molecular volumes of a few substances at the critical point and at absolute zero :—

Substance.	$M\phi_0$	Mv_0	Ratio.
Oxygen	49·2	20·8	2·37
Nitrogen	70	25·0	2·80
Carbon dioxide . . .	96	25·5	3·77
Ethyl ether	280	71·7	3·91
Benzene	256	70·6	3·63
Carbon tetrachloride . .	276	72·2	3·82
Propyl acetate	345	86·2	4·00

The critical volume is therefore not always three times the volume at absolute zero; the ratio, however, is never very different from the theoretical value 3, and for many substances assumes a value in the neighbourhood of 4.[4]

[1] Young, *Proc. Phys. Soc. Lond.*, 1894-95, p. 602.
[2] Riecke, *Gött. Nachr.*, 1894, No. 2 ; further K. Meyer, *Zeitschr. phys. Chem.* **32**, 1, 1900.
[3] *Zeitschr. phys. Chem.* **32**. 116 (1900).
[4] See Van't Hoff, *Theoret. Chemie*, iii. p. 21 (1903).

The Vapour Pressure Curve.—If the theorem of corresponding states held good, the problem of the calculation for vapour pressure curves, already touched upon on p. 61, would be capable of a very simple solution; for if we knew the vapour pressure curve of a normal substance, we could calculate that of any other substance from a knowledge of the critical data.

If, in a co-ordinate system, reduced temperatures are plotted as

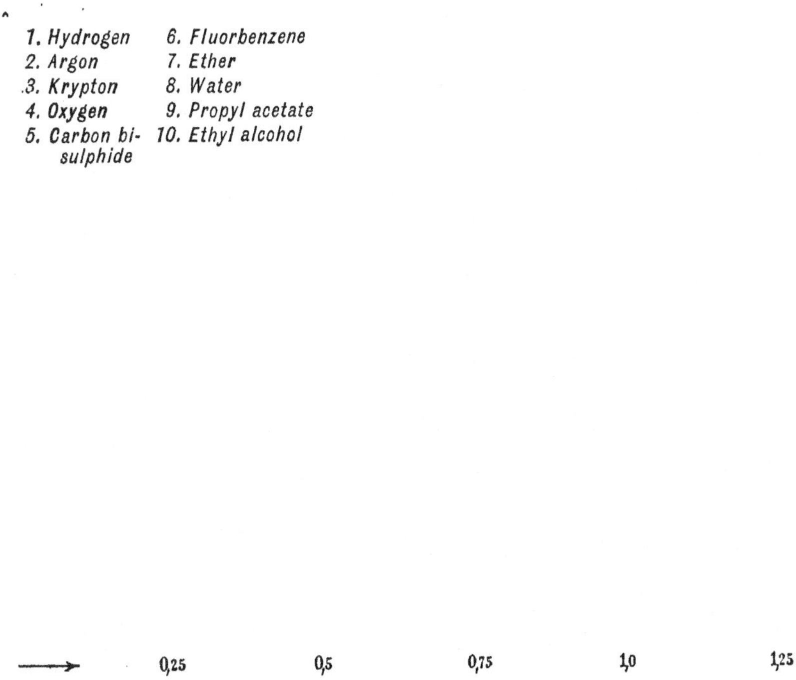

1. Hydrogen   6. Fluorbenzene
2. Argon   7. Ether
3. Krypton   8. Water
4. Oxygen   9. Propyl acetate
5. Carbon bi-   10. Ethyl alcohol
   sulphide

0,25	0,5	0,75	1,0	1,25

Fig. 19.

abscissae and reduced vapour pressures as ordinates, then, according to the equation (p. 226)

$$\pi = f_3 \ (\theta),$$

an identical curve should result; the calculations on p. 230 have already shown that this is not the case.

If, instead of $\theta = \dfrac{T}{\theta_0}$ we plot the values of $\left(\dfrac{\theta_0}{T} - 1 \right)$ as abscissae, and instead of $\pi = \dfrac{p}{\pi_0}$, the expression $\log \dfrac{\pi_0}{p}$ as ordinates, we obtain a very simple picture of the relations under consideration, for then practically straight lines are obtained, as van der Waals himself observed [1]; or in other words, we get the relation

$$\log \frac{\pi_0}{T} = a \left(\frac{\theta_0}{T} - 1 \right)$$

where a is a constant within certain limits. Van der Waals held the opinion that the value of a should be the same (about 3·0) for all normally behaving substances, but experiment has not supported this view, which must therefore be given up. The diagram [2] (Fig. 19) shows that the inclination of the straight lines is very different for different substances; excluding curves 8 and 10, which refer to substances (water and alcohol) which are without doubt highly polymerised in the liquid state (see the following chapter), it is at once obvious that the higher the molecular weight, and the more atoms there are in the molecule, the greater are the curves inclined to the abscissa axis. In accordance with this rule there is a considerable difference between krypton and argon, so that the law of corresponding states is not even obeyed by monatomic substances. Substances, like alcohol and water, which are associated in the liquid condition, give curves which are relatively more strongly inclined to the axis, but which also approximate to straight lines. We can now understand [3] that Young's proof (p. 226 ff.) of the theorem of corresponding states was carried out under much too favourable conditions, for he confined himself to substances of much the same molecular weight, which at the same time contained a large number of atoms in the molecule; if he had taken for comparison monatomic substances, or at any rate such substances as H_2, O_2, N_2, we should have obtained quite another picture of the relations in question.

We can express the above result as follows: the theorem of corresponding states is at any rate approximately true when we compare substances with not very different critical temperatures, but it does not hold at all when the critical temperatures are widely different. It is possible that in the latter case a number of other regularities (pp. 229, 232) also fail.

I have attacked the problem of the calculation of vapour pressure curves in the following way (*Gött. Nachr.*, 1906, vol. 1). The equation

$$p_0(v_0 - v_0') = RT \left(1 - \frac{p}{\pi_0} \right)$$

agrees closely with observations made on fluorbenzene up to pressures of about 15 atm.; p, v_0, v_0', denote respectively vapour pressure, molecular volume of saturated vapour, and that of the liquid. Since volume ratios

---

[1] *Kontinuität*, etc., p. 147.
[2] The values for H_2, A, Kr, O_2, are taken from M. W. Travers' *Experimental Study of Gases*.
[3] Nernst, *Gött. Nachr.*, 1906, vol. i.

at corresponding pressure very nearly agree with those required by the law of corresponding states (p. 231) the above equation must hold good generally. The equation of Clausius-Clapeyron (p. 58)

$$\lambda = T\frac{dp}{dT}\Big(v_0 - v_0{}'\Big),$$

where λ is the molecular heat of vaporisation, becomes therefore

$$\lambda = RT^2\frac{d\ln p}{dT}\Big(1 - \frac{p}{\pi_0}\Big).$$

For λ, I find the empirical formula

$$\lambda = (\lambda_0 + 3\cdot5T - \epsilon T^2)\Big(1 - \frac{p}{\pi_0}\Big),$$

where ϵ is a specific constant.

Hence

$$\lambda_0 + 3\cdot5T - \epsilon T^2 = RT^2\frac{d\ln p}{dT},$$

which becomes when integrated

$$\ln p = -\frac{\lambda_0}{RT} + \frac{3\cdot5}{R}\ln T - \frac{\epsilon}{R}T + \text{const.}$$

The Heat Content of Compressed Gases and of Liquids.—

We will now finally consider the answer to certain questions regarding the heat content of *gaseous and liquid substances* in the light of the kinetic theory of van der Waals. Disregarding the question of the amount of work performed against the external pressure, which can be ascertained in all cases exactly and easily in calorific equivalents, heat introduced into gas and liquids will increase the kinetic energy of the molecules on the one hand, and on the other will perform a certain amount of work against the molecular forces, because in consequence of the thermal expansion the molecules remove farther apart. But now, since the molecular forces increase greatly with condensation, they will be much greater in liquids than in gases, where they are inconsiderable at ordinary condensation; this explains why the specific heat of a liquid is always greater than that of its vapour (p. 58). If a liquid is kept at constant volume during the warming, then, provided that the theory of van der Waals is rigorously applicable to it, its specific heat must be exactly the same as that of its vapour, provided, of course, that this latter is taken at constant volume.

The same conclusion holds good for compressed gases; Mallard and Le Chatelier (p. 44) found, in fact, that up to pressures of 6000 to 7000 atm. the specific heat at constant volume was independent of the volume.

The following result also speaks emphatically in favour of the preceding conclusion. From the equation developed on p. 54, viz.—

$$\frac{\partial C_v}{\partial v} = T\frac{\partial^2 p}{\partial T^2},$$

when

$$\frac{\partial C_v}{\partial v} = 0, \text{ it follows that } p = AT + B,$$

if we denote by A and B two integration constants. As a matter of fact, Ramsay and Young[1] found that the pressure of a liquid or gaseous substance, when kept at *constant volume*, varied linearly with the temperature; or, in other words, that the *isochores* (*i.e.* curves which are obtained from varying pressure at constant volume) are straight lines.

Moreover, it is possible to derive this last result directly from the equation of condition (p. 209), by writing it in the form

$$p = \frac{R}{v - b}T - \frac{a}{v^2};$$

thus we have

$$A = \frac{R}{v - b}; \text{ and } B = -\frac{a}{v^2}.$$

As was shown (on p. 47), the work performed in compressing an ideal gas appears in the interior as heat. This law, like the other gas laws, becomes inexact with a high degree of compression, and thus the interesting question arises as to how we are to conceive of these deviations in the light of the theory of van der Waals.

The answer is very simple. On the approach of the molecules towards each other by compression, their mutual attraction performs a certain amount of work which appears in the form of heat; the conditions, therefore, require that a *greater amount of heat* should appear from compression than what corresponds exactly to the work applied. The molecular pressure,

$$K = \frac{a}{v^2},$$

may be regarded as a measure of the force of attraction. The heat developed by this force, by compressing the volume from v_1 to v_2, amounts to

$$\int_{v_1}^{v_2} K dv = \int_{v_1}^{v_2} \frac{a}{v^2} dv = a\left(\frac{1}{v_1} - \frac{1}{v_2}\right).$$

Moreover, the theory affords many explanations regarding the *heat of evaporation.* For, in the first place, it is at once obvious that the heat of evaporation *must become zero at the critical point,* because the distinction between a liquid and its saturated vapour ceases at that point. Mathias[2] found experimental proof for this corollary from

[1] *Zeitschr. phys. Chem.* **1.** 433 (1887); **3.** 49, 63 (1889.)
[2] *Ann. chim. phys.* [6], **21.** 69 (1890).

measurements conducted with carbon dioxide and nitrous oxide. This necessarily follows from the formula of Clausius

$$\lambda = T \frac{dp}{dT} (v_0 - v_0') \, ;$$

for at the critical point,

$$v_0 = v_0', \quad \text{therefore } \lambda = 0.$$

It now becomes possible to go a step farther and calculate the *heat of vaporisation* from the molecular forces.[1] If a gas is condensed, without performance of external work, the molecular forces perform the work calculated above, which must reappear in the form of heat ; by calculating the latter for 1 mol. (according to p. 57), we obtain

$$\lambda - p(v_0 - v_0') = a\left(\frac{1}{v_0'} - \frac{1}{v_0}\right). \qquad . \qquad . \qquad . \qquad (1)$$

By comparison with the equation deduced on p. 225,

$$RT \ln \frac{v_0 - b}{v_0' - b} + \frac{a}{v_0} - \frac{a}{v_0'} = p(v_0 - v_0'), \qquad . \qquad . \qquad (2)$$

we get

$$\lambda = RT \ln \frac{v_0 - b}{v_0' - b}. \qquad . \qquad . \qquad . \qquad (3)$$

From the critical data (according to p. 220),

$$a = \frac{27}{64} \frac{R^2 \theta_0^2}{\pi_0} ;$$

now on considering the heat of evaporation at the boiling-point, it follows that v_0 must be very large compared with v_0', and therefore similarly $\frac{1}{v_0'}$ as compared with $\frac{1}{v_0}$; and we thus find as the value of the molecular heat of evaporation

$$\lambda = \frac{27}{64} \frac{R^2 \theta_0^2}{\pi_0 v_0'} + RT.$$

For benzene we have

$$\theta_0 = 561° \, ; \quad \pi_0 = 42 \text{ atm. } ;$$
$$v_0' = 0.096 \text{ lit. } ; \quad T = 273 + 80 :$$

now by writing $R = 0.0821$, we obtain λ in litre-atm. (p. 48): then by reducing to g.-cal., by dividing by 24.19 we obtain $\lambda = 5400$ instead of 7200 g.-cal. The theoretical value is therefore only very approximately correct ; but it is not without interest to know that it is possible to calculate roughly the heat of evaporation so easily from the critical data ; and also that the formula is in harmony with experiment in showing a gradual diminution [for the value of λ], till the critical point is reached, when λ becomes zero.

[1] Bakker, *Zeitschr. phys. Chem.* **18.** 519 (1895).

Similarly is found for

Ether	$\lambda = 4600$	instead of 6640	at the boiling-point.	
Carbon tetrachloride	$\lambda = 5250$	,,	7100	,,	,,
Tin tetrachloride	$\lambda = 6270$	,,	7900	,,	,,
Ethyl alcohol	$\lambda = 5640$	,,	10500 at 0°.	,,	,,
Ethyl acetate	$\lambda = 5500$	,,	9000	

In all cases experiment gives a higher value than the theory.

Equation (3) is obtained by combination of (2) derived entirely from the kinetic theory with (1), which is purely thermodynamic; it can also be deduced kinetically as Kammerlingh Onnes showed (*Verh. d. Ak. Wiss.*, Amsterdam, 1881; *Arch. Néerl.* **30.** 101 (1897); see also W. Voigt, *Gött. Nachr.*, 1897, Heft 3). This problem, obviously associated with that of the kinetic explanation of the second law of thermodynamics, is fully treated by Boltzmann (*Gas Theory*, ii. p. 167 ff.).

If the molecules are considered as points of mass, and hence the change of internal energy associated with the condensation of a vapour is taken as equivalent to the work performed by the molecular attraction, we have

$$\int_{v_1}^{v_2} K dv = \int_{r_1}^{r_2} \frac{A}{r^n} dr = \frac{A}{n-1}\left(\frac{1}{r_1^{n-1}} - \frac{1}{r_2^{n-1}}\right),$$

where r_1 and r_2 denote the average distance between the molecules in the liquid and gaseous states, and their mutual attraction is inversely proportional to the nth power of the distance apart. Now, as specific volume is proportional to the cube of this average distance, equation (1) would be satisfied if $n - 1 = 3$ or $n = 4$, and this, as J. W. Mellor (*Phil. Mag.* [6], **3.** 423, 1902), showed, would be in agreement with Sutherland's laws.

If we accept the view of J. E. Mills (*Jour. Phys. Chem.* **6.** 209, 1902, and **8.** 383 and 593, 1904) that the force, like ordinary gravitation, is inversely proportional to the square of the distance apart, it follows that

$$\int_{v_1}^{v_2} K dv = \lambda - p \, (v_0 - v_0^1) = A\left(\frac{1}{\sqrt[3]{v_0^1}} - \frac{1}{\sqrt[3]{v_0}}\right).$$

The author finds, in fact, that the factor A is constant for any given substance within wide ranges of temperature, provided that the substance behaves normally, *i.e.* does not polymerise in the liquid condition like water and alcohol, for example. But the above equation, as well as equation (1), is probably only a first approximation.

Joule-Thomson Effect.

—Joule and Thomson (1854) made use of an ingenious apparatus to investigate the heat effect on expansion of non-ideal gases.. The gases were driven through a tube which contained a closely fitting wad of cotton wool or some similar substance. The velocity of streaming through the narrow pores of the wad was so small that the kinetic energy of the movement could be neglected. If T_1, p_1, v_1, denote temperature, pressure, and molecular volume of the gas on entering the wad, and T_2, p_2, v_2, the same magnitudes on leaving the wad, the energy conveyed to the gas in the form of external work is

$$p_1 v_1 - p_2 v_2.$$

In order to arrive at the change of internal energy accompanying the process, we must first imagine the gas to emerge at constant temperature T_1 and with the volume v_2, whereby internal work of $\dfrac{a}{v_1} - \dfrac{a}{v_2}$ is performed, and then the temperature to sink from T_1 to T_2, whereby an amount of heat $C_v (T_1 - T_2)$ is given up. Hence, since the total amount of energy must be the same,

$$p_1 v_1 - p_2 v_2 = \frac{a}{v_1} - \frac{a}{v_2} - C_v (T_2 - T_1). \qquad . \qquad . \qquad (1)$$

Writing van der Waals' equation in the form

$$p\left(1 + \frac{a}{v^2 p}\right)v\left(1 - \frac{b}{v}\right) = RT,$$

we observe that in the case of a gas which behaves nearly ideally $\dfrac{a}{v^2 p}$ and $\dfrac{b}{v}$ must be small compared to unity. As in any case we are only concerned with small corrections, we can introduce the simple gas equation without perceptible error and write

$$pv = \frac{RT}{\left(1 + \dfrac{ap}{(RT)^2}\right)\left(1 - \dfrac{bp}{RT}\right)},$$

which, neglecting infinitesimals, becomes

$$pv = RT\left[1 + p\left(\frac{b}{RT} - \frac{a}{(RT)^2}\right)\right]. \qquad . \qquad . \qquad (2)$$

If we introduce this into (1), remembering that $T_1 - T_2$ is very small compared to T_1, we get

$$C_v (T_1 - T_2) = R(T_2 - T_1) + \left(\frac{2a}{RT_1} - b\right)(p_1 - p_2),$$

or finally, substituting

$$C_p = C_v + R,$$

(which is, of course, only approximately correct for non-ideal gases),

$$C_p (T_1 - T_2) = \left(\frac{2a}{RT_1} - b\right)(p_1 - p_2).$$

This equation was shown by van der Waals to agree very well with the measurements of Joule and Thomson.

As a rule

$$\frac{2a}{RT_1} > b,$$

so that cooling results, but with hydrogen the reverse is the case (see also p. 211), and Joule and Thomson found correspondingly that the expansion of this gas was accompanied by a warming effect. Under $-80°$ the above inequality holds good also for hydrogen.

The Linde apparatus for the liquefaction of air depends on the Joule-Thomson effect (1898). The previously cooled gas, compressed to 200 atmospheres, is allowed to expand without performance of external work; the cooler gas thus obtained sweeps back over the oncoming gas, and further cools the latter. In this way the temperature becomes lower and lower till the boiling-point of the air under the pressure used is reached. Hydrogen could not be 'liquefied under ordinary conditions in such an apparatus, as the gas would be continually warmed instead of cooled. But if the original temperature of the gas is lower than $-80°$, it can be liquefied, as Dewar, Ramsay, Olszewski, and others have shown.

Critique of the Results.—By means of the numerical material given above, it is shown that the theorems of van der Waals are not strictly proved by experiment, but that, although they explain qualitatively the behaviour of liquid and gaseous substances, there are certain undoubted deviations between theory and fact.

Now the question arises whether these deviations are of such a sort that the whole theory must be given up, or is it possible to account for them by some change in developing the theory. The verdict cannot be doubted for a moment; for the results of the theory are so undeniable, and the region of the phenomena which it claims to control is so extensive, that it would be a very profitable problem to follow up these deviations, and to prove carefully what is necessary, *i.e.* whether a re-shaping or an extension of the theory is required. The study of the changes which must be made in the gas laws in order to adapt them better to the facts, was what led van der Waals to his wonderful discoveries. Is it not probable that the desire to invest the laws of van der Waals with yet greater accuracy would be rewarded with surprising and unexpected results ?

The results so far arrived at with regard to van der Waals' theory may be summarised as follows : the equation

$$\left(p + \frac{a}{v^2}\right)(v - b) = RT$$

only holds exactly for not too strongly compressed gases; it quite fails near the critical point. The theory of corresponding states, which does not depend upon the special form of the above equation, is of wide applicability ; in especial it allows of calculating accurately the volume, thermal expansion, and compressibility of liquids. The assumption that the deviations are due to polymerisation in the liquid state is shown to be improbable by the considerations on page 234. It will perhaps be possible to characterise the behaviour of a substance by the introduction of a few specific constants beside the critical data ; at any rate this possibility should be thoroughly tested, now that the theorem of corresponding states (determination of the behaviour of a substance simply from the critical data) has been shown untrue ; cf. the paper (p. 232) by Kirstine Meyer, who introduced two new specific constants. An excellent monograph on the above questions has been written by J. P. Kuenen, *Die Zustandsgleichung*, Braunschweig, 1907.

The Kinetic Theory of the Solid State of Aggregation.—

The attempt to penetrate into the nature of the constitution of solid substances by means of molecular considerations has as yet only begun.. The assumption, that the kinetic energy of the translatory motion is proportional to the absolute temperature, and independent of the nature of the molecule, may possibly be introduced here, as was the case with gases and liquids ; but it is very probable that the heat motion of the molecules of solid substances consists of an oscillation within very sharply-defined limits, in which they are restrained by the forces of cohesion, and that no single molecule can continue to change its place as is the case with gases and liquids. In fact, the peculiarities of the solid state become intelligible in this way.

Thus heat introduced becomes effective in the following ways :—

1. It will increase the kinetic energy of the molecule, or of the atoms within the molecule.

2. In consequence of 1, it will alter the potential energy of the molecules towards each other.

3. It will perform work against the forces of cohesion.

4. It will perform work against the external pressure.

On account of the slight change of volume occasioned by heating solid bodies, in general the fourth change in energy is negligible ; that under 3 is also small, as is shown by calculation according to equation (7) p. 54.[1]

For monatomic bodies it is possible to show under certain conditions that (1) and (2) are equal in magnitude. For if we consider the case when the atoms rotate in circleਿ round their positions of equilibrium, and assume that the force attracting the atom towards its centre of equilibrium is proportional to its distance from it, the centrifugal force must equalise the force of attraction, *i.e.*

$$\frac{m}{r} u^2 = Ar$$

(m = mass, u = velocity, r = radius of circle. A = proportional factor of the attractive force). If the atom, supposed at rest, fell back towards its centre of equilibrium, it would arrive there with the kinetic energy

$$\frac{m}{2} u_1{}^2 = A \int_0^r r dr = A \frac{r^2}{2} ;$$

from these equations it follows that

$$\frac{m}{2} u^2 = \frac{m}{2} u_1{}^2,$$

[1] See especially Grüneisen, *Ann. d. Phys.* [4], **26**. 393 (1908).

R

i.e. that kinetic and potential energies are equal. Now as, according to p. 200, the kinetic energy of an atom is $\frac{3}{2}$ R = 2·98, the atomic heat of a monatomic solid body must be ·

$$C_v = 2 \times 2 \cdot 98 = 5 \cdot 96.$$

According to Boltzmann [1] this relation holds good generally, whatever the motion of the atom round its equilibrium position, and thus we not only arrive at the result that the atomic heats of monatomic solid bodies must be constant, but also obtain a number agreeing with the rule of Dulong and Petit. But as long as we are not in a position to give quantitative expression to the many and considerable deviations (p. 170) from this rule, the admissibility of the above considerations must be considered doubtful. In view of the rapid decrease of specific heats at very low temperatures, it seems to me particularly doubtful whether the molecules can possess in the solid state the same kinetic energy as in the gaseous state.

If we follow up the above considerations, and make a few special assumptions on the nature of the forces existing between the atoms, we arrive at some interesting conclusions,[2] which can be subjected to experimental proof, and have, as a matter of fact, been confirmed to a certain extent in the cases already investigated. As examples we may mention the following laws :— [3]

1. The product of potential coefficient and atomic volume of monatomic bodies is a linear function of the atomic heats.

2. The potential coefficient of monatomic solid and liquid substances is a certain multiple of the number of atoms in unit volume.

3. All monatomic solid and liquid substances are raised in temperature to the same extent by the same adiabatic compression.

Finally, Lämmel's [4] empirical modification of Dulong and Petit's law is worthy of mention. The atomic heats of elements are practically constant at corresponding temperatures, where by the latter is meant temperatures which are equal fractions of the temperature at the melting-point of the body in question. For example, the atomic heats in the neighbourhood of the melting-point all approximate to the value 9.

The process of crystallisation is especially noteworthy from the point of view of molecular theory. We have to imagine that to form a crystal (*e.g.* in an undercooled fused mass or a supersaturated solution) a considerable number of molecules have to meet in one spot, and in an appropriate constellation ; most probably the smallest crystalline individual capable of existence consists of very many molecules. Thus the probability of formation of crystals may be very small ; experience

[1] *Wiener Sitzungsber.* **63**. 2. Abt. p. 731 (1871).
[2] Mie, *Ann. d. Phys.* [4], **11**. 657 (1903). Grüneisen, *l.c.*
[3] Grüneisen, *l.c.*   [4] *Ann. d. Phys.* [4]. **16**. 551 (1905).

shows, in fact, that it may take a very long time before crystals appear in an undercooled fused mass, and that crystalline precipitates possess a number of centres of crystallisation (nuclei) that is excessively small compared with the number of molecules concerned.

The circumstance that discrete centres of crystallisation can arise in apparently homogeneous melts or solutions is a striking instance of the appropriateness of the molecular theory ; for this alone makes it intelligible that even in the interior of an apparently homogeneous fluid, local differences should occur due to special constellations of molecular movements, and that these should be very sparsely scattered in comparison with molecular distances.

According to G. Tammann (*Zeitschr. phys. Chem.* **25**. 441, 1898) the points at which crystallisation begins in a melt are hardly 1000 per minute per cubic millimetre under the most favourable circumstances. With increase of undercooling the number of these nuclei at first increases, then diminishes, to practically zero.

The molecular explanation of this remarkable fact seems to me this. The greater the undercooling, the smaller the smallest possible crystalline individual must be, and so the greater the probability of the molecular constellation required to form it. But, on the other hand, the molecular movements fall off in vigour with fall of temperature, so that the occurrence of any particular constellation is rendered more difficult, and at the absolute zero, impossible. These two factors in combination would give the results observed by Tammann. See especially Küster (*Zeitschr. anorg. Chem.* **33**. 363 (1903).

The Kinetic Theory of Mixtures.—In all our theoretical considerations regarding molecules thus far, we have always had in mind a substance which should be simple from a chemical standpoint, *i.e.* one consisting of nothing but molecules *of one kind*. The question now arises, how the preceding considerations will be modified when we study a mixture.

And here we must distinguish between two cases, viz. the different kinds of molecules may react chemically upon each other, or they may behave indifferently towards each another.

It must be noticed, in the first case, that the condition of chemical equilibrium prevailing in the mixture will, in general, vary with the pressure, volume, and temperature ; such a mixture, for example, is the vapour of acetic acid, which consists partly of doubled molecules and partly of normal ones, the ratio of which changes with the external conditions. We shall consider such mixtures more thoroughly in the part devoted to "the doctrine of affinity." In the following we consider only mixtures which consist of molecules which are chemically indifferent.

Now, the van der Waals' equation of condition,

$$\left(p + \frac{a}{v^2}\right)(v - b) = RT,$$

can, of course, be applied directly to a homogeneous mixture of this last sort, whether it be a liquid or a gas. In fact, it is as fully applicable to strongly-compressed atmospheric air as to a simple gas, only the meaning of the constants " a " and " b " is somewhat different from that which they have in the case of pure substances, and their magnitudes also change with the relative proportions of the ingredients in the mixture.

Van der Waals (*Zeitschr. phys. Chem.* 5. 134, 1890) gives the following equations to calculate the constants a_x and b_x of a mixture containing $1 - x$ mols of one component to x of the other.

$$a_x = a_1(1 - x)^2 + 2a_{12}x(1 - x) + a_2x^2$$
$$b_x = b_1(1 - x)^2 + 2b_{12}x(1 - x) + b_2x^2.$$

Here a_1 and b_1 are constants of the first component, a_2 and b_2 of the second ; a_{12} is the attraction constant between the two, and b_{12} the volume constant for the combination. Also, for b_{12},

$$\sqrt[3]{b_{12}} = \tfrac{1}{2}\{ \sqrt[3]{b_1} + \sqrt{b_2}\}$$

holds.

According to this the properties of a mixture can be deduced from those of its components by the help of one new constant a_{12} only.

The treatment of the question regarding the coexistence of liquid and vapour is entirely different in the case of mixtures, since in general, in distinction from simple substances, the composition of the liquid and vapour differ. As shown on p. 225, this question has not yet been treated for the case of a simple substance from a pure kinetic standpoint. Much less, therefore, would this be the case for mixtures ; and van der Waals' quoted work, although entitled *The Molecular Theory of Bodies consisting of two Different Substances*, is emphatically a thermodynamic study, a description of which does not belong to this chapter. It should, however, be observed that, in addition to the investigation of the coexistence of liquid and vapour of mixtures, there also arises the question of the coexistence of liquids of different composition (mutually saturated solutions).[1]

The Kinetic Theory of Solutions.—We learned, in the last chapter of the first book, a fact drawn from experiment, viz. that. the laws of gases are applicable also to dissolved substances, and that there is a very far-reaching analogy between the condition of matter in dilute solution and in the gaseous state. Now it is but a step to *transfer this analogy also to the molecular condition* ; and the conception is at once suggested that the osmotic pressure of a solution, like gas pressure, has a *kinetic nature, i.e.* that it results from the bombardment of the molecules of the dissolved substance against the semi-permeable partition.

[1] See the important new work of van Kuenen (especially *Zeitschr. phys. Chem.* **24.** 667, 1897 ; **41.** 43, 1903) and the second part of V. d. Waals, *Kontinuität*, etc. (Leipzig, 1900).

Boltzmann,[1] Riecke,[2] and Lorentz[3] have made attempts of this sort to develop the laws of dilute solutions immediately from the play of molecular forces and of molecular movements, without having recourse to the aid of thermodynamics.

Each of these investigators assumed that the *mean kinetic energy of the translatory motion of the molecules in solution was as great as in the case of the molecules of a gas at the same temperature as the solution.* This assumption appears the more probable, because the theory of van der Waals has been already applied to liquids with good results.

According to Boltzmann, in the calculation of the osmotic pressure, one must take into consideration not only the mutually opposed action between the wall and the molecules bounding against it, as was done in explaining gas pressure, but also the mutual action between the dissolved molecules and those of the solvent. But it is a difficult problem to state in just what way this occurs, and to make such a supposition as shall be explanatory and shall harmonise with the facts, and the satisfactory solution of this problem remains for the future. Boltzmann assumed, on the one hand, the distance between the centres of two neighbouring salt molecules, to be very great as compared with the distance between the centres of two neighbouring molecules of the liquid solvent ; and, on the other hand, the space changed by the presence of the molecule of the dissolved salt, to be small in comparison with the total space occupied by the liquid solvent ; and in this way he obtained the result *that the osmotic pressure exerted by the dissolved substance on a semi-permeable membrane is equal to the corresponding gas pressure.*

Lorentz assumed that the dissolved substance is subjected to an attractive force proceeding from the solvent, which is equal and opposite to the force acting upon the quantity of the liquid displaced. Riecke proceeds upon the supposition that the number of collisions between the molecules of the dissolved substance is infinitesimally small as compared with the number of collisions between the molecules of the solvent. Both these investigators arrived at the same conclusion as Boltzmann.

Boltzmann and Riecke both showed in this way, that the same results are obtained for the diffusion of dissolved substances, and of electrolytes especially, which I have already developed independently from the special kinetic conceptions preceding (p. 152). Riecke succeeded in deriving the *mean free path* of a dissolved substance from its diffusion velocity : the following is the value, in which D denotes the coefficient of diffusion (p. 151), and u denotes the mean calculated velocity of the molecule (p. 200) :

$$L = \frac{3D}{8 \,.\, 64 \times 10^4 \,.\, u}.$$

[1] *Zeitschr. phys. Chem.* **6.** 474 (1890) ; **7.** 88 (1891),
[2] *Ibid.* **6.** 564.   [3] *Ibid.* **7.** 36.

In this way he found, for instance, the mean free paths, at 8° to 10°, as follows :—

Substance.	D.	Mean Free Path " L."
Urea .	0·81	$0·68 \times 10^{-8}$ mm.
Chloral hydrate	0·55	0·94 ,, .
Mannite	0·38	0·68 ,,
Cane sugar	0·31	0·77 ,,

It is somewhat remarkable that the mean free paths so calculated are extremely small compared to the dimensions of the molecules (*cf.* Chapter XII. of this book).

It cannot be denied that kinetic considerations applied to solutions by no means lead to the simple results which distinguish their application to the behaviour of an ideal gas ; even for single laws, such as, for example, the relative lowering of the vapour pressure of the solvent (p. 143), no plausible kinetic explanation has yet been found.

The explanation recently offered by J. H. Poynting (*Phil. Mag.* 42. 289, 1896), that the relative lowering of vapour pressure is due to association of the dissolved molecules with those of the solvent is an arbitrary *ad hoc* hypothesis. There is no proof that this hypothesis can explain anything but the particular fact it was brought forward to explain, *e.g.* electrolytic conductivity. The hypothesis of electrolytic dissociation gives deductions in harmony with the facts of conduction, whereas the association hypothesis contradicts them.

Finally, I will refer to one more point which seems to have some importance. It was shown in the case of many liquids, for example ether, that at room temperature the space actually occupied by the molecules is about 0·3ths of the space apparently occupied. If we dissolve any substance in ether, then the space at the disposal of the oscillating molecules is certainly much smaller than the volume of solution ; therefore it would be expected that this " volume correction " would exercise as correspondingly great an influence on the osmotic pressure as on the pressure of a strongly compressed gas ; and it is inconceivable that it should nevertheless be so nearly equal to the gas pressure. Yet a more careful examination shows that *this correction may be neglected in the methods hitherto applied for measuring the partial pressures of the dissolved substances.* The methods thus far used always give the osmotic work P, *i.e.* the work required to remove a unit volume of the pure solvent from the solution, and this value of the pressure (being multiplied by the unit of volume) turns out to be equal to the gas pressure. But if we assume that the pressure of the dissolved substance must be increased on account of the volume correction, in the ratio of $1 : 1 - \beta$, when β denotes the diminution of the space at the disposal of the movement of the dissolved molecules, then this pressure P will become

$$\frac{P}{1 - \beta};$$

therefore the osmotic work required to remove unit volume of the solvent would be calculated as the product of the pressure and the volume, *i.e.*

$$\frac{P}{1 - \beta} \times (1 - \beta) = P,$$

since the volume through which the pressure is to be forced back is also diminished in the ratio $1 - \beta : 1$, and for the same reasons. In the methods thus far employed for measuring the osmotic pressure, the volume correction is thus wholly neglected. It would be very interesting to find a method for measuring directly the actual pressure of the dissolved substance, viz.

$$\frac{P}{1 - \beta}.$$

Tammann's Theory of Concentrated Solutions.—Tammann [1] has developed a very simple theory of the behaviour of solutions towards pressure and temperature. He found, namely, that the equation of condition of a solvent under a certain pressure is the same as that of a solution of a certain concentration. Tamman concludes from this result that the solution of a substance brings the solvent under a certain pressure, and hence causes the solution to behave in a similar manner to the solvent under the corresponding pressure, which varies with the nature and concentration of the dissolved substance.

From the standpoint of van der Waals' theory, it is in fact obvious that a change in internal pressure $\frac{a}{v^2}$ could be exactly compensated in the term $(p + \frac{a}{v^2})$ by a change in external pressure, so that the equations of condition of solution and solvent become identical.

As one of the many examples which Tammann has brought forward in support of his theory, we will choose the expansion by heat of water and alcohol under pressure, and of certain concentrated solutions of calcium chloride in these two solvents.

In Fig. 20 the three curves, 1, 2, 3, refer to water under pressures of 1, 1000, and 3000 atmospheres; the three dotted curves, I. II. III. to solutions of 10, 20, and 30 per cent of calcium chloride in water. It is obvious that the second group of curves is precisely similar to the

[1] *On the Relations between Internal Forces and the Properties of Solutions* (Hamburg, 1907).

first, or that, in other words, to every concentration of calcium chloride in water corresponds, in fact, a pressure under which the expansion of water by heat is exactly the same as that of the corresponding solution. The curves 4, 5, 6, show the expansion of alcohol under pressures of 1, 500, and 1000 atmospheres ; the dotted curves IV. and V. represent

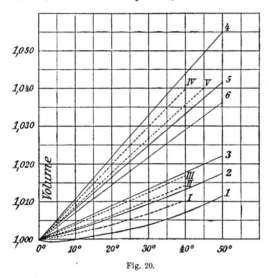

the expansion of solutions of 8·6 and 25·1 per cent calcium chloride in alcohol. In this case also the two groups of curves follow the same course. It should be especially noticed that alcoholic solutions of calcium chloride have a smaller coefficient of expansion the greater the concentration, which corresponds to the fact that the expansion of alcohol is smaller the higher the external pressure. Water behaves in the reverse

Fig. 20.

way ; its expansion is greater the higher the pressure, and the greater the concentration. In order to make the curves easily comparable, the volume at 0° has been invariably taken as unity.

The pressure to which the pure solvent must be subjected in order to make its coefficient of expansion equal to that of a solution under atmospheric pressure, has been named by Tammann the *internal pressure of the solution*. It is practically proportional to the concentration of the solution up to high concentrations, but varies with the nature of the dissolved substance.

The investigation of compressibility has led to the same result, and the value of the internal pressure of a solution has been found to be the same, whether deduced from measurements of compressibility or expansion by heat. This is, of course, a striking confirmation of the theory. Deviations are only found when the concentration is extremely high.

Tammann draws a number of very remarkable conclusions on specific heat, viscosity, electrical conductivity, and optical rotatory power, from the internal pressure of the solution in question ; *e.g.* the fact, which has been long observed, that the specific heat of a solution is usually smaller than that of the water it contains, is explained by the diminution of the specific heat of water under pressure.

The Molecular Weight of Gaseous Substances.—Formerly gases were the only substances the molecular weights of which could be directly determined, and it is only recently that it has become possible to measure the same values for substances in dilute solution. The theoretical reasons which underlie these methods have been already thoroughly treated in discussing the theory of the gaseous state and of solutions. The chief aim of this chapter will be devoted to the experimental realisation of these methods.

Since, according to Avogadro's rule (p. 201), under similar conditions of temperature and pressure, different gases contain the same number of molecules in a litre, therefore the *densities of any two gases are in the ratio of their molecular weights.* It is customary to refer the density, D, of a gas *to atmospheric air at the same temperature and pressure.* The density of air at 0° and atmospheric pressure in latitude 45° is 0·0012932, compared with water at 4°; hence the density of the gas under the same conditions is

$$0·0012932D.$$

Since 1 mol of an ideal gas under normal conditions occupies 22412 c.c., the density is

$$\frac{M}{22,412}$$

if M be the molecular weight.

Hence

$$M = 0·0012932 . 22,400D = 28·983D,$$

or nearly enough

$$M = 29·0D.$$

All the practical methods for the determination of the density of a gas amount to determining either

(1) The mass of a gas filling a measured volume at a known temperature and pressure;

Or (2) the volume filled by a weighed amount of a vaporised substance;

Or (3) the pressure exerted by the evaporation of a known amount of the substance in a measured volume at a given temperature.

Moreover, in practical work in the laboratory, it is not so necessary that a vapour density method shall be capable of measurement with a high degree of accuracy, as that it shall be certain and simple. For since the percentage composition is furnished by the analysis, a determination of the vapour density within 1 per cent is amply sufficient to determine *which one* of the different possible molecular weights in question is to be selected as the correct one.

Regnault's Method.—For the determination of the density of a substance which is already gaseous under the ordinary conditions of temperature and pressure, Regnault used two glass bulbs of nearly the same size, which were hung from the arms of a sensitive balance. One of the bulbs was first exhausted, and then filled with the gas to be investigated at a known pressure. The second bulb merely served to avoid the very considerable correction due to the buoyancy of the air.[1]

As is well known, Regnault in this way was able to measure the density of the permanent gases with satisfactory accuracy (p. 40). But for use in the chemical laboratory, when liquid and solid substances are to be investigated, other methods are employed, of which the following are the most important.

Dumas's Method (1827).—A light glass bulb, holding about 0·25 l, is drawn out at the opening to a long thin point, and then weighed. After partially exhausting it, by previous warming, about 1 g. of the liquid substance is drawn up into it. It is then placed in a heating bath, which has a measured constant temperature which must be above the boiling-point of the substance to be volatilised. After the contents have been completely volatilised, the point of the opening is sealed by melting the glass with a blow-pipe. The bulb, when cooled and cleaned, is then weighed again. Then it is filled with water by breaking off the sealed point under water. The experiment is regarded as satisfactory, only when it is filled completely with water, showing that only traces of air remain in the bulb. Its volume is obtained by weighing it filled, including the point broken off; an approximate weight suffices here.

Let m denote the weight of the bulb filled with air, m′ that when filled with the vapour, and finally M that when filled with water. Let t and b be the temperature and barometric pressure at the moment of sealing the opening, and t′ and b′ the corresponding values

---

[1] This method has been used recently by Rayleigh, Crafts, Leduc, Morley, etc., and worked out more thoroughly; see Morley, *Zeitschr. phys. Chem.* **17**. 87 (1895); **20**. 68 and 242 (1896).

at the first weighing. Let λ be the weight of 1 c.c. of air at pressure b' and temperature t'. Then will the density D be equal to

$$D = \left(\frac{m' - m}{M - m}\frac{1}{\lambda} + 1\right)\frac{b'}{b}\frac{1 + 0.00367t}{1 + 0.00367t'}.$$

Since 1 c.c of atmospheric air at $0°$ and 760 mm. weighs 0.001293 g., therefore λ amounts to

$$\lambda = \frac{0.001293}{1 + 0.00367t'}\frac{b'}{760}.$$

The Gay-Lussac-Hofmann Method (1868).

—A measured quantity, m, of the liquid in question is enclosed in a tiny bottle with a glass stopper. This is then introduced into an upright barometer and allowed to rise into the vacuum above the mercury. By means of a steam jacket, heated with the vapour of a suitable liquid, the barometer is warmed to such a temperature that the contents of the tiny bottle are vaporised. From the volume v, finally occupied by the vaporised substance at the temperature t, the density D is found to be

$$D = \frac{m}{v}\frac{1}{\lambda};$$

where again the value of λ, the weight of 1 c.c of air, at the temperature and pressure of the vaporised substance, is obtained from the formula,

$$\lambda = \frac{0.001293}{1 + 0.00367t}\frac{b - h - e}{760}.$$

Here the pressure, at which the vapour in the barometer tube stands, is equal to the external barometric pressure, b, at the time of the experiment, reduced to zero, minus the height, h, of the mercury column over which the vapour stands, reduced to zero, and minus also the vapour tension of mercury e, at the temperature t.

Victor Meyer's Method by the Displacement of Air (1878).

—All the methods thus far described are far surpassed in simplicity and certainty by this method. It shares with Hofmann's method the advantage of requiring only a very small quantity of a substance.

A long "pear-shaped" vessel, A in Fig. 21, is heated to *a constant temperature*, which must be above the boiling-point of the substance to be investigated, either by means of a heating bath,[1] or in any other suitable manner. It is not necessary to know this temperature in order to calculate the vapour density. The pear tube extends into a long tube of smaller diameter. This is closed

---

[1] For the description of a simple bath, see V. Meyer, *Ber. deutsch. chem. Ges.* **19.** 1861 (1886).

at its upper end, near which are two side tubes. One of these leads to a small delivery tube or to a gas burette. The other carries a glass rod which is provided at the opening with a tightly-fitting rubber tubing. This serves to drop the substance. It is somewhat enlarged in Fig. 21. On the small glass rod rests the substance to be used, enclosed within a tiny glass flask if it is a liquid, or if a solid, in the form of a little rod, obtained by sucking the molten substance up into a glass tube.

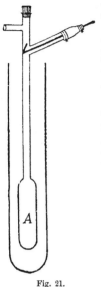

Fig. 21.

After the temperature has become nearly constant, as will be shown by the cessation of bubbles from the delivery tube, the substance is dropped by slipping back the glass rod, which is drawn back into position again by the elastic rubber. The substance falls to the bottom of the pear-shaped flask, which is provided with a cushion of asbestos, spiral wire, mercury, or the like, to avoid its being broken. The substance is at once vaporised. The disengaged vapour displaces the air above it, blocking its way; and if this occurs before there is any marked diffusion or condensation into the colder parts of the apparatus, then the vaporisation occurs quickly enough. The volume of air displaced is measured in the eudiometer, or in the gas burette; and this represents the volume which would be occupied by the substance at the same conditions of temperature and pressure. Thus the density D is

$$D = \frac{m}{b} \frac{760}{0 \cdot 001293} \frac{1 + 0 \cdot 004t}{v} = 587,800 \frac{m}{bv} (1 + 0 \cdot 004t).$$

Here m denotes the quantity of the substance used in grams, b the pressure in millimetres, and t the temperature at which the displaced volume, v, of air (measured in c.c.) is observed. The factor $0 \cdot 004$ is taken instead of the usual coefficient of expansion $0 \cdot 00367$, in order to take account of the moisture of the air.

One may also drop the substance into the pear-shaped flask by opening the stopper and closing as quickly as possible. A heating-jacket of glass around the " pear " may be used when the temperatures do not run too high.

It must be observed that the partial pressure at which the vaporised substance stands is *neither definite nor constant* ; but that from the bottom, where the substance is only slightly intermixed with the air present, and therefore where the pressure is almost equal to the atmospheric pressure, the partial pressure gradually sinks to zero at the top, and thus that it diminishes at all intermediate points with increasing diffusion. But this variation of the partial pressure, resulting from dilution with the obstructing air, may be disregarded in the measurement (*i.e.* in the measurement of the displaced air), *provided that the disengaged vapour conducts itself as an ideal gas and obeys Boyle's law*. Only in such cases will the quantity of displaced air be as great as though no intermixture had occurred through diffusion.

But the behaviour is entirely different when the substance which is to be studied exhibits dissociation (see Chapter VI.), and when it dissociates more and more as the partial pressure diminishes. In that case, the quantity of air displaced will be greater the more quickly the mingling occurs, and the results obtained will no longer bear a simple interpretation, because one does not know how far the mixture had gone at the time of the measurement, and therefore what the relative pressures may be under which the vaporised substance was studied.

The way in which the air is displaced may thus indicate qualitatively, whether the vaporised substance is conducting itself normally, or whether dissociation is taking place ; *in the latter case, the method is unsuitable for exact measurements, and will not give simple results*. (See Book III. Chapter II., " Influence of Indifferent Gases.")

The Determination of the Vapour Density at Very High Temperatures.—At high temperatures, Hofmann's method is debarred on account of the great vapour tension of mercury, and also for other reasons. The method of Dumas is quite difficult to use, since we are debarred from using a glass bulb at high temperatures (above 650°), and if a porcelain flask is used according to the modification of Deville and Troost, its point must be sealed with the oxyhydrogen blow-pipe. On the other hand, the method of the displacement of air has been used recently with very good results, even at very high temperatures (up to 2000°).

For the material of the heating bath there may be used boiling sulphur (444°), or boiling phosphorus pentasulphide (518°), or boiling stannous chloride (606°), and for still higher temperatures a charcoal furnace, or a Perrot's gas furnace which is fed with an air blast. As shown by the researches of Nilson and Pettersson (1889), and also by those of Biltz and V. Meyer (1889), it is possible in this way to reach and measure high temperatures which are sufficiently constant during the investigation ; these temperatures were easily regulated by controlling the supply of gas, and mounted as high as 1730°.

Using water-gas in a Perrot [1] furnace Biltz [2] attained a temperature of 1900° ; suitable materials for a vessel to use at this temperature are not known however (see below).

The pear-shaped vessels and the extension tubes are protected against injury, by making them of platinum free from soldering with any other metal, or of porcelain glazed both inside and outside. The latter has the advantage that it can be subjected directly to the gas

[1] For a description of the Perrot furnace see V. Meyer and C. Meyer, *Ber. deutsch. chem. Ges.* **12**. 1112 (1879).
[2] *Zeitschr. phys. Chem.* **19**. 385 (1896).

flames ; while the former, on account of its ready permeability by gases at high temperatures, must be protected from direct contact with the flame by a surrounding mantle of porcelain. Inasmuch as the porcelain "pears" begin to soften at 1700°, it is recommended that they be wrapped in thick platinum foil in order to increase their resistance to heat.

The dropping apparatus, and the tube delivering to the gas burette, are as before made of glass, and provided with rubber fittings at the ends of extension tubes which reach far enough out of the furnace ; they are protected from being heated by a screen at the side of the furnace.

In general the measurement differs in no detail from that conducted at lower temperatures, except that the substance cannot be vaporised in air on account of the great chemical activity of oxygen at high temperatures ; therefore, before the experiment, the apparatus must·be filled with some neutral gas, as nitrogen or carbon dioxide.

Although, as previously emphasised, it is not necessary to know the temperature at which the substance is vaporised, yet it is never-theless of great advantage in the case of substances which change their molecular weight with rising temperature. As a matter of fact, Nilson and Pettersson, 'V. Meyer, and others, without making the apparatus very complicated, succeeded in making vapour density determinations, combined with quite reliable determinations of the · temperature.

This experiment [1] consisted simply in using the "pear" as an *air thermometer* by heating it from the initial temperature (as 0° or the temperature of the room), and measuring the volume of the air dis-placed ; from this the final temperature was calculated from the well-known expansion coefficient of gases.

It is necessary to introduce a correction due to the expansion of the "pear" with the temperature ; this is given by the coefficient of volume expansion of the material of which it consists. Now it must be noticed that only the "pear" itself is exposed to the temperature which it is desired to measure, and this temperature diminishes along the extension tube down to the temperature of the room. As the correction which this involves introduces much difficulty into the calculation, it is determined directly by means of a *compensator ;* this is a companion tube closed below, of the same material as the extension tube, of the same form, and placed parallel to it and as near it as possible.

By subtracting the amount of gas driven out of the compensator, from that driven out·of the vapour density apparatus, one obtains the amount actually driven out of the "pear" by the elevation in tem-perature, which, reduced to 760 mm. and 0°, amounts to v. Further,

· [1] Nilson and Pettersson, *J. pr. Ch.* [2], **33**. 1 (1886) ; Biltz and Meyer, *Zeitschr. phys. Chem.* **4**. 249 (1889).

if V denotes the content of the pear (= the total content minus the content of the compensator), a the coefficient of expansion of gases (0·00367), and γ the cubic coefficient of expansion of the material of the pear (0·0000108 for porcelain and 0·000027 for platinum), then the final temperature is given by the simple formula :

$$t = \frac{v}{V (a - \gamma) - va}.$$

At very high temperatures, when only about $\frac{1}{4}$th of the original air remains in the apparatus, the method loses its accuracy, because here a very great increase in temperature causes the expulsion of only a very slight quantity of air.

Another method, used at the same time by Crafts and V. Meyer,[1] works much better ; this requires a more complicated apparatus, and consists in driving out the air or nitrogen contained in the apparatus at atmospheric temperature, and again at the temperature of the experiment by carbon dioxide or by hydrochloric acid ; measuring the former in a gas burette, while the displacing gas, in a quick stream, is absorbed by a solution of caustic potash, or by water in a gas burette. The displacing gas is introduced into the apparatus through a narrow tube which is fused into the lower part of the pear, and runs parallel with the extension tube ; and similarly the introduction of the gas into the compensator is effected by means of a tube sealed into it, and running parallel with the extension tube. The use of such an apparatus is rendered impossible in the case of porcelain pears by reason of technical difficulties, but pears of glass and platinum prove well suited for this purpose.

If V denotes the volume of the pear at 0° and 760° mm., and v that of the heating jacket containing dry nitrogen referred to 0° and 760 mm., then the temperature of the experiment (as before) is

$$t = \frac{V - v}{va - V\gamma}.$$

Of course V and v are regarded as corrected by the subtraction of the corresponding quantity of air driven out of the compensator.

The author[2] has recently succeeded both in simplifying the procedure described above and in extending the range of temperature available to 2000°. A small iridium vessel (made by Heraeus of Hanau) containing about 3 c.c. was heated by an electrically heated iridium tube : the small amount of gas driven out was measured by the movement of a mercury drop in a calibrated glass tube. The

[1] Crafts and Fr. Meier, *C.R.* **90**. 606 (1880) ; V. Meyer and Züblin, *Ber.* **13**. 2021 (1880). See also Langer and V. Meyer, *Pyrochemische Untersuchungen*, Brunswick (1885) ; Mensching and V. ·Meyer, *Zeitschr. phys. Chem.* **1**. 145 (1887).

[2] W. Nernst, *Z. f. Elektroch.* (1903), p. 622 ; cf. further Löwenstein, *Zeitschr. phys. Chem.* **54**. 707 (1906) ; and V. Wartenberg, *Ber. deutsch. chem. Ges.* **39**. 381 (1906) ; *Zeitschr. anorg. Chem.* **56**. 320 (1908).

substance to be gasified was weighed—usually a fraction of a milli-gram—on a "microbalance," constructed like a letter balance, the pan being fastened at right angles to horizontally stretched quartz fibre. The temperature was measured by the emission of light from the bottom of the iridium vessel; this was compared with a photometric, electrolytic glower (of a Nernst lamp). With this apparatus fairly accurate measurements could be taken easily and rapidly.

The Determination of the Vapour Density at Diminished Pressure.—An important method of vaporising substances consists not only in raising the temperature, but also in diminishing the pressure ; and indeed the latter alone is applicable when an elevation of temperature is attended by a decomposition of the substance which makes the determination of its vapour density impossible. The method of Hofmann is the only one of those described above, which permits the evaporation of the substance in a vacuum, and which therefore gives a determination at any desired diminished pressure. By combining the bulb used in the method of Dumas, with a water-pump and a manometer,[1] the pressure can be reduced very low ; but it is obvious that, on weighing the very small residue remaining in the bulb, the method loses in accuracy very considerably.

Finally, it has been recently shown by V. Meyer[2] that it is possible to determine the vapour density of a substance at temperatures from 20° to 40° below its boiling-point *by taking pains to vaporise it quickly.* In order to accomplish this it is necessary to spread the substance out quickly on the bottom of the pear. This is accomplished by dropping solid substances in the form of tiny rods ; and liquids enclosed in little flasks of Wood's metal, which melt immediately on arriving at the bottom of the pear. Also the use of hydrogen, as the packing gas, was found to be of advantage in increasing the speed of vaporisation, on account of its ready diffusibility [mobility].

Finally, a number of particular methods have been described for the determination of vapour densities at diminished pressures.

Malfatti and Schoop,[3] and Eykmann[4] as well as Bleier and Cohn[5] also in a modified way, measure the increase of pressure occasioned, in a space of known volume which is almost completely exhausted, by the vaporisation of a known quantity of the substance in question. Schall[6] compares the increase of pressure, resulting from such evapora-tion as that just described, with the increase of pressure from the admission of a known quantity of air into the exhausted apparatus, or from the escape of carbon dioxide from a known quantity of soda ; in

[1] Habermann, *Lieb. Ann.* **187.** 341 (1877).
[2] Demuth and Meyer, *Ber.* **23.** 311 (1890) ; Krause and V. Meyer, *Zeitschr. phys. Chem.* **6.** 5 (1890).
[3] *Zeitschr. phys. Chem.* **1.** 159 (1887).
[4] *Ber.* **22.** 2754 (1889).   [5] *Monatshefte f. Chem.* **20.** 909 (1900).
[6] *Ber.* **22.** 140 ; **23.** 919, 1701 (1890).

this method it is not necessary to know the volume of the apparatus. An apparatus has been described by Lunge and Neuberg,[1] which consists of a combination of V. Meyer's apparatus with a Lunge gas burette, and allows a very elegant control of the pressure under which the substance is vaporised.

The gas baroscope of Bodländer's[2] arrangement depends on the method of displacement, but the increase in pressure at constant volume is measured; a special advantage of this is that it avoids reduction to normal volume.

Calculation of Atomic Weight from Gas Density.—Atomic weights can be calculated from the molecular weights determined according to Avogadro's law (p. 167); usually this has only been done in an approximate manner, the exact value being subsequently arrived at by analysis.

Now, according to all probability Avogadro's law is strictly true for ideal gases; hence if the measurements on ordinary gases and vapours can be reduced to the ideal state, we have a purely physical method for exact determination of atomic weights from gas densities.

This method has been carried out with remarkable results by D. Berthelot.[3]

Let v_0 be the actual volume of a mol. of gas under normal conditions, V_0 that which a mol. of ideal gas would occupy under the same circumstances, then (p. 212)

$$V_0 = v_0\left(1 - \frac{b}{v_0} + \frac{a}{v_0{}^2}\right).$$

Hence to reduce the measured density of a gas to the ideal condition and obtain the exact molecular weight it must be multiplied by

$$\frac{v_0}{V_0} = \left(1 + \frac{b}{v_0} - \frac{a}{v_0{}^2}\right).$$

The simplest way to get the expression in brackets is by measurements of compressibility. As we are only concerned with gases in a condition approaching the ideal, the quantities $\frac{b}{v}$ and $\frac{a}{v^2}$ in van der Waals' formula are small compared with unity; we may therefore write with sufficient accuracy (see p. 239)

$$pv = RT\left[1 + p\left(\frac{b}{RT} - \frac{a}{(RT)^2}\right)\right],$$

i.e. pv must, for constant temperature, be a linear function of the pressure p. If, then, pv be measured for various pressures and extrapolated linearly to p = 0, we shall have accomplished the

[1] Ber. **24.** 724 (1891).   [2] Ibid. **27.** 2263 (1894).
[3] J. de phys. [3], **8.** 263 (1896); cf. Guye, Bull. Soc. Chim. [2], 33.

reduction to the ideal state.   D. Berthelot found the following
molecular weights :—

	H_2	N_2	CO	O_2	CO_2
d	0·062865	0·87508	0·87495	1·0000	1·38324
A	− 0·064	+ 0·038	0·046	0·076	0·674%
M	2·0145	28·013	28·007	32·000	44·000

	N_2O	HCl	C_2H_2	SO_2
d	1·38450	1·14836	0·81938	2·04835
A	+ 0·761	0·790	0·840	2·358%
M	44·000	36·486	26·020	64·050

Under A are given the corrections in per cent, calculated as
described above ; the observed densities must be reduced by these
amounts to yield- correct molecular weights.   The atomic weights
deduced from the latter are given in line (I.) below, while in (II.) are
the atomic weights from the table, p. 34 :

	O	H	C	N	S	Cl
(I.)	16·000	1·0075	12·004	14·005	32·050	35·479
(II.)	16·000	1·008	12·00	14·01	32·07	35·46

The remarkable agreement is evidence that Avogadro's law is true,
in the limit, with great, or perhaps complete accuracy.

The Determination of the Molecular Weight from the Osmotic Pressure of the Dissolved Substance.

—It has been
already stated that it is possible to determine the molecular weight of
any desired substance in any selected solvent, provided the concentration is not too great ; this depends upon van't Hoff's generalisation of
Avogadro's rule ; according to this, *the osmotic pressure of a substance in
solution, like the pressure of a gas, is independent of the nature of the
molecules, but simply proportional to their number, and is identical with
the corresponding gas pressure* (see p. 150).   Thus, if there are c grams
of a substance dissolved in 1 litre of any selected solvent, and if the
pressure at the temperature t, exerted by this on a partition (which is
permeable for the solvent, but not for the dissolved substance),
amounts to p atmospheres, then the molecular weight of the dissolved
substance is calculated to be

$$M = 22·41(1 + 0·00367t)\frac{c}{p} ;$$

for (p. 40) 1 mol. of any selected gas, when enclosed in the space
of 1 litre, at 0°, exerts a pressure of 22·41 atm., and at t° a pressure of
22·41 (1 + 0·00367t) ; and the osmotic pressure is equal to this,
multiplied by the relative number of molecules, viz. $\frac{c}{M}$: 1, from
which we derive the preceding formula.

Now the direct experimental determination of osmotic pressure is
attended by great difficulties : hence osmotic measurements for
molecular weight determination have been used only occasionally, as

once by de Vries,[1] who determined the molecular weight of raffinose by comparing a solution of it with the known osmotic pressure of a plant-cell, by the plasmolytic method.

On the other hand, we possess several methods for the indirect measurements of the osmotic pressure, which give simple and exact results ; we are indebted to Raoult especially for their discovery. Since the lowering of the freezing-point, of the vapour pressure, and of the solubility, experienced by *a solvent* on adding a foreign sub-stance, are all proportional to the osmotic pressure of the substance added, by measuring these depressions we obtain directly the molecular weight of the dissolved substance.

The Depression of the Freezing-Point.—If the addition of m grams of a substance to 100 g. of a solvent lowers the freezing-point of the latter t degrees, then the molecular weight of the dissolved substance is calculated from the formula

$$M = E\frac{m}{t};$$

here E, the "molecular depression of the freezing-point" of the particular solvent used, is obtained from the heat of fusion w, of 1 g. of the solvent, expressed in g.-cal. and from its fusing-point T in absolute temperature ; thus

$$E = R\frac{T_0^2}{100w} = 0.02\frac{T^2}{w}.$$

The molecular depressions of the freezing-point for the solvents thus far investigated are given in the table on p. 147. The accuracy of the formula requires that the *pure* solvent shall freeze out of the solution, and not a mixture of the solvent with the dissolved substance (p. 163).

A great variety of pieces of apparatus which, however, are essentially the same in principle, have been described to measure the depression of the freezing-point.[2] Of these we will describe the apparatus constructed by Beckmann,[3] which was universally adopted in a very short time, and which enables one to measure the lowering of the freezing-point very simply and accurately.

The vessel A, Fig. 22, which is designed to hold the solvent, con-sists of a thick-walled test-tube, having a side tube. After pouring in the solvent, about 15 or 20 g. being weighed or measured out with a pipette, there is introduced a stirrer made of thick platinum

---

[1] *C.R.* **106.** 751 (1888).

[2] Raoult, *Ann. chim. phys.* [6], **2.** 93 (1884) ; **8.** (1886) ; *Zeitschr. phys. Chem.* **9.** 343 (1892) ; Hollemann, *Ber.* **21.** 860 (1888) ; Auwers, *ib.* 701 ; Eykmann, *Zeitschr. phys. Chem.* **4.** 497 (1889) ; Fabinyi, *ib.* **2.** 964 (1888) ; Klobukow, *ib.* **4.** 10 (1889).

[3] *Zeitschr. phys. Chem.* **2.** 638 (1888). See especially G. Fuchs, *Anleitung zu Molekulargewichtsbestimmungen*, Leipzig (1895).

wire, and then the thermometer D, fitted with a cork. In order to hold the test-tube in place, and also to protect it with an air-jacket, it is fitted with a cork ring into another wider test-tube B. The whole is placed in a glass jar C filled with the cooling mixture, the temperature of which should be carefully kept constant during the experiment, and at about 4° below the freezing-point of the solvent.

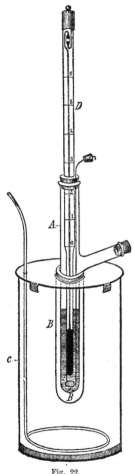

A measurement is conducted in the following way : First, the test-tube containing the requisite quantity of the pure solvent is dipped into the cooling mixture, and at the same time is constantly stirred till the whole is a little undercooled, and there occurs a separation of *finely-divided ice*, attended by a sudden rise in the thermometer to the freezing-point of the solvent. In this way, when the test-tube is protected by the air-jacket, which prevents its heat from being given off too suddenly, we obtain an exact measurement of the freezing-point of the solvent itself. We then add, through the side tube, a weighed amount of the substance to be investigated, and, after melting the solvent by careful warming, redetermine the freezing-point of the solution in exactly the same way as before. The resulting depression of the freezing-point is obtained by subtraction.

Although we are now in possession of all the data requisite for the calculation of the molecular weight, yet it is recommended that a series of observations be made by adding successive portions of the substance, in order to determine whether the molecular weight is independent of the concentration, or whether the degree of dissociation varies with the concentration.

Fig. 22.

In investigating solutions of greater concentration, the amount of ice separated must be as little as possible, in order to avoid the errors consequent upon too great a change of concentration from the freezing out of too large a portion of the solvent. This can be accomplished easily with a little practice. The side tube serves to introduce the solid substances. To introduce liquid substances one may use as a wash bottle the Sprengel-Ostwald pyknometer. More recently Beckmann has described a simple apparatus which enables one to use solvents which are strongly hygroscopic.[1]

As the measurement of the freezing-point can be accomplished with a little practice, within some thousandths of a degree, it is recommended to use a thermometer divided to read directly to hundredths of a degree. In order to use such a thermometer over wide ranges of temperature ($-6°$ to $+60°$), Beckmann devised a thermometer where the capillary above passed into a bent mercury reservoir (see Fig. 22). According as the thermometer is to be used with solvents having a higher or lower freezing-point, more or less of the mercury is passed from the capillary into the lower part of the reservoir by warming and carefully tapping the thermometer. The value of the scale of the thermometer practically remains unchanged, since we are merely concerned in measuring differences of temperature.

A method, given by the author, for measuring the freezing-point of solutions, especially at high concentrations, has been worked out by M. Roloff.[2] The principle of the method is to determine the composition of the solution that is in equilibrium with the frozen solvent at a given temperature. This may also be looked upon as a measurement of the solubility of the solvent in the given solution. In working out the method the first difficulty met with was to maintain constant low temperatures. Cryohydrates formed by mechanical mixture of snow and·salts are not finely enough divided to give really constant temperatures. If, however, the cryohydrates be formed. by freezing saturated salt solutions, they keep their cryohydric temperatures exactly till the freezing is complete. By the use of appropriate salts all temperatures from $0°$ to $-30°$ can be obtained.

The principle of the method is to measure the composition of a solution corresponding to a certain freezing-point, instead of determining the freezing-point of a given solution.

Water, acetic acid, and benzene are the solvents most used. Very remarkable results were obtained by using Glauber salt as solvent ($E = 32·6$). Löwenherz, *Zeitschr. phys. Chem.* **18.** 70 (1895).

Freezing-point of very Dilute Solutions.—It is important to make sufficiently exact measurements on very dilute solutions, both on account of the theoretical importance of such solutions and practically to obtain the molecular weight of slightly soluble substances. Early observers obtained somewhat erroneous values for the aqueous solutions with which, in the first place, they concerned themselves ; but recently results of value seem to have been arrived at.

It has been found that the influence of the cooling-bath and of

---

[1] *Zeitschr. phys. Chem.* **7.** 323 (1891) ; **22.** 616 (1897).
[2] *Ibid.* **18.** 572 (1895). The method described later by T. W. Richards (*Journ. Amer. Chem. Soc.* **25.** 291, 1903) is entirely identical.

the heat generated by stirring produce errors of some thousandths of a degree or more ; this is of no consequence in careful measurements of molecular weight of substances at moderate concentrations, but must—and can—be avoided in dealing with very dilute solutions.

The following is a brief account of the theory of the establishment of equilibrium on freezing [1] :—Given a large mass of freezing liquid : let the true freezing-point be T_0, *i.e.* the temperature at which the separated solid and residual liquid are in equilibrium ; let the temperature at time x be t. Then t will approach T_0 by the melting or freezing of some of the solvent, and the accompanying absorption or evolution of heat, according as t is above or below T_0. The outside temperatures exert no influence, since we have assumed a large mass of liquid.

According to experience on the solution of solids (Book III. Chapter V.), the rate of solution of the solid solvent may be taken as proportional, other circumstances being equal, to its difference in temperature from the point of equilibrium ; but as the heat absorbed is proportional to the mass dissolved, the rate of change of temperature at any moment may be put proportional to the difference between T_0 and t. Thus

$$dt = K(T_0 - t)dz \qquad . \quad . \quad . \quad . \quad (1)$$

We need not trouble as to the meaning of K except that it is proportional to the total area of the solid solvent and its heat of fusion. On integrating we get

$$K(z_2 - z_1) = \ln \frac{T_0 - t_1}{T_0 - t_2} \qquad . \quad . \quad . \quad (2)$$

where t_1, t_2 are the temperatures at times z_1, z_2.

Actually the mass of liquid is limited, so that there will be an interchange of heat with the surroundings by radiation, etc., as well as a production of heat by stirring. If we call t_0 the temperature that the solution would tend towards if no freezing took place (the " convergence temperature "), the course of the temperature, if there were no separation of solid, would be given by Newton's law as

$$dt = k(t_0 - t)dz \qquad . \quad . \quad . \quad . \quad (3)$$

with the integral

$$k(z_2 - z_1) = \ln \frac{t_0 - t_1}{t_2 - t_0} \qquad . \quad . \quad . \quad (4)$$

Again the physical meaning of k is unimportant ; we need only remark that k is smaller the greater the ratio of thermal capacity of the solution to surface exposed.

The actual course of the thermometer in a finite mass of solution is found by adding (1) and (3) :

$$dt = [K(T_0 - t) + k(t_0 - t)]dz \qquad . \quad . \quad (5)$$

which gives, on integration,

$$(K + k)(z_2 - z_1) = \ln \frac{KT_0 + kt_0 - (K + k)t_1}{KT_0 + kt_0 - (K + k)t_2} \qquad . \quad (6)$$

[1] Nernst and Abegg, *Zeitschr. phys. Chem.* **15.** 681 (1894).

The final temperature t', which may conveniently be called the apparent freezing-point, is given by

$$\frac{dt}{dz} = K(T_0 - t') + k(t_0 - t') = 0,$$

or
$$t' = T_0 - \frac{k}{K}(t' - t_0) \qquad . \quad . \quad . \quad . \quad (7)$$

The thermometer settles therefore, not at T_0, but at the somewhat different temperature t'; the latter is the closer to the former, the nearer the convergence temperature t_0 is to the freezing-point T_0, and also the larger K by comparison with k.   The true and apparent freezing-points are only identical when

$$t_0 = t',$$

or
$$K = \infty .$$

Hence, to obtain correct values, either the temperature of the freezing mixture must be carefully regulated, so that the convergence temperature practically coincides with the point to which the thermometer settles, or else the correction $\frac{k}{K}(t' - t_0)$ must be obtained by special experiments (see the work of Abegg and Raoult already quoted on p. 139).   It should be observed that for electrolytes, as for water, K is usually so large that the correction is negligible (though K of course varies according to the way ice separates). It is otherwise with non-electrolytes, such as sugar ; for these Raoult,[1] Jones,[2] and others found erroneous values, which were only corrected by means of experiments conducted in accordance with the above theory of Abegg and the present writer.   Only recently have Raoult[1] and Loomis[3] taken up the same standpoint as ourselves.   Hausrath[4] has succeeded, by refinements in temperature measurement, in measuring the freezing-point of solutions to $0\cdot00001°$.   Beckmann (*Zeitschr. phys. Chem.* **44.** 161 (1903)) has shown how the accuracy of the experiments can be increased by lessening the above corrections (*e.g.* by electrical stirring).

The Lowering of the Vapour Pressure.—The law which was developed theoretically by van't Hoff, and experimentally by Raoult, states that the lowering of the vapour pressure experienced by a solvent on adding a non-volatile substance, is equal to the number of molecules of the dissolved substance divided by the number of molecules of the solvent ; this leads at once to the determination of the molecular weight.   Let p be the vapour pressure of the pure solvent at a selected temperature, and p' that of a solution containing m grams of a foreign substance dissolved in 100 g. of the solvent; then, according to the preceding law, we shall have

$$\frac{p - p'}{p'} = \frac{mM_0}{M100},$$

where M denotes the molecular weight of the dissolved substance, and M_0 that of the solvent, as ascertained from a determination of the

[1] *Zeitschr. phys. Chem.* **9.** 343 (1892).   [3] *Ibid.* **32.** 584 (1900).
[2] *Ibid.* **11.** 529 ; **12.** 623 (1893).   [4] *Wied. Ann.* **9.** 522 (1902).

vapour density. Then we shall have, in terms of those quantities only which are directly accessible,

$$M = M_0 \frac{mp'}{100(p - p_1)}.$$

But considerable experimental difficulties are found to interfere with the practical application of this formula. For many reasons the exact measurement of the vapour pressure of a solution is not a simple problem. Also, since the difference in the preceding formula, between any two vapour pressures to be measured, amounts to only a small percentage, it is necessary that this measurement should be very exact. Moreover, the selection of a method [1] for measuring simply and accurately the difference between the vapour pressure of a solvent and of the solution has not hitherto been attended with good results. It is only recently that Beckmann [2] accomplished this in an indirect way; instead of determining the lowering of the vapour pressure after the method of Raoult, *he determined the corresponding elevation of the boiling-point.*

It follows directly from the equations, developed on p. 136, that

$$M = E \frac{m}{t},$$

where m has the same meaning as above, and t denotes the observed elevation of the boiling-point. E, the "molecular elevation of the boiling-point" [for the particular solvent], is calculated as follows, from the heat of vaporisation l, of 1 g. of the solvent at its boiling-point T, in the absolute scale; thus

$$E = \frac{0 \cdot 02 T^2}{l}.$$

The following table shows E, calculation and experiment giving results in agreement for the solvents thus far investigated :—

	E	T – 273			E	T – 273
Benzene . . .	26·7	80	Ethyl alcohol . .	11·5	78
Chloroform . .	36·6	61	Ethyl acetate . .	25·1	75
Ethylene bromide .	63·2	132	Ethyl ether . .	21·2	35
Carbon disulphide .	23·7	46	Acetone . . .	16·7	56
Acetic acid . .	25·3	118	Aniline . . .	32·2	182
Phenol . . .	30·4	132	Water . . .	5·2	100
Nitrobenzene . .	50	205			

[1] Raoult, *Ann. chim. phys.* [6], **20.** (1890) ; Will and Bredig., *Ber.* **22.** 1084 (1888) ; Beckmann, *Zeitschr. phys. Chem.* **4.** 532 (1889). [An accurate method for determining the vapour pressures of solutions has been introduced by Berkeley and Hartley, *Proc. Roy. Soc.* **77.** 156 (1906) ; *Phil. Trans.* **209.** 177. The results obtained by this method for the osmotic pressures of solutions agree closely with those found by direct measurement.—Tr.]

[2] *Zeitschr. phys. Chem.* **4.** 532 (1889) ; **6.** 437 (1890) ; also Raoult, *C.R.* **87.** 167 (1878).

The measurement of the elevation of the boiling-point can be conducted very accurately by means of the apparatus shown in Fig. 23.[1] The three-neck flask A serves to heat the liquid ; the bottom is pierced

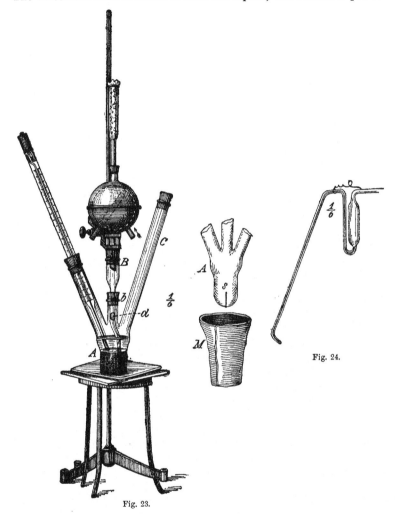

Fig. 23.

Fig. 24.

with a short thick piece of platinum wire, set in with cement glass (*Einschmelzglas*), and is also half-filled with glass beads.   A thermometer, provided with a mercury reservoir as in the freezing apparatus, and thus made serviceable for temperatures from 30° to 120°, is fitted

[1] Beckmann, *Zeitschr. phys. Chem.* **4.** 543 (1889) ; see also the short monograph by Fuchs, and further Beckmann, *ibid.* **40.** 129 (1902) ; **44.** 161 (1903).

in one opening. An inverted condenser is fastened into the middle opening (b) ; this condenser has an opening at d, which serves to give free passage for the steam. On account of its ready condensation, the apparatus of Soxhlet is used, and this is protected from the moisture of

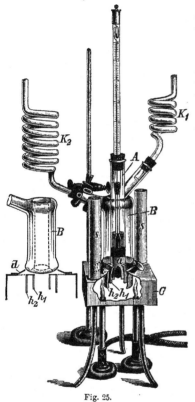

the air by a chloride of calcium tube. A third opening, C, serves to introduce the substance to be dissolved.

In conducting the operation, the flask is first partly filled with a definite quantity of the solvent, which is either weighed or measured with a pipette. It is then heated by a gas lamp, which can be suitably regulated, and is protected against too sudden heating by an asbestos jacket. The flame is so regulated that a drop shall fall from the condenser B every ten or twenty seconds. The upper part of the apparatus is protected against the heat by two pieces of asbestos paper, one of which is cut out with a circular opening for a support. The heat is largely transmitted through the platinum wire which is fused into the bottom of the flask, and which touches the lower asbestos paper. As a result of this, bubbles of vapour form at its upper end, when the liquid boils ; and on account of the glass beads present, the bubbles must pass up through the liquid in serpentine courses, thus having sufficient time to bring

Fig. 25.

themselves into temperature equilibrium corresponding to the external pressure, and to the concentration. After the temperature has been kept constant within a few thousandths of a degree, the substance to be dissolved is introduced in a weighed quantity, through the opening C, solid substances being in the shape of little sticks or lozenges, and liquids being introduced by means of the pipette shown in Fig. 24. As was done in the case of the freezing-point method, so here also it is recommended to make several determinations with increasing concentration.

Beckmann[1] has since described a modified form of his boiling-

[1] *Zeitschr. phys. Chem.* **8.** 223 (1891) ; see also Beckmann, Fuchs, and Gernhardt, *ibid.* **18.** 473 (1895).

point apparatus, by the use of which it is not only possible to employ liquids of a higher boiling-point, but it is also so shaped that a very little of the solvent and of the dissolved substance will give very exact results.   The flask A, containing the liquid, is shaped (Fig. 25) like the flask in the freezing-point apparatus figured on p. 260.   It is a side-necked test-tube, 2·5 cm. wide, is provided with a thick platinum wire sealed into the bottom, and is filled to a depth of 3-4 cm. with glass beads.   The thermometer is fitted in by means of a cork.   The boiling-flask is surrounded by a steam-jacket of glass, B, containing about 20 c.c. of the solvent, and shown in a special figure. Between the boiling-flask and the vapour jacket is a roll of asbestos paper, and both are provided with return condensers, K_1 and K_2, which can be replaced in the case of volatile solvents by small Liebig condensers.   Bunsen burners serve for heating, and, as shown in the figure, these are placed at the side of the vapour jacket.   Where the

flames strike there are pieces of wire gauze, and also cres- cent-shaped plates of asbestos paper, which are arched above by a little asbestos saucer d ; also the rings h_1 and h_2 protect the boiling-flask from the direct flame ; ss are little chimneys of asbestos paper for the flame gases.   If necessary, the boil- ing-flask itself is also heated directly by a small flame which does not touch it, but, as a rule, the heat introduced from the

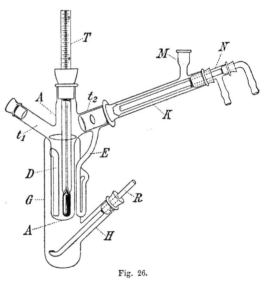

Fig. 26.

outer vapour jacket is sufficient to bring the inner liquid to com- plete boiling.   The right condition of boiling will be shown, as in the other form of apparatus, by the constant reading of the thermometer.

Finally a boiling-point apparatus of new construction [1] is shown in Fig. 26 ; in this apparatus the solution is heated by the vapour of the solvent.

The apparatus therefore depends on the phenomenon that the vapour

[1] Beckmann, *Zeitschr. phys. Chem.* **40.** 129 (1902) ; a few improvements in the method (*e.g.* electrical heating of the liquid) are given in *Zeitschr. phys. Chem.* **63.** 177 (1908).

of the solvent partially condenses in the solution because of the lower vapour pressure of the latter, and the heat of condensation brings the solution exactly to its boiling-point.   The boiling tube, as in the earlier apparatus, consists of the glass tube A, with a side tube t_1 for introducing the substance; to a second side tube t_2 the reverse condenser is attached.   The boiling mantle G is fused on to the boiling tube.   The vapour given off passes through the tube D, (which is 7 mm. wide, and somewhat jagged at the lower end), down to nearly the bottom of the boiling tube, in which it is partially condensed.   The non-condensed part passes into the reverse condenser K, and is completely liquefied in the cooler N.   The resulting liquid can be led back into the boiling tube or boiling mantle as required. In the drawing (Fig. 26) a direct flow back into the boiling tube takes place; but by turning the condenser round, the liquid can be made to flow through a hole in the glass joint back into E, and thence into G.   In this manner it is possible to regulate the amount of liquid in the boiling tube.   The concentration is determined by weighing the amount of substance introduced, and measuring the volume of the solution, for which purpose the boiling tube is graduated in millimetres.   The boiling mantle can be filled with liquid through the side tube H; R is a safety tube, which makes it impossible for the liquid to suck back from the boiling tube into G.   M can be fitted into a calcium chloride tube.   The heating is conducted as in the other apparatus.

The accuracy of measurement is certainly greatest with the apparatus first described; but as the determination of molecular weights in practice only needs moderate accuracy, it is better to use the last apparatus, on account of its greater convenience.

The Investigation of Volatile Substances.—The use of the forms of apparatus just described implies that the substance dissolved is not lost by volatilisation.   Experience shows that this condition is met when its boiling-point lies about 130° above that of the solvent.

If the dissolved substance begins to volatilise in a noticeable way, then, according to the statements on p. 148, it has the same molecular weight in the state of a vapour and in the solution, if the partial pressure of its vapour is proportional to its concentration in the solution; or, in other words, if the vapour of the dissolved substance follows Henry's law of absorption.   If the dissolved substance has a molecular weight different from that in the gaseous condition, then there occur striking deviations from a simple ratio.   We will consider these laws further in the Third Book, Chapter III.

There is no difficulty,[1] on the basis of these considerations, in extending the theory of the boiling-point apparatus to the case where the dissolved substance has its own vapour pressure.   I will here

[1] Nernst, *Zeitschr. phys. Chem.* **8.** 16 (1891); Beckmann, *ibid.* **17.** 110 (1895).

merely indicate briefly that the boiling apparatus, in this case also, is able to afford information regarding the molecular condition of the dissolved substance. Provided the dissolved substance is sufficiently volatile, then if Henry's law is true, changes of the boiling-point, which in this case (see also p. 106) may consist in an elevation or a lowering, according to circumstances, will be proportional to the concentration. If this is so, the substance has the same molecular condition in the state of vapour as in solution. If the latter condition is not fulfilled, there is not even approximate proportionality between the changes of boiling-point and concentration.

Of course it is immaterial for the freezing-point method whether the dissolved substance is volatile or not.

The Lowering of Solubility.—A third method, recently added to the two so-called Raoult-van't Hoff methods, by the author, has both a theoretical and an experimental basis (see pp. 136 and 145). According to this, *the relative lowering of solubility experienced by a solvent, as ether, in another solvent, as water, on the addition of a third substance [which is soluble only in the first solvent], is equal to the number of dissolved molecules of this third substance divided by the number of molecules of the [first] solvent.* Thus, let L denote the solubility of the [first] pure solvent in the second solvent, and L' its solubility when m grams of the substance are dissolved in 100 g. of the first solvent ; then the molecular weight of the dissolved substance can be calculated as accurately as from the lowering of the vapour pressure (p. 263), and with only such magnitudes as can be determined directly, as follows :—

$$M = M_0 \frac{mL'}{100(L - L')}.$$

Here M_0 denotes the molecular weight which the first solvent has when dissolved in the second.

There are several chemical and physical methods which can be used to determine the solubility, and it is not necessary to determine the absolute values, but only the ratio of the solubility before and after adding the substance. When using ether and water, one can advantageously employ Beckmann's freezing apparatus with 20 c.c. of ether and 5 c.c. of water, to determine the change of solubility.[1] Then the freezing-point of water is at that temperature which corresponds to the depressed freezing-point (– 3·85°), occasioned by its saturation with ether. Now, if a third substance is added to the ether, according to the aforesaid theorem, the solubility of ether in the water will diminish in proportion to the molecular content of the third substance that it [*i.e.* the ether] absorbs, and thus the freezing-point of the water will *rise*. This elevation of the freezing-

[1] *Zeitschr. phys. Chem.* **6.** 573 (1890).

point can be exactly determined, and, as numerous experiments have shown, the method is capable of exactly the same degree of accuracy as the Raoult-van't Hoff method.   As the non-volatility of the substance in question was presupposed in the boiling-point method, so here we must assume that the [third] substance is insoluble in water [or in the second solvent used, whatever it may be].

The above method has been worked out further by F. W. Küster,[1] who used phenol as one solvent and saturated common salt solution as the other, measuring the solubility of the phenol by titration; also by Tolloczko,[2] who used ether and a relatively large quantity of water, and measured the change in volume of the latter due to solution of foreign bodies directly.   The latter method leaves nothing to be desired in simplicity, especially for strong solutions.

The Distribution of a Substance between Two Solvents.— A very simple and exact method for comparing the molecular condition of a substance in two solvents, which are only partially soluble in each other, is to *determine the dependence of the relative distribution upon the concentration.*   If the dissolved substance has the same molecular condition in the two solvents the distribution is independent of the concentration (p. 149).   If the molecular condition is not the same, then the coefficient of distribution will vary with the concentration in a very pronounced way.   This subject will be considered again in the third book.

The Rôle of the Solvent.—All the methods thus far described for the determination of the molecular weights of substances in solution are based on the same principle; this consists in the measurement of the osmotic pressure and its evaluation, in the sense of Avogadro's rule as generalised by van't Hoff.   Therefore all these methods thus far used, though apparently very diverse, lead to the same results when the investigation concerns the same substances in the same solvents.   But numerous instances are known where the aforesaid substances when dissolved in different solvents show a *different* molecular condition.   Thus acetic acid when dissolved in benzene, at a sufficient degree of concentration, consists almost entirely of molecules having the formula $(CH_3CO_2H)_2 = 120$; when dissolved in ether, of $CH_3CO_2H = 60$; and when dissolved in water, as will be

$$\overset{-}{}\qquad\overset{+}{}$$

seen later, it is split electrolytically into the ions, CH_3COO and H. In the gaseous state, according to the external conditions, we find acetic acid to consist more or less entirely of the "normal" molecules, CH_3CO_2H.

This result does not, of course, speak against the correctness of the methods, neither is it at all surprising.   The molecular condition of a

[1] *Ber. deutsch. chem. Ges.* **27.** 324 and 328 (1894).
[2] *Zeitschr. phys. Chem.* .**20.** 389 (1896).

vaporised or of a dissolved substance varies not only with the external conditions of temperature and pressure, as shown in numerous instances, but also, in the case of dissolved substances, with the nature of the solvent employed.

The question now arises whether the difference between the molecular condition of a substance in the gaseous state, and of the same substance in solution, is to be ascribed to *a chemical action* by the solvent.   This question is of surpassing interest, but it is impossible to answer it at present.   For it must be emphasised that any compound of the molecules of the solvent with the molecules of the dissolved substance, at slight degrees of concentration, *would have no effect in changing the osmotic pressure of the latter,* and therefore would not appear in the figures of the lowering of the freezing-point and the like.

We do not know at present, and we have no good reason to show whether the possibility that the *"dissociating force"* of water, in its capacity as a solvent, may cause it to form compounds with the dissolved substance in the way of hydration, is well grounded or not.[1] One fact that is often overlooked is that the measurements of osmotic pressure make no disclosures regarding any compounds of the molecules of the solvent with those of the dissolved substance.   (See Book III. Chapter II.)

We must be forewarned also against another very common error concerning the osmotic method ; it has been supposed that it afforded some information regarding the molecular condition of the *solvent* itself in the liquid state.   Thus Raoult and Recoura,[2] instead of obtaining the formula (as on p. 263)

$$M = 60 \frac{mp'}{100(p - p')}$$

for the lowering of the vapour pressure of acetic acid, where 60 denotes the [normal] molecular weight, actually obtained

$$M = 1\cdot61 \, . \, 60 \frac{mp'}{100(p - p')} \, ;$$

from which they concluded the molecular weight of liquid acetic acid to be

$$M_0 = 1\cdot61 \, . \, 60 = 97.$$

This conclusion is not well grounded ; the results of this investigator can be more simply explained, by supposing that the density of the saturated vapour of acetic acid at the temperature of the experiment (118°) was 1·61 times as great as the theoretical value, 2·08 ; and therefore that its calculated molecular weight (97) should be introduced into the formula.   At the same time, these experiments

[1] Bruhl, *Zeitschr. phys. Chem.* **18.** 514 (1895) ; **27.** 319 (1898).

[2] *C.R.* **110.** 402 ; *Zeitschr. phys. Chem.* **5.** 423 (1890).

show that the osmotic pressure of dissolved substances is normal, *i.e.* that it obeys the gas laws, even when the vapour of the solvent itself is abnormal.

The relation that seems to exist between dissociating power of a solvent and its dielectric constant is discussed in Chapter VII. of this Book.

Molecular Weight of Strongly-Compressed Gases and of Liquids.—Avogadro's rule does not hold good for strongly-compressed gases, but, as we have seen in the previous chapter, van der Waals' formula may be applied.

It is assumed, in the derivation of this formula, that the molecular condition does not alter on compression ; conversely we may conclude that when a substance does not obey the equation, the condition in question is not fulfilled.

In a similar way, half empirical and half theoretical, corresponding conclusions may be drawn from the rules deduced in the preceding chapter for substances which behave normally.

We have seen (p. 231) that the critical densities are 3·7 to 3·8 times the theoretical. For ethyl alcohol this ratio is 4·02, which indicates polymerisation—in agreement with the other methods to be described in this and the following paragraph.

A further criterion [1] is deviation from the rule of Cailletet and Mathias (p. 228), which alcohol shows in a marked way. The course of the vapour-pressure curve seems to be especially influenced by polymerisation ; we have already (p. 234) seen examples of this in alcohol and water. Corresponding, finally, to the fact that polymerisation of molecules in the liquid state is accompanied by an evolution of heat, which is shown by a high heat of evaporation, we shall find, in Chapter V. of this Book, that the determination of this magnitude gives us a very reliable test for the existence of polymerisation. Although we are thus easily able (see also the two following paragraphs) to decide whether association in the liquid state takes place or not, we are nevertheless unhappily still in want of a certain method to determine accurately the degree of association.

Molecular Weight and Heat of Evaporation.—For the molecular heat of evaporation we have the relation (p. 59)

$$\lambda = RT^2 \frac{d \ln p}{dT} \qquad . \qquad . \qquad . \qquad (1)$$

or, transformed,

$$\frac{\lambda}{T} = R \frac{d \ln p}{d \ln T} \qquad . \qquad . \qquad . \qquad (2)$$

According to the theory of van der Waals (see especially p. 224), the differential quotient on the right-hand side should be of the same

[1] See especially Guye (*Archives des sciences phys. et nat. de Genève*, **31.** 38 (1894)).

value for all substance at corresponding states. Now Guldberg[1] pointed out that the boiling-point on the absolute scale is nearly always about $\frac{2}{3}$ the critical absolute temperature even for widely different substances. This is shown in the following table :—

Substance.	Abs. Critical Temp. (T_1).	Abs. Boiling-point (T_2).	$\frac{T_2}{T_1}$
Oxygen . . .	155	90	0·58
Nitrous oxide . .	309	184	0·60
Chlorine . . .	414	240	0·58
Sulphur dioxide . .	429	263	0·61
Ethyl ether . . .	467	308	0·66
Ethyl alcohol . .	516	351	0·68
Phenol . . .	691	454	0·66

It follows that *the quotient of molecular heat of evaporation and absolute boiling-point must be approximately the same for all substances.* This law has, in fact, been put forward, and until quite recently has been assumed at least approximately correct (Trouton's Rule); the value of the quotient is about 20-22.

A more rigid examination of the law, with substances of widely different boiling-points, shows, however, that the ratio is by no means constant, but increases regularly with the temperature.[2]

In the thermodynamic calculation of heats of evaporation it must be borne in mind that saturated vapour at the boiling-point, especially that of substances of high molecular weight, does not obey the gas laws (see also p. 60); from the formulae developed on page 235 it follows easily that

$$\lambda = R\frac{T_1 T_2}{T_1 - T_2}\left(1 - \frac{p}{\pi_0}\right) \ln \frac{p_1}{p_2} \qquad . \qquad . \qquad . \qquad (3)$$

where p_1, p_2, are the vapour pressures corresponding to the two absolute temperatures T_1, T_2; the latter must be near enough together for their arithmetic and geometric means to be practically the same. Formula (3) is well supported by direct measurements; as a rule the values calculated from the formula will be more accurate than those determined calorimetrically.

The following table contains the boiling-points T_0 of a few substances, and their heats of evaporation λ_0 at the boiling-points, calculated for formula (3); for hydrogen alone is given the apparently very accurate value determined calorimetrically by Dewar[3] :—

---

[1] *Zeitschr. phys. Chem.* **5.** 374 (1890).

[2] Nernst, *Gött. Nachr.* Heft 1, 1906 ; cf. also Bingham, *Journ. Amer. Chem. Soc.* **28.** (1906).

[3] *Proc. Roy. Soc.* **76.** 325 (1905).

Substance.	T_0	λ	$\dfrac{\lambda}{T_0}$	$9{\cdot}5 \log T_0 - 0{\cdot}007 T_0$.
Hydrogen . . .	20·4	248	12·2	12·3
Nitrogen . . .	77·5	1362	17·6	17·4
Argon	86·0	1460	17·0	17·8
Oxygen . . .	90·6	1664	18·3	18·0
Methane . . .	108	1951	18·0	18·6
Ethyl ether . . .	307	6466	21·1	21·5
Carbon bisulphide	319	6490	20·4	21·6
Benzene . . .	353	7497	21·2	21·7
Propyl acetate . .	375	8310	22·2	21·8
Aniline . . .	457	10,500	23·0	22·1
Methyl salicylate .	497	11,000	22·2	22·1

It is at once seen that $\dfrac{\lambda}{T_0}$ rises considerably and regularly with the absolute temperature ; the expression given in the last column (which I have derived from certain considerations which will not be gone into here)—

$$\frac{\lambda}{T_0} = 9{\cdot}5 \log T_0 - 0{\cdot}007 T_0 \qquad . \qquad . \qquad . \qquad (4)$$

agrees well with observation, and may suitably be called the "*revised rule of Trouton*."

Substances which are considerably polymerised in the liquid state, but possess normal densities in the gaseous state, show higher values than those corresponding to the above formula—

	T_0.	λ	$\dfrac{\lambda}{T_0}$	$9{\cdot}5 \log T_0 - 0{\cdot}007 T_0$.
Alcohol . . .	351	9448	26·9	21·7
Water . . .	373	9650	25·9	21·8

This is, therefore, a further criterion for association in the liquid condition. As both λ_0 and T_0 must be increased by association, it must be concluded that the first value is more strongly influenced than the second.

The behaviour of acetic acid is peculiar :

	T_0.	λ	$\dfrac{\lambda}{T_0}$	$9{\cdot}5 \log T_0 - 0{\cdot}007 T_0$.
Acetic acid . .	391	5400	13·8	21·9

But acetic acid has a molecular weight of 97 in the gaseous state at the boiling-point (p. 271) instead of the normal value $CH_3 \cdot COOH = 60$; if we refer λ correspondingly to 97 g. acetic acid, $\dfrac{\lambda}{T_0}$ becomes $\dfrac{8730}{391} = 22{\cdot}1$, and therefore practically coincides with the calculated value 21·9. It can therefore be concluded with some degree of certainty, that acetic acid in the liquid state also has a mean molecular weight of 97, which corresponds to a high degree of association.

Molecular Weight and Surface Tension.—A very important method of determining molecular weight of liquids is due to Eötvös,[1] who found the following rule confirmed by a series of experiments : if γ is the surface tension of a liquid expressed in dynes, v its molecular volume (that is, the volume occupied by one mol in the liquid state), then

$$\gamma v^{\frac{2}{3}} = k(T - T_0) \qquad . \qquad . \qquad . \qquad . \qquad (1)$$

where T_0 is a temperature not very different from the critical, and k is a constant independent of the nature of the liquid. This relation was later tested experimentally by Ramsay and Shields[2] in a very thorough manner, and found in good agreement with the observations. Conclusion (1) was put in the form

$$\gamma v^{\frac{2}{3}} = k(\tau - d) \qquad . \qquad . \qquad . \qquad . \qquad (2)$$

where τ is reckoned downwards from the critical temperature, and d is usually about 6 ; conclusion (2) only holds accurately when τ is greater than $35°$; not, therefore, in the immediate neighbourhood of the critical point.

Imagine that we have a mol of the liquid in question in spherical form, its radius is $\sqrt[3]{v}$, its surface is proportional to $v^{\frac{2}{3}}$, and accordingly $\gamma v^{\frac{2}{3}}$ is a quantity proportional to the *molecular surface energy of the sphere*. Equations (1) and (2) therefore state *that the temperature coefficient of the molecular surface energy* (except in the immediate neighbourhood of the critical point) *is independent of the special nature of the liquid*.

Putting the molecular surface energy at $\gamma v^2_{\frac{3}{3}}$, then the temperature coefficient k is $2\cdot27$ according to Eötvös, and $2\cdot12$ according to Ramsay and Shields.

Eötvös's law may be expressed in this manner ; the work required *to form the surface of a spherical mol* of a liquid varies with the temperature in the same manner for all liquids. This is the case with the production of a mol of gas under constant pressure according to Avogadro's law ; in the latter case, according to the laws of gases, the work required is simply proportional to the absolute temperature.

The following liquids behave normally—that is, give a temperature coefficient of the molecular surface energy in the neighbourhood of $2\cdot12$:—

	k.
Nitrous oxide	$2\cdot27$
Benzene	$2\cdot17$
Chloro-benzene	$2\cdot08$
Tetrachloride of carbon	$2\cdot11$

[1] *Wied. Ann.* **27.** 452 (1886).
[2] *Trans. Chem. Soc.* **63.** 1089 (1893).

							k.
Ethyl ether	.	.	.	.	.	.	2·17
Bi-sulphide of carbon	.	.	.	.	.	.	2·02
Benzaldehyde	.	.	.	.	.	.	2·16
Nitrobenzene	.	.	.	.	.	.	2·09
Aniline	.	.	.	.	.	.	2·05
Pyridine	.	.	.	.	.	.	2·23
Phosphorus trichloride	.	.	.	.	.	.	2·10

and a large number of esters.[1]

Anomalous values of k (lower and varying with the temperature) are given by the alcohols (1·0 - 1·6), organic acids (·8 - 1·6), acetone (1·8), propionitril (1·5), nitro-ethane (1·7), methyl-urethane (1·6), valeroxime (1·7), water (0·9 - 1·2). To obtain the normal value of the temperature coefficient for these liquids their molecular weight must be raised—that is, association of molecules must be assumed. But it does not appear possible in the present state of our knowledge to conclude satisfactorily *the degree of association* from the divergence from the normal value.

The rule of Eötvös can be derived theoretically in the following way. The work required to bring a molecule from the interior of a liquid to the surface layer, is the same as that required to bring it from the surface layer into the vapour space.[2] The first magnitude is proportional to the molecular surface energy, the second to the molecular heat of evaporation; it follows therefore that these two magnitudes must be proportional, the ratio depending on the units chosen. Now we have seen above that, according to the theory of corresponding states, the quotient of molecular heat of evaporation and temperature must be the same at the same reduced temperature for all liquids; this must therefore also be true for the quotient of molecular surface energy and temperature. If we write the (empirical) equation (1) in the form

$$\frac{\gamma v^{\frac{2}{3}}}{T} = k\left(\frac{T_0}{T} - 1\right)$$

it follows that k must be independent of the nature of the liquid—this is the rule of Eötvös.[3]

Hence a considerable deviation of the value of k from the normal value, simply means that the substance in question does not obey the law of corresponding states; association can only be indirectly assumed. It is also obvious, as has already been emphasised above, that we cannot at present calculate the degree of association from the deviation of k from the normal value. It appears, however, that the

[1] Ramsay and Aston, *Zeitschr. phys. Chem.* **15.** 98 (1894); Guye and Baud, *ibid.* **42.** 379 (1903). Grummach, *Drudes Ann.* **15.** 401 (1904); Bolle and Guye, *Journ. chim. phys.* **3.** 38 (1905).

[2] Stefan. *Wied. Ann.* **29.** 555 (1886); see also A. Brandt, *Drudes Ann.* **10.** 783 (1903).

[3] See further the theoretical considerations of van der Waals, *Zeitschr. phys. Chem.* **13.** 713 (1894).

value of k is only slightly affected by the inaccuracy of the theorem of corresponding states, but considerably by polymerisation, and this is ⎰why the rule of Eötvös is such a useful means of deciding the molecular condition of a liquid. Of course care must be taken in applying the rule at very low or very high temperatures (just as with Trouton's rule p. 274). The above analogy between molecular surface energy and heat of evaporation would of course demand the same relations for the difference between molecular heats of liquid and vapour (Mc – C_p p. 57) as for k. Nothing is yet known on this point.

A third method that can be used to study the molecular condition of a liquid is given in Chapter V. of this book, in the section on rules of boiling-point. Linebarger [1] has given an interesting study of the vapour pressure of mixtures, and uses the partial pressure of the components to decide the question whether association exists. Finally, it may be remarked that all the methods here quoted agree remarkably in showing that the majority of liquids studied are not polymerised, and that certain classes of bodies, such as acids, alcohols, and, in particular, water, form complexes (mostly double molecules) in the liquid state, and that the last-mentioned substances show a tendency to do the same in the gaseous and dissolved conditions.

Guye [2] has investigated the application of the critical density to decide the question of molecular condition in the critical state, but the measurements of this quantity so far obtained are too uncertain to form the basis of a further step in this direction.

Molecular Weight of Solids.—There is no method known at the present time which leads to a knowledge of the molecular weight of solids ; indeed, our molecular conceptions on the nature of the solid state are very vague (p. 241). The case is somewhat more hopeful with *dilute solid solutions*, and perhaps Avogadro's law can be applied to them (p. 164).

The results obtained in the last-mentioned way are not free from objection ; see Nernst, [3] Küster, [4] Hoitsema, [5] Würfel, [6] Bodländer. [7]

---

[1] *Amer. Chem. Journ.* **17.** 615, 690 (1895).
[2] *Compt. rend.* **112.** 1257 (1891) ; more fully, *Thèse*, Paris (1891).
[3] *Zeitschr. phys. Chem.* **9.** 137 (1892).
[4] *Ibid.* **13.** 445 (1894) ; **17.** 357 (1895).
[5] *Ibid.* **17.** 1 (1895).   [6] *Dissertation*, Marburg (1896).
[7] *Neues Jahrbuch f. Mineralogie*, Beil. 12 (1898).

CHAPTER IV

THE CONSTITUTION OF THE MOLECULE

Allotropy and Isomerism.—The properties of all substances vary with the external circumstances under which they are studied. Those external conditions which exert the greatest influence upon the physical and chemical conduct of substances are the *temperature* and the *pressure*; also, according to circumstances, the properties are modified in one way or another by *magnetisation, electrification, illumination*, etc. In describing the behaviour of a chemically simple substance, it must always be stated what the external conditions are under which it is studied.

Further, under all circumstances the properties of any two substances having a different chemical composition, are different: if only one atom in the molecule be replaced by another, even then there is a difference in both the physical and the chemical behaviour of the compound; but this change is a variable quantity. Those atoms which can replace each other in the molecular group without occasioning a deep-seated change in the whole behaviour of the compound, are said to be related chemically. A number of such related groups of elements have been already pointed out in the vertical columns of the periodic system (p. 180). Although the change in the properties of a compound, when one atom is replaced by one of another element of similar behaviour, may be very slight, yet it is definite in all cases; *two substances which behave alike in all their properties must have the same composition.*

But the converse of this is by no means true; viz. that two substances which conduct themselves differently under the same external conditions have a different composition. This is neither true of elements nor of compounds, as has been already seen in the capacity of substances to assume different states of aggregation under the same external conditions. It is also known that many elements exist in the solid state, in different modifications, called "allotropic forms." Phosphorus is an element known to us in two modifications, called the yellow and the red; and these varieties are so different

278

under the same external conditions, both in their physical and in their chemical behaviour, that one might easily believe that they were two essentially different substances. Carbon occurs in nature in the forms of the diamond, of graphite, and of so-called amorphous carbon. Sulphur appears in crystalline forms of the orthorhombic and the monoclinic system, according to the method of formation, etc. etc.

We do not certainly know the reason for the difference between the allotropic forms of solid elements, but the probability, in the light of the atomic hypothesis, is very strong that the atoms unite either with a different number in the molecule, or with a different mode of union. To be sure, certain proof for this supposition is wanting at present, since hitherto it has been impossible to obtain a glimpse into the molecular constitution of solids.

More often we find the case where a chemical compound can occur in different modifications, not only in the solid state, but in all the states of aggregation. Such compounds are called *isomeric*.[1] The molecular hypothesis has done much good work in explaining these cases of isomerism, by showing how to obtain new examples of isomerism; and, on the other hand, it has repeatedly been found in the history of theoretical chemistry, that the attempt to explain new isomeric phenomena has led to a bold extension of the molecular hypothesis, which, in turn, reacted in new requirements on experimental research.

These are some of the points in the *history of the knowledge of isomerism*, which is, at the same time, the history of constitutional theories: in 1823 Liebig remarked that the silver fulminate analysed by him had the same constitution as the silver cyanate discovered by Wöhler in 1822; in 1825 Faraday found that benzène, discovered by him, agreed in composition with acetylene; and in 1828 Wöhler succeeded in directly converting one isomer into another, namely, ammonium cyanate into urea. The number of cases of isomerism grew very rapidly; in 1832 Berzelius discovered the isomerism of racemic and tartaric acids, and very many instances were discovered in organic chemistry, especially after the theoretical explanation had been given. The most striking advance towards the development of stereochemistry of carbon was the investigation of Wislicenus on isomerism in lactic acids (1871), and that of fumaric and maleic acids in 1887, whilst the first experimental material discovered for stereo-chemistry of nitrogen was in the isomerism of benzil-dioxime discovered in 1882 by Goldschmidt, and in 1888 by V. Meyer and Auwers. In 1891, Le Bel discovered the first example of optically active pentad nitrogen.

The Constitution of the Molecule.—The question may now be asked at once, whether or not the differences in the properties of isomeric compounds are based upon a difference in the size of the molecule; *i.e.* whether the atoms unite to form the different molecules in the same relative proportions, but not in the same number.

---

[1] Oxygen and ozone form an example of isomerism amongst the elements.

Experience shows that this circumstance often explains some material differences, but by no means can it explain all cases of isomerism. For, on the one hand, there are isomeric substances having the same per cent composition and different molecular weights, as acetylene C_2H_2, and benzene C_6H_6 (*isomerism* in the broader sense of *polymerism*); and, on the other hand, there are isomeric substances with physical and chemical properties clearly distinct, and these are found especially in the carbon compounds, which have both the same per cent composition and the same molecular weight (*isomerism* in the special sense of *metamerism*).

The existence of metameric compounds at once gives us a chance to frame more definite conceptions regarding the mode of union of the atoms in the molecule; it at once excludes the supposition that the atoms can unite in a chemical molecule in all conceivable positions with reference to each other, like the molecules in a homogeneous liquid mixture. For otherwise, just as by bringing together definite quantities of different substances—*e.g.*, water and alcohol,—there can result only one physical mixture of definite properties, so also by the union of a certain number of atoms of different elements into a molecule there could, in that case, result only one chemical compound, having the same properties; and thus the formation of metameric compounds would be impossible.

Therefore it must be assumed that certain forces are exerted between the atoms in the molecule, which determine the relative positions of the atoms; also that the relative positions of the atoms can vary with the mode of union of the atoms with each other.

The differences shown in the physical and chemical behaviour of metameric compounds, must thus be ascribed to differences in the arrangement of the atoms in the molecule, or as is said, to differences in the constitution of the molecule.

The Chemical Forces.—At present scarcely anything definite is known about the nature of the forces which bind the atoms together in the molecule and which hinder them from flying apart in consequence of the heat motion, or their laws of action; but there are many reasons which lead us to suppose that these forces, like the forces in the explanation of capillarity and related phenomena, act only in the immediate neighbourhood of the atoms, and diminish in strength very rapidly as the distance from the atoms increases.

Further, in order to explain the various capacities for reaction of the elements, and the various degrees of stability with which the atoms are linked together, we must assume that the mutual action of the atoms varies greatly with their nature; and in order to explain the fact that atoms of the same sort unite to form molecules, we must assume that chemical forces are active between the atoms of the same element, and vary very much with their nature.

The answer to the question, how these forces vary with the reacting elements, is rendered exceedingly difficult from the fact that in the great majority of cases we have to explain, not a single exchange, but the sum total of several exchanges. Thus in the formation of hydrochloric acid,

$$H_2 + Cl_2 = 2HCl,$$

we find that the reaction is determined not only by the affinity between hydrogen and chlorine, but that before a single atom of the reacting elements can enter into the exchange, the bonds holding the two atoms in the molecules H_2 and Cl_2 respectively, must be loosened. When the reaction takes place from left to right in the sense of the preceding equation, as happens at temperatures not too high, then it works against the affinities holding two hydrogen atoms and two chlorine atoms together, and tends to come to rest with the affinity between hydrogen and chlorine predominant. But when the reaction takes place from right to left, as happens at high temperatures, then it works against the affinity between different kinds of atoms, and tends to come to rest with the affinity between atoms of the same sort predominant. And the case is similar in almost all reactions which are carefully studied, so that it is very rarely that the course of the reaction can enable us to draw any certain conclusion on the intensity of the chemical forces. The affinity certainly changes with the external conditions of temperature and pressure in all cases, although it may be very different in degree ; but we usually are entirely ignorant as to the cause. Thus, in the preceding case, we cannot state how the affinity changes between the like and the unlike, with the temperature ; we can merely conclude from the course of the reaction, that at lower temperatures the affinity between unlike atoms prevails, and at higher temperatures that between like atoms.

In order to obtain a deeper insight into the manner of the action of the forces of affinity, it is, of course, necessary at first to direct our attention to those reactions where the simplest conditions find expression. This is found in those cases where a complex molecule breaks up into simpler ones (dissociation), or conversely where several simpler molecules condense into a more complicated one (addition). In such a case the chemical change occurs either against, or with, only *one* affinity. The simplest case is where two elementary atoms unite to form a single molecule, or conversely where a diatomic molecule of an element breaks up into its atoms ; as is the case, for example, in the dissociation of iodine vapour ; thus

$$I_2 = I + I.$$

The study of the conditions under which these reactions come to a pause will throw some light on the affinity between the elementary atoms in question.

The Doctrine of Valence.—Without framing any definite conception of the nature of chemical affinity, it is possible to consider the mode of union of the atoms in the molecule, according to a certain scheme, which not only gives us much general information on the classification of chemical compounds, but which also serves to make their capacities for reaction intelligible in many respects, and also renders it easy to remember them.

Much observation has taught us that often certain elements and radicals may replace each other without occasioning a deep-seated change in the properties, and especially in the reaction capacity of the molecule. Thus in many instances it is possible to replace a hydrogen atom in a molecule, by an atom of F, Cl, Br, I, Li, Na, K, etc., or by certain radicals as NH_2, NH_4, CH_3, C_2H_5, C_6H_5, always to be sure with some associated change in the physical and chemical behaviour of the compound, but never entirely destroying the clearly expressed similarity between the new and the original compound. The experience based on an enormous amount of observation is embraced in the statement that *such elements or radicals are chemically equivalent.*

Some other similarly chemically equivalent elements are O, Mg, Zn, Ca, Sr, Ba, etc. ; these, as a rule, easily replace each other, and in such a way as not to change radically the whole habit of the compound. A number of such groups of elements are given in the vertical columns of the table on p. 180.

A further observation has been made, that elements which are not of the same equivalent group can replace each other, but not in such a way that an atom of one sort can replace an atom of another sort in the molecule ; but the replacement takes place so that in the place of a certain number of atoms of one group, there are substituted a different number of atoms of another group. Thus two atoms of H, Li, Na, F, Cl, etc., can usually replace one atom of O, Mg, etc.

In this way it is possible to compare the *chemical value or valence* of the elements belonging to the different groups, and to make a quantitative determination of this. Since no element is known where more than one of its atoms are required to take the place of an atom of hydrogen, the valence of this latter element is assumed as standard ; and, accordingly, hydrogen and the related elements are said to be *univalent* ; then oxygen and the related elements are *bivalent*, phosphorus is *trivalent*, carbon, silicon, etc., are *quadrivalent*, and the like.

It is usually assumed, in order to explain these relations, that the chemical force of the elementary atoms does not act equally in all directions in space—like the attraction of a gravitating mass-point, or the mutual attraction of the molecules of a liquid—but rather that the *affinity is entirely, or at least chiefly, active in certain directions ; according to this view, the number of these directions or rays corresponds to the chemical value (valence) of the atoms.* Thus the chemical force of hydrogen acts in one direction, that of oxygen in two, that of carbon in four, etc. The union of the atoms in the molecule is to be conceived of thus: the outgoing line of force of one atom coincides with one from another atom ; or in other words, the valences of the different atoms *mutually and oppositely satisfy each other.*

By such conceptions as these it is possible to obtain a general view, if not of all the possible compounds, at any rate of those which are formed most readily, and which are characterised by great stability.

Thus two univalent elements, as hydrogen and chlorine, or two bivalent elements, as calcium and oxygen, will unite, in the sense of what has preceded, and in harmony with experiment, in very stable forms in such compounds as the following :

$$H—Cl \text{ and } Ca=O.$$

The uniting dashes, as commonly used, represent the force-lines which anastomose into each other. Similarly we can explain the ready formation of such molecules as

$$N{\Big\langle}\begin{matrix} H \\ H \\ H \end{matrix} \quad \text{or} \quad H—\overset{\displaystyle H}{\underset{\displaystyle H}{C}}—H,$$

and also molecules composed of the same kind of atoms, as

$$H—H, \ O=O,$$

and the like ; for it is to be expected that the same scheme will be used to explain the constitution of molecules composed of like, as of those of unlike, atoms. Regarding the saturation capacity of the valences, it must be supposed that each valence is satisfied by another valence, whether it be from the same kind of element or from a different kind, although there do occur very pronounced quantitative distinctions in the complete saturation of the linking of the atoms.

The Dualistic and the Unitary View.—It must be admitted that, according to previous experiments, the power of saturation of valences is almost unlimited, that as all ponderable matter produces mutual attraction regardless of what its character may be, so also two valences can unite their lines of force under certain circumstances whatever the atoms may be from which they arise. On the other hand, the intensity of this action is in the highest degree dependent on the nature of the two atoms and *also on the number and character of the other atoms present in the molecule.* It is, therefore, remarkable that on the whole the atoms and atom complexes comparable to them in behaviour (radicals) may be placed in two groups, between which a polar distinction is recognisable. Whilst the atoms and radicals belonging to either group are more or less indifferent to one another, the members of one group show marked affinity towards those of the other group. Hydrogen, the metals, radicals such as NH_4, etc., belong to one group ; halogens and other nonmetals, further radicals such as OH, SO_4, etc. belong to the other.

The existence of a polar contrast in their chemical action is undoubted, and will be explained more clearly in the subject of electrolysis, where it will be shown how the representatives of the first class (positive) "wander" to the cathode, and those of the second class (negative) to the anode. It was the discovery of these which led Davy, and especially Berzelius (1810), to the advancement of the electrochemical theory ; this regarded the undeniable dualism in mutual affinity, as the guiding star of chemical investigation, and compared the polar contrast to that between the positive and negative electrostatic charges.

But very soon it appeared that it was impossible to carry out this supposition ; for, apart from the faulty consideration of the physical side of this question implied in the theory, which shows the premises to be inadmissible, there are well-known chemical processes which occur in distinct contradiction to an exclusively dualistic conception.

For on that basis, how can one explain the mutual and very active capacity for union shown by two atoms of the same sort, and illustrated in the molecules of many elements, as H_2, O_2, Cl_2, etc.? Or how explain the abnormal behaviour of carbon, which can unite firmly with such characteristically positive and negative elements as hydrogen and chlorine ?

Instead of drawing the conclusion that, in chemical action, apart from the polar forces (analogous to electric attraction and repulsion), there is some other force acting simply (like the Newtonian attraction of ponderable matter) which must be taken into account, the tendency has been for a long time, and also is at present, to develop a one-sided *unitary* theory in opposition to the one-sided *dualistic* theory of Berzelius ; this is easily explained by the historical consideration that the dualistic view was unsuited to the treatment of the carbon compounds, which form the subject of the flourishing department of organic chemistry. It seems that at the present time, when the phenomena of electrolysis are again exciting great interest, the dualistic theory is being justified, and we are gaining a deeper insight into the "positive" or "negative" behaviour of many elements or radicals—a conception which is indispensable also to the modern chemist.

The Variability of Chemical Valence.—The great variety of chemical transformations are explained by the fact that the properties of the chemical forces vary with external conditions of temperature and pressure, with the presence of other substances, and finally and especially with the nature of the atoms concerned in the exchange. It may be regarded as the chief problem of theoretical chemistry, to express numerically the dependence of affinity on these factors. How far this problem has been solved will be considered under the subject of the " Doctrine of Affinity " ; we will here only anticipate what is most important from the standpoint of the doctrine of valence.

Both the number of valences acting from an atom in a molecular group, and the intensity with which each one preserves the integrity of the union, vary within certain limits. There has hardly ever been any doubt regarding the latter [*i.e.* the variation of the intensity of the valences] ; but the attempt to maintain the doctrine of a constant valence was very general till recently ; for to explain the cases in question, it was urged, on the one hand, that certain valences remained unsatisfied, when an atom used less valences than were allotted to it ; and, on the other hand, the conception of " molecular compounds " was advanced to account for the possibility of the existence of those molecular complexes where the number of effective valences seemed too small to explain their constitution.

We cannot discuss here how far in this method of investigation mere words helped on the faulty conceptions of the nature of valence ; but, at all events, the fact remains that all chemical compounds cannot be arranged under the structure plans of the accepted chemical rubric, and also that nothing else primarily remains but to give careful attention to any change in the chemical valences, since this implies no especial encroachment on the significance of valence in systematic chemistry.

At all events, in the case of many compounds, where at first glance the number of active valences appeared to be too small, it later appeared possible to devise a constitution formula which harmonised well with the doctrine of valence ; this is shown in the structure-plans of the so-called "unsaturated compounds," which maintain the four-valence theory of carbon. The simple device which here brought about the desired result consisted in making the well-known assumptions, that several valences may be mutually satisfied between any two carbon atoms, and that the carbon atoms also can form *rings*. This assumption has been accorded great triumph both in theory and in experiment.

But such results as these, for which we are indebted to the application of the doctrine of constant valence, must not therefore blind our eyes to the fact that there are many things which appear, at least temporarily, to be unexplained by this same view. A brilliant example of this is shown in a recent discovery of Nilson and Petterson,[1] who proved that three chlorides of indium can undoubtedly exist in the gaseous state, viz.

$$\mathrm{In-Cl,\ In\!\!\diagdown_{Cl}^{Cl},\ In\!\!\diagup_{\diagdown Cl}^{\diagup Cl}_{Cl}}$$

Even among the carbon compounds change of valency is to be found, although it is rare.

[1] *Zeitschr. phys. Chem.* **2.** 669 (1888).

As a matter of fact, the considerations of the kinetic theory of gases lead to the result that we should hardly expect to find such simple conduct as is implied in the doctrine of constant valence. The so-called stability of chemical compounds, accordingly, appears to be the resultant of two opposing forces, one of which, the chemical force proper, tends to hold the atoms in the molecular group, while the other, controlling the atoms by heat motion, strives to break the molecule apart. It is probable that the latter force changes, and probably increases with the temperature. Of the former we know nothing, and nothing can be stated regarding its variation with the temperature. The more the chemical force preponderates, the more stable will the compound be.

Here we meet with relations which are comparable with those considered in the kinetic theory of liquids (p. 212). The vapour tension of a liquid (which results from the concurrence of the forces which control the heat motion of the molecules, and those forces which exert an attraction between the molecules), can be regarded as a standard of the capacity of the liquid to be vaporised. So in the same way, the capacity of compounds for dissociation, and for chemical reaction also, can be regarded as conditioned by the con-currence of analogous forces. Thus the well-known dependence of the stability of molecular groups upon the external conditions of temperature and pressure is at once explained on the basis of these considerations. The laws which prevail here will be thoroughly considered in detail in the section on the Doctrine of Affinity.

Thus we can easily account in this way for the numerous instances observed of the variation of the chemical valence, by supposing that the heat motion of the atom within the molecule may cause some particular lines of force, called valences, to vanish.

Molecular Compounds.[1]— More difficult to explain than the occurrence of unsaturated valences, or, in other words, of atoms employing less valences in many compounds than the normal number, is the formation of those well-characterised chemical compounds where more valences appear to be active than can be ascribed to the atoms in question in any of their other relations.

Water, and also many salts, must be classified under the compounds which are completely saturated, in which no more free valences are available for use in uniting with other atoms ; yet, in spite of this, salts containing water of crystallisation are obviously chemical compounds which are built up in accordance with the rules of multiple proportion. The phenomenon of water of crystallisation is analogous to that where many salts crystallise together as double salts in stoichiometric proportions.

Methyl ether is able to unite with a molecule of hydrochloric

[1] See A. Naumann, *Die Molekulverbindungen* (Heidelberg, 1872).

acid, which is in striking contradiction to the well-developed valence theory of organic compounds.

If we regard oxygen as regularly divalent, then the existence of the molecules $(H_2O)_2$ is unexplained, and yet we cannot hesitate to assume the existence of molecules of this size both in water vapour and also in solutions.

Molecular complexes of this sort, occasioned by the union of saturated compounds, are called "*molecular compounds.*" It is assumed on the basis of the valence doctrine, that the components of this aggregate retain to a certain extent their individuality in the new complex, and that the binding force does not inhere in force lines passing between the single atoms, but that the union centres in the attraction of the original molecules acting as units.

In recent times many attempts have been made to bring molecular compounds under a valence scheme by assuming the existence of forces between molecules analogous to those existing between atoms; no satisfactory result has yet been arrived at. It seems to me that all these attempts are wrong in one particular. We must, namely, make a sharp distinction between compounds which only exist in the solid state, and at once decompose on solution or evaporation, and compounds which can also exist as gases or in solution. It is quite possible[1] that compounds belonging to the first category are simply formed by the interlacing of the different crystals of the components; we should thus obtain complexes obeying the laws of constant and multiple proportions, but not calling into play any particular valence action between the components. But if the molecules of a compound also exist in the gaseous condition or in solution (in the amorphous condition generally), we are forced to assume some valence action which holds together the complexes, for otherwise the heat motion of the molecules would cause the components to separate.

A remarkable attempt of A. Werner's to systematise molecular compounds will be dealt with in Chapter VII.

The Compounds of Carbon.—The valence doctrine has been hitherto applied almost exclusively, but with great and undoubted results, to the carbon compounds, or the so-called organic compounds; and thus it has been already done, or it is already possible, to construct for every actual compound, whose reactions are known to a fairly satisfactory degree, a structure scheme which represents the quintessence of its chemical reactions. The reason of this is to be found in the fact that the theory of valence here found, in the abundance of material and the great variety of behaviour, ample opportunity for an experimental "baptism by fire"; but the great development of organic structural chemistry is to be explained, as far as we know, from the fact that the behaviour of organic compounds is actually

[1] See Sohncke (*Zeitschr. f. Krist.* **14.** 417 and 426 (1888)).

much simpler than that of other groups, and also that carbon surpasses other elements in its more regular behaviour, and in the great variety of its compounds.

The quadrivalence of carbon is the basis of organic structural chemistry; after the preparatory work of Frankland, this was distinctly emphasised by Couper and Kekulé contemporaneously (1858); its fruitfulness was recognised and proved by the latter in particular.

If one imagines the hydrogen atoms as in the formula

$$
\begin{array}{c}
\text{H} \\
| \\
\text{H—C—H} \\
| \\
\text{H}
\end{array}
$$

to be substituted by other atoms or radicals successively, or two hydrogen atoms to be replaced by one divalent atom or radical, and so on, it is possible to represent structure formulæ for the whole host of carbon compounds; and these formulæ cannot only be regarded as possible, but they also will disclose, to those who are familiar with the language, much regarding the reaction capacities and the physical properties of the compounds in question.

The Peculiarities of the Carbon Compounds.—The very fact that there is an "organic chemistry" gives rise to the question, What are the peculiarities which so characterise the compounds of this branch of chemistry, that they receive a special method of treatment, a treatment which is distinct from the general domain of chemistry, not only on the part of the teacher, but also on the part of the investigator? We are not here taking into account the fact that the materials of organic chemistry claim the interest of the animal and plant physiologist in particular, and are of particular value for the physician and technologist,—a circumstance which, though perhaps external and casual, has nevertheless a most impressive significance. We will rather inquire after the causes which make the organic compounds, in their physical and chemical behaviour, actually appear so different in many respects from other compounds.

It is doubtless carbon itself which stamps its character on the "chemistry of the carbon compounds." We must consider carefully to what extent this element occupies a special position. The following items are from a statement of van't Hoff.[1]

1. The quadrivalence of carbon necessitates an enormous number of derivatives of a carbon compound.

2. The capacity of carbon atoms of uniting with each other in very many ways, allows the possibility of the greatest variety of combination.

[1] *Ansichten über die org. Chemie*, I. p. 34 ff. ; II. p. 240 ff. (Braunschweig (Brunswick), 1881).

3. The position of carbon, standing as it does between positive and negative elements, invests it with a peculiar capacity for uniting with the most different elements, as hydrogen, nitrogen, oxygen, chlorine, etc. To this is due the property of adapting itself alternately to the processes of oxidation and reduction, which have such significance in animal and plant life. If we consider the first horizontal row of the periodic system (p. 180),

Li   Be   B   C   N   O   F,

we find carbon well balanced between the affinity extremes; for the elements to the right are emphatically negative; and those to the left are emphatically positive in character. Moreover, the temperature clearly exerts an influence, for at high degrees of heat the affinity of carbon for oxygen grows, and it is emphatically *positive* itself; possibly a lowering of temperature might act in the inverse way.

4. According to the style and manner of the saturation of three of the carbon valences, the fourth will have a decided positive or negative character, or something intermediate; thus the free valence of the following group is usually negative,

$$\begin{array}{c} H_2 \\ \diagdown \\ C- \; ; \\ \diagup \\ NO_2 \end{array}$$

but that of the methyl group,

$$H_3 \equiv C-,$$

is most nearly comparable to hydrogen in its reaction value, and is distinctly positive; finally, the cyanogen group,

$$N \equiv C-, \; [\text{or } C = N-, \; \text{Tr.}],$$

may be at times positive or negative in reaction.

5. Another characteristic property is the *inertia* of the carbon compounds, and the *slowness of reaction* associated therewith, which characterises organic chemistry where carbon compounds come into play, and which, therefore, is found exhibited in the life activity of plants and animals. Thus it is probable that the existence of the compound

$$Zn \Big\langle \begin{array}{c} CH_3 \\ CH_3 \end{array}$$

its analogous hydrogen compound being unknown, viz.

$$Zn \Big\langle \begin{array}{c} H \\ H \end{array}$$

U

is to be explained, not by the greater affinity of the methyl groups for zinc as compared with hydrogen, but rather in that the former compound decomposes much more slowly than the latter. Further, it is well known that many carbon derivatives are more stable than the mother substances; thus methyl sulphonic acid $CH_3 \cdot SO_2 \cdot OH$ is much more stable than sulphurous acid $H \cdot SO_2 \cdot OH$; also esters of the unstable ortho-carbonic acid are known, etc.

This same inertia renders it possible to build on to molecules, the arrangement of which is very artificial, so to speak, and therefore unnatural; by a more or less energetic blow, there occurs a transformation to a more stable form, and a closer union of the atoms. Usually there is a great quantity of energy set free in this, and the rearrangement leads to an explosion, which in turn leads to the dissolution of the molecule; in this way we find the explanation for the large number of explosive compounds produced in organic chemistry.

The Methods for the Determination of the Constitution.— The great development of organic chemistry and the extraordinary experimental results, for which we are indebted to the most deliberate application of the conception of the "constitution of the molecule," prove, in a most striking way, how fortunate the application of this idea has been. In what follows I have tried to represent, in brief, according to van't Hoff,[1] the principles which guide the organic chemist in representing the structure of organic compounds.

1. The *composition* of the compound, which is known to be pure, must first be ascertained from an *analysis*, and from a molecular weight determination by some one of the methods described in Chapter III. Next, in the attempt to trace the *method of union* of the atoms in the molecule, attention must be given to the *valence* of the atoms entering into the compound in question; thus carbon has a valence of four, nitrogen of three or five, oxygen of two, hydrogen and the halogens of one, etc.; this gives a foothold, so that the number of conceivable formulæ is seen to be very limited, and the more limited according as the number of valences of each element is more constant.

2. *The method of preparation* of the unknown compounds from those of known constitution, or conversely the transformation of the former into the latter, gives a still better grasp of the subject. It may be assumed in many cases that the new compounds have a constitution which is related to that of the original, and this is the more probable when the change and the retransformation occur easily, and when the changes of energy associated with the decomposition are very slight. The peculiar *inertia* of the carbon compounds, which gives the chemistry of this element its peculiar character (p. 289), in certain cases justifies the assumption that *the number of old valences discharged, or of new ones attached*, is reduced to a minimum. This method of deter-

---

[1] *Ansichten über die org. Chem.* (Brunswick, 1881).

mining the constitution is altogether the most reliable, and the one most commonly employed. On account of the readiness with which the valences in inorganic compounds are accustomed to change their *rôles*, this method is almost entirely limited to the carbon compounds.

3. On the basis of a very extended experience, showing that the reaction capacity of certain atomic groups, as OH, CO, C_6H_5, NH_2, etc., usually remains unchanged, irrespective of the composition of the rest of the molecule, one may make certain inferences regarding the existence of these groups in the molecule from the reaction capacity of the compound. This is the *Principle of Analogous Reactions*.

4. A very elegant principle consists in the investigation of the *number of isomeric derivatives*. Thus, by ascertaining how many new compounds can result by the same sort of substitution, as of a hydrogen atom by a chlorine atom, one may safely infer whether the variously substituted atoms exert the same functions in the molecular group or not. Thus the existence of only one phenyl-chloride, C_6H_5 . Cl, led to the recognition of the identical union of the hydrogen atoms in benzene. Similarly, the discovery of three hydroxy-benzoic acids necessitated the distinction between the ortho, para, and meta positions, which is of fundamental significance in representing the structure of benzene. See also the discussion on p. 296 regarding the number of methylene chlorides.

5. From the degree of readiness with which a cleavage product is formed from a compound, a probable conclusion may be drawn as to the contiguity of the components of the separated products in the molecule of the original compound. Thus, other things being equal, the nearer together that the hydroxyl group and the hydrogen of the detached water molecule are in the original compound, so much the more readily can an anhydride be found. It will be seen later what important service has been given to stereochemistry by this *principle of intermolecular action*.

6. Sometimes certain elements or radicals, in the molecule, exert a *mutual influence on their aptitude for reaction*.[1] This will be manifested more clearly, as the reacting atoms are nearer to each other. From this aptness of reaction of particular atoms or radicals in a compound of unknown constitution, one may make some inference as to their *respective distances from each other*, and thus get a starting-point for the representation of their structural formulæ. Thus various atoms and radicals, according to their position in the molecule, exert a very remarkable influence on the reaction capacity of the acid hydrogen atoms in organic acids.

7. All isomeric compounds are distinguished more or less by their properties, such as the melting-point, the boiling-point, the density, the refractive index, etc. ; and the constitution is no less a standard

---

[1] For a very interesting summary of this line of argument see Remsen, *Theoret. Chem.* 4th edit., chapter xix.—TR.

factor than the composition in determining the respective physical conduct. Thus, when we have found a connection between the constitution and the physical properties of a large number of compounds which are known to be related in their structure, then conversely from the *physical properties* of an unknown compound, we can safely draw some inference regarding its constitution. Usually such relations as these, as for instance the connection between the constitution and the refractive index, are of a purely empirical nature, and the safety with which they may be employed in any given case will depend simply on the number of the analogous cases. But others of these relations, such as *e.g.* that between constitution and optical activity, rest on a firmer theoretical basis, and we may make use of them with a very considerable degree of confidence. The material thus far discovered in this direction is collected in the following chapter.

Benzene Theory.—By means of the methods described, it is possible to ascertain with great certainty the constitution of a daily increasing number of carbon compounds. These constitutional formulæ so obtained are of great importance even for those who would entirely abstain from all molecular-theoretical speculations, for they represent, in a very condensed form, the kernel of many and various empirical observations, and he who is skilled in reading this symbolism, learns very much regarding the nature of the compound, from what is expressed through the formula.

Thus if we consider, for instance, the constitutional formula of phenol,

at first glance it is apparent that one hydrogen atom will react differently from all the others, since it can be substituted quite readily by a positive radical; also that in substituting any one of the other hydrogen atoms by a univalent atom or radical, it is possible to obtain any one of three isomers, according to the location of the substitution; also that a dissolution of the ring union would be accompanied by a fundamental change in the molecular structure, etc., etc.

The three isomers that can be formed by replacement of a hydrogen atom directly combined with carbon in phenol and analogous compounds are distinguished as ortho- meta- and para-compounds, but, strictly speaking, the number of cases of isomerism should be greater; for example, a difference should exist between substitution of the two atoms next the hydroxyl group in phenol. The fact that this case of isomerism has not been realised has led to many explanations and to the suggestion of many modified forms of Kekulé's benzene formula.[1] Quite recently a modified view of the nature of a double link has been developed which is worth inserting here.

It has often been remarked that the expression "double link" and the symbol for it, $C = C$, corresponds but little to the actual behaviour and does not lend itself to calculation of the characteristic peculiarities of the double bond, its instability and its tendency to addition products. J. Thiele[2] has offered an extension of the concept of a double bond which certainly brings in a new hypothetical element, but is well suited to bring together a number of observed facts. He believes that, in the formation of a compound with a double bond, only *partial saturation of the two valencies occurs*. Thiele found the strongest support for this belief in the behaviour of the so-called conjugate double compounds. When a hydrogen or bromine molecule is added to the atomic complex $C = CH -- CH = C$, the result is not the elimination of one double bond by formation of a group like $CBr - CHBr - CH = C$, but both disappear, and another double bond appears in the middle instead ; thus we get $CBr - CH = CH - CBr$.

This is difficult to understand according to accepted views. Thiele assumes that the affinities are not completely used up in the formation of a double bond, but that a residue of affinity or partial valency remains in each atom. The two neighbouring partial valencies saturate each other mutually, whilst the extreme one remains unsaturated and capable of forming addition products. He writes the following symbol for it :—

$$C = CH \smile CH = C$$

The addend is attached to the carbon atom with the free partial valencies, and hence the product $BrC - CH = CH - CBr$. Other phenomena of addition that have been noticed in the aldehydes, quinone, benzyls, and so forth, are explained in a similar manner.

An especially good application of these views is to be found in the ·benzene problem. Thiele's modification of the old formula is explained by the symbol

---

[1] See especially the critical study by Marckwald, *Benzoltheorie* (Stuttgart, 1897). F. Enke.

[2] *Lieb. Ann.* **306.** 87 (1889).

$$
\begin{array}{c}
\text{H} \\
\diagup\text{C}\diagdown \\
\text{HC} \quad \text{CH} \\
\| \quad \text{)} \\
\text{HC} \quad \text{CH} \\
\diagdown\text{C}\diagup \\
\text{H}
\end{array}
$$

or, if all the bonds are regarded as equivalent, by

$$
\begin{array}{c}
\text{H} \\
\diagup\text{C}\diagdown \\
\text{HC} \quad \text{CH} \\
\| \quad \| \\
\text{HC} \quad \text{CH} \\
\diagdown\text{C}\diagup \\
\text{H}
\end{array}
$$

Since benzene, according to this formula, contains six inactive bonds, it is to be regarded as a saturated compound in harmony with its chemical behaviour.

The objection made above against Kekulé's formula disappears in the case of Thiele's, on account of its complete symmetry.

But, at the same time, experience has shown that the constitutional formulæ are not adequate to the complete description of the compounds represented. For on the one hand it appears that the anticipated compounds cannot in all cases be represented by the constitutional formulæ; thus the two isomers, methyl cyanide and methyl isocyanide (the nitril and the isonitril), are known,

$$\text{N}\equiv\text{C—CH}_3, \quad \text{and} \quad \text{C}\equiv\text{N—CH}_3,$$

or more probably $C = N - CH_3$ (just as in $C = O$ and $C = NOH$), but only one hydrocyanic acid is known, although there should be *two*, corresponding to the formulæ

$$\text{N}\equiv\text{C—H}, \quad \text{and} \quad \text{C}\equiv\text{N—H, (or } C = N - H\text{)}$$

In this case the constitutional formulæ cover too much ground, since fewer compounds are known than were to be expected. Yet this proves nothing against the formulæ, because it is entirely possible that the desired isomer may exist, but that the proper method of preparation has not as yet been found, nor the conditions suitable for its existence. Also the assumption is not improbable that both molecules may exist in the case of hydrocyanic acid, and that these two forms are converted into each other so readily, that the *one* acid may be able to react in the sense of *both* structural formulæ. (For further details see Book III., chapter on Chemical Kinetics, Tautomerism.)

On the other hand, it would be an entirely different case *if more isomers were known than were required by the theory, or than could be accounted for by it.* The classical case is that of lactic acid. This was shown by the investigations of Wislicenus[1] to have several distinct forms of really different properties, all of which yet had *one and the same formula,* viz.

$$CH_3CH(OH)CO_2H.$$

It was this observation chiefly that led (1877) van't Hoff[2] to bring forward the question, What change or extension must be introduced into the theory of structural chemistry in order to adapt it to all the observed compounds ? The following abstract gives the essentials of the order of thought by which van't Hoff was led to the creation of stereochemistry. Le Bel developed similar views simultaneously.

The Stereochemistry of Carbon.—The fundamental assumption on which all the following considerations are based is *that the four valencies of carbon are like each other in every particular.* The correctness of this is shown by the negative proof that not nearly so many isomers are known as would be known, if one or several of the valencies of carbon were different. Thus, for example, only one methyl chloride is known ; but there would be several if the mode of union with the chlorine atoms varied with their location.

The question regarding the number of mono-substitution products has been treated very systematically by L. Henry.[3] We will briefly indicate the course pursued by this investigator, on account of its great importance as the basis of stereochemistry.

If we assume that the four valencies of carbon are different, then we must write the formula of methane thus, $CH_IH_{II}H_{III}H_{IV}$; here the Roman numerals denote that the respective hydrogen atoms are united to the carbon each in a different way ; then there would be four monosubstitution products, according to the particular hydrogen atom substituted. Now, let the univalent radical A replace H_I, producing the compound $CAH_{II}H_{III}H_{IV}$. We will now place A by the radical B, producing the compound $CBH_{II}H_{III}H_{IV}$; and again in this latter compound introduce A, which, let us say, takes the place of H_{II}, producing $CBAH_{III}H_{IV}$; finally, B is replaced by hydrogen, producing $CH_IAH_{III}H_{IV}$. Now if the valencies I and II are different, then $CAH_{II}H_{III}H_{IV}$ and $CHAH_{III}H_{IV}$ should have different properties [*as is not the case*] ; and in the same way all the other valencies of

[1] *Lieb. Ann.* **156.** 3 ; **157.** 302 (1871).

[2] *Dix années dans l'histoire d'une théorie* (Rotterdam, 1877). The arrangement of atoms in space, 3rd edition (Braunschweig, 1908). See also A. Hantzsch, *Grundriss der Stereochemie* (Breslau, 1893) ; A Werner, *Lehrbuch der Stereochemie* (Braunschweig, 1905).

[3] *Bull. Acad. Belg.* (3), **12.** No. 12 (1886) ; **15.** 333 (1888).

carbon were investigated.   In this way Henry successively prepared all of the four nitro-methanes, *and always obtained the same substance.*

Let us next advance the question as to the directions in which the four valencies radiate from the carbon atom.   Now it follows from the likeness of the four valencies, that they must be symmetrically distributed in space, and there are only two conceivable modes of such arrangement : the four valencies must either lie in a plane, intersecting each other at angles of 90°, or else they must be symmetrically distributed in space as the four axes of an equilateral tetrahedron.   Here again the isomeric forms must decide between these two possibilities. Thus, in the former case, by replacing two hydrogen atoms by chlorine, we should obtain the two following isomeric methylene chlorides, thus,

$$
\begin{array}{ccc}
\text{H} & & \text{H} \\
| & & | \\
\text{Cl—C—Cl,} & \text{and} & \text{Cl—C—H ;} \\
| & & | \\
\text{H} & & \text{Cl}
\end{array}
$$

these should be distinguished by the circumstance that in one the chlorine atoms are opposite each other, while in the other they are beside each other.   On the other hand, if the four valencies are arranged tetrahedrally, two chlorine atoms when introduced into the molecule would always lie beside each other, and the conditions would allow of only one methylene chloride.   Now, as a matter of fact, only one methylene chloride is known.

The case is similar when two hydrogen atoms in methane are replaced by two different radicals, or when three hydrogen atoms are replaced by two radicals of one kind and one of another.   In all cases, unless we assume, as is very improbable, that there are isomers which have not yet been observed, *we are forced to regard the tetrahedron arrangement of the valencies in space as correct.*

Optical Isomerism.—Accepting this view then, the only possible case of isomerism of the substitution products of methane is found when three of the hydrogen atoms are replaced by different radicals, or expressed in more general terms, *where the four carbon valencies are replaced by four different radicals [or atoms].*

By denoting the four different atoms or radicals which satisfy a carbon atom, by the letters *a, b, c,* and *d,* we obtain such formulæ types as those shown in Fig. 27.

These formulæ, in all probability, should correspond to two different compounds, because they cannot be made to coincide by superposition ; the difference between them is comparable to that between the right and left hand, or between a real object and its reflected image.

A single glance at Fig. 27 shows that such isomers as these two must represent the slightest conceivable difference between their respective physical and chemical properties. The degree of separation between the atoms is the same in both cases ; thus the distance between *a* and *b* is the same. The sole difference is that if we consider any selected angle as that marked by the radical *d*, then in the left figure the course *a*, *b*, *c* is directed like the movement of the hands of a watch, while the corresponding order *a*, *b*, *c* in the right figure is in the inverse direction. Inasmuch as these two types, figured above, have no planes of symmetry, such a carbon atom, the valencies of which

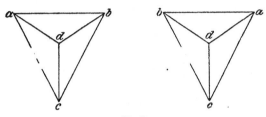

Fig. 27.

are satisfied by four different [atoms or] radicals, is said to be *unsymmetrical*.

In 1874 Le Bel and van't Hoff[1] independently and contemporaneously suggested that the right- and left-handed optically active isomers correspond to these two types. As a matter of fact, the physical and chemical properties are exactly the same, and only their property of rotating the plane of polarisation equally strongly but in opposite directions, shows that the respective substances have a difference in their molecular structure. This kind of isomerism is accordingly called "*optical*" ; the subject of optical rotation will be further considered in the next chapter.

This kind of isomerism usually exhibits itself in the solid state by occasioning the crystallisation of the two substances in two respectively opposite enantiomorphic forms (forms turned back upon themselves).

The two isomers shown in Fig. 27 obviously have the same constitution, since the conditions are alike in every respect ; they differ only in the spatial arrangement of the particular groups in the molecule, or they are said to have a different "*configuration.*"

Optical isomerism can also occur in compounds which have no particular asymmetric carbon atom, but whose space formulæ have no plane of symmetry, *i.e.* are not congruent with their mirror images. An example of this kind is the optically active inosite $C_6H_6(OH)_6$. Bonocault (*Bull. Soc.*

---

[1] See references on p. 295.

Chim. [3] 11, 144, 1894) assigns the following space-formulæ to the two optical isomers :

A second example is the optically active methyl-cyclo-hexylidene acetic acid, prepared synthetically by Marckwald and Meter (*Ber. deutsch. chem. Ges.* **39**. 1171, 1906).

Geometrical Isomerism.—Another variety of isomerism, which is clearly inexplicable by means of the ordinary structure formulæ, is met in the case of compounds which have a " double linkage " between two carbon atoms. And here again it was due especially to the experimental work of Wislicenus[1] that there was recognised a 'distinction between isomers of this sort, and again it was to van't Hoff that their theoretical explanation was due.

When two valencies of two different carbon atoms mutually satisfy each other, or, in the language of stereochemistry, when two corners of one tetrahedron are joined to two corners of another tetrahedron, then the four free valencies lie in one plane ; thus, if the four free valencies become satisfied by the four radicals R_1, R_2, R_3 and R_4, so that one carbon atom holds the first two, and the other the last two, then there is produced the compound

$$\underset{R_2}{\overset{R_1}{>}}C=C\underset{R_4}{\overset{R_3}{<}}$$

Now, according to van't Hoff's view, two compounds of this sort would be looked for, in one of which R_1 and R_3, in the other R_1 and R_4, would lie on the same side of the double tetrahedron.

A similar case of isomerism would also be expected when the two free valencies of each of the doubly linked carbon atoms become united to a like pair of radicals, as in the compound

$$\underset{R_2}{\overset{R_1}{>}}C=C\underset{R_2.}{\overset{R_1}{<}}$$

[1] *Abh. d. kgl. sächs. Akad.* (1887).

This case is illustrated in the following diagram of the isomerism between fumaric and maleic acids, as in Fig. 28.

This isomerism is also very frequently satisfactorily expressed by the following constitutional formulæ, where the spatial relations are illustrated :—

Maleïc Acid.	Fumaric Acid..
H—C—COOH	H—C—COOH,
‖	‖
H—C—COOH	HOOC—C—H.

It would not be expected that this variety of isomerism would exhibit optical activity, because the four radicals satisfying the four

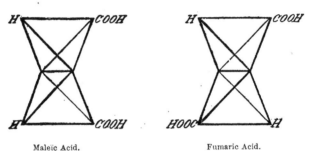

Maleïc Acid.   Fumaric Acid.

Fig. 28.

valencies of the double tetrahedron all lie in the same plane.   Also, since the relative degree of separation of the radicals from each other, as shown in Fig. 28, is not the same, the two isomers will have different reaction capacities, boiling-points, melting-points, solubilities, etc.   The question of the relative contiguity of the respective groups, in any such case of which Fig. 28 is a type, can be decided by means of the principle of intermolecular reaction (p. 291).

The theory suggests no new case of isomerism in the formation of a triple bond, or so-called "acetylene bond," but as in the case of di-methylene (ethylene), so in the poly-methylenes, cases of geometric isomerism must occur.   Considering the simplest carbon ring,

tri-methylene $\begin{array}{c} CH_2 \\ \diagup \diagdown \\ CH_2—CH_2 \end{array}$, it may be seen that in the arrangement of

the atoms in space, geometrical isomerism must be possible by the entry of two substituting groups, according as they take a "cis" position on the same side of the plane of the ring, or a "trans" position on both sides of the plane.   In the latter case two isomers are possible, forming non-congruent images; we get, therefore, altogether three isomers which can be understood by the following models :—

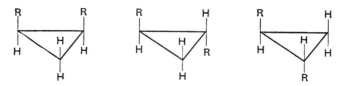

Actually two different tri-methylene di-carboxylic acids have been observed,[1] one of which can probably be split into opposed active components.

Cases of geometrical isomerism are also known in derivatives of larger rings; the investigations of v. Baeyer's[2] on the reduced phthalic acids have been largely productive of material confirming this theory. Whilst no case of isomerism is known in the singly substituted derivatives of hexa-methylene two hexa-hydro-terephthalic acids are known corresponding to the formulæ

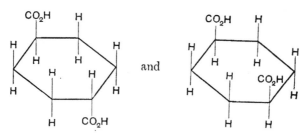

The first is analogous to fumaric, the second to maleïc acid.

The Stereochemistry of Nitrogen.—There has recently been begun, in addition to the stereochemistry of carbon, a stereochemistry of nitrogen, which has already led to considerable results. According to experiments thus far made, there are two groups of stereo-isomeric nitrogen compounds, which are completely analogous to the two groups of stereo-isomeric carbon compounds described above.

Firstly, Le Bel[3] has recently prepared a compound which contains, instead of the asymmetric carbon atom, the group NX, where X denotes a univalent radical, the four free valencies being saturated by four different radicals. The compound produced by Le Bel was isobutyl-propyl-ethyl-methyl-ammonium chloride, which was obtained

[1] Buchner, *Ber. deutsch. chem. Ges.* **23.** 702 (1890).
[2] *Lieb. Ann.* **245.** 103 (1888) ; **251.** 258 (1889) ; **258.** 1, 145 (1890).
[3] Le Bel, *C. R.* **112.** 724 (1891); **129.** 548 (1899). [See Pope and Peachey, *Journ. Chem. Soc.* **75.** 1127 (1899).]

in an optically active form by means of a fungus (*Pilz*). It has the formula

$$CH_3$$
$$|$$
$$C_4H_9\!-\!NCl\!-\!C_2H_5$$
$$|$$
$$C_3H_7.$$

The activity remained even when the chlorine was replaced by the acetyl radical. The preceding compound seems to be completely analogous to the optical isomers of carbon.[1]

Secondly, certain compounds were prepared before that of Le Bel, and were claimed to be geometrical isomers by Hantzsch and Werner.[2] These compounds can be regarded as analogous to the corresponding carbon isomers, by supposing the group CR to be replaced by *trivalent nitrogen.* Now, since this latter is very often possible, according to experiments, the inference is a direct one that the three nitrogen valencies do not lie in a plane, but that they occupy relative positions which are similar in direction, at least approximately so, to the three free valencies in the group CR. Therefore it follows that when *two nitrogen valencies are bound to one carbon atom, there must result a case of geometrical isomerism which is completely analogous to that described on p. 299, and which may be expressed by spatial formulæ written as follows :*—

$$R_1\!-\!C\!-\!R_2 \qquad\qquad R_1\!-\!C\!-\!R_2$$
$$\|\qquad\quad \text{and} \qquad\quad \|$$
$$R_3\!-\!N \qquad\qquad\qquad N\!-\!R_3$$

Numerous examples of this interesting variety of isomerism have been found among the asymmetric oximes, *i.e.* compounds where the hydroxyl group plays the part of the radical R_3.

The question as to which of the isomers corresponds to which of the configurations given above, can be answered by means of the principle of intermolecular reaction between groups which are spatially contiguous. Thus one of the aldoximes,

$$\begin{matrix} H \\ R \end{matrix}\!\!\bigg\rangle C\!=\!N\!-\!OH,$$

produced by the reaction between aldehydes and hydroxylamine, decomposes with difficulty, but the other readily into the nitrile $R\!-\!C\!\equiv\!N$; therefore the inference is drawn directly that in the one, the H and the OH, expelled as water, are nearer neighbours than in the other ; and therefore they are given the respective formulæ, viz.—

---

[1] See E. Wedekind, *Stereochemie des fünfwertigen Stickstoffs* (Leipzig, 1907).
[2] See references on p. 288.

Synaldoxime.   Antaldoxime.

$$R\!-\!C\!-\!H \qquad R\!-\!C\!-\!H$$
$$\|\qquad\qquad\qquad \|$$
$$N\!-\!OH \qquad HO\!-\!N.$$

In an analogous way the three isomeric benzil dioximes expressed by the respective formulæ :—

$$RC\!-\!CR \qquad RC\ -\ CR \qquad RC\ -\ CR$$
$$|\quad\||\qquad\quad \|\qquad \|\qquad\quad \|\qquad\qquad \|$$
$$HON\ \ NOH \qquad HON \quad HON \qquad NOH \ \ HON.$$

Optically active compounds of other elements besides car nitrogen have recently been prepared. Thus Pope and prepared active sulphur and tin compounds.[2] Example :

Pope and Neville,[3] an active selenium compound. In some c two opposite optical isomers were both obtained.

[1] *Journ. Chem. Soc.* **77.** 1072 (1900).
[2] *Proc. Chem. Soc.* **16.** 42 (1900).   [3] *Ibid.* **18.** 198 (1902)

CHAPTER V

General Observations.—According to the views advanced in the preceding chapter regarding the structure theory of molecules, there are three circumstances which are of fundamental significance in determining the physical properties of any compound.   These are—

1. The chemical composition.
2. The cónstitution, *i.e.* the mode of linking of the atoms.
.3. The configuration, *i.e.* the spatial arrangement of the atoms.

A change in any one of these factors occasions a more or less extended change in the properties of the compound.

The knowledge of this at once suggests the problem of determining the relations which exist between the physical and chemical properties of a compound, and the *structure of the molecule*; this latter expression denotes the sum and substance of the three factors mentioned above.   The complete solution of this problem will enable us to infer in every respect the behaviour of a substance from its structural formula; and further, to predict the conditions for the existence of, and the properties of, compounds not yet prepared; and this would mean the attainment of a goal, to reach which has been the chief aim of all chemical investigation.

Even at present, structural chemistry, at least among organic compounds, has already progressed so far that the structural formula of a substance enables us to draw many inferences regarding its aptitude for reaction, as has been repeatedly mentioned in the preceding chapter; in the " doctrine of affinity " we shall also deal with the relations between structure and capacity for reaction.

In this chapter will be given only the other side of the question, namely, that concerned with the regularities which have been found thus far between the *physical properties* and the structure of the molecule of a substance.   Naturally the question will be almost entirely limited to the consideration of carbon compounds, because thus far it is only here that we find well-grounded notions regarding the arrangement of the atoms in the molecule.   It may be remarked here that salt solutions occupy in many respects a special position, and therefore a special chapter will be devoted to their physical relations.

Specific Volume and Molecular Volume.—By the *specific volume* of a substance is meant the volume, expressed in c.c., occupied by a gram; the reciprocal of this specific volume, *i.e.* the weight of a unit volume, is the so-called *specific gravity*. It is of much advantage, for purely algebraic reasons, to derive the relations between the density and the composition of substances from the specific volume.

The essentials of the determination of the specific volumes of gases, and their relations to the respective molecular weights, have been already described in the chapter on the determination of the molecular weight (p. 249); the simple result was obtained that the molecular volumes of the most different gases are the same, under the same external conditions. We will consider here only those substances which exist in the *liquid* and *solid* states.

The *specific volume of liquids* can be easily and exactly determined, either by measuring the resistance caused by the immersion of a solid body of known volume (the araömeter, Mohr's balance, etc.), or by weighing the liquid contained in a vessel of known volume (the pykno-meter). Of the many forms of pyknometer which have been described, that shown in Fig. 29, which was designed by Sprengel and modified by Ostwald, is at once the simplest and the most convenient. It consists of a small bent pipette, provided on one side with a capillary opening at *a*, and on the other side with a narrow tube *b* with a mark; it is filled by dipping the capillary opening *a* into the liquid in question, and sucking through a rubber tube which is attached to *b*; it is then hung in a bath which has the temperature of the determination, the liquid meniscus being adjusted to the mark in *b*, either by sucking out the excess of the liquid from the capillary opening at *a*, by means of a bit of filter paper, or by adding what liquid is wanting by a drop on a glass rod applied at *a*, when it will be sucked in by the capillary force.

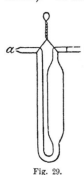

Fig. 29.

Let p, p_1, and p_2 be the weights respectively of the pyknometer empty, when full of a liquid (as water) of known density s, and when filled with the liquid which is to be studied; and if Δ is the weight of the air displaced, and which is approximately equal to $(p_2 - p_1)$ 0·0012, then the specific gravity sought is

$$S = s\,\frac{p_2 - p - \Delta}{p_1 - p - \Delta}.$$

F. Kohlrausch and Hallwachs [1] have lately perfected the areometric

[1] *Wied. Ann.* **53.** 14 (1894); see also F. Kohlrausch, *Wied. Ann.* **56.** 185 (1895). G. Mie, *Boltzmann Festschrift*, p. 326 (1904).

method to such an extent that changes in the specific gravity of aqueous solutions of one-millionth can be distinguished with certainty, a notable result for the investigation of very dilute solutions. Smooth cocoon silk was used for the suspension, and as immersed body a glass bulb of 133 grammes weight and 129 c.cm. content.

While by this method the density of a liquid can be determined without any difficulty, yet the methods used to determine the *specific gravities of solid bodies* are not quite satisfactory in accuracy, for the reason that only small pieces of the substance can be used ; and this is true of the methods which depend upon the measurement by means of the buoyancy in a liquid of known density, or by weighing it in a liquid pyknometer, or by the application of gas laws (volumenometer), or by its swimming free in a liquid mixture, the density of which is already determined. The "swimming method" usually gives the best results when small pieces only can be used. This method has at the same time the advantage, which should not be undervalued, that from the way the substance floats in the liquid, by observing whether a part of it floats at the top, and whether another part sinks to the bottom, one can infer very much regarding the purity of the substance, and thus one can raise the grade of purity.[1]

A liquid, in which the substance shall swim free, without either rising or sinking, can be made by a mixture of methylene iodide, CH_2I_2, which has a sp. gr. of 3·3, with such lighter hydrocarbons as toluene, xylene, etc. The specific gravity of the solid substance is then equal to that of the liquid in which it swims free, and that of the liquid can be determined by a suitable method.

The question regarding the dependence of the specific volume upon the composition and the constitution of compounds has thus far, as is the case with many other properties, been successfully studied *only for carbon compounds.* It is well known, as shown by Kopp (1855), that it is possible to calculate the volume occupied by 1 mol of a liquid organic substance at its boiling-point from its composition ; this volume is equal to the product of the molecular weight and the specific volume, and therefore is suitably called the "*molecular volume*" ; it is calculated in the following way.

If a molecule of the substance in question contains m atoms of carbon, n_1 atoms of "carbonyl oxygen" (*i.e.* oxygen with both its valencies united to the same carbon atom), n_2 atoms of oxygen which has its two valencies distributed between two carbon atoms or between two atoms of other elements, o atoms of hydrogen, p atoms of chlorine, q atoms of bromine, r atoms of iodine, and s atoms of sulphur ; then its molecular volume at the boiling point amounts to

$$M.V. = 11·0m + 12·2n_1 + 7·8n_2 + 5·5o + 22·8p + 27·8q + 37·5r + 22·6s.$$

---

[1] Retgers, *Zeitschr. phys. Chem.* **3**. 289 (1889).

This formula is by no means strictly exact, as deviations amounting to several per cent are not uncommon; but nevertheless it should be particularly noticed that by means of a few empirical constants it is possible to calculate, at least approximately, the molecular volume; and thus by dividing this value by the molecular weight, it is possible to obtain the specific gravity of numerous compounds which are made up of the aforenamed elements. Thus the measurement of the molecular volume of acetone at its boiling-point gave as the result 77·5; and from its formula $CO\begin{smallmatrix}CH_3\\CH_3\end{smallmatrix}$ it was estimated as follows :—

3 atoms of carbon	33·0
1 atom of carbonyl oxygen. . .	12·2
6 atoms of hydrogen	33·0
Sum . . .	78·2

The presence, in the molecule, of carbon atoms with doubled linkage increases the molecular volume proportionally.[1] Reference should be made to the thorough epitome of this material, which has been compiled by Horstmann.[2] He has shown from extended researches that, in general, simple additive relations really exist with some very considerable deviations, and has ascribed these deviations to peculiarities in the constitution.

The specific gravities of liquid chlorine and bromine at the boiling-points amount respectively to 1·56 and 2·96;[3] *the atomic volumes deduced from these figures are* 22·7 *and* 26·9 *respectively, or nearly the same as the figures* 22·8 *and* 27·8, *which Kopp calculated from the organic compounds;* we may therefore with great probability take $\frac{1}{5·5} = 0·18$ as the approximate specific gravity of liquid hydrogen.[4]

Concerning the question as to how far Kopp was justified *in selecting the boiling-point as the point for comparison,* we shall obtain information from the following. In the light of the theory of van der Waals, the molecular volume at the critical point should be three-eighths of that calculated from the laws of ideal gases. Experience vindicates this law (p. 231) to this extent, viz. that the critical volume of many substances amounts to the same fraction, namely, $\frac{1}{3·8}$.

Further, from the equation given on p. 219,

$$\phi_0 = 3b,$$

it follows that the molecules of all substances at their critical points

---

[1] Horstmann, *Ber.* **20**. 766 (1887).
[2] Graham Otto, *Lehrbuch der Chemie,* 3rd edit. (Braunschweig, 1893).
[3] Dammer's *Handbuch der anorg. Chem.* I. pp. 474 and 520 (1892).
[4] [Dewar found 0·07, *Journ. Chem. Soc.* **73**. 535 (1898).]

occupy the same fraction of the critical volume ; *this latter therefore may be regarded as a measure of the space actually occupied by the molecules.* But now the volume of liquids in corresponding states is the same fraction of the critical volume. *Therefore the molecular volumes measured in corresponding states,* i.e. *at equal reduced pressures and temperatures, may be regarded as a measure of the space actually occupied by the molecules ;* and this suggests that we should take as comparison temperature an equally reduced temperature, *i.e.* a temperature which is the same fraction of the (absolute) critical temperature. It is not necessary for the reduced pressures to be the same, for, as already shown on p. 222, the volume of a liquid would be subject to only very slight change if it were measured at a pressure of one-half, and then at two atmospheres ; and no greater variations of pressure are concerned here.

But now the absolute boiling-point of the most various substances is about two-thirds of the critical temperature ; i.e. *for the most various substances, the boiling-point at atmospheric pressure is itself an identical reduced temperature.* The fact that the identity may not be strictly fulfilled is unimportant, because the volume of a liquid is only slightly affected by changes of 5° or 10° ; and only such variations as these are found.

We thus obtain the result that not only is the boiling-point a suitable temperature for comparison, but also that the molecular volumes so determined, for the most different substances, represent very nearly the same multiple of the space occupied by the molecules. Now, as we must regard Kopp's molecular volumes as a measure of the volumes actually occupied by the molecules, therefore *we must conclude that the volume of the molecule can be calculated additively from the volumes of the atoms.* This result will also be established later in an entirely different way.

The Density of Solid Bodies.—The volume relations of solid compounds have as yet been only slightly investigated. The molecular volume is obviously additive in certain cases, as of salts of analogous constitution, as shown by the following table :—

I.	Diff.	II.	Diff.	Diff. I.—II.
KCl $= 37 \cdot 4$		NaCl $= 27 \cdot 1$		$10 \cdot 3$
	$6 \cdot 9$		$6 \cdot 7$	
KBr $= 44 \cdot 3$		NaBr $= 33 \cdot 8$		$10 \cdot 5$
	$9 \cdot 7$		$9 \cdot 7$	
KI $= 54 \cdot 0$		NaI $= 43 \cdot 5$		$10 \cdot 5$

We find constant differences both between the corresponding potassium and sodium salts, and also between the corresponding chlorides, bromides, and iodides, and this is a necessary condition for the calculation of the molecular volume in summation from the atomic volumes, by the choice of suitable constants. Schröder, who has done good service by investigating these relations, stated, in 1877, in harmony with the preceding, that in the homologous series of the silver salts of the fatty acids, the molecular volume increases quite constantly, about 15·3, for every additional CH_2 group.

The question as to what is the proper temperature for comparison is here of less importance on account of the slight change of density of solid substances from a change in temperature. The relation between the atomic weight and the density of the elements in the solid state has been already treated in the description of the periodic system (p. 188).

The Refractive Power.—The optical coefficient of refraction for homogeneous gases, liquids, or solids can be measured very accurately by enclosing them in a hollow prism with a prismatic cavity, and then measuring, by means of a spectrometer, the deviation of a ray of monochromatic light. The method of total reflection, which is employed in the refractometers devised by Kohlrausch, Abbe, and others, can be used much more easily, and this method has recently been applied by Pulfrich in the construction of a very convenient apparatus for the special study of liquids. As we are practically concerned only with the determination of the optical behaviour of liquids, in the exigencies of the chemical laboratory, and as also the Pulfrich[1] refractometer combines ease of manipulation with an accuracy which is more than sufficient for most purposes, we will give here a description of this apparatus.

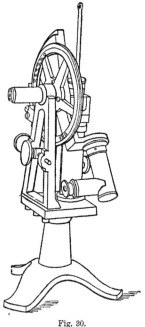

Fig. 30.

The monochromatic light given out by a Bunsen burner, fed with salt, for instance, and concentrated by passing through a lens which is adjusted to the apparatus (but not shown in the cut, Fig. 30), is allowed to fall on the horizontal surface of a prism, which must be provided with a refractive angle of 90°. The top of the prism is adjusted to receive the glass cylinder, which is to hold the liquid to be studied, in the following way :—The lower edge of the glass cylinder

[1] *Zeitschr. f. Instrumentenkunde,* **8.** 47 (1888) ; **15.** 389 (1895) ; *Zeitschr. phys. Chem.* **18.** 294 (1895).

rests a little lower than the round flat upper face which fits into it, and thus the cemented edge does not interfere with the passage of the light. Then it is necessary to moisten the upper surface of the prism with only a few drops of the liquid to be investigated, an advantage which is not to be undervalued in chemical work. The prism, with its smoothly ground hypothenuse surface, rests on a bevelled block, of brass, which in turn rests on a wooden support. This rests on a heavy tripod base. By means of this it is possible to obtain very certain manipulation, so that after removing the prism it can be returned again to its original position, and a readjustment is not required even after long use. The normal positions of the two surfaces of the prisms are determined by means of an adjusting apparatus which is fastened, with the wooden support, to the brass block on which the prism rests, parallel with the plane of rotation of the divided circle. The observer may convince himself of the correct adjustment most easily, by observing the refractive index of pure water at the atmospheric temperature, which is known, and deducing from it the small correction which must be introduced into all readings.

The measurement consists simply in adjusting the telescope which moves round the divided circle, until the cross wires coincide with the sharply defined boundary between the light and the dark portions of the field, and thus obtaining the exit angle i of the light ray. Then, as follows from the simple application of the law of refraction, we have for the desired value of the refractive index of the liquid in question—

$$n = \sqrt{N^2 - \sin^2 i},$$

where N denotes the value of the index of refraction of the glass prism, for the kind of light used. A table furnished with the instrument gives, without further calculation, the value of the refractive index for the angle i for sodium light. Whenever it is necessary to identify an unknown substance, this determination should never be neglected, as scarcely any other property of liquids can be determined so easily and exactly. The apparatus may also be used for analytical purposes, as in the study of solutions.

Further, Le Blanc[1] has suggested a very simple method for measuring very exactly the refractive index of solid bodies which are optically isotropic by means of this same instrument. A decigram or so of the finely powdered substance is shaken into the glass cylinder of the refractometer, and this is then covered with a mixture of two liquids, for example, brom-naphthalene and acetone, between the refractive indices of which that of the substance in question must lie : if that of the latter is very far removed from that of the mixture, the field of the telescope will remain almost uniformly dark ; then more of either brom-naphthalene or acetone is added, when a light

[1] *Zeitschr. phys. Chem.* **10**. 433 (1892).

field appears after the addition of one or the other liquid. If the desired point is already nearly obtained, so that two parts of the field are somewhat different in brightness, then one can easily judge whether the liquid of the greater, or of the lesser refractive index must be added. Thus, if the refractive index of the liquid mixture is greater than that of the powder, there appears a light band at the limit between the light and the dark parts; this band is due to the total reflection of the incident light by the solid substance; it is wanting in the opposite case. *It is possible, by the further addition of the required liquid, to so nearly equalise the coefficients of the solid substance and of the mixture, that the limit between the light and dark half of the field will be as sharp as in the case of a single pure liquid.* When this sharp limit is found, the refractive index of the solid substance can at once be obtained from the table furnished with the apparatus.

This method is also applicable to the measurement of the refractive index of the ordinary ray of optically uniaxial bodies; but not, at least not in this form, to the measurement of the extraordinary rays, nor to the investigation of substances which are optically poly-axial.

The Molecular Refraction of Organic Compounds.—The refractive coefficient of a substance changes with its temperature, and also especially with its state of aggregation. If, as in the preceding case, we are only concerned with a clear statement of the relations between the optical and the chemical behaviour, then the only way in which we may hope for results is *to find some function of the refractive index which, when freed from other influences, shall be conditioned essentially by the chemical nature of the substance.*

The specific refractivity, expressed by the index minus 1, and divided by the density, thus

$$\frac{n-1}{d}$$

partially satisfies the preceding requirements, as shown by Gladstone and Dale,[1] and especially by Landolt.[2] In fact, in most cases, the specific refractivity is only slightly dependent upon the temperature; moreover, each particular substance in a mixture preserves its own specific refractivity nearly unchanged, as already shown on p. 103. But the preceding expression does not apply to changes in the state of aggregation, and the specific refractivity of a liquid, in general, is considerably different from that of its vapour.

This condition of being independent of changes in the state of aggregation is very well satisfied by a formula which was suggested at the same time (1880) by Lorenz in Copenhagen and by Lorentz in Leyden; it was developed from the following considerations.[3]

The Clausius-Mossotti theory of dielectrics proceeds upon the

[1] *Phil. Trans.*, 1858, p. 8; 1863, p. 523.　　[2] *Pogg. Ann.* **123.** 595 (1864).
[3] Lorentz, *Wied. Ann.* **9.** 641; Lorenz, *ibid.* **11.** 70 (1880).

assumption that the molecules, assumed to be spherical, are electrical conductors, and that to this is due the weakening action experienced by the mutual attraction or repulsion of two electrically charged points, on interposing a dielectric.   Let u denote a fraction, assumed to be very small, of the total volume which is actually occupied by the molecules; then, according to this view, the dielectric constant [1] is calculated to be

$$K = \frac{1 + 2u}{1 - u} \, ;$$

from which it follows that

$$u = \frac{K - 1}{K + 2}.$$

Now according to the electromagnetic theory of light,

$$K = N^2,$$

if N denotes the refractive index for light of very long wave-length; by introducing this, and then dividing by d, we obtain

$$\frac{u}{d} = \frac{N^2 - 1}{N^2 + 2} \cdot \frac{1}{d} = R \, ;$$

and this expression must be independent of the temperature, the pressure, and of changes in the state of aggregation, because, according to the definition, $\frac{u}{d}$ denotes the real specific volume of the molecule, i.e. the volume actually occupied by the molecules of 1 gram of the substance.   R *denotes the specific refraction.*

Now, as a matter of fact, experiment leads, in a very remarkable way, to the result that the specific refraction is a very characteristic quantity for the given substance, irrespective of the conditions under which it may be studied; and this holds true, not only when calculated from the so-called "refractive index of light of infinitely long wave-length," but also when calculated from the definite refractive index of any selected kind of light in the visible spectrum; it is best to take the red hydrogen line, or the sodium line, so that the influence of dispersion is not too great.   As already shown on p. 104, the rule of mixtures gives better results by calculating with the n^2 formula than with the n formula; and all experiment supports the view that the former decidedly ought to be preferred in studying the connection between the chemical composition and the optical behaviour.

Both expressions are very satisfactory in the relatively small changes of the refractive indices, due to the expansion by heat, as is shown by the following table of values for water from the determinations of Rühlmann, referred to the D-line :—

---

[1] Clausius, *Ges. Abh.* (Separate Papers), II. 135 (1867).

t	$\dfrac{n-1}{d}$	$\dfrac{n^2-1}{n^2+2}\cdot\dfrac{1}{d}$
0°	0·3338	0·2061
10°	0·3338	0·2061
20°	0·3336	0·2061
90°	0·3321	0·2059
100°	0·3323	0·2061

A comparison of the n^2 expression with the old formula shows that it alone is independent of the state of aggregation, as is illustrated by the following example,[1] in which again the refractive index n is referred to the sodium line.

	$\dfrac{n-1}{d}$			$\dfrac{n^2-1}{n^2+2}\cdot\dfrac{1}{d}$		
	Vapour.	Liquid.	Diff.	Vapour.	Liquid.	Diff.
Water . . .	0·3101	0·3338	− 0·0237	0·2068	0·2061	+ 0·0007
Carbon-disulphide .	0·4347	0·4977	− 0·0630	0·2898	0·2805	+ 0·0093
Chloroform . .	0·2694	0·3000	− 0·0306	0·1796	0·1790	+ 0·0006

The temperature of the liquid was 10°, of the vapour 100°.

The product of the specific refraction R and the molecular weight M is called the *molecular refraction*; thus

$$MR = \frac{n^2-1}{n^2+2}\cdot\frac{M}{d}.$$

It is therefore a measure of the true volume of the molecules contained in a mol. A regularity of conduct is shown in the case of the molecular refraction, which is similar to that in the case of molecular volume; but the influence of the constitution on the optical behaviour is manifested much more decidedly than in the relations between the density and the nature of the substance. *The molecular refraction of a compound can be calculated by the summation of the atomic refractions*; but the atomic refraction is fairly constant, *i.e.* independent of the other elements occurring in the molecule, only in the case of the univalent elements; it varies considerably for oxygen and carbon according to the mode of union.

It is to J. W. Brühl[2] that we are chiefly indebted since 1880, together with Landolt, for the development of the science of the molecular refractions, in that he has worked up and calculated a great

[1] Brühl, *Zeitschr. phys. Chem.* **7.** 4 (1891).
[2] *Zeitschr. phys. Chem.,* **7.** 140 (1891). See also the voluminous investigations of Kannonikoff, *J. pr. Chem.* [2], **31.** 339 (1885).

number of observations.   The following table contains the principal atomic refractions recently recalculated by Brühl.   The figures which refer to sodium light are taken from the calculations of Conrady.[1]

TABLE OF SOME OF THE ATOMIC REFRACTIONS

	For the Red H-line.	For the Na-line.	For the Blue H-line.	Atomic Dispersion Blue-Red.
Simply bound carbon	2·365	2·501	2·404	0·039
Hydrogen	1·103	1·051	1·139	0·036
Hydroxyl oxygen	1·506	1·521	1·525	0·019
Ether oxygen	1·655	1·683	1·667	0·012
Carbonyl oxygen	2·328	2·287	2·414	0·086
Chlorine	6·014	5·998	6·190	0·176
Bromine	8·863	8·927	9·211	0·348
Iodine	13·808	14·12	14·582	0·774
Ethylene union	1·836	1·707	1·859	0·23
Acetylene union	2·22	...	2·41	0·19

Atomic refractions of a great number of other elements have been determined mostly from their organic compounds by the use of the above values.   They have generally been found to show considerable variation according to the nature of the chemical combination into which they enter, so that the atomic refractions have no wide range of applicability for the other elements.   The variation increases naturally with the variety of the modes of combination ; it is therefore greatest for multivalent elements.   On the other hand, this constitutive variability of the atomic refraction, if only its dependence on constitution is thoroughly studied, serves as a valuable help in determining the constitution, as was shown especially for the nitrogen compounds by the extensive investigations of Brühl.[2]   A further constitutive influence was brought to light by Brühl,[3] who showed that neighbouring unsaturated atomic groups (especially $C = C$) caused an increase in molecular refraction, and especially also in molecular dispersion.   Recent investigations of Moureu [4] have shown that the acetylene union has a very variable value, which is usually considerably greater than 2·2, so that here additive relations seem to fail entirely.

Oxygen itself in some states of combination shows an atomic refraction different to that given above, as appears from the investigations of Nasini, Carrara, Anderlini, and others.[5]

The refractive power of the enol- and keto- forms are markedly different in a number of solvents.[6]

[1] *Zeitschr. phys. Chem.* **3.** 210 (1889).
[2] *Ibid.* **16.** 193, 226, 497, 512 ; **22.** 373 ; **25.** 577 (1895-1898).
[3] *Ber.* **40.** 878, 1153 [1907].   [4] *Ann. chim. phys.* [8], **7.** I. 1906.
[5] *Gazz. chim. ital.* **24.** I. (1894) ; **25.** II. (1895) ; *Zeitschr. phys. Chem.* **17.** 539 (1895).   [6] Bruhl, *Zeitschr. phys. Chem.* **30.** 61 (1899).

The use of these figures may be most easily explained by means of an example ; we will calculate the molecular refraction of benzene, C_6H_6, referred to the figures for the red H-line.

$$
\begin{aligned}
\text{6 carbon atoms} &= 6 \times 2 \cdot 365 = 14 \cdot 190 \\
\text{6 hydrogen atoms} &= 6 \times 1 \cdot 103 = 6 \cdot 618 \\
\text{3 double unions} &= 3 \times 1 \cdot 836 = 5 \cdot 508
\end{aligned}
$$

$$\text{Sum} \quad . \quad MR = 26 \cdot 32$$

Observation with the same kind of light and at $20°$ gave $n = 1 \cdot 4967$, $d = 0 \cdot 8799$, $M = 78$, and therefore

$$MR = \frac{n^2 - 1}{n^2 + 2} \frac{M}{d} = 25 \cdot 93,$$

which coincides well with the value as calculated above.

The molecular refraction calculated for acetone $CO(CH_3)_2$, and with the Na-light, gives 3 carbon atoms + 6 hydrogen atoms + 1 carbonyl oxygen = $16 \cdot 10$; while observation gives $16 \cdot 09$.

Small variations of the expression $\frac{n^2 - 1}{n^2 + 2}$ from proportionality with the density on change of temperature have been found which, however, exceed errors of observation. Eykman[1] suggested from a large and varied collection of observations the expression $\frac{n^2 - 1}{n + 0 \cdot 4}$ as expressing this proportionality more completely, but, as this has no theoretical foundation, it can only be considered as an interpolation formula.

The figures given in the last column of the preceding table (p. 313), and called the atomic dispersions, are the differences of the respective values, referred to the blue and the red hydrogen lines. Brühl finds, by a discussion of the material thus far observed, that the *molecular dispersion* of a compound for a definite substance, liquid or gaseous, is independent of the temperature, and fairly independent of the state of aggregation ; this *molecular dispersion*, in a manner analogous to that for the molecular refraction, may be defined by the formula

$$\left(\frac{n_\gamma^2 - 1}{n_\gamma^2 + 2} - \frac{n_a^2 - 1}{n_a^2 + 2} \right) \frac{M}{d},$$

where n_a and n_γ are the respective refractive indices for the H_a and the H_γ lines. Thus the molecular dispersion, like the molecular refraction, becomes of value as a specific manifestation of the material nature and composition of chemical substances.

As far as the available data extend, it is possible in many cases to calculate the molecular dispersion from the sum of the atomic dispersions ; yet in this case it appears that the constitutive influence appears more often and in a more decided way than in the case of

[1] *Rec. trav. chim. Pays-Bas*, **14**. 185 ; **15**. 52 (1895 and 1896).

the molecular refraction. A comparison of atomic refraction and atomic dispersion shows that there is no simple connection between refraction and dispersion. The atomic refraction of carbon is about twice as great as that of hydrogen, but their atomic dispersions are about the same. The atomic refraction of bromine is once and a half as large as that of chlorine; while its atomic dispersion is twice as great. The iodine atom refracts twice as strongly as the chlorine atom ; but it disperses four times as strongly, etc., etc. It is interesting to know that the influence of multiple unions of atoms in the molecule is manifested more clearly in the case of dispersion than in the case of refraction.

An observation of Brühl [1] is very important, to the effect that the atomic refractions of hydrogen and chlorine, as calculated from their behaviour in their compounds, coincide respectively with the powers of refraction of these gases in the free state ; the former, according to the table on p. 313, are respectively 1·05 and 6·00 for Na-light ; the latter are found by observation to be 1·05 and 5·78 respectively. On the other hand, the atomic refraction of free oxygen amounts to 20·5, which is considerably greater than the value for hydroxyl oxygen, 1·52.

Since the mixture formula on p. 104 usually holds, solids can be investigated and their molecular refraction determined in a suitable solvent (that is, a chemically indifferent one). It is not improbable that, if these substances were studied in dilute solution, more remarkable results might be obtained than by the investigation of pure liquids. For in the latter the degree of polymerisation introduces complications as to which the constitutional formula gives us no indication. To perform such experiments it would be advisable to use an optical differential method which would yield directly the difference of refractive index between solution and solvent.

The following may be said in brief, regarding the *theoretical foundation* of the regularities which obtain in molecular refraction. According to the results given on p. 311, the molecular refraction is a measure of the space actually occupied by the molecules ; it had been previously (p. 307) inferred that the molecular volume is made up additively, or at least approximately so, from the volumes of the atoms ; and the same must also be true for the molecular refraction, as in fact was found to be the case.

The molecular volumes and the molecular refractions thus appear to be closely related values, because they are both proportional to the space occupied by the molecules.

Now, as a matter of fact, it cannot be denied that there is a certain parallelism between the relations of the molecular volume on the one hand and of the molecular refraction on the other, to the molecular structure. Both properties are peculiarly additive. Also

[1] *Zeitschr. phys. Chem.* **7**. 1. (1891).

the influence of constitution is clearly the same in both cases, in that carbonyl oxygen has a greater atomic volume and a greater atomic refraction than that possessed by hydroxyl oxygen, or by ester oxygen. Also, both the molecular volume and the molecular refraction are increased by the presence of a doubled carbon union.

The attempt to express the molecular refraction of a *gaseous compound* as the sum of the molecular and atomic refractions of its components, employing the n^2 formula, has given the following results : [1]—

Substance.	Molecular Refraction.	
	Observed.	Calculated.
Hydrochloric acid . . .	6·70	$H + Cl = 6·83$
Carbon dioxide . . .	13·32	$CO + 2Cl = 16·59$
Hydrocyanic acid . . .	6·63	$H + CN = 7·21$
Water	3·82	$2H + O = 4·14$
Ammonia	5·63	$3H + N = 5·36$
Carbon dioxide . . .	6·71	$CO + O = 7·08$
Ethyl chloride . . .	16·35	$HCl + C_2H_4 = 17·49$
Nitric acid	4·46	$N + O = 4·25$
Nitrous acid . . .	7·58	$2N + O = 6·45$

The refractive values of the components used were obtained from the direct measurements which Dulong, Mascart, Jamin, and others have made on the free gases, and are as follows :—

H	O	N	Cl	CO	CN	C_2H_4
1·5	2·05	2·20	5·78	5·03	6·16	10·66

The differences between experiment and calculation cannot be ascribed to errors of observation; they show that the molecular refraction is not a purely additive property, but constitutive influences make themselves felt. Thus oxygen in the free state has undoubtedly a different atomic refraction than in the carbon compounds, and in the latter there is a difference according as the oxygen has both its valencies saturated by the same or by two different carbon atoms. The atomic refraction of elements such as sulphur or nitrogen is still more variable.

Dielectric Constants.—The mutual electrostatic action of two electrically charged bodies varies with the nature of the medium in which they are placed; if in a vacuum they attract with a force k, then in another medium the force amounts to $\dfrac{k}{D}$, in which D, the dielectric constant of the medium in question, is always greater than one, though in gases only slightly greater. Electrostatics teaches that the mutual action of two bodies kept at a constant potential difference

[1] Brühl, *Zeitschr. phys. Chem.* **7.** 140 (1891).

is proportional to the dielectric constant of the medium, that, further, if c is the capacity of a condenser in a vacuum (or, what is practically the same thing, air), it becomes cD when the condenser is placed in a medium of dielectric constant D.   It follows from the theory of electric oscillations that the velocity of propagation of electric waves in wires is inversely proportional to the square root of the dielectric constant of the surrounding insulator.

From these facts arise a number of experimental methods for determining the dielectric constant ; we may mention the following :—

1. *The electrometer method* consists in observing the throw of the needle of a suitably constructed quadrant electrometer, first in air, then in the liquid in question (Silow, 1875).   Cohn and Arons[1] used alternating currents instead of continuous currents to charge the electrometer.   With this method, slightly conducting liquids may be investigated.

2. *The condenser method* consists in comparing by any suitable method the capacity of condensers, first in air, and then when filled with the liquid to be studied.   Measurement by means of a telephone and Wheatstone's bridge is to be recommended ; the chief difficulty which arises from want of insulation of the substance under investigation can be eliminated by the use of variable resistances placed in parallel to the condensers to be compared.   The method thus becomes suitable for the investigation of slightly conducting liquids, and is simpler and more exact in practice than the electrometer method.[2]

3. *Measurement of the length of stationary electric waves.*—Some arrangement is used for producing stationary electric waves and for measuring their length, which is directly proportional to the velocity of propagation and, therefore, according to what precedes, inversely to the square root of the dielectric constant of the medium.   A convenient apparatus has recently been described by P. Drude,[3] and used for numerous experiments.   By working with short waves this method allows of studying relatively good conductors.

Dielectric action can be simply explained, as was remarked on p. 311, by assuming conducting particles surrounded by an insulator (luminiferous ether) ; the greater the volume of these conducting particles, the greater the dielectric constant of the medium in question.

The following table contains the dielectric constants of a number of liquids at 18° ; the numbers show that the dielectric constant varies extraordinarily from one substance to another, and so is highly suited for characterising the substances :—

---

[1] *Wied. Ann.* **33.** 13 (1888).   For the description of simple and suitable electrometers see F. Smale, *Wied. Ann.* **57.** 215 (1896).

[2] Nernst, *Zeitschr. phys. Chem.* **14.** 622 (1893).

[3] *Zeitschr. phys. Chem.* **23.** 267 (1897).

DIELECTRIC CONSTANTS OF SOME LIQUIDS AT 18°

Benzene	. . .	2·29	Ethyl alcohol	. .	26·1
Xylene	. . .	2·35	Propyl alcohol	. .	22
Carbon disulphide	. .	2·58	Isobutyl alcohol	. .	19
Ether	. . .	4·35	Amyl alcohol	. .	16
Aniline	. . .	7·28	Ortho-nitro-toluene	.	28
Chloroform	. .	5·0	Nitro-benzene	. .	36
Ethyl chloride	. .	11	Water	. . .	80
Ethyl bromide	. .	4·8	Ethyl acetate	. .	6·3
Methyl alcohol	. .	32			

If in the expression (p. 311)

$$R = \frac{N^2 - 1}{N^2 + 2} \cdot \frac{1}{d},$$

N^2 be replaced by D,

$$R = \frac{D - 1}{D + 2} \cdot \frac{1}{d}$$

means *the specific refraction for very long waves*, since the measurements of dielectric constants are always made with wave lengths considerably greater than those of visible light. It may be expected, therefore, that the regularities observed in optically measured refraction would become much more obvious if there were used, instead of the optical refractive index N, the corresponding value of the electric refractive index ($= \sqrt{D}$) which is free from the influence of dispersion (that is, refers to very long waves). This anticipation does not turn out to be true, as was shown by the extensive investigations of Landolt and Jahn.[1] The expression for the electric refraction is not even approximately constant for the same substance with varying temperature and state of aggregation, nor can the specific refraction of mixtures be calculated with any certainty from the mixture formula.[2]

The explanation of this behaviour lies in the fact that the refractive index extrapolated from Cauchy's formula for very long waves rarely agrees with the square root of the dielectric constant. To take the strongest example, the refractive index of water extrapolated for long waves is 1·3, the square root of its dielectric constant is 9; in other words, there is a region of very strong and, in fact, anomalous dispersion in the infra-red spectrum. Dispersion phenomena in the infra-red region of the spectrum have so far been but slightly studied, we have, therefore, no means of tracing the complete dispersion curve; for the long heat waves investigated are still very much shorter than the shortest electric waves which have been produced and measured, so that a large and certainly highly interesting region remains inaccessible to experiment; but the recent investigations of Drude (*l.c.* p. 317) bring out clearly that dispersion is mainly associated

[1] *Zeitschr. phys. Chem.* **10**. 289 (1892).
[2] See also, amongst others, the researches of F. Ratz, *Zeitschr. phys. Chem.* **19**. 94 (1896); Linebarger, *ibid.* **20**. 131 (1896); J. Philip, *ibid.* **24**. 18 (1897).

with presence of *hydroxyl groups* in the molecule, and that the observed phenomena of anomalous dispersion accompanied by the appearance of absorption bands in the infra-red part of the spectrum is in accordance with Helmholtz's theory.

The circumstance that mixtures of pyridine or betaine with water show much more marked anomalous dispersion than these substances in the pure state is explained by Bredig[1] as due to formation of hydrates in solution after the analogy of $NH_4(OH)$.

From the point of view of the above theory of Clausius and Mossotti these facts may mean that the molecules consist of a well-conducting core, or several such, and a less conducting sheath; then the optical refraction would be the measure of the volume of the well-conducting core, whilst the electric refraction measured for very long waves would give the volume of the core plus the badly conducting sheath. The additive behaviour of the optical molecular refraction would show that the volume of the core is practically equal to the sum of the volumes of its components, whilst the volume of the surrounding sheath would be greatly influenced by constitution. Of course this assumption is, at the present time, very hypothetical; still we may draw certain conclusions on the molecular constitution of matter from the explanation of anomalous dispersion in the region of long waves.

Magnetic Rotation of the Plane of Polarisation.—In 1846 Faraday discovered that transparent substances, when placed in a magnetic field, acquire the property of rotating the plane of polarisation in the direction of the lines of force; and also that the observed rotation is proportional to the thickness of the layer, and to the intensity of the magnetic field. The sense of this rotation is the same for most substances, as for all organic substances for instance; it is in the same direction, as seen by the observer, in which the magnetising current circles; but its magnitude is dependent upon the nature of the particular substance.

The problem of explaining the relation between the degree of rotation and the chemical nature of the substance was recently (since 1882) attacked in a very thorough way by W. H. Perkin. As a measure of the coefficient of the magnetic rotation of substances, Perkin took the observed angle of rotation in a definite intensity of the magnetic field, divided by the density of the substance and by the rotation angle of a layer of water of the same thickness in the same field; this value he named the *specific rotation*; and the product of this with the molecular weight of the substance divided by the molecular weight of water, he called the *molecular rotation*. Here we meet with relations which are similar to the dependence of the molecular refraction upon the composition and the constitution respectively. The molecular rotation of organic compounds can usually be calculated very approximately, by summation of the *atomic rotations*, the values

---

[1] *Zeitschr. f. Elektrochem.* **7.** 767 (1901).

of which must be suitably chosen; and here also, in the case of the multivalent elements, the atomic rotation varies very distinctly with the mode of union.[1]

Magnetism.—The molecular magnetism, *i.e.* the specific magnetism referred to that of water as unity, and multiplied by the molecular weight, has recently been investigated for a number of organic compounds by Henrichsen,[2] who used the torsion method of G. Wiedemann. All of the substances studied were *diamagnetic.* As the molecular magnetism could be calculated by summation of suitably chosen *atomic magnetisms*, it proves that this property is also emphatically *additive.* The presence of double carbon-unions in the molecule seems to increase the diamagnetism.

According to recent investigations by G. Jäger and St. Meyer,[3] the atomic magnetism of the paramagnetic elements, nickel, cobalt, iron, manganese in equivalent solutions of their compounds stands in the simple ratio 2 : 4 : 5 : 6, and chromium appears to lie between nickel and cobalt.

It is remarkable that the magnetic susceptibility appears to be independent not merely of the anion, but of the valency of the cation; for solution of ferrous and ferric salts containing equal amounts of iron are equally susceptible.

The Heat of Combustion.—By the heat of combustion of a substance is meant the quantity of heat produced by the complete oxidation of 1 g. of the substance. It makes a slight difference whether the combustion is conducted at constant *pressure,* or at constant *volume,* the former value being a trifle smaller, viz. by the amount of the heat value of the external work performed by the combustion. In the case of the hydrocarbons, *e.g.*, this difference is usually less than 0·5 of a per cent of the total value. The details of this, as well as the methods of the determination of the heat of combustion, will not be given till the chapter on " Thermochemistry." We will give in this place only a statement of the regular relations which were ascertained by a study of organic compounds.

The *hydrocarbons* in particular have been carefully studied ; according to J. Thomsen,[4] the following may be theoretically prefaced regarding these values. The process of combustion may be regarded as occurring in two stages :—

1. The decomposition of the molecule into the individual atoms.

2. The combination of the individual atoms with oxygen.

The quantity of heat produced in the combustion of a hydrocarbon

[1] For further information see Ostwald, *Lehrbuch der allg. Chem.* 2nd edit. I. p. 499 (1891). [Also see Walker's translation of Ostwald's *Outlines*, p. 105.—Tr.]

[2] *Wied. Ann.* **34.** 180 (1888) ; **45.** 38 (1892).

[3] *Ibid.* **63.** 83 (1897).

[4] *Thermochem. Untersuchungen,* Bd. IV., Leipzig, 1886 ; *Zeitschr. phys. Chem.* **1.** 369 (1887).

is equal to the *heat developed* by the union of the isolated atoms with oxygen, minus the *heat absorption* which would be observed in the dissociation of the hydrocarbons into separate carbon atoms and separate hydrogen atoms.   It is a matter of indifference whether the process actually occurs in this way ; because according to the law of the conservation of energy, the quantity of heat developed must be the same, whatever may be the order in which it occurs.

Now, if we make the assumption that the same quantity of heat absorption S is always required in the separation of one hydrogen, wherever the separation occurs ; and that there are required the same amounts of heat, U, V, and W, in the separation of single, double, or triple carbon unions respectively, wherever the separations occur ; then in the dissociation of a carbon compound C_aH_{2b}, the amount of heat absorption A_1, is,

$$A_1 = 2bS + xU + yV + zW,$$

where x, y, and z denote respectively the number of single, double, or triple unions.

Now, since there are in the molecule 4a carbon valencies, 2b of which are satisfied by hydrogen, then $4a - 2b$ carbon valencies must be satisfied *in pairs*; and therefore, and because every single union employs two valencies, every double union four valencies, and every triple union six valencies, it follows that

$$4a - 2b = 2x + 4y + 6z.$$

Therefore

$$x = 2a - b - 2y - 3z,$$

and therefore for the heat absorption A_1, we find

$$A_1 = 2bS + (2a - b - 2y - 3z)U + yV + zW.$$

Now, if P denotes the heat of combustion of an isolated carbon atom, and Q that of an isolated hydrogen atom, then the heat developed A_2 in the combustion of the isolated atoms amounts to

$$A_2 = aP + 2bQ.$$

And thus for the heat of combustion at constant volume, we have

$$A_2 - A_1 = aP + 2bQ - 2bS - (2a - b - 2y - 3z)U - yV - zW.$$

In order to obtain the heat of combustion at constant pressure, it must be observed that the combustion of the gaseous molecule C_aH_{2b} requires $a + \dfrac{b}{2}$ molecules of oxygen, and that there are produced a molecules of gaseous carbon dioxide, and b molecules of liquid water ; there results, therefore, a diminution in volume of $1 - \dfrac{b}{2}$ mol, which corresponds to

$$0{\cdot}580 - 0{\cdot}290b \text{ Cal.}$$

Now, if we add this correction, which is usually very small, to $A_2 - A_1$, we obtain *as the heat of combustion* $\mathfrak{B}(C_aH_{2b})$ *of the hydrocarbon* (C_aH_{2b}), *at constant pressure,*

$$\mathfrak{B}(C_aH_{2b}) = aA + bB + yC + zD + 0.580,$$
where

$A = P - 2U,$	$C = 2U - V,$
$B = 2Q + U - 2S - 0.290,$	$D = 3U - W.$

As a matter of fact, this formula allows a very exact calculation of the heat of combustion of the *hydrocarbons of the fatty series*, expressed in large calories, if we assume the following values :—

$A = 106\cdot17,$	$C = 15.465,$
$B = 52.53,$	$D = 43\cdot922.$

Thus, for example, by the calculation of the heat of combustion of di-allyl, we find

$$\mathfrak{B}(C_6H_{10}) = 6A + 5B + 2C + 0\cdot58 = 931\cdot2 \text{ Cal.,}$$

while Thomsen determined it experimentally as $932\cdot8$ Cal. Of course it is not possible to ascertain the particular values of P, Q, S, **U**, V, and W from the empirically determined values of A, B, C, and D.

The preceding formula is not applicable to closed chain hydrocarbons, such as trimethylene or benzene. Thus the heat of combustion of the latter substance, C_6H_6, in the gaseous state, on the assumption of nine single unions, according to the preceding formula, would give

$$
\begin{aligned}
6A &= 637\cdot02 \\
+3B &= 157\cdot59 \\
+0\cdot580 &= 0\cdot58 \\
\hline
\text{Sum} &= 795\cdot19
\end{aligned}
$$

while by assuming three doubled unions in benzene, we would have

$$795\cdot19 + 3 \times 15\cdot465 = 841\cdot585.$$

Both of these values differ too much from that obtained by direct measurement, namely, $787\cdot5$, which, however, is fairly near the value calculated on the supposition of nine single carbon unions.

It happened by chance that Thomsen, in using his universal burner, obtained heats of combustion which were a little too high, and so his old values for the heat of combustion of gaseous benzene, uncorrected, coincide quite well with the value calculated on the assumption of nine single unions,—a circumstance which induced him at the time to speak against the Kekulé formula, and gave opportunity for much controversy.

Thus it resulted, particularly by the work of Berthelot in Paris, and Stohmann in Leipsic, both of whom worked with the calorimetric bomb, that more extended material gave a broader basis for the theoretical development of the relations between the heat of combustion and the chemical constitution.   Then a renewed discussion of the observations led Thomsen[1] to the conclusion *that the benzene union has a heat value different from that of the ethylene union.*

In order to obtain satisfactory material to prove this view, Thomsen then calculated the heat of combustion of a number of aromatic hydrocarbons, which were measured *in the solid state.*

The assumption that the same formula, of course with changed constants, would hold good here, was justified by the circumstance, that the heat of sublimation, which obviously is the excess of the heat of combustion in the gaseous state over that in the solid state, in all cases has a regular connection with the constitution, and that, at all events, *this value is only a very small fraction of the heat of combustion.*

In fact, it was shown that the heat of combustion of benzene, naphthalene, anthracene, phenanthrene, and chrysene, all being taken *in the crystallised state,* can be calculated from the formula

$$\mathfrak{B}(C_aH_{2b}) = 104 \cdot 3b + 49 \cdot 09m + 105 \cdot 47n,$$

where m denotes the number of single hydrocarbon unions, and n the number of double unions.   The formula harmonises very well with the results of experiment when we ascribe to benzene three double unions, to naphthalene four, to anthracene, phenanthrene, and chrysene each six.   This is of course, not quite in agreement with the constitutional formulæ of these substances.   It is also possible to calculate the heat of combustion of the phenyl methanes, by ascribing a heat value of $723 \cdot 7$ to the radical $C_6H_5 - C$.   The preceding formula is also in harmony with other determinations; thus the heat of combustion of methane in the solid state is calculated to be

$$\mathfrak{B}(CH_4) = 2 \times 104 \cdot 3 = 208 \cdot 6,$$

a result a little smaller than that for gaseous methane $(211 \cdot 9)$, as it should be.

A comparison of the numerical values obtained by the new formula, with those given on p. 322, which were obtained for gaseous hydrocarbons of the open-chain variety, leads to the conclusion *that the heat of formation of an ethylene union is considerably smaller than that of the formation of a benzene union.*   And this result is entirely in harmony with the well-known fact that the formation of addition products is attended with much greater difficulty in the case of aromatic nuclei than in the case of the olefines; or, in other words, that the double benzene unions are much harder to dislocate than the olefine unions.   This difference is all the more remarkable because the compounds have the same optical behaviour (p. 314).[2]

---

[1] *Zeitschr. phys. Chem.* **7.** 55 (1891).

[2] Further attempts to calculate heats of combustion on the assumption of a practically additive behaviour were made by Lemoult, *Comp. rend.* **136.** 895 ; **137.** 979 (1903).

In the other organic compounds [1] the heats of combustion show a prevailingly additive character. But the unmistakable influence of constitutional differences (for instance, in isomeric acids) may be distinguished with some certainty in the difference in the value of the heats of combustion, and can be compared with the much more remarkable variations of other physical properties, specially the dissociation constant.[2] In the sense of Berthelot's principle (Book IV. Chap. V.) the less stable isomeric form has usually, but not always, the greater content of energy, and consequently the greater heat of combustion; but as, according to Baeyer's [3] stereochemical theory, double and treble bonds between carbon atoms are more unstable the more their valencies vary in direction from the tetrahedric arrangement, *i.e.* the greater the tension inside the molecule, so usually the heat of combustion increases with the magnitude of the tension, as was found by Stohmann [4] in general, and especially for the poly-methylenes $(CH_2)_n$.

The heats of combustion of the hydrogenised benzenes measured by Stohmann [5] are very characteristic of the thermal behaviour of the aromatic compounds. He found the heat of combustion under constant pressure—

					Diff.
Benzene	.	.	.	. 779·8	
					68·2
Di-hydro-benzene	.	.	.	.. 848·0	
					44·0
Tetra-hydro-benzene	.	.	.	. 892·0	
					41·2
Hexa-hydro-benzene .	.	.	.	. 933·2	
					58·0
Hexane	.	.	.	. 991·2	

Similar differences were found for the terephthalic acids and their products.[6] The transformation of benzene into its first reduction product is accompanied by a much greater absorption of heat than the transformation of already hydrogenised products to the next higher product of reduction. The entire thermal behaviour of benzene and its derivatives agrees well with Thiele's assumption (p. 293), according to which the saturation in aromatic compounds is much more complete than was formerly supposed.

Regularities in the Boiling-Points of Organic Compounds.
—The problem of calculating the boiling-points of organic compounds from their composition and constitution, and with the same exactness that is possible in the case of the molecular refraction, has not been solved as yet; and, indeed, this problem, which is interesting both in a practical and a theoretical way, presents no little difficulty, for the reason that the boiling-point, doubtless, depends to a large degree

[1] Stohmann, *Zeitschr. phys. Chem.* **6.** 334 (1890).
[2] Stohmann and Schmidt, *Zeitschr. phys. Chem.* **21.** 314 ref. ; *Journ. pr. Chem* **53.** 345 (1896). [3] *Ber. deutsch. chem. Ges.* **18.** 2278 (1885).
[4] *Journ. pr. Chem.* **45.** 305, 475 ; **46.** 530 (1892).
[5] *Sitzungsber. der sächs. Akad.*, 1893, 477.
[6] Stohmann and Kleber, *Journ. f. prakt. Chemie*, **43.** 1 (1891).

upon the constitution, and that certainly makes the problem all the more fascinating.

Now, investigation has disclosed a number of instances of regular behaviour [1] which are sufficiently remarkable to deserve a more thorough treatment, although it has not been possible, as yet, to group them from any general standpoint. These regularities, for the most part, consider the *change of boiling-point* experienced by an organic compound from substitution.

Substitution of CH_3.—It was early recognised that the melting-point of homologous organic compounds rose fairly regularly with the molecular weight; it is only quite recently that Young [2] has succeeded in bringing these regularities under a general scheme.

Firstly, as always in such questions, a distinction must be drawn between normal and associated substances. Young expresses the boiling-points in absolute measure, and shows that for normal substances, the increase Δ corresponding to the substitution of CH_3 for hydrogen, is simply a function of the absolute boiling-point:

$$\Delta = \frac{144 \cdot 86}{T^{0 \cdot 148 \sqrt{T}}}.$$

The following table contains the (absolute) boiling-points of the paraffins calculated according to this formula:

Paraffin.	Boiling-points (abs.).		Difference.
	Obs.	Calc.	
CH_4	108·3	106·75	− 1·55
C_2H_6	180·0	177·7	− 2·3
C_3H_8	228·0	229·85	+ 1·85
C_4H_{10}	274·0	272·6	− 1·4
C_5H_{12}	309·3	309·4	+ 0·1
C_6H_{14}	341·95	341·95	—
C_7H_{16}	371·4	371·3	− 0·1
C_8H_{18}	398·6	398·1	− 0·5
C_9H_{20}	422·5	422·85	+ 0·35
$C_{10}H_{22}$	446·0	445·85	− 0·15
$C_{11}H_{24}$	467·0	467·35	+ 0·35
$C_{12}H_{26}$	487·5	487·65	+ 0·15
$C_{13}H_{28}$	507·0	506·8	− 0·2
$C_{14}H_{30}$	525·5	525·0	− 0·5
$C_{15}H_{32}$	543·5	542·3	− 1·2
$C_{16}H_{34}$	560·5	558·85	− 1·65
$C_{17}H_{36}$	576·0	574·7	− 1·3
$C_{18}H_{38}$	590·0	589·9	− 0·1
$C_{19}H_{40}$	603·0	604·5	+ 1·5

[1] These have been compiled by W. Marckwald, *Dissertation*, Berlin, 1888 ; see also Fehling's *Handwörterbuch*, art. " Siedepunkt " (" boiling-point "), (1893), to which also reference should be made for the bibliography ; and Nernst and Hesse, *Siede- und Schmelz-punkt*, Braunschweig, 1893.   [2] *Phil. Mag.* **9.** 6 (1905).

This formula, which was proved on about 250 substances, holds good also for the alkyl halides, isoparaffins, olefines, polymethylenes, toluenes, xylols, ethers, aldehydes, amines, and mercaptans. It should be noticed, however, that the first member of a series always shows a greater deviation than the higher members. This is illustrated in the following small table :

RCl.

R.	T abs.	Δ obs.	Δ calc.	Diff.
CH_3	249·3			
		36·2	39·85	+3·65
C_2H_5	285·5			
		33·5	35·25	+1·75
C_3H_7	319·0			
		32·0	31·55	−0·45
C_4H_9	351·0			
		28·6	28·55	−0·05
C_5H_{11}	379·6			
		26·4	26·15	−0·25
C_6H_{13}	406·0			
		27·0	24·15	−2·85
C_7H_{15}	433·0			
		24·0	22·4	−1·6
C_8H_{17}	457·0			

Every homologous series must therefore be divided into two groups, for one of which the formula agrees approximately, for the other very closely. The first member of each series that contains a − CH_2 group attached to two carbon atoms ($C - CH_2 - C$) is the end of the first group and the beginning of the second.

The same formula holds good (but with differences of a few degrees), for the homologous series of substances associated in the liquid condition, such as nitriles, nitrocompounds, ketones, aliphatic acids and alcohols ; while the esters come between the normal and the associated substances, both in their degree of association, and in the closeness with which they obey the rule.

The Substitution of Cl, Br, and I.—The introduction of the first chlorine atom into a methyl group occasions a rise in the boiling-point of about 60° ; the actions of the second and third Cl atoms are much weaker, as shown in the example of the chlor-acetic acids ; thus

				Diff.
CH_3CO_2H boils at	.	.	118°	
				67°
CH_2ClCO_2H ,,	.	.	185°	
				9°
$CHCl_2CO_2H$,,	.	.	194°	
				1°
CCl_2CO_2H ,,	.	.	195°	

The replacement of Cl by Br makes the rise about 24° greater throughout ; by I about 50° greater.

The Substitution of H by OH.—This in general occasions a rise of about 100° ; the phenols and the corresponding amines have the same boiling-points; thus here the effect of the substitution of NH_2 and of OH is the same.

A very complete and valuable study on the action of substituting negative radicals has been made by L. Henry,[1] who established that the accumulation of negative radicals, especially oxygen, at one point of the molecule of an organic compound causes great increase of volatility, that the influence is greatest when the substituting negative radicals are attached to a single carbon atom, whilst the action is still noticeable if the substitution takes place in two carbon atoms directly combined.

When two compounds unite with each other *with elimination of water*, the boiling-point of the resulting product can be roughly calculated by adding the boiling-points of the two components, and then subtracting 100°-120°.   Thus

Acetic acid boils at	.	.	.	. 118°
Ethyl alcohol ,,	.	.	.	. 78·5°
				Sum = 196·5°
Acetic ether boils at	.	.	.	. 77·0°
				Diff. = 119·5°

A Comparison of Isomeric Compounds shows that in the fatty series the normal compound has the highest boiling-point.[2]   The more the chain of carbon atoms assumes a "branching" type, or the more "spherical" the molecule becomes, so much more does the volatility increase.   Pentane, C_5H_{12}, may serve to illustrate this—

$$CH_3(CH_2)_3CH_3 ; \qquad (CH_3)_2CHCH_2CH_3 ; \qquad (CH_3)_4C.$$
$$\text{B.-P.} \quad 38° \qquad\qquad 30° \qquad\qquad\qquad 9·5°$$

In general a change of $CH_3(CH_2)_2$ into $(CH_3)_2CH$ corresponds to a fall in boiling-point of about 7°.

Further, in the case of isomers containing oxygen, the boiling-point will be the lower the nearer the oxygen atom approaches the centre of the molecule: a change from a primary to a secondary alcohol corresponds to a fall in the boiling-point of about 19°; thus

$$CH_3(CH_2)_2CH_2OH \text{ boils at} \qquad . \qquad . \qquad . \quad 116·8°$$
$$CH_3(CH_2)CH(OH)CH_3 \text{ ,,} \qquad . \qquad . \qquad . \quad 99·0°$$
Diff. = 17·8.

Moreover, in the case of the isomeric halogen substitution products, that one will have the lower boiling-point where the chlorine seems to be more central in the chain of atoms; thus

$$CH_3CH_2CH_2Cl \text{ boils at} \qquad . \qquad . \qquad . \qquad . \quad 46·5°$$
$$CH_3CHClCH_3 \qquad ,, \qquad . \qquad . \qquad . \qquad . \quad 37°$$

Of the *isomers of the benzene derivatives*, in general the *ortho compounds*

[1] *Bulletin de l'Académie belgique* [3], **15**. Nos. 1 and 2 (1888).
[2] B. Tollens, *Ber.* **2**. 83 (1869).

boil at a higher temperature than the *meta compounds*, and these in turn about the same as, or higher than, the *para* compounds.

Regarding the influence of *the double union* in hydrocarbons, there is no general rule; but it is found that the hydrocarbons corresponding to the formula C_nH_{2n+2}, and those corresponding to C_nH_{2n}, have the same boiling-point, so that in this case the double union seems to have the same influence as the two hydrogen atoms; the same applies to alcohols, acids and esters. But in other cases a corresponding change in the molecular structure, *e.g.* carbon union instead of two hydrogen atoms, is associated with a decided change in the boiling-point; thus compounds of the type

$$\begin{matrix} C_6H_5 \\ \diagdown \\ \diagup \quad R \\ C_6H_5 \end{matrix}$$

boil about 40°-41° lower than those of the type

$$\begin{matrix} C_6H_4 \\ | \quad \diagdown \\ \diagup \quad R, \\ C_6H_4 \end{matrix}$$

where R represents any selected divalent radical, as O, CH_2, S, NH, etc.

When an *acetylene compound* is produced by further elimination of hydrogen, the boiling-point rises: thus the propargyl compounds boil about 19·5° higher than the corresponding propyl compounds.

The attempt of Vernon [1] to apply regularities of boiling-point to determine molecular condition of a liquid is noticeable as he starts from the very plausible assumption that the deviations which individual substances show from general rules have their ground in polymerisation of the liquid molecules. Thus usually doubling the molecular weight raises the boiling-point about 100° (ethylene boils at − 105, butylene at − 5, octylene at 126, the hydrocarbon $C_{16}H_{32}$ at 274); now in the series hydroiodic acid, hydrobromic acid, hydrochloric acid, the boiling-point falls from − 25, − 73, to − 100. We may therefore expect for hydrofluoric acid about − 120, whereas its boiling-point is actually + 19·4°, that is, 140° too high. Vernon concludes therefore for a molecular formula of hydrofluoric acid lying between H_2F_2 and H_4F_4. Similarly water, by analogy with sulphuretted hydrogen, should boil at − 100°, as the boiling-point lies 200° higher the formula $(H_2O)_4$ is probable. By similar considerations Vernon found the molecular formulæ S_{12}, SO_2, $SOCl_2$, SO_3, $(H_2SO_4)_4$, $(SeO_2)_4$. It is especially noticeable that the hydroxyl compounds, according to these observations, are in general strongly polymerised; for the thio-compounds which contain SH instead of OH boil 30° or more below the corresponding hydroxyl compounds, whereas in general replacing of oxygen by sulphur causes a rise of 40° or 50° in the boiling-point; further, many ethers boil at a lower temperature than the corresponding alcohols (for instance,

---

[1] *Chem. News*, **64**. 54 (1891).

methyl ether at − 23°, methyl alcohol at + 66°), whereas otherwise replacing of oxygen by an alkyl raises the boiling-point. These considerations lead to results which must be qualitatively correct; the conclusions on the degree of polymerisation are, however, uncertain (see pp. 272-277).

The Critical Data.—The conclusions arrived at in the second chapter of this book leave no doubt that the critical data have great significance for every well-defined chemical substance, and that the problem of tracing out their relationship to the constitution is a very important one. Unfortunately the experimental data thus far accumulated are neither very extensive nor very exact, as there is considerable difference between the results of different observers. For this reason, the results up to date are very small, and we will limit ourselves to the description of a rule discovered independently by Guye and Heilborn.

In keeping with experiment (p. 230), and according to van der Waals, the critical volume, which is determined experimentally with great difficulty, may be made proportional to the critical temperature divided by the critical pressure, i.e. proportional to the so-called "critical coefficient" k,

$$k = \frac{\theta_0}{\pi_0}.$$

But now since, according to the reasoning on p. 307, the critical molecular volume is an additive property, then the critical coefficient must be so also (Heilborn). On the other hand, the critical coefficient, like the molecular refraction (p. 310), is a measure of the space actually occupied by the molecules; and since the latter is decidedly an additive property, therefore the former is also (Guye).[1]

Now as a matter of fact it is found that it is possible to make

$$k = \frac{\theta_0}{\pi_0} = 1 \cdot 8MR,$$

if the critical pressure is estimated in atmospheres, and the refraction R refers to infinitely long wave-lengths (p. 312). This rule is only a rough approximation, inasmuch as the numerical factor in the preceding equation varies between the limits of 1·6 and 2·2; therefore in calculation one may use the red rays, the refraction of which is only slightly different, in comparison. And conversely, it is possible to calculate the critical coefficient from the atomic refraction given on p. 313, with about the same degree of approximation, i.e. about 10-20 per cent.

The Melting-Point.—The melting-point is best determined experimentally by surrounding the thermometer with the finely pulverised substance and heating it to incipient fusion. On account of the latent

[1] *Ann. chim. phys.* [6], **21**. 206 (1890) ; *Thèse*, Paris, 1892.

heat the thermometer remains constant for some time, when it is carefully stirred till all is melted at a fixed temperature, which can be exactly measured, and which is the melting-point. We can in this way obtain very exact measurements, especially by using large quantities of the particular substances, and by fixing the zero-point of the thermometer scale very accurately by observing the melting-point of water according to this method.

Another method, which allows of very accurate determination, and which also makes it possible to use considerably smaller quantities of the substance, say 10-20 g., depends upon the phenomenon of *under-cooling*. For although a solid substance at its melting-point assumes the liquid form under all circumstances, yet there is usually a marked delay in the reverse process, and it requires some external stimulus to induce the liquid to assume the solid state which corresponds to its temperature. If one brings this about by stirring with a glass rod, or more certainly still by introducing a bit of the substance in the solid state, the freezing of the under-cooled substance occurs; and then, as a result of the latent heat, the temperature rises to the freezing-point. This pause in the fall of the temperature may be determined with great precision and certainly by this method (see also p. 260).

The methods of melting and of freezing with large quantities of the substance give results which coincide to the hundredth part of a degree. These methods, according to a recent publication by Landolt,[1] are the *only* ones which give certain results. In practice, however, extreme accuracy is often superfluous, either because the substance is not completely pure, or because very small quantities of it are at disposal; the determination is then usually made by introducing the substance into a capillary tube which is fastened to a thermometer bulb, and the two together are dipped into a bath of water, oil, paraffin, or sulphuric acid. The temperature shown by the thermometer at the moment when the substance (which is opaque in the solid state) begins to become transparent is noted as the melting-point. The moment of the change of colour, as a rule, can be sharply noted in a clear bath and with favourable light; but sometimes, when the substance exhibits an appearance of translucency before it really melts, the error of observation may amount to several degrees. In such a case the moment when the melted substance begins to flow down into a deeper part of the tube may be taken as the sign of incipient fusion. This point may be made more visible to the eye by a simple apparatus suggested by Piccard.[2]

Mention was made on p. 186 of the regularity in the melting-point

[1] *Zeitschr. phys. Chem.* **4.** 349 (1888); see also R. v. Schneider, *ibid.* **22.** 225 (1897).
[2] *Ber.* **8.** 687. See also art. "Schmelzpunkt" ("melting-point") in Fehling's *Handwörterbuch* (1890).

of the elements.   A rule announced by v. Baeyer [1] for organic compounds has general interest.   According to this, the even members of homologous series are clearly different from the odd members—

SERIES OF THE FATTY ACIDS

	M.-P.
Normal $C_2 H_4 O_2$	$+16\cdot5$
$C_3 H_6 O_2$	-22
$C_4 H_8 O_2$	$-7\cdot9$
$C_5 H_{10} O_2$	$-58\cdot5$
$C_6 H_{12} O_2$	$-1\cdot5$
$C_7 H_{14} O_2$	$-10\cdot5$
$C_8 H_{16} O_2$	$+16\cdot5$
$C_9 H_{18} O_2$	$+12\cdot5$
$C_{10} H_{20} O_2$	$+31\cdot4$
$C_{16} H_{32} O_2$	$+62\cdot6$
$C_{17} H_{34} O_2$	$+60$
$C_{18} H_{36} O_2$	$+69\cdot3$

SUCCINIC ACID SERIES

Normal Succinic acid	$C_4 H_6 O_4$ . .	183
Glutaric ,,	$C_5 H_8 O_4$ . .	97·5
Adipic ,,	$C_6 H_{10} O_4$ . .	153
a-Pimelic ,,	$C_7 H_{12} O_4$ . .	105
Suberic ,,	$C_8 H_{14} O_4$ . .	140
Azelaic ,,	$C_9 H_{16} O_4$ . .	107
Sebacic ,.	$C_{10} H_{18} O_4$ . .	133
Brassylic ,,	$C_{11} H_{20} O_4$ . .	110

In both series, without exception, the member with an uneven number of carbon atoms has a lower melting-point than the preceding member with one less carbon atom.   In the succinic acid series, with increasing molecular weight, the melting-point of the acids having an uneven number of carbon atoms rises, and that of acids having an even number of carbon atoms falls, so that the two sets of numbers together seem to tend towards the same mean curve.

Tsakolotos [2] has shown that in the case of the simple hydrocarbons, this curve which fits the melting-points of the higher homologues of the series, can be expressed by an empirical equation.   While the melting-points of the compounds CH_4 to $C_{15}H_{32}$ alternately rise and fall, just as with the fatty acids, the difference from $C_{16}H_{34}$ to $C_{60}H_{122}$ can be expressed by the relation :

$$\triangle_n = \frac{85 - 0\cdot01882\,(n-1)^2}{n-1}$$

where $\triangle_n$ is the difference between the melting-points of two neighbouring homologues, and n, the number of C atoms, is the lower of the two.

[1] *Ber.* **10**. 1286 (1877).   [The melting-points have been corrected in accordance with the tables in the latest edition of Meyer and Jacobsen, *Lehrbuch der org. Chem.*, 1909-10.—Tr.]   [2] *Compt. rend.* **143**. 1235 (1900).

ABSOLUTE MELTING-POINTS OF THE HYDROCARBONS.

				Obs.	Calc.
$C_{16}H_{34}$	.	.	.	291°	—
$C_{17}H_{36}$	.	.	.	295·5	296
$C_{18}H_{38}$	.	.	.	301	300·7
$C_{19}H_{40}$	.	.	.	305	305
$C_{20}H_{42}$	.	.	.	309·7	309·2
$C_{21}H_{44}$	.	.	.	313·4	313·1
$C_{22}H_{46}$	.	.	.	317·4	316·7
$C_{23}H_{48}$	.	.	.	320·7	320·2
$C_{24}H_{50}$	.	.	.	324·1	323·6
$C_{27}H_{56}$	.	.	.	322·5	322·2
$C_{31}H_{64}$	.	.	.	341·1	342·0
$C_{32}H_{66}$	.	.	.	343·5	344·2
$C_{35}H_{72}$	.	.	.	347·7	350·0
$C_{60}H_{122}$	.	.	.	374-375	374·3

The following may be stated respecting other irregularities :—

Bromine compounds appear to have a higher melting-point than the corresponding chlorine compounds ; and the nitro-compounds higher than the corresponding bromine and chlorine compounds.[1]

In the pyrotartaric acid series the melting-point is higher the more the structure of the acid deviates from the normal type, i.e. the more side chains are built on to the normal. This may be formulated in the statement that in the pyrotartaric acids the melting-point rises with the number of methyl groups.[2]

Of the isomers of the aromatic series, the para derivatives seem to have the highest boiling-points, but there is an exception to this rule in the case of the amido derivatives of the substituted benzene sulphonic acids,[3] and also in the case of the isomers of the toluene sulphonic amides, anilides, and toluidides.

Among the amides of the halogen derivatives of the benzene sulphonic acids, in the para series, the melting-point rises about 20°, when a halogen is substituted by the next heavier halogen. Thus the chlorine compound melts at 143°-144°, the bromine compound at 160°-166°, and the iodine compound at 183°. Also the melting-points of the halides of any particular series appear to rise from the fluorine to the iodine compounds, but not regularly.[4] For a series of further rules see the monograph quoted on p. 325. Another point which is of much consequence for this question must not be overlooked ; it gives to melting-points occasionally, perhaps more often than is supposed, a certain arbitrary character. Many solids have the faculty of existing in several modifications, possessing different physical properties, and in particular often very different melting-points (p. 93). This is especially common among organic compounds, and it is not impossible that allotropy (polymorphism) is a general phenomenon, i.e. that every

[1] Petersen, Ber. **7**. 59 (1874).   [2] Markownikoff, Lieb. Ann. **182**. 340.
[3] Beilstein, Handbuch, **1**. 60 (1886).   [4] Lenz, Ber. **12**. 582 (1879).

solid substance can exist in several modifications corresponding with different conditions of pressure and temperature. If this view is correct, then when comparing melting-points the question must first be settled *what modifications are comparable*, and it is quite possible that many exceptions to the rules of melting-point so far discovered are only apparent, and would be avoided by the discovery of new modifications.

Although in the case of the other physical properties, the theory of their relation to the constitution of organic compounds in particular has been developed much further than in the case of the melting-point, yet, on the other hand, there is no other physical constant so well suited to identify a well-defined chemical substance. The melting-point has a pre-eminent place among all the physical properties, as is shown by the fact of its easy and accurate determination, by its great sensitiveness to foreign adulteration, and also by the fortunate circumstance that these foreign adulterations almost always act in the same way, viz. to lower it (p. 137), and finally, it varies considerably, even with very slight changes in the composition.

Internal Friction.—According to the gas theory, p. 204, the internal friction in the case of *gases* and *vapours* is directly proportional to the path of the molecule, and this latter is inversely proportional to the cross-section of the molecule ; therefore by measuring the internal friction of gases, one may obtain a measure of the space occupied by the molecule. As a matter of fact, L. Meyer [1] found a proportionality, which was at least approximate, between the volumes of molecules determined in this way and Kopp's values ; and we have already seen that the latter (p. 307) may be regarded as a measure of the space actually occupied by the molecules. It would be very interesting to have a comparison between the values as obtained by internal friction, and those from the molecular refraction, since these latter values, according to p. 312, are also a measure of the volumes of molecules.

The internal friction of liquids has been the subject of much investigation, but without affording any regularities of a general nature.[2] It is noticeable that the peculiar influence on other physical properties of the mode of combination of oxygen appears also in the viscosity.[3]

The Natural Rotation of the Plane of Polarisation.—While the property of being optically active under the influence of magnetism is a universal property (p. 320), only certain substances are able of themselves to rotate the plane of polarisation. The natural rotation,

[1] *Wied Ann.* **7.** 497 (1879) ; **13.** 1 (1881) ; **16.** 394 (1882). See also Steudel, *ibid.* **16.** 369 (1882).

[2] Ostwald, *Allg. Chem.* 2nd edit. **1.** 550 (1891).

[3] Thorpe and Rodger, *Philosophical Transactions*, London, 1894 and 1896 ; *Zeitschr. phys. Chem.* **14.** 361 ; **20.** 621.

like the magnetic, is proportional to the thickness of the section used, and varies with the temperature, and also with the wave-length of the light used.

The rotation may be measured by the polarisation apparatus or by the polari-strobometer; this in its simplest form, as devised by Mitscherlich, consists of two Nicol's prisms, which, when placed respectively before and behind the stage, produce darkness; the stage is for the reception of the substance. The angle of rotation is read directly from the divided circle of the ocular, or else the rotation is compensated by a quartz wedge which can be interposed to any desired thickness (Soleil). Finally, a number of changes have been proposed in order to obtain still greater accuracy; these have been applied in the so-called "half-shadow" apparatus, which has been well received in both scientific and practical work. The fundamental principle of this is that the field of view of the polarising apparatus is filled, not with one bundle of light rays, but with two; their planes of vibration form a certain angle with each other, and by turning the analysing Nicol, the two halves of the field of view are brought to the same degree of brightness.[1]

The natural circular polarisation was discovered in quartz by Arago in 1811, and was afterwards observed in many other crystals.

The natural circular polarisation of liquids, or of amorphous solids, was first observed by Biot in 1815 in sugar solutions, and although it has been found since then in very many substances, yet these are all carbon compounds.

The rotation property of crystallised substances depends apparently upon their molecular arrangement (crystal structure); while that of organic compounds depends upon the constitution of the molecule. A fact among others, in favour of this latter view, is that Biot (1819) found that those organic substances, which were active in the liquid state, were also capable of rotating the plane of polarisation in the gaseous state; this was more thoroughly studied by Gernez (1864) for the vapour of oil of turpentine. We will consider here only the property of rotation of the carbon compounds.

The property of rotation of organic substances has primarily been of great importance as an aid in analysis. This can be determined not only directly for active substances, as, for instance, sugar in water solution, but also under certain circumstances, as shown by Landolt,[2] indirectly, in that the influence of inactive substances on active substances may be measured by the polari-strobometer. An active substance is characterised by its specific coefficient of rotation [α]; α denotes the rotation angle for a definite kind of light (sodium light for example), measured at a definite temperature (20° for example), and expressed in degrees of the divided circle; 1 denotes the length

---

[1] For a more detailed description, see Landolt, Optisches Drehungsvermögen org. Substanzen, 2nd edit., Braunschweig, 1898   [2] Ber. **21**. 191 (1888).

of the section used, expressed in decimeters ; c denotes the number of grams contained in 1 c.c. of the liquid used (whether of a solution or a pure substance) ; then we have

$$[\alpha]\frac{20^\circ}{D} = \frac{\alpha}{lc}.$$

Moreover, the specific coefficient of rotation of the substance in solution in general varies with the nature of the solvent, and also with the concentration [1] ; it therefore will be advisable to give a statement of this phase of the rotation property. The product of the specific coefficient of the rotation and the molecular weight is called the *molecular coefficient of rotation.*

The connection with constitution is shown in no other physical property so clearly as it is in this of optical rotation. As already stated on p. 296, if we omit the asymmetrical nitrogen compounds, p. 300, which are as yet only very little known, *only those compounds are active which have one or more unsymmetrical carbon atoms, i.e.* carbon atoms, the four valencies of which, in the sense of structural organic chemistry, are satisfied by four different atoms or radicals. But, on the other hand, the existence of such carbon atoms by no means conversely necessitates optical activity ; this is explained by the following fundamental laws regarding the polari-strobometric behaviour of organic compounds, which in turn are an immediate consequence of the views developed on p. 297.

1. Only those compounds are active in an amorphous state, whether solid, liquid, or gaseous, which possess one or more unsymmetrical carbon atoms in the molecule.

2. There corresponds to every optically active substance a twin, which polarises light with the same degree of strength, but in the opposite direction ; if the compound has only one *unsymmetrical* carbon atom, then the two twins have the relative rotations, $+ A$ and $- A$. But if several unsymmetrical carbon atoms exist in the molecule, two, for instance, then, if we denote by A and B the rotations produced by each of these respective carbon atoms, there will result the following combinations :—

$$A + B ; \quad - A - B ;$$
$$A - B ; \quad - A + B.$$

The pairs in the horizontal rows are isomeric twins, since they have the same degree of rotation but in contrasted directions. If the compound has n unsymmetrical carbon atoms, then the number of optical isomers is 2n, every pair of which are twins.

---

[1] C. Winter has shown that the influence of concentration and temperature on the optical rotatory power of dissolved substances, can be theoretically accounted for by means of the internal pressure of liquids (p. 248). See *Zeitschr. phys. Chem.* **60**. 563, 641, 685 (1907).

3. But, conversely, it is not necessary that all compounds containing asymmetric carbon atoms must be optically active; for these may be—

(a) *Compounds having a very small coefficient of rotation*, so that it baffles measurement. The quantitative relations between the strength of the rotation and the nature of the atoms or radicals satisfying the four valencies of the carbon atoms have not been determined as yet; so that nothing certain can be stated at present regarding the absolute degree of the rotation.

(b) *Compounds exhibiting internal compensation*; if a molecule contains an even number of unsymmetrical carbon atoms, then it may happen that the particular action is exactly neutralised, and that the molecule as a whole is inactive, in case the carbon atoms are alike in pairs. This is the case with tartaric acid,

$$CHOH—CO_2H$$
$$|$$
$$CHOH—CO_2H,$$

which has two similar unsymmetrical carbon atoms; the possible isomers are, of course, as follows:—

$+ A + A$	$+ A - A$	$- A - A$
Dextro tart. acid;	Inactive tart. acid;	Lævo tart. acid.

Of course $+ A - A$ and $- A + A$ correspond to identical substances, which are optically inactive in consequence of internal compensation.

(c) *Compounds consisting of an equi-molecular union (racemic mixture) of the right and left varieties.* Thus this is the case with racemic acid, which is an equi-molecular union of right and left tartaric acid.

Such mixtures as the latter are obtained in the *synthetic production* of compounds with unsymmetrical carbon atoms from inactive substances. This follows necessarily from the fact that the synthesis of such a compound consists in the replacement of one c in the compound $Cabc_2$ by d, and on account of the complete equality in value between the places occupied by the two c valencies, two kinds of substitution must always occur to the same extent.

The Decomposition of a Mixture of Optical Isomers.[1]—It remains as a problem for the experimenter to separate the equi-molecular mixture of the dextro and laevo compound. There is no particular difficulty in the synthetical preparation of such a mixture above the other syntheses of organic chemistry; but certain special methods of treatment are requisite for the separation. The customary

[1] For details see Van't Hoff, *Lagerung der Atome im Raume*, Braunschweig, 1894, and especially in the extensive work of Landolt referred to on p. 334.

methods applicable to the separation of physical mixtures, which depend upon incidental differences in the melting-points, the vapour pressures, or the solubilities, all fail here completely, because, according to p. 297, both components have the same melting-point, the same vapour pressures, and the same solubility.   There are three methods applicable in this case, for all of which we are indebted to Pasteur. A short sketch of these follows.

1. By allowing an active substance, + B, to react on the mixture, the components of which are designated as + A and − A, we obtain thereby a mixture of B + A and B − A.   Now, these last compounds are no longer twins, but will in general exhibit greater or smaller differences in melting-point, vapour pressure, and solubility, therefore they can be separated by the usual methods.   By decomposing the separated compounds, the isomers + A and − A are obtained in the pure state, and the desired separation of the original inactive mixture is accomplished.

In this way Pasteur used cinchonine to neutralise a solution of racemic acid, which is an equi-molecular mixture of dextro and laevo tartaric acids; the respective salts were separated from each other by crystallisation, and then by decomposing these cinchonine salts the dextro and laevo tartaric acids were obtained in the free state: the velocity of reaction in the saponification of an optically active alcohol by a racemic mixture of an active acid is noticeably different for the two components of the mixture.[1]

2. Certain organisms affect the two isomers differently.   Thus Pasteur observed that the vegetation of *penicillum* in a dilute solution of ammonium racemate destroyed the dextro acid, while the laevo acid remained.

Since the organisms in question, or the enzymes contained in them, possess themselves an asymmetrical structure, this method is essentially the same as the first.

3. Sometimes the dextro and laevo compounds can be separated from each other in contrasted hemihedral crystals, which can be picked out from each other.   Pasteur observed this in the crystallisation of sodium-ammonium racemate.   But usually the two isomeric salts crystallise out as a compound.   This is the case with the tartaric acids which, in an equi-molecular solution, unite in crystallising out as racemic acid.   Of course in such a case the method is debarred.

To produce an optically active compound from its antipodes the following method can sometimes be used.   On rise of temperature an optically active compound is commonly converted into the racemic mixture, which then, by any suitable process of decomposition, will give both the dextro and laevo compound.

Quantitative Relations.—The fact that optical activity is con-

---

[1] Marckwald and McKenzie, *Ber. deutsch. chem. Ges.* **32.** 2130 (1899).

ditioned by the presence of an unsymmetrical carbon atom suggests another question : What are the relations between the nature of the radicals which saturate the four valencies of the unsymmetrical carbon atom on the one hand, and the degree and direction of the rotation on the other hand ?   Although not very much is certainly known at present, yet a few general remarks will be given regarding the kind of relation which should be looked for here.

We will denote by e the numerical value of the property of a radical which is influential in occasioning the polarisation ; then the power of rotation $[a]$ will be determined by the combination of the values e_1, e_2, e_3, and e_4, which this property assumes for each one of the four respective radicals of the unsymmetrical carbon atoms ; and the mathematical expression which may be calculated as the power of rotation from these values must obviously fulfil the following conditions :—

1. It must become equal to zero when two or more of the four values of e are the same, for in the latter case the asymmetry, and, therefore, of course, the rotation, will disappear.

2. It must remain unchanged in degree, but in the opposite direction, when two values of e exchange places with each other.   Such an exchange means nothing more than that a dextro-isomer is changed into lævo-isomer, or the reverse.

By a few trials it is found that an expression of the following form is suited to the conditions outlined above :—

$$(e_1 - e_2)(e_1 - e_3)(e_1 - e_4)(e_2 - e_3)(e_2 - e_4)(e_3 - e_4),$$

or

$$\ln\frac{e_1}{e_2}\ln\frac{e_1}{e_3}\ln\frac{e_1}{e_4}\ln\frac{e_2}{e_3}\ln\frac{e_2}{e_4}\ln\frac{e_3}{e_4}.$$

Of course many such expressions as the preceding may be found, but these two are the simplest.   They are, moreover, fundamentally identical, for it is only necessary to use log e in the second expression, $i.e.$ to regard this property as a measure of the power of rotation, in order to obtain the first expression.   It is also probable that there exists a property of the atom or radical, which is related to the molecular rotatory power according to the following law :—

$$M[a] = (e_1 - e_2)(e_1 - e_3)(e_1 - e_4)(e_2 - e_3)(e_2 - e_4)(e_3 - e_4).$$

Of course it cannot be determined on *a priori* grounds, whether or not the value of e may depend both on the nature of the particular radical and also on the nature of the other three radicals which constitute the unsymmetrical carbon atom group, $i.e.$ whether or not there exists a mutual influence between the radicals.   If such were the case the problem would be much complicated, because then the calculation would have to take account· of the mutual influence of each of the values of e, though probably this mutual influence would not be very great.

It was suspected by Guye[1] that the product of the mass of the radical, by its distance from the central point [centre of gravity], of the unsymmetrical carbon atom, or, since the latter is approximately constant, that the *mass of the radical* is a measure of the degree of the rotatory power.   The molecular rotation accordingly would be

$$M[\alpha] = (m_1 - m_2)(m_1 - m_3)(m_1 - m_4)(m_2 - m_3)(m_2 - m_4)(m_3 - m_4),$$

where the values of m are either proportional to the weights of the four radicals, or at least are greater the greater the weights become. But this has not been confirmed by experience.

The Absorption of Light.—If monochromatic light, *i.e.* light having a definite wave-length, falls at right angles upon an absorbent layer which has the thickness d, then a part of the light will be used in warming the substance permeated, and thus will be lost by absorption.   The fundamental law of absorption states that the intensity of the emerging light J' is proportional to that of the immerging light J, and that there exists the relation

$$J' = J(1 - \gamma)^d ;$$

here γ denotes a numerical factor which is characteristic of the absorbing substance ; this *absorption coefficient* γ varies with the wave-length of light.   In order to detect this variation, it is best to illuminate the absorbing substance with white light, and then decompose the emerging rays by the aid of a spectral apparatus (see also p. 190).

The construction of the spectral apparatus is described in handbooks of physics.[2]   It should be noted that the apparatus usually made for laboratory use depends upon the dispersive power of transparent substances, glass in particular, and therefore *give refraction spectra* ; it is only quite recently that scientific investigation has commonly begun to use spectra produced by *diffraction gratings*.   As this latter method gives regular and strong dispersion, and is also entirely free from the absorption phenomena of glass, it now commonly finds almost universal application, as it thus has a great advantage, especially in studying the infra-red and the ultra-violet parts of the spectrum.   *Photography* is employed to study the ultra-violet rays, and it is also possible to render the ultra-violet rays visible by *fluorescence.*   In the study of the infra-red part of the spectrum, use is commonly made of heat effects caused by these rays on the thermopile, bolometer, radiometer, etc.

The following kinds of absorption are recognised :—

[1] *C.R.* **110.** 744 (1890) ; thoroughly in a Thesis, Paris (1891) ; see also the work of Landolt quoted on p. 334.
[2] See also the monographs on spectral analysis by Kayser, Berlin, 1883 (new edition being prepared), and by H. W. Vogel, Berlin, 1886, and the literature quoted on p. 191.

1. Absorption which steadily increases or decreases with the wave-length of light : *uni-lateral absorption.* As a rule the absorption increases with decreasing wave-length, *i.e.* the violet end of the spectrum is absorbed more strongly than the red end.

2. Absorption which exhibits a minimum in the spectrum, with regular increase on both sides of this minimum : *bi-lateral absorption.*

3. Absorption exhibiting shaded maxima ; the spectrum appears to be crossed by *absorption bands.*

4. Absorption exhibiting sharply-defined maxima ; the spectrum appears to be crossed by *absorption lines.*

This latter variety, which is altogether the most characteristic, is met in incandescent gases.

Inasmuch as the absorption capacity of substances varies with the nature of the substance to such an extraordinary degree and in such a variety of ways, and beyond all other properties, therefore both light absorption and light emission would appear to be primarily suited to give us some information regarding molecular structure. But the results thus far obtained in this line do not at all justify the anticipations. We know of innumerable examples where very slight changes in molecular structure are associated with deep-seated changes in the capacity for absorption. But we cannot infer a single generalisation regarding the laws according to which this happens. Thus, for example, if we break up the unstable variety of nitrogen peroxide, N_2O_4, by raising the temperature into a simpler molecule NO_2, we obtain a very slight change in the chemical behaviour ; but the gas changes from a slight yellow to a dark reddish-brown ; this gas, when interposed in the path of a bundle of light rays, gives a spectrum crossed by innumerable absorption lines. Also the absorption may vary strongly with unchanged molecular weights. Thus iodine, when dissolved in carbon disulphide, gives a violet colour ; in ether, a reddish-brown ; yet in both cases the iodine was shown, by the boiling-point method, to have the molecule I_2. Of course it is not impossible that the different colours are occasioned by reaction with the solvent, *i.e.* by forming compounds consisting of $I_2 + n$ molecule of the solvent. Moreover, the cases are not rare where, as in this case, the absorption varies more or less strongly with the nature of the solvent. Usually, but not always, the absorption bands advance towards the red, according as the refractive power of the solvent increases.

Up to the present the most thorough study of absorption in solution has been done in the case of organic compounds ; here there were found certain remarkable regularities regarding the influence of substitution on the position of the absorption bands.[1]

[1] G. Krüss and Oeconomides, *Ber.* **16.** 2051 (1883) ; Kruss, *Ber.* **18.** 1426 (1885) ; *Zeitschr. phys. Chem.* **2.** 312 (1888) ; E. Koch, *Wied. Ann.* **32.** 167 (1887) ; E. Vogel, *ibid.* **43.** 449 (1891) ; M. Schutze, *Zeitschr. phys. Chem.* **9.** 109 (1892) ; G. Grebe, *ibid.* **10.** 674 (1892) ; Hartley and Dobbie, *Trans. Chem. Soc.* 1899, p. 640.

According to this, the introduction of hydroxyl, methyl, hydroxy-methyl, carboxyl, phenyl, and the halogens occasions a displacement towards the red ; the introduction of the nitro and amido groups, and also the addition of hydrogen, occasions a displacement towards the violet ; exceptions, however, occur. For reasons which will be given in the following paragraph, the former group is designated as *batho-chromic*, and the latter as *hypso-chromic*. In the case of all chemically related groups, the displacements increase with increasing *molecular weight* of the radical introduced : thus it is greater in the case of iodine than of bromine, and again greater in the case of phenyl than of methyl. Of the solvents used, concentrated sulphuric acid gave the sharpest colour reactions.

The Theory of Colouring Substances.—Inasmuch as the colour of a substance depends, as is well known, upon its selective absorption, therefore, as has been shown by M. Schütze,[1] the regularities observed regarding the absorption of light give opportunity for some interesting observations upon organic colouring matters. The mixture of all the colours of the sun's spectrum appears to be white, because for every colour there is an equally strong *complementary* colour ; and these two, when combined, produce in the eye the sensation of whiteness. There-fore, when any colour of the spectrum is extinguished by absorption, the substance appears to have the colour of the complementary emerg-ing rays. The paired complementary colours are as follows :—

> Violet—Greenish-yellow.
> Indigo—Yellow.
> Cyanide blue—Orange.
> Bluish-green—Red.
> Green—Purple.

Many colourless substances produce absorption bands in the violet. These bands are displaced towards the less refrangible [red] end of the spectrum by the introduction of batho-chrome groups ; by the entrance of bands into the visible part of the spectrum, *violet* will be first absorbed, when the substance will have a *greenish-yellow* hue. As the bands retreat regularly back towards the red, the colour of the substance will pass successively into yellow, orange, red, purple, and finally back up into violet, when the absorption bands pass from green into greenish-yellow. Continued displacement in the same direction will cause the appearance of the colours indigo, cyanide blue, bluish-green, and when the bands pass into the infra-red spectrum, the body will again be colourless.

This series of absorption colours, which is the simplest possible, is very rarely seen, because usually, before the one set of bands has passed down through the spectrum, another set appears in the violet end of the spectrum, and of course there occur complications between these two sets.

---

[1] *Zeitschr. phys. Chem.* **9.** 109 (1892).

The introduction of "hypso-chromic" groups works in a way contrary to that of the batho-chromic groups; the former produce an elevation of the "tone colour," the latter a depression, whence their respective names. As the hypso-chrome groups are of exceptional occurrence, the following law may be stated:—*the simplest colouring substances are in the greenish-yellow and yellow, and with increasing molecular weight the colour passes into orange, red, violet, blue, and green.* In fact, this law was empirically discovered in 1879 by Nietzki; it is by no means perfect, because disturbances arise from various sources— thus the very groups introduced to increase the molecular weight may have a specific hypso-chrome action in displacing the bands towards the violet, or else complications may arise from the existence of several bands in the region of the visible spectrum.

One remark of Schütze is very interesting, viz. that in the case of analogous elements an increase of atomic weight is attended by a deepening of colour; a beautiful illustration of this is found in the series including colourless fluorine,[1] yellowish-green chlorine, reddish bromine, and violet iodine.

Now experience shows that the colour of many organic colouring substances is due to the presence of certain specific groups in the molecule; thus the colour of the azo derivatives is due to the presence of the azo group; it may be therefore assumed that these same groups are responsible for the absorption of light in the molecule, and that the change of colour is due to the effect of the influence exerted by the group which is introduced on the group producing the colour.

O. N. Witt,[2] who first developed this view, called those groups which produce the colours *chromophores.* Inasmuch as their influence becomes greater the nearer spatially the group introduced is placed to the chromophore, this theory suggests an interesting method for determining the value of the influence of relative distance of the groups in the molecule, by means of spectroscopic investigation. In fact Schütze, in his work to which repeated reference has been made, by the spectroscopic study of a number of azo colouring substances, showed that the distances of the atoms as given by the structure formulæ corresponded, on the whole, to the distances evaluated in the way mentioned above.

Interesting direct applications of the above theory were made by Wallach,[3] who recognised the combinations

$$C = CH . CO \quad \text{and} \quad C = CHCOCH = C$$

as chromophores. All these considerations rest on the fundamental assumption that every molecule has a distinct absorption spectrum. Baly[4]

---

[1] Fluorine has been recently found by Moissan to have a light greenish-yellow colour similar to, but lighter than, that of chlorine.—Tr.

[2] *Ber.* **9.** 522 (1876).   [3] *Gött. Nachr.* 1896, Heft 4.

[4] See Henrich, *Neuere theoretische Anschauungen auf der Gebiete der organischen Chemie,* Braunschweig, 1908, p. 179.

has recently put forward the idea that tautomeric equilibrium (see Book III. Chapter V. par. " Tautomerism ") gives rise to specific absorption bands.   He supports this by the observation (*inter alia*) that neither the enol nor the keto form of acetoacetic ester shows by itself an absorption band, but that under the conditions when a tautomeric equilibrium, *i.e.* a quick mutual transformation, exists, an absorption band appears.   But the fact that no similar phenomena have yet been found to attend chemical equilibria makes it more probable that the tautomeric change is accompanied, perhaps to a very small extent, by the formation of new molecular species, and these give rise to the absorption.

Fluorescence.—According to the investigations of C. Liebermann [1] and R. Meyer,[2] the somewhat singular property of fluorescence is associated with the existence of certain atomic groups in the molecule, the *fluorophores* ; such groups are chiefly rings of six members, mostly heterocyclic, such as pyrine, azine, oxazine, and thioazine rings, and further atomic rings contained in anthracene and acridine.   As in the case of colour the nature of the surrounding atomic groups influences the action of the fluorophores.   For further details see the monograph by Henrich just referred to.

Crystal Form. — The connection between crystal form and molecular structure has not been very thoroughly studied as yet, and the results thus far obtained are limited to some rules given by Groth [3] regarding the change in the ratio of the axes occasioned by the substitution of certain radicals.   This phenomenon in mineralogy is called *morphotropy.*

It has been already stated that optical isomerism is shown in the solid state by the contrasted *right and left hemihedral (or tetartohedral) crystal forms* (pp. 78 and 337).   This is doubtless due, like the optical rotatory power, to an asymmetric structure of the molecule.   But such a development of planes may also occur when the structure of the molecule is not unsymmetrical ; in such cases it is highly probable that the molecules unite in an unsymmetrical way to build up the crystal. Hemihedrism may, like the rotatory power of crystallised substances (p. 334), be produced in two entirely different ways, one of which, the chemical, refers to the method of *the arrangement of the atoms in the molecule* ; the other, the physical, to *the arrangement of the molecules in the crystal.*   Both conditions allow of spatial isomerism ; but by passing into the liquid or gaseous state, the latter variety of isomerism is destroyed, while the former persists.

Retgers gives some interesting statistics with regard to a law proposed by Buys-Ballot in 1846 that the simple *chemical* compounds take for

[1] *Ber.* **13.** 913 (1880).   [2] *Zeitschr. phys. Chem.* **24.** 478 (1897).
[3] *Pogg. Ann.* **141.** 31 (1876) ; see also Hintze, *Zeitschr. Kryst.* **12.** 165 (1887) ; and Retgers, *Zeitschr. phys. Chem.* **6.** 193 (1890).

preference a regular or hexagonal shape, that is, crystallise in the *simpler forms*.[1]

Of 40 monatomic substances (elements) there are—

	%
regular	50
quadratic	5
hexagonal	35
rhombic	5
monoclinic . . .	5
triclinic	0

Thus : regular and hexagonal 85 %, all other systems 15 %.

Of 67 diatomic substances there are—

	%
regular	68·5
quadratic . . .	4·5
hexagonal . . .	19·5
rhombic	3·0
monoclinic . . .	4·5
triclinic	0·0

Thus : regular and hexagonal 88 %, all other systems 12 %.

Of 63 triatomic substances there are—

	%
regular	42·0
quadratic . . .	19·0
hexagonal . . .	11·0
rhombic	23·5
monoclinic . . .	3·0
triclinic	1·5

Thus : regular and hexagonal 53 %, all other systems 47 %.

Of 20 tetratomic substances there are—

	%
regular	5
quadratic	5
hexagonal	35
rhombic	50
monoclinic . . .	5
triclinic	0

Thus : regular and hexagonal 40 %, all other systems 60 %.

Of 50 pentatomic substances there are—

	%
regular	12
quadratic	6
hexagonal	38
rhombic	36
monoclinic . . .	6
triclinic	2

Thus : regular and hexagonal 50 %, all other systems 50 %.

Of 673 polyatomic inorganic compounds there are—

	%
regular	5·8
quadratic . . .	7·0
hexagonal . . .	14·6
rhombic	27·3
monoclinic . . .	37·3
triclinic	8·0

Thus : regular and hexagonal 20·4 %, all other systems 79·6 %.

Of 585 organic substances there are—

	%		%
regular	2·5	rhombic	33·0
quadratic . . .	5·0	monoclinic . . .	47·5
hexagonal . . .	4·0	triclinic	7·0

Thus : regular and hexagonal 6·5 %, all other systems 93·5 %.

The Systemisation of the Physical Properties.—We will give in the concluding paragraph of this chapter only a summary of the rather heterogeneous material found here ; for unfortunately space does not allow more than a short sketch of a subject which is broad and which deserves generous treatment.

A large number of physical properties have been shown to be clearly additive, *i.e.* the value of the property in question can be calculated as though the compound were such a mixture of its elements that they experience no change in their properties ; thus *we can calculate the properties of a compound from the properties of its components in*

[1] *Zeitschr. phys. Chem.* **14.** 1 (1894).

exactly the same way as was done for many properties of the physical mixture (p. 100). This, as already mentioned in a preceding chapter (p. 168), is more clearly shown by the specific heat of solid salts than is the rule elsewhere ; but there are many properties of organic compounds which are more or less clearly additive, as the volume, refraction, magnetism, heat of combustion, etc. Several of these have this in common, viz. *that their numerical values are a measure of the space actually occupied by the molecule.* Thus we can infer from quite different sources, *that the volume of a molecule may be often calculated approximately as the sum of the volumes actually occupied by the atoms.*

In some cases the numerical values deduced for the properties of the elements from their compounds coincide with the values actually shown by the elements in the free state ; thus this is the case for the specific heat of solid elements for the atomic volume and the atomic refraction of chlorine, but not for the atomic refraction of oxygen. We have seen previously, in the case of isomorphic mixtures (p. 117), that in some cases the specific volume of a salt in a mixed crystal was the same as in the free state, but in other cases very different.

Now the properties of compounds are no more *strictly* additive than those of physical mixtures. For with compounds the deviations from simple additive relations are, as a rule, much more emphatic. This is not to be wondered at ; for the mutual influence of the properties is much smaller in a *simple mixture of the molecules*, whereby there results a physical mixture, than when the atoms unite to form a *chemical compound*.

The kind of influence of the atom in a compound is primarily dependent upon the mode of its union, *i.e.* upon the constitution and configuration of the compound. Those properties which are *clearly* influenced in this way (very exact measurements would probably show this to be true of all properties) are called " *constitutive,*" following the example of Ostwald,[1] who has done such great service in the systemisation of the physical properties. An excellent example of a strongly constitutive property is the absorption of light. Similar examples are found in the optical activity, the melting-point, etc. Moreover, our knowledge as to how far the influence of constitution is shown in certain cases varies with the different properties, but in general it is developed to only a slight degree.

Moreover, it does not seem to me to be certainly established that the deviations from simple additive relations are to be ascribed to the influence of constitution alone. It is quite possible that the *molecule as a whole* may exert an influence upon these deviations, as is evidenced by many experiments with physical mixtures ; for, in addition to the forces which are active between the atoms, there are also forces active between the molecules, but the action of the latter may be eliminated by studying substances in the gaseous state.

---

[1] Ostwald, *All. Chem.* 2nd edit. **1.** 1121 (1891).

A third species of properties depends, neither upon the na
the atom in the molecule, nor upon the mode of the union
atoms, but only upon the sum total of the molecule. Prope:
this kind, which are called "*colligative*" by Ostwald, we have con
in the chapter on the Determination of the Molecular Weight.
these properties are based the methods for ascertaining the :
weights of molecules.[1]

---

[1] Additive properties give no foothold in determining the molecular weights,
as shown in the specific heats of solid salts, they are not affected by a change in
of the molecule ; but constitutive properties sometimes do render accessory :
determining the molecular weights.

CHAPTER VI

Abnormal Vapour Densities.—In a preceding chapter (p. 249) we have considered the methods which enable us to determine the molecular weights of gaseous and of dissolved substances; in this and the two following chapters a discussion will be given regarding some conclusions which are necessitated by the experimental results obtained by the methods mentioned above. These conclusions deal with the *molecular condition of gaseous and of dissolved substances.*

In some cases, which, to be sure, are not very numerous, one at once finds values for the molecular weights which are in glaring contradiction to those chemical formulæ which are probable from all analogies. Thus the vapour of ammonium chloride has a density about one-half as large as it should have if calculated from the formula NH_4Cl; that of ammonium carbamate has a value about one-third of what it should be if calculated from the formula $NH_2CO_2NH_4$; acetic acid, on the other hand, at lower temperatures, has a density considerably greater than that corresponding to the formula CH_3CO_2H.

Now it could be supposed that, in spite of this unexpected behaviour, Avogadro's rule still holds good, and that the *abnormal vapour densities* were to be explained by *abnormal molecular conditions.* Thus, at almost the same time, Cannizzaro (1857), Koppe (1858), and Kekulé (1858) expressed the opinion that the low vapour densities must be ascribed to a more or less complete decomposition; in fact, on the basis of this, Kopp succeeded in showing in many cases that the decrease of vapour density followed in accordance with the increase in the number of molecules resulting from the decomposition. Thus ammonium chloride has about only a little more than half its theoretically normal vapour density, because it is almost entirely decomposed into $NH_3 + HCl$; and similarly ammonium carbamate only about a third of its vapour density, because it is decomposed into $2NH_3 + CO_2$, etc. Similarly, on the basis of this view, it must be concluded that acetic acid is partially polymerised, and that in

347

addition to the simple molecules, more complicated ones occur in greater quantity.

This question, the importance of which was fully realised, was attacked in the most different ways, and soon an abundant collection of experimental data spoke overwhelmingly in favour of the applicability of Avogadro's law even when the vapour densities were abnormal. Thus, in detail, it was not only shown that the gaseous decomposition products of the substances in question could be recognised by their special physical and chemical behaviour, but also that these ingredients could be at least partially separated from each other into the free state by means of diffusion.

Dissociation.—The more or less complete dissociation of a molecule into its components or *dissociation products*, we will call *dissociation*, following the usage of St. Claire Deville,[1] to whom we are greatly indebted for his investigations on these phenomena, which are of fundamental importance for the conception of chemical processes.

The thorough treatment of dissociation phenomena belongs to the department of the so-called "reversible" chemical reactions, and the theoretical derivation of the laws of dissociation forms a special case, and a very simple one, of the universal laws of reaction. These will be considered under the subjects of the *doctrine of affinity*, and also of *thermochemistry*. Yet, nevertheless, in order to understand what follows, it is necessary to introduce some remarks on the dissociation of gases.

The Extent of Dissociation.—Dissociation is a chemical reaction, and consists in separating a complex molecule into simpler ingredients, thus leading to a *continual increase* in the number of molecules. The pressure exerted on the walls of a vessel by a definite quantity of a gas, other things being equal, will be greater the greater the number of new molecular species produced from the original molecules, and the further the decomposition of the latter proceeds; and also the density of the original gas must diminish in the same proportion, if it is not maintained at constant volume, but at constant pressure.

Let us denote by δ the vapour density observed when no dissociation occurs, and by Δ that actually observed; then Δ must always be smaller than δ. Let the number of molecules into which the original molecules become decomposed be n; thus in the dissociation of iodine vapour

$$I_2 = I + I.$$

Here $n = 2$; and in the case of ammonium carbamate, viz.

$$NH_4CO \cdot ONH_2 = 2NH_3 + CO_2,$$

---

[1] "Sur la dissociation ou la décomposition spontanée des corps sous l'influence de la chaleur," *Compt. rend.* **45.** 857 (1857). The term "thermolysis," suggested by Fr. Mohr, has not come into extensive use.

n = 3. If the decomposition were complete, Δ would be the nth part of δ. In general Δ lies between δ and δ/n.

Let the dissociated part of the gas mass, or the extent of the dissociation amount to a; then the undissociated part is $1 - a$; *i.e.* of 100 molecules, $100a$ are dissociated and produce $100na$ new molecules, while $100(1 - a)$ molecules remain undecomposed. Thereby the number of molecules is increased by dissociation from

$$100 \text{ to } 100na + 100(1 - a) = 100[1 + (n - 1)a],$$

and the vapour density diminishes in the same proportion, viz.

$$\frac{1}{1 + (n - 1)a} = \frac{\Delta}{\delta}.$$

The extent of the dissociation a is calculated, therefore, to be

$$a = \frac{\delta - \Delta}{(n - 1)\Delta}.$$

When $\Delta = \delta/n$, then the extent of the dissociation $a = 1$, and we have complete dissociation; but when $\Delta = \delta$, then $a = 0$, and no dissociation has occurred.

According to experiment, the extent of dissociation varies with the temperature and the pressure. It increases with increasing temperature, and diminishes with increasing pressure. This is expressed by the statement that by lowering the temperature and increasing the pressure, the values of the vapour densities Δ and δ are brought nearer together.

The Physical Conduct of Dissociated Gases—Effusion.—If a

gas which exists in a state of dissociation is allowed to escape (effuse) through a narrow opening into a vacuum, or into a space filled with an indifferent gas, then the velocity of the effusion will decrease as the density or the molecular weight of the gas increases. Moreover, there occurs a partial separation of the products of dissociation, as the effusate will contain an excess of the lighter molecules, and the residue an excess of the heavier molecules.

On this phenomenon is based the method of research of Pebal[1] in proving that ammonium chloride owes its diminished density to an extended dissociation into ammonia and hydrochloric acid. This method may be demonstrated in a lecture in the following simplified form given by Skraup.[2] In a combustion tube of about 10-12 mm. diameter, near the middle there is fastened an asbestos plug about 5 mm. thick. A piece of ammonium chloride is then placed at one side of the plug in the middle of the tube, and, in addition, a piece of litmus paper in each division of the tube. A blue piece is placed

[1] *Lieb. Ann.* **123.** 199 (1862).
[2] Exner's *Répert. d. phys.* **21.** 501 (1884).

on the same side of the asbestos plug with the ammonium chloride, and a red piece on the other side.   On heating the piece of ammonium chloride by a Bunsen burner, there occurs a change of colour in the inner ends of the litmus paper in both parts of the tube.   This proves that the effusate reacts alkaline, while the residue reacts acid.   The experiment should be interrupted in season, as the reaction is reversed after a little.

Colour.—The physical properties of a mixture of any two gases are intermediate between those of the particular components, while the properties of a compound of two gases exhibit in many respects a deep-seated change, as shown for example in the absorption of light.   Now, dissociation must cause the physical properties of gases to approach those of their components, and thus it is usually possible to draw some inference from the change in the physical properties of gases relative to the progress of dissociation.   In this way Deville observed that the colourless vapour of phosphorus pentachloride became distinctly green at higher temperatures.   This is explained by a dissociation in the sense of the following equation :

$$PCl_5 = PCl_3 + Cl_2,$$

which is likewise in harmony with the vapour density determinations.

An experiment which can be easily carried out consists in heating a flask filled with nitrogen dioxide.   This will become almost colour-less by cooling, and then, on gentle heating, it will appear to be filled with a dark-brown vapour, which is again decolorised by cooling.   In this case Salet[1] succeeded in showing, in a quantitative way, that the colour varied with the change in vapour density, and that it was entirely explained on the supposition that nitrogen dioxide consists of a mixture of colourless compound N_2O_4, and a brownish-red gas NO_2, and that the latter molecular species increases with increasing tempera-ture at the expense of the former.

Specific Heat.—The specific heat of a gas, existing in a state of dissociation, is abnormally great.   This is due to the fact that the heat introduced is used not only in raising the temperature, but also in effecting dissociation, which is attended with considerable absorption of heat.   We are indebted to Berthelot and Ogier for measurements of this sort.   These measurements were made with nitrogen dioxide[2] and acetic acid vapour.[3]   The molecular heat of nitrogen dioxide (referred to $NO_2 = 46$ g. and at constant pressure) at $0°$ is about 95·1 ; at $100°$ it is only about 39·1, while at $157°$ it falls to 7·1.   At this latter temperature, where the dissociation is almost

---

[1] *Compt. rend.* **67.** 488 (1868).
[2] *Ibid.* **94.** 916 ; *Bull. Soc. chim.* **37.** 434 (1882).
[3] *Bull. Soc. chim.* **38.** 60 (1882).

complete, we find a value of the molecular heat which would naturally be expected from the figures on p. 45.

Gaseous acetic acid conducts itself in a similar way.   In this case the investigators mentioned above found the following values for the molecular heat C_p at the respective temperatures :

$$t° = 129°   160°   200°   240°   280°$$
$$C_p = \;\; 90·1   76·2   57·0   38·2   28·5 \text{ g.-cal.}$$

Inasmuch as the degree of dissociation varies not only with the temperature, but also with the pressure, it is to be expected that the specific heat of those gases, which are already in a state of dissociation, would vary considerably when compared with those gases which either are not at all dissociated, or only partly so, according to the pressure.

Thermal Conductivity.—The kinetic theory allows of an interesting application of the thermal conductivity of gases in a state of dissociation.   As we have already seen (p. 203), heat is carried through an ideal gas in the direction of the fall of temperature by equalisation of the mean kinetic energy of the molecules ; in gases in a state of dissociation a new factor enters.   At the higher temperature the dissociation is more considerable than at the lower ; the result is that when, in consequence of the irregular heat movements, undissociated molecules pass into the hotter part of the gas, they partly decompose there ; conversely, when the products of dissociation come into the colder parts they partially recombine to form non-dissociated gas. But since dissociation is accompanied by absorption of heat and reformation of undissociated molecules by generation of heat, the above described process furthers the equalisation of temperature between the two parts of the gas, that is, it *considerably increases the thermal conductivity.*

Actually Magnanini and Malagnini found that the thermal [1] conductivity of nitrogen dioxide in the dissociating state is more than three times as great as when the gas is completely dissociated.   This appears to be a remarkable confirmation of the kinetic conception of matter.

The quantity of heat transported in the form of heat of dissociation in a partially dissociated gas can be calculated if the amount of dissociated and non-dissociated molecules which pass through an area in the gas at right angles to the temperature gradient be known ; the quantity of heat in question is then proportional to the excess of un-

---

[1] *Nuovo Cim.* **6.** 352 (1897) ; later Magnanini and Zunino, *Mem. Acad. Modena* [3], **2.** (1899).   R. Goldschmidt has shown ("Sur les rapports entre la dissociation et la conductibilité thermique des gaz," *Thèse*, Brussel, 1902) that, in determining the thermal conductivity of gases, we possess a means of detecting dissociation at very high temperatures where measurement is hardly possible otherwise.

dissociated molecules which travel in unit time against the temperature gradient over the quantity that travels in the opposite direction.[1]

The Condition of Dissociation.—The results given in this
chapter show that the state of an ideal gas is realised only when there
is no dissociation at all, or else when it is complete.   In the first case
we have a simple gas; in the latter case a gas mixture, the properties
of which are a combination of the properties of the components.   The
gas laws cease to hold good only in the case of *partly dissociated* gases,
for here changes in the temperature and the pressure are associated
with changes in the molecular condition, and the gases vary enormously
in their behaviour, not only as regards their compressibility and
their expansion by heat, but also as regards all their other physical
properties.

This passage from the normal behaviour of a simple gas to
another normal behaviour of a gas mixture is called passing to the
state of dissociation.   The laws of the state of dissociation will be considered in the section devoted to the *doctrine of affinity.*   Here we will
only refer to the results of pure experiment.   These show that those
vapour densities which seemed to contradict Avogadro's rule most
decidedly are associated with very remarkable deviations in all their
physical behaviour, and these deviations which at first seemed to contradict Avogadro's rule really argue strongly in its favour.

---

[1] See Nernst, *Jubelband Boltzmann*, p. 904 (1904), for the quantitative calculation
of the influence of dissociation on the thermal conductivity from the standpoint of the
kinetic theory, and for the general theory of this phenomenon and others related to it.

CHAPTER VII

ELECTROLYTIC DISSOCIATION

Dissociation in Solutions.— As already stated on p. 270, abnormal vapour densities are completely analogous to the abnormal values of the osmotic pressure of dilute solutions observed in many cases. It is an immediate inference to explain these abnormal osmotic pressures, in the sense of van't Hoff's generalised form of Avogardo's rule, in a similar way, viz. as being due to abnormal molecular conditions. This assumption almost amounts to a certainty from the fact that almost all the instances of dissociation which have been met with thus far in the case of gases are also observed if the particular gas is investigated, in a suitable solvent, at about the same temperature. *Very often the abnormal vapour density of a substance is also found to correspond to an abnormal value of its osmotic pressure.*

Let us suppose a molecule, existing in solution, to decompose into n new and smaller molecular species. These may consist of one or of several atoms, and may be similar or dissimilar. Let t_0 denote the lowering of the freezing-point (or a value which is proportional to the osmotic pressure, as, for example, the lowering of the vapour pressure, the raising of the boiling-point, etc.) calculated from the molecular proportions of the substance in question, on the assumption that the dissolved substance is not at all dissociated; and in accordance with this, let nt_0 be the lowering of the freezing-point corresponding to complete dissociation. Then the value of t, as observed, will lie between these limiting values. An increase in the number of molecules, in the proportion of $1 : 1 + (n - 1)a$, will correspond to the degree of dissociation a. Therefore it follows that

$$1 + (n - 1)a = \frac{t}{t_0} \; ;$$

and therefore

$$a = \frac{t - t_0}{(n - 1)t_0}.$$

Numerous experimental investigations, for which we are par-

353   2 A

ticularly indebted not only to Raoult, but also to Beckmann [1] and Eykmann,[2] have led to the result that it is usual to find substances in solution not existing as simple molecules, but in a state of dissociation. Thus the organic acids in benzene solution, as in the gaseous state, consist of double molecules, but these separate into single ones on further dilution. Chloral hydrate in acetic acid, as in the gaseous state, decomposes partially into chloral and water, as is shown from the following table :—

m.	t.	a.
0·266	0·095	0·52
1·179	0·385	0·38
2·447	0·755	0·31
4·900	1·450	0·25

Here m denotes the number of grams of chloral hydrate dissolved in 100 g. of acetic acid. The lowering of the freezing-point t_0, which would be observed in the normal behaviour of chloral hydrate, is calculated from the formula given on p. 146—

$$t_0 = 39 \frac{m}{165 \cdot 5}.$$

Here 39 denotes the molecular depression of acetic acid, and 165·5 the molecular weight of the undissociated chloral hydrate. The degree of dissociation, given in the third column of the preceding table, is calculated from the formula

$$a = \frac{t - t_0}{t_0}.$$

It is obvious that, with increasing concentration, this becomes smaller ; and that, conversely, with decreasing concentration, it converges towards a value of one. At a high degree of concentration the behaviour of the solution would approach that of an ideal one, provided that certain discrepancies did not occur, independently of dissociation, at high degrees of concentration. At a high degree of dilution there would be a mixture of the two substances, water and chloral, which would perfectly obey the laws of ideal solutions, while between these extremes a state of dissociation exists.

Aqueous Solutions.—It was a striking fact that abnormal values of the osmotic pressure were very often found in the case of water

---

[1] *Zeitschr. phys. Chem.* **2.** 715 (1888) ; **6.** 437 (1890).
[2] *Ibid.* **4.** 497 (1889).

solutions. All the methods of measuring the osmotic pressure led, with quantitative coincidence, to this result ; that it is much greater for *acids, bases,* and *salts* in water solution than it should be if calculated from the molecular weights of the respective substances, either in the gaseous state or in other solvents than water. If we assume that the Avogadro-van't Hoff law holds good here, we are forced to the unavoidable conclusion that these substances, when dissolved in water, are in a peculiar molecular condition, and *must be dissociated to a greater or less degree.*

But one of the first difficulties here consists in answering the question, What are the products of the dissociation ? Such a substance as hydrochloric acid, for instance, undoubtedly has, as a gas, a molecular weight corresponding to the formula HCl. But inasmuch as the lowering of the freezing-point, in water solution, is almost twice as great as that which should correspond to that molecular formula, the original molecule, when dissolved, must be separated into two new ones, *i.e.* HCl must be dissociated into H and Cl. Both of these dissociation products are such that we cannot recognise them in any other way. At ordinary temperatures hydrogen and chlorine are known to us as H_2 and Cl_2 respectively : if we boil a water solution of hydrochloric acid, we obtain HCl to be sure, but no free hydrogen or free chlorine. So an assumption like that mentioned above appears, at first glance, very improbable ; and there would be some difficulty in understanding it if the same assumption were not shown to be necessarily true from an entirely different aspect, and if we did not have, at the same time, more detailed explanations regarding the nature of the dissociation products of salts, acids, and bases, in water solution.

In the case of salts one would at once think of separation into the acid and the base, and thus explain their great osmotic pressure : in fact, we will consider later this so-called *" hydrolytic dissociation "*; but it is not possible to consider it such a common phenomenon as the abnormal pressures are, because salts can be separated, by diffusion, into the respective acids and bases in only a very few cases. For, disregarding for the moment many other reasons which contradict such a method of explanation, and to which we will return later, this assumption fails utterly in the case of acids and bases, which, as well as salts, show abnormal osmotic pressures. Therefore we are forced to seek another explanation.

Now it happens that those substances, and only those substances, which can conduct the galvanic current in water solution, i.e. the electrolytes, are the ones which exhibit osmotic pressures very much greater than those which are calculated for their concentration and their molecular weight in the gaseous state ; and, moreover, if the same substances, when dissolved in other solvents, are unable to conduct electricity in any marked degree, then they also lose their abnormal behaviour. Thus we are forced to the view that, if dissociation actually takes place, it is intimately connected with the conduction of electricity by electrolytes.

Electrolytic Conduction.—Let us try to frame a mental image of electrolytic conduction. It is a well-known fact that, in contrast to the metallic conduction of electricity, it is associated with a transportation of matter ; and, moreover, that the passage of the galvanic stream from the metallic electrode into the solution is, according to circumstances, either associated with the solution of the metal, or else with the separation of the substance in the solution and its deposition on the electrode.

Thus if we introduce gaseous hydrochloric acid between the platinum electrodes of a galvanic battery, no appreciable transference of electricity occurs ; neither is there any transference of electricity if we introduce *very pure water* between the poles ; but the electricity passes readily if the poles are introduced into water containing hydrochloric acid. Thus, it is fair to suppose that the hydrochloric acid, which is dissolved in water, is in a molecular condition *different* from that in the gaseous state ; because in the one case it can conduct electricity, but not in the other. The following picture is both clear and simple in attempting to account for the definite conception entertained.

When a current passes through the solution, free chlorine is separated at the anode, where the current enters the solution ; and free hydrogen at the cathode, where it leaves the solution : one component of the electrolyte " wanders " in one direction, the other in the other direction. This is explained most simply by supposing that the electrolytes consist of different parts which are oppositely polarised, *i.e.* of molecules charged respectively as electro-positive and electro-negative. These parts, after the usage introduced into science by Faraday, are called "*ions.*" According to this view, in the solution, the galvanic current consists in the passage of the positively charged oins, the "*cations,*" in one direction, and in the passage of the negatively charged ions, the "*anions,*" in the other direction. The passage of positive electricity from the [one] electrode *into* the solution is accordingly associated with a separation of anions ; and the passage of positive electricity *out* of the solution into the [other] electrode is associated with a separation of cations.

The capacity of dissolved substances to conduct the electric current thus assumes a decomposition into positively and negatively charged molecules, which we will call "*electrolytic dissociation.*"[1] Of course it is not necessary for the decomposition to be complete, for in addition to the electrolytically dissociated molecules, there may also

[1] The expression "*ionisation*" sometimes used 'should rather be reserved for the formation of ions in gases produced by the action of Röntgen rays and the like (see Chap. IX. of this Book).

exist in the solution undecomposed molecules, which are electrically neutral.

Only the former are instrumental in current conduction, and it is apparent, other things being equal, that a solution will have a greater conductivity, or a less resistance, the larger the fraction of the electrolytically dissociated molecules in the solution. Cane sugar, when dissolved in water, does not conduct electricity noticeably; therefore it must consist entirely, or at least almost entirely, of uncleaved molecules which are electrically neutral. On the other hand, hydrochloric acid is a good conductor of electricity; and therefore the gas which has been absorbed by water must have attained a high degree of electrolytic dissociation.

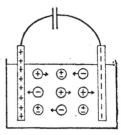

Fig. 31.

On the basis of these preceding remarks, we will now attempt to draw a picture of the mechanism of electrolytic conduction. Let there be a water solution of hydrochloric acid between two platinum plates (Fig. 31). These two platinum electrodes are in connection with a source of electricity, as, for example, with a galvanic battery. The first result of this is that the platinum plate, which is connected with the positively conducting pole, becomes charged with positive electricity, and the other becomes charged with negative electricity.

As a result of these charges, the free electricities of the electrodes will exert an electrostatic attraction or repulsion on the free ions in the solution, which are charged with free electricity; the positive ions will be attracted by the negative electricity of the cathode, and will be repelled by the positive electricity of the anode; thus a force will be developed, acting in the direction of the arrows. The reverse of this will happen in the case of the negative ions; and thus there will be developed a force in the opposite direction. No force of this sort will be exerted upon the electrically neutral molecules.

As a result of this electrical attraction and repulsion, there results a displacement of the free ions in the solution, whereby the positive ions wander from the anode to the cathode, and the negative ions in the opposite direction. *This wandering [or "migration"] of the ions represents to us that which we call an electric current in an electrolyte.*

The Free Ions.—It now remains to determine the material nature of the ions and of the electrically neutral molecule. In the electrolysis of hydrochloric acid, free hydrogen is separated at the cathode and free chlorine at the anode : therefore the former must be positively charged, the latter negatively. Thus we arrive at the result that hydrochloric acid, when dissolved in water, must be dissociated into positively charged hydrogen ions and negatively charged chlorine ions. Of course we must regard the undissociated hydrochloric acid molecules as being electrically neutral.   A similar inference must of course be drawn for all other electrolytes.

We may learn something about the molecular dimensions of the ions, and about the degree of electrolytic dissociation, by the aid of principles developed previously.

The osmotic pressure in a dilute solution of hydrochloric acid, as shown by the quantitative coincidence of results obtained in different ways, is almost twice as great as that corresponding to its gaseous molecular weight ; therefore two new molecules must result from the solution of one in water.   This means nothing else than that the electrolytic dissociation is *almost complete* ; thus—

$$HCl = \overset{+}{H} + \overset{-}{Cl}.$$

The ions of hydrochloric acid are thus monatomic.

Now since two opposite kinds of electricity are produced in equivalent quantities by this cleavage, the positive charge of the hydrogen must be exactly as great as the negative charge of the chlorine, *i.e. an atom of hydrogen and an atom of chlorine are electrically equivalent.*   An important conclusion follows from this.   If a definite quantity of electricity passes through our electrolytic cell, then electrically equivalent quantities of the ions must separate out on the two electrodes ; for otherwise there would occur an enormous accumulation of free electricity in the circuit, which is impossible.   Thus hydrogen and chlorine must be set free, at the electrodes, in equivalent electrical quantities, or, what amounts to the same thing, *in equivalent chemical quantities.*

Now if we put into the same electric circuit a cell filled with hydrobromic acid, then on the cathodes of the two electrolytic cells the same quantities of hydrogen will be set free ; and on the respective anodes there will be set free equivalent quantities of chlorine and bromine.   And in general it may be said that *chemically equivalent quantities of the most various ions are set free from the most various solutions by the same quantity of electric current.*

As is well known, this statement is most completely substantiated by experience ; it is simply the fundamental law of electrolysis, advanced by Faraday and demonstrated most exactly by experiment.

Those ions which are charged with the same equivalent quantities of electricity as the hydrogen ion, the chlorine ion, etc., are called *univalent* ; those ions which are charged respectively with a twofold, or a threefold, etc., quantity of electricity are called *divalent, trivalent,* etc.

Thus sulphuric acid, for instance, in dilute solution, exhibits an osmotic pressure which is *three times* as great as that which should correspond to its concentration, and to the molecular formula H_2SO_4 : this means simply that, under these circumstances, three new molecules

have been produced from one ; and that an almost complete dissociation
has occurred, in the sense of the following equation :—

$$H_2SO_4 = \overset{+}{H} + \overset{+}{H} + \overset{=}{SO_4}.$$

The negative ion, SO_4, must be as heavily charged as the two positive
ions together, *i.e.* with twice as great a quantity of electricity as a
hydrogen ion ; this is indicated by a double dash ($\overset{=}{SO_4}$).

Accordingly we call the SO_4 a *divalent* ion, and sulphuric acid a
di-basic acid ; and in general we call an acid which produces n hydrogen
atoms, by complete dissociation, *n-basic.*

The radical hydroxyl (hydroxyl ion) OH, which has a negative
charge, is a univalent ion ; it is produced by the electrolytic dissociation of water, which happens to only a very slight degree under
ordinary circumstances, thus—

$$H_2O = \overset{+}{H} + \overset{-}{OH} ;$$

and also in the dissociation of bases, as sodium hydroxide, *e.g.*—

$$NaOH = \overset{+}{Na} + \overset{-}{OH}.$$

Those bases, the molecules of which, like the preceding, give only one
hydroxyl ion on ionisation as above, are called *monacid* ; those bases
which, like barium hydroxide, produce two hydroxyl ions, are called
di-acid, etc. ; thus

$$Ba(OH)_2 = \overset{++}{Ba} + \overset{-}{OH} + \overset{-}{OH}.$$

It is very remarkable that similar ions may have very different
charges, even in the same solution ; thus the iron ion, produced by
the dissociation of ferrous chloride, is *divalent*, thus—

$$FeCl_2 = \overset{++}{Fe} + \overset{-}{Cl} + \overset{-}{Cl},$$

while the iron ion, produced by the dissociation of ferric chloride, is
trivalent, thus—

$$FeCl_3 = \overset{+++}{Fe} + \overset{-}{Cl} + \overset{-}{Cl} + \overset{-}{Cl}.$$

Thus we see that the *electric value of an element is by no means a
constant property*, but may vary by leaps in certain cases. It is possible
that a thorough investigation of this change in the electrical value of
certain elements might prove the starting-point for a deeper insight
into the reason for the change in valence, and into the nature of
valence.[1]

In the manner just described, it is usually possible to answer the
question regarding the nature and value of the ions quite certainly,

[1] In this connection see the paragraph on "The Variability of Chemical Valence"
(p. 284).—TR.

by combining the results of the determination of the molecular weight and of the conductivity.

Moreover, the *chemical behaviour* of solutions usually yields important information on this point (see Chap. IV. of the Third Book).

The Determination of the Degree of Electrolytic Dissociation.—It is not only important to answer the question regarding the nature of the ions, but also another question, viz. *how far the decomposition of the electrically neutral molecules in the solution has proceeded.* Therefore a knowledge of the degree of dissociation of an electrolyte is of great significance, inasmuch as many other properties, besides the conductivity and the osmotic pressure, depend upon the extent of the electrolytic dissociation; and especially is this true of the *share of the dissolved substances in chemical reactions*: a thorough reference will be made to this point under the subject of the *doctrine of affinity.*

The degree of dissociation, or the value of the coefficient of dissociation, by which is meant the ratio of the dissociated molecules to the whole number of molecules, can be directly obtained in two independent ways: from the osmotic pressure and from the conductivity.

The first method is of course exactly similar to that by which the ordinary (*i.e.* the non-electrolytic) dissociation in solution is determined (p. 353). Thus if P_0 denotes the osmotic pressure, as calculated from the gas laws without reference to dissociation, and if P denotes that actually observed, then it will follow that

$$1 + (n - 1)a = \frac{P}{P_0}, \quad \text{and} \quad a = \frac{P - P_0}{(n - 1)P_0},$$

where a denotes the degree of electrolytic dissociation and n the number of ions into which one molecule dissociates. Instead of the ratio of the respective osmotic pressures, we may, of course, use the relative depressions of the freezing-point, or of the vapour pressure.

Another way is given by the determination of the electrical conductivity; this can be easily and exactly done by the method proposed by F. Kohlrausch.[1] A full description of this method, so commonly used in the laboratory, need hardly be given here. It need only be mentioned that this method depends upon the use of Wheatstone's bridge; and that instead of a constant current, an alternating current produced by an induction coil is used, whereby the disturbing effect of polarisation is ·eliminated; and that instead of a galvanometer, as a current indicator, use is made of a telephone which is sensitive to the alternating current.

The unit of conductivity now adopted is that of a body of which

---

[1] This method is found in F. Kohlrausch, *Lehrb. d. prakt. Physik.* 9 Aufl. S. 409 ; see further Ostwald, *Physiko chem. Messungen*, Leipzig. 1902, p. 395 ; and especially Kohlrausch and Holborn, *Leitvermögen der Elektrolyte*, Leipzig, 1898.

a column 1 *cm. long and* 1 *cm.*[2] *in cross-section has a resistance of* 1 *ohm.* If, therefore, a body of this size possesses a resistance w, it has a conductivity κ :—

$$\kappa = \frac{1}{w}.$$

The conductivity of an electrolyte divided by its concentration (= number of g-equivalents in cm.[3]) is called the *molecular conductivity* Λ—

$$\Lambda = \frac{\kappa}{\eta}.$$

Formerly the conductivity of mercury at 0° was adopted as the unit of conductivity; in the above measure it is 10,630, hence the conductivity in terms of mercury

$$k = \frac{\kappa}{10,630}.$$

Similarly the molecular conductivity λ was formerly defined as

$$\lambda = \frac{k}{c},$$

where $c = 1000\eta$, that is, expresses the normality.

Now, according to the statements on p. 356, the conductivity is proportional to the number of free ions, *i.e.* it is proportional to the product $a\eta$, and therefore it is directly proportional to the degree of dissociation, a itself. That is, we may put

$$\Lambda = Ka,$$

while K is a proportional factor. For very great dilution the electrolytic dissociation becomes complete, that is, $a = 1$; if the molecular conductivity measured for sufficiently great dilution be written $\Lambda\infty$, we simply get

$$\Lambda\infty = K \text{ and } a = \frac{\Lambda}{\Lambda\infty}.$$

The following table gives the molecular conductivities obtained by Kohlrausch [1] for various dilutions of *potassium chloride* at 18° :—

KCl.

$c=1000\eta$.	Λ.	a.	$c=1000\eta$.	Λ.	a.
1·0	98·2	0·748	0·005	124·6	0·950
0·5	102·3	0·780	0·001	127·6	0·973
0·1	111·9	0·853	0·0005	128·3	0·978
0·03	118·3	0·902	0·0001	129·5	0·987
0·01	122·5	0·934	$\frac{1}{\infty}$	131·2	1·000

$$\Lambda\infty = 131\cdot2.$$

[1] *Wied. Ann.* **26.** 161 (1885) ; *Leitvermögen*, etc., p.159.

It may be remarked here that the change of the conductivity with the concentration from 0·1 normal downwards is very nearly the same for all salts made up by combination of univalent radicals, *i.e.* *that in equivalent solutions these salts experience the same high dissociation.* Therefore the value of a in the preceding table can be used to calculate the degree of dissociation of almost all these salts, *e.g.* NaCl, LiNO$_3$, CH$_3$CO$_2$NH$_4$, etc.

The combination of these two methods for the determination of a gives

$$a = \frac{\Lambda}{\Lambda\infty} = \frac{P - P_0}{(n - 1)P_0}.$$

This law was established by Arrhenius,[1] who was the first to develop clearly the hypothesis of electrolytic dissociation; it unites the abnormal values of the osmotic pressure of electrolytes with the changes of conductivity with varying concentration. The law has been well established not only by the preliminary calculation of the available material by Arrhenius, but also by its subsequent more exact proof.[2] The following table will serve as an illustration; here are given the values of the factor $1 + (n - 1)a$, *i.e.* the ratio in which the number of molecules is increased by dissociation; under column I. are given the results according to the plasmolytic method (p. 129); under II. the results according to the freezing-point method; and under III. the results according to the method of conductivity.

Substance.	n.	c.	1+(n–1)a.		
			I.	II.	III.
Cane sugar . .	0	0·3	1·00	1·08	1·00
CH$_3$CO$_2$H . .	2	0·33	...	1·04	1·01
KCl . .	2	0·14	1·81	1·93	1·86
LiCl . .	2	0·13	1·92	1·94	1·84
MgSO$_4$ . . .	2	0·38	1·25	1·20	1·35
CaN$_2$O$_6$ . .	3	0·18	2·48	2·47	2·46
SrCl$_2$ . .	3	0·18	2·69	2·52	2·51
K$_4$FeCy$_6$ . .	5	0·356	3·09	...	3·07

Hittorf's Transport Numbers and Kohlrausch's Law of the Independent Migration of Ions.

—On turning back to consider the mechanism of electric conduction, the question at once arises as to the velocity with which the ions are transported through the solution, at a given difference of potential between the electrodes, and with given dimensions of the electrolytic cell. The magnitude of the force

[1] *Zeitschr. phys. Chem.* **1.** 631 (1887).
[2] Arrhenius, *Zeitschr. phys. Chem.* **2.** 491 (1888); Van't Hoff and Reicher, *ibid.* **3.** 198 (1889).

acting on the ions, and depending upon the charges of the electrodes, other things being equal, is of course equally great for all univalent ions ; and, moreover, the pull exerted upon the positive ions in the direction of the current is just exactly as strong as the pull exerted upon the negative ions in the opposite direction; and of course the force which drives n-valent ions is n-fold as great.

But the *frictional resistance* of the different ions will vary with their varying nature. It may be predicted, with a large degree of probability, that this frictional resistance will be very great ; for, if we notice how slowly a fine precipitate in water sinks to the bottom, and that it requires more time the finer the precipitate is—then it follows that such extraordinarily fine particles as the ions are would require an enormous force to transport them through the solution with any noticeable velocity. *On this assumption, which will be justified later, we may regard the ions as points of mass with very great friction* (p. 14), *and therefore set their velocity proportional to the forces acting on them.* But as the intensity of current is proportional to the velocity at which the ions travel in the solvent, it is proportional to the electromotive force, that is, *Ohm's Law* holds.

It appears from equation 7, p. 15, that force and velocity are not proportional at the first moment, but on account of the very large friction this initial stage is not accessible to experimental proof (see Cohn).[1]

The term *frictional resistance* will be understood as meaning that force—expressed *e.g.* in kilogram weights—which will be required to drive 1 g.-ion, *i.e.* the molecular weight of the ion expressed in grams, against the solvent, with a velocity of 1 cm. per sec. ; and the term *mobility* or *velocity of transport* will mean the reciprocal of this force, *i.e.* the velocity with which 1 g.-ion will be transported under the influence of a pull of 1, *e.g.* 1 kilogram weight.

Now, for the sake of simplicity, let us consider a binary electrolyte, *i.e.* one composed of two univalent ions, and let us suppose that the quantity of electricity, E, is sent through the electrolytic cell. Then transference of ions occurs so that the positive ones are carried "in the direction of the current" through the solvent, and the negative ones in the opposite direction. If we take a cross-section through the electrolytic cell, at any selected place, at right angles to the current, then the electricity conveyed by the positive ions in the direction of the current, plus that conveyed by the negative atoms in the opposite direction, is equal to E.

Now if we denote the mobility of the positive and negative ions by U and V, then their respective velocities will be in the same ratio as their mobilities ; since they are, at every instant of the passage of electricity, under the influence of the *same forces*. The transport of a

[1] *Wied. Ann.* **38.** 217 (1889).

quantity of electricity, E, occurs therefore in this way : in the direction
of the current, there " wander "

$$E \frac{U}{U + V} \text{ positive ions,}$$

and in the opposite direction

$$E \frac{V}{U + V} \text{ negative ions.}$$

Now at the cathode, E equivalents of + electricity separate in the
form of positive ions ; and these disappear from the solution, and are
precipitated, as gas or metal, on the electrode (of course in an electrically neutral state): $E \frac{U}{U + V}$ ions have thus passed by the "ionic
migration." Moreover, at the close of the experiment, there will be
found a diminution of concentration in the solution in the neighbourhood of the cathode, corresponding to the removal of $E \frac{V}{U + V}$ cations ;
or, according to what has preceded, to the removal of the same
quantity of negative ions by the wandering [in the opposite direction],
and therefore corresponding to $E \frac{V}{U + V}$ equivalents of the electrolyte.
In a precisely analogous way it follows that the liquid in the neighbourhood of the anode must lose $E \frac{U}{U + V}$ equivalents of electrolyte.

Now it is usually the case that the separated quantities of anion
and cation respectively react, in a secondary way, either upon the
solution or upon the metal of the electrode. Thus by the electrolysis
of potassium chloride, the metallic potassium, which is deposited upon
the cathode by the passage of the quantity of electricity E through
the cell, does not remain there as such ; but, as is well known, it
reacts upon the solvent, forming potassium hydroxide and hydrogen.
If we electrolyse silver nitrate between silver electrodes, there does
not result an accumulation of the free radical NO_3, equivalent to E, at
the anode, but this reacts with the metal of the electrode forming the
equivalent quantity of silver nitrate. Therefore the variations in
concentration in the neighbourhood of the electrodes are changed in
a corresponding way, to be sure, but in such a way that it can be
easily calculated in each particular case.

For the thorough study of these changes in concentration produced
by the wandering of the ions, and also for their theoretical interpretation in the sense given above, we are indebted to Hittorf.[1] His work
is of fundamental importance, both in framing a conception of electrolysis and also in the theory of solutions. Following the usage of

[1] *Pogg. Ann.* **89.** 177 ; **98.** 1 ; **103.** 1 ; **106.** 337 (1853-59) ; see also Ostwald's
Classiker, Nos. 21 and 23.

Hittorf, we will designate the following ratios, which can be determined directly by experiment, as the *transport values* of the *cations* and *anions* respectively, viz.

$$n = \frac{U}{U + V}; \quad \text{and} \quad 1 - n = \frac{V}{U + V}.$$

In practice it is often possible to decide upon the nature of the ions by measurements of migration velocities, especially in the case of complex molecules.

The discovery of the relation between the conductivity and transport numbers was made by Friedrich Kohlrausch:[1] we will proceed to derive it by the consideration of electrolytic dissociation.

Kohlrausch's Law of the Independent Wandering of Ions.

—The conductivity of a solution of a binary electrolyte is greater in accordance as it contains more free ions, and according as these have a greater mobility ; and since the particular quantities of electricity transported by the anion and cation are directly proportional to their mobility, therefore the conductivity must be proportional to their sum ; that is, the specific conductivity κ of a solution, which contains η mols of the electrolyte in a c.cm, must be

$$\kappa = a\eta F(U + V),$$

where a denotes the degree of dissociation at the respective concentration. F is a proportional factor, depending on the system of units chosen. By making

$$u = FU \quad \text{and} \quad v = FV,$$

we obtain

$$\kappa = a\eta(u + v) ;$$

or, writing for $\dfrac{\kappa}{\eta}$ the molecular conductivity Λ,

$$\Lambda = (u + v)a.$$

At very great dilution $a = 1$; then by noticing that u and v are proportional to the magnitudes U and V introduced above, we obtain the three equations,

$$\Lambda\infty = u + v ; \quad u = n\Lambda\infty ; \quad v = (1 - n)\Lambda\infty .$$

These express Kohlrausch's law of the *independent wandering of the ions*. They state primarily *that the molecular conductivity of a binary electrolyte is equal to the sum of the conductivities of the two ions*, i.e. *that it is an additive property* ; further, that there exists between the conductivity and the transport values an intimate relation, such, that if the transport value of one electrolyte is known, the transport values of the other electrolytes can be calculated from the respective conductivities.

These rules hold good for those electrolytes which are completely

[1] *Wied. Ann.* **6.** 1 (1879) ; **26.** 161 (1885).

dissociated, but they likewise apply to the comparison of electrolytes existing in the same state of dissociation, as one can easily convince oneself. When Kohlrausch developed his law, the difference between the conducting molecules (*i.e.* the free ions) and the inactive molecules of an electrolyte was not recognised ; and Kohlrausch, on proving his law by means of the conductivities measured by himself and the transport values obtained earlier by Hittorf, found good coincidence in all cases between calculation and experiment, when he compared electrolytes in the same degree of dissociation, but otherwise he found decided deviations. As is obvious from the deduction given above, Arrhenius showed that Kohlrausch's law must necessarily fail when electrolytes are compared which are dissociated to different degrees.

Soon afterwards an experimental investigation [1] was especially directed to this point. The conductivity and transport values of dilute silver salts were measured, and it was shown that Kohlrausch's relation between the conductivity and the transport values was strictly accurate when the two values refer to electrolytes which are completely dissociated.

The following table gives the molecular conductivity for a number of ions : the values are referred to a temperature of $18°$:—

	K	NH$_4$	Na	Li	Ag	H		
u =	65·3	64·2	44·4	35·5	55·7	318		

	Cl	Br	I	NO$_3$	ClO$_3$	CO$_2$H	C$_2$H$_3$O$_2$	OH
v =	65·9	66·7	66·7	60·8	56·5	45	33·7	174

Thus from the preceding table the molecular conductivity of potassium chloride, *e.g.*, is 131·2 at infinite dilution ; and its transport value is calculated to be 0·50 ; while the respective values obtained by experiment are 131 and 0·51.

The great practical value of this law consists in the fact that *we may calculate quite certainly the limiting value of the molecular conductivity of those electrolytes at infinite dilution, in the cases of which we cannot reach the limit by experiment.* Thus we can obtain the limiting value of the potassium chloride quite certainly by extrapolation (p. 361) ; but this is not the case with ammonia, as is shown by the following figures :—

Concentration	.	.	.	=1·0	0·1	0·01	0·001 g. equivalents per litre.
Mol. conductivity of NH$_3$	.			=0·89	3·3	9·6	28

At dilutions when measurement begins to become very uncertain, ammonia falls too far short of complete dissociation to enable us to assume a constant molecular conductivity. But from Kohlrausch's law we can calculate, with full certainty, the limiting value of the molecular conductivity of ammonia (ammonium hydroxide = $NH_4 + OH$) at infinite dilution, by means of the mobility of the two ions, thus—

$$\Lambda \infty = 64·2 + 174 = 238·2.$$

[1] M. Loeb and W. Nernst, *Zeitschr. phys. Chem.* **2.** 948 (1888). Cf. F. Kohlrausch, *Zeitschr. f. Elektrochemie,* **13.** 333 (1907).

Thus the conception that those salts which conduct the galvanic current when they are dissolved in water are more or less dissociated into their ions, is seen to be supported in every respect, both by the phenomena and by the laws of electrolysis ; moreover, the law of Avogadro, which has been applied by van't Hoff to solutions, can be also shown to meet the requirements fully in the case of electrolytes.

Ionic Mobility and Temperature Coefficient.—Ionic mobilities increase about 1·5 to 2·7 per cent per degree rise of temperature ; the temperature coefficient is smaller the greater the mobility, so that the differences between the mobilities of different ions tend to diminish with rising temperature. Kohlrausch [1] has expressed the relation between the migration velocity (u) of an ion, and its temperature coefficient (a) by means of the equation :

$$a = 0·0136 + \frac{0·67}{18·5 + u} \qquad . \qquad . \qquad . \qquad (1)$$

It is more simple to make use of a logarithmic formula :

$$a = \frac{0·0348}{\log u + 0·207} \qquad . \qquad . \qquad . \qquad (2)$$

The quadratic equation

$$a = 0·0134 + 0·64\left(\frac{1}{u}\right) - 6·94\left(\frac{1}{u}\right)^2 \qquad . \qquad . \qquad (3)$$

also gives good results.

It has not yet been found possible to give any of these formulæ a theoretical interpretation ; a only changes slightly (from 0·0265 to 0·0154), and this is probably why all three equations—in spite of the difference between them—give results which agree well with observation. The following table shows this :—

			a_{18} Calc.		
	u_{18}	a_{18} Obs.	Form I.	Form II.	Form III.
Li	33·4	0·0265	0·0265	0·0264	0·0264
Na	43·5	0·0244	0·0244	0·0243	0·0245
Ag	54·3	0·0229	0·0228	0·0228	0·0228
Cl	65·5	0·0216	0·0216	0·0216	0·0216
Br	67·0	0·0215	0·0214	0·0215	0·0214
H	315	0·0154	0·0156	0·0152	0·0154

The above behaviour may possibly be explained on the grounds that the slowly migrating ions carry a large quantity of water molecules with them, and that the number of these decreases with rise of temperature.

[1] *Zeitschr. f. Elektrochemie*, **8.** 288, 626 (1902) ; **14.** 129 (1908).

The Characteristics of Electrolytic Dissociation.—Electrolytic dissociation differs from ordinary dissociation chiefly in this, viz. that in the former the dissociation products are electrically charged, but not in the latter. The introduction of the idea of electrical dissociation into science marks a new era in our molecular conceptions, since it has revealed to us an entirely new species of molecule, viz. the *electrically charged ion.* According to circumstances, the same substance may decompose either into electrolytic or into non-electrolytic molecules. Thus by dissolving ammonium chloride in a good deal of water it dissociates electrolytically, and almost completely, in the sense of the equation,

$$NH_4Cl = \overset{+}{N}H_4 + \overset{-}{Cl},$$

while by volatilisation, at sufficiently low pressures, it decomposes quite completely, in the sense of the following equation, into non-electric molecules, thus—

$$NH_4Cl = NH_3 + HCl.$$

These two processes are distinctly different, and no connection between them, however probable, is known at present.

The products of ordinary dissociation may be mixed together in any selected proportion ; but in electrolytic dissociation there are in the system the same number of positive and of negative ions, so that they neutralise each other electrically.

In ordinary dissociation no other expenditure of work is requisite in order to separate the products than that usually required to effect the separation of a mixture (p. 97) ; but in the case of electrolytic dissociation, in addition to this work, there is required the expenditure of the much greater work necessary to overcome *the electric attraction of the oppositely charged ions.* Such a separation of this kind is observed to only a very inconsiderable degree by electrostatic influence on electrolytes ; [1] here the free electricities collect on the surfaces in the form of ions ; but no one has ever detected a weighable quantity of "free ions" in this sense, which are unaccompanied by the opposite kind. This could not be very easily produced, because the accumulation of free ions of the same kind is opposed by the enormous electrical forces resisting it.

The Diffusion of Electrolytes.—The preceding observations explain at once why we cannot conduct an experiment like that described on p. 349 [effusion] for the separation of the ions. If we allow a dissociated gas to diffuse, through a small opening, for instance, there will occur a partial separation of the components, since the more mobile components will outstrip the sluggish ones ; but it is quite otherwise in the case of electrolytic dissociation. Let us imagine two solutions of hydrochloric acid, having a

[1] Ostwald and Nernst, *Zeitschr. phys. Chem.* **3.** 120 (1889).

different concentration, to be brought into contact with each other; and let these be sufficiently diluted, in order that we may disregard the undissociated molecules of HCl. Then on every molecule existing in the solution, on the positively charged hydrogen and on the negatively charged chlorine ions, there will be exerted the same force due to the gradient of the osmotic pressure; this will tend to move them from places of a higher to those of a lower concentration. But we know from the conductivities, that a hydrogen ion has a greater mobility than a chlorine ion (p. 366); then the former will, to a corresponding extent, outstrip the latter, and thus there will occur *a partial separation of the two ions.*

But this can only happen to a limited degree. For as soon as one dilute solution contains an excess of H-ions, and the other an excess of Cl-ions, then the one will become positively charged, and the other negatively. As a result of these electric charges, there will arise an electrostatic force; this will drive the H-ions from places of a lower to those of a higher concentration, and the Cl-ions from those of a higher to those of a lower concentration. Thus the diffusion of the H-ions will be retarded, and that of the Cl-ions will be accelerated; and the equalised condition will obviously be that where both ions diffuse with the same velocity. A separation of the ions will occur only during the first instant, and, on account of the great electrostatic capacity of the ions, only to an inappreciable degree.

Thus the decomposition products of electrolytic dissociation cannot be separated from each other, like the products of ordinary dissociation, by diffusion, to any marked degree. On the contrary, this can easily be done by removing the electrostatic charges which result from diffusion, *i.e.* the solution can be *electrolysed.*

The theory of diffusion of dissolved electrolytes can now be given in the following way [1] : let a diffusion cylinder, having the height x, be filled with a highly dissociated solution of a binary electrolyte, having the concentration η, in the total cross-section q, and let the osmotic pressure of each particular ion be p; then at the position $x + dx$ these values will become respectively $\eta - d\eta$ and $p - dp$; the volume of the section thus increased is qdx, and it contains a quantity of electrolyte (of hydrochloric acid, *e.g.*) equal to ηqdx mols. This is acted upon by the force qdp; or, per mol,

$$\frac{1}{\eta}\frac{dp}{dx}.$$

Now the resistance friction, which must be overcome by the two ions in their movement, amounts respectively (according to p. 363) for the cation to

$$\frac{1}{U}$$

[1] Nernst, *Zeitschr. phys. Chem.* **2.** 613 (1888).

2 B

and for the anion to

$$\frac{1}{V}.$$

The quantity of each ion which will migrate in unit of time dz, through a cross-section of the diffusion cylinder, if acted upon only by the forces due to the osmotic pressure, can be obtained by the product of the cross-section × the concentration × the force per mol × the mobility × the time; it amounts respectively to

$$- Uq\frac{dp}{dx}dz, \quad \text{and} \quad - Vq\frac{dp}{dx}dz.$$

But, as a matter of fact, the electrostatic forces described above come into play; these equalise the velocity of the two kinds of ions; let their electrostatic potential amount to P. Then the electrostatic attraction or repulsion, exerted per g.-ion, will amount respectively to

$$- \frac{dP}{dx}, \quad \text{and} \quad + \frac{dP}{dx};$$

and the quantities of each ion which will migrate through the cross-section, from the influence of this force alone, calculated by means of the same products as above, are respectively

$$- Uq\eta\frac{dP}{dx}dz, \quad \text{and} \quad + Vq\eta\frac{dP}{dx}dz.$$

Now, as a matter of fact, the two forces act together; and the quantity of salt which will migrate through the cross-section, in the time dz, is

$$dS = - Uqdz\left(\frac{dp}{dx} + \eta\frac{dP}{dx}\right) = - Vqdz\left(\frac{dp}{dx} - \eta\frac{dP}{dx}\right);$$

or, after the elimination of $\frac{dP}{dx}$,

$$dS = - \frac{2UV}{U + V}q\frac{dp}{dx}dz.$$

Now, according to the law of the osmotic pressure (p. 144),

$$p = \eta RT.$$

By introducing this, we obtain

$$dS = - \frac{2UV}{U + V}RTq\frac{d\eta}{dx}dz.$$

A comparison of this formula with that on p. 151 (where the concentration was denoted by C) shows that

$$D = \frac{2UV}{U + V}RT \quad . \qquad . \qquad . \qquad . \qquad (1)$$

and this denotes *the diffusion coefficient of the electrolyte.*

We know already (p. 365) that U and V are proportional to the ion mobilities u and v ; thus

$$u = FU \quad \text{and} \quad v = FV \qquad . \qquad . \qquad . \qquad (2)$$

The value of the proportional factor, F, depends upon the choice of the unit of measurement ; its absolute value can be calculated from the equation derived by Kohlrausch on p. 365, where $\alpha = 1$, in the case of fully dissociated electrolytes, viz.,

$$\kappa = \eta F(U + V).$$

If we express all these magnitudes on the same system of measurement, then F, of course, will $= 1$. We may suitably choose the C.G.S. system.[1]

In order to obtain the *conductivity* κ, on this scale, we must multiply it by 10^9 because an Ohm $= 10^9$ C.G.S. Further, the unit of *ion concentration*, of course, is that which holds the quantity of electricity ± 1 bound to the ions contained in 1 c.c. If the unit quantity of electricity is held by v-equivalents of a positive ion, then a c.c. contains $\dfrac{\eta}{v}$ units of $+$ electricity ; and of course the same quantity of $-$ electricity.

We thus find that

$$\kappa 10^{-9} = (U + V) \frac{\eta}{v} ;$$

or, after introducing the molecular conductivity (p. 365),

$$U + V = \Lambda v \cdot 10^{-9}. \qquad . \qquad . \qquad (3)$$

Now 96,540 Coulomb (Ampère seconds) ($= 9654$ C.G.S. units) deposit 1 mol of a univalent ion (Book IV. Chap. VI.) ; hence we have for univalent ions

$$v = \frac{1}{9654} ;$$

further

$$U + V = \frac{\Lambda}{9654} \cdot 10^{-9} = 1\cdot036\Lambda \cdot 10^{-13},$$

or, according to p. 365,

$$U = 1\cdot036u \cdot 10^{-13}, \quad V = 1\cdot036v \cdot 10^{-13}. \qquad . \qquad (4)$$

These were the expressions calculated by Kohlrausch[2] in 1879 for the *absolute* velocities with which the ions migrate when they are acted upon by unit force, *i.e.* for example when there is a unit fall of potential per centimetre in an electrolyte through which a current is

[1] See the Text-books of Physics, *e.g.* Kohlrausch, *Prakt. Physik*, Leipzig, 1892, Appendix. [In English, see, *e.g.* Daniel's *Physics*, 2nd edit., p. 13.—TR.]
[2] *Wied. Ann.* **6.** 160 (1879).

passing.   If the fall of potential is $10^8 = 1$ volt (the conventional unit of electromotive force), the velocities are

$$U' = 1 \cdot 036u \cdot 10^{-5}, \quad V' = 1 \cdot 036v \cdot 10^{-5}.$$

If we think of an electrolytic cell (p. 357) as connected with the poles of a Daniel's element which has an electromotive force of $1 \cdot 11$ volt ; and if we separate the electrodes $1 \cdot 11$ cm., then we have a potential gradient of 1 volt per cm., provided we disregard the internal resistance of the element and the polarisation of the electrodes ; if the electrolytic cell is filled with dilute hydrochloric acid, then from the values of u and v, given on p. 366, we get

$$U' = 0 \cdot 000329, \quad \text{and } V' = 0 \cdot 00068 \, \frac{\text{cm.}}{\text{sec.}}$$

It thus becomes apparent that the velocities controlled by the current are very small in comparison with the velocities of the molecules moving back and forth ; now these latter were introduced (p. 244) to explain the osmotic pressure, and they constitute the measure of the temperature in the sense of the kinetic theory.   The increase in the kinetic energy of the ions occasioned by the current is extremely slight ; and the work which the current does is practically completely used up in overcoming the friction, *i.e. in developing Joule's heat.*

The migration in the case of coloured ions, such as the anion of potassium permanganate, can. be made visible by a method suggested in 1887 by O. Lodge.   Using a U-shaped apparatus [1] the migration may not only be made visible, but the absolute velocities may be measured with fair accuracy in a lecture.

Now if we introduce into equation (1), developed for the diffusion coefficients, the values of U and V, from equations (3) and (4), we obtain

$$D = \frac{2uv}{u + v} \cdot \nu RT \cdot 10^{-9} \qquad . \qquad . \qquad . \qquad (5)$$

Now, it remains to express the gas constant R, in the same system of measurement, *i.e.* in its evaluation, to select that unit of volume in c.c., and that unit quantity of ions which shall hold the unit quantity of electricity 1.   Now the pressure in a space containing this quantity of ions per c.c., according to p. 40, at T = 273, is

$22,412 \, \nu$ atm. $= 22,412 \times 981,000 \times 1 \cdot 033 \, \nu$ abs. units,

and, therefore, in the C.G.S. system (for univalent ions $\nu \doteq \frac{1}{9654}$),

$$RT = 2 \cdot 351 \frac{T}{273} \times 10^6 \qquad . \qquad . \qquad . \qquad (6)$$

Now, by introducing this into equation (5), we obtain the diffusion

[1] See *Zeitschr. f. Elektr.* **3.** 308 (1897).

coefficients on the absolute scale, *i.e.* the quantity of salt which will migrate per sec. through a cross-section of 1 sq. cm., where the gradient of concentration per centimetre is 1. It is a matter of indifference what 'scale we take to express the quantity of salt, provided only that we measure the concentration (*i.e.* the quantity of salt × cm.$^{-3}$) on the same scale. It must be noticed, however, that the numerical values usually given are based on the day as unit of time, and thus the factor $8·64 \times 10^4$, the number of seconds in a day, must be introduced in order to express the diffusion coefficient D in the conventional system of measurement; then

$$D = \frac{2uv}{u+v} \nu . 2·351 . \frac{T}{273} \times 10^6 \times 10^{-9} . 8·64 \times 10^4 . \qquad (7)$$

or, simplified and calculated for $T = 273 + 18$,

$$D = 0·04485 \frac{uv}{u+v}[1 + 0·0034(t-18)] \qquad . \qquad . \qquad (8)$$

The temperature coefficient, as calculated theoretically for 18°, from that of the mobility of the ions, and from that of the osmotic pressure, is in complete accord with observation, viz. 0·024 for bases and acids, and 0·026 for neutral salts. The following table contains the observations of Scheffer [1] calculated for 18°, and the theoretical values calculated from the ion mobilities u and v, according to equation (8) :—

Substance.	D obs.	D theor.	Substance.	D obs.	D theor.
HCl	2·30	2·45	NaNO$_3$	1·03	1·15
HNO$_3$	2·22	2·29	NaCO$_2$H	0·95	1·00
KOH	1·85	2·13	NaCH$_3$CO$_2$	0·78	0·86
NaOH	1·40	1·58	NH$_4$Cl	1·33	1·46
NaCl	1·11	1·19	KNO$_3$	1·30	1·41

W. Oeholm has made a thorough experimental study of the accuracy of the diffusion theory; the numbers he obtained [2] for very dilute solutions (about 0·01 normal) at 18° are given in the following table :—

Substance.	D obs.	D theor.	Substance.	D obs.	D theor.
HCl	2·32	2·45	KCl	1·46	1·46
KOH	1·90	2·13	KI	1·46	1·47
NaOH	1·43	1·58	LiCl	1·00	0·994
NaCl	1·17	1·19	CH$_3$CO$_2$H	(0·930)	1·37

[1] *Zeitschr. phys. Chem.* **2.** 390 (1888).
[2] *Ibid.* **50.** 309 (1904).

Since acetic acid at this concentration is only dissociated to a small extent, the observed value 0·93 is considerably less than that calculated for complete dissociation 1·37. Otherwise the agreement found, especially in the recent measurements of Oeholm, is surprising, when one thinks that the calculated value involves diffusion coefficients and laws of gases and electrical measurements, and that parts of physics are thus brought in relation between which a connection was hardly imagined previously. The fact that not only in acetic acid but in the other substances the calculated values are usually a little larger than the observations may be attributed to incomplete dissociation, since the undissociated molecules diffuse more slowly than free ions.

The theory of diffusion in mixtures of salts can also be completely developed; observation again supports the results of the theory, as was shown by me in 1888, and subsequently in a series of researches by Arrhenius.[1]

If we measure the molecular conductivity, the mobility of ions, the diffusion coefficient, and the gas constant, by one system of measurement, consistently applied, it will be found that

$$\Lambda = U + V,$$

and according to equation (5)

$$\frac{1}{D} = \left(\frac{1}{U} + \frac{1}{V}\right) \frac{1}{RT}.$$

That is, that while the molecular conductivity is simply equal to the sum of the ion mobilities, the reciprocal of the diffusion coefficient is proportional to the sum of the reciprocals of the mobilities, these being also included under the additive properties.

The Friction of the Ions.—The friction of the ions can be calculated on the absolute scale from the mobilities found on p. 371. Now, since the velocities assumed by the ions, when unit force acts on v-equivalents, according to equation (4), are respectively,

$$U = 1·036u \times 10^{-13}, \quad \text{and} \quad V = 1·036v \times 10^{-13};$$

then, per v-equivalents, there will be respectively the forces

$$\frac{1}{1·036u \times 10^{-13}}, \quad \text{and} \quad \frac{1}{1·036v \times 10^{-13}} \text{ abs. units};$$

or, per g.-ion respectively, the forces

$$K = \frac{1}{1·036u \times 10^{-13} \cdot 981000v} = \frac{0·950}{u}, \quad \text{and} \quad \frac{0·950}{v} \times 10^{+11} \text{ kg.} \quad (9)$$

required to cause the ions to move with velocity 1 cm./sec. (Kohlrausch).

[1] *Zeitschr. phys. Chem.* **10.** 51 (1892); see also the interesting studies of U. Behn, *Wied. Ann.* **61.** 54 (1897); and Abegg and Bose, *Zeitschr. phys. Chem.* **30.** 545 (1899).

We may apply the same formula to a non-electrolyte or to a salt, by making u = v, and then calculating its mobility according to equation (8) ; then we obtain

$$u = \frac{D}{0\cdot02242[1 + 0\cdot0034(t - 18)]},$$

and by considering equation (9), we obtain

$$K = \frac{2\cdot13}{D}[1 + 0\cdot0034(t - 18)] + 10^9 \text{ kg.} \qquad . \qquad (10)$$

a formula which was already referred to.

Now we will use equations (9) and (10) in order to calculate the resistance friction for an ion and for an electrically neutral molecule of any related molecular structure. Thus the conductivity v of the ion of caproic acid, $H_3C—CH_2—CH_2—CH_2—CH_2—C\begin{smallmatrix}O\\\diagdown OH\end{smallmatrix}$, at $10°$, amounts to 18 ; and, therefore, according to equation (9), the force in kilograms required to give it a velocity of 1 $\frac{\text{cm.}}{\text{sec.}}$ is

$$K = 5\cdot3 \times 10^9.$$

Moreover, from the diffusion constant $0\cdot38$ of mannite, $C_6H_{14}O_6$, measured at the same temperature, according to equation (10), we calculate this force to be

$$K = 5\cdot5 \times 10^9.$$

The fact that these resistance frictions are so nearly coincident, in spite of the very different ways in which they are derived, is a new proof that the views developed in the preceding pages are based on a sure foundation.

Further comparisons are given in the following table [1] :—

Anion or Kation of	Molecular Weight.	v or u.	$K\,10^{=9}$	Diffusing substance.	Molecular Weight.	D.	$K\,10^{-9}$.	Temperature.
Acetic acid .	59	45	2·1	Acetic acid .	60	·90	2·4	18
Tartaric acid .	149	30	3·2	Tartaric acid	150	·50	4·2	18
Racemic acid .	149	30	3·2	Racemic acid	150	·52	4·1	18
Isobutyl-Sulphuric acid .	153	29	3·3					
Ammonium Ion	18	64	1·5	Ammonia .	17	1·64	1·3	19

Other Solvents.—The faculty of breaking up dissolved substances into ions and so yielding good conducting electrolytes, which is most marked in the case of water, is found also in other solvents, but mostly

[1] Euler, *Wied. Ann.*, Jubelband, p. 273 (1897).

only to a small extent and hardly ever to an extent comparable with water.

It should be noticed that conductivity depends not only on the number of ions, that is, on the degree of dissociation, but also upon their mobility. According to the preceding pages, the velocity of diffusion is a measure of this. This is important because in weakly dissociating solvents we can neither determine $\Lambda\infty$ directly nor obtain a from freezing-point determinations on account of its smallness; hence to find a and $\Lambda\infty = u + v$ separately in the equation

$$\kappa = a\eta \, (u + v)$$

one is thrown back upon measurements of diffusion. Walden[1] found the relation

$$\Lambda\infty \; \eta = \text{constant}$$

for the numerous solvents he investigated. As η changed in the ratio of $1:30$ it is evident that this rule is extremely important.

We may form the following conclusions on the power of solvents to break up dissolved substances into ions. Clearly the electrostatic attraction of oppositely charged ions plays an important *rôle* in electrolytic dissociation; that force naturally tends to recombine the ions into electrically neutral molecules.[2] We must therefore assume that other actions whose nature is unknown to us, perhaps the kinetic energy of the components of the molecule, cause separation, and that dissociative equilibrium has its origin in the concurrence of these two opposed tendencies. If the electrostatic force is weakened the electrolytic dissociation should increase; now electrostatics shows that two oppositely charged bodies attract each other more weakly the higher the dielectric constant of the medium in which they are placed. It follows, therefore, *ceteris paribus*, that electrolytic dissociation will be greater the higher the dielectric constant of the medium. This view is supported by the following table :—

Medium.	Dielectric constants.	Electrolytic Dissociation.
Gaseous space .	1·0	Indistinguishable at normal temperatures.
Benzene . .	2·3	Extremely small but measurable conductivity indicates a trace of dissociation.
Ether . .	4·1	Noticeable conductivity of the dissolved electrolyte.
Alcohol . .	25	Moderately strong dissociation.
Formic acid .	62	Strong dissociation of dissolved salts.
Water . .	80	Very strong dissociation.
Prussic acid .	96	Very strong dissociation.

[1] *Zeitschr. phys. Chem.* **55.** 246 (1906).
[2] Nernst, *Gött. Nachr.* Nov. 12, 1893; *Zeitschr. phys. Chem.* **13.** 531 (1894). In the same year, but later, J. J. Thomson put forward similar considerations (*Phil. Mag.* **36.** 320, 1893).

The parallelism between electrostatic dissociation of dissolved substances and the dielectric constant of the solvent is put beyond doubt by this and a number of other examples ; but absolute proportionality is not to be expected, for other influences have to be taken into account, especially as we are unable to say how far the forces tending to separation of the ions vary with the nature of the medium.

The behaviour of formic acid as a solvent, studied by Zanninovitch-Tessarin,[1] is especially noticeable. Salts, such as NaCl, KBr, etc., are hardly less dissociated in this solvent than in water, as measurements of conductivity and freezing-point both show ; hydrochloric acid, on the other hand, hardly conducts at all, and consists for the most part of double molecules ; tri-chlor-acetic acid also, which is extensively dissociated in water, has almost its normal molecular weight in formic acid. This shows, as was to be expected, that besides the undoubted influence of the dielectric constant other specific influences make themselves felt. Apparently association of the ions with molecules of the solvent is important in this respect. The molecular conductivity in certain solvents often decreases with increasing dilution, instead of increasing. This phenomenon is observed in extremely dilute solutions of acids and bases in water itself, but is usually attributed to secondary phenomena caused by impurities. But in certain non-aqueous solvents it is so pronounced that this explanation cannot be accepted. It is possible that in such cases dissociation takes place in steps, so that electrolytic dissociation is only noticeable at certain concentrations, and diminishes when the dilution becomes very great. Thus, to take an arbitrary example, we may suppose that an acid can exist in a tri-molecular form, and be ionised as such, while the simple monomolecular acid is an extremely weak electrolyte :

$$\text{I} \quad (RH)_3 = \overset{-}{R_3H_2} + \overset{+}{H}$$
$$\text{II} \quad (RH)_3 = 3RH.$$

According to this conception, ions would only be present in appreciable quantities at moderate dilutions (Equation I), for when the dilution becomes very great, electrically neutral molecules would again be formed (Equation II).

A good summary of the work done in this direction has been made by Carrara, " Elektrochemie der nicht wässerigen Lösungen." (German translation by K. Arndt, Stuttgart, 1908.)

It is worth mentioning that solvents with considerable dissociating power are also those which have a tendency to polymerisation in the liquid state.[2] This favours the assumption that electrolytic dissociation is helped by association of the free ions with the molecules of the solvent, an assumption which is all the more plausible, as the ions have a strong tendency to form molecular compounds, as will appear in the following section.

The fact noted by F. Kohlrausch[3] that we know of no good electrolytically conducting liquids at usual temperatures, that consequently electrolytic conduction is first seen in mixtures, supports this view.

[1] Zeitschr. phys. Chem. 19. 251 (1896).
[2] Nernst, ibid. 14. 624 (1894) ; Dutoit and Aston, Compt. rend. 125. 240 (1897).
[3] Pogg. Ann. 159. 270 (1875).

Werner's Theory of Molecular Compounds.—Whilst in dealing with the carbon compounds the unitary conception is the most helpful, in dealing with the majority of the inorganic compounds, especially the salts, acids, and bases, Berzelius's dualistic hypothesis is more suitable, the hypothesis which, as we have seen in this chapter, can be referred to decomposition into negative and positive ions. Werner has shown that the investigation of ionic dissociation gives valuable insight into the constitution of so-called molecular compounds, especially the metal ammonia derivatives.

The following observations serve as starting-point. Amongst the metallic ammonia compounds of the trivalent metals, cobalt, chromium, and rhodium, four series are known with 3, 4, 5, and 6 molecules of ammonia. Thus, considering the chlorides, we have as the member richest in ammonia the luteo salts $Me(NH_3)_6Cl_3$ where Me is one of the metals mentioned. In these salts, as in other metallic chlorides, the chlorine atoms can be separated as ions ; this is shown by the conductivity and by chemical behaviour, for instance, immediate reaction with silver nitrate, decomposition by sulphuric acid with formation of hydrochloric acid, etc. When these compounds lose a molecule of ammonia and turn into the purpureo salts $Me(NH_3)_5Cl_3$, the remarkable phenomenon appears that *one of the chlorine atoms can no longer be separated as ion.* This can be rendered symbolically by the formula

$$\left(\begin{matrix} Me(NH_3)_5 \\ Cl \end{matrix}\right)Cl_2,$$

which is to express that the complex within the bracket does not dissociate on solution. Coming to the next members of the series we find that as each molecule of ammonia disappears the chlorine atom becomes incapable of acting as iron. Thus we have the series

$$\left(\begin{matrix} Me(NH_3)_6 \end{matrix}\right)Cl_3 \qquad \left(\begin{matrix} Me(NH_3)_5 \\ Cl \end{matrix}\right)Cl_2 \qquad \left(\begin{matrix} Me(NH_3)_4 \\ Cl_2 \end{matrix}\right)Cl \qquad Me\left(\begin{matrix} (NH_3)_3 \\ Cl_3 \end{matrix}\right).$$

Luteo salts.   Purpureo salts.   Praseo salts.   Hexamine salts.

The last member of the series is not dissociated.

The series of the cations of these salts is

$$\overset{+++}{Me(NH_3)_6} \qquad \overset{++}{Me(NH_3)_5} \atop Cl \qquad \overset{+}{Me(NH_3)_4} \atop Cl_2 \qquad Me(NH_3)_3 \atop Cl_3.$$

Thus we here find the neutral ammonia molecule replaced by univalent anions, so that, naturally, the negative charge of the anions is neutralised by the positive charge of the complex. Hence for each atom of chlorine that enters it the complex loses one charge and finally becomes electrically neutral. If an anion be introduced in the place of an ammonia molecule in the neutral hexamine salt, we obtain the anion

$$Me\frac{(\overline{NH_3})_2}{(NO_2)_4}$$

which is capable of forming salt with potassium.

These relations are excellently shown by the platin-ammonia compounds investigated by Werner ;[1] the following series of radicals has been found :—

$$\overset{++}{Pt}(\overset{++}{NH_3})_6, \quad \overset{+}{Pt}(\overset{++}{NH_3})_5 Cl, \quad \overset{+}{Pt}(\overset{+}{NH_3})_4 Cl_2, \quad Pt(\overset{+}{NH_3})_3 Cl_3, \quad Pt(NH_3)_2 Cl_4,$$

$$Pt(\overset{-}{NH_3})Cl_5, \quad Pt\overset{=}{Cl_6}.$$

The original platin-ammonia ion with a quadruple charge loses its charge by substitution of chlorions, becomes electrically neutral, and finally even negative. The following curve gives the observed molecular conductivity of the chlorides and potassium salts of the above radicals :

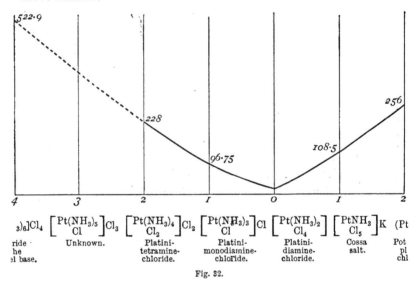

Fig. 32.

Similarly a series can be obtained by the substitution of chlorions in compounds of divalent platinum :

$$\left(Pt(NH_3)_4\right)Cl_2 \quad \left(Pt\frac{(NH_3)_3}{Cl}\right)Cl \quad \left(Pt\frac{(NH_3)_2}{Cl_2}\right) \quad \left(Pt\frac{NH_3}{Cl_3}\right)K \quad \left(PtCl_4\right)K_2.$$

The position of ammonia in the examples here given can be taken by other atomic groups such as water. Thus we know the

[1] *Zeitschr. anorg. Chemie*, **3.** 267 (1893); **8.** 153 (1895) ; Werner and Miolati. *Zeitschr. phys. Chem.* **12.** 35 (1893).

roseo compounds $\left(\text{Me}^{(\text{NH}_3)_5}_{\text{H}_2\text{O}}\right)\text{Cl}_3$ and the tetramine-roseo compounds $\left(\text{Me}^{(\text{NH}_3)_4}_{(\text{H}_2\text{O})_2}\right)\text{Cl}_3$. In these the radical remains trivalent because the substituent is neutral. By introducing this water molecule we obtain hexahydrates, and this is actually the form in which the heavy metals most commonly appear. When a hydrate contains more than 6 molecules of water, for example the vitriols, this is attributed by Werner to a combination of water with the anion.

Werner and Gubser [1] have given an interesting case of "hydrate isomerism" in the chromium chlorides. It has long been known that, like other chromium salts, these exist in two modifications, a green and a violet. The solid salts both have the composition $\text{CrCl}_3 . 6\text{H}_2\text{O}$. In solution the green form changes into the violet, whilst the conductivity rises about threefold. In the violet solution the three chlorine atoms are present as ions, it has therefore the constitution $(\text{Cr}(\text{H}_2\text{O})_6)\text{Cl}_3$; in the green solution only one chlorine atom is present as ion, the constitution is therefore $\left(\text{Cr}^{(\text{H}_2\text{O})_4}_{\text{Cl}_2}\right)\text{Cl} + 2\text{H}_2\text{O}$. That we have here actually two molecules of water combined in a different way to the others, is shown by the fact that the green salt can be transformed into the tetra-hydrate without losing any of its characteristic properties. It may be seen from these examples that the negative atom can be combined in two different ways : one so that it is easily separated as an ion, the other so that it combines with the metallic atom to form a radical ; the latter is the case when it takes the place of ammonia or water. Werner believes that in the latter case the radical is directly attached to the metallic atom and exists in the inner sphere of the latter. Ions which contain other kinds of molecules added in this way are called complex ions. The number of radicals directly combined is a characteristic constant of each metal known as the co-ordination number ; it is to be distinguished from the valency.

Werner's views are valuable for the systematisation of molecular compounds, but we are still far from a satisfactory theory. A very remarkable research of Abegg and Bodländer [2] shows how the affinity of the elements for the electron regulates the formation of complex compounds ; the less firmly the ion holds its electric charge the more readily it forms "molecular compounds" in general. This hypothesis cannot, however, be followed out with exactness, since we do not know how to give precise determination to the electro-affinity.

Ions with Positive and Negative Charge.—A peculiar kind of

[1] *Ber. deutsch. chem. Ges.* **34**. 1579 (1901) ; for further cases of isomerism, see Werner, *Neue Anschauungen auf dem Gebiete der anorganischen Chemie*, Braunschweig, 1909 (2nd edition).

[2] *Zeitschr. anorg. Chem.* **20**. 453 (1899).

ion must be formed, as Küster[1] showed first, when an electrically neutral molecule gives off simultaneously a positive and a negative ion (either uni- or multi-valent); in that case an electrically neutral molecule remains, but one which must be regarded as an ion, since it carries free electric charges; Küster gave such the name *zwitter-ion.* An example is to be found in methyl orange and other substances which possess the formula

$$N(CH_3)_2 - R - SO_3H.$$

There are in solution both a base (substituted ammonia) and an acid (sulphonic acid), therefore must form the ion

$$\overset{+}{N}H(CH_3)_2 - R - \overset{-}{SO_3}.$$

Evidently this conception of a *zwitter-ion* is partly identical with that of an "internal salt"; the new theory therefore admits the possibility of two isomers, according as the charges remain free or neutralise each other. Nothing is known experimentally as to the existence of these two isomers; they would correspond to the difference, for example, between dissociated and non-dissociated acetic acid.

It would evidently be of much importance to find a means of testing for *zwitter-ion*; since the entire ion suffers no force in an electric field, such ions do not, like the ordinary kind, contribute to the conductivity. But the electric field must exert a moment of rotation on their free charges, and hence must have a directive action on them, but on this subject nothing is known at present. It is possible that *zwitter-ions* are much commoner than has hitherto been assumed, for example, the carbon in carbonic oxide would be tetravalent if the latter substance had the constitution

$$\overset{+}{C} = O,$$

but this view can neither be confirmed nor disputed at the present time. See Bredig. *Zeitschr. phys. Chem.* **13.** p. 323, Anm. I. (1894).

Incandescent Gases.—Arrhenius,[2] on the basis of his own investigations, has recently developed the view that the conductivity of incandescent gases, which had been repeatedly studied, is an electrolytic phenomenon, and, therefore, that it argues the existence of ions. The flame of a Bunsen burner was fed by means of an atomiser (*Zerstäuber*) with a mixture of air and little drops of different salt solutions, and thus was brought to a degree of saturation which was fairly constant and capable of approximate determination. Of course, this was proportional to the concentration of the solutions used, and was determined on an absolute scale by photometric measurement. Inasmuch as it was possible to measure the intensity of a galvanic current which was sent through, by means of two platinum electrodes adjusted in the

---

[1] *Ibid.* **13.** 136; see also Winkelblech, *Zeitschr. phys. Chem.* **36.** 546 (1901).
[2] *Wied. Ann.* **42.** 18 (1891).

flame, it was thus possible to measure the conductivity of the incandescent salt vapours. The. flames which were free from salt vapours did not conduct in a marked degree.

In the case of the alkali salts the conductivity was nearly proportional to the square root of the quantity present. It was independent of the nature of the negative ingredient of the salt. Thus, for example, all potassium salts having the same degree of concentration conducted equally well. The conductivity of the salts of the alkali metals increased with the atomic weights. Mixtures of the vapours of potassium and sodium salts showed a conductivity similar to that which can be calculated for the mixture of two electrolytes in water solution. Acids and ammonium salts did not conduct in a marked way.

The salts of the heavy metals showed only traces of conductivity. The behaviour of the alkaline earths was much more complicated.

According to Arrhenius, the reaction which leads to the formation of free ions, and which consists of the action of the water vapour of the flame on the alkali salt, is probably as shown by the equation :—

$$KCl + H_2O = HCl + KOH.$$

The potassium hydroxide formed then breaks up slightly into ions, as follows :—

$$KOH = \overset{+}{K} + \overset{-}{OH}.$$

Since direct observation shows that the resulting acid does not conduct in the flame, there follows immediately from this view a result obtained experimentally, but which is, at first sight, very surprising, viz. that *salts having the same positive ion, when in the same degree of concentration, conduct equally well.* Moreover, a number of other phenomena are explained by the view given above, as, particularly, the fact that the conductivity increases in proportion to the square root of the concentration. All weak electrolytes, as we shall see in the third book, show a similar behaviour.

It should, however, be added to the above, that recent work has shown that conductivities in flame may possibly be due to quite different phenomena ; thus Stark .*e.g.* (*Physik. Zeitschr.* 5. 83, 1904), assumes the negative ions in flames to consist of free electrons.

Historical Observations.—The idea of electrolytic dissociation, which has exerted such a fruitful and regenerating effect upon various departments of physics and chemistry, like other discoveries of· this sort, had its historical anticipation. As early as the year 1857, Clausius,[1] from the laws of electrolytic conductivity, developed the view, that in conductors of that sort there must be traces of free ions leading, at least, an ephemeral existence.

[1] *Pogg. Ann.* **101**. 338 (1857).

H. v. Helmholtz,[1] in 1880, from a similar starting-point, arrived at similar conclusions.

"*Since the complete equilibrium of electricity is produced in the interior of electrolytic liquids, as well as in metallic conductors, by the weakest distribution of the electric forces of attraction, therefore it must be assumed that no other (chemical) force is opposed to the free movement of the positively and negatively charged ions, save the forces of their electrical attraction and repulsion.*"

In this law Helmholtz has clearly formulated the fundamental idea of the theory of electrolytic dissociation. From an experimental point of view the cryoscopic investigations of Raoult [2] are of importance. This investigator showed in 1884 that the abnormally great lowering of freezing point caused by salts in aqueous solutions was distinctly connected with the number of their ions. He even gave approximate rules by which the lowering of freezing point could be calculated from the number and valency of the ions of the salt. The further development of these conceptions is due to Arrhenius (1887), who derived exact formulæ and taught us on the one hand how to determine the nature and the number of the ions, while on the other hand, by a series of applications, he clearly showed the fruitfulness of the theory.

---

[1] *Wied. Ann.* **11.** 737 (1880).
[2] *Compt. rend.* from August 18, 1884.

CHAPTER VIII

THE PHYSICAL PROPERTIES OF SALT SOLUTIONS

The Necessity of the Additive Relation.—A solution which is sufficiently dilute contains the electrolytes in a state of complete dissociation. The dissolved substance has now become a mixture of different molecules, *i.e.* of its ions. Now it is a common experience that, in a dilute solution, or in a gas mixture (p. 97), the properties of each particular component remain unchanged, and, moreover, if the components are known, the properties of the mixture can be predicted. From this there follows the fundamental law that—

The properties of a salt solution are composed, additively, of the properties of the free ions.

Inasmuch as this simple law has been at times subject to much misconception, particular warning should be given against certain illegitimate applications.

The law presupposes *complete* dissociation of the electrolytes. Nothing can be said *a priori* regarding the behaviour in cases where the dissociation is incomplete.

The law may hold good in cases where the dissociation is not complete; and this would obviously be the case where the properties in question are not changed by the union of the ions to form electrically neutral molecules. To what extent this may happen in any given case depends expressly upon this, viz. whether the property in question is decidedly additive or not.

It is unreasonable to reject this law because it occasionally holds (*e.g.* with regard to absorption of light) even in cases in which it is not obviously necessary that it should.

The Density of Salt Solutions.—If we add to water a salt which is completely dissociated electrolytically when in solution, then the change in volume so occasioned will be brought additively by intermixture of the particular ions, and therefore this will be an additive property of the ions. A similar thing may occur in the case of salts which are only slightly dissociated, as, for instance, when the electrolytic dissociation is associated with no change of volume. But

384

here this is not a necessary consequence.   It has not been possible as yet to state *what part of the change of volume is due to each particular ion.*

Let us denote by s the density of a solution containing in m grams of water 1 mol of a salt having a mol wt. of M ; and by s_0, the density of pure water at the same temperature ; then the change of volume occasioned by the solution of that quantity of salt will be

$$\Delta v = \frac{M + m}{s} - \frac{m}{s_0}.$$

The following table contains some values of the change of volume,[1] as calculated from dilute solutions :—

I.	Diff.	II.	Diff.	Diff. I.-II.
KCl $= 26 \cdot 7$		NaCl $= 17 \cdot 7$		$9 \cdot 0$
	$8 \cdot 4$		$9 \cdot 0$	
KBr $= 35 \cdot 1$		NaBr $= 26 \cdot 7$		$8 \cdot 4$
	$10 \cdot 3$		$9 \cdot 4$	
KI $= 45 \cdot 4$		NaI $= 36 \cdot 1$		$9 \cdot 3$

.These values are uncertain within the limit of one unit.   But within this limit of error, the preceding law holds good, as shown by the constancy of the differences between Cl and Br, Br and I, and Na and K.

The change in volume, Δv, is, as a rule, no longer additive, when weakly dissociated acids are concerned ; thus

KAc $= 50 \cdot 6$	NaAc $= 40 \cdot 0$	HAc $= 51 \cdot 1$
KCl $= 26 \cdot 7$	NaCl $= 17 \cdot 7$	HCl $= 17 \cdot 4$
Diff. $= 23 \cdot 9$	$= 22 \cdot 3$	$= 33 \cdot 7$

The differences refer to differences in the increase of volume occasioned by Ac (the acetic acid radical) and Cl.   They are equal when salts are compared which exhibit the same degree of dissociation ; but they have an entirely different value when the highly dissociated hydrochloric acid is compared with the slightly dissociated acetic acid. Acetic acid also is highly dissociated at great dilution ; then its Δv would diminish to about $40 \cdot 5$.

If the change of volume, as defined above, is an additive property, the same thing of course will not be strictly true regarding changes in the specific gravity, for algebraic reasons.   But it is approximately true, because the changes of density amount to only a small part of the total density.   In fact, it is found that the densities of normal solutions of Na and K compounds, *e.g.* show a constant difference when combined with the same negative component.   And

[1] *J.* Traube, *Zeitschr. anorg. Chem.* **3.** 1 (1892).

2 C

furthermore, as the changes in density are nearly proportional to the amount of the content, then the difference must also be proportional to the content.

These regularities can be used to calculate, from a few data which are empirically determined, the density of any selected solution of a salt having the ions A and B.[1]

Let us denote by D_μ the density of a μ-fold normal solution of ammonium chloride, which is chosen as the starting-point, and let a and b represent the differences between the densities of a normal ACl solution and of a normal NH_4B solution respectively ; then the density of a μ-fold normal AB solution is calculated from the formula

$$d = D_\mu + \mu(a + b).$$

The constants a and b, which are to be empirically determined, are called the *moduli* of the respective ions. In the following table there are given the densities of solutions of ammonium chloride, and also the moduli of a number of ions.[2] All the values refer to a temperature of 15°.

μ	Densities of NH_4Cl Solutions.
1	1·0157
2	1·0308
3	1·0451
4	1·0587
5	1·0728

MODULI IN $\frac{1}{10000}$ UNITS

$NH_4 = 0$; $K = 289$; $Na = 238$; $Li = 78$; $\frac{1}{2}Ba = 734$: $\frac{1}{2}Sr = 500$; $\frac{1}{2}Ca = 280$; $\frac{1}{2}Mg = 210$; $\frac{1}{2}Mn = 356$; $\frac{1}{2}Zn = 410$; $\frac{1}{2}Cd = 606$; $\frac{1}{2}Pb = 1087$; $\frac{1}{2}Cu = 434$; $Ag = 1061$.

$Cl = 0$; $Br = 373$; $I = 733$; $NO_3 = 163$; $\frac{1}{2}SO_4 = 206$; $C_2H_3O_2 = -15$.

Thus the density of a threefold normal solution of $Sr(NO_3)_2$, which contains 1·5 g.-mol per litre, is calculated to be

$$d = 1·0451 + 0·0003(500 + 163) = 1·2442 ;$$

while a direct determination gave the result 1·2422. Sometimes the differences are considerably greater.

Electrostriction by Free Ions.—It is very remarkable that the above values of Δv for dissociated substances are extraordinarily small, being considerably smaller than the molecular volume of the solid substance ; in some cases (*e.g.* sodium carbonate, magnesium sulphate, zinc sulphate) they are even negative. It seems, therefore,

[1] Valson, *C.R.* **73**. 441 ; **77**. 806.
[2] Bender, *Wied. Ann.* **20**. 560 (1883).

that with increasing separation of ions, Δv has in general a marked tendency to fall off; this may be clearly seen from the exact measurements of Kohlrausch and Hallwach (see p. 305). The effects hitherto observed can be most easily explained by supposing the *solvent water to be strongly contracted by the presence of free ions.* It is of interest to know that such a contraction might be expected from the electric charges of the ions; every electric liquid must suffer a contraction if, as usually happens, the dielectric constant increases with pressure. It is therefore natural to suppose that the observed contraction of water by dissolved electrolytes is due to the electrostatic field of the ions; the theory of this electrostriction by free ions has been developed by Drude and Nernst.[1]

This electrostriction, which, according to firm physical principles, must always be present, causes therefore a contraction of the solvent; the increase in internal pressure thus brought about will not be distributed equally over the whole solvent, but on the contrary will be very great in the immediate neighbourhood of each ion, where a strong potential gradient exists, and will fall off rapidly at a short distance away. In many respects, however, the solvent will behave as if it were evenly subjected to a higher pressure. In this way we arrive at a very simple physical interpretation of the internal pressure of solutions (p. 247).

Of course it must be admitted that the internal pressure may also be brought about by other causes; it is found, for example, that non-electrolytes can also exhibit not inconsiderable values of internal pressure. But on the whole, a review of Tamman's experimental data (p. 248) can leave, in my opinion, no doubt that electrolytes are distinguished by relatively high internal pressures, as the above considerations demand; it is possible that the high internal pressure of some non-electrolytes may be due to the presence of "zwitter ions," which must, of course, also produce electrostriction. When Tamman states in his monograph that the ions have no specific action, he puts himself somewhat in opposition to his own data; moreover his considerations on electrostriction appear to me to be physically not quite sound.

In aqueous solution the contraction caused by the dissociation of a binary electrolyte is on the average 10-12 cm. Carrara and Levi[2] observed that the molecular volumes of electrolytes dissolved in methyl alcohol, ethyl alcohol and urethane also decreased with increasing dissociation; Walden[3] recently investigated the density of solutions of the good electrolyte tetra-ethyl ammonium iodide in many different solvents, and always found that increasing dissociation was accompanied by contraction; the contraction was approximately the same in all cases, being about 13 c.c. at complete

[1] *Zeitschr. phys. Chem.* **15.** 79 (1894).
[2] *Gazz.-chim. ital.* **30.** II., 197 (1900).
[3] *Zeitschr. phys. Chem.* **60.** 87 (1907).

dissociation, *i.e.*, only slightly different from the value found for aqueous solutions.

The Refractive Power of Salt Solutions.—For the reason that the change of volume, on adding a salt to a solvent, must be necessarily an additive property of the ions the same would be expected of the change in the specific refractive power. In fact, it is found to be true that *the molecular refractive power of a salt, in water solution, is an additive property*, provided that the salt is completely, or at least nearly, decomposed into the free ions ; but this may (not necessarily must) cease to hold good when electrolytic dissociation is slight. Gladstone [1] has stated that the specific molecular refractive powers of similar K and Na compounds show quite constant differences. Le Blanc [2] has shown most conclusively that the same is true of the differences between the specific refractive powers of acids and of their Na salts, in so far as the former are highly dissociated ; but not so when the dissociation is slight, *i.e. there is a marked difference between the atomic refraction of combined hydrogen, and that of hydrogen which is electrolytically separated.*

No way has yet been found to determine the specific refraction of particular ions ; nor any method to determine the amount by which each ion changes the specific volume of water (compare p. 385).

It would be simpler, but less rational, to calculate from the refractive index instead of from the specific refractive power. The change experienced by the refractive index of pure water, on the addition of a salt, is, at least approximately, made up additively of the changes occasioned by the particular ions ; and, therefore, by the use of suitably chosen numerical values or moduli of the ions, it is possible to calculate the refractive coefficients of salt solutions in exactly the same way that was shown to be possible for the specific gravities (p. 386). Thus let us denote by N_μ the refractive index of a solution of KCl containing μ equivalents per litre ; then the refractive index n of a solution of a salt of this concentration, when the moduli of the ions are a and b, may be calculated from the formula

$$n = N_\mu + \mu\ (a + b).$$

Bender,[3] using the following refractive coefficients for KCl solutions at $t° = 18°$, as a starting-point, found the following moduli :—

μ.	Hα.	D.	Hβ.	Hγ.
1	1·3409	1·3428	1·3472	1·3505
2	1·3498	1·3518	1·3565	1·3600
3	1·3583	1·3603	1·3651	1·3689

---

[1] Gladstone, *Phil. Trans.*, 1868 ; Kanonikoff. *J. pr. Chem.* [2], **31.** 339 (1885).
[2] *Zeitschr. phys. Chem.* **4.** 553 (1889).
[3] *Wied. Ann.* **39.** 89 (1890) ; see also Valson, *Jahresber. f. Chem.*, 1873, p. 135.

MODULI IN $\frac{1}{10000}$ UNITS

	Hα.	D.	Hβ.	Hγ.
K	0	0	0	0
Na	2	2	2	2
½Cd	38	...	40	41
Cl	0	0	0	0
Br	37	38	41	43
I	111	114	123	131

Thus the refractive coefficient for a twofold normal NaBr solution, and the line Hα, is calculated to be [1]

$$n = 1\cdot3498 + 0\cdot0002(2 + 37) = 1\cdot3576 ;$$

while experiment gave $1\cdot3578$. The coincidence usually is not so good as this.

Light Absorption and Colour.—The theory of electrolytic dissociation requires that *the absorption of an electrolyte, which is completely dissociated, should be made up additively from the absorption of the positive and negative ingredient*; and therefore that the colour of a dilute salt solution depends upon the colour of the free ions. Some arguments in favour of this view are the well-known facts that, when in very slight concentration, all chromates are yellow, all copper salts are blue, and all salts made up of nothing but colourless ions—as Cl, Br, I, NO_3, SO_4, etc., and as K, Na, Ba, Ca, NH_4, etc.—in water solution are colourless. Moreover, this has been recently subjected to a quantitative proof. Ostwald,[2] in particular, has investigated the absorption spectra of a number of salts of permanganic acid, of flourescein, of eosin, of rosolic acid, of aniline violet, etc., and fixed them photographically, thus obtaining actual proof, undistorted by any subjective influence. The paper on the subject included some accompanying illustrations, made up of the photographed spectra, which were compared with each other as exactly as possible. These represented a number of dilute solutions of salts containing one coloured ion, and contributed, in a striking way, to demonstrate the question at issue regarding the dissociation theory ; *it was found that the spectra of dilute solutions of salts containing the same coloured ion are identical.*

---

[1] In accordance with this it has recently been found by Chénevau (*Ann. phys. chim.* [8], **12**. 145, 289, 1907) that the difference between the refractive indices of salts and their aqueous solution is independent of the dissociation and is an additive property of the ions.

[2] *Abh. d. kgl. sächs. Akad.*, **18**. 281 ; *Zeitschr. phys. Chem.* **9**. 579 (1892) ; also Ewan, *Phil. Mag.* [5], **33**. 317 (1892).

The accompanying cut (Fig. 33) shows the absorption spectra of a number of salts of permanganic acid, which were studied in equivalent solutions, *i.e.* in solutions containing the same number of coloured ions : they all show absolutely identical bands in the yellow and green.   If we remember that the absorption of light is usually (p. 340) changed considerably by very slight changes in the structure of the molecule,

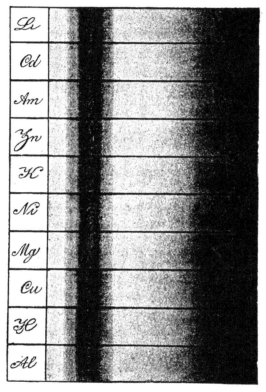

Fig. 33.

it would appear very strange not to seek its simple explanation in the dissociation theory.

General rules for the behaviour of the spectrum, when the ions unite to form molecules which are electrically neutral, have not been found as yet ; thus the change is quite small when a solution of copper sulphate, *e.g.* is diluted, but this change in the colour is clearly recognisable when one adds water to a solution of copper chloride ; in the latter case, the original green solution gradually assumes the blue colour of the copper ions, a clear and simple experiment.

Of course the same ion may change its colour by changing the value of its electrical equivalent [*i.e.* its valence]; thus the trivalent chromion is violet, the divalent blue. The spectrum also changes when a coloured ion unites with another substance to form a new ion; thus the negative ions of the different chrom-acids have colours different from those of the free chromions.

‡The Natural Power of Rotation.— *Those salts which contain one optically active ion must, when in equivalent solutions, and when in a state of complete dissociation, have the same power of rotation.*   This law was first established from certain measurements of Landolt,[1] but the results of Oudemans[2] are still more striking; he developed the law in a purely empirical way, and formulated it as follows. Alkaloids, in their salts, are independent of the acid with which they are combined; and optically active acids are independent of the nature of the metal with which they are combined: these show the same rotation, at the same degree of concentration; thus the molecular rotation of the following salts of quinine acid, as measured in about $\frac{1}{4}$th normal solution, were nearly identical, viz. :—

$K = 48\cdot8$; $Na = 48\cdot9$; $NH_4 = 47\cdot9$; $Ba = 46\cdot6$; $Sr = 48\cdot7$; $Mg = 47\cdot8$.

The *power of magnetic rotation* is also an *additive* property, as is inferred from the investigations of Jahn.[3]   It should also be mentioned here, in brief, that, according to the investigations of G. Wiedemann,[4] the atomic magnetism of dissolved salts of magnetic metals is independent of the nature of the acid (see p. 319), and the phenomenon of *fluorescence* can be shown by ions as well as by electrically neutral molecules.[5]

Ionic Mobility.—Ostwald, Walden, and especially Bredig,[6] investigated the relation between the chemical nature of a number of anions and cations and their mobilities (see Chap. VII.) as deduced from the limiting values of the molecular conductivities. The relations so far known are chiefly the following :—

The mobility of *elementary* ions is a marked *periodic function of their atomic weight*, and *rises* in each series of similar elements when the atomic weight increases until the latter reaches the value 35.

Compound ions travel equally fast when they are *isomeric* and of *equal degree of substitution* with respect to the dissociating group; thus we find equal mobility for

the anions of ortho-toluic acid $CH_3 . C_6H_4 . COOH$ ($29\cdot9$) and a-toluic acid $C_6H_5 . CH_2 . COOH$ ($29\cdot8$), butyric acid $CH_3CH_2CH_2COOH$ ($30\cdot7$) and isobutyric acid $(CH_3)_2CHCOOH$ ($30\cdot9$) ;

[1] *Ber.* **6.** 1073 (1873) ; W. Hartmann, *ibid.* **21.** 221 (1882).
[2] *Beibl.* **9.** 635 (1885).   [3] *Wied. Ann.* **43.** 280 (1891).
[4] See art. "Magnetismus" in Ladenburg's *Handwörterbuch*, **7.** (1889).
[5] Compare the interesting study of Buckingham, *Zeitschr. phys. Chem.* **14.** 129 (1894).   [6] *Zeitschr. phys. Chem.* **13.** 242 (1894).

the cations of propyl amine $CH_3CH_2CH_2NH_3OH$ (40·1) and isopropylamine $(CH_3)_2CHNH_3OH$ (40·0);
on the contrary, when the degree of substitution is not the same the mobilities are unequal as with the
cations of propyl amine $C_3H_7NH_3OH$ (40·1) and trimethyl amine $(CH_3)_3NHOH$ (47·0).
The higher the degree of substitution of isomeric ions the faster they travel.

The substitution of the same group in different ions alters the mobility in the *same sense*; mobility in general falls off with increase in the number of atoms, but less so when the number of atoms is already large, so that the mobility tends with increasing complexity of the ion asymptotically to the minimum value of 20 (the fastest ions are $\overset{+}{H} = 318$ and $OH = 174$). Numerical relations have not been established on account of numerous imperfectly known constitutive influences.

Systematic Résumé of the Properties of Ions.—In the study of any casual physical property of a salt solution, the first attempt made is to give it an additive form. This is usually very simple in the case of the so-called " uni-lateral " [or " one-sided "] properties (p. 105), *i.e.* those where the dissolved substances alone are efficient, but not the solvent. Thus the conductivity, the colour of a substance when dissolved in a colourless solvent, etc., are " uni-lateral " properties ; but not the density, the refractive power, the internal friction, and the like, because here the solvent contributes to the values measured. In the latter case this problem must first be solved, viz. the determination of the very interesting action exerted by the *dissolved substance*. We have, in the preceding sections, several illustrations of the way that this is done in special cases.

When the property in question has been finally brought into an additive form, as by combining it with another property, according to circumstances (as, *e.g.* by combining the refraction of light with the density), then there remains the further question, *How far does each particular ion contribute to the observed value of the property ?*

In certain instances, only one ion is active, as in the case of salts where a coloured or an optically active radical is combined with a colourless or optically inactive radical ; then in such a case the preceding question answers itself. In other cases, the attempt to answer the question has not met with good success, as shown, *e.g.* in the increase of the volume of water on dissolving a salt ; on the other hand, the attempted explanation was successful in the conductivity, and in the capacity of diffusion, *i.e.* in the case of those properties regarding the nature of which we have some clear conceptions.

Not until these preliminary questions are solved, can we undertake with safety the investigation of the problem *as to how far the properties considered are dependent upon the nature of the ion.* But, in general, it may be predicted that the property will have a more or less decidedly *constitutive nature* ; hence the same considerations may be applied here which we brought forward in the paragraph on the properties of electrically neutral molecules (p. 345).

Moreover, in addition to the composition and constitution of the ion, it appears that sometimes another factor in the case of ions is of considerable importance, viz. the *magnitude of the electric charge, i.e.* the same ion may conduct itself with varying electrical valencies. This question regarding the influence of a change in the electric charge on the physical properties, although interesting in many respects, has not yet been subjected to a systematic examination.

Finally, *regarding the electrolytes which are not completely dissociated,* the question arises, What part of the observed value of the respective properties of the dissolved substances is due to the electrically neutral components, and what part is due to those which are dissociated ? This question decides itself in the conductivity, since the dissociated part alone is active. But in every case where the problem is settled, we have *a method for determining the degree of electrolytic dissociation.* The most important result of the two preceding chapters can be stated in the theorem : *that the ions show all the properties of ordinary molecules as well as certain new ones due to the electrical charge.*

CHAPTER IX

General.—In the two foregoing chapters we have been concerned with the properties of free ions, that is with positively or negatively charged molecules ; in the third book we shall see that the theory of free ions is of the greatest importance in understanding numerous chemical processes.

We are thus naturally led to the question of the nature of electricity itself, a problem which certainly belongs more to the region of pure physics, but is of such extreme importance for the theoretical chemist that some mention of it appears to be in place here, the more so as a chemical conception of electricity has come forward in recent times.

It is not superfluous to warn the reader against a misunderstanding of the recent development of electricity which was associated with the names of Maxwell and Hertz : a misunderstanding that is somewhat widespread, and which makes the following theory difficult or impossible to understand. It is generally known that recent physics has been occupied with electrical vibrations ; it is clearly under this influence that a notion has arisen that the so-called fluid theory of electricity regarding the latter as a corporal agent is superseded, and now one often finds the entirely needless supposition that electricity is a state of vibration. The electromagnetic theory of light has given a conclusive proof that the phenomena of light, which have long been referred to wave motion, are closely connected with electrical phenomena, or, in other words, that there is no essential difference between optical and electrical vibrations. Hence optics has become a special chapter in the theory of electricity, just as has long been the case with magnetism. But the question as to the nature of electricity remains the same as before.

This may be made clear by an example. Physics has shown that the sensations of tone are to be attributed to vibrations of the air, hence acoustics becomes a special branch of hydrodynamics, viz. the theory of vibrations of gaseous substances. If any one were to say on the strength of acoustics that air was a state of vibration, the absurdity of this expression would be obvious; yet the same false conclusion has been drawn recently with regard to electricity. Purely chemical investigations have shown us the nature of air, and the development of acoustics has hardly even contributed a detail towards it. Similarly we may look for knowledge of electricity, and perhaps also of the luminiferous ether, to investigations that have a great similarity to the methods used in chemistry.

Ion and Electron.—The consideration of electrolytic phenomena has shown that the quantity of free electricity which the ions are capable of taking up is as invariable a quantity as that of the atoms of the chemical elements; the simplest explanation of this behaviour is that put forward by Helmholtz [1] that electricity itself has an atomistic structure, that therefore we must assume the existence of *positive and negative elementary particles.*

Just as the law of constant and multiple proportions was unintelligible without an atomistic conception of matter, so the existence of ions—that is, of atoms or radicals which are always capable of taking up a defined quantity of free electricity, or twice or three times that quantity—would be quite unintelligible if electricity were a continuum. But if we attribute an atomic structure to electricity, which we know is as indestructible as matter, and can be regarded as an elementary substance like the chemical elements, it is clear that each ion can only combine with a whole number of electrical elementary particles.

Thus we have to assume two new univalent elements whose atoms exert no, or very little, Newtonian attraction on the other elements but act on each other, similar atoms repelling each other, and dissimilar attracting (Coulomb's law). We shall use the signs $\oplus$ and $\ominus$ as symbols for these elements, and call their atoms positive and negative electrons. The chemical compounds of these two univalent elements with the others are to be considered ions; Faraday's law is then nothing else than the law of constant and multiple proportions, applied to the compound atoms of ordinary elements with the positive and negative electrons.

The compound $H\oplus(=\overset{+}{H})$ arises by substitution of a positive electron in a molecule of hydrochloric acid (HCl) in the place of the chlorine; similarly, if a negative electron be substituted for the hydrogen, we obtain the compound $Cl\ominus(=\overline{Cl})$; double substitution of negative electrons in the molecule of sulphuric acid H_2SO_4 in the place of hydrogen gives the compound $SO_4 < {\ominus \atop \ominus}(=\overline{\overline{SO}}_4)$, and so on. This formation of free ions comes into the scheme of valence (p. 282). The dualism which is found in the valence theory, and which leads to

---

[1] *Die neuere Entwicklung von Faradays Ideen über Elektrizität* (1881), *Vorträge und Reden*, 4th ed. vol. ii. p. 251; *Ges. Abh.* iii. p. 97.

a distinction into positive and negative elements, is to be explained by the faculty of some elements (such, for instance, as strongly positive hydrogen) to combine with positive electrons, with others (such, for example, as strongly negative chlorine) to combine with negative electrons.

The ions behave as saturated chemical compounds in the sense of the valence theory, as may be seen from their behaviour towards molecular compounds ; as we saw on p. 378 that ions are capable of replacing ammonia molecules in the platin-ammonia compounds.

The relation between positive and negative electrons recalls that between optically isomeric twins (p. 297). It is a question of much importance whether a compound of the positive and negative electrons ($\oplus\ominus$ = neutron, an electrically neutral massless molecule) really exist ; we shall assume that neutrons are everywhere present like the luminiferous ether, and may regard the space filled by these molecules as weightless, non-conducting, but electrically polarisable, that is, as possessing the properties which optics assumes for the luminiferous ether.

Free Electrons.—The chemical theory of electricity put forward above raises the question whether the elementary atoms of electricity can be isolated, or whether they are only found in chemical combination with ordinary atoms or radicals.

The following consideration [1] makes it probable that free electrons can exist at least momentarily. If we consider the chemical equilibrium (see Book III. Chap. I.)

$$2\bar{C}l + Br_2 = Cl_2 + 2\bar{B}r.$$

which exists kinetically in aqueous solution, we must suppose that an exchange of negative electrons occurs between the bromine and chlorine atoms, and hence we are driven to assume that the electrical atoms must be capable of independent existence apart from matter at least momentarily. The question as to the amount of free electrons in that or similar cases has not been answered so far.

It has been found possible by two quite different means to isolate at least negative electrons, that is, to get them free from original matter. Closer investigation of the cathode rays discovered by Hittorf has led to the knowledge (Wiechert, 1897) that they consist of negative electrons projected with great velocity. By studying the action which electrostatic and electromagnetic fields of force exert on the cathode rays, it has been found possible to measure the velocity of these electrical particles with certainty ; according to W. Kaufmann's measurements [2] for discharge potentials of 3000 to 14,000 volts, it amounts from $0\cdot31$ to $0\cdot68 . 10^{10}$ cm. per second, that is, from $\frac{1}{10}$ to about $\frac{1}{4}$ of the velocity of light.

[1] Nernst, Ber. deutsch. chem. Ges. 30. 1563 (1897).
[2] See also Riecke, Lehrbuch der Physik, 2nd edit. vol. ii. p. 348 ff.

As we shall see in Chap. XII. of this book, the Becquerel rays also consist partly of free negative electrons ; their velocity in these rays attains a value of 2.8×10^{10}, that is, only a trifle less than the velocity of light (3×10^{10}).

It has not so far been found possible to prove the existence of free positive electrons in any similar way.   Probably the positive electron has much greater affinity for ordinary atoms and radicals than the negative, so that its isolation is much more difficult.[1]   There appears to me at the present time to be no reason to doubt that positive electrons might be isolated.

For numerous details, especially on the experimental side of this remarkable region of investigation, see the exposition by E. Riecke, *Lehrbuch der Physik*, 2nd ed. vol. ii. p. 339.

The fact that negative electrons can be projected by electrostatic forces in the cathode rays, and by chemical forces in the Becquerel rays, and that they travel with constant velocity (in a vacuum) shows that, like ordinary matter, they possess a certain inertia or mass.   This mass can be calculated from the magnetic or electrostatic deviation of the rays, and has been found in the cathode rays to be $\frac{1}{2000}$ of the mass of a hydrogen atom.   But this mass is considerably greater at higher velocities.   Apparently it is not mass in the ordinary sense, but an inertia of electromagnetic character, due to the action of the moving electrons on the luminiferous ether.[2]

It should be mentioned that the theory given by Lorentz of the Zeemann phenomenon (see Riecke, *l.c.* p. 447) is based on the vibrations of free negative electrons round positively charged metallic atoms, and that, in this case also, the mass of the negative electrons is about the same as in the cathode rays.

Action of Electrons on Gases.—The rays of electrons are characterised by their penetrative power, by their electrostatic and electromagnetic deviation, by their action on photographic plates, and by the phosphorescence they produce.   All these actions therefore are due to the enormous velocity of the electrons ; it is therefore of great importance that we possess indications of slowly moving or motionless electrons in the action of electrons on gases.

It has been observed in fact that electrons immediately form ions, that is, electrically charged molecules in a gas ; it is true that the ions are of quite a different kind to those known in the theory of electrolytic dissociation.   To distinguish these from the electrolytic ions, since they are produced only in gas, we shall describe them as *gas ions*.

The numerous observed facts on this subject may be simply shown

[1] See Nernst, *Bedeutung elektrischer Methoden und Theorien für die Chemie*, Göttingen, O. Vandenhoek u. Ruprecht, 1901, p. 25.
[2] See H. A. Lorentz, *Physikal. Zeitschr.* **2.** 78 (1900) ; Abraham, *Gött. Nachr.* Heft 1, 1902, and W. Kaufmann, *ibid.* Heft 3, 1903.

and described by means of the following conceptions.[1] With free electrons in a mass of gas, for example air, each electron attaches to itself a certain number of molecules of the gas and so forms a *gas ion ;* if the velocity of the electron is very great, it may produce a relatively large number of positive and negative gas ions.

The formation of gas ions may be most simply conceived as due to the dielectric attraction of the free electrons of the gas molecules, just as on p. 386 we were obliged to assume that an electrolytic ion surrounded by a sheath of water molecules can cause a contraction of the solvent. The complex thus produced must go into thermal equilibrium with the other molecules, that is, it must assume an amount of kinetic energy corresponding to the temperature of the gas.

If the free electron possesses a very high velocity, it may break up a large number of neutrons in the course of gradually losing its excess of kinetic energy, that is, it may form new positive and negative electrons, each of which, according to its kinetic energy, will either form a gas ion at once, or will break up fresh neutrons.

As with electrolytic ions in a solvent the gas ions impart a certain conductivity of the gas. Cathode rays which penetrate into a gas through a thin metallic window from a Geissler tube, or Becquerel rays, projected by a radio-active preparation brought into the mass of gas, give to the gas a noticeable conductivity, since the negative electrons thus entering with high velocity produce a considerable number of positive and negative gas ions.

This conductivity, unlike the ordinary electrolytic conductivity, is not stable or lasting, but recombination of the gas ions, or, more correctly, the combination of the electrons contained in a positive gas ion with the electron contained in a negative gas ion, causes it to disappear in a short but measurable time. Here, also, then is an important difference between the electrolytic and the gas ions ; in the former equilibrium is produced in an immeasurably short time, in the second case quickly, but not so fast as to prevent any measurement.

Many measurements have shown that the law of Guldberg and Waage (Book III. Chap. I.) is applicable to the recombination of the gas ions ; if η is the concentration of positive, and $\acute{\eta}$ of positive ions, we have

$$- \frac{d\eta}{dt} = K\eta\acute{\eta} ;$$

usually but not always η can be put $= \acute{\eta}$. Apparently the gas molecules with which the free electrons are loaded cause the recombination of the two kinds of gas ions to be measurably slow, though probably the reaction

$$\oplus + \ominus = \oplus\ominus$$

---

[1] See the lengthy exposition of *J.* Stark, *Elektrizität in Gasen*, Leipzig, 1902, Ambrosius Barth ; a short but extraordinarily clear and precise summary by Langevin, *Recherches sur les gaz ionisés*, Thèse, Paris, 1902 ; *Ann. chim. phys.* [7], **28.** 289 and 433 (1903).

which takes place in a vacuum, that is, in the luminiferous ether, occurs with a prodigious velocity, so that ether cannot be made conducting.

It is of very great importance that the chemical nature of the gas is of secondary consequence to the degree of ionisation;[1] this is in accordance with the views put forward here, that the process of ionisation consists primarily in the dissociation of neutrons, while the gas molecules play only a small part in forming a sheath round the free electrons in consequence of dielectric forces. According to the customary view that the ionisation consists primarily in breaking up the gas molecule into a positive ion and a free negative electron it might be expected, contrary to the observations, that the chemical nature of the gas would be of as much importance as in electrolytic dissociation.

Other Methods of Formation of Gas Ions.[2]—Gases can be made conducting by various ways other than by rays of negative electrons. Apparently the reaction

$$\oplus\ominus = \oplus + \ominus$$

is always produced by a sufficiently high potential gradient, such, for example, as that at a charged point, when gas molecules are present which can attach themselves to the free electrons and so delay their recombination. At any rate gases can be made decidedly conducting by means of the so-called point discharge.

Röntgen rays have a very strong ionising influence on gases; it is not unlikely that the violently impulsive ether waves, such as Röntgen rays are supposed to be, produce potential differences capable of decomposing neutrons.

Whether the ionic content of flame gases is due to spontaneous formation of gas ions by high temperature is doubtful; it must be observed in passing that at high temperatures gases possess a certain amount of stable conductivity which depends largely on the chemical nature of the substance, and must be due to ordinary electrolytic dissociation (p. 382).

Mobility of the Gas Ions.—The number of gas ions present in the gas at the highest degree of ionisation hitherto produced is very small compared with the whole number of molecules in the gas, less than one gas ion in a billion gas molecules.[3] Hence the gas ions, like an extremely dilute electrolytic solution, must have a mobility independent of their concentration.

---

[1] See Stark, *l.c.*, p. 74. For distinction from the stable electrolytic dissociation of solutions, salts, and also gases (p. 382), the transitory conductivity of gases by means of gas ions may be described as ionisation.

[2] Our knowledge of gas ions is mainly due to the valuable investigations of J. J. Thomson and his students (Rutherford, Zeleny, McClelland, Wilson, Townsend, and others) in Cambridge, 1897 to 1900.   [3] Langevin, *l.c.*, p. 322.

The conductivity K of an ionised gas is therefore

$$K = k\eta + k'\eta',$$

where η and η' are the concentrations, k and k' the mobilities of the positive and negative gas ions.

The values of k and k' have been obtained by widely differing methods; without going into experimental details we will give here the most reliable values given by Zeleny.[1]

	k.	k'.	$\dfrac{k'}{k}$.	Temp.
Dry air	1·36	1·87	1·37	13·5
Damp air	1·37	1·51	1·10	14
Dry oxygen	1·36	1·80	1·32	17
Damp oxygen	1·29	1·52	1·18	16
Dry carbon dioxide . . .	0·76	0·81	1·07	17·5
Damp carbon dioxide . . .	0·82	0·75	0·92	17
Dry hydrogen	6·70	7·95	1·19	20
Damp hydrogen	5·30	5·60	1·05	20

The numbers are the velocities in cm. per second which the gas ions assume with a potential gradient of 1 volt per cm.

On comparison with the mobility of the hydrogen ion (p. 372) we see that the positive ions in dry air move some 400 times faster under the same potential gradient; evidently the friction of the ions in air must be very much smaller than in water; the positive gas ions in hydrogen travel 2000 times faster than the hydrogen ions in water.

In spite of these relatively great mobilities the conductivity due to ionisation in gas is very small because the content in gas ions, as remarked above, is less than 10^{-12} of the gas, or since the latter at atmospheric pressure contains only $\frac{1}{22}$ of a mol per litre the normality only reaches about $0·45 . 10^{-13}$. Even in hydrogen, in which we have seen the mobility is 2000 times that of the hydrogen ion, the conductivity is only of the same order of magnitude as that of an acid solution of 10^{-10} normal. Consequently the conductivities of the ionised gases must usually be determined by electrostatic measurement, but even the small amount of electricity required to charge an electrometer usually causes noticeable changes of concentration in the gas ions. Consequently the methods of investigation of the conductivity of ionised gases differ considerably from these for the investigation of electrolytic conductivity. They cannot be discussed here however.

The numbers given above for the mobility refer to gases at atmospheric pressure; according to the kinetic theory (p. 203), the

[1] *Phil. Trans.* **195**. 193 (1901).

mobility of a gas ion must be inversely proportional to the number of collisions it makes with the gas molecules; in other words, it must increase in inverse proportion to the pressure of the gas.

This conclusion is confirmed by measurements made at pressures of 0·1 to 0·2 atmospheres; for lower pressures than this the mobility increases much faster than inversely proportionally to the pressure; this is the case especially with the negative gas ions.[1]

This result clearly means that at low pressures the number of gas molecules which surround the electron diminishes, and that hence the gas ion is more mobile. The circumstance that this diminution is more noticeable in the negative than in the positive gas ions confirms the conclusion drawn on other grounds that the positive electrons hold ordinary matter more firmly than negative; so too the invariably greater mobility of the negative ion as compared with the positive (see the ratio $\dfrac{k'}{k}$ in the table, p. 400) shows that the number of gas molecules attached to a positive electron is greater than to a negative.

The great influence that water vapour exercises on the mobility, and also, as may be seen from the table in the following section, on the diffusivity, is clearly to be attributed to the greater number of water molecules which attach themselves to electrons, perhaps on account of their greater dielectric constant (see also the next section).

Diffusion of Gas Ions.—The theory of the diffusion of electrolytes in dilute solution given by the author is applicable without change to the diffusion of gas ions. The diffusion coefficient is therefore, according to p. 370 (7),

$$D = \frac{2UV}{U + V} RT \qquad . \qquad . \qquad . \qquad (1)$$

Here, if instead of volts we introduce absolute units,

$$U = k \cdot 10^{-8}, \quad V = k' \cdot 10^{-8}.$$

We have found for the gas constant of univalent ions, p. 372 (6),

$$RT = 2 \cdot 351 \frac{T}{273} \cdot 10^6,$$

and since an equivalent of an n-valent ion possesses one nth of the osmotic pressure we have for n-valent ions

$$RT = \frac{2 \cdot 351}{n} \frac{T}{273} \cdot 10^6,$$

and thus finally

$$D = \frac{2kk'}{k + k'} \frac{0 \cdot 02351}{n} \frac{T}{273} \qquad . \qquad . \qquad . \qquad (2)$$

---

[1] See Langevin, *l.c.* p. 514.

Townsend[1] has given the following values of the diffusion constant at $15°$ (cm.^{2} sec.^{1}) :—

	Obs.	Cal.
Air dry	D = 0·0347	0·0391
Air damp . . .	D = 0·0335	0·0356
Oxygen dry . . .	D = 0·0323	0·0384
Oxygen damp . . .	D = 0·0323	0·0386
Carbon dioxide dry . .	D = 0·0245	0·0194
Carbon dioxide damp .	D = 0·025	0·0194
Hydrogen dry . . .	D = 0·156	0·1805
Hydrogen damp . .	D = 0·135	0·1345

According to p. 205, the diffusion coefficient, for example, of CO_2 into NO_2 is 0·089, and since these two gases have almost the same free path and molecular weight, the diffusion of carbon dioxide molecules in carbon dioxide (Maxwell's "*Diffusion into itself*") must be equally great. Now we saw, p. 375, that an electrolytic ion has about the same mobility as an ordinary molecule; we may therefore reasonably expect that the mobility, and hence the diffusivity of a gas ion would be the same as that of an ordinary molecule if the two are of the same magnitude. We find, further, that in carbon dioxide—and other gases behave similarly—the gas ion travels only about one-third as fast as the carbon dioxide molecules (0·0245 as compared with 0·089); hence the assumption is made very plausible that a greater number of molecules is grouped round the electron in a gas ion (Langevin, *l.c.* p. 332, assumes that there are 7).

Carrying out for gas ions calculations analogous to that on p. 373, we find agreement between the observed and calculated diffusion coefficients when

$$n = 1 ;$$

this indicates *that a gas ion is electrically univalent, that is, it is only a single positive or negative electron.*

We saw on p. 369 that the diffusion of an electrolyte produces potential differences when the mobility of the positive and negative ions is different. The corresponding phenomenon for gas ions has been demonstrated by Zeleny,[2] who stated that a metallic conductor dipping into an ionised gas is negatively charged because the more mobile negative gas ions diffused to it faster than the positive.

Condensation by Gas Ions.—When air saturated with water vapour is expanded it cools, and therefore becomes supersaturated with water, which, when there is dust in the air, condenses to form a

---

[1] *Physikalische Zeitschrift*, **1.** 313 (1900); more fully, *Phil. Trans.* **193.** 129 (1889).
[2] *Phil. Mag.* **46.** 134 (1898).

cloud ; when the air is free from dust it remains supersaturated ; but when the supersaturation is sufficiently great, gas ions are capable of acting as centres of condensation, so that we have an important new means of detecting them.

J. J. Thomson,[1] who, with his students, cleared up this phenomenon by his brilliant researches, showed that when the ratio of expansion is greater than 1·33, both the positive and negative gas ions act as nuclei for the condensation of cloud drops ; if it lies between 1·29 and 1·33 all the negative but only some of the positive ions act as nuclei. When the ratio of expansion is between 1·27 and 1·29 only the negative ions act as nuclei ; and below 1·27 these cease to be effective.

The action of the gas ions just described is probably, like the attachment of gas molecules to the electrons, referred to dielectric forces ; in the last chapter of this book we shall return to this phenomenon, which is of the greatest importance for atomic conceptions. It is especially remarkable that the negative ions produce condensation more strongly than the positive.

Positive and Negative Elements.—The electron theory allows us to form a clear picture of the relation between the dualistic and unitary conceptions. The different elements and radicals have different chemical affinities towards the positive and negative electrons ; those which have a strong tendency to combine with the positive electrons form positive groups of elements ; similarly negative elements are characterised by their affinity for negative electrons. Besides this different elements exercise a chemical attraction on each other which is not of a polar character. Accordingly, two atoms of an element may form a stable chemical compound without any action on the part of the electrons ; the stability with which the two hydrogen or two nitrogen atoms unite with one another in the molecule is an example of this. The same is true of many of the compounds of the metalloids with each other, such as iodine chloride, phosphorus sulphide, and so on. So too the metals make numerous compounds with each other, in which we have no reason to suppose that the electrons take part. Carbon especially, which forms a transition between the well-marked positive and negative elements, reacts with both groups of elements, and since electrons seem here to be out of the question, a purely unitary conception of the carbon compounds is possible.

But so soon as a positive and a negative element react with one another we have separation of ions, that is, the additional separation of a massless electrically neutral molecule is associated with this chemical process ; it is remarkable that this process involves a far deeper change in the ordinary behaviour than one in which the electrons do not take part ; whilst the compounds of the metals with each other retain their metallic character, and similarly, compounds of metalloids

[1] *Phil. Mag.* [5], **46**. 528 (1898) ; [6], **5**. 346 (1903).

recall the properties of their components, when a metal reacts with a metalloid something entirely new and peculiar is produced. Substances like sodium chloride show the greatest possible difference of character from that of their components, and in the formation of such compounds clearly the chemical forces acting are the most intense.

It is of course possible that in the non-polar reactions electrical forces are in the background, just as it has often been hoped to refer the Newtonian attraction to electrical phenomena, as has been accomplished with optics. That, however, is a matter of the future; at present it is necessary to distinguish the forces of polar character from unitary actions.

The views put forward here admit of supposing that an element or radical can react with a positive or negative electron, without a simultaneous reaction between another element of the opposite character combining with the electron which is set free. If this happens the free electrons should possess a certain dissociation pressure in analogy with that of ordinary chemical processes; this would cause differences in the kinetic energy of the electrons given out; possibly the Becquerel rays are due to some such chemical process. (See Chap. XI.)

In any case the recent investigations in the region of the electron theory have an importance for purely chemical questions that can hardly be overrated.

CHAPTER X

THE METALLIC STATE

General.—Matter is found in a singular condition as metal, and although transition stages are known, there is on the whole a sharp distinction between this and the non-metallic state.

The noticeably distinct position of the metallic substances may be seen in the first place in their facility for combining to form homogeneous mixtures with one another, but not with non-metallic substances; no single non-metallic solvent is known for any metal apart from obvious cases of chemical combination, nor are any cases of isomorphous mixtures of a metallic and a non-metallic substance known.[1] Selenium forms a very characteristic example of this; its metalloid modification is soluble in carbon bisulphide, while the metallic form is insoluble.

A second, and perhaps the most important, criterion for the metallic state is the power of conducting electric currents "*metallically*," that is, unlike electrolytic conduction, without any transport of matter; metallic and electrolytic conductors behave so differently that they are distinguished as conductors of the first and second class.

The opacity of metals is closely related to their electric conductivity; there are no known non-metallic substances which are so opaque in thin films as the metals. According to the electromagnetic theory of light, the opacity of the metallic state is due to the fact that conduction in the metal takes place without transport of matter, in contradistinction to electrolytic conduction; metals behave, therefore, as good conductors even towards electric oscillations as rapid as the waves of light.

It is noteworthy that metallic conductivity is usually at ordinary temperatures of a much higher order of magnitude than the highest known conductivity of electrolytes, and it seems from numerous observations that metallic conduction would assume enormous values

---

[1] The fact that hydrogen and the other gases, for which many non-metallic solvents are known, are also occluded by many metals, may perhaps be regarded as an exception but occlusion by metals is probably merely a phenomenon of adsorption, p. 123.

in the neighbourhood of the absolute zero of temperature, at which electrolytic conduction would almost vanish ; and on the other hand, at very high temperatures, whilst electrolytes gain considerably in conductivity, metallic conduction tends to cease.

Certain partly conducting materials, such as carbon, silicon, tellurium, and similar elements lie on the boundary between the metallic and non-metallic states.[1] Metallic conduction in chemical compounds is rare and not well marked.[2]

The characteristics of the metallic state vanish in gases ; vapours of metals ·mix with all other gases and show no trace of metallic conductivity.

Metallic Solutions.[3]—The general behaviour of liquid metallic mixtures is quite analogous with that of mixtures of non-metallic substances. Metals are known, for example lead and tin, which mix in all proportions in the liquid state and behave in this respect therefore like water and alcohol ; others, such as zinc and lead, form two separate layers, which only dissolve each other to a small extent, and recall the behaviour of water and ether.

When a liquid mixture freezes, usually one of the components separates out in the pure state first, and in the same way the components of a metallic mixture can usually be separated by fractional distillation. Consequently the thermodynamic theory of metallic mixtures follows the same lines as that for non-metallic substances, and, in particular, molecular weight determinations in dilute solution can be made on metals as on other substances. The most important result that has been obtained in this respect is that the metals in dilute solution are for the most part *monatomic*; this has also been shown by vapour pressure determinations for mercury and cadmium vapour ; it is of course possible that the dissolved metal forms a compound with the solvent, but this can only contain a single atom of the dissolved metal.

Molecular weight determinations in metallic solutions have been made according to the Raoult-van't Hoff method by Ramsay,[4] Tammann,[5] and recently in a very complete manner by Heycock and Neville ;[6] the most important results of their investigations have been collected by Bodländer in the publication referred to. They found [7] that *tin* is deposited in the pure state from alloys with sodium, aluminium, indium, copper, zinc, silver, cadmium, gold, mercury, thallium, lead, and bismuth ; that the molecular

[1] See also the arrangement of the elements, p. 180.
[2] See also F. Streintz, *Leitvermögen gepresster Pulver*, Stuttgart, 1903, F. Enke.
[3] See also the article "Chemische Natur der Metall-Legierungen," by F. Förster, *Naturw. Rundschau*, **9**. Nos. 36-41 ; and "Konstitution einiger Legierungen," by G. Bodländer, *Berg- und hüttenmanische Zeitung*, 1897, Nos. 34 and 39.
[4] *Zeitschr. phys. Chem.* **3**. 359 (1889).
[5] *Ibid.* **3**. 441 (1889). [6] *Journ. of Chem. Soc.*, since 1888.
[7] *Chem. Zentralblatt*, **1889**, Bd. I. p. 666.

weight of these metals in the liquid mass is the same as their atomic weight; that, therefore, the molecules consist of single atoms like those of vapour of mercury. Aluminium and indium form double atoms in tin. *Antimony* alone raises the melting-point of tin. *Sodium*[1] deposits in the pure state from alloys containing gold, thallium, mercury, and lead, and these metals occur in sodium in the form of single atoms. Cadmium, potassium, lithium, and zinc lower the melting-point of sodium less than the same number of atoms of the former metals, they therefore probably form double atoms as well as single. *Bismuth*[2] also separates in the pure state from alloys with most metals, and the following metals form monatomic molecules in fused bismuth: lead, thallium, mercury, tin, palladium, platinum, gold, cadmium, sodium, and silver. Zinc, copper, and arsenic form larger molecules, di- or triatomic; antimony raises the melting-point of bismuth, and must therefore be deposited in the form of a mixture or compound. *Cadmium* forms compounds with silver, since the latter metal raises its melting-point; otherwise cadmium separates in the pure state. Antimony, platinum, bismuth, tin, sodium, lead, and thallium exist in these alloys in the state of monatomic molecules. Copper, zinc, mercury, palladium, potassium, gold, and arsenic form polyatomic molecules in fused cadmium. *Lead* seems always to separate in the pure state from its fused alloys. Whilst gold, palladium, silver, platinum, and copper form mainly monatomic molecules in fused lead, the molecules of the other metals in this solvent are larger. Antimony, cadmium, mercury, and bismuth in particular occur as double atoms in fused lead. If gold and cadmium are simultaneously dissolved in *tin*, the compound AuCd is formed in solution,[3] and crystallises out as such if the concentration is sufficiently great. The same alloy has been found in later investigations,[4] when gold and cadmium are dissolved in tin, thallium, bismuth, or lead. Silver forms with cadmium in solution in tin, lead, or thallium, the compound Ag_2Cd, but in fused bismuth Ag_4Cd. Gold combines with aluminium when both are dissolved in tin to form the crystalline compound Al_2Au, which is insoluble in tin. By adding aluminium to tin containing gold the whole of the gold is precipitated in this form, so that pure tin is left behind. Pure *thallium* separates from a solution of gold, silver, or platinum in thallium;[5] the dissolved metals, namely, gold, silver, and platinum, form monatomic molecules in thallium. Tin, bismuth, thallium, lead, antimony, and magnesium are monatomic in *zinc*, and all these solutions on freezing deposit zinc in the pure state.[6] In recent years Tammann and his pupils have discovered a large number of compounds between metals; see *Zeitschr. anorg Chem.* since 1904, and especially the summary in *Zeitschr. f. Elektrochemie* **14.** 789 (1908).

The dissolved metals, like ordinary dissolved materials, show the phenomenon of *diffusion* as might be expected, since they obey the laws of osmotic pressure. G. Meyer[7] has shown that the diffusion constants of metals dissolved in mercury are of the same order of magnitude as

[1] *Chem. Zentralblatt*, **1889**, Bd. II. p. 1043.   [2] *Ibid.*, **1891**, Bd. I. p. 123.
[3] *Ibid.*, **1892**, Bd. I. p. 153.   [4] *Ibid.*, **1894**, Bd. I. p. 410.
[5] *Ibid.*, **1894**, Bd. I. p. 266.   [6] *Journ. Chem. Soc.* **71.** 383 (1897).
[7] *Wied. Ann.* **61.** 225 (1897).

those of the salts in water, and that this is also true of the frictional resistance. Metallic powder can be welded at high pressure, as has been shown by Spring[1] in a series of interesting researches, so that even solid metals are capable of diffusing into each other (see also p. 162).

Metallic Alloys.—The components of a mixture of liquid metals can be deposited on cooling either in the form of an intimate mechanical mixture, or in the pure state, or as compounds, or, finally, in the form of homogeneous mixed crystals. The opacity of metals often makes it difficult to decide in any special case what the nature of a metallic alloy is; the constitution can, however, usually be ascertained by microscopic examination of layers and etched surfaces, or, finally, by the use of Röntgen rays. The most certain way of deciding the question is, however, to investigate the cooling curve of the solidifying mixture. (See Book IV. chap. II., paragraph "Thermal Analysis.")

Electric Conductivity of Alloys.—The electric conductivity of alloys is very characteristic. If the alloy is merely a mechanical mixture, its conductivity is an additive property of the volume percentages of the components. The conductivity of an isomorphous mixture, on the other hand, is very much diminished by the addition of small quantities of the separate components, and hence is always much smaller than the value calculated from the law of mixtures. Finally, metallic compounds have a relatively high conductivity in the pure state, and additions of foreign substances have the same effect as upon pure metals.

By means of these simple rules, which were laid down by Le Chateleir,[2] the various phenomena observed can be easily explained. A theoretical explanation, which has the advantage of great simplicity and high intrinsic probability, has been given by Liebenow.[3] According to this theory, the conductivity of all alloys consisting of a mixture of different kinds of molecules must be smaller than that reckoned according to the rule of mixtures, *because thermoelectric forces arise which oppose the electric current.*

Let us suppose a conductor, for simplicity, to consist of thin alternate layers of the two metals which form the alloy, then at the surface of contact Peltier effects will be produced (alternate heating and cooling), that is, the points of contact will be alternately heated and cooled, so that the conductor

---

[1] *Zeitschr. phys. Chem.* **15.** 65 (1894).

[2] Le Chatelier, *Revue générale des sciences,* **6.** (1895), 531 ; *contribution à l'étude des alliages* (Paris, 1901), p. 446.

[3] *Zeitschr. f. Elektrochemie,* 1897, vol. iv. p. 201. Separately in *Der electrische Widerstand der Metalle* (Knapp), Halle, 1908. Lord Rayleigh pointed out in 1896 (*The Electrician,* **37.** 277), that opposing thermoelectric forces were to be expected in alloys.

becomes a thermopile whose electromotive force must oppose the current. Since, as is easily seen, this opposing force must be proportional to the strength of current, its effect appears simply as an increase in the resistance of the alloy. The same effect must be found when the two metals are not arranged in plates, as was assumed above, but in the form of very small particles, as actually occurs.

We get for the specific resistance of an alloy the formula.

$$C_0(1 + \gamma t) = A_0(1 + \alpha t) + B_0(1 + \beta t) \ ;$$

here A_0 is the true resistance at $0°$, B_0 is the apparent resistance due to the thermoelectric effect, or what is physically the same, the opposing electromotive force per unit strength of the current ; C_0 is the observed resistance, α, β, γ are the temperature coefficients.

It is found that the temperature coefficient of most pure metals is $0·004$ (about the same as the expansion coefficient of gases), or, in other words, the resistance of most pure metals increases approximately in proportion to the absolute temperature, as was pointed out by Clausius (1858). As to the thermoelectric effect, it may be assumed in the first place that it is little affected by temperature ; since the experimental results support this assumption we may put

$$\beta = 0$$

as the first approximation.

Then from these assumptions a series of interesting conclusions may be drawn :—

1. In general (when B_0 possesses a considerable value) the specific resistance of an alloy will be . much greater than that of its components, but the temperature coefficient much smaller than that of the pure metals.

2. When the metals are mechanically mixed B_0 is small, therefore the specific resistance can be calculated from that of the components ; the temperature coefficient for such alloys is the same as that of the pure metals.

3. If the two metals in mixing form a compound, and if the proportions are taken so as to produce it, B_0 must vanish and the temperature coefficient must be the same as that of the pure metals ; but if either of the components is present in excess, B_0 must reach a noticeable value, and therefore the temperature coefficient must fall.

These conclusions were thoroughly tested by Liebenow so far as the experimental material would allow, and were found correct to a surprising degree ; more recent measurements, especially those designed to test opposing theories, have supported Liebenow's considerations in every respect ; it appears, however, that a small value of B_0 (see above under 2) is due not to thermoelectric indifference, as Liebenow had to assume in the then state of affairs, but rather to the fact that the metals are mechanically, and not molecularly, mixed.

It is probably better not to refer these effects to the ordinary thermoelectricity of metals, but to consider them in the light of the electron theory. For example, we may assume that when an electron passes from the sphere of influence of one molecule into that of another kind of molecule, its velocity

is increased on entering and decreased on leaving. This conception is really
practically identical with that of Liebenow, and leads, as far as I can see, to
the same results. We can thus determine the existence of definite metallic
compounds under given conditions from the electric conductivity, or often,
more simply still, from the temperature coefficient—as Liebenow also showed ;
if, namely, the compound in question forms mixed crystals with the two
components, then the conductivity as well as temperature coefficient exhibits
a sharp maximum at the point where the ratio of the two components
corresponds to the constitution of the compound. For further details, see
e.g. R. Ruer, *Metallographie* (Hamburg, 1907).

The Theory of Metallic Conduction..—It is hardly doubtful
from what precedes that the theory of metallic conduction should lead
to a deeper knowledge of the metallic state, just as the theory of
electrolytic conduction has led to a knowledge of the peculiar constitution of the electrolytes.

Only the beginnings of this line of progress exist at the present
time. The first assumption is obviously that electric particles are
present in the metals and travel in the direction of the current, but
these, unlike the ions, appear to be massless. The remarkable conductivity of many metals leads to the supposition that the number of
such particles is very great; this view is supported by the fact that
matter in the metallic state has a very great density, *i e.* that the
numerous electric particles cause very great *electrostriction* (p. 386).
The existence of massless electric atoms is rendered probable by the
considerations on p. 395 ; according to these, we must regard the
metals as solvents in which the dissociation

$$\oplus\ominus = \oplus + \ominus$$

reaches considerable magnitude.

If it is assumed that the free electrons and metals follow the principles
of the kinetic theory of gases, and especially that their kinetic energy can be
considered as in equilibrium with that of ordinary molecules, the ratio of
thermal and electric conduction in the metals can be calculated in good
agreement with experience (see Drude).[1]

[1] *Ann. d. Phys.* **1.** 566 (1900) ; Reinganum, *ibid.* **2.** 398 (1900).   G. Jäger,
Sitzungsber. d. Wiener. Akad. **117.** June 1908.

CHAPTER XI

RADIOACTIVITY

Historical.—Soon after the discovery of the Röntgen rays, and led on by this discovery, Becquerel (1896) observed that uranium compounds, and also metallic uranium itself, were capable of affecting a photographic plate through light-tight screens (sheet aluminium and so on); gas in the neighbourhood of such "radioactive" preparations becomes a conductor in consequence of the formation of gaseous ions (p. 398). The latter manifestation of the phenomena of radioactivity is especially adapted for their closer investigation, on account of the great sensitiveness of electrometric measurements.

A few years later (1898), C. G. Schmidt and S. Curie found independently of each other, and almost simultaneously, the like behaviour on the part of thorium compounds.

A very thorough chemical investigation undertaken by the two Curies led to the surprising result that an extraordinarily strongly active barium preparation could be obtained from pitchblende, and further investigation showed that the activity of this preparation was to be ascribed to the presence of a small amount of a new element, homologous to barium, and with the atomic weight 226. To this element the discoverers gave the name *Radium*. Chemical as well as spectro-analytical behaviour supports the contention that we have to do here with a well-defined chemical element. Bismuth contained in the pitchblende also proved to be strongly radioactive; closer investigation showed the presence in this case of a radioactive element closely related to tellurium. It was named *Polonium* by the Curies, and first obtained by Marckwald (1902) in a pure state. Finally, the rare earths, which are present to a very slight degree in pitchblende, also contain, as Debierne showed, a radioactive companion, *actinium*, which is characterised by giving forth an emanation (see further below) of very short life. Giesel found later (1902) the presence of actinium in the earths which had collected in radium bromide mother-liquors, and showed it to be analogous to lanthanum.

The intensity of the radiation of pure radium, which, up to now, is the only one of the strongly radioactive elements to be prepared

411

pure in workable quantities, is enormously greater than that of uranium, and so a series of new radioactive phenomena was discovered with the aid of radium preparations ; these exhibit strong phosphorescence, like that caused by cathode and Röntgen rays ; radium-barium salt mixtures are strongly phosphorescent, the radium rays causing the barium salt to phosphoresce strongly ; many salts, as well as glass, are coloured by radium rays after some time ; oxygen is ozonised, and what is probably connected with this, organic tissues are quickly destroyed ; water is decomposed into knallgas, and so on.

Particularly striking is the property of radium preparations to develop heat continuously ; 100 g. cal are produced in an hour per gram of radium content.

To all these wonderful phenomena was added in 1903 the discovery of Ramsay and Soddy, that radium preparations evolve helium, the presence of which could be easily and with certainty proved by spectrum analysis. Rutherford's hypothesis of atomic disintegration, which appears at first sight, even stranger, if possible, than radioactivity itself, yet explains the phenomena of radioactivity in a simple, and, as far as can be seen at present, complete way.

The Nature of the Rays.—Rutherford's investigations in particular have given us very conclusive information on the nature of the radiation from radioactive substances. It was shown to be made up of different kinds of rays, which were distinguished as α, β, and γ rays, to which must now be added the recently discovered δ rays :

1. The α rays, like the so-called canal-rays of Geissler tubes, consist of positively charged particles (gaseous ions) ; it has been recently assumed on apparently good grounds, that these particles are helium atoms combined with two positive electrons. Their velocity can be exceedingly great, up to $\frac{1}{10}$ the velocity of light. It is therefore obvious what enormous kinetic energy the particles can possess. A further result of their high velocity is their penetrative capacity ; not too thin aluminium foil, thick paper, and the like, can nevertheless absorb α rays practically completely. If the velocity of the particles sinks to about $\frac{1}{30}$ of that of light, they can no longer ionise the air ; and as their velocity is diminished on passing through air, their capacity to ionise is completely destroyed after a certain length of path ; for instance, after 3·86 cm. for polonium rays. The measurement of this length provides a method by which the characteristic initial velocity of the particle from different radioactive preparations can be determined.

2. β rays consist of negative electrons, and are therefore identical in behaviour with the so-called cathode rays. Their velocity can attain that of light ; and the greater it is, the more penetrative will the rays be ; for example, they can pass through fairly thick aluminium leaf. They excite strong fluorescence, especially on barium platino-

cyanide; their presence is best shown by means of a photographic plate.

3. The γ rays have the greatest penetrative powers, but are not deflected by a magnet; they have therefore the same properties as Röntgen rays. It is probable that these rays are secondarily produced by β rays, through the obstruction of electrons shot forth from the middle of the radioactive preparation, just as Röntgen rays result from the absorption of cathode rays by matter.

4. δ rays, finally, consist of relatively very slow moving, negatively charged particles; they are correspondingly easily absorbed, and are strongly deflected by magnets in the opposite direction to α rays on account of their charge, and in the same direction to, but much stronger than, β rays.

As the different kinds of rays are given forth by different preparations with different relative strength, an investigation of the nature of the rays of a radioactive substance under consideration gives us important information. It is extremely desirable that the methods used in the investigation of the different kinds of rays should be improved as far as possible. Especially important is the measurement of the deflection of the rays in a magnetic or electric field, because from the extent of the deflection can be calculated the velocity and the mass of the particles expelled. A radiation consisting of *uncharged* particles expelled with very high velocity could be detected by the accompanying development of heat, but, as a matter of fact, generally escapes notice owing to the inaccuracy of this method. It is, at the same time, quite probable that a radiation of this kind is given forth from radioactive elements. On the other hand, a radiation consisting of charged particles moving with sufficient speed to ionise air, can be detected extraordinarily sharply by means of an electroscope; thus, according to V. Lersch,[1] "if we distributed 1 mg. of radium C amongst all the inhabitants of the earth (about 2000 million), then each person would receive enough to discharge five electroscopes in a fraction of a second."

The energy of the α radiation from radium is by far greater than from any other radioactive element; the absorption of the radiation is the main cause of the development of heat mentioned above. If a radium preparation is enclosed in a small glass tube, only β and γ rays penetrate, and as the former rays carry negative electricity with them, the preparation becomes charged positively.

Theory of Radioactivity.—Rutherford, as has been already observed, has succeeded in explaining the phenomena of radioactivity by a simple hypothesis, according to which they are due to a *kind of explosive disintegration of the atom of a chemical element.* Such an hypothesis seems at first sight extremely bold, but it is well to

[1] *Zeitschr. f. Elektrochemie,* **13.** 383 (1907).

remember that the extremely complicated structure of the emission spectra of chemical elements gave rise long ago to the conception that the atoms of an element are by no means simple points of mass, but must have a very complicated structure. We do not know what the component parts of an atom are, but it is likely that helium atoms and electrons play an especially important part—at any rate in the building up of the atoms of elements of high atomic weight. We can well imagine that the different parts of an atom are in lively motion, and the assumption that from time to time such a mechanism explodes is merely a direct consequence of the kinetic point of view.

When this happens often, the element in question will be unstable, or practically incapable of existence; if it happens extraordinarily seldom, the element will be, practically speaking, entirely unchangeable, and this is therefore the condition in which the chemical elements formerly known exist, with the possible exception of uranium and thorium. If, on the other hand, the atom of an element is neither extraordinarily unstable, nor extraordinarily stable, then single atoms will continually decompose, and, at the same time, a radiation in the form of pieces of the atom shot out with high kinetic energy will be maintained; in this condition exist, according to the above hypothesis, the radioactive elements (uranium, thorium, and especially radium). From this point of view, radioactivity is obviously quite a general phenomenon; but it only lends itself to observation, when the atomic disintegration takes place neither too often nor too seldom. That relatively few elements are in this condition is not to be wondered at; much rather must it be considered fortunate that strongly radioactive elements are capable of being investigated. Now that investigation has been directed to these phenomena, it is to be hoped that, through the extraordinary improvements, of which electrostatic methods especially are capable, even the measurement of an exceedingly slow atomic disintegration, i.e., of an exceedingly weak radioactivity, will be made possible.

The Time Constant of Chemical Elements.—The atoms of a chemical element are capable of various changes of place; e.g. collision with atoms of another element is the cause of chemical phenomena. Besides these changes the atom leads, so to speak, an independent existence, and although we know no details of this existence, yet we can follow Rutherford and make the simple assumption that the number of atoms $- dn$ which a given quantity of the element loses in time dt, should be set proportional to the number n of the atoms still present:

$$- dn = \lambda \, n \, dt,$$

or, if at time $t = 0$, the number of atoms is n_0, then the value for the time constant is given by integration

$$\lambda = \frac{1}{t} \ln \frac{n_0}{n}.$$

The time τ which elapses till half the atoms are destroyed is therefore given by

$$\tau = \frac{1}{\lambda} \ln 2,$$

and is called the *period of half decay*.[1]

Investigation of radioactive substances has shown that neither temperature, state of aggregation, nor even the nature of other elements with which the element under consideration is combined, has any influence on its length of life. In the light of the above hypothesis this means that so far as we know at present, there is no kind of influence which can be brought to bear on intra-atomic movements. From an experimental point of view, the result signifies that although the change of one chemical element into another is possible (*e.g.*, formation of helium from radium) yet we possess no means by which we can influence the change in any way.

It therefore seems as if the period of half decay, like the atomic weight, has a characteristic value for each element. Just as the atomic weight of an element remains unchanged in all ordinary chemical processes, so the same thing holds good for the period of half decay. Should, therefore, the atomic disintegration hypothesis stand the test of time, the determination of the period of half decay with the greatest possible accuracy, and for as many elements as possible, will be one of the most important tasks before us.

The following are the chief methods for determination of this constant :

1. In the case of elements of short life, the gradual decay in radioactivity is measured, or, more directly, the time which elapses before the radioactivity has fallen to half its original value is determined.

2. The mass of charged corpuscles given forth by the preparation is electrometrically measured, and from this the rate of decay can be indirectly determined.

3. As a rule, the decay of a radioactive element gives rise to new radioactive elements ; hence after a very long time a stationary condition will be set up, in which as much of these intermediate products is destroyed as is formed in unit time. We conclude therefore from the fact that all uranium earths existing for geological time contain radium, that radium is a product of the decay of uranium ; now, as the rate of decay of radium has been determined by several methods, the rate of decay of uranium can be calculated from the relative proportions of radium to uranium in the earths mentioned.

---

[1] Radioactive decomposition obeys therefore the law of monomolecular reactions (of Book II., Chap. V.). If we have a mixture of radioactive elements, as is often the case, then each element has its particular constant λ, and the decay curve of the radioactivity is more complicated. Nevertheless by taking enough measurements the separate values of λ can be determined.

The Products of the Decay of Uranium.—In order to obtain a picture of the variety of the relations here prevailing, a table is given of the length of life of uranium, and as many of its products of decay as are known at present; investigation is, of course, in no way to be considered complete.

Element.	Period of Half Decay.	Properties.	Kind of Radiation.
Uranium . .	$7 \cdot 10^9$ years	Nitrate soluble in ether . .	a
Uranium X .	22 days	Nitrate difficultly sol. in ether.	β, γ
Ionium . .	?	Very similar to Thorium . .	a, β
Radium . .	2600 years	Homologue of Barium . .	$a (\delta)$
Ra (emanation)	3·8 days	Noble gas, condenses at $-150°$	$a (\delta)$
RA . . .	3 minutes	Difficultly volatile . . .	a
RB . . .	26 minutes	,, ...	β
RC . . .	19 minutes	,, ...	$a, \beta, \gamma.$
RD . . .	40 (?) years	,, ...	Inactive
RE_1 . . .	6 days	,, ...	,,
RE_2 . . .	4·8 days	,, ...	β
RF (Polonium).	140 days	Similar to Tellurium . .	$a (\delta)$

Pure uranium has a certain activity; by different chemical means it is possible to separate a substance (uranium X) which possesses the whole of the activity originally ascribed to the uranium (at any rate as regards the β rays). This is true only for a moment; after some time uranium X loses its activity, while the original uranium regains it to exactly the same degree, for uranium X is continually produced from uranium by the decay of its atoms. The separated uranium X itself, on the other hand, decomposes quickly further, and its activity therefore falls off.[1]

The mass of uranium X present in uranium must increase till in the same time as much uranium X is formed from uranium as is decomposed further. To the stationary condition obtained in this way has been given the name *radioactive equilibrium*.

The question into what bodies polonium changes has not yet been solved. It is supposed that lead is the final product of uranium decay, but it has not been found possible up to the present time to prove this assumption directly.

Ra, which is, according to the above, an easily volatile radioactive element, is also called radium emanation. This emanation changes into other non-volatile radioactive elements, and so objects which have been for some time in the neighbourhood of a radium preparation become themselves active. This is the cause of the so-called *induced radioactivity*.

---

[1] Whether ionium is formed from uranium directly, or through another intermediate product, has not yet been cleared up.

Chemical properties seem to bear no relation to the mean length of life; according to R. Lucas (1906), however, a connection exists with the electrochemical properties, for with progressive decay, electrochemically nobler transformation products are formed. As is also shown in the above table, quickly decaying elements exist, which do not send forth any noticeable rays; but it must be remembered that we have no certain test for rays which consist of electrically neutral particles.

Radioactivity and the Atomic Conception.—It might be thought that doubt is thrown on the atomic conception by the theory of radioactivity. It is true that in the light of this theory, the atom can no longer be considered absolutely indivisible. But it must be emphasized that the conception of the atom as such, for all ordinary physical and chemical processes, is the same now as it was before, because we have no means whatsoever by which we can influence in any way the occasional spontaneous decomposition of atoms. The atomic conception itself seems rather to be capable of an extraordinary extension and strengthening through the phenomena of radioactivity. Finally, the condition that new sources of energy of undreamt-of magnitude appear to be made accessible by the transformation of chemical elements is of universal importance; for instance, by the complete decay of radium we can obtain about one hundred thousand times the amount of heat which would be yielded by the combustion of an equal weight of coal.

In this connection Marckwald,[1] pertinently says, " It was the alchemist's dream to change ignoble into noble metals. Radioactive substances teach us that if this process were possible, we should either gain so much energy that the value of the noble metal obtained would be negligible in comparison, or, conversely, the consumption of energy required to bring about the change would make the ennoblement practically worthless."

The literature on radioactivity is extremely comprehensive; references to special papers have been given in this chapter. Special attention may be called to the excellent reports on the subject by M. Toepler (*Abhandlungen der Naturwissenschaftlichen Gesellschaft Isis*, 1905, Heft 1); W. Marckwald (Muspratt, *Chemie*, unter " Uran "); Stefan Meyer (*Vierteljahrsbericht des Wiener Vereins zur Förderung des physikalischen und chemischen Unterrichts*, 1906).

A collection of the most important results and a complete index to the literature has been made by R. Lucas (Gmelin-Kraut, *Handbuch der anorganischen Chemie*, 7. Aufl. 1906, under " Radioaktive Stoffe "). A series of lectures, and the discussions which arose from them, can be found in the report on the " 14te Hauptversammlung der Deutschen Bunsengesellschaft " (*Zeitschr. für Elektrochemie*, 1907, Heft 27). Finally the comprehensive lecture by Marckwald, mentioned above, can be especially recommended.

---

[1] *Ber. d. deutsch. chem. Ges.* **41.** 1561 (1908).

CHAPTER XII

Colloids and Crystalloids.—From his examination of hydro-diffu-sion, Graham [1] came to the conclusion that substances existing in solution fall into two groups, the physical and chemical behaviour of which are characteristically different. These differences appeared to Graham so pronounced that he designated them as "two different worlds of matter," the *crystalloidal condition* of matter being in the sharpest contrast to the *colloidal condition*.

The difference between them is shown most clearly in their solutions. Up to this point we have considered only solutions of crystalloids; let us now turn to the examination of solutions of *colloids*.

The most important examples of the latter are silicic acid, aluminium hydroxide, ferric hydroxide, and many other metallic hydroxides; also starch-flour, dextrin, gum, caramel, tannin, white of egg, glue, etc. etc.; also colloidal solutions of certain elements, as silver, selenium, platinum, gold, etc., have been recently prepared.

The distinctions consist in this, viz. that crystalloidal substances are characterised by the facility with which they assume the crystal-lised condition; while the colloids, which were named by Graham from their representative *glue* [κόλλα], are incapable of crystallising, or at least do so very slowly. Still more important are the differences between the conduct of these two classes when in a state of solution. It will be shown shortly *how pronounced is the difference between crystalloid and colloid solutions regarding their osmotic pressures.*

As has been mentioned already, Graham was led to his discovery of the peculiar nature of colloidal solutions by the study of their diffusion velocity; the diffusion of colloids, in general, resembles that of crystalloids, but is relatively a much slower operation. This is shown by the following time periods found by Graham to be required to effect the same degree of diffusion at 10°.

[1] *Lieb. Ann.* **121.** 1 (1862).

Crystalloids.		Colloids.	
Hydrochloric acid .	. 1	White of egg . . .	. 49
Sodium chloride .	. 2·33	Caramel . . .	. 98
Sugar . . .	. 7		
Magnesium sulphate	. 7	...	

Osmotic Pressure.—The question was formerly raised whether a colloidal solution was to be regarded as a simple emulsion, or as a true solution. But, at present, when we can detect a "head" of pressure directly from the phenomena of diffusion, we must in all probability suppose that there is no essential difference between solutions of colloids and of crystalloids.[1] But the extreme slowness of the diffusion of colloids indicates emphatically two things, viz. on the one hand, the driving force must be very small, *i.e.* the osmotic pressure is very small; and, on the other hand, the resistant friction experienced by the molecules in their passage through the water must be enormous; both these conditions are explained by the assumption *that the colloids possess exceedingly high molecular weights.*

Now, as a matter of fact, the experiments conducted with colloid solutions show very small values for the osmotic pressure. Thus Pfeffer,[2] by the use of a membrane of cupric ferrocyanide, obtained the following values for gum-arabic at the respective concentrations, and at a temperature of 15°; the corresponding values for cane sugar are appended for comparison:—

Con.	Gum-Arabic.	Cane Sugar.	Mol. Wt. of Gum-Arabic.
1 %	6·9 cm. Hg	51·8 cm. Hg	2570
6 %	25·9 ,, ,,	310·8 ,, ,,	4110
14 %	70·0 ,, ,,	725·2 ,, ,,	3540
18 %	119·2 ,, ,,	932·4 ,, ,,	2680

The molecular weights of the gum-arabic given in the last column are obtained by the well-known rules (p. 258), from the mol. wt. (342) of cane sugar, multiplied by the ratio of the corresponding osmotic pressures.

In the following table are given some molecular weights, calculated in a similar way, from the osmotic pressures observed by Pfeffer:—

[1] Suspensions are to be distinguished from solutions in the fact that they exercise no measurable osmotic pressure, and also that they do not diffuse; this criterion has been overlooked in many recent researches.

[2] *Osmotische Untersuchungen*, Leipzig, 1877.

Substance.	Membrane.	Con.	Temp.	Pressure.	Mol. Wt.
Dextrin . .	Cupric ferrocyanide	1 %	16°	16·6 cm. Hg	1080
Conglutin .	Calcium phosphate	2 %	16°	3·8 ,, ,,	9500
Glue . .	Cupric ferrocyanide	6 %	23·3°	23·7 ,, ,,	4900
Glue . .	Parchment	6 %	23·3°	21·3 ,, ,,	5200

Further Linebarger [1] has determined the osmotic pressure of colloidal tungstic acid, using parchment paper as the semi-permeable membrane, as it is impermeable for the dissolved colloid. A solution, containing 24·67 g. of H_2WO_4 per litre at 17°, showed a pressure of 25·2 cm. of Hg, which gives a mol. wt. of 1700; while that from the formula $(H_2WO_4)_7$ require 1750, a fairly good coincidence; another solution containing 10 g. per litre gave a mol. wt. of 1720.

The Freezing-Point and the Vapour Pressure.—In harmony with the small osmotic pressure stands the observation, that *the freezing- and boiling-points of colloidal solutions are only slightly different from the respective values of pure water.* Tammann [2] showed that the vapour pressure of water is only slightly depressed by the addition of considerable quantities of gelatin and gum. The following table of figures, given by Sabanejeff and Alexandrow,[3] gives an illustration of the slight depression of the freezing-point of colloidal solutions :—

Quantity of White of Egg in 100 g. of water.	Depression of the Freezing-Point.	Mol. Wt.
14·5	0·020°	14,000
26·1	0·037°	13,000
44·5	0·060°	14,000

Of course such results as these are open to the objection that the observed depression of the freezing, small as it is, may be accounted for on the supposition that the colloid is impure, and therefore that the mol. wts. given in the third column are to be regarded *only as the lower limit.* But at all events it is an evidence that the remarkable magnitude of the mol. wt. of substances occurring in colloidal solution is one of their chief characteristics. It is worth mentioning that Graham [4] himself raised the question " whether the complex nature of

---

[1] Silliman's *Journal [Am. Jour. Sci.]* [3], **43.** 218 (1892).
[2] *Mem. d. Petersb. Akad.* **35.** No. 9 (1887).
[3] *Journ. russ. Ges.* **2.** 7-19 (1891); ref. in *Zeitschr. phys. Chem.* **9.** 88 (1892).
[4] *l.c.* p. 71.

the molecule is not the basis of the colloidal condition." Although
colloidal solutions may represent the transition state intermediate
between emulsions and true solutions, yet they doubtless resemble the
latter much more than they resemble a coarse mechanical suspension.

The Molecular Weight of Colloids.—The osmotic method
described above is particularly suitable for the further investigation
of colloidal solutions, and especially for the more exact determination
of their molecular weights.   For while exact measurements of the
lowering of the vapour pressure and of the freezing-point are open
to question, because of the extreme difficulty in purifying the colloids
from foreign salts, yet these impurities may be disregarded in the
measurement of the osmotic pressure, because these salts can easily
penetrate the parchment paper, and thus do not affect the observed
pressure action.   Moreover, the differences of the freezing- or boiling-
points here, although very small, some hundredths of a degree,
correspond to pressures which can be easily measured by the manometer.

The same method of investigation, when applied to a mixture of
several colloids, would lead to some conclusions respecting *the mutual
action of colloid molecules*.   Of course the very dark question regarding
the relative capacity of the colloid molecules for reaction claims
especial interest.

In the following table are given some figures collated from the
results by the freezing-point method :—

Substance.	Mol. Wt.	Observer.
Inulin	2200	Brown and Morris.[1]
Maltodextrin . . .	965	
Starch	ca. 25000	
Gum	,, 1800	Gladstone and Hibbert.[2]
Caramel	,, 1700	
Ferric hydroxide . .	,, 6000	
Tungstic acid . .	,, 800	
Glycogen . . .	> 140,000	Gatin-Gruzewska.[3]
Silicic acid . . .	at least 49000	Sabanejeff.[4]
Tannin	1100	

Although the results may be uncertain on account of the smallness
of the depressions observed, yet at the same time they undoubtedly
show that colloids do have a very large mol. wt.

Moreover, it appears that other solvents besides water may be

[1] *Chem. Zentralbl.* **2.** 122 (1889).
[2] *Ibid.* 189 ; *Phil. Mag.* **28.** 38 (1889).
[3] *Pflügers Archiv*, **103.** 282 (1904).
[4] *Chem. Zentralbl.* **1.** 10 (1891).

utilised to prepare colloidal solutions ; thus caoutchouc dissolved in benzene shows a mol. wt. of 6500 (Gladstone and Hibbert) ; and tannin in acetic acid a mol. wt. of 1100 (Sabanejeff). Further, it should be mentioned that Graham explained the peculiar inactivity of colloid substances as a result of their high mol. wt. ; also, from the fact that arabic acid, e.g. (Gummi-säure), could be neutralised by very small quantities of calcium hydroxide or potassium hydroxide, he concluded that its mol. wt. must be much greater than $C_{12}H_{11}O_{11}$, the formula commonly given.

Another way of determining the molecular weight, which is free from the sources of error mentioned, but does not rest on so firm a theoretical basis, consists in the direct measurement of the diffusion coefficient. Riecke's kinetic theory (see p. 245) requires that the diffusion coefficient should be inversely proportional to the square root of the molecular weight :

$$D = \frac{k}{\sqrt{M}}$$

The experiments of Thoverts[1] have shown that k has the value of 59·2. Herzog[2] who determined the diffusion coefficients of a few solutions of albumens, found the following molecular weights :

Egg Albumen	.	.	.	.	17,000
Egg mucus	.	.	.	.	30,000
Pepsin	.	.	.	.	13,000
Inversin	.	.	.	.	54,000
Emulsin	.	.	.	.	45,000

The order of magnitude of these results agrees satisfactorily with that obtained by the freezing-point method.

Optical Properties.—Colloidal solutions, like ordinary solutions, appear perfectly clear when examined (even microscopically) by transmitted light. But if a strong beam of light is allowed to fall on a colloidal solution at right angles to the observer, the solution often appears cloudy in the path of the light ; it is therefore not homogeneous, or " optically empty " (Tyndall phenomenon).

Although this phenomenon should not be considered a criterion for colloidal, as opposed to true, solutions, yet from the strength of the effect we can draw an approximate conclusion as to the size of the dissolved or suspended particles. The determination of the size of the particles by ultra-microscopical observation, really depends on this same method (see below, p. 431). In this way Zsigmondy[3] showed the presence, in colloidal gold solutions, of particles of diameters from 10^{-6} to 10^{-3} mm., according to the method of preparation ; the colour

[1] C.R. **133.** 1197 (1901) ; **134.** 564 (1902).
[2] Biochem. Zeitschr. **11.** 172 (1908).
[3] Zeitschr. f. Elektrochemie, **12.** 631 (1906).

by transmitted, as well as the appearance by reflected light, varies in the most pronounced way with the size of the particles. Zsigmondy has also shown that very small particles, which cannot even be observed by means of the ultra-microscope, may be enlarged and made apparent by the following beautiful method, analogous to photographic development; in reducing mixtures containing gold or silver, the particles grow at the expense of the metal in the (chemical) solution, every particle acting as a core.

Gelatination.—Many colloidal solutions are able to coagulate or gelatinise, either on the addition of foreign substances or sometimes spontaneously. They must therefore be regarded as supersaturated, and in a state of labile (unstable) equilibrium. Other colloidal solutions, as those of gelatin, agar-agar, etc., *e.g.* will solidify only below certain definite temperatures, and will become liquid again only when raised to the same temperature. Here of course we have to do with a condition of equilibrium between the gelatinous and the liquid states, and this is a parallel to that between the salt and the saturated solution.

The simplest conception of the nature of gelatinised solutions is that a solid amorphous substance is separated which has a " network " structure, and hence an enormous surface. Hardy [1] has in fact succeeded in showing by microscopic observation that a jelly consists of a fine network; the solid frame formed by the colloid contains a certain amount of dissolved water, while the interstices are filled with an aqueous solution of the colloid. The two phases are held together by capillary forces; the greater part of the water, which is held by " capillary affinity " [2] is removed by evaporation, but where the interstices of the network are very fine, the water is given off only by drying thoroughly.

If a dried jelly is brought into contact with water, it begins to swell. This process apparently indicates an inward suction of the water into the capillaries, resulting in a large increase of the volume. That the force which drives the water into the colloid substances is very great is obvious from the fact that blocks of granite are split by the swelling of wood. The work performed by the capillary and adhesion forces occasions the development of heat, although this is not very considerable. This was observed by E. Wiedemann and Lüdeking.[3]

By the addition of plenty of water, some colloids, as gelatine, glue, etc., can be brought back to solution; but others, as silicic acid, cannot be. As stated by both the observers mentioned above, the

[1] *Zeitschr. f. phys. Chem.* **33.** 326 (1900).
[2] Graham, *l.c.* p. 72, and interesting researches by Linebarger on velocity of coagulation, *J. Amer. Chem. Soc.* **20.** 375 (1898).
[3] *Wied. Ann.* **25.** 145 (1885).

solution is attended *by an absorption of heat.* This is in harmony with the fact that the heat of solution of solids is as a rule negative. The coagulation of colloidal silicic acid is accordingly attended by the development of a corresponding degree of heat.

A gelatinised solution presents several peculiarities,—an intermediate thing between a solid and a liquid, its enormous internal friction relates it to solids. It also has clearly defined elasticities of deformation which clearly distinguish it from true pulpy substances. Yet it preserves many properties of liquid solutions ; thus it can dissolve crystalloids and allows them to diffuse freely. Thus, according to the older researches of Graham, who worked with solutions of gelatine, and especially according to the more recent work of Voigtländer,[1] who worked with agar-agar solutions, it appears that crystalloids diffuse through gelatinised solutions *with velocities which are remarkably near to those which they diffuse through pure water.*

In harmony with this, the electric conductivity of salts, which, as shown by the principles already established, is closely connected with the capacity of diffusion, is only slightly changed by the gelatinisation of the solution. A similar thing seems to hold good for the reaction capacity, as is inferred from an observation made by Reformatzky.[2] According to this, the velocity with which methyl acetate is decomposed by acids in a solution gelatinised by agar-agar is within 1 per cent of the velocity in pure water.

By means of these properties we can explain some of the applications which have been made of gelatinised solutions, and which possess great interest.

Thus the sensitive layer of photographic plates which were *wet* by the old methods, by the new methods are made of a *dried* gelatinised solution or emulsion of the sensitive substance, so that their practical use is rendered much easier than was formerly supposed to be possible.

When galvanic elements are to be transported, the electrolytic liquid with which they are provided is gelatinised. This led to the construction of the so-called " dry cell."

The introduction of " culture gelatine " into bacteriology by Robert Koch marked a new epoch in this science.

Finally, it should be noted that the technology of explosives has experienced an extended regeneration by the use of gelatinised solutions of pyroxylin (smokeless powder), and especially so since Alfred Nobel gelatinised the pyroxylin with " nitroglycerin," and thus used an explosive itself as the solvent.

It is remarkable that *a gelatinised solution is unable to absorb another colloid,* because it retards its diffusion almost completely ; for this reason it makes a semi-permeable membrane, which gives free passage to water and its dissolved crystalloids, but not to colloids dissolved in water.

[1] *Zeitschr. phys. Chem.* **3**. 316 (1889).   [2] *Ibid.* **7**. 34 (1891).

This fact, which was known by Graham, and which he rightly re-garded as very important, explains why a clearly defined osmose is to be observed only when an animal membrane, parchment, or unsized (*planirtes*) paper is used with colloid solutions. Membranes of this sort have the property of colloid solutions, of offering not a very much greater resistance to crystalloids than to pure water, but they hinder colloids almost completely. Before the membranes, which are semi-permeable for many crystalloids, and which are described on p. 129, were known, the tendency was to ascribe a very strong osmotic activity to colloidal solutions, and it was not until Pfeffer's experi-ments that the contrary was known to be the case.

It cannot be certainly stated at present why a gelatinised solution is impermeable to a dissolved colloid. Perhaps it may be reasonable to suppose that the meshes of the network are too fine to allow the colloid molecules to diffuse, but are wide enough to allow the smaller crystalloid molecules to diffuse.

Dialysis.—The property of gelatinised solutions just described is very important for the preparation of pure colloid solutions, because it makes the separation of colloids and crystalloids possible. Thus let a piece of parchment paper or of animal membrane be fastened to the lower part of a frame, and let this be filled with the solution to be purified, and let it be dipped into pure water ; then, after a sufficient lapse of time, the crystalloids in the solution diffuse through into the water, especially if the water bathing the frame be replaced from time to time with fresh water ; the colloid substances remain behind in the frame. Thus to prepare colloidal silicic acid, *e.g.* we decompose a solution of sodium silicate by hydrochloric acid, and then pour it into the "dialyser," for so the discoverer, Graham, called the simple apparatus, the method being called "dialysis." After several days the sodium chloride formed, and the excess of hydrochloric acid, diffuse away, and there remains a solution of silicic acid which is almost absolutely pure. As a result of the osmotic action of the dissolved colloid during the process, the solution [of the colloid] becomes diluted with water.

Hydrosols and Hydrogels.—Colloids which can be redissolved by a solvent after separating from it in the solid state are called *hydrosols*, those which cannot be so redissolved are called *hydrogels*, or simply *gels* ; the solid hydrosols are thus *reversible colloids* and the hydrogels *irreversible colloids*, and it would probably be better to use these expressions instead of the inconvenient terms hydrosol, etc., which make a wholly unnecessary demand on the memory.

Colloidal Solutions of Metals.—If solutions of metallic salts are acted upon by reducing agents under certain definite experimental conditions, the metal is obtained in so finely divided a state, that the so-called colloidal solution of the metal is formed.   Bredig[1] has shown that the same solutions can be obtained by allowing an electric arc to pass between metallic electrodes under water.   Probably the high temperature causes the material of the electrodes to vaporise, the subsequent cooling being so rapid that the particles do not collect to form large complexes, but remain in a state of extremely minute division.   In this way colloidal solutions of some metals (*e.g.* cadmium) could be obtained which had not previously been prepared by any other method.   The Svedberg[2] has recently improved this method.

Even colloidal solutions of the alkali metals can be obtained in indifferent solvents by using an alternating current of high capacity instead of the direct current usually employed, excluding oxygen, and keeping the solution at a low temperature.   It is unnecessary to make the electrodes specially out of the metal in question; it is sufficient to place pieces of the metal in the liquid, and bring them into contact with the sources of the current.   Solutions of the alkali metals are highly coloured, the absorption band moving towards the region of greater wave-lengths with increasing combining weight.

Precipitation Phenomena.—A colloid can be precipitated from its solution by addition of an electrolyte.   The action of the electrolyte depends either on the cation or on the anion, according to the nature of the colloid to be precipitated.   The phenomenon has been investigated quantitatively by Schulze[3] and others who determined the minimum quantity of the electrolyte necessary for precipitation of the colloid, and found at the same time that the precipitating power of an electrolyte is a function of the valency of the ion that causes precipitation, and increases strongly with increase of valency.

Between the precipitating power K of an electrolyte and the valency R of the precipitating ion, the relation

$$R_1 : R_2 : R_3 = K_1 : K_2 : K_3$$

approximately holds.[4]   K is expressed by the dilution of the solution just capable of causing coagulation.   Hydrogen and hydroxyl ions have especially great precipitating power.

The adsorbent power of the colloid for dissolved substances probably plays an important part in the precipitation phenomena.   Van Bemmelen[5]

---

[1] *Anorganische Fermente.*   Leipzig, 1901.
[2] *Ber. d. deutsch. chem. Ges.* **39.** 1703 (1906), "Studien zur Lehre von den kolloiden Lösungen."   Upsala, 1907.
[3] *Journ. prakt. Chem.* [2], **32.** 390-407 (1885).
[4] See Hardy, *Ber.* **37.** 1095–1116 (1904); Freundlich, *Zeitschr. phys. Chem.* **44.** 129-160 (1903); Perrin, *Compt. rend.* **137.** 564-566 (1903).   This relation has been applied to the determination of the valency of the Beryllium ion by Galecki *Zeitschr. f. Electrochemie*, **14.** 767 (1908).
[5] *Zeitschr. f. anorg. Chem.* **23.** 321-372.

found that the partition of a dissolved substance between a solution and a solid colloid can be expressed by the formula

$$\frac{C_1{}^n}{C_2} = K,$$

where C_1 is the concentration of the dissolved substance in the colloid, and C_2 is the concentration of the solution ; n is usually greater than 1.

Electrical Phenomena.—Both Quincke[1] and Helmholtz[2] observed that suspensions move under the influence of an electrical potential gradient. That colloids are affected in the same way has been established by many investigators[3]; it has been shown that some colloids, as *e.g.* the hydroxides $Fe(OH)_3$, $Al(OH)_3$, $Zr(OH)_4$, etc., move in the opposite direction to the current, while others, *e.g.* Pt, Au, Se, the sulphides, silicic acid, etc., move in the same direction as the current.

The actual *conductivity* of colloids is, however, so small that it has not yet been determined with certainty.[4] Cotton and Mouton[5] showed, however, that the *migration velocity* of all colloids is of the same order of magnitude, while Whitney and Blake[6] state that the migration velocity of the colloidal particles is approximately equal to that of a monovalent ion of an inorganic salt.

As colloidally dissolved substances exist in conglomerates of numerous chemical molecules (in the narrow sense), it is to be expected that a colloidal particle can also contain electrically charged molecules (ions); if one kind of ion is in excess, an electric charge must result, and this causes the migration phenomena. Now the electric charge of colloidal particles must obviously be of extreme importance for the stability of the solution. For the separate colloidal particles must tend (under the influence of adhesive and capillary forces) to combine with each other to form flocks, *i.e.* to coagulate. But colloidal particles which have similar electric charges repel each other, and so hinder the coagulation, and the colloid remains in stable solution.

Every circumstance which removes the electric charge of the colloid must therefore in general cause coagulation. If an electrolyte is added, coagulation will only be brought about by the ion charged oppositely to the colloid, while the other ion is either without influence or tends to prevent coagulation ; in fact, it is only by addition of

[1] *Pogg. Ann.* [2]. **113.** 513-598 (1861).
[2] *Wied. Ann.* **7.** 337 (1879).
[3] See, *e.g.* B. Coehn, *Zeitschr. f. Elektrochem.* **4.** 63-67 (1897) ; *Wied. Ann.* **64.** 217 (1898) ; Hardy, *Zeitschr. f. phys. Chem.* **33.** 385-400 (1900) ; Linder and Picton, *Journ. Chem. Soc.* **71.** 568-573 (1897) ; Lottermoser, *Samml. chem. u. chem.-techn. Vortr.* **6.** vols. 5 and 6, p. 76.
[4] See Duclaux, *Compt. rend.* **140.** 1468-1471 (1905) and Malfitano, *Compt. rend.* **139.** 1221-1223 (1904).
[5] *Compt. rend.*, 1904, from 27th June.
[6] *Journ. Amer. Chem. Soc.* **26.** 1339-1387 (1904).

oppositely charged ions that an electrically neutral complex can result.

From the same point of view we can explain the rule of Linder and Picton [1] that colloids can mutually coagulate each other which migrate in opposite directions in an electric field; in this case electrical neutralisation occurs when the two oppositely charged colloids coalesce. W. Biltz [2] investigated quantitatively this mutual precipitation and succeeded in showing the existence of a maximum effect. He obtained the following results when 10 c.cm. gold solution containing 1·4 mg. Au were acted upon by 5 c.c. of zirconium hydrate solutions of variable concentrations.

ZrO_2 in mg.	Phenomena observed.
16·2	No precipitation.
3·2	No precipitation.
1·9	Formation of flocks which settled very slowly.
1·6	Complete precipitation.
0·65	Very fine flocks, settling very slowly.
0·32	Extremely fine flocks.
0·065	No precipitation.

A maximum effect occurs therefore at 1·6; when the amount of ZrO_2 is either above or below certain limits, no precipitation takes place.

According to Biltz this must be explained in the following way. In order to neutralize the electric charge of one colloid by the opposite charge of a second, a certain definite quantity of the latter is necessary. If either more or less than this is added, the charge of the second or first colloid is in excess, and precipitation is only partial, or may not take place at all.

The question to what extent the two colloids combine (without formation of flocks) at a great distance from the maximum, seems worthy of further investigation. Although it is thus possible to bring many observations under the same point of view, "yet we are still far from a complete comprehension of all the phenomena occurring in this wide field." [3] Considering the extreme importance of colloids for all organisms, their closer investigation is obviously one of the most urgent tasks of physical chemistry; especially important are the questions how far, and with what alterations, the laws of chemical statics and dynamics can be applied also to colloids.

The ingenious experiment of Arrhenius, who applied the principals of chemical equilibrium directly to the mutual neutralization of toxins and antitoxins, has been proved unsuccessful by Ehrlich.[4] It is obvious that the slow processes in question were mistaken by Arrhenius for equilibrium phenomena.[5]

[1] *Journ. Chem. Soc.* **71.** 572 (1897).
[2] *Ber.* **37.** 1095 (1904).
[3] Lottermoser, *Zeitschr. f. Electrochemie,* **12.** 630 (1906).
[4] See *ibid.* **10.** p. 661 ff. (1904).
[5] Cf. my critique *ibid.* **10.** p. 377 (1904).

recent literature on the subject of the colloids see Lottermoser, . Kolloide," *Sammlung chem. techn. Vorträge*, Heft 6 ; A. Müller, *der Kolloide*, Leipzig, 1903 (Deuticke) ; Bredig, *Anorg. Fermente*, 1901 ; R. Zsigmondy, *Zur Erkenntnis der Kolloide*, Jena, 1905 ischer) ; also the short summaries by W. Beltz, *Chemikerzeitung* **29**. 00) ; *Medizin. naturw. Archiv*, **1**. 267 (1907) ; and Lottermoser, *f. Electrochem.* **12**. 624 (1906) ; **14**. 634 (1908).

CHAPTER XIII

THE ABSOLUTE SIZE OF MOLECULES

The Superior Limit.—We have treated thus far of the properties of molecules, of their kinetic conditions, of the various forces exerted by them, etc. In this concluding chapter we will discuss briefly the problem of *their absolute dimensions.*

The assumption that matter is not infinitely divisible requires that these dimensions [of the molecule], no matter how small, must yet be finite.

Many experiences of daily life speak in favour of the view that the divisibility of matter extends to a high degree. Infinitesimal quantities of strong perfumes can impart their odour to whole rooms; they have entirely filled them with their molecules. Infinitesimal quantities of strong colouring substances can distinctly colour large quantities of water. One part of fluoresceïn, when dissolved in more than a hundred million parts of water, suffices to impart to it a distinct fluorescence. Faraday prepared gold-foil, the thickness of which, at the most, was 0·5 millionths of a mm. Röntgen[1] succeeded in preparing layers of oil on water, having about the same thickness.

The attempt has been made repeatedly from determinations of this sort to find an upper limit of the size of the molecule, or at least the limit of the *sphere of activity of the molecular forces, i.e.* the distances within which the mutual attraction of the molecules begins to have a "noticeable value." As is obvious, there is no precise definition of this sphere of activity, for it leaves the question open regarding the boundary between the "noticeable" (*merklich*) and the "unnoticeable" action; nor will this be possible until we know something certain regarding the law of the variation of the molecular forces, with their distances apart.[2] Nevertheless, by means of the capillary forces, an estimation of these magnitudes can be attempted; in this way van der Waals found the order of the magnitude to be about 0·2 millionths of a mm.

[1] *Wied. Ann.* **41.** 321 (1890).
[2] See, *e.g.* Bohl, *Wied. Ann.* **36.** 334 (1889); Galitzine, *Zeitschr. phys. Chem.* **4.** 417 (1889).

If it were possible to make lamellæ of a homogeneous liquid sufficiently thin, then the otherwise constant surface-tension (p. 56) would begin to diminish as soon as the thickness of the lamellæ should become smaller than the sphere of activity of the molecular forces; because, from this point, the resultant of the forces, which are directed towards the interior of the liquid, would begin to diminish. The phenomenon of the dark spots in soap-bubble films has been employed for this purpose; but even disregarding the fact that such a heterogeneous and ill-defined substance, chemically, as "soap solution," must at the outset be discarded for investigations like these, it is stated by Drude[1] that the surface-tension of these dark parts is not noticeably different from that of the other parts; this observer determined their thickness to be 17×10^{-6} mm.; while Reinold and Rücker[2] found it to be 12×10^{-6} mm. A. Overbeck[3] conducted an interesting research, in which he determined the slightest thickness with which a platinum plate must be covered by another metal, in order that this layer may receive an electric charge; but this method cannot give a safe determination of the sphere of activity of the molecular forces, because the observations can be explained by the formation of an alloy (a solid solution, p. 161), on the surface of the platinum.

A very interesting and promising method of detecting small particles whose refractive index differs sufficiently from that of the medium has been discovered by Siedentopf and Zsigmondy;[4] by strong side illumination they succeeded in producing a diffraction image of the particles which are made self-luminous by the illumination; this can be done even when their dimensions are small compared with the wave-length of light. The method was found to be applicable to particles of about $6 \cdot 10^{-6}$ mm., so that direct observation has already approached molecular dimensions. The authors applied their method to ruby gold glasses; they succeeded in showing that the gold is distributed in small particles in these glasses. Although no doubt the gold particles (colloidal molecules?) thus made visible consist of many single gold atoms, it is none the less of the highest interest that by refining the observation the apparent continuum can be resolved into discrete points.

The Space occupied by the Molecules.—According to the present view, the molecules do not completely fill the space which is occupied by the body as a whole, but are separated from each other by intervening spaces. We have already repeatedly studied properties which are to be regarded as measures of the volume actually occupied by the molecules (p. 310 ff.), or which at least are related more or less

[1] *Wied. Ann.* **43**. 158 (1891).
[2] *Phil. Trans.* (1881), 447; (1883), 645.
[3] *Wied. Ann.* **31**. 337 (1887).
[4] *Ann. d. Phys.* [4], **10**. 1 (1903).

closely in this way.   We will now proceed to see how far *the absolute value* of this magnitude is determined.

The first method to determine this is derived from van der Waals' theory, according to which the constant "b" of the equation of condition is equal to fourfold the volume of the molecule; now its value can be calculated, either by means of the deviation of gases from the law of the ideal gas condition, or from the relation that it is threefold as large as the critical volume; or finally, from the equation (p. 220)

$$b = \frac{1}{8} \frac{\theta_0}{273\pi_0};$$

if we calculate the critical pressure π_0 in atmospheres, then our unit of volume will denote the space occupied by a mol of the gas under normal conditions of temperature and pressure, and the equation

$$x = \frac{b}{4} = \frac{1}{32} \frac{\theta_0}{273\pi_0} \qquad . \qquad . \qquad . \qquad \text{I.}$$

denotes the fraction of the volume actually occupied by the molecules.

The three methods given above to determine the value of b give only approximately coincident results, on account of the inexactness of the theory, to which reference has often been made; but these deviations are of no importance in view of the object here considered. We find abundant data for calculations of this sort.[1] Equation I. is naturally not applicable to substances that are strongly dissociated (p. 276).

The Clausius-Mossotti theory of dielectra (p. 311) gives another method; according to this, when D denotes the dielectric constant, the value of the space filled is

$$x = \frac{D-1}{D+2} \qquad . \qquad . \qquad . \qquad \text{II.}$$

The following table, taken from a work of Lebedew,[2] contains some results calculated by these two independent methods.   The dielectric constant D is obtained from the equation

$$\frac{D-1}{D+2} \cdot \frac{1}{d} = \text{const.,}$$

which is well established, both by theory and by experiment; here d denotes the density reduced to the gas condition at 0°, and to a pressure of 1 atm.   The table is based on the measurements of Boltzmann (1875), Klemencic (1885), and Lebedew (1891).

---

[1] *Kontinuität*, etc., p. 136.
[2] *Wied. Ann.* **44.** 288 (1891).

Substance.	x.		$\dfrac{M}{22412x}$
	Acc. to I.	Acc. to II.	
Nitrous oxide . . .	0·00048	0·00038	3·7
Carbon dioxide . . .	0·00050	0·00033	4·0
Ethylene	0·00056	0·00054	2·4
Carbon disulphide . .	0·00082	0·00097	4·3
Benzene	0·00128	0·00123	2·7

Although the deviations between the two columns of figures are far greater than any error due to observation, yet it is very remarkable that the orders of magnitude coincide so well. Therefore it need not appear questionable if these values should be used to develop further conclusions.

The Density of the Molecules.—The specific gravity w of the molecules may be calculated directly from the value of x. 22,412 c.c. of a gas at 0°, and a pressure of 1 atm., contain 1 mol M ; therefore the density of the molecule, referred to water at 4°, amounts to

$$w = \frac{M}{22,412x}.$$

In the third column of the preceding table are given the respective values of this quantity, on the basis of the value of x, according to van der Waals' figures.

Values of the same order of magnitude are obtained by calculating w from the dielectric constant ; thus

$$w = d\frac{D+2}{D-1}.$$

The specific refraction (p. 310) gives therefore a measure of the specific volume $\dfrac{1}{w}$ of the molecule, which is at least approximate.

The Size of Molecules.—By combining these units, obtained as just described, with the formula of Clausius and Maxwell (p. 203), viz.

$$L = \frac{\lambda^3}{\sqrt{2}\pi s^2}, \quad \text{or} \quad \frac{1}{\lambda^3} = \frac{1}{\sqrt{2}L\pi s^2} \qquad . \qquad . \qquad (1)$$

we are led a step further. The mean wave-length L has been determined, with at least an approximate coincidence, by three different methods, so that we are certain of the approximate value. Then λ^3, a cube, the cross-section of which contains a molecule of the gas, may be denoted by the reciprocal value of the number of molecules N in unit volume, so that for the sum Q, of the cross-section of the molecules, we may write

$$Q = \frac{N\pi s^2}{4} = \frac{1}{4\sqrt{2}L}. \qquad . \qquad . \qquad . \qquad (2)$$

2 F

Now if we assume that the molecules are *spherical*, it obviously results that the following equation,

$$x = N\frac{s^3\pi}{6} = \frac{2}{3}sQ \quad . \quad . \quad . \quad . \quad (3)$$

represents the volume of the molecules; and therefore the molecular diameter would be expressed by the following formula, containing only magnitudes which can be determined, viz.

$$s = 6\ \sqrt{2}xL = 8\cdot5xL.$$

Thus for carbon dioxide (p. 204) we find

$$s = 8\cdot5 \times 0\cdot000068 \times 0\cdot00050 = 0\cdot29 \text{ millionths mm.,}$$

and similar values for other substances.

The Number and the Weight of Molecules.—The number of molecules contained in 1 cubic mm. of a gas at $0°$ and at atmospheric pressure is obtained directly from the formula

$$N = \frac{1}{\sqrt{2}L\pi s^2} = \frac{1}{72\ \sqrt{2}L^3x^2\pi} = \frac{1}{320L^3x^2}.$$

According to Avogadro's law this must be the same for all gases, *i.e.* L^3x^2 must be a constant.

If we again use the mean free paths derived from the internal friction (p. 204), we obtain—

	$L \times 10^6.$	$x \times 10^5.$	$L^3x^2 \times 10^{20}.$
Nitrous oxide . .	68	48	7·2
Carbon dioxide . .	68	·50	7·8
Ethylene . . .	58	56	6·1
		Mean	$7\cdot0 \times 10^{20}$

Therefore it follows that the number of molecules N contained in 1 cubic mm. of a gas at $0°$ and at atmospheric pressure is

$$N = \frac{1}{320 \times 7\cdot0}10^{20} = 4\cdot5 \times 10^{16}.$$

Now 1 cubic mm. of hydrogen weighs $0\cdot000090$ mg.; therefore an atom weighs [1]

$$\frac{0\cdot000090}{2N} = 1\cdot00 \times 10^{-21} \text{ mg.,}$$

and a molecule of any gas of mol. weight M has the weight expressed by the formula

$$y = M \times 10^{-21} \text{ mg.}$$

[1] [Taking $2\cdot8 \times 10^{16}$ as the most probable value for N (see below), the mass of the hydogen atom becomes $1\cdot6 \times 10^{-21}$ mg.]

Sirk[1] derived values for x from the refractive indices $\left(x = \dfrac{n^2 - 1}{n^2 + 2},\right.$ p. 312), and so made use of a wealth of experimental material for the calculation of a^3x^2. As n for gases is very little different from 1, we obtain as a close approximation

$$x = \frac{2}{3}(n - 1).$$

In this way the mean value of $\dfrac{4}{9}L^3(n - 1)^2$ for 32 different gases and vapours was found to be $3\cdot24.10^{-20}$; hence it follows that $N = 9\cdot65 . 10^{16}$.

These calculations were first given by van der Waals, though Loschmidt still earlier (1865) had tried to obtain an estimate of these values.

The colloidal molecule, for which M may be over 10,000, may weigh about 10^{-17} mg. If we dissolve 1 mg. of white of egg in a litre of water, there will be about 10^{11} molecules in each cubic mm.

The Electric Charge of an Ion.—1·008 mg. of hydrogen, when in the ion condition, carries 9·65 absolute units of electricity (p. 371), and therefore an atom has

$$\frac{9\cdot65 . 4\cdot5 . 10^{-5}}{1\cdot008N} = \frac{4\cdot307 . 10^{-4}}{N};$$

by making use of the more exact value for N obtained below, it follows that the charge on a hydrogen ion is 1.54×10^{-20}. To convert this into absolute electrostatic units we must multiply by $3 . 10^{10}$. This number in general represents the magnitude of the electric charge of a univalent ion or electron. The n-valent ions of course have an n-fold charge.

If a particular ion moves with a velocity of 1 $\dfrac{cm}{sec}$, then this represents a galvanic current of an intensity of $15\cdot4 \times 10^{-20}$ of an ampere. Now, by the aid of a very sensitive galvanometer, one can detect a current of about 10^{-11} of an ampere, i.e. what would correspond to the movement of about 100 millions of ions, with the velocity mentioned above.

Determination of the Absolute Charge of an Ion.—In the earlier editions of this book it was suggested that the magnitude of the charge of single ions might perhaps be determined, and hence the absolute magnitude of the molecule.

This hope has meanwhile been most completely realised in more than one way.

1. We saw on p. 403 that a gas ion can serve as the nucleus for cloud formation, and that with sufficient under-cooling all the gas ions act in this way.

[1] *Sitzungsber. d. Wiener Akad., Math.-nat. Klasse*, 117 [IIa], 1 (1908).

Now the mass of condensed water can be reckoned from the degree of under-cooling ; the size of the single drops may be determined from the rate at which they sink, so that the number of drops formed is known. But as the degree of ionisation produced, for example by means of Röntgen rays, is also known, we have a means of determining the amount of electricity contained in each drop, and this is identical with the charge of a single ion.

In this way Thomson found (*loc. cit.* p. 403) $11\cdot3 \times 10^{-21}$ absolute (magnetic) units as the charge of a single ion. It follows that the number of gas molecules in a cubic millimetre of a gas at $0°$ atmospheric pressure is $N = 3\cdot8 \times 10^{16}$. Thomson's experiments have been repeated by other English investigators, who obtained similar results. Thus Wilson[1] found $N = 4\cdot17 \times 10^{16}$, Millikan and Begeman[2] found $N = 3\cdot18 \times 10^{16}$.

[Recently Millikan[3] has repeated his measurements with various refinements, and obtained a value for N of $2\cdot78 \times 10^{16}$, the probable error being only about 2 per cent.]

2. A second method of determining directly the elementary quantity of electricity rests on the possibility of counting the number of a particles shot out by radium in a second, and then determining the total charge of these particles by electrical measurements. In this way the charge of a single a particle can be determined. The number of particles shot out in a second can be determined by different methods. One a particle produces a large number of ions in a gas, and each of these ions can, under certain experimental conditions (*e.g.*, when the gas, highly expanded, is in a very strong electric field) give rise to new ions by *collision*. In this way the action of a single a particle can be so magnified that its appearance can be directly detected by the deflection of an electrometer. In order to make use of this phenomenon to count the a particles, only an extremely small, but accurately known fraction of the total radiation is allowed to enter the ionisation vessel. The number of deflections of the (ballistic) electrometer is then counted, and thus the total number of a particles can be easily calculated (on the assumption that the radiation is the same in all directions).

Another method of determining the a particles is to observe the so-called scintillations which they excite on a screen of Sidot's blende —a phenomenon which was discovered by Crookes[4] and by Elster and Geitel. [5]

It is reasonable to assume that each a particle gives rise to one scintillation, so that by counting the latter, we can find the number of a particles.[6]

---

[1] *Phil. Mag.*, April 1903.   [2] *Phys. Rev.*, February 1908, p. 197.
[3] *Phil. Mag.*, February 1910, p. 209.   [4] *Proc. Roy. Soc.* **81.** 405 (1903).
[5] *Phys. Zeitschr.* **5.** 437 (1905).
[6] Rutherford *l.c.* ; further Regener, *Verh. d. Deutsch. phys. Ges.* **10.** 78 (1908).

The results of these two methods agree closely; one gramme of radium sends out $3\cdot4 \cdot 10^{10}$ α particles in a second.

The total charge on the α particles sent out by one gramme of radium was found by Rutherford and Geiger[1] to be $31\cdot5$ electrostatic units, so that the charge on one particle is $9\cdot3 . 10^{-10}$ units. The comparison of this number with the values obtained by other methods (see above) makes it appear highly probable that an α particle carries two elementary quantities of electricity, so that by this method we obtain $4\cdot65 . 10^{-10}$ for this fundamental number, and for N the value $2\cdot78 . 10^{16}$. Regener (*l.c.*) calculates provisionally from his experiments $N = 3\cdot1 . 10^{16}$.

3. Planck, from his electromagnetic theory of radiation[2] obtains $N = 2\cdot76 . 10^{16}$ by using the accurately determined empirical constants of some laws of radiation.

[4. Finally, Perrin[3] has arrived at a value for N from an investigation of the Brownian movement (p. 206). He assumes that the granules of a dilute uniform emulsion behave as the molecules of a perfect gas, and shows this assumption to be justified within the errors of observation by comparing the behaviour of granules of different emulsions which differ widely in size and mass. It follows from this hypothesis that the Brownian particles have the same mean kinetic energy as the molecules of a gas (p. 203 ff.), and also that the concentration of the particles decreases exponentially as a function of the height. In this way N may be determined by directly counting the number of particles present at different heights in the emulsion. A theory of Einstein makes possible another determination of N from an investigation of the activity of the movement. Perrin gives $3\cdot17 \times 10^{16}$ as the mean of a large number of determinations by these methods.]

The following values have thus been obtained by different methods for the number of molecules of an ideal gas in a cubic millimetre at $0°$ and under atmospheric pressure :—

Kinetic Theory	$N = 4\cdot5 . 10^{16}$
Method of Cloud formation . . .	$N = 2\cdot78 . 10^{16}$
Counting of α particles . . .	$N = 2\cdot78 . 10^{16}$
Theory of radiation	$N = 2\cdot76 . 10^{16}$
Brownian movement	$N = 3\cdot17 . 10^{16}$

The first value can only be considered approximate, as it is obtained by making certain simplifications (*e.g.* assuming spherical molecules, etc.); the agreement between the four other values is very good.

In any case we may regard the molecular dimensions as established with a remarkable degree of certainty, so that the atomistic conception begins to lose its hypothetical character.

[1] *Proc. Roy. Soc.* **81.** 161 (1908). *Physik. Zeitschr.* **10.** 1 (1909).

[2] *Vorlesungen über die Theorie der Wärmestrahlung,* Leipzig, 1906, p. 167.

[3] *Annales de chimie et de physique* [8], September 1909, English translation by F. Soddy. "Brownian Movement and Molecular Reality" (Taylor and Francis).

BOOK III

THE TRANSFORMATION OF MATTER
(THE DOCTRINE OF AFFINITY, I.)

CHAPTER I

THE LAW OF CHEMICAL MASS-ACTION

The Aim of the Doctrine of Affinity.—As the final goal of the doctrine of affinity, this problem is proposed, viz., to ascribe those forces which are efficient in the transformation of matter to well-investigated physical transformations. The question of the nature of the forces which come into play in the chemical union or decomposition of substances was agitated long before a scientific chemistry existed. As long ago as the time of the Grecian philosophers, the "love and hate" of the atoms were spoken of as the causes of the changes of matter; and regarding our knowledge of the nature of chemical forces, not much further advance has been made even at the present time. We retain anthropomorphic views like the ancients, changing the names only when we seek the cause of chemical changes in the changing *affinity* of the atoms.

To be sure, attempts to form definite conceptions [regarding these affinities] have never been wanting. All gradations of opinion are found, from the crude notion of a Borelli or a Lemery, who regarded the tendency of the atoms to unite firmly with each other as being due to their hook-shaped structure (and we employ the same view at present when we speak of "the linking of the atoms in the molecule"), to the well-conceived achievements of a Newton, a Bergman, or a Berthollet, who saw in the chemical process a phenomenon of attraction which was comparable with the fall of a stone to earth.

The idea that a deeper insight into the nature of the chemical forces could be gained by identifying them with the attractions of the different electricities was only transitory; for chemistry has completely emancipated herself, in spite of the authority of a Berzelius, from a theory which, instead of leading to further discoveries, was only suited to obscure the impartial estimation of the facts. It is not too much to say that there is no discovery of any physical interchange of bodies with each other which has not been used by some speculative brain in the explanation of the chemical forces also; but up to the present the results are not at all commensurate with the ingenuity displayed. It cannot be emphasised enough that we are as yet very far from reaching the goal, viz. the explanation of chemical decompositions by the play of well-defined and well-investigated physical forces.

In view of this undeniable fact, we must ask ourselves the question, whether this problem has been well chosen, and also whether it is not too premature. And, in fact, it appears that the strenuous endeavours made to reach the goal at present do not promise very much; and it seems as though the ladder, from which some one will pluck the ripe fruit, is not at present built firmly enough nor high enough.

Nowhere does a master mind show itself more clearly than in the wise restraint which imposes upon the investigator the choice of the mark to be aimed at; and nowhere is danger more imminent than when valuable ability for work is squandered in attacking useless problems—problems which offer difficulties which are almost insuperable at present, but which may perhaps be easily overcome in a short time by the use of results gained from sources which [previously] seemed entirely foreign to the subject.

The history of chemistry offers a striking example of this. As long as the alchemists attempted to convert the worthless metals into gold, their endeavours remained fruitless; scientific chemistry did not develop until it began to consider questions which had been previously regarded as insignificant.

The most immediate aim requires that we must deliberately ignore the question regarding the *nature* of the force which is instrumental in chemical decompositions, and must fix the eye upon *its mode of action*, and especially as regards its dependence upon the external conditions, such as the mass-ratio, the temperature, and the pressure. And here brilliant results have undoubtedly been obtained. Similarly the laws which control the pressure exerted by gases were *discovered* before they were *explained* by ascribing them to the collisions of the gas molecules. For, supposing that it had happened that some genius had gained an insight into the kinetic gas theory a little before the gas laws themselves were discovered, even then, as a matter of fact, the way leading to the kinetic conception of the gaseous state had to be levelled down by much painstaking endeavour.

We are as yet very far distant from having a clear conception of the course of a chemical combination, but we possess some fundamental laws which control it. The investigation of such laws should not be regarded as less worthy than the aim designated above; for, ultimately, that standpoint will receive vindicated recognition which recognises, *e.g.* the *experimental* discovery of the laws of gases as being on an equality with their *theoretical* establishment.

We may compare the present condition of the doctrine of affinity in many respects with that of theoretical astronomy. The latter, on the basis of Newton's law, attained a development which at that time was not reached by the other sciences. This law, according to which two mass-points attract each other directly as the product of their masses, and inversely as the square of their distance, merely describes the mode of action of attraction; it does not explain its nature, which is unexplained, even at present. The question which anticipated the important discovery of this law was not *why* does a stone fall to the earth, but *how* does it fall.

Similarly, a great result in chemical mechanics was obtained when the question was asked, not *why*, but *how*, do acids invert water solutions of cane-sugar. And although such a simple and universally efficient law as Newton's law has not been formulated as yet for the complexities of chemical phenomena,—where, in strong contrast to astronomy, the specialised nature of matter is expressed most clearly, —yet, nevertheless, theoretical chemistry does possess a number of universal natural laws, which make a formal description of the course of a chemical reaction possible, just as theoretical astronomy predicts the paths of the heavenly bodies.

The demonstration and application of these laws will form the second part of this description of theoretical chemistry.

The Condition of Chemical Equilibrium.—When we bring together a number of substances which are capable of chemical reaction,—and thus constitute *a chemical system*, as we will call it,—a reaction occurs which will terminate after the lapse of a sufficient interval of time; then we say that the system reaches a state of *chemical equilibrium*.

In general, the state of equilibrium is associated with definite conditions of temperature and pressure; and a change in these latter values implies a change in the state of equilibrium. Moreover, it requires great precaution before one can regard a system as actually having arrived at a state of equilibrium. For the observation that no material change can be observed, even after the lapse of quite a long time, is by no means always sufficient.

Thus, as many observations have shown, a mixture of hydrogen and oxygen may be preserved for years in sealed glass bulbs, without the formation of a noticeable amount of water. Yet, in spite of this, the two gases are by no means in equilibrium; in fact, we have every ground for the assumption that at ordinary temperatures, the reaction goes on spontaneously, but far too slowly to be recognised in such a lapse of time as is practically feasible; that the actual equilibrium would be reached after a practically, but not entirely, complete union of the gases to form water; and that the time required for the completion of this equilibrium, at ordinary temperatures, would be enormously long.

Reversible Reactions.—In what follows, we shall use the general equation

$$n_1A_1 + n_2A_2 + \ldots = n_1'A_1' + n_2'A_2' + \ldots$$

to denote that n_1 molecules of the chemically simple substance A_1, and n_2 molecules of the substance A_2, etc., react to form n_1' molecules of the substance A_1', and n_2' molecules of the substance A_2', etc. The substances A_1, A_2 . . ., A_1' A_2', . . ., may be present in any number and quantity, and may exist in any of the states of aggregation. We say that the substances present, in certain proportions, in reference to the preceding reaction are in chemical equilibrium when they can remain together for an indefinitely long time in these same proportions, without the occurrence of a decomposition, in the sense of the preceding equation, either in one direction or the other.

We call a reaction which progresses in the sense of the preceding scheme, *reversible* when, in the sense of the reaction equation, it goes on from left to right, with any arbitrary excess of some (not all) of the reaction products A_1', A_2', etc., if we start out with any arbitrary quantity of the substances A_1, A_2, etc.; and also if the reaction occurs spontaneously, in the opposite sense, with some arbitrary excess of the reaction products A_1, A_2, etc., if we start out with arbitrary quantities of A_1', A_2'. etc.; so the final state of equilibrium reached will be the same in both cases if we start out with equivalent quantities.

An excellent illustration of a reversible reaction is the production of an ester, which takes place according to the equation

$$C_2H_5OH + CH_3CO_2H \underset{\longleftarrow}{\overset{\longrightarrow}{}} CH_3.CO_2C_2H_5 + H_2O$$

Alcohol   Acetic acid   Ethyl acetate   Water

One molecule of alcohol and one molecule of acetic acid react to form one molecule of the ester (ethyl acetate in this case) and one molecule of water, or the reverse. If we bring together alcohol and acetic acid, a reaction occurs, in the sense of the equation from left to right. On the other hand, if we mix a molecule of the ester with a molecule of water, a reaction occurs in the sense of the equation from right to left. In neither case are all the reacting components used up, but the reaction stops when such a condition of equilibrium is established as shall allow some of all four of the reacting components to exist beside each other.

If we start out with equivalent quantities, *i.e.* with those proportions which are convertible into each other, in the sense of the reaction equation, then in both cases we arrive at the same [final] condition of equilibrium. Thus, to select the simplest case, if we mix 1 g.-mol. of alcohol (46 g.) with 1 g.-mol. of acetic acid (60 g.); or if we mix 1 g.-mol. of ethyl acetate (88 g.) with 1 g.-mol. of water (18 g.); then in both cases, as shown by experience, the final composition of the reaction mixture is

$\frac{1}{3}$ mol. alcohol + $\frac{1}{3}$ mol. acetic acid + $\frac{2}{3}$ mol. ester + $\frac{2}{3}$ mol. water.

We call a chemical system *homogeneous* when it has the same physical and chemical nature at every point; and when this is not the case, we call it *heterogeneous*. Thus a system consisting of a gas mixture or of a solution, *e.g.* we call *homogeneous*; but if solid substances are also present, or if the liquid is separated into different layers, then the system is *heterogeneous*.

The opinion was formerly entertained that " reversible actions " were exceptional; or, at least, that reactions should be divided into two classes, the *reversible* and the *non-reversible*. But such a sharp distinction as this does not exist; and, moreover, there can be no doubt that by suitable adjustment of the conditions of the experiment, it would be possible to make a reaction take place, now in one direction, now in the opposite—that is, *in principle every action is reversible*.

If in the following considerations we limit ourselves expressly to reversible reactions, then we place a restriction upon ourselves only in so far that we assume that the conditions for the reversibility of the reaction in question have been already found. Thus, if one reaction is complete, from a practical standpoint, as *e.g.* the union of oxygen and hydrogen to form water, we are not justified, on this basis, in laying down an essential distinction between this and the formation of an ester, where the equivalent proportions of the acid and alcohol react only to $\frac{2}{3}$ of the possible extent. The distinction is only a quantitative one; for hydrogen and oxygen, even in equivalent proportions, are surely unable to unite with each other in absolute completeness; but here also the reaction doubtless comes to a pause before the possible limit of the change is reached, although the quantity of the two gases which remain uncombined in equilibrium with each other at ordinary temperatures is too insignificant to be detected.

We will first develop the law of mass-action for reversible reactions which take place in a *homogeneous* system; then there will be no difficulty in developing it later for heterogeneous systems.

According to the usage of van't Hoff, we will introduce into the reaction equation, in place of the sign of equality, two parallel arrows pointing in opposite directions, thus ($\rightleftarrows$), to denote that we are dealing with a reversible reaction.

The law of mass - action will instruct us, not only about the *variation* of equilibrium in a chemical system, with the relative proportions of the reacting components, but also concerning the *velocity* with which this equilibrium is attained. It is the fundamental law of *chemical statics* as well as of *chemical kinetics*.

On the other hand, the law of mass-action has nothing to say regarding the influence of temperature ; the law which deals with this will be discussed in Book IV. (Transformation of Energy).

The Kinetic Development of the Law of Mass-Action.—

We will assume that the molecular species $A_1, A_2 \ldots A_1', A_2' \ldots$ have been brought together in a *homogeneous system*, and react on each other, according to the scheme

$$A_1 + A_2 + \ldots \underset{\longleftarrow}{\overset{\longrightarrow}{\rule{0pt}{1.2em}}} A_1' + A_2' + \ldots .$$

If we compare this with the general equation on p. 441, we shall notice that here we have the simple case that $n_1, n_2 \ldots n_1', n_2' \ldots$ are all equal to 1, *i.e. only one molecule* of each substance takes part in the reaction.

The reacting substances may be either gaseous, or may form a liquid mixture, or finally may be dissolved in any selected solvent. The following considerations on the course of the reaction apply to each case.

In order that a decomposition may occur in the direction from left to right, in the sense of the reaction equation, it is obviously necessary that the molecules $A_1, A_2 \ldots$ shall *collectively* collide at one point ; for otherwise a reaction would be impossible, because side reactions must be at first excluded. Such a collision as this need not of course lead at once to a rearrangement of the atoms in those molecules, as the preceding reaction requires. Rather must this collision take place at a time when the atoms in each molecule are in the requisite state of loose union which must necessarily precede the rearrangement. The result is, that of a large number of collisions, there will be only a definite percentage (always the same under identical external conditions), which will cause a rearrangement from left to right in the sense of the equation. But this rearrangement will be greater the more frequent the collisions ; and *therefore a direct ratio must exist between these two magnitudes*. Now the number of these collisions must obviously be proportional to each of the concentrations of the bodies $A_1, A_2 \ldots$, *i.e.* collectively it must be proportional *to the product of these concentrations*. Therefore the velocity v of the change from left to right, in the sense of the reaction equation, is

$$v = kc_1c_2 \ldots,$$

where $c_1, c_2 \ldots$ denote respectively the spatial concentration, *i.e.* the number of g.-mol. of the substances $A_1, A_2 \ldots$ contained in a litre, and where k is a constant for the given temperature, and may be called the *velocity coefficient*.

Exactly the same considerations apply to the molecules A_1', A_2' . . .; here also the rate of change from right to left, in the sense of the reaction equation, will increase with the number of collisions of all these molecules at one point; and the latter, again, will be proportional to the product of their spatial concentrations. If we denote the corresponding proportional factor [velocity coefficient] by k', then the velocity v', with which the change occurs from right to left, in the sense of the reaction equation, will be

$$v' = k'c_1'c_2' \ . \ . \ .;$$

where again c_1', c_2' . . . denote the number of g.-mol. of each of the substances A_1', A_2' respectively, contained in 1 litre.

These spatial concentrations are commonly called *the active masses of the reacting components*. The reaction velocity in the sense of the reaction equation, from left to right, or the reverse, is thus proportional to the product of the active masses of the components on the left side, or on the right side, respectively.

We cannot observe either v or v' alone. The tracing out of the course of a reaction by measurement gives us always the *difference* between these values. For the *total* reaction velocity, which is actually observed, is made up of the difference between the two *partial* reaction velocities noted above ; because the change actually observed, at every moment of time, is equal to the change in one direction, minus the change in the opposite direction, during this moment of time.

Therefore, when the condition of equilibrium has been reached, we are not to conclude that no further change takes place ; but we should rather assume merely that the change, in the sense of the reaction equation, from left to right, is exactly compensated by the change, in the sense of the reaction equation, from right to left ; and, therefore, the *total change* observed is equal to zero, *i.e.* the system is in equilibrium. Hence we have the relation

$$v - v' = 0,$$

and, therefore,

$$kc_1c_2 \ . \ . \ . = k'c_1'c_2' \ . \ . \ .,$$

which is the fundamental law of chemical statics.

The view that, at equilibrium, there is no absolute indifference between the reacting substances, but rather that the reacting ingredients persist unchanged in their mutual action, and that only the total [apparent] change becomes zero, is of fundamental importance for our conception of changes of matter. It is ordinarily expressed by the statement that in this and in all analogous cases the equilibrium is not a static but a *dynamic* one.

This view was derived as an immediate conclusion from the kinetic-molecular mode of explanation, and it has been employed with especial success in the development of the kinetic gas theory.

Thus the equilibrium between water and water vapour, according to Clausius, is not to be conceived of as though there occurred neither the evaporation of liquid water nor the condensation of gaseous water vapour ; but rather, when saturated water vapour is in contact with water, both of these processes continue uninterruptedly in equilibrium, *i.e.* through a definite area of the surface of the liquid water, in any interval of time, there are the same number of molecules going in the one direction as in the other (see also p. 213).

This view was first applied to chemical changes by Williamson (1851), and later was more fully developed by Guldberg and Waage, Pfaundler, and others.

The progress of the reaction, *i.e.* the velocity with which the chemical change strives to reach the condition of equilibrium at any moment, is expressed by the following equation, viz.

$$V = v - v' = kc_1c_2 \ldots - k'c_1'c_2' \ldots$$

This *is the fundamental law of chemical kinetics.*

The formula for the equilibrium is, of course, only a special case of those already developed; it is obtained by making the total velocity equal to zero ; in the same way, in analytical mechanics, from a specialisation of the general equations of motion, one obtains at once the conditions of equilibrium.

There is no difficulty in generalising the preceding equations, for the reaction which shall occur, according to the scheme,

$$n_1A_1 + n_2A_2 + \ldots = n_1'A_1' + n_2'A_2' + \ldots,$$

where n_1, n_2 . . . n_1', n_2' denote the number of molecules with which each particular substance takes part in the reaction ; these numbers (n_1, n_2 . . . n_1', n_2') are necessarily *whole* numbers, and, as a rule, they are small, rarely being larger than three.

Here also we must put v and v' proportional to the number of collisions of all the kinds of molecules necessary to the reaction ; we must remember however that n_1 molecules A_1, n_2 molecules A_2, and so on, must collide *simultaneously* in order that the reaction may take place from left to right, and similarly n_1' molecules A_1', n_2' molecules A_2', and so on, in order that the reverse reaction may be possible.

If we consider the path of a single molecule arbitrarily chosen for a fixed time, the number of its collisions with other similar molecules will be proportional to c, the concentration of the kind of molecule in question ; the number of collisions between two similar molecules of a given kind during the same time is therefore c-times as many, that is, the number of collisions between two similar molecules is proportional to the square of the concentration c, and in general it follows that the number of collisions between n similar molecules of one kind must be considered proportional to c^n.

The number of collisions of n_1 molecules A_1, n_2 molecules A_2, is therefore proportional to $c_1^{n_1} c_2^{n_2} \ldots$, and for the velocity of reaction which is proportional to that number we have

$$v = k c_1^{n_1} c_2^{n_2} \ldots,$$

and similarly the velocity of the reverse reaction is

$$v' = k' c_1'^{n_1'} c_2'^{n_2'} \ldots ;$$

the total velocity of reaction being again the difference between the partial velocities

$$V = v - v' = k c_1^{n_1} c_2^{n_2} \ldots - k' c_1'^{n_1'} c_2'^{n_2'} \ldots,$$

a formula which represents the most general application of the law of mass-action of *homogeneous systems*. If V is equal to 0, the formula

$$\frac{c_1'^{n_1'} \cdot c_2'^{n_2'} \ldots}{c_1^{n_1} \cdot c_2^{n_2} \ldots} = \frac{k}{k'} = K$$

for the state of equilibrium is arrived at. K is called the "equilibrium constant."

It should be emphasised that the kinetic proof,[1] given above, of the law of chemical mass-action, can lay no claim to be in the rank of the laws which are proven with universal completeness ; but it can only be considered as a means of making this law appear probable. Thermodynamics, in the last book, will furnish us a stricter theoretical proof ; this will find its demonstration in an abundance of facts, part of which are unintelligible without it, and part of which were furnished by means of the universal laws [of thermodynamics].

The History of the Law of Mass-Action.—The first theory of the action of chemical forces is that which was developed by the Swedish chemist, Bergman, in the year 1775. The essential principle of this may be stated in the following law, viz. :—

The magnitude of chemical affinity may be expressed by a definite number ; if the affinity of the substance A *is greater for the substance* B *than for the· substance* C, *then the latter* (C) *will be completely expelled by* B *from its compound with* A, *in the sense of the equation*

$$AC + B = AB + C.$$

This theory fails entirely to take account of the influence of the *relative masses* of the reacting substances ; and had therefore to be given up as soon as this influence was recognised.

An attempt to consider this factor was made by Berthollet (1801), who introduced into the science the conception of chemical equilibrium. The views of this French chemist may be summed up in the following law :—

Different substances have different affinities for each other ; these exhibit their value only when they are in immediate contact with each other. The

---

[1] A more stringent proof will be found in Boltzmann, *Wied. Ann.* **22.** 68 (1884).

condition of equilibrium depends not only upon the chemical affinity, but also essentially upon the relative masses of the reacting substances.

The genuine kernel of Berthollet's idea is to-day the guiding principle of the doctrine of affinity. This holds good, especially for the conception regarding many reactions which, in the sense of Bergman's notion, proceed to a completion, *i.e.* until the reacting substances are all used up; but only for this reason, viz., that one or more of the products of the reaction either crystallise out or evaporate off from the reaction mixture, and hence the inverse reaction becomes impossible.

Two Norwegian investigators, Guldberg and Waage, clinging to Berthollet's idea, succeeded in formulating the influence of the reacting masses in a simple law, viz. the law of chemical mass-action given above. The results of their theoretical and experimental studies were given in a book [1] which appeared at Christiania in 1867, and which was entitled *Études sur les affinités chimiques*. A new epoch of theoretical chemistry dates from the appearance of this book.

Already, before this, formulæ to describe the progress of certain chemical reactions, which must be regarded as applications of the law of mass-action, had been described by Wilhelmy (1850) and by Harcourt and Esson (1856). The service of Guldberg and Waage is still undiminished, since they grasped the law in its full significance and applied it logically in all directions.

The treatise of the two Scandinavian investigators remained quite unknown; and so it happened that Jellet (1873), and van't Hoff (1877), and others independently developed the same law.

The *thermodynamic basis* of the law of mass-action is due to Horstmann, Gibbs, and van't Hoff; it will be dealt with more closely in Book IV.

---

[1] Given in abstract, *Jour. prakt. Chem.* [2], **19.** 69 (1879). Translated into German with notes by Abegg, Ostwald's *Klassiker*, No. 104.

CHAPTER II

Equilibrium between Gases.—Corresponding to the different states of aggregation, the particular system considered as being in equilibrium, which must be both physically and chemically homogeneous in all its parts, may be either gaseous, liquid, or solid. In accordance with the old fundamental law: *corpora non agunt nisi fluida*, the last species of homogeneous systems [*i.e.* the solids], in particular would be excluded from the foregoing consideration. But some facts, though they are but few, lead us not exactly to a repudiation of this law, but rather to limit its universal availability. Thus, for the sake of completeness, a short notice, at all events, must be given to the equilibrium, which is exhibited by homogeneous mixtures existing in the solid state.

The conception of "active-mass" has for gaseous systems a very simple and obvious meaning. By the "active-mass" of a substance (a molecular species), we mean the number of mols which are present in 1 litre. But now the partial pressure under which a gas stands in a gas mixture corresponds simply to this value; because, according to Avogadro's law, the pressure of a gas depends only upon the number of molecules which it contains in unit volume. Thus in the equation on p. 446, instead of the concentrations, we may introduce the respective partial pressures of the different molecular species, as they participate in the reaction.

Thus, if a reaction occurs in a gaseous system, in the sense of the equation,

$$n_1 A_1 + n_2 A_2 + \ldots \underset{\longleftarrow}{\overset{\longrightarrow}{}} n_1' A_1' + n_2' A_2' + \ldots,$$

and if the partial pressures of the molecular species A_1, A_2, etc., are respectively p_1, p_2, etc., and for the molecular species A_1', A_2', etc., p_1', p_2', etc., then the following relation holds good for the condition of equilibrium:

$$\frac{p_1'^{n_1'} p_2'^{n_2'} \ldots}{p_1^{n_1} p_2^{n_2} \ldots} = K'.$$

The Formation of Hydrogen Iodide.—The preceding formula

448

will be first applied to the formation of hydrogen iodide from hydrogen and iodine vapour; it occurs in the sense of the equation

$$H_2 + I_2 = 2HI.$$

This equation was first investigated by Hautefeuille,[1] but afterwards, and very thoroughly, by Lemoine.[2] The latter allowed a weighed quantity of iodine to act upon a measured volume of hydrogen in a sealed bulb. After equilibrium had been reached, the contents of the bulb were introduced into a eudiometer, and the residual hydrogen was measured, while the hydrogen iodide which had been produced was absorbed by the water. At ordinary temperatures, the reaction progresses so very slowly that the two substances seem absolutely indifferent towards each other; and they can, accordingly, be separated from each other (e.g. by absorption, as in Lemoine's work) without any marked displacement of equilibrium taking place during the separation.

But with rise of temperature—and this is quite a universal phenomenon—the velocity of the reaction increases enormously. At 265° (oil-bath) the time required to bring about the state of equilibrium was counted in months; at 350° (boiling mercury) in days; at 440° (boiling sulphur) in hours.

Moreover, with increasing pressure the velocity of the reaction increased, which is in perfect harmony with kinetic considerations.

Special researches proved that the final condition of equilibrium reached was the same, whether one started with a mixture of hydrogen and iodine vapour, or with the corresponding quantities of hydrogen iodide with an excess of one of the reaction products; thus the final condition could be reached either by a change from left to right, in the sense of the reaction equation, or in the inverse direction.

If we denote the partial pressure of the hydrogen iodide by p, and that of the hydrogen and of the iodine respectively by p_1 and by p_2, then at equilibrium we have

$$\frac{p_1 p_2}{p^2} = K'.$$

The total pressure of the gas mixture, according to Dalton's law, is of course

$$P = p + p_1 + p_2.$$

We will first investigate the way in which the condition of equilibrium changes with the external pressure. If we compress the reaction mixture to the nth part, then the particular partial pressures will rise to n-fold their [original] value. But now we have

$$\frac{n p_1 n p_2}{n^2 p^2} = \frac{p_1 p_2}{p^2} = K,$$

i.e. the new pressure values meet the requirements of the equilibrium

[1] C.R. **64.** 608 (1867).   [2] Ann. chim. phys. [5], **12.** 145 (1877).

formula, and therefore there is no change in the relative quantities resulting from changes in the pressure.

Thus the condition of equilibrium is independent of the external pressure. This result is general *if there is no change in the number of molecules caused by the reaction.*

Lemoine found for the values of the total pressure P, as given below, the following corresponding values of the decomposition co-efficient x (*i.e.* the quantity of the free hydrogen divided by the quantity of the total hydrogen). In all of these researches the glass bulb was filled at first with hydrogen iodide.

P.	x.	
4·5 Atm.	0·24	
2·3 ,,	0·225	
1·0 ,,	0·27	t = 440°
0·5 ,,	0·25	
0·2 ,,	0·29	

The above numbers hardly bring out the influence of pressure on the degree of decomposition of hydriodic acid, as the numbers show irregular variations. Similarly, the reduction of the other researches of Lemoine (see p. 350 of the first edition of this book) leaves no doubt that the results are affected by some source of error.

In fact, M. Bodenstein,[1] who repeated the investigations of Lemoine, found that the glass walls absorb considerable quantities of hydriodic acid, and that consequently less of this gas takes part in the equilibrium than was calculated in Lemoine's experimental arrangement from the amount of free hydrogen; Bodenstein, however, in arriving at the equilibrium, determined besides. the volume of free hydrogen, the quantities of free iodine and free hydriodic acid separately by titration; he was thus able to prove exactly that the decomposition of hydriodic acid is independent of the pressure, and to arrive at a precise application of the law of mass action of this case.

If we express, as above, the degree of decomposition of the pure hydriodic acid by x, we have

$$p = P(1 - x), \quad p_1 = p_2 = \frac{P}{2}x,$$

and therefore

$$\frac{x^2}{4(1 - x)^2} = \frac{p_1 p_2}{p^2} = K'.$$

If in a given volume a mols of iodine and b mols of hydrogen react, and 2γ is the number of mols of hydriodic acid formed, there

[1] *Zeitschr. phys. Chem.* **22.** 1 (1897).

remains $a - \gamma$ mols of free iodine, and $b - \gamma$ mols of free hydrogen, so that

$$p = P\frac{2\gamma}{a+b}, \quad p_1 = P\frac{a-\gamma}{a+b}, \quad p_2 = P\frac{b-\gamma}{a+b},$$

and consequently, $\quad \dfrac{(a-\gamma)(b-\gamma)}{4\gamma^2} = K',$

and this solved for γ gives [1]

$$\gamma = \frac{a+b}{2(1-4K')} - \sqrt{\frac{(a+b)^2}{4(1-4K')^2} - \frac{ab}{1-4K'}}.$$

The following tables show the good agreement between calculation and observation; a and b here stand for the number of cubic centimetres of gaseous iodine and hydrogen, reduced to $0°$ and 760 mm. pressure, that were contained in the glass bulb of about 13 cubic centimetres volume; γ is the amount of hydriodic acid formed expressed in the same manner. The quantities directly determined as mentioned above were $a - \gamma$, $b - \gamma$, and γ.

HEATED IN SULPHUR VAPOUR : $x = 0\cdot2198$, $K' = 0\cdot01984$

a.	b.	2γ.		Difference.
		Obs.	Cal.	
2·94	8·10	5·64	5·66	+ 0·02
5·30	7·94	9·49	9·52	+ 0·03
9·27	8·07	13·47	13·34	− 0·13
14·44	8·12	14·93	14·82	− 0·11
27·53	8·02	15·54	15·40	− 0·14
33·10	7·89	15·40	15·12	− 0·28

HEATED IN MERCURY VAPOUR : $x = 0\cdot1946$, $K' = 0\cdot01494$

a.	b.	2γ.		Difference.
		Obs.	Cal.	
2·59	6·63	4·98	5·02	+ 0·04
5·71	6·22	9·55	9·60	+ 0·05
10·40	6·41	11·88	11·68	− 0·20
26·22	6·41	12·54	12·34	− 0·20
23·81	6·21	12·17	11·98	− 0·19
22·29	6·51	12·71	12·68	− 0·03

[1] In solving quadratic equations there can be no doubt as to whether to give the positive or negative sign to the root ; only one solution gives a physically possible result. In the above case, for example, the positive sign would yield for γ values higher than a and b, which of course is nonsense.

The above tables certainly give the most exact confirmation of the law of mass-action for homogeneous gaseous systems that has so far been arrived at.

The Dissociation Phenomena of Gases.—A class of reactions which deserves especial consideration, because of the simplicity and the frequency of their occurrence, is found in the so-called *phenomena of dissociation.* These are distinguished by the fact that, in the general equation of reaction, the substances standing on one side are reduced to a single molecule, and the change proceeds according to the scheme

$$A = n_1' A_1' + n_2' A_2' + \ \ldots \ ;$$

here A is the [original] molecular species advancing to the state of dissociation, and A_1', A_2' . . . are the [corresponding] dissociation products. If p denotes the partial pressure of the former, and p_1', p_2' . . . those of the latter respectively, then, according to what has preceded, the relation for the condition of equilibrium is

$$\frac{p_1'^{n_1'} p_2'^{n_2'} \cdot \cdot \cdot}{p} = K'.$$

K' is called the *dissociation constant.*

The number of molecules in the system grows with increasing dissociation. Inasmuch as we have an easy and exact method of learning this [*i.e.* the relative number of molecules], by means of the vapour density determination, there is, therefore, no difficulty here in investigating the condition of equilibrium.

For a simple case, we will consider a gas which dissociates into two new molecules, which may be identical, as in the dissociation of nitrogen dioxide,

$$N_2O_4 \rightleftarrows NO_2 + NO_2 \ ;$$

or different, as in the case of the dissociation of phosphorus pentachloride into chlorine and phosphorus trichloride,

$$PCl_5 \rightleftarrows PCl_3 + Cl_2.$$

Let δ be the density of the undecomposed gas, as calculated from its molecular weight; at complete dissociation the number of molecules will be doubled, and the vapour density therefore will amount to $\delta/2$. Now, according to p. 349,

$$1 + a = \frac{\delta}{\Delta}, \quad \text{and } a = \frac{\delta - \Delta}{\Delta}.$$

The total pressure P, at which Δ is measured, is made up of the pressures of the undecomposed molecules, and of the products of dissociation; if we denote the former by p, and the latter by p', then, according to Dalton's law, we shall have

$$P = p + p'.$$

Now, since the ratio of the number of the undecomposed molecules to the number of the dissociated ones is as $1 - a$ to $2a$, therefore we obtain

$$p = P\frac{1 - a}{1 + a} = P\left[2\frac{\Delta}{\delta} - 1\right]$$

$$p' = P\frac{2a}{1 + a} = 2P\left[1 - \frac{\Delta}{\delta}\right].$$

Now the law of mass-action gives us the relation

$$p'^2 = K'p,$$

where K' denotes the constant of dissociation; then by the substitution of the expressions obtained for the partial pressures, we obtain as the equation of the *isotherm of dissociation*

$$\frac{4[\delta - \Delta]^2 P}{[2\Delta - \delta]\delta} = K' \quad . \qquad . \qquad . \qquad . \qquad (1)$$

from which we obtain

$$\Delta = \delta + \frac{K''}{P} - \frac{K''}{P}\sqrt{1 + \frac{\delta P}{K'}} \quad . \qquad . \qquad . \qquad (2)$$

where

$$K'' = \frac{K'\delta}{4};$$

that is, the vapour density of a gas existing in a state of dissociation (at constant temperature) changes with the pressure; at very small pressures, it converges towards the lower limit of the vapour density; at very high pressures, it converges towards the upper limit of the vapour density.

The Dissociation of Nitrogen Dioxide.—The vapour density of nitrogen dioxide has been measured by E. and L. Natanson,[1] and has also been calculated according to the preceding formula. Although there are small deviations between the vapour densities required by the theory and those found experimentally, yet on the whole the results are to be regarded as a satisfactory verification of the theory. This is shown in the following table :—

$$t = 49 \cdot 7°.$$

P.	$\frac{K''}{4}$.	Δ Obs.	Δ Calc.	γ.
0 mm.	...	...	1·590	1·000
26·80 ,,	106	1·663	1·670	0·930
93·75 ,,	112	1·788	1·783	0·789
182·69 ,,	124	1·894	1·906	0·690
261·37 ,,	130	1·963	1·984	0·630
497·75 ,,	121	2·144	2·148	0·493

[1] *Wied. Ann.* **24.** 454 (1885); **27.** 606 (1886).

At a temperature of 49·7° and a pressure 497·75 mm., of 1000 molecules of N_2O_4, 493, *i.e.* about one-half, are dissociated. At the same pressure, but with increasing temperature, the dissociated fraction becomes greater, a phenomenon observed almost invariably in gaseous dissociation. The dissociation constant K increases with the temperature.

The quantity K'' in the second column of the above table is derived from the former equation (1)

$$K'' = \frac{K'\delta}{4} = \frac{(\delta - \Delta)^2 P}{2\Delta - \delta},$$

and should be constant according to theory; it shows large but irregular variations due to small errors of observations, especially when Δ is not very different from δ or $\frac{\delta}{2}$. If we take the mean

$$K'' = 119 \times 4 = 476$$

and recalculate Δ from equation (2) of the previous section, we arrive at the fourth column. The agreement with the observed values of the vapour density is within the error of observation, and shows that the conclusions of the theory are thoroughly satisfied.

As already referred to on p. 350, the colour of nitrogen dioxide increases with increasing dissociation, because the molecules of NO_2 are reddish-brown, while those of N_2O_4 are colourless.

At about 500° the gas begins to decolourise again in consequence of a decomposition into oxygen and nitric oxide, thus

$$2NO_2 = 2NO + O_2.$$

The following vapour densities were measured by Richardson,[1] by the methods of Dumas and of others :—

Temp.	Pressure.	Δ.	γ.
130°	718·5	1·600	...
184°	754·6	1·551	0·050
279°	737·2	1·493	0·130
494°	742·5	1·240	0·565
620°	760·0	1·060	1·000

At 620°, under ordinary pressure, the decomposition is complete. The fraction a of the decomposed molecules may here be calculated from the equation

$$a = 2\frac{1·590 - \Delta}{\Delta}.$$

The Influence of Indifferent Gases.—Experience has shown in a large number of cases that *the condition of dissociation of a gas is not*

---

[1] *Journ. Chem. Soc.* **51.** 397 (1887).

changed when another indifferent kind of gas (i.e. *a gas which does not react chemically*) *is introduced at constant volume.* This is seen to be in perfect harmony with the equation of the isotherm of dissociation, if one considers that, according to Dalton's law, the presence of a foreign kind of gas does not influence the partial pressures of the reacting ingredients.

This law is, moreover, one of extraordinary importance, and one which throws much light on the general view. Later it will be thoroughly proved from thermodynamic principles.

Of course it is entirely a different case when the mixing with the indifferent gas is attended with an *increase of volume*, the latter acting then as a diluting agent. Then the dissociation increases with the increase of volume, independently of the nature of the kind of gas which is added. If one studies a gas which exists in a state of dissociation by the method of the displacement of air (p. 251), the dissociation is found to increase the more the evaporating substance is diluted with the indifferent gas; and, therefore, results are obtained which depend upon the mutual diffusion, *i.e.* the values of the vapour densities are very irregular. It is erroneous and misleading to speak of the " *dissociating influence* " of other gases.

The Influence of an Excess of the Dissociation Products.— The theory allows us to anticipate the influence of the addition of one of the dissociation products. Thus, for example, let a gas, which gives rise to two different kinds of molecules on decomposition, be brought into equilibrium with its dissociation products; and between the partial pressure p of the undissociated molecules, and that of the dissociation products, which may be p' for both, let there exist the relation

$$p'^2 = Kp.$$

Now, let an amount of one of the dissociation products corresponding to a partial pressure of p_0 be added in excess, and let the increase which p experiences be π. Then the partial pressure of the other decomposition product will sink to $(p' - \pi)$, and the total pressure of the first decomposition product will amount to $p_0 + p' - \pi$. The calculation of π is obtained by the law of mass-action, from the equation

$$(p' - \pi)(p_0 + p' - \pi) = K(p + \pi).$$

By comparing this equation with the preceding formula, it will be found that π must always have a positive value. That is, *admixture of one of the decomposition products, at constant volume, tends to diminish the degree of dissociation.* This is a very important phenomenon. We shall make repeated application of this rule.

Moreover, research verifies this conclusion. The dissociation of phosphorus pentachloride diminishes when phosphorus trichloride is added in excess.[1]   The determination of the vapour density of ammonium chloride by the method of the displacement of air, gives higher values when ammonia or hydrochloric is used as the packing gas [2] [instead of air or some indifferent gas].   We will consider later several ways in which this law is indirectly verified.

If the admixture of the dissociation product occurs with increase of volume, then it also acts as a *diluting agent*, and hence it occasions an *increase* of dissociation.   Therefore, according to the special conditions, on the whole, there may result an increase or a decrease of the dissociation.   Thus, *e.g.* if any selected volume of gaseous phosphorus pentachloride is mixed with another selected volume of chlorine, or of phosphorus trichloride, so that the resulting mixture occupies a volume which is equal to the sum of two volumes, then, as can be easily shown, *the condition of dissociation remains unchanged, if the pressure of the added chlorine is exactly as great as its partial pressure in the pentachloride.*

The Frequency of Dissociation Phenomena.—Dissociation

phenomena are much more common than was formerly supposed to be the case; and no doubt can be entertained that, under suitable conditions of temperature and pressure, not only all chemical compounds, but also all poly-atomic molecules would be reduced to a state of decomposition more or less considerable.   Thus, the diatomic molecule of iodine, at high temperature and low pressure, decomposes into its two atoms, and a similar thing would doubtless happen in the case of other diatomic gases, like oxygen, nitrogen, etc., although no such decomposition could be established at $1700°$, and at atmospheric pressure.[3]

Sulphur, the vapour density of which has been investigated by H. Biltz,[4] and Biltz and Preuner,[5] at temperatures varying from $468\text{-}606°$, behaves exceptionally ; the vapour density falls with decrease in the temperature and only gives values agreeing with the formula S_2 at high temperatures.   This may apparently be explained by the assumption of molecules S_8 formed by vaporisation of sulphur which partially decompose according to the equation

$$S_8 \rightleftarrows 2S_4,$$

and that the S_4 molecules simultaneously decompose according to the equation

$$S_4 \rightleftarrows 2S_2,$$

therefore the sulphur vapour consists of three kinds of molecules S_8, S_4, S_2, the last of which gains at the expense of the former on decrease

---

[1] Wurtz, *C.R.* **76.** 60 (1873).
[2] Neuberg, *Ber. deutsch. chem. Ges.* **24.** 2543 (1891).
[3] C. Langer and V. Meyer, *Pyrochem. Unters.*, Brunswick (Braunschweig), 1885.
[4] *Zeitschr. phys. Chem.* **2.** 920 (1888).   [5] *Ibid.* **39.** 323 (1902).

of pressure or increase of temperature. The equation of the dissociation isotherm of sulphur vapour is consequently given by the formula

$$K_1 p_1 = p_2^2, \quad \text{and} \quad K_2 p_2 = p_3^2,$$

where p_1, p_2, p_3 show the partial pressures of the three kinds of molecules, K_1 and K_2 the dissociation constant of the two reactions. Sulphur is accordingly an example of "*dissociation in two stages.*" The present author has found by means of the apparatus described on p. 255 that at $1900\text{-}2000°$ the S_2 molecules are broken up into atoms to the extent of about 45%.

We shall return in the fourth book to the further discussion of methods and results in the dissociation of, and chemical equilibrium in, gases.

Equilibrium in Homogeneous Liquid Systems—Esterification.

—The dependence of the equilibrium upon the relative quantities of the reacting substances is the same with liquid systems as with gaseous ones; only here we do not have to take account of the partial pressure, but rather of the *concentration* of the reacting substances; and by this is meant the number of mols contained in 1 litre.

The number of special cases which have been investigated here is very large. This is to be explained by the following reasons; firstly, the study of the chemical equilibrium of a liquid system is much easier for the experimenter in many ways than the study of a gaseous system; and secondly, the decompositions which occur in liquid systems are very important, both in the usage of the laboratory, and also in the economy of nature.

We begin with esterification, a reaction to which reference has already been made (p. 441); the thorough study of this by Berthelot and Péan de St. Gilles[1] has had great influence in defining the conception of chemical equilibrium.

If one mixes any organic acid, as acetic acid, with an alcohol, as ethyl alcohol, there is formed water, and also the corresponding ester; the latter results from the combination of the positive component of the alcohol with the negative component of the acid; thus—

$$CH_3COOH + C_2H_5OH = CH_3COOC_2H_5 + H_2O$$

Acetic acid   Alcohol   Ethyl acetate   Water.

This reaction, which is comparable with the neutralisation of an acid by a base, progresses very slowly at ordinary temperatures; several days elapse before the state of equilibrium is approximately established, and the reaction comes to a standstill. If this liquid system is heated in a sealed glass tube to $150°$, the state of equilibrium is reached after a few hours. The reaction never advances

[1] *Ann. chim. phys.* **65.** and **66.** (1862), and **68.** (1863).

to a completion, *i.e.* until all of the [original] reacting substances are consumed, but each of the four reacting substances is present at equilibrium.

It can be easily ascertained how far the reaction has proceeded at any moment, by titrating the acetic acid which is present, or which has been produced; on account of the slowness of the reaction no marked displacement of the momentary condition need be feared during the operation (of titration).

If equivalent quantities are allowed to react on each other, *i.e.* if we start with 1 mol of acetic acid (60 g.) and 1 mol of alcohol (46 g.), or with 1 mol of methyl acetate (88 g.) and 1 mol of water (18 g.); then after the lapse of a sufficiently long time, there results a homogeneous system, which has the composition, in both cases, of

$\frac{1}{3}$ mol acetic acid + $\frac{1}{3}$ mol alcohol + $\frac{2}{3}$ mol water + $\frac{2}{3}$ mol ester.

This ratio of the relative quantities remained constant, even after a lapse of seventeen years. Moreover, this ratio changes very slightly with the temperature; the reason for this will be given later, Book IV.

Let v be the volume of the preceding reaction mixture, and let 1 mol of acetic acid be mixed with m mols of alcohol, and n mols of water (or ester; it is immaterial which, for the form of the equation). Then at equilibrium, if x denotes the number of mols of alcohol decomposed (and of acetic acid also, of course), there exists the relation—

$$k\frac{(1-x)(m-x)}{v^2} = k'\frac{(n+x)x}{v^2};$$

here k corresponds to the velocity with which the alcohol and the acid unite, and k' the velocity with which the ester and the water unite with each other. The denominator common to both sides of the equation can be neglected.

In the preceding special case, we had m = 1; n = 0; and x = $\frac{2}{3}$; therefore

$$\frac{k}{9} = \frac{4k'}{9},$$

i.e. the constant of equilibrium becomes

$$K = \frac{k}{k'} = 4.$$

By introducing this value into the general equation, and then solving it for x, we obtain as the quantity of ester formed—

$$x = \frac{1}{6}\left(4(m+1) + n - \sqrt{16(m^2 - m + 1) + 8n(m+1) + n^2}\right).$$

And this simplified for n = 0, becomes

$$x = \frac{2}{3}\left(m + 1 - \sqrt{m^2 - m + 1}\right).$$

The equation is very satisfactorily verified by experiment, as was first shown by Guldberg and Waage, and later and very thoroughly by van't Hoff.[1]   Thus Berthelot and Péan de St. Gilles, allowing 1 mol of acid to act upon m mols of alcohol, found that the following quantities of ester were formed, the latter being denoted by x :—

m.	x Obs.	x Calc.
0·05	0·05	0·049
0·18	0·171	0·171
0·33	0·293	0·311
0·50	0·414	0·423
[1·00	0·667	0·667]
2·00	0·858	0·845
8·00	0·966	0·945

Results which were fully as satisfactory were obtained by calculation for any particular quantities of water or ester.   It is a very important and significant result of the law of mass-action, that such apparently complicated ratios as were found by Berthelot and Péan de St. Gilles in their experimental researches, could be expressed in such simple formulæ.

We see, moreover, that by the action of a large quantity of acetic acid upon a little alcohol, or by the action of a large quantity of alcohol upon a little acid, the esterification is almost complete ; and conversely, by the action of a large quantity of water upon a little ester, the latter is almost entirely decomposed.

By properly choosing the mass-ratios, we can therefore make the reaction proceed as far as we like in one direction or the other.

The Influence of the Nature of the Reacting Components.—After it had been ascertained, as already shown, that the action of acids on alcohols could be expressed in mass and number, this question at once arose — *how does the reaction - capacity depend upon the nature of the particular acid, and the particular alcohol used ?* We are indebted to Menschutkin[2] for attacking this problem in a very extended research.   He determined the limit of esterification, on bringing together equi-molecular quantities of the most various acids and alcohols ; and at the same time he directed the research so as to determine, at least approximately, the velocity with which the limiting state was reached.   Of the numerous details of his research, we will merely state that in general—

In homologous series, the relative quantities of ester produced increased with the molecular weight.

In using the same acids, secondary alcohols afforded less ester than

[1] *Ber. deutsch. chem. Ges.* **10**. 669 (1877).
[2] *Ann. chim. phys.* [5], **20**. 229 (1880) ; **23**. 14 (1881) ; **30**. 81 (1883).

primary alcohols, and tertiary alcohols less ester than secondary alcohols.

There was no simple connection observable between the limit of esterification and the velocity with which this was reached.

The Dissociation of Esters.—As Menschutkin observed in his researches, in using tertiary alcohols, the ester produced decomposes into an acid and a hydrocarbon. This reaction was investigated later by Konowalow,[1] who allowed acids to act upon amylene ; in this way it appeared that the reaction concerned a dissociation phenomenon, which proceeded according to the scheme

$$CH_3COO(C_5H_{11}) = CH_3COOH + C_5H_{10}.$$

The reaction advances with marked velocity only in the presence of a sufficient quantity of free acid ; the pure ester is stable, even at quite high temperatures ; and the addition of acid at once occasions dissociation which then advances to a definite limit. The same limit is reached when one starts with free amylene and free acid.

Here we meet *catalytic reactions* for the first time, *i.e.* cases where the presence of a certain substance will strongly accelerate the progress of a reaction, which can also take place without it. As the law of mass-action was applicable to this, therefore the writer, together with Hohmann,[2] attempted to prove in a more extended way just how the simple relations which were anticipated were obtained.

If 1 mol of acid is added to 1 mol of amylene, the law of mass-action requires that

$$\frac{(a - x)(1 - x)}{xV} = K,$$

where x denotes the ester produced, V the volume of the reaction mixture, and K the equilibrium constant. The figures in the following table were obtained by heating the amylene and trichlor-acetic acid in a sealed glass tube to 100° for a sufficiently long time (some hours, up to a day), and then determining the quantity of ester produced by the decrease in the acidity titration :—

a.	V.	x Found.	K.	x Calc.
2·15	361	0·762	0·00120	0·762
4·12	595	0·814	0·00127	0·821
4·48	638	0·820	0·00126	0·826
6·63	894	0·838	0·00125	0·844
6·80	915	0·839	0·00126	0·845
7·13	954	0·855	0·00112	0·846
7·67	1018	0·855	0·00113	0·848
9·12	1190	0·857	0·00111	0·852
9·51	1237	0·863	0·00111	0·853
14·15	1787	0·873	0·00107	0·861

[1] *Zeitschr. phys. Chem.* **1.** 63 (1887) ; **2.** 6 and 380 (1888).
[2] *Ibid.* **11.** 352 (1893).

By making $K = 0·001205$, and then calculating x, by the help of this mean value, from the equation

$$x = \frac{1}{2}\left(1 + a + KV - \sqrt{(1 + a + KV)^2 - 4a}\right)$$

we obtain the figures given in the last column, which coincide remarkably well with the results of observation.

As is seen, the quantity of ester produced varies only inconsiderably, whether 4 or 14 mol of amylene are added to 1 mol of acid. One might infer at first glance that the esterification could be carried as far as desired by a sufficient excess of amylene, just as an acid can be completely esterified by an excess of alcohol (p. 459).

But this is not the case; the esterification of amylene and an acid is different from that of an alcohol and an acid; for in the former case only one molecular species is formed, viz. the ester; but in the latter case there are two, viz. the ester and the water.

In the formula of equilibrium for the first reaction, the volume of the reaction mixture *does not disappear* as it does in the second case, which thus shows a different behaviour.

Theoretically one could add an infinite quantity of amylene to a limited quantity of acid, without occasioning the esterification of more than 88 per cent of the acid; but as a matter of fact, the acid is soon used up on account of the difficulty in purifying the amylene.

Equilibrium in Solutions.—When one of the pure substances in a homogeneous liquid mixture is present in great excess, we have a *solution*. The great importance which attaches to those reactions which occur in water solutions, both in nature—as in plant and animal organisms—and also in the analytical operations of the chemist, justifies a particular and thorough description of the state of equilibrium which is established between substances which are capable of mutual reaction when existing in solution.

We will first consider those cases where the solvent is indifferent, *i.e.* where none of the molecular species which take part in the reaction are from that ingredient which is present in great excess, viz. the solvent. It will be shown later that actually the participation of the solvent in the reaction is immaterial for the form of the conditions of equilibrium.

At first, great difficulty was found in getting an insight into the condition of equilibrium which prevails in a solution. The methods which were applicable in studying the action of iodine on hydrogen, or of acetic acid on alcohol, and which depended upon the direct analytical determination of one of the molecular species taking part in the reaction, are usually out of the question here, because equilibrium is too quickly displaced by the removal of one of the reacting molecular species.

Thus, for example, if we wished to ascertain the state of equilibrium of such a reaction as the following,—taking place in water,—

$$K_2CO_3 + 2CH_3COOH = 2CH_3COOK + CO_2 + H_2O \; ;$$

by removing the free CO_2 by a stream of air, and thus determining it analytically, we should obtain false results; because during this operation the condition of equilibrium would be displaced, in the sense of the equation, from left to right.

We are therefore limited almost exclusively to physical methods of determination which, like the vapour-density determination in a gaseous system, can be performed without changing the composition of the reaction mixture. It is only recently that investigators have come into the possession of a method which is almost as universally applicable to solutions as the vapour density determination is to gas mixtures. Before this it was necessary to employ, according to the given case, certain physical properties of the solution, such as the power of optical rotation, the heat developed in preparing the solution, the refraction of light, the absorption of light, the colour, etc., in order to infer the composition of the solution; and this had to be preceded by an investigation of the dependence of the property in question upon the composition of the system as far as this was possible.

The Distribution of Hydrochloric Acid between Alkaloids.

—As an example of such an investigation, which was conducted with great skill and which led to significant theoretical developments, we will discuss the results of a paper communicated by J. H. Jellet[1] on the distribution of hydrochloric acid between alkaloids in alcoholic solution. It appears that Jellet made use of the correct formulation and application of the law of mass-action in this investigation; and although this was subsequent to the work of Guldberg and Waage, yet it was done independently.

The question which Jellet proposed to solve was this, viz.—Such alkaloids as quinine and codeïne, combine in alcoholic solution with 1 mol of hydrochloric acid. What will be the distribution of acid when two alkaloids are present in the solution, but when the total acid present is not sufficient to saturate the total quantity of alkaloids?

The physical property which was employed in ascertaining the molecular condition of the reacting substances when in equilibrium, was the optical rotatory power of their solutions. This, for quinine dissolved in alcohol, was 2·97, for codeïne, 2·63. By the addition of equi-molecular quantities of hydrochloric acid these values increased 1·344 fold and 1·909 fold respectively.

Moreover, since these substances do not mutually influence each

[1] *Trans. Irish Acad.* **25.** 371 (1875), Ostwald's *Klassiker*, No. 163.

other's rotatory power, when in the same solution, except when they react chemically on each other at the same time, it is possible to draw conclusions regarding the mutual action of the dissolved substances from the rotatory power of the solution.

Thus in a definite volume v of the solution, let n mols of HCl be added to a_1 mols of quinine (Ch), and a_2 mols of codeïne (Cod). Then when there are produced x mol. of quinine hydrochloride (ChHCl), and accordingly n − x mol. of codeïne hydrochloride, the observed rotation α of the plane of polarisation of light will be—

$$\alpha = (a_1 - x)D_{Ch} + (a_2 - [n - x])D_{Cod} + xD_{ChCHl} + (n - x)D_{CodCHl}.$$

The values of D here denote respectively the molecular rotatory power for the compound annexed as the sub-index. By means of this equation, the values of x may be expressed in only those terms which can be directly measured.

The observations gave the following results :—

a_1.	a_2.	n.	x.	$\frac{(a_2 - [n-x])x}{(a_1 - x)(n-x)}$.
100	104	70·7	42·7	1·91
100	104	91·9	55	2·08
100	104	112·4	66	2·10
100	104	130·3	73	2·02
				Mean 2·03

From the reaction equation,

$$Ch + CodHCl \rightleftarrows ChHCl + Cod,$$

we obtain the formula of equilibrium—

$$K = \frac{(a_2 - [n - x])x}{(a_1 - x)(n - x)},$$

since the active masses of the four molecular species participating in the reaction are respectively—

$$\underset{Ch}{\frac{a_1 - x}{v}}, \quad \underset{CodHCl}{\frac{n - x}{v}}, \quad \underset{ChHCl}{\frac{x}{v}}, \quad \text{and} \quad \underset{Cod}{\frac{a_2 - (n - x)}{v}}.$$

The volume v of the solution cancels out, *i.e.* the condition of equilibrium does not change when the volume of the solution is largely increased by the addition of the solvent, alcohol. And, in fact, in all the mixtures observed above, the rotation angle was proportional to the concentration, and this could not have happened unless the condition of equilibrium remained unchanged with the dilution.

The coefficient of equilibrium K was calculated as in the last column, and showed itself to be a constant as far as was possible with the errors of observation, which were not inconsiderable.

In the same way, Jellet studied the distribution of hydrochloric acid between codeïne and brucine; the rotatory power of the latter is $1·66$, and it increases $1·291$ fold by neutralisation with HCl. He also studied the distribution of HCl between brucine [Bru] and quinine. The following constants of equilibrium were found for these various reactions :—

$$
\begin{array}{lll}
 & & \text{K} \\
\text{Ch} + \text{CodHCl} = \text{ChHCl} + \text{Cod} & . \quad . \quad . & 2·03 \\
\text{Cod} + \text{BruHCl} = \text{CodHCl} + \text{Bru} & . \quad . \quad . & 1·58 \\
\text{Bru} + \text{ChHCl} = \text{BruHCl} + \text{Ch} & . \quad . \quad . & 0·32
\end{array}
$$

From the theory we can develop a characteristic relation which must exist between the three constants of equilibrium, and which leads at the same time to a deeper insight into the mechanism of the preceding reaction and also of related reactions. The hydrochloric acid is almost, but not quite entirely, combined with the alkaloids, a very slight quantity remaining free. This amounts to the statement that the alkaloidal hydrochlorides are dissociated, at least in traces, into free alkaloid and hydrochloric acid.

If K_1 denotes the dissociation constant of quinine hydrochloride, and K_2 that of codeïne hydrochloride, and if ϵ denotes the (very small) quantity of hydrochloric acid remaining free, then according to the law of dissociation, as already stated for gases, and which, according to the law of mass-action, holds good of course also for substances existing in solution, we shall have—

$$xVK_1 = \epsilon(a_1 - x),$$

and

$$(n - x)VK_2 = \epsilon(a_2 - [n - x]).$$

Then by division we obtain—

$$\frac{(a_2 - [n - x])x}{(a_1 - x)(n - x)} = K = \frac{K_2}{K_1}.$$

That is, *the constant of equilibrium is equal to the ratio of the dissociation constants of the two compounds between which the hydrochloric acid is divided.*

Other things being equal, the quinine hydrochloride is, therefore, dissociated $2·03$ times as much as the codeïne hydrochloride. Now this relation also holds good for the two other reactions. If we denote the dissociation constant of brucine hydrochloride by K_3, then the product of the three constants of equilibrium should be—

$$\frac{K_2}{K_1} \cdot \frac{K_3}{K_2} \cdot \frac{K_1}{K_3} = 1.$$

As a matter of fact, we find that—

$$2·03 \times 1·58 \times 0·32 = 1·026.$$

Jellet previously obtained this result in a somewhat different way.

Obviously, in all cases in which the salts of an optically active base have different rotatory power to the base, it may be studied in a similar way, so that the chemical equilibrium may be found even when the second base added is optically inactive. This is a good method of comparing the strength of bases, as was shown by Skraup.[1]

Dissociation in Solutions.—In order to investigate the condition of equilibrium, in a reaction which involves a change in the number of molecules, as *e.g.* a dissociation, we may make use of a general method which amounts to the same as the determination of the vapour density of a gaseous system. The depression of the freezing-point, of the vapour pressure, and of the solubility, experienced by a solvent on the addition of soluble substances, are each directly proportional to the number of molecules of the dissolved substance. This has been shown by the new theory of solutions (see p. 145); and therefore very generally, by the determination of these magnitudes, we may learn the state of equilibrium of those reactions, the progress of which is identified with a change in the number of molecules. This method has, in fact, already given fairly extended information concerning the dissociation phenomena in solutions; but unfortunately it is not sufficiently accurate in all cases, because measurements of this sort are uncertain at small concentrations, and at higher concentration the calculation can only be approximate, on account of the inexactness of the gas laws.

The writer [2] succeeded in showing, in an indirect way, viz. by the study of the distribution of acids between water, and benzene or chloroform, that the equation of the isotherm of dissociation holds good, in the broadest sense, for the decomposition of double molecules into single ones. Thus if c denotes the concentration of the double molecule of the acid, and c_1 that of the normal [single] molecule, then it was shown that

$$Kc = c_1^2, \quad \text{or} \quad KV(1 - a) = 4a^2,$$

where a denotes the degree of dissociation, and V the volume of the solution containing 2 g.-mol of the acid.

The preceding formula, of which much use will subsequently be made, can be considerably simplified when the substance in question is either *very highly or only very slightly* dissociated. In the former case a is almost constant, and nearly equal to 1, and we have

$$V(1 - a) = \text{constant};$$

i.e. *the concentration of the undissociated molecules* $\left(= \dfrac{1 - a}{V} \right)$, *at extreme*

dissociation, is proportional to the square of the total concentration $\left(= \dfrac{1}{V^2} \right)$.

[1] *Monatshefte für Chemie*, **15.** 775 (1895).
[2] *Zeitschr. phys. Chem.* **8.** 110 (1891).

In the second case, a is small as compared with 1, and therefore $\frac{a^2}{V}$ = constant; i.e. *the concentration of the dissociated molecules* $\left(\frac{a}{V}\right)$, *at very slight dissociation, is proportional to the square root of the total concentration* $\left(=\frac{1}{\sqrt{V}}\right)$.

Such simple laws as these assist greatly in the general treatment of the subject.

Esterification in Benzene.—The esterification of amylene and acids already described on p. 460 was also investigated when the reacting substances were *dissolved in benzene*. Under these conditions the acid is *bi-molecular* when the concentration is not too low, *i.e.* the reaction here progresses according to the scheme

$$S_2 + 2A = 2E,$$

where S_2 denotes the double molecule of the acid, and A and E respectively denote the amylene and the ester.

In consequence of this the law of mass-action does not require as before that

$$\frac{(1-x)(a-x)}{xV} = K,$$

but that

$$\frac{(1-x)(a-x)^2}{x^2V}$$

or else the expression

$$\frac{a-x}{x}\sqrt{\frac{1-x}{V}} = K'$$

must be constant.

The following table contains some results of an investigation conducted with trichlor-acetic acid at 100°. Here V denotes the volume of that reaction mixture in litres, which contains the double equivalent of acid.

a.	V.	x.	K.	K'.
0·481	3·00	0·181	0·453	0·87
0·963	4·00	0·298 ·	0·392	0·94
0·481	7·77	0·135	0·282	0·85
0·963	13·54	0·197	0·230	0·94

As a matter of fact, in the sense of the theory, and within the limits of the errors of experiment, K' alone is constant. It should be noticed that if one applies the law of mass-action to the reaction

$$S + A = E,$$

then the active mass of the acid obviously will be

$$a\frac{1-x}{V},$$

when we denote the degree of the dissociation of the acid by a. Therefore the following expression,

$$a\frac{(1-x)(a-x)}{xV},$$

must be constant. But now, according to the equation of dissociation (p. 465), the following expression must be constant, viz.

$$\frac{a^2}{1-a}\cdot\frac{1-x}{V};$$

or, as a is very small compared with 1 at slight concentration, a must be inversely proportional to the expression $\sqrt{\dfrac{1-x}{V}}$, *i.e.* the square root of the concentration of the acid; and thus we find in this way that the expression, designated above as K', must be constant.

Thus the requirements of the law of mass-action are found to be unequivocal throughout, as appears from the course of the reaction.

Evidence of Chemical Action from the Osmotic Pressure of Solutions.—Just as the question whether a substance is dissociated in solution or not can be decided by measurement of the osmotic pressure (or the proportional quantities, such as the lowering of the freezing-point), so we can investigate whether, in dissolving two or more different substances, a chemical reaction occurs which causes a change in the number of dissolved molecules. If the freezing-point is lowered by each of the substances in the mixture as if the others were not present, no such reaction can have occurred, in the contrary case a reaction is indicated.

As an example of this method, we may mention that, according to the measurements of H. C. Jones,[1] solutions of water and alcohol in acetic acid produce the same lowering of freezing-point as if each was present separately, hence there is no formation of alcohol hydrates under these circumstances. But water and sulphuric acid influence each other's depression of the freezing-point, the effect in the mixture being smaller than when the two substances are present alone. The results thus obtained indicate that when a considerable excess of water is present the hydrate $H_2SO_4 . 2H_2O$ is formed, in other cases $H_2SO_4 . H_2O$, but in dilute solutions the latter hydrate is partly dissociated into water and sulphuric acid by the dissociating power of the solvent, acetic acid.

[1] *Zeitschr. phys. Chem.* **13.** 419 (1894).

The Influence of the Solvent.—Many investigations have led to the very remarkable result that *the nature of the solvent has a very great influence on the molecular condition of the dissolved substance* (p. 270). Thus the organic acids, which exist in the form of *double* molecules in *benzene solution,* at not too low concentration, have their normal molecular weight in *ether, ethyl acetate, acetic acid,* and similar solvents. In *water solution* they suffer *electrolytic dissociation,* more or less strongly. Similar results are found in other cases.

It has been shown that, on the whole, the different solutions can be arranged in a series as regards their "power of dissociation" (Beckmann).

At the head stands *water,* which has the property of splitting many dissolved substances into their respective ions, and of decomposing others at least to their normal molecular size.

The former property is possessed by such solvents as *the alcohols, the phenols, the esters,* and *the ethers,* and also by *acetone,* only in the very slightest degree. On the other hand, substances dissolved in these solvents just enumerated, at not too·high concentration, usually have their respective *normal molecular weights.*

Many substances, such as the organic acids, the oximes, the phenols, etc., when dissolved in anethol, azobenzene, paratoluidine, etc., show a tendency, which is more or less strongly expressed, towards the formation of *large molecular complexes,* and especially of *double molecules.* These solvents represent the transition from the preceding group [*i.e.* the slightly ionising group of solvents] to the next following group, which contains solvents having a still greater tendency to promote polymerisation, such as the *hydrocarbons, benzene, naphthalene, di-phenyl-methane, di-phenyl,* etc., *carbon di-sulphide, chloroform, ethylene bromide,* and the like.

Accordingly, we find that acids form more ester with amylene, when dissolved in benzene, other things being equal, than when dissolved in ether, in which latter solvent the substances do not react to any marked extent. Beckmann called attention to the fact that, excepting acetone, these solvents, which are characterised by great dissociating power,[1] are built on the water type.

We may clearly assume from the observations made hitherto that a high *dielectric constant* of the solvent is favourable not only to dissociation into ions, but also for the dissociation of complex molecules into simpler. To this corresponds the fact that substances in solution are more strongly dissociated than when they exist in a vacuum or in an indifferent gas under the same conditions of temperature and concentration. Thus acetic acid occurs with normal molecular weight in water under circumstances such that, as a gas, it would consist almost entirely of double molecules. Many solutions have a greater dissociating force than a vacuum, and hence there follows the

---

[1] Beckmann, *Zeitschr. phys. Chem.* **6.** 437 (1890).

practical result that *the measurements conducted according to Raoult's method usually give more certain information regarding the normal molecular weight than the determinations of the gas density afford*, provided that by the normal molecular weight we mean the smallest form which the substance in question can assume without a complete dissolution of the molecular union.

The tendency of many substances, especially those containing hydroxyl, to form double molecules in solvents of small dissociating power, such as benzene or naphthalene, has been thoroughly investigated by Auwers and his pupils (*Zeitschr. phys. Chem.* 12. 689 ; 15. 33 ; 18. 595 ; 21. 337 ; 32. 39 ; 42. 513). The constitution of the dissolved substances seems to exert a regular influence, especially in the cases of phenol and acid anilides. In both these cases, ortho-substitution either weakens or entirely destroys the tendency towards formation of double molecules. The substituent exerting the greatest influence in this sense, is the aldehyde grouping CHO. Carboxyl CO_2R and CN are somewhat weaker, NO_2 and the halogens weaker still, and alkyl weakest of all. Meta- or para-substitution exerts much less influence, and may, as in the case of the phenols, increase the polymerisation.

The Participation of the Solvent in the Reaction.

—Thus far we have always considered the solvent as excluded from taking any part in the reaction, and we will now consider how such a participation can be taken into account.

The simplest case is that where only one molecular species, A, occurs in solution, and reacts on the molecules of the solvent, water, *e.g.* when hydration of the dissolved substance would occur. Then there would take place the following reaction, viz.

$$A(H_2O)_n = A + nH_2O,$$

which also has the form of an equation of dissociation. Let c denote the concentration of the hydrated molecules of the substance A ; and c_1 the concentration of the non-hydrated molecules ; and c_2 the concentration of the water. Then we obtain the equation

$$Kc = c_1 c_2^n.$$

Now it must be noticed that c_2 is very large in comparison with c and c_1 ; and therefore, especially when the solution is sufficiently diluted, the active mass of the solvent will only change inconsiderably if the point of equilibrium is displaced in one direction or the other, i.e. *the active mass of the solvent is almost constant.* But then there is a proportionality between c and c_1, and therefore in a dilute solution *the hydrated fraction is independent of the concentration.* This deduction from the law of the mass-action has not been properly noticed hitherto.[1]

But now, since we have no means at present of answering the question, whether a molecular species existing in aqueous solution

---

[1] Thus the view is very commonly found expressed in the literature that hydrates decompose with increasing dilution.

combines with water or not, and also since the Raoult-van't-Hoff methods for molecular weight determination give us no evidence concerning this, the experimental determination of the state of equilibrium of such reactions as the preceding, or of analogous ones, has hitherto eluded us. Yet the experiment described on p. 461, that in an excess of amylene the esterified portion of the acid is almost independent of the quantity of amylene, speaks in favour of the preceding law.

Moreover, a more stringent calculation, on the basis of thermo-dynamic principles (see Chap. III. of the last Book), shows that the active mass of a solvent at constant temperature is proportional to its *vapour pressure*. Now, in keeping with the preceding considerations, this must be regarded as constant in the case of solutions fairly dilute, because it is only very slightly different from that of the pure solvent.

Equilibrium in Solid Systems.—From the van't Hoff method of treatment of "solid solutions" (p. 161), and especially from the undoubted, though slight, capacity of solid substances to diffuse into each other, there follows immediately the suggestion that mutual chemical reaction may take place even in homogeneous solid systems, and that ultimately a condition of equilibrium will be established. But it is easily conceivable that chemical processes in the solid state of aggregation would usually take place too slowly for one to trace out their progress ; and thus, of course, their experimental study would be impossible.

Now, in fact, illustrations of the gradual progress of molecular changes of solids are not wanting. Here would be included the so-called elastic and thermal "effects" (*Nachwirkungen*), which are doubtless to be explained by a more or less considerable change of the molecular structure. Also the brittleness of some metals occasioned after a time ; as, *e.g.*, that of tin by the cold, or by lively agitation. Also the gradual change of the crystal form, and the change from the so-called amorphous to the crystallised condition, which is illustrated in devitrification.

Moreover, Spring[1] succeeded in one case in demonstrating the probable establishment of equilibrium, viz. in the reaction between solid barium carbonate and solid sodium sulphate ; here the change into barium sulphate and sodium carbonate ceased when about 80 per cent had been so transformed ; and conversely, the mutual reaction between barium sulphate and sodium carbonate ceased when about 20 per cent of the equi-molecular mixture had been changed. This reaction takes place on energetic shaking of the finely-powdered substances, and is also very much accelerated by the application of high pressures (up to 6000 atmospheres). Its progress was ascertained by extraction with water, and then weighing the insoluble ingredients.

[1] *Bull. soc. chim.* **46**. 299 (1886).

CHAPTER III

The Kind of Heterogeneity.—The heterogeneity of a chemical system existing in equilibrium obviously cannot consist in any variation of the composition of the liquid, or of the gas mixture, from point to point ; because, if this were the case, there would occur a migration of matter, as a result of diffusion, *i.e.* the system would not as yet have reached its state of equilibrium. The heterogeneity must essentially consist only *in the intimate association of different complexes, each of which is homogeneous in itself,* such as solid salts and saturated solutions, mixtures of liquids and of gases, solids and their gaseous dissociation products, etc. ; the degree of heterogeneity will be conditioned and estimated by the number of these complexes. The particular system may, of course, be either gaseous, liquid, or solid. There is no limit to the number of solid substances, and of liquids which do not dissolve each other, which participate in material decompositions by a displacement of the point of equilibrium resulting from reactions. On the other hand, we know that, on account of the complete miscibility of gases, there can be present [in any case], *only one gaseous complex.*

The different complexes which are both physically and chemically homogeneous in themselves, which may be either a physical mixture or a chemical compound, and which make up the heterogeneous system, are called *the phases of the system,* after the usage of W. Gibbs. Thus, *e.g.,* in considering the state of equilibrium between calcium carbonate and its decomposition products, carbon dioxide and calcium oxide, we must distinguish in this system three phases, two of which, viz. $CaCO_3$ and CaO, are solid, and one, CO_2, is gaseous.

General Law regarding the Influence of the Relative Proportions.—An unusually large number of experiments have led to the following law, which is universal, viz. :—

The condition of equilibrium of a heterogeneous system is independent

471

of the relative quantity by weight in which each phase is present in the system.

Thus, *e.g.*, after equilibrium has been established in the aforesaid system, viz.—

$$CaCO_3 \rightleftharpoons CaO + CO_2,$$

if there should occur an increase or a diminution in the quantity by weight, in which each of the enumerated substances is present, and if care is taken to preserve the external conditions, temperature and pressure, unchanged, then the state of equilibrium remains unchanged, *i.e.* in the sense of the reaction equation, there is no change in either direction, and the composition of each particular phase remains undisturbed.

Among other deductions from the preceding law are these well-known facts : that the vapour tension of a liquid is independent of its quantity ; and that the concentration of a saturated solution is the same, whether much or little of the solid salt be present, and the like.

The law may be demonstrated, on the basis of the molecular theory, in the following way. The establishment of chemical equilibrium does not mean that all chemical change has absolutely ceased ; but rather that, in the sense of the reaction equation, the change, at any moment and at any point in the one direction, is exactly as great as the change in the opposite direction (p. 444).

Thus if we consider any selected part of a surface which separates two different phases of a system from each other, there will be a continual change of molecules in the portion of the surface, and molecules will be continually going out and in at the same time. In order that equilibrium may become established and remain so, the condition must be fulfilled, that the same number of molecules of each species must pass through the portion of the surface in the one direction as in the other. Thus we are considering the necessary extension of the same considerations which earlier (p. 213) led us to conceive of the equilibrium between a liquid and its saturated vapour, as a *dynamic* condition ; and there also the state of equilibrium was associated with the condition, that at each portion of the surface separating the liquid and the saturated vapour, at every moment, as many gaseous molecules condense as evaporate from the liquid.

The forces, under the influence of which there occurs the continuous exchange of molecules between two different phases, like all molecular forces, have only very small spheres of action and sink rapidly to zero at measurable distances. This exchange only takes place as a result of the forces which are active in the immediate vicinity of the limiting surface between molecules which exist in two different phases, and it is indifferent whether the extension of the two phases on both sides of the separating surface is large or not. For the same reason the exchange of molecules is not influenced either by the form [1] or by the extension of the separating surface. This can only mean that *the condition of equilibrium is independent of the relative mass of each of the phases.*

Complete Heterogeneous Equilibrium.—Among the simplest cases of equilibrium are the so-called "physical," *i.e.* the equilibrium between two different states of aggregation of the same substance; as, *e.g.*, the equilibrium between ice and liquid water; the equilibrium between liquid water and water vapour; and the equilibrium between ice and water vapour, *i.e.* where the reaction—in regard to which an equilibrium has been established—consists in the melting of a solid body, in the evaporation of a liquid, or in the evaporation of a solid (sublimation).

The relations here are very simple. For a definite external pressure there corresponds a definite temperature at which the two systems can exist beside each other; thus ice and water are co-existent at atmospheric pressure at 0°; and liquid water and water vapour at atmospheric pressure at 100°. If we change the external pressure, at a temperature which is kept constant, or if we change the temperature, at an external pressure which is kept constant—then the reaction advances to a completion in one sense or in the other.

We may obtain complete knowledge of the conditions of equilibrium by ascertaining the dependence of the pressure at which the two respective states of aggregation are capable of existing beside each other—upon the temperature, *i.e.* the dependence of the melting-point upon the external pressure, and the vapour-pressure curve of the liquid or solid substance.

Now there are a number of reactions of a purely chemical nature which are completely analogous to the above physical reactions, for they have the common peculiarity that *when the reaction takes place isothermally, each one of the phases may change its mass but not its composition.*

In all reactions of this sort the same thing holds true which was true in the case of the physical reactions, *i.e.* with a certain external pressure, the phases of the system are, collectively, coexistent only at a certain definite temperature; and under all other conditions, the reaction advances in one sense or the other to a completion, *i.e.* till one of the phases is exhausted.

After the example of Roozeboom,[2] whose many-sided experimental investigations have very largely contributed to clearing up these questions, we will call the equilibrium "*completely heterogeneous.*"[3]

---

[1] Excepting very great curvatures, where possibly the capillary forces may come noticeably into play (Book IV. Chap. III.).

[2] *Rec. trav. chim. des Pays-Bas* since 1884; *Zeitschr. phys. Chem.* since 1888.

[3] It must be strongly emphasised that the "complete equilibrium" has no special importance or superiority as compared with the "incomplete equilibrium." Exactly

A complete [heterogeneous] equilibrium, *e.g.*, is that between calcium carbonate and its decomposition products. To a definite temperature there corresponds one, and only one, pressure at which the three reacting substances can exist beside each other, according to the reaction equation

$$CaCO_3 \rightleftharpoons CaO + CO_2.$$

Let us think of the $CaCO_3$ as being at the bottom of a cylinder which is closed with a movable air-tight piston. Then, if we increase the volume by raising the piston, the reaction progresses, in the sense of the preceding equation, from left to right; and if we diminish the volume by depressing the piston, the reaction progresses, in the sense of the preceding equation, from right to left. Equilibrium can exist only at a definite pressure exerted from without upon the piston, viz. the so-called "*dissociation pressure.*" If we make the external pressure only a trifle smaller, always at a temperature which is kept constant, then the reaction advances from left to right until the calcium carbonate is exhausted, *i.e.* until it is *complete*. If we make the external pressure only a trifle greater, there results, conversely, the *complete* reunion of the carbon dioxide with the calcium oxide, in the sense of the equation, from right to left. When the reaction occurs, with the equilibrium pressure and temperature remaining constant, none of the phases changes its composition: this is the necessary pre-existing condition for the occurrence of the reaction under constant equilibrium pressure.

The peculiarity of such reactions is, that they may occur at constant temperature without change in the composition, or in any other property of each of the phases, and with no change except in their total mass; it follows from this quite generally, that for a given composition, there can be but one corresponding external pressure, *and to every definite temperature there corresponds one, and only one, equilibrium pressure.*

In this manner the way is clearly pointed out which must be followed for the experimental investigation of special cases of complete equilibrium. We may become completely familiar with such a case if we ascertain for each temperature the corresponding pressure at which the different phases are coexistent, and if we also ascertain the composition of each of the phases. Sometimes, as was the case with the system,

$$CaCO_3 + CaO + CO_2,$$

the contrary is the case. For example, investigation of the freezing-points of salt solutions, where a change of concentration is produced by the solid freezing out, and where, therefore, we are dealing with incomplete equilibria, has led to the most valuable results, while the corresponding complete equilibrium (coexistence of ice and salt with the solution) possesses an absolutely arbitrary character. The old erroneous idea that these mixtures were definite substances has been historically perpetuated by giving them the name of "cryohydrates."

the composition may remain unchanged, even with a change in the temperature; but this is often not the case.

Let us consider, as an example of the last case, the equilibrium between a solid salt, its saturated water solution, and the water vapour: here we have a case of complete equilibrium, for, at any definite temperature, the three phases are coexistent only at one pressure, namely, the vapour pressure of the saturated solution; and, moreover, the reaction which occurs isothermally (the evaporation of the water and the precipitation of the salt) does not result in a change of composition of any of the phases. But the composition of the liquid phase (the solution) varies with the temperature as a result of the varying solubility of the salt.

As it is *the influence of the temperature* which especially concerns us in complete equilibrium, its further description belongs to the sections on *thermo-chemistry*.

Phases of Variable Composition.—The relations are very different when one or more of the phases changes its composition while the reaction proceeds isothermally. Here, in general, a change of the external pressure establishes a new condition of equilibrium, because one or more of the phases of the system changes its composition.

An illustration will serve to make the case intelligible.

If we allow pure water to evaporate at the exact pressure of its saturated vapour, then, while the reaction (evaporation) is going on, neither the liquid nor the gaseous phase changes its composition. If we make the external pressure a little smaller, then all the water evaporates; if we increase it, then all the vapour condenses.

Now this is at once changed as soon as a salt is dissolved in the water; then, as is well known, the vapour pressure is lowered in proportion to the concentration [of the solution].

Let a definite volume of water vapour be in equilibrium with the solution. If we now diminish the external pressure a little, not all the water evaporates but only a definite fraction. For, as a result of the evaporation, the concentration of the solution increases, whereby the maximal pressure is still further reduced, and this goes on until it has sunk to the new and lower value of the external pressure, and thus a new state of equilibrium becomes established. But if the concentration proceeds so far that the solid salt is precipitated, then the concentration remains constant, and equilibrium pressure also remains constant, and does not increase any more with further evaporation.

Thus in those systems in which there occur phases having a variable composition, the equilibrium depends upon *the relative masses* of the reacting components in these phases, and thus the problem arises of formulating this influence.

In what follows, as we advance from the simplest conditions of equilibrium to the more complicated examples which have been experimentally examined, this simple result will be found, *that without the introduction of any new assumptions, the law of mass-action may be also applied to heterogeneous systems.*

We will first consider the case where there occurs *only one phase having a variable composition* in the system, and will then proceed to the more complicated cases where the number of such phases is greater than one. This one phase may be either gaseous or liquid. *Solid substances* (except mixed crystals), *in contrast to gaseous and liquid phases, do not change their composition on a displacement of the point of equilibrium; and therefore they occupy an exceptional position, because they form only phases of constant composition.*

Equilibrium between a Gaseous Phase and a Solid Substance—Sublimation.—According to Dalton's law, the sublimation pressure, *i.e.* the maximal partial pressure under which the solid vaporises into a gas, with which it forms no new compound, is as great as though the sublimation took place in a vacuum. The composition of the gaseous phase is thus completely determined by the vapour pressure of the corresponding solid substance, and by the mass of the foreign gases which are present.

The Dissociation of a Solid Substance which produces only one Gas.—This case conducts itself in the same way as the last. Here also, for each temperature, there is a corresponding maximal pressure (*the dissociation pressure*) of the gas resulting from the dissociation, and which is not changed by the presence of indifferent gases. The dissociation pressure is also independent of the relative masses of the solid bodies which take part in the reaction.

The classical example of this case is the dissociation of calcium carbonate, the regularity of which was observed by Debray (1867):

$$CaCO_3 \underset{\longleftarrow}{\longrightarrow} CaO + CO_2$$
Solid   Solid   Gaseous.

The dissociation pressures of this system have been measured very exactly by Le Chatelier;[1] in measuring the temperatures he used a thermocouple made of platinum and an alloy of platinum and rhodium.

THE DISSOCIATION TENSIONS OF CALCIUM CARBONATE

t.	p.	t.	p.
547°	27 mm. Hg.	745°	289 mm. Hg.
610°	46 ,, ,,	810°	678 ,, ,,
625°	56 ,, ,,	812°	753 ,, ,,
740°	255 ,, ,,	865°	1333 ,, ,,

[1] *C.R.* **102.** 1243 (1886).

The observation that the dissociation pressure like the maximal pressure of saturated vapours increases rapidly with the temperature appears to be quite general; moreover, there is a very close analogy between these phenomena.

The dissociation pressure is independent of the ratio between the relative quantities of solid carbonate and calcium oxide, as also follows if we apply the general law stated on p. 476 to the particular system considered. This is usually expressed as follows : viz. *the active masses of solid bodies which participate in the chemical equilibrium are constant* (Guldberg and Waage, Horstmann).

The explanation of this behaviour, from the kinetic-molecular standpoint, presents some difficulty. Thus one might incline to the view that the more the relative mass of oxide increased, the more CO_2 molecules would be taken up and held fast by the mixture of oxide and carbonate; and that the more the mass of carbonate decreased, the fewer CO_2 molecules would be sent out. In this way, however, the mass ratios would exert an influence on the dissociation pressure, which is contrary both to the general law already mentioned, and to experience.

We have already given on p. 472 a general discussion according to the molecular theory showing that the relative quantity of the various phases must be without influence on equilibrium; it is worth while, however, to go through some considerations which show simply and easily the constancy of the dissociation pressure.

Both the calcium oxide and also the carbonate must each certainly possess a certain vapour pressure, or, more correctly, a pressure of sublimation; by this is meant the respective partial pressures of the molecular species CaO and $CaCO_3$, standing in a gas space which is in contact with the oxide and the carbonate. Now, these sublimation pressures are independent of the presence of foreign gases; they remain unchanged when the oxide and the carbonate are present at the same time. We cannot ascertain the magnitudes of these pressures, because they evade direct measurement by reason of their smallness.

Hence in the vapour space, which is in contact with the two solid substances, there occur the three molecular species, $CaCO_3$, CaO, and CO_2; and respecting the reaction,

$$CaCO_3 \underset{\longleftarrow}{\overset{\longrightarrow}{}} CaO + CO_2,$$

a condition of equilibrium will be established, and to this we may directly apply the law of chemical mass-action.

Let us denote by π_1 and π_2 the sublimation pressures of the oxide and of the carbonate respectively; and by p the vapour pressure of the carbon dioxide; this latter, on account of the smallness of the values of π_1 and π_2, will not be very different from the vapour pressure (*i.e.* the dissociation pressure) of the whole system. Then, according to the law of mass-action, it follows that

$$K' \pi_2 = p \pi_1,$$

where K' denotes the dissociation constant of the *gaseous* $CaCO_3$ molecules. Now, since π_1 and π_2 are independent of the quantity of the solid substances [CaO and $CaCO_3$ respectively], then p, *i.e.* the dissociation pressure at any given temperature, must also be constant. But it will vary greatly with the temperature, because the same also holds good both for K' and for π_1 and π_2.

Considered on the basis of the molecular theory, this same proof is the reason for the view that the reaction occurs exclusively in the gaseous phase, and that the solid substances participate in the reaction to the extent of their previous sublimation. This view leads, as an immediate consequence, to the constancy of the dissociation pressure, though, on the other hand, this is not a necessary condition for its derivation.[1]

To the dissociation phenomena of solid bodies there also belong *the dehydration of salts containing water of crystallisation*, resulting from raising the temperature. This has been thoroughly studied by Mitscherlich, Debray, G. Wiedemann, Pareau, Müller-Erzbach, and others. Here also the pressure of decomposition is constant for any given temperature, but increases strongly with increasing temperature. But here *dissociation by stages* is usually found, *i.e.* the salts do not lose *all* their water at a constant pressure, but several stages can be recognised, at which points the different molecules of water suddenly evaporate as the pressure changes.

Thus, for example, copper sulphate ($CuSO_4 + 5H_2O$) gives off the first two molecules of water with constant pressure, the following two also with constant but much lower pressure, and finally, the last molecule of water with the least pressure, so that the dissociation occurs in three stages—

$$\text{I. } CuSO_4 \cdot 5H_2O = CuSO_4 \cdot 3H_2O + 2H_2O$$
$$\text{II. } CuSO_4 \cdot 3H_2O = CuSO_4 \cdot H_2O + 2H_2O$$
$$\text{III. } CuSO_4 \cdot H_2O = CuSO_4 + H_2O,$$

each of which possesses its own maximal pressure. A simple and certain method of determining the various stages of hydration is due to Müller-Erzbach.[2] The researches of Andreae[3] show that the *change in question is discontinuous*. The *ammonia compounds of the metal chlorides* behave like salts with water of crystallisation (Isambert [1868], Horstmann [1876]).

R. Hollmann[4] has shown that mixed crystals containing water possess a vapour pressure which is independent of the water content within certain

---

[1] The considerations advanced by Horstmann, *Zeitschr. phys. Chem.* **6.** 1 (1890), which derived the same result from the same standpoint of "solid solutions" *do not at all* contradict the preceding statements.

[2] See especially *Zeitschr. phys. Chem.* **19.** 135 (1896).

[3] *Zeitschr. phys. Chem.* **7.** 241 (1891).   [4] *Ibid.* **37.** 193 (1901).

limits. He showed also that small quantities of an isomorphous mixture in all cases lowered the vapour pressure of the crystal. The discovery that double salts also behave like simple crystals is of great interest; if the vapour pressure of a series of mixtures of two salt hydrates which are isomorphous in all proportions be investigated, it is found that the vapour pressure curve shows a break where the composition corresponds with that of a pure double salt. This is the only method at present known for deciding whether a double salt is found in a complete isomorphous mixture series (p. 116).

The Production of one Gas from several Solid Substances.—It can be shown here, by the same considerations which were advanced above, that for every temperature there is a corresponding development pressure (*Entwicklungsdruck*) which is independent of the relative quantities of the solid substances. In fact, Isambert[1] demonstrated that the evolution of ammonia from lead oxide and ammonium chloride, in the sense of the equation

$$PbO + NH_4Cl = NH_3 + Pb(OH)Cl,$$

took place at the following maximal pressures for the corresponding temperatures :—

t	Pressure.	t	Pressure.
17·5°	296 mm. Mercury	36·3°	599 mm. Mercury
27·0°	420 ,, ,,	48·9°	926 ,, ,,

At about 42° the maximal pressure is equal to the atmospheric pressure, and thus this point is the "boiling-point" of the system.

Another interesting example of the preceding case has been found by Rothmund[2] when calcium carbide is formed according to the equation

$$CaO + 3C = CaC_2 + CO,$$

a single gas is generated from this solid substance, and can therefore be in equilibrium with the system only at one given pressure for a given temperature. In point of fact it is found that above 1620° carbon monoxide is violently evolved with formation of carbide, and that conversely below that temperature carbon monoxide at atmospheric pressure completely decomposes calcium carbide into lime and carbon.

The Dissociation of one Solid Substance which produces several Gases.—When the volatilisation of a solid substance is attended, at the same time, with a more or less complete dissociation, then for a definite temperature there corresponds a definite dissociation pressure; this latter amounts to the same, in the presence of an indifferent gas, as in a vacuum. But the case where one of the resulting gaseous products of decomposition is present in excess, requires special treatment.

Thus ammonium hydrosulphide has at each temperature a definitely

[1] *C.R.* **102.** 1313 (1886).   [2] *Gött. Nachr.*, 1901, Heft 3.

corresponding vapour pressure; but, as must be inferred from its vapour density, the gas mixture above it is almost completely dissociated into ammonia and hydrogen sulphide, *i.e.* in the sublimation the following reaction occurs:

$$NH_4SH \rightleftarrows NH_3 + H_2S.$$

At 25·1° the dissociation pressure of the gas amounted to 501 mm., without excess of the decomposition products, *i.e.* the partial pressures of the two gases, NH_3 and H_2S, were equal to each other, each being 250·5° mm.

According as one or the other of the two gases were present in excess, the partial pressures $[p_1$ and $p_2]$ for the state of equilibrium had the following values: [1]—

NH_3 p_1	H_2S p_2	p_1p_2
208	294	60700
138	458	63200
417	146	60800
453	143	64800
	Mean	62400

As is obvious, the partial pressure of that gas which is not present in excess is diminished by the presence of the other, *i.e. the dissociation pressure has fallen.* This result may be theoretically developed in the following way.

In the vapour of the ammonium hydro-sulphide, aside from the decomposed molecules, there are also some undecomposed molecules, though the number of the latter may be very small; let their partial pressure amount to π. Then by applying the equation of the isotherm of dissociation to the gaseous, we obtain

$$K'\pi = p_1p_2.$$

But now, according to Dalton's law, at constant temperature, the vapour pressure π of the undecomposed molecules of ammonium hydrosulphide must be constant; and, according to the preceding formula, the same thing holds true for the product p_1p_2. Now, denoting the dissociation pressure by P, for the case where $p_1 = p_2$ (*i.e.* where there is no excess of either of the decomposition products), we obtain

$$K'\pi = p_1p_2 = \frac{P^2}{4}.$$

[1] Isambert, *C.R.* **92.** 919; **93.** 731 (1881); **94.** 958 (1882).

Now, in fact, this equation is found to be established by the preceding table. The value of p_1p_2 varies irregularly, and the mean value 62,400 approximately coincides with the [theoretical] value,

$$\frac{P^2}{4} = \frac{501^2}{4} = 62,700.$$

The relations are very similar in the case of ammonium carbamate, a substance studied by Horstmann,[1] to whom we are indebted for the first application of the law of mass-action to the dissociation of solid compounds, and therefore at the same time for one of the most striking demonstrations of the law. The substance, on sublimation, decomposes almost entirely in the sense of the equation

$$NH_4\text{-}O\text{-}CONH_2 \rightleftharpoons NH_3 + CO_2.$$

If we denote the partial pressure of the ammonia by p_1, and that of the carbon dioxide by p_2, then the application of the equation of the isotherm of dissociation gives

$$K'\pi = p_1^2 p_2,$$

where K denotes the dissociation constant of the gaseous ammonium carbamate molecules, and π their partial pressure. Now, since the latter is constant, in the presence of the solid salt, for any given temperature, therefore the right side of the preceding equation must also be constant; and since π, in contrast to the total pressure, has an infinitesimal value, on account of the almost complete dissociation of the ammonium carbamate, therefore we obtain

$$p_1^2 p_2 = \frac{4P^3}{27},$$

where P denotes the dissociation pressure at the respective temperature, without excess of either of the dissociation products: and, therefore, two-thirds P denotes the partial pressure of the ammonia, and one-third P, that of the carbon dioxide. The addition of NH_3, then, will depress the dissociation pressure a good deal more than the addition of CO_2. Horstmann, and Isambert[2] later, found the preceding formula to be well established.

Reaction between any Arbitrary Number of Gases and Solid Substances.

—This general case can be dealt with, according to what has preceded, without the introduction of any new assumptions.

Thus, let ν_1 molecules of the solid substance a_1, and ν_2 molecules of the solid substance a_2, etc., come together with n_1 molecules of the gas A_1, and n_2 molecules of the gas A_2, etc.; and let them form ν_1' molecules of the solid substance a_1', and ν_2' molecules of the solid substance a_2', etc., and also n_1' molecules of the gas A_1', and n_2' mole-

---

[1] *Lieb. Ann.* **187.** 48 (1877).   [2] *C.R.* **93.** 731 (1881); **97.** 1212 (1883).

cules of the gas A_2', etc. Thus the reaction will occur, according to the general scheme,

$$\nu_1 a_1 + \nu_2 a_2 + .. + n_1 A_1 + n_2 A_2 + .. \leftrightarrows \nu_1' a_1' + \nu_2' a_2' + .. + n_1' A_1' + n_2' A_2' + ..$$

As above, let the partial pressures of the reacting gases be respectively $p_1, p_2 \ldots, p_1', p_2' \ldots$ Now some of the molecules of the solid substances $a_1, a_2 \ldots, a_1', a_2' \ldots$, will certainly occur in the gaseous system, though, under the circumstances, in very small quantities, since each of these solid substances will have a certain vapour pressure; let this latter amount respectively to $\pi_1, \pi_2 \ldots, \pi_1' \pi_2' \ldots$, etc. Thus the application of the law of mass-action to the gaseous system will give the following condition :—

$$k\pi_1^{\nu_1}\pi_2^{\nu_2} \ldots \, p_1^{n_1}p_2^{n_2} \ldots = k'\pi_1'^{\nu_1'}\pi_2'^{\nu_2'} \ldots \, p_1'^{n_1'}p_2'^{n_2'} \ldots$$

Here k and k' denote the velocity coefficients of the two mutually opposed reactions.

Now if we observe that, according to Dalton's law, the vapour pressures of solid bodies are independent of the presence of other gases, and that they remain constant at constant temperatures, then we can bring the preceding equation to the form

$$Kp_1^{n_1}p_2^{n_2} \ldots = p_1'^{n_1'}p_2'^{n_2'} \ldots ,$$

where K denotes a constant, which again we will call the *equilibrium* constant. We arrive thus at the simple result that in a consideration of the equilibrium conditions of a system containing gases reacting on each other in presence of solid bodies, we proceed just as before, and neglect only those molecular species which are present at the same time in the solid form.

As has been already noted, Guldberg an Waage expressed this result in the statement, that *the active mass of a solid substance is constant.*

As an example of this, let us consider a reaction which was studied by Deville,[1] viz.

$$3Fe + 4H_2O = Fe_3O_4 + 4H_2.$$

By the reaction of steam at the pressure p upon iron at quite high temperatures, the reaction reached its completion when the partial pressure p' of the hydrogen produced reached a definite value. The application of the general equation preceding led to the relation that p^4 and p'^4 must be proportional, and therefore p and p' must be so also.

Deville's experiments were carried out in the following way. A tube containing finely divided iron, and heated to a high temperature communicated with a retort containing liquid water at constant temperature. Hence at equilibrium the partial pressure of the water vapour in the whole apparatus was equal to the vapour pressure of the liquid water, corresponding to its temperature. The gradual increase of total pressure which took place was due to the hydrogen

[1] *Lieb. Ann.* **157.** 76 (1870).

evolved during the reaction.   The numbers obtained by Deville only partially agree with theory : the supposition that the gas mixture in his experiments never became homogeneous owing to slowness of diffusion has been confirmed by Preuner.[1]   This investigator repeated Deville's experiments with a more suitable apparatus, and obtained values which agree fully with the law of mass-action—as the following table shows :—

p.	p′.	$\frac{p}{p'}$.
8·8	13·5	0·65
12·7	18·0	0·71
25·1	37·4	0·67
25·4	54·1	0·65
49·3	71·8	0·68

The pressures are given in millimetres of mercury.   The temperature of the iron was 900°.

Explanation of the preceding General Case by Means of Sublimation and Dissociation.

—When a number of bodies react with a single gas phase we may consider the reaction in general, as has already been shown on p. 476 for the special case of the dissociation of calcium carbonate, as occurring in the form of a sublimation of the solid bodies which then react as gases.   We may similarly consider the reaction in the gaseous phase as consisting in a dissociation of the reacting molecules into simpler components, which then recombine to new molecules.

The chemical process is thus reduced to sublimation and dissociation, and, however complicated the case, it may be calculated when we know the sublimation pressure and dissociation constants of all the reacting molecules.   It would be an important problem for future chemical investigation to determine these quantities for as many gases as possible and to find general rules for their calculations.

This may be elucidated by one or two applications.   Ammonium chloride at ordinary temperatures has an exceedingly small sublimation pressure, probably to be reckoned in thousandths of a millimetre of mercury ; ammonia and hydrochloric acid in the gaseous phase can remain in equilibrium with solid sal-ammoniac, and the product of the partial pressure of these gases is constant at a constant temperature.   If, then, by any means we reduce the partial pressure of hydrochloric acid, that of ammonia must increase, if the partial pressure of hydrochloric acid is made excessively small that of ammonia will become very considerable.   If solid lime be added to sal-ammoniac, the hydrochloric acid is almost completely absorbed; the partial pressure of ammonia must therefore increase, since the product of the partial pressure of hydrochloric acid and ammonia must remain constant so long as solid sal-ammoniac is present. Actually even at room temperature ammonia is evolved from a mixture of sal-ammoniac and lime with considerable partial pressure, and it is certainly very noteworthy that small sublimation pressures of bodies that dissociate on volatilisation can be raised to considerable amounts by *sufficiently thorough absorption of one of the components.* On the other hand if sal-ammoniac is mixed with phosphorus anhydride, the pressure of ammonia is made exceedingly small and hydrochloric acid is violently evolved. The formation of carbon dioxide from calcium carbonate by acids may be regarded in the same manner. The partial pressure of calcium oxide in the gaseous phase is extremely reduced, that of carbon dioxide is consequently considerably raised, since so long as solid calcium carbonate is present the product of the partial pressure of CO_2 and CaO must be constant. Mercury salts are little volatile at low temperatures, but if copper filings are brought in contact with them the negative radical of the mercury salt is combined, and the partial pressure of the mercury vapour reaches such an amount that, on moderate warming, enough mercury is given off to serve as the basis of an analytical test for mercury.

Lead peroxide gives no perceptible partial pressure of oxygen; if, however, we make the partial pressure of PbO extraordinarily small by adding sulphuric acid, oxygen is evolved.

These conclusions indicate an indirect way of measuring sublimation pressures which in themselves would be extremely small.

The Equilibrium between a Liquid Phase and Solid Substances—The Solubility of Solid Substances.—The description of the particular cases in which solid substances are in equilibrium with a liquid (solution), should be prefaced by the general remark, that here a behaviour is found which is completely analogous to the equilibrium between a gaseous phase and solid substances. Thus the solution of a solid substance in any solvent is a process which has the greatest similarity to sublimation. In both cases the process is ended as soon as the expansive force of the evaporating or dissolving substance is held in equilibrium by the gas pressure of the vaporised molecules, or by the osmotic pressure of the dissolved molecules, respectively. And, therefore, for the reason already mentioned (p. 140), we call the osmotic pressure of a saturated solution, "the solution pressure" of the respective substance, in order to make quite clear the analogy to vapour pressure or sublimation pressure.

The solubility varies with the nature of the particular substance, and will always be affected more or less by any change in its chemical composition, or physical properties (as the crystal form, *e.g.*); thus, *e.g.*

in general, the different solid hydrates of a salt will have different solubilities.

In determining solubilities, the condition of the solid substances which exist in equilibrium with the solution must always be carefully noticed.

Moreover, the solubility depends also upon the nature of the solvent, and upon the temperature; usually, but not always, it rises with the temperature.

The analogy between solution and sublimation, or dissociation, of solid substances is very clearly shown by *the influence of foreign substances which are present.* The solubility of a solid substance is no more changed by the (moderate) addition of another substance—provided that the foreign substance does not react chemically on the first—than is the sublimation pressure changed by the presence of foreign indifferent gases.

In the following, we shall fix our principal attention on dilute solutions, as before. It is practically only these whose laws have been investigated, and so we shall consider mainly the behaviour of *difficultly soluble* substances. At higher concentrations the whole nature of the liquid, including of course its capacity as solvent, undergoes a considerable change, and therefore the laws which will be developed below must experience large modifications, which, however, are seldom so sweeping as to prevent us from obtaining at any rate a qualitative idea of the phenomena involved.

The particular "specific" influences which enter here and tend to obliterate the simple regularities of dilute solutions have great interest and deserve a thorough study. It is only recently that the first deliberate step has been made in this direction.[1]

Solubility varies very greatly with the nature of the solvent; this may be described as an effect of "*the nature of the medium,*" but nothing more about it is at present known. If another substance be added to a solvent in a very small quantity the nature of the medium is not altered—that is, a dilute solution of a given substance has the same solvent action as the pure solvent. When, however, a considerable quantity of the added substance is present the nature of the medium is altered, and according to present observations this may take place somewhat rapidly—that is, with a higher power (for example, the second) of the concentration of the added component. Thus if alcohol is added to an aqueous solution of cane-sugar, the sugar is precipitated because it is much less soluble in the newly formed medium.

According to recent investigations[2] the solvent action of water is usually much reduced by addition of electrolytes, especially those with multivalent

---

[1] G. Bodländer, *Zeitschr. phys. Chem.* **7.** 308 and 358 (1891).
[2] See especially Roth, *Zeitschr. phys. Chem.* **24.** 114 (1897); Rothmund, *ibid.* **33.** 401 (1900); W. Biltz, *ibid.* **43.** 41 (1903).

ions ; this is in all probability related to the fact (p. 386) that the density of water is considerably influenced by the presence of other ions.

A good example of the influence of the nature of the medium is to be found in the researches of Villard on the solvent action of compressed gases.[1] In a vacuum or in a *dilute* indifferent gas solids and liquids dissolve in accordance with their vapour pressure ; if, however, the indifferent gas is strongly compressed, say at 100 atmospheres, specific solvent action appears ; thus bromine evaporates in an atmosphere of compressed oxygen in much greater quantity than in a vacuum ; compressed hydrogen has much smaller solvent power.

Solubility of Hydrates.—It may be expected on theoretical grounds that the action of other substances should affect the solubility in water of salts containing water of crystallisation even when the action is too small to alter the nature of the medium. We will not go into the thermodynamic consideration of this influence here ; it is easily seen, however, that the water contained in the dissolving solid is taken up by the solvent the more easily the lower the vapour pressure of the dissolving water, and hence is more strongly dissolved ; in other words, the solubility of a hydrate in water is increased by the addition of a foreign substance the more such addition reduces the vapour pressure of water. For further details see the complete theoretical and experimental investigation of H. Goldschmidt.[2]

Equilibrium between Solids and Solutions.—This case is obviously to be treated in the same way as the equilibrium between solids and gaseous phases. The concentration of each kind of molecule present in the solid state remains constant when the equilibrium is displaced, and the law of mass-action can be applied to homogeneous solutions in the manner given in the preceding chapter.

The simplest case of this kind is *dissociation on solution*, such as occurs with racemic acid and similar compounds which, on solution, break up into dextro and lævo modifications, and also with many double salts and salts with water of crystallisation which break up into their components (the two single salts or salt and water), and most frequently of all with the solution of salts which dissociate into ions.

The equations for this case are as follows.[3] If u is the concentration of the undissociated component we have

$$u = \text{const.} \ ;$$

if u_1 and u_2 are the concentrations of the two components into which the compound breaks up in solution the equation of the dissociation isotherm is

$$Ku = u_1 u_2.$$

[1] *Journ. de phys.* [3], **5.** 453 (1896) ; ref. *Zeitschr. phys. Chem.* **23.** 373 (1897).
[2] *Zeitschr. phys. Chem.* **17.** 148 (1895).
[3] Nernst, *Zeitschr. phys. Chem.* **4.** 372 (1889).

So long as the dissociated substance is present in the solid state u is constant, and we have therefore

$$u_1 u_2 = \text{const.}$$

We thus have the same equation as that given on p. 480 for the dissociation of ammonium sulphydrate.

R. Behrend[1] has carried out a study of the foregoing equation. If anthracene and picric acid are mixed in alcoholic solution, anthracene picrate is formed according to the equation

$$C_{14}H_{10} + C_6H_2(NO_2)_3OH = (C_{14}H_{10}) \cdot (C_6H_2[NO_2]_3OH) \, ;$$

this becomes evident to the eye from the marked red coloration of the solution, but the compound is only formed to a small extent, *i.e.* it is largely dissociated in solution.

Now the solubility of anthracene and picric acid were determined and found to be 0·176 and 7·452 grms. in 100 parts of solution at 25°. Then a series of solutions of varying composition were analysed, some containing anthracene and some anthracene picrate in solid form ; the results of these determinations are given in the following table :—

	1	2	3	4	5	6	7	8	9	10
Anthracene a	0·190	0·206	0·215	0·228	0·236	0·202	0·180	0·162	0·151	0·14
Picric acids p	1·017	2·071	2·673	3·233	3·469	3·994	5·087	5·843	6·727	7·511
nthracene diss. u_1	0·176	0·176	0·176	0·176	0·183	0·149	0·127	0·109	0·098	0·096
'icric acids diss. u_5	0·999	2·032	2·623	3·166	3·401	3·926	5·019	5·775	6·659	7·443
Picrate u	0·032	0·069	0·089	0·119	0·121	0·121	0·121	0·121	0·121	0·121
$\dfrac{u_1 \cdot u_2}{u}$	5·5	5·2	5·2	4·7	5·1	4·8	5·3	5·2	5·4	5·9

a and p are the amounts of the two components present in the solution partly free, partly combined. In solutions 1-4 anthracene was in excess, in solutions 6-9 solid anthracene picrate was present ; 5 was saturated with both bodies, 10 with the picrate and picric acid.

Solutions 1-4 contain more anthracene than corresponds to its solubility (0·176) ; the excess must be in the form of picrate in solution ; this quantity is given in the fifth line of the table. If the amount of picric acid present in the form of picrate be subtracted from p we obtain the values of u_2 given in the fourth horizontal line.

[1] *Zeitschr. phys. Chem.* **15.** 183 (1894).

Solution 5 is saturated both with anthracene and with picrate; the amount of picrate here present, which is equivalent to $0.236 - 0.176 = 0.060$ grms. of anthracene, and therefore amounts to $0.060\dfrac{229 + 178}{178} = 0.137$ (since 229 and 178 are the molecular weights of picric acid and anthracene), gives the amount of undissociated picrate which must be present in all the solutions containing solid picrate in excess. This amount may, however, also be calculated from solution 10, which is saturated with picric acid and picrate, and contains $7.511 - 7.452 = 0.059$ of picric acid more than corresponds to the solubility of picric acid. This quantity can also only be present as picrate, and we thus find for the amount of undissociated picrate $0.059\dfrac{229 + 178}{229} = 0.105$. The mean of these two determinations (0.137 and 0.105) is 0.121; this is taken as the value of u in solutions 5-10 with solid picrate present. u_1 in these solutions is naturally calculated by subtracting u equivalents of anthracene from the total amount of anthracene present as picrate, and u_2 is determined in a similar manner.

The theory requires that for all the solutions the expression

$$K = \frac{u_1 u_2}{u};$$

should hold, and, in point of fact, this expression was found constant so far as the errors of observations would allow. In solutions 5-10 on account of the constancy of u

$$u_1 u_2 = \text{const.},$$

and for the solutions 1-5 on account of the constancy of u_1

$$\frac{u_2}{u} = \text{const.}$$

If we evaporate an alcoholic solution of anthracene and picric acid, then according to the ratios of the masses present, either anthracene, picrate, or picric acid will separate out—according to which first reaches its solubility limit. If we assume that the solution contains picric acid in slight excess, then, on evaporation, anthracene will first separate. The picrate will only be deposited when the mass of picrate acid is $\dfrac{3.469}{0.236} = 14.7$ times as great as that of the anthracene in solution.

In this case both anthracene and picrate will be present in the solid state, i.e. u and u_1 are constant. Hence u_2 is also constant, and the solution remains unaltered on further evaporation. But evaporation will cause at first a rise in the concentration of picric acid. This can only be counteracted by more anthracene going into solution, combining, and then separating again as picrate. In this way the anthracene already deposited gradually disappears. When the disappearance is complete, only picrate is present in the solid form, and we now have a condition such as solutions 6-9 represent. Finally, on continued evaporation, the solution becomes saturated with respect to picric acid. The solid bodies present are now picrate and picric acid, i.e., u and u_2 and hence also u_1 are constant. On further concentration the solution remains therefore unchanged, and a mixture of picric acid and picrate is deposited until all the alcohol is evaporated off. Thus if we know the respective solubilities of the separate ingredients as well as the conditions of equilibrium in the solution, we have a means within certain limits of crystallising out, and obtaining in pure form, any desired molecular species. For instance, in order to obtain pure anthracene picrate, we must crystallise from an alcoholic solution containing a large excess of picric acid.

If the solubility of picric acid happened to be less than 3·401 it would be obviously impossible for the picrate to crystallise out (i.e. excluding supersaturation). Hence it follows that compounds formed in solution cannot necessarily be obtained in the solid form by crystallisation. Their constitution in this case can only be ascertained by a careful study of the equilibrium obtaining in solution. If we treat the pure picrate with alcohol, its solubility is great enough to cause the resulting solution to become supersaturated with respect to the anthracene formed by dissociation. Hence solid anthracene is deposited, i.e., the compound is decomposed by alcohol.

The behaviour of double salts on crystallisation and solution is very similar, only here we have the extra phenomenon to deal with, that the component salts are usually highly electrolytically dissociated by the water.[1]

Several Phases of Variable Composition—The Vapour Pressure of Solutions.

—We may now advance a step further and consider the case where *several phases of variable composition occur in a system: these phases may occur in the gaseous or liquid state.*

The state of equilibrium which is established between a dilute solution of a substance which is not noticeably volatile, and the vapour emitted, is completely determined by the formula for the vapour pressure: according to this, *the relative depression of the vapour pressure, which is experienced by the solvent on adding a strange substance, is equal to the ratio of the number of dissolved molecules to the number of molecules of the solvent* (p. 145). For concentrated solutions, this law is at least suitable as a first approximation.

[1] See the detailed work of Van't Hoff, *Bildung und Spaltung von Doppelsalzen,* Leipzig, 1897.

In the sense of the kinetic method of the consideration of chemical equilibrium, we must conceive of this law also in a dynamic way; thus, *e.g.* in the coexistence of a water solution and of water vapour, at every moment, as many molecules of water vapour will be emitted, from every portion of the surface of a solution, as are precipitated by condensation.

We will now consider that case which is in extreme contrast to the last—namely, where only the *dissolved substance* evaporates from the solution, or at least where its volatility is more pronounced than that of the solvent ; and where the vapour pressure, exerted by the vapour emitted by the solvent and by the solution, is due almost exclusively to the molecules of the dissolved substance. When the dissolved substance, as such, stands at the same osmotic pressure that its vapour has at the same concentration, or in other words, when its molecular condition does change on evaporation, then, according to p. 148, a proportionality must exist between the concentrations of the dissolved substance in the two phases of the system considered.

Under these circumstances, Henry's law of absorption holds good. Let us denote the osmotic pressure of the dissolved substance in the solution by π ; and by p, the gas-pressure which the evaporated substance has in the space in contact with the solution. Then at constant temperature, we have

$$\pi = Lp,$$

or

$$c = LC,$$

where c and C are the concentrations in the two phases.

The proportional factor L we will call the *solubility coefficient* of the respective substance. It has this simple relation to the *absorption coefficient*, in that it may be obtained from the latter by multiplication by $(1 + 0 \cdot 00366t)$, where t denotes the temperature of the experiment. By the term "absorption coefficient," according to Bunsen,[1] is meant the volume (referred to 0° and 760 mm. pressure) of the gas which is absorbed by unit volume of the solution.

The proportionality between the osmotic pressure and the gas pressure may be easily understood by means of the molecular theory. When the solution is in equilibrium with the vapour in the space above it, then at every moment there are as many molecules of the dissolved substance emitted by the solution as are precipitated upon it from the gas space. But now since the quantity both of the emitted and of the absorbed molecules is proportional to their number, therefore these quantities must also be proportional respectively to the concentration in the solution and in the gas space ; and there must also be a proportionality between the two latter values.

It thus becomes obvious how the *identity of the molecular weights* of

---

[1] *Gasometrische Methoden*, Braunschweig (Brunswick), 1877.

the dissolved substance in the solution and in the gas space is a necessary condition for the relevancy of Henry's law; because otherwise
the number of emitted and of precipitated molecules would not be
proportional to the concentration. If different molecular species, but
such as do not react upon each other, are present, they, of course, do
not have any influence on each other, *i.e.* each of the different gases
of a mixture is dissolved as though the others were not present
(absorption law of Dalton).

The Law of Distribution.—Moreover, the case where several
molecular species (which may react chemically upon each other)
evaporate at the same time, from any selected solvent,—this may likewise be referred to the preceding case by means of a kinetic treatment. For the method of treatment, which was advanced for the case
of one molecular species, may be applied unchanged to each of several
molecular species participating in the chemical equilibrium, which has
become established in the solution and in the vapour space above it.
For in order that equilibrium can be attained it is obviously necessary
that just as many molecules of each species enter the liquid at any
moment as are driven out—because otherwise equilibrium would be
continually disturbed.

We thus arrive at the result, that *at a given temperature for every
molecular species there exists a constant ratio of distribution between a solvent
and its vapour space ; and this is independent of the presence of other molecular species, whether the particular molecular species is chemically reactive
with the other or not.*[1]

**The simultaneous Evaporation of the Solvent and of the
Dissolved Substances.**—This case, which, strictly speaking, should
be considered alone, may be solved by a combination of the laws just
given. It may be stated as follows :—

1. The partial pressure of the solvent in the vapour which stands
in equilibrium with the solution is equal to the vapour pressure p of
the pure solvent at the respective temperature, diminished by the
depression occasioned by the dissolved substance ; this depression,
according to van't Hoff's vapour-pressure formula, is estimated to be

$$p\frac{n}{N + n},$$

where n denotes the total number of dissolved molecules, in proportion to N molecules of the solvent.[2]

[1] Nernst, *Zeitschr. phys. Chem.* **8.** 110 (1891) ; see also Aulich, *ibid.* **8.** 105.

[2] If the total pressure changes considerably in the gas phase, it must be remembered
that the vapour pressure of the solvent changes with external pressure, as will be proved
thermo-dynamically later. See Book IV., chap iii., "Influence of unequal pressures."

2. The vapour pressure p_1, p_2 . . . of the dissolved substances can be calculated from the formulæ

$$p_1 = \frac{\pi_1}{L_1}, \quad p_2 = \frac{\pi_2}{L_2} \ldots ,$$

if π_1, π_2 . . . denote the partial osmotic pressures of the particular molecular species existing in the solution, and if L_1, L_2 . . . denote their respective solubility coefficients.

The partial pressure of each of the particular molecular species in the gas space is, moreover, proportional to the concentration in the solution. When no change of the molecular state (*i.e.* neither dissociation nor any other reaction between the dissolved and the evaporating substances) is associated with a change in the concentration, either in the solution or in the gas space, then *the total pressure* of the dissolved substances in the saturated vapour is proportional to the concentration in the solution. But this ceases to be true when there occurs a displacement of the equilibrium existing between the dissolved substances (the displacement being identified with a change in the number of molecules), as a result of a change in the concentration.

In order to prove these requirements of my theory, I investigated the equilibrium existing between solutions of acetic acid in benzene and their saturated vapour. Acetic acid, both in solution and in a state of vapour, is a mixture of the molecules (CH_3CO_2H) and $(CH_3CO_2H)_2$; and since the degree of dissociation changes with the concentration, it was anticipated that Henry's law would not hold good for the vapour of acetic acid.

The measurements of the partial pressure of the vapour of acetic acid were accomplished by determining the changes of the boiling-point occasioned by the addition of acetic acid to benzene, and were exactly measured by Beckmann's apparatus.

The partial pressures sought were obtained by the differences between the observed changes in the boiling-point and those calculated from the vapour pressure formula. In the following table, m denotes the number of g. of acetic acid dissolved in 100 g. of benzene ; and x its degree of dissociation, as is inferred from the boiling-point determinations of dilute solutions of related non-volatile acids, and calculated for the different concentrations, according to the equation of the isotherm of dissociation, viz.

$$\frac{mx^2}{1-x} = \text{constant.}$$

Here p is derived from the changes in the boiling-point, the partial pressure of the acetic acid being expressed in mm. of mercury.

m.	x.	p Obs.	p Calc.	Δ.	α.
0·150	0·20	2·4	2·6	2·24	0·87
0·663	0·10	6·6	6·5	2·44	0·70
1·64	0·065	11·8	11·6	2·61	0·60
1·87	0·061	12·9	12·6	2·63	0·58
2·60	0·055	16·1	15·7	2·71	0·54
4·13	0·042	21·8	21·4	2·81	0·48
5·00	0·038	23·6	23·9	2·83	0·47
6·83	0·033	31·4	31·1	2·96	0·40
7·53	0·031	33·5	33·4	2·99	0·38
8·42	0·029	36·4	36·4	3·02	0·36

Here we are not concerned with the proportionality bétween m and p which is required by the ordinary conception of Henry's law ; but this holds true, nevertheless, for the two particular molecular species, viz. the double and the single molecules, of which the acetic acid vapour is composed. This is shown by the following calculation.

The number of *normal molecules* in the solution is proportional to the value of mx, or also of $\sqrt{m(1-x)}$. The degree of dissociation α for the gaseous state is calculated from the vapour density Δ of acetic acid to be

$$\alpha = \frac{4\cdot146 - \Delta}{\Delta},$$

where $4\cdot146$ represents the value of the vapour density of acetic acid when $\alpha = 0$. The vapour densities Δ, given in the fifth column, and corresponding to the temperature of observation (the boiling-point of benzene being 80°), are calculated from the equation of the isotherm of dissociation (p. 465), viz.—

$$\frac{\Delta - 2\cdot073}{(4\cdot146 - \Delta)^2 p} = K',$$

where, according to Gibbs,[1] at 80°, K′ may be placed at $0\cdot0201$.

Now, since the number of normal molecules in unit volume of the vapour is proportional to the product of the mass of the acetic acid vapour in unit volume and its degree of dissociation ; therefore, corresponding to the expression

$$\Delta p \alpha = \Delta p \frac{4\cdot146 - \Delta}{\Delta} = p(4\cdot146 - \Delta),$$

a proportionality must exist between the values,

$$\sqrt{m(1-x)}, \quad \text{and} \quad p(4\cdot146 - \Delta).$$

Now, as a matter of fact, we find that the values of p given in the fourth column, and calculated from the formula

$$p = 14\cdot4\frac{\sqrt{m(1-x)}}{4\cdot146 - \Delta}\text{mm. Hg.}$$

[1] *Sill. Journ. (Am. J. Sci.)*, **18.** 371 (1879).

coincide with the results of observation in a remarkable way. The proportional factor 14·4 corresponds to the solubility coefficients of the CH_3CO_2H molecules.

Similar results are obtained in the measurement of the pressures of ethereal solutions of water, which substance, like acetic acid, tends to form double molecules, in this case $(H_2O)_2$.

The Mutual Solubility of Liquids.—Many liquids have the property of mutually dissolving each other to a limited extent, as water and ether, *e.g.* For each temperature there is a corresponding solubility of the one in the other, and conversely of the other in the one.

Usually both of the mutual solubilities increase with increasing temperature. Then the compositions of the two solutions approach nearer and nearer together on raising the temperature, until *complete miscibility* occurs, a phenomenon which reminds one of the *critical temperature.*

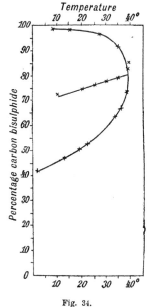

Fig. 34.

Sometimes both solubilities diminish with increasing temperature, or finally, the one may increase and the other may diminish, as is the case with water and ether. Thus if one warms water saturated with ether [the water being the solvent], or cools ether saturated with water [ether being the solvent], in both cases it is noticed that a cloudiness is formed in the originally clear liquids. From this it follows that the solubility of ether in water diminishes with rising temperature ; but, inversely, that that of water in ether increases with the temperature.

These relations have been thoroughly investigated first by Alexejew [1] and later by Rothmund.[2] The diagram represents some results obtained by the last-named author from measurements of the mutual solubility of carbon bisulphide and methyl alcohol.

The upper branch of the curve represents the composition of saturated solutions of methyl alcohol in carbon bisulphide, the lower the composition of those of carbon bisulphide in methyl alcohol. At 40·5° the curves are concurrent—*i.e.* above this temperature the two liquids are miscible in all proportions. As a rule all the pairs of

[1] Alexejew, *Wied. Ann.* **28.** 305 (1886).
[2] *Zeitschr. phys. Chem.* **26.** 433 (1898).

liquids investigated behaved similarly ; very occasionally a maximum or minimum was found in one or both curves. If we plot the mean values of the composition of two corresponding solutions we obtain in every case a straight line (see diagram), a regularity which is analogous to the law of Cailletet and Mathias (p. 228). As the " critical solution temperature " can be relatively easily and exactly determined, the ordinate which corresponds to the critical temperature, and gives the composition at which the two solutions become identical, can be easily found by a straight line of interpolation. The direct determination of the composition is less simple, because it changes very sharply with the temperature in the neighbourhood of the critical solution temperature.

Two liquids, which are mutually soluble to a limited degree, are in equilibrium with each other when they have dissolved each other to saturation. From this it follows that the *saturated vapours emitted by each of the two layers have the same pressure and the same composition.* For, since the two layers of the mixture are in equilibrium with each other, their saturated vapours must be also; for otherwise the condition of · equilibrium would be destroyed, resulting from a distillation process which would change the composition of the two layers. This requirement of the theory has been experimentally established by Konowalow (p. 107).

Moreover, the partial pressure of each one of the two ingredients must be smaller than that corresponding respectively to each of the pure solvents, because each of the solvents has experienced a depression of its own particular pressure, by reason of having dissolved some of the other solvent. The magnitudes of these depressions depend of course upon the respective molecular weights, and upon the mutual solubilities. They are very small when the solubility is at a minimum, as is the case, *e.g.*, with water and carbon disulphide. In such cases the resulting vapour pressure is simply [nearly] equal to the sum of the two vapour pressures which each of the two liquids respectively would have independently.

When one of two liquids [A and B] (the mutual solubility of which for each other is limited) dissolves still another substance [C], then the mutual solubility of the former [A or B] for the other [B or A] is diminished, in accordance with the laws of solubility already stated (see p. 145).

The Distribution of a Substance between Two Solvents.—

The laws which have already been stated for the evaporation of a substance existing in solution, *i.e.* for the distribution of a substance between a gaseous and a liquid phase, may be applied without further remark to the distribution of a substance between two liquid phases.

Now, by the *partition coefficients* of a substance between two solvents, we mean the ratio of the concentrations which the one substance has in these two solvents, after equilibrium is established ; and thus, by a simple extension of the law developed on p. 491, we arrive at the following results, viz. :—

1. If the dissolved substance has the same molecular weight in each of the two solvents, then *the partition coefficient* is constant for any given temperature (compare also p. 149).

2. In the presence of several dissolved substances, each molecular species distributes itself as though the others were not present.

3. If the dissolved substance does not exist as a unit, but is influenced by dissociation, then law 1 holds good for each of the molecular species resulting from the dissociation. This also follows immediately from the application of law 2.

Thus succinic acid is divided between ether and water, with the following constant *partition coefficient* :—

c_1.	c_2.	$\dfrac{c_1}{c_2}$.
0·024	0·0046	5·2
0·070	0·013	5·2
0·121	0·022	5·4

Here c_1 and c_2 denote the number of g. of acid dissolved in 10 c.c. of water and of ether respectively. This was to be expected, because succinic acid has its normal molecular weight both in ether and also in water, disregarding its very slight electrolytic dissociation in the latter. Similar results were found by Berthelot and Jungfleisch[1] for similar cases.

But, as was to be expected, very different results were found by the writer[2] in the study of the distribution of substances which have *different molecular weights* in the two solvents. Thus, c_1 and c_2 denoting the varying concentrations (*i.e.* the number of g. in 10 c.c. of the solvent) of benzoic acid in water and benzene respectively, the following results were found :—

c_1.	c_2.	$\dfrac{c_1}{c_2}$.	$\dfrac{c_1}{\sqrt{c_2}}$.
0·0150	0·242	0·062	0·0305
0·0195	0·412	0·048	0·0304
0·0289	0·970	0·030	0·0293

[1] *Ann. chim. phys.* [4], **26**. 396 (1872) ; Berthelot, *ibid.* 408.
[2] Nernst, *Zeitschr. phys. Chem.* **8**. 110 (1891).

Here we are not concerned with the constancy of the quotient $\frac{c_1}{c_2}$, because the acid has its *normal mol. wt.* in water (disregarding again a very slight electrolytic dissociation), while in benzene the *double molecules* preponderate. Now, the number of normal molecules in the latter solvent [benzene], according to the laws of dissociation, is proportional to the square root of the concentration; and thus the law of distribution requires a proportionality between c_1 and $\sqrt{c_2}$; and as a matter of fact we find the values of the expression $\left(\dfrac{c_1}{\sqrt{c_2}}\right)$, as given in the last column, very constant.

This constancy disappears at extreme dilution, because in this case the benzoic acid in the benzene is decomposed increasingly into single molecules. The writer calculated the degree of dissociation from the change in $\dfrac{c_1}{\sqrt{c_2}}$, and thus proved that the equation of the isotherm of dissociation also holds good for the decomposition, in solution, of double molecules.

Hendrixson [1] has made more exact measurements of this kind and thoroughly established the theory. The following table refers to the partition of benzoic acid between benzene and water at $10°$; c_1 is the number of grms. of benzoic acid contained in the aqueous phase for 200 grms. of water, c_2 the corresponding quantity for the benzene phase; α is the degree of electrolytic dissociation in water (see the following chapter), $c_1(1-\alpha)$ therefore the quantity of benzoic acid in its normal state in the aqueous phase. Taking as the ratio of partition for normal molecules $k = 0\cdot700$, it follows that the number of normal molecules in the benzene phase is

$$m = \frac{c_1(1-\alpha)}{0\cdot700};$$

the number of double molecules in the benzene phase is therefore naturally $c_2 - m$. To test the theory the last column gives the dissociation constant

$$K = \frac{m^2}{c_2 - m},$$

which is found to be constant within the limit of errors of observation; this proves both that the dissociation isotherm holds for the dissociation of double molecules into simple, and that the simple molecules (as also the double molecules) possess a ratio of partition independent of concentration or degree of dissociation.

[1] *Zeitschr. anorg. Chem.* **13.** 73 (1897).

2 K

c_1.	c_2.	α.	$c_1(1-a)$.	m.	$c_2 - m$.	$\dfrac{m^2}{c_2 - m}$.
0·0429	0·1449	0·169	0·0357	0·0510	0·0939	0·0277
0·0562	0·2380	0·149	0·0474	0·0677	0·1703	0·0269
0·0823	0·4726	0·125	0·0720	0·1029	0·3697	0·0286
0·1124	0·8843	0·104	0·1007	0·1439	0·7404	0·0279
0·1780	2·1777	0·0866	0·1626	0·2323	1·9454	0·0277
0·2430	4·0544	0·0747	0·2249	0·3213	3·7331	0·0276
0·2817	5·4851	0·0695	0·2621	0·3743	5·1108	0·0274
					Mean K=	0·0277

In the same way it was found that at 44°

$$k = 0·477 \qquad K = 0·122.$$

Application of the Law of Partition to Determination of Chemical Equilibrium.

—Just as on p. 486 the solubility was applied to determine the ratio in which the different species of molecules take part in equilibrium, so we may make use of a partition of a substance between two solvents for the same object. This has been done practically in the table in the foregoing paragraph ; the following examples, which illustrate the application of this method to more complicated cases, show that the law of partition has a certain advantage as compared with the principle of constant solubility in application to such cases, for the latter refers only to a single concentration, namely that of saturation, whereas the former is not so limited.

1. Bromine is shared between water and carbon disulphide in a constant ratio, the molecular weight corresponding to the formula Br_2 in both solvents. If potassium bromide is added to the water, it is found that a considerably larger amount of bromine passes into the aqueous layer. This quantity must be used in forming a new species of molecule ; Roloff,[1] who, at my instance, first made use of the law of partition to study chemical equilibrium, was able to show that bromine forms, by addition of potassium bromide, the electrolytically strongly dissociated salt KBr_3.

2. The ratio of partition of chlorine between water and carbon tetrachloride varies considerably with the concentration. This, as was shown by A. A. Jakowkin,[2] depends upon the fact that chlorine acts on water according to the equation

$$Cl_2 + H_2O = HCl + HClO.$$

[1] *Zeitschr. phys. Chem.* **13.** 341 (1894). The corresponding investigation on the formation of potassium triodide has been carried out by A. A. Jakowkin (see *ibid.* **20.** 19, 1896).

[2] *Ber. deutsch. chem. Ges.* **30.** 518 (1897) ; *Zeitschr. phys. Chem.* **29.** 613 1899).

If the amount of unchanged chlorine is used for the calculation, a constant ratio of partition is arrived at ; in calculating this the electrolytic dissociation of the hydrochloric acid formed must be taken into account.

Adsorption Equilibrium.—Just as the partition of a substance between two solvents leads to an equilibrium, so also does adsorption— equilibrium generally being reached quickly and exactly.   Freundlich [1] found the empirical relation :

$$\frac{y}{m} = \beta c^{\frac{1}{p}} \qquad . \qquad . \qquad . \qquad . \qquad (1)$$

where y is the mass of adsorbed substance, m that of the adsorbent, c the concentration of the unadsorbed portion in solution, and β and p are constants.   For example, W. Biltz [2] showed that the adsorption of arsenious acid by freshly precipitated iron hydroxide could be expressed by the relation :

$$\frac{y}{x^{\frac{1}{5}}} = 0 \cdot 631$$

(y = mass of adsorbed acid, x that remaining in solution).   This table

x found.	x calc.	y.
0·010	0·010	0·251
0·107	0·123	0·415
0·495	0·498	0·549
0·952	0·881	0·615
1·898	1·826	0·712
3·875	3·740	0·824

brings out clearly a characteristic of all adsorption phenomena : the percentage adsorbed of the total amount of substance is greater, the more dilute the original solution.   A well-known example of this is the adsorption of gases by charcoal at very low temperatures ; if the original pressure of the gas is extremely small, a practically absolute vacuum can be obtained (Dewar).   At the same time, the above relation shows that the adsorbent is not simply a solvent for the adsorbed material.   For if this were true, arsenious acid would have a molecular weight in iron hydroxide, one-fifth of that which it has in water (partition law).   In water, however, its molecular weight is practically normal ; the assumption of so large a dissociation in iron hydroxide is therefore untenable.   No theoretical interpretation has yet been given to the above relation.   Freundlich (*l.c.*) has also shown

[1] *Zeitschr. phys. Chem.* **57.** 385 (1907).
[2] *Ber. deutsch. chem. Ges.* **37.** 3138 (1904).

that it is derived from a differential equation, which is equally incomprehensible from a theoretical point of view.   He has replaced this by another :

$$\frac{dy}{dm} = \lambda \frac{x}{v}$$

(v = volume of solution) ; this means that if a small fresh amount of adsorbent is added to a solution in adsorption-equilibrium, then the increase of adsorbed substance is proportional to its concentration in the solution$\left(\frac{x}{v}\right)$.   The factor λ can be empirically expressed as a function of (x + y) and v :

$$\lambda = a\left(\frac{x+y}{v}\right)^{-\frac{1}{n}},$$

where a, and $\frac{1}{n}$ are characteristic constants for every substance, and independent of the temperature.   Integration gives :

$$\frac{v}{m} \ln \frac{x+y}{x} = a\left(\frac{x+y}{v}\right)^{-\frac{1}{n}} \qquad . \qquad . \qquad . \qquad (2)$$

and it is not difficult to show by evolution in series that this equation is identical with (1) up to terms of high order.   It agrees with observations as well as (1), and has the advantage that it is derived from a differential equation capable of a theoretical explanation.

The Freezing of Solutions and Crystallisation from Solutions.—The separation of solid substances from solutions, in many respects, may be compared with the process of the evaporation of a mixture, *i.e.*, the separation of one of its components in the gaseous form.   When this process results in the precipitation of that ingredient of the solution which is present in excess, *i.e. the solvent*, it is called *a freezing of the solution* ; and when it results in the separation of *the substance dissolved*, then it is called *a crystallising out of the substance dissolved.*   The processes of freezing and of crystallising out are both to be considered from the same point of view ; and if we are not dealing with dilute solutions, where one ingredient is present in large excess, but with a mixture, where both ingredients are present in about the same proportions, then we are in actual doubt whether the separation should be regarded as a freezing or a crystallising out.

Now it is probable that neither ingredient is ever separated in an absolutely pure form, but that there crystallises out an *isomorphous mixture containing both ingredients*, just as every solution emits a vapour which is a mixture containing *both ingredients.*

But experiment shows that usually one ingredient preponderates so much in the product which is crystallised out, that we may practically regard it as a separation in a pure form.   Then, according to this conception, the two cases which are distinguished above are to be regarded as only two limiting cases of the many which occur in nature ; and in fact examples are known, though they are not very numerous, where the solvent and the dissolved substance crystallise out from the solution in an isomorphous mixture (pp. 163 and 277).

The Freezing-Point of Dilute Solutions.—There is no difficulty in solving the case where *the pure solvent freezes out* from a dilute solution. For the condition of equilibrium between the solidified solvent and the solution is completely made known by means of the laws which have been already described (p. 146). These laws may be formulated as follows :—

1. The addition of a foreign substance lowers the freezing-point in all cases.

2. The depression of the freezing-point of the solvent, occasioned by the addition of a foreign substance, is, in most cases, proportional to its concentration (Blagden) ; in all cases, namely, where the dissolved substance exists in the solution in its unit molecules, *i.e.* when there is neither dissociation nor polymerisation (van't Hoff).

3. The depression t of the freezing-point, occasioned by the addition of a foreign substance whose mol. wt. is M, is

$$t = E\frac{m}{M} ;$$

where m denotes the number of grams of the foreign substance in 100 g. of the solvent ; E denotes the *molecular depression of the freezing-point*, *i.e.* the depression occasioned by the addition of 1 g.-mol. of the foreign substance to 100 g. of the solvent ; it varies with the particular solvent used (Raoult).

The *molecular depression of the freezing-point* may be theoretically calculated from the *melting-point* T, on the absolute scale, and from the *heat of fusion* r, expressed in g.-cal per g. of substance, from the formula (van't Hoff),

$$E = \frac{0.02T^2}{r}.$$

These laws make it possible to ascertain by calculation, from the known concentration of the solution, that temperature-point at which (under atmospheric pressure) the solution and the solidified solvent may exist together in stable equilibrium.

The influence of *pressure* on the freezing-point of a solution has not as yet been experimentally studied ; but it may be anticipated that the lowering of the freezing-point experienced by the solvent on the addition of a foreign substance is practically *independent* of the external pressure. The laws formulated above strictly hold good only for *dilute solutions*, and in concentrated solutions (*e.g.* 10 to 20 per cent) they merely serve as *approximations.*

The Crystallising out of Dissolved Substances.—Reference has already been made (p. 484) to the condition of equilibrium which prevails when the dissolved substance is separated in a pure form. Here we will merely show the connection of the preceding section with the new point of view to which we have attained. Thus, *e.g.* we may conceive of the condition of equilibrium between a solid salt and its saturated water solution in this way ; that the freezing-point of the solid salt is depressed by the presence of the water to the temperature of the saturated solution. Thus, while on the one hand we may justly parallelise the process of solution with that of evaporation, there is also, on the other hand, an undeniable analogy with the melting of a solidified solvent in presence of its solution.

The so-called " Cryohydrates."—If we cool sufficiently a water solution in contact with a solid salt, we finally arrive at the freezing-point of the saturated solution, where, with the separation of ice, there is also associated a separation of the salt existing in the solution. At this temperature-point there is precipitated a mechanical (not a really isomorphous) mass (the eutectic mixture, p. 120), containing ice and the solid substance, in those proportions which correspond to the particular concentration of the saturated solution. This temperature-point is determined by the intersection of the solubility curve of the salt in question, with the curve which represents the dependence of the freezing-point of the solution upon its concentration. Such a solution does not change its composition by fractional freezing, and it must, therefore, have a constant freezing-point, *i.e.* one which is *independent* of the quantity frozen out.[1]

The Equilibrium between Liquid and Solid Solutions.— The most general case, where an isomorphous mixture of the solvent and of the dissolved substance crystallises out of the solution, gives us a system in which a solid and a liquid solution are in equilibrium with each other.

We may distinguish the following cases of equilibrium corresponding to the degree of miscibility of the solid substances :—

1. The two salts[2] may form isomorphous mixtures in all proportions : then in crystallising out a common solution of both salts, mixed crystals of every composition could be formed.

2. The series of mixtures of the two solid salts is not continuous. Then the two inner members must be in equilibrium with each other, in a way similar to the equilibrium between two mutually saturated liquids (p. 494) ; and, therefore, for exactly the same reason that the

---

[1] Amongst the more recent work see especially the investigation of Roloff, *Zeitschr. phys. Chem.* **17.** 325 (1895).

[2] Of course, what is said above respecting salts may be applied without further remark to other substances.

two mutually saturated liquids are in equilibrium with vapour having the same composition, these two inner members must be in equilibrium with the same saturated solution.

In fact, Roozeboom [1] succeeded in verifying this experimentally by mixed solutions of potassium and thallium chlorates. If solutions of thallium chlorate which contain increasing quantities of potassium chlorate are allowed to crystallise, at first there appear mixed crystals containing the thallium chlorate in excess. The greater the quantity of the potassium salt added, the larger is the proportion of this substance contained in the mixed crystals. But when the proportion of the potassium salt in the mixed crystals has reached 36·3 per cent, then there appear also mixed crystals which contain 98·0 per cent of the potassium salt, i.e. the same solution is at the same time in equilibrium with these two inner members of the series of mixtures. If the proportion of the potassium salt in the solution is carried further, then there separate only mixed crystals which contain more than 98 per cent of the potassium salt.

The phenomena observed on evaporating the solution of these two salts are thus completely analogous to those observed on the condensation of a mixture, e.g. of ether and water vapour.

3. If a double salt is found in the gap of the series of mixtures, then, from solutions of the one salt, by successive and increasing additions of the other, there separate—firstly, the mixed crystals on one side [of the gap] of the series of mixtures ; then, secondly, when a definite concentration is reached, at the same time there appear both the inner end member of the first mixed series and also the double salt ; then, thirdly, within a certain concentration interval, the double salt alone appears ; then, fourthly, at a definite point, the double salt, and at the same time the inner end member of the second series of mixtures ; and finally [with increasing addition of ·the second salt], the successive mixed crystals of the second series alone. An example of this kind is found in Roozeboom's [2] investigation of the crystallisation of solutions of ferric and ammonium chlorides.

There is thus often a complicated series of stable solutions, and it is necessary in referring to a saturated solution to state the solid substances present.

All that we know at present about the case where a *dilute solid solution* takes part in the equilibrium, shows that the same laws hold good which we have learned in the foregoing sections regarding the equilibrium between phases of variable composition, which are composed of gases or of dilute liquid solutions. Especially the laws regarding the distribution of a substance between two solvents hold good also for this case. [3]

[1] *Zeitschr. phys. Chem.* **8.** 504 and 530 (1891).   [2] *Ibid.* **10.** 145 (1892).
[3] See further the literature mentioned on p. 277 and the observations of Muthmann and Kuntze, *Zeitschr. f. Kristallographie*, **23.** 368 (1896).

An interesting application of these laws appears to be possible in the theory of dyeing processes. According to O. N. Witt,[1] the absorption of the colour by the fibre *consists in a solution of the dye-stuff in the fibre,* i.e. *in the formation of a solid solution.*

Of the many reasons which Witt has adduced for the plausibility of this view, it should be mentioned that the coloured fibre does not show the colour of the solid dye-stuff, but of the dissolved dye-stuff; thus, *e.g.,* fibres coloured with fuchsine are not coloured a metallic-green, but red. Rhodamine does not fluoresce in the solid state, but in solution; but silk, coloured with rhodamine, shows a clear fluorescence, which argues for the view that the colouring matter exists in the dissolved state.

In the sense of these views, the colouring process is completely comparable to the shaking out of a substance from a water solution by any other solvent, as by ether, carbon disulphide, etc.

Further, the fact that the same dye-stuff may introduce itself into different fibres, producing different colours, is completely analogous to such cases, as where iodine, *e.g.,* is dissolved in different solvents, producing different colours.

The nature of the so-called "adjective colours" was thus explained by Witt, viz. that the associated mordant is first dissolved by the fibre, and then, in its turn, dissolves the dye-stuff, as a result of a chemical action, as it diffuses into the fibre; and thus there results an increase of the solubility of the dye-stuff in the fibre.

Probably when the yarn takes up colouring matter adsorption phenomena occur and perhaps even chemical processes, so that it is not a simple case of the partition of a substance between two solvents; this is evidenced by the abnormal values obtained in attempts to ascertain the molecular weight of the substances absorbed by the yarn by means of the partition laws.[2]

Similarly no theoretical conclusions can be made about the carrying down of dissolved salts by precipitation of oxides, sulphides, and the like—so important in analytical chemistry. This phenomenon occurs exclusively with colloidal (amorphous) precipitates. The observations of van Bemmelen,[3] Linder and Picton,[4] and Whitney and Ober[5] show that there must be some chemical combination of the salt with the colloidal precipitate.

The Most General Case.—Finally, the following very general case will be considered.

Let there be a reaction between a number of vaporised substances, which are at the same time dissolved in any selected solvent, and let the reaction proceed according to the scheme

---

[1] *Färberzeitung,* **1.** (1890-91). Ref. in *Zeitschr. phys. Chem.* **7.** 93 (1891), also in the *Jahrbuch der Chem.* **1.** p. 18 (1891), and very thoroughly in the *Chem. Zentralbl.* **2.** 1039 (1891).

[2] See the literature mentioned on p. 124, and also Zacharias, *Zeitschr. phys. Chem.* **39.** 468 (1902), and Kaufler, *ibid.* **43.** 686 (1903).

[3] *Zeitschr. anorg. Chem.* **23.** 321 (1900).   [4] *Chem. Soc. Journ.* **67.** 63 (1895).

[5] *Zeitschr. phys. Chem.* **39.** 630 (1902).

$$n_1 A_1 + n_2 A_2 + \ldots = n_1' A_1' + n_2' A_2' + \ldots$$

That is, let n_1 mols of a substance A_1, and n_2 mols of a substance $A_2 \ldots$, etc., unite to form n_1' mols of a substance A_1', and n_2' mols of a substance $A_2' \ldots$, etc. Let equilibrium be established when the partial pressures of the particular molecular species are respectively p_1, $p_2 \ldots$, p_1', $p_2' \ldots$, and when their concentrations in the solution amount respectively to c_1, $c_2 \ldots$, c_1', $c_2' \ldots$

Then the application of the Guldberg-Waage law of chemical mass-action gives the two equations—

$$\frac{p_1^{n_1} p_2^{n_2} \cdots}{p_1'^{n_1'} p_2'^{n_2'} \cdots} = K' \qquad \qquad (1)$$

$$\frac{c_1^{n_1} c_2^{n_2} \cdots}{c_1'^{n} c_2'^{n_2'} \cdots} = K . \qquad \qquad (2)$$

Here K and K', the reaction coefficients, depend only upon the temperature.

The law of distribution gives us several equations, viz.

$$c_1 = p_1 k_1, \quad c_2 = p_2 k_2 \ldots, \quad c_1' = p_1' k_1', \quad c_2' = p_2' k_2' \quad . \qquad (3)$$

Here k_1, $k_2 \ldots$, k_1', $k_2' \ldots$ denote respectively the solubility coefficients of the particular molecular species; and these again depend only upon the temperature.

From reactions (1) to (3) we obtain

$$K' = K \frac{k_1'^{n_1'} k_2'^{n_2'} \cdots}{k_1^{n_1} k_2^{n_2} \cdots} \qquad \qquad (4)$$

In most cases the solubility coefficients of a molecular species for any solvent may be directly determined, and this information allows one to say beforehand how a number of substances will react on each other in any solvent, provided that their reaction capacity in the gaseous state is known, and conversely.

Of course a similar relation holds good for the partition coefficients. When *solid substances* take part in the equilibrium, their active mass is constant,[1] and the same is true of reacting molecules, which at the same time play the *rôle* of solvents (p. 469). Therefore, we may state the following general theorem :—

If we know the coefficients of equilibrium of a reaction which progresses to a finish at a definite temperature, and in any selected phase ; and if we know the partition coefficients of all the molecular species with reference to another phase ; then the condition of equilibrium is also known in the second phase at the same temperature.

This theorem should have great practical significance, because it enables us to anticipate, from the partition coefficients, the reaction capacity in the most various solvents or in the gaseous state, after we

---

[1] Provided that these form no mixed crystals, double salts, or the like.

have studied it in one particular phase; and thus the problem of "dissociating force" (p. 468), or even of the influence of the medium is referred to the simpler one of the study of the *partition coefficients*, and of the relation of these to the nature of the substance in question, and to the particular phase under consideration.

Applications.—The vapour above a mixture of acetic acid, alcohol, water, and ester in equilibrium must also be in equilibrium; hence the relation

$$\frac{\text{Ester} \times \text{water}}{\text{Alcohol} \times \text{acid}} = \text{const.}$$

must hold for the vapour also; but the constant in the gaseous phase will in general have a different value to that for the liquid. The experimental verification of this law would be not without interest.

Kuriloff[1] made a very thorough investigation of the above general theorem, the results of which we will calculate in a somewhat different manner to the author. The investigator mentioned determined the equilibrium of solid β-naphthol-picrate in contact first with water and then with benzene, and also the ratio of partition of the reacting molecules, so that all the data necessary for testing the theory are available.

The equilibrium in water was determined by solubility measurements in the same way as in the example of anthracene picrate given on p. 486. The solution contains 6·09 free β-napthol and 8·80 free picric acid, besides 1·20 of picrate when the latter substance was present in the solid state. The numbers are in thousandths of a mol per litre. The picric acid under these circumstances is electrolytically dissociated to the extent of 94·6%; hence the product of the free naphthol and the free undissociated picric acid is

$$\mu_1 \mu_2 = 6{\cdot}09 \,.\, 8{\cdot}80(1 - 0{\cdot}946) = 2{\cdot}89.$$

Further, the coefficients of partition of the two latter species of molecule between benzene and water are 67 for naphthol and 39 for the undissociated molecules of picric acid. Hence in benzene the value must be

$$\mu_1' \mu_2' = \mu_1 \mu_2 \,.\, 67 \,.\, 39 = 7550,$$

and when both species of molecules are present in equivalent quantities their concentrations must be

$$c_0 = \sqrt{\mu_1' \,.\, \mu_2'} = 86{\cdot}9.$$

Now the solubility of the picrate in benzene is 104·5; hence the saturated solution of this substance must be dissociated to the extent

$$\frac{c_0}{104{\cdot}5} = 0{\cdot}83,$$

whilst measurement of the equilibrium by means of solubility, with excess of one or the other component, gives 0·64 to 0·85 for the degree of dissociation of the saturated solution.

Thus from the dissociation of the aqueous solution saturated with picrate, and from the ratio of partition of the components, we can calculate how much dissociated substance is contained in a saturated solution of picrate in benzene.

---

[1] *Zeitschr. phys. Chem.* **25**. 419 (1898).

CHAPTER IV

The Reaction Capacity of Ions.—In the preceding chapter we have become familiar with the general theory of chemical equilibrium in any selected system, and regarding the dependence of this equilibrium upon the relative quantities of the reacting components. But there is one case which we have not as yet considered : viz. *the part played in the reactions by the free ions, i.e.* the study of *water solutions of electrolytes,* or in short, of *salt solutions.* A special chapter is devoted to the consideration of salt solutions, *partly for the purpose of a general view, and partly to show that when the law of mass-action is applied to the study of salt solutions, then the hypothesis of electrolytic dissociation becomes an imperative necessity, at least, according to the present state of our knowledge.*

From the standpoint of the hypothesis of electrolytic dissociation (p. 353), the whole question is at once solved by the simple conclusion, that *the free ions must participate in reactions in proportion to their concentration (their active mass), just like every other molecular species.* Without the introduction of any new hypothesis, we are now in a position to handle the chemical equilibrium between substances, which conduct electrolytically, in just the same simple manner which was employed in considering the reactions between those molecular species which were exclusively electrically neutral.

And thus nothing that is especially new in principle is contained in the following paragraphs, but many new and surprising applications of the law of Guldberg and Waage will be given.

The great honour of giving this point of view its proper value belongs to Arrhenius.

Electrolytic Dissociation.—When a molecular species A, which is electrically neutral, decomposes into ions, thus

$$A = n_1 A_1 + n_2 A_2 + \ldots ,$$

the law of mass-action requires that

$$Kc = c_1^{n_1} c_2^{n_2} \ldots ,$$

where c denotes the concentration of the undissociated part, and $c_1, c_2 \ldots$ etc., the respective concentrations of the products (ions) resulting from dissociation, and K, as usual, denotes the *constant of dissociation*. Of course, the ions are always produced in quantities which are electrically equivalent. For a binary electrolyte, we have

$$Kc = c_1^2;$$

then since

$$c = \frac{1 - a}{V}, \text{ and } c_1 = \frac{a}{V},$$

when a denotes the degree of dissociation, and V the volume containing 1 mol of the electrolyte; we obtain

$$KV(1 - a) = a^2,$$

from which it follows that

$$a = \frac{KV}{2}\left(\sqrt{1 + \frac{4}{KV}} - 1\right).$$

Two methods (p. 360) are already known to us for the determination of a; viz. the measurement of *the osmotic pressure* (the freezing-point, etc.), and the measurement of *the electrical conductivity*; the latter is much more exact, and depends on the formula

$$a = \frac{\lambda}{\lambda_\infty}.$$

This formula, which was first experimentally proven by Ostwald,[1] by application to electrolytic dissociation, was established with the best results for a large number of organic acids. The following table, given by van't Hoff and Reicher,[2] may serve as an illustration :—

THE MOLECULAR CONDUCTIVITIES OF ACETIC ACID AT $14 \cdot 1°$.

V.	λ.	100 a Obs.	100 a Calc.	
0·994	1·27	0·402	0·42	
2·02	1·94	0·614	0·60	
15·9	5·26	1·66	1·67	
18·1	5·63	1·78	1·78	
1500	46·6	14·7	15·0	log K $= 5\cdot25 - 10$
3010	64·8	20·5	20·2	
7480	95·1	30·1	30·5	
15000	129	40·8	40·1	
[∞	316	100	100]	

[1] *Zeitschr. phys. Chem.* **2.** 36 and 270 (1888); see also Planck, *Wied. Ann.* **34.** 139 (1888).
[2] *Zeitschr. phys. Chem.* **2.** 779 (1888).

The coincidence between the degree of dissociation—as determined by the conductivities, and as calculated according to the theoretical formula, where $K = 0\cdot0000178$—is very remarkable.

Inasmuch as the same form of the isotherm of dissociation holds good for the ordinary binary, and also for the electrolytic, dissociation, therefore the laws developed (p. 465) for the former also apply to the latter.

In particular when the dissociation is but slight, the concentration of the ions (and therefore of the conductivity also), of a binary electrolyte, is proportional to the square root of the total concentration.

The formula does not hold for highly dissociated acids and salts. This is perhaps to be ascribed partly to the fact that the determination of

$$1 - \alpha = \frac{\lambda_\infty - \lambda}{\lambda_\infty},$$

is exposed to *great uncertainty*, on account of the smallness of the difference between λ_∞ and λ; here, most probably, for reasons unknown at present, the electrical conductivity is not a perfectly exact measure of the degree of dissociation. An explanation of this point would be exceedingly important, but it has not been forthcoming as yet.

The practical use of the law of mass-action is scarcely affected by those comparatively slight exceptions.

According to M. Rudolphi,[1] in strongly dissociated electrolytes the expression $\dfrac{\alpha^2}{(1 - \alpha) \sqrt{V}}$ is much more constant than $\dfrac{\alpha^2}{(1 - \alpha) V}$, and for analogous compounds possesses somewhat similar values. Van't Hoff[2] a little later pointed out that the expression $\dfrac{\alpha^{\frac{3}{2}}}{(1 - \alpha) \sqrt{V}}$ or the square of it $\dfrac{\alpha^3}{(1 - \alpha)^2 V}$ is equally or more constant than that of Rudolphi. Considering that

$$c = \frac{1 - \alpha}{V}, \quad c_1 = \frac{\alpha}{V},$$

we have

$$\frac{c_1{}^3}{c^2} = \text{const.},$$

that is, *the third power of the ionic concentration is proportional to the square of the undissociated molecules.* As F. Kohlrausch[3] showed, van't Hoff's expression may also be put in the form that the ratio of the concentration of the undissociated molecules to that of the ions is proportional to the mean distance between the undissociated molecules.

The above equations are purely empirical; in reality the law of mass-

---

[1] *Zeitschr. phys. Chem.* **17.** 385 (1895).   [2] *Ibid.* **18.** 300 (1895).
[3] *Ibid.* **18.** 662 (1895).

action probably holds good, for *apparent* anomalies may be caused by a slight combination of ions and neutral molecules in water.

Electrolytic Dissociation and Chemical Nature.—The question now arises,—How does the *degree* of the electrolytic dissociation depend upon the *nature* of the respective electrolyte ?—a question which is all the more important because the reaction-capacity depends, in a very pronounced way, upon the degree of dissociation. In what follows, there will be grouped together some of the most important rules thus far recognised in this region of work ; a knowledge of these rules will serve, in a remarkable way, to elucidate the general view of chemical equilibrium in salt solutions.

1. *The salts of the alkalies, of ammonium, of thallium, and of silver, with monobasic acids, in dilute solutions and at equivalent concentrations, are dissociated to the same degree ; and, moreover, are highly dissociated, as is shown by the figures for potassium chloride, given on p. 361.*

2. On the other hand, the greatest differences are found among *the monobasic acids* and the *monacid bases.* Thus, some substances, like acetic acid, ammonia, etc., in tenth-normal solutions, are dissociated only to a small percentage ; while other substances, such as hydrochloric acid, potassium hydroxide, etc., are as highly dissociated as the salts enumerated above.

3. Certain electrolytes, such as zinc sulphate, cupric sulphate, etc., *which on dissociation are cleaved into only two ions, but each with doubled electrical charges,* are comparatively much less dissociated ; zinc sulphate and copper sulphate, in a concentration of 1 mol per litre, are dissociated only about 25 per cent (see also p. 362).

4. The behaviour of those *electrolytes which dissociate into more than two ions,* is much more complicated. According to what is known at present, in general, a *dissociation in stages* seems to take place. Thus sulphuric acid does not decompose all at once into the SO_4 group with a double electro-negative charge, and two hydrogen ions, each with a single electro-positive charge ; but the decomposition rather progresses according to the two following equations—

$$\text{I. } H_2SO_4 = \overset{-}{H}SO_4 + \overset{+}{H}.$$
$$\text{II. } \overset{-}{H}SO_4 = \overset{=}{S}O_4 + \overset{+}{H}.$$

The decomposition is similar in the case of such substances as $BaCl_2$, K_2CO_3, etc.

In general this law holds good here, viz., *salts which have an analogous composition, in equivalent solutions are dissociated electrolytically to the same degree.* But this latter law is by no means a rule which holds good without exception ; thus the chlorides of calcium, strontium, barium, magnesium, and copper are dissociated nearly to the same extent ; but the chlorides of cadmium and of mercury, though of analogous constitution, are cleaved into their respective ions much less strongly.

For dissociation such as $\overset{+}{Pb}Cl \mid \overset{-}{Cl}, \overset{+}{K} \mid \overset{-}{KSO_4}$ etc., it may be assumed with considerable probability that it follows the rule of binary neutral salts, such as potassium bromide. Von Ende [1] has recently demonstrated this experimentally in the case of lead. chloride.

5. Many polybasic acids, within a wide concentration interval, act like monobasic acids, *i.e.* the equation of the isotherm of dissociation, which was developed on p. 508, for binary electrolytes, is also applicable to them. It is only at extreme dilution that these polybasic acids begin to separate the second, the third, etc., hydrogen ions.

The fact that extensive dilution is always required in order to separate the last hydrogen ions, would indicate that it is increasingly difficult for the acid residue to assume the last *quanta* of negative electricity.

6. Electrolytic dissociation, as compared with ordinary dissociation, changes with the temperature but slightly; for with rising temperature, it sometimes slowly diminishes, sometimes increases,—in contrast to ordinary dissociation, which always rapidly increases with ·the temperature.

These rules, as shown by Ostwald,[2] may be well applied to the determination of the basicity of acids. Since the state of dissociation, *e.g.* of a sodium salt, varies in a characteristic way with the basicity of the respective acid, therefore the simple study of the conductivity, in its dependence upon the concentration, may be directed to the explanation of this point. Of course the same question may be decided by the measurement of the depression of the freezing-point.

The Strength of Affinity of Organic Acids.—It is to the extended researches of Ostwald [3] that we are chiefly indebted for our knowledge of the relations prevailing here ; he, in common with his students, has given especial attention to the problem, *how does the capacity of organic acids to dissociate electrolytically depend upon the structure of the particular radical?* Unfortunately not enough space is available to consider in detail the many interesting points which have been developed by research in this region ; and it will be merely mentioned that *the dissociation constants*, or as they will also be called, for reasons to be given below, *the affinity strengths* (which, as shown on p. 508, can be ascertained with the greatest exactness), *vary in a most pronounced way with the constitution of the acid radical.* This relation to the constitution has not as yet been explained, so as

[1] *Dissertation*, Göttingen, 1900.
[2] *Zeitschr. phys. Chem.* **1.** 74 (1887) ; **2.** 901 (1888).
[3] *Jour. pr. Chem.* **31.** 433 (1885) ; *Zeitschr. phys. Chem.* **3.** 170 (1889) ; Walker, *ibid.* **4.** 319 (1889) ; Bethmann, *ibid.* **5.** 385 ; Bader, *ibid.* **6.** 289 (1890) ; Walden, *ibid.* **8.** 435 (1891) ; Bredig, *ibid.* **13.** 289 (1894).

to allow the value of the dissociation constant to be numerically derived from the constitution ; our knowledge thus far is limited to the recognition of the regularity of the influence exerted by the substitution of certain radicals.

According to this the radicals may be divided into *negative* and *positive*, according as they favour the assumption of a negative anionic charge (acids) and therefore hinder the positive cationic charge, or *vice versa*.

The following substances act *negatively* : aromatic radicals (*e.g.* C_6H_5), hydroxyl, sulphur, halogens, carboxyl, and cyanogen ; *positively* : fatty radicals (*e.g.* CH_3) addition of hydrogen, and especially the amido group.

This appears from the affinity constants of the following series of acids :—

	100 K
Acetic acid CH_3COOH	0·00180
a-Toluic acid $CH_2(C_6H_5)COOH$ . .	0·00556
Glycollic acid $CH_2(OH)COOH$ . . .	0·0152
Thiacetic acid CH_3COSH . . .	0·0469
Chloracetic acid $CH_2ClCOOH$ . . .	0·155
Tri-chlor-acetic acid CCl_3COOH . .	121
Malic acid $CH_2(COOH)COOH$ . . .	0·158
Cyanacetic acid $CH_2(CN)COOH$ . .	0·370
Propionic acid $CH_2(CH_3)COOH$ . .	0·00134
Glycocol $CH_2(NH_2)COOH$ . . .	very small

and of *bases* :—

	100 K
Ammonia NH_4OH	0·0023
Methylamine $NH_3(CH_3)OH$ . .	0·050
Benzylamine $NH_3(CH_2C_6H_5)OH$ . .	0·0024
Aniline $NH_3(C_6H_5)OH$	0·000000011

The *spacial position* of the substituent in the molecule is of considerable influence on its action ; the nearer the substituent is to the point at which the ionic charge is taken up the more effective it is ; thus we have 100 K in

o-nitrobenzoic acid 0·616 > m-nitrobenzoic acid 0·0345

$$\frac{\text{Trichloracetic acid}}{\text{Acetic acid}} \quad \frac{CCl_3 . COOH}{CH_3 . COOH} = \frac{121}{0·00180} > \frac{\text{Trichlorlactic acid}}{\text{Lactic acid}}$$

$$\frac{CCl_3 . CHOH . COOH}{CH_3 . CHOH . COOH} = \frac{0·465}{0·0138}$$

Benzylamine $C_6H_5CH_2NH_3OH$ 0·0024 > Toluidine $CH_3C_6H_4NH_3OH$ circa 10^{-12}

Oxalic acid COOH–COOH 10 > Malonic acid $CO_2H.CH_2.CO_2H$ 0·158

> Succinic acid $CO_2H.CH_2.CH_2.CO_2H$ 0·00665

We have already met on p. 341 with similar relations in considering the influence of substituting radicals on the absorption of light in the chromophore. It is obvious that the affinity constants are of considerable importance for stereochemistry; they have indeed been repeatedly used with success in that connection.

The behaviour of the *dicarboxylic acids* is especially interesting: the distance between the two carboxyls is the determining factor between the isomeric maleic and fumaric acids, as in the previous case of oxalic, malonic, and succinic acids; these constants are for

$$\text{Maleic acid } \begin{array}{l}\text{H}.\text{C}.\text{COOH}\\ \text{H}.\text{C}.\text{COOH}\end{array} 1\cdot17 > \text{Fumaric acid } \begin{array}{l}\text{H}.\text{C}.\text{COOH}\\ \text{COOH}.\text{C}.\text{H}\end{array} 0\cdot09 ;$$

on the other hand the dissociation of the hydrogen ion of the second carboxyl group occurs much sooner in fumaric acid than in maleic, which dissociates as a monobasic acid only up to more than 80 %. The explanation of this given by *Ostwald*[1] lies in the *electrostatic repulsion* between a negative charge and another of the same sign so that the charge due to dissociation of the first hydrogen ion hinders that of the second more effectively the nearer the two carboxyls stand, since on dissociation they acquire similar charges.

The principle which is at the foundation of the investigations briefly described above, and to which reference has already been made (p. 291), consists in *the study of the mutual influence on the reaction capacity of different elements or radicals in the molecules.* The measurement of the electrolytic dissociation constant of an acid, as will be shown clearly below, consists merely in the determination of the reaction capacity possessed by the "acid hydrogen" in water solution.

Instead of studying the reaction capacity of "acid hydrogen" we could study the reaction capacity of another element or radical in the molecule: *but here the problem is to find out a method to determine the reaction-capacity with satisfactory sharpness, and under conditions which are suitably comparable.* Comparable conditions may be obtained most easily by determining the reaction-capacity in *the same solvent.* The quantitative determination of the reaction-capacity of the radical in question, may be accomplished by the measurement of a suitable chemical equilibrium. Thus it would be very interesting to study in an extended way the question of the capacity of the nitrogen bases to fix hydrochloric acid or any other acid; this could be done very easily by means of a method like that of Jellet (p. 462), since one could allow an optically active base to compete for the acid at the same time with the base to be investigated.

It should be remarked, as a matter of history, that Menschutkin (p. 460) was the first to attack a problem of affinity in an extended way; perhaps the results of his extended investigations would have been greater, if he had studied the state of equilibrium of the esterification under conditions which were more nearly comparable, *e.g.* in a suitable solvent.

[1] *Zeitschr. phys. Chem.* **9.** 553 (1892).

Finally, there are here appended some of the most important affinity constants of the acids investigated by Ostwald.

Acid.					100 K.
Malic acid $C_2H_3(OH)(CO_2H)_2$	.	.	.	.	0·0395
Formic acid HCOOH	.		.	.	0·0214
Benzoic acid C_6H_5 . COOH	.	.	.	.	0·0060
Butyric acid C_3H_7 . COOH	.	.	.	.	0·00149
Lactic acid $CH_3CH(OH)COOH$	.	.	.	.	0·0138
Salicylic acid $C_6H_4(OH)$. COOH	.	.	.	0·102
Cinnamic acid $CH(C_6H_5)$. CH . CO_2H	.	.	.	0·00355

Walker [1] has measured certain very weak acids, making use of exceedingly pure water for the conductivity (indirect methods for determining the dissociation of extremely weak acids will be given below); acetic acid is taken for comparison :

				$K \cdot 10^{10}$
Acetic acid $C_2H_3O_2 - H$	.	.	.	180000
Carbon dioxide $HCO_3 - H$	.	.	.	3040
Sulphuretted hydrogen $HS - H$	.	.	.	570
Boric acid $H_2BO_3 - H$	.	.	.	17
Hydrocyanic acid $CN - H$	.	.	.	13
Phenol $C_6H_5O - H$	.	.	.	1·3

The Mixture of Two Electrolytes containing the same Ion.

—As the simplest case of equilibrium between several electrolytes, we will first investigate the reaction which occurs *on bringing together any two electrolytes with a common ion*, e.g. two acids having the hydrogen ion in common. The progress of the reaction can be followed without recourse to calculation.

Let a second acid be added to an acid solution keeping the volume constant, *i.e.* by adding the second acid in the pure form to a dilute water solution of the first acid, so that the concentration of the hydrogen ions will be increased ; then the immediate result of this is that the undissociated part of the first acid is no longer able to maintain equilibrium with the increased product of the active masses of the hydrogen ion and of the negative ingredient ; *i.e. the dissociation of the acid retrogrades.* This phenomenon is similar to that on adding free chlorine to phosphorus penta-chloride, whereby the dissociation is diminished by the addition of one of the dissociation products (p. 455).

In order to observe the relations in a quantitative way we need employ only the law of mass-action. Let c denote the concentration of the electrically neutral molecules, and c_1 that of the two ions, so that the total concentration C, will be

$$c + c_1 = C.$$

Then we shall have

$$cK = c_1^2.$$

Now let a second electrolyte be added, which has one ion the same as

[1] *Zeitschr. phys. Chem.* **32.** 137 (1900).

one ion of the first electrolyte ; and let the concentration of the ion so added be c_0. Then the new equilibrium will be satisfied by the condition,

$$c'K = c_1'(c_1' + c_0),$$

where again, of course, $c' + c_1'$ must be equal to C. Obviously c' will be greater than c ; and conversely c_1 will be smaller than c_1' ; i.e. the dissociation of the electrolytes retrogrades, on the addition of a second electrolyte containing an identical ion, and in a ratio capable of exact calculation.

This phenomenon may be very well shown qualitatively by a solution of paranitrophenol ; the negative ion of this acid is coloured an intense yellow, whilst the electrically neutral molecule is colourless. If therefore any acid is added to an aqueous solution of this substance the yellow coloration directly vanishes, because the slight dissociation of this weak acid is reduced to almost nothing by even a small addition of hydrogen ions.   (See the section on "The Theory of Indicators.")

Arrhenius [1] succeeded in proving this law quantitatively in the following way.   Thus, e.g. sodium acetate was added to a solution of acetic acid, and then he determined the velocity of the inversion of cane sugar contained in the solution ; this velocity of sugar inversion (as. will be thoroughly demonstrated in the chapter on Chemical Kinetics), is a measure of the number of the free hydrogen ions existing in the solution.   Thus, this velocity amounted to 0·74 in a solution containing $\frac{1}{4}$ of a mol of acetic acid to the litre, and when the equivalent quantity of sodium acetate was added, the value sank to 0·0105, the calculated value of the latter being 0·0100.

If any selected volumes of any two electrolytes having ions in common, as two acids, e.g., are mixed, then, in general, the state of dissociation of each of these will change as a result of their mixture ; and consequently the electrical conductivity of the mixture will not be identical with that corresponding to the *mean* of the conductivities of the unmixed components.

But if the concentrations of the two acids are so selected that each shall contain the same number of free hydrogen ions in a litre,—such solutions are called "*isohydric,*"—*then there is no change of their state of dissociation resulting from their mixture.*   For let c and c_1 be the concentrations of the electrically neutral molecules and of the ions, and k the dissociation constant for one solution ; then we have the relation

$$kc = c_1^2 \qquad . \qquad . \qquad . \qquad . \qquad (1)$$

and similarly for the second solution

$$KC = C_1^2. \qquad . \qquad . \qquad . \qquad (2)$$

If the volume v of the first solution be mixed with the volume V of

[1] *Zeitschr. phys. Chem.* **5.** 1 (1890) ; also **2.** 284 (1888) ; and *Wied. Ann.* **30.** 51 (1887).

the second, the concentration of the electrically neutral molecules and of the not common ions

$$c, c_1 \; C, C_1$$

will become

$$\frac{cv}{V+v}, \quad \frac{c_1 v}{V+v}, \quad \frac{CV}{V+v}, \quad \frac{C_1 V}{V+v},$$

whilst the concentration of the ion common to the two solutions reaches the value $\frac{C_1 V + c_1 v}{V+v}$. Applying the law of mass-action to determine the equilibrium in the common solution we have

$$kc = c_1 \cdot \frac{C_1 V + c_1 v}{V+v}, \qquad . \quad . \quad . \quad (3)$$

$$KC = C_1 \cdot \frac{C_1 V + c_1 v}{V+v}; \qquad . \quad . \quad . \quad (4)$$

but the equations (1) to (4) are only satisfied if

$$C_1 = c_1,$$

that is, in mixing isohydric solutions no displacement of the dissociation occurs, *hence the conductivity of the mixture must be the mean of the conductivities of the two solutions,* as is shown by experience.

If we mix solutions of any two electrolytes which have a common ion and *the same dissociation constant,*—as, *e.g.,* two chlorides of univalent basis,—then these solutions contain the common ion in the same concentrations when the solutions are equivalent. Hence it follows that, in a mixture of such electrolytes, each one is dissociated equally strongly, and just as strongly as though it alone formed a solution in proportions corresponding to the total concentration.

The case of a mixture of two acids in solution can easily be treated by the above method, especially the question of how the conductivity of a mixture of two acids changes with increasing dilution. See for particulars A. Wakemann.[1] It is especially interesting to note that the dissociation constant, calculated from the conductivity according to p. 508, is by no means constant for a mixture of two acids, but varies considerably with the dilution, so that, as has been shown by Ostwald, it can serve as a criterion of the purity of the acid under consideration.

The Equilibrium between any Selected Electrolytes.—The state of equilibrium is much more complicated in the case of a solution containing two binary electrolytes *having no common ion.* Then care must be given to discriminate between the different molecular species in the solution, viz., the four free ions and the four electrically neutral molecules produced by the combination of the former. By a displacement of the point of equilibrium, four reactions may take place

[1] *Zeitschr. phys. Chem.* **15.** 159 (1894).

beside each other ; namely, the dissociation of the (four) electrically neutral molecules into the respective ions, to each of which reactions there always corresponds an equilibrium condition of the form

$$Kc = c_1 c_2,$$

where K denotes the corresponding dissociation constant, c the concentration of the molecular species that is electrically neutral, and c_1 and c_2 respectively the concentrations of the two ions.

It is easy to see that equilibrium can be with certainty determined if we know the dissociation constants and the total concentration (which is given by analysis). The determination is, however, attended by no inconsiderable difficulties of calculation. Simplifications can be made, however, especially if we regard all binary salts of monatomic radicals as being dissociated to the same (considerable) extent. Arrhenius[1] gives the following laws :

1. The degree of dissociation of a weak acid, in the presence of salts of this acid, is inversely proportional to the quantity of salt present.

2. When a weak acid and several strongly dissociated electrolytes exist together in the same solution, their respective degrees of dissociation may be calculated as though the dissociated part of the particular electrolyte were a dissociated part of a salt (as a sodium salt, e.g.), of this acid.

There is hardly any special proof needed to show that the case, where any arbitrary number of electrolytes are in a solution, can be solved by the application of the preceding equation. Before advancing any farther, we will now discuss a case which has not been considered as yet, namely, the participation of water in the equilibrium ; i.e. where the hydrogen ion and the hydroxyl ion react on each other.

Neutralisation.—It may be concluded from the fact that water conducts worse the more carefully it is purified, and accordingly that the traces of conductivity which the most carefully prepared water shows are mainly due to traces of salt in solution, that water itself is only very slightly dissociated into ions.

It follows directly from this that these two kinds of ions (H and OH), are capable of existing beside each other in water only in the merest traces. Thus if we bring together in a water solution two electrolytes, such that on decomposition one affords a hydrogen ion and the other a hydroxyl ion,—or, in other words, if we mix an acid with a base,—then in all cases the same reaction occurs, viz.

$$\overset{+}{H} + \overset{-}{OH} = H_2O,$$

and practically in absolute completeness, i.e. until one of the reacting components is exhausted.

[1] Zeitschr. phys. Chem. **5.** 1 (1890).

Now this reaction, the necessity of which, as already shown, was derived theoretically, is in fact well known and of the greatest importance ; it is called *the process of neutralisation.*

If the acid and the base are completely dissociated, then the aforesaid reaction will be the only one which takes place ; and from this there follows directly a very remarkable conclusion, to which attention was first called by Arrhenius, viz. *the same reactions must correspond to the same evolution of heat* (*" heat of reaction "*). Therefore by mixing any selected strong base with any selected strong acid in a sufficiently large quantity of water, there always results the same development of heat ; this is proved by experiment (see the chapter "Thermo-Chemistry," I. Book IV.).

If, on the other hand, the acid or the base is not completely dissociated, then side reactions other than the aforesaid reaction, take place, namely, decomposition into the ions ; and since this is also associated with a certain, though often very slight, heat change, a slight variation in the heat of neutralisation is observed under these circumstances.

The law of mass-action applied to the dissociation of water causes, since the active mass of the solvent must be constant (p. 469), the relation that in dilute aqueous solutions the product of the concentrations of the hydrogen ions $[\overset{+}{H}]$ and the hydroxyl ions $[\overset{-}{OH}]$ must be constant ; if the concentration of each of these ions in pure water is c_0, we have

$$[\overset{+}{H}]\, [\overset{-}{OH}] = c_0{}^2.$$

Electrolytic Dissociation of Pure Water.—Although it would seem to be very difficult to determine this exceedingly small dissociation of pure water, the problem has been solved of late years by different investigators in very varied methods, and with good agreement.

1. The electromotive force of the acid alkali cell allows of calculating the concentration of the hydrogen ions in an alkaline solution by means of the osmotic theory of currents (Book IV. Chap. VII.) ; it was found in this way that in a normal solution of a strongly (80 %) dissociated base it amounts at 19° to $0.8 \cdot 10^{-14}$. It follows for such a solution

$$[\overset{+}{H}] = 0.8 \cdot 10^{-14},\ [\overset{-}{OH}] = 0.8\ ;\ \text{therefore}\ c_0 = 0.8 \cdot 10^{-7}\ \text{at}\ 19°.$$

At a higher temperature it was found in the same way[1] that

$$c_0 = 1.19 \cdot 10^{-7}\ \text{at}\ 25 - 26°.$$

Ostwald[2] and Arrhenius[3] attempted simultaneously to determine c_0 in

[1] Löwenherz, *Zeitschr. phys. Chem.* **20·** 283 (1896).
[2] *Ibid.* **11.** 521 (1893).   [3] *Ibid.* **11.** 805 (1893).

this manner; the present writer showed shortly afterwards that the calculation was somewhat different to that given by these writers, and that the value obtained is that given above.[1]

2. A second process lies in measuring the *hydrolytic decomposition of salts*, the theory of which is given below on p. 530. Arrhenius [2] found in this way

$$c_0 = 1 \cdot 1 \times 10^{-7} \text{ at } 25°.$$

Kanolt [3] has recently found somewhat smaller results by the same method. He measured the hydrolysis of the ammonium salt of diketotetrahydrothiazol:

$t =$	$0°$	$18°$	$25°$
$c_0 = 0 \cdot 30$		$0 \cdot 68$	$0 \cdot 91 \times 10^{-7}$

3. Both hydrogen and hydroxyl ions cause acceleration of the process of saponification of esters dissolved in water; Wiis,[4] at van't Hoff's suggestion, determined the velocity of saponification of methyl acetate in pure water, and calculated according to a theory given by van't Hoff (see the following Chapter) that

$$c_0 = 1 \cdot 2 \, . \, 10^{-7} \text{ at } 25°.$$

4. Finally, Kohlrausch and Heydweiller [5] succeeded in purifying water to such an extent that it showed its own conductivity, that is, was practically free from conductivity due to impurities.

It was known from previous work of Kohlrausch that water conducts the less the more carefully it is purified; it appears, however, that a limiting value can be reached below which the conductivity cannot be reduced, that is that water possesses measurable *conductivity of its own account*. The method of purification is distillation in vacuum. A U-shaped tube, one leg of which ended in a large reservoir and the other in a smaller conductivity cell, was provided with water already very thoroughly purified, and boiled for a long time under the mercury pump. On slightly warming the large vessel a fraction of the water was distilled over into the resistance cell and its conductivity measured.

At 18° the conductivity of the purest water was found to be $0 \cdot 0384 \, . \, 10^{-6}$ (that of ordinarily good water is about 2×10^{-6}); the temperature coefficient at 18° is $5 \cdot 8 \, \%$, much larger therefore than that of salt solutions (2 to $2 \cdot 5 \, \%$) and that of ordinary distilled water ($2 \, \%$).

The degree of electrolytic dissociation of the water may be calculated from the conductivity found by Kohlrausch and Heydweiller; according to p. 365 the conductivity is

$$\kappa = \eta_0(u + v) = 0 \cdot 0384 \times 10^{-6},$$

[1] Löwenherz, *Zeitschr. phys. Chem.* **14.** 155 (1894).   [2] *Ibid.* **11.** 805 (1893).
[3] *Journ. Amer. Chem. Soc.* **29.** 1402 (1907).
[4] *Zeitschr. phys. Chem.* **12.** 514 (1893).   [5] *Wied. Ann.* **53.** 209 (1894).

where u, the mobility of the hydrogen ion, is 318, and v, that of the hydroxyl ion is 174 ; hence we may calculate the ionic concentration c_0 of the pure water in g-ions per litre ($= 1000\eta_0$).

$$c_0 = \frac{1000\kappa}{u + v} = 0{\cdot}78 \times 10^{-7} \text{ at } 18^\circ ;$$

at 25° this becomes $1{\cdot}05 \times 10^{-7}$; *i.e.* is in *satisfactory agreement with the values mentioned above, arrived at in entirely different ways.*

Even the surprisingly large temperature coefficient of pure water was predicted by Arrhenius and exactly calculated by him (see Book IV. Chap. III.).

Water is clearly capable of a second electrolytic dissociation, namely

$$\overset{-}{OH} = \overset{=}{O} + \overset{+}{H},$$

that is, water can be treated as a dibasic acid. Since therefore the separation of the second hydrogen ion from a dibasic acid is always much harder than that of the first, we may expect that the second stage in the electrolytic dissociation of water is extremely slight, or that the oxygen ions with a double negative charge in water exist in infinitesimal quantities. Nothing more is known at present as to this second dissociation.

The Most General Case of Homogeneous Equilibrium.— Consideration of the preceding paragraph now finally allows us to remove the last limitation, viz. that the ions of water are not included among the reacting molecular species ; in accordance with this we will develop the general equilibrium of a solution containing any casual electrolytes. This is possible by means of the following propositions.

1. The *total quantity* of each radical which is present in the solution, partly as a free ion and partly combined with other ions,—this is either known from the conditions of the experiment, or else may be ascertained by analysis.

2. For every combination of ions, we have an equation, according to which the undissociated part per unit of volume is proportional to the product of the active masses of the ions contained in the combination. The proportional factor is the *dissociation constant*, which, according to p. 511, is known for most molecular species, and can be determined, if necessary, for any particular case, by means of the conductivity, by the freezing-point, etc.

3. Hydrogen ions and hydroxyl ions are capable of existing together in only the slightest quantities ; their product is (nearly) constant, and its magnitude is extremely small ($0{\cdot}64$ or $1{\cdot}14 \times 10^{-14}$ at 18° or 25°).

By means of the formulæ afforded by the immediate application of these propositions, the state of equilibrium is definitely determined.

We are thus enabled to state in every case what part of each radical exists in the solution as a free ion, and what part is combined with other ions, provided we know the dissociation constants of the combinations of all of the ions.

This is a result of the greatest importance. It indicates a partial solution of the problem which is to be regarded as the final goal of the doctrine of affinity, namely, *the expression of the mutual reactions between substances, by means of certain characteristic numerical coefficients.*

To this class of coefficients belong the dissociation coefficients of electrolytes, a knowledge of which enables us to anticipate the kind of action which takes place between them in dilute solution.

We shall later obtain the result, that by means of the solubilities of solid salts, we can also definitely determine the state of equilibrium which is established in dilute solution in the presence of solid (difficultly soluble) salts.

In the following paragraphs, some applications will make the meaning of the preceding results more intelligible.

The Distribution of one Base between two Acids.—We can now answer, in its most general form, a question which was formerly much discussed, and fruitlessly too, in default of the aid of the dissociation theory. This question refers to the distribution of a base between two acids, when the total quantity of the latter is greater than that required for neutralisation; and the distribution of an acid between two bases, when the total quantity of the bases is greater than that required for neutralisation.

The state of equilibrium is definitely determined by the absolute quantities of each of the four radicals of the solution (either two acid radicals, the basic radical, and the hydrogen ion, or else respectively the two basic radicals, the acid radical, and the hydroxyl ion), together with the dissociation constants of the four electrically neutral species which may be produced by the combination of the four radicals aforesaid; and the calculation of this equilibrium offers no difficulties except in the way of pure calculation, which, though usually not inconsiderable, are nevertheless not insuperable.

As an example of such a calculation, we will consider the following simple case.

Thus let two weak (slightly dissociated) monobasic acids, SH and S'H, compete for a base, *e.g.* NaOH; *and let there be in the volume* V 1 mol *of each of the three electrolytes.*

Let the quantity of the undissociated part of *the first acid* SH, be x; and therefore the undissociated part of S'H will be $1 - x$. Then the quantity $1 - x$ of the first acid SH, will be concerned with the base in two ways, for the negative radical S will partly exist as a free ion, and will be electrically neutralised by the equivalent quantity of the positive radical of the base, and will partly unite with the basic radical to form the electrically neutral molecule SNa. Then let the first of these fractions amount to a_1 $(1 - x)$, and the second to $(1 - a_1)$ $(1 - x)$; here a_1 denotes the degree of dissociation of the salt SNa.

And regarding *the second acid* S'H, the quantity x of this is concerned with the base; and of this quantity x, a_2x is in the form of negative ions S'; and $(1 - a_2)x$ is employed in the formation of electrically neutral molecules having the composition S'Na; here a_2 denotes the degree of dissociation of the salt S'Na.

Moreover, a fraction of the two acids will be electrically dissociated; let the quantity of *the free H-ions be denoted by* γ. But, according to the proviso, both acids are weak, and by the presence of the sodium salt the dissociation is caused to retreat considerably. Therefore γ will represent an *infinitesimal quantity*, as compared with x and $1 - x$.

We have now to apply the equation of the isotherm of dissociation to the four following dissociations, viz.,

$$\text{I. NaS} = \overset{+}{\text{Na}} + \overset{-}{\text{S}}. \qquad \text{III. HS} = \overset{+}{\text{H}} + \overset{-}{\text{S}}.$$

$$\text{II. NaS'} = \overset{+}{\text{Na}} + \overset{-}{\text{S}}'. \qquad \text{IV. HS'} = \overset{+}{\text{H}} + \overset{-}{\text{S}}'.$$

In the case of the first two,—according to the law that binary salts composed of univalent ions are decomposed to the same extent,— we make the dissociation constant equal to K; and thus we obtain respectively,

$$\text{I. } K(1 - x)(1 - a_1) = \frac{([1 - x]a_1 + xa_2)(1 - x)a_1}{V},$$

$$\text{II. } Kx(1 - a_2) = \frac{([1 - x]a_1 + xa_2)xa_2}{V}.$$

Here $(1 - x)$, $(1 - a_1)$ and $x(1 - a_2)$ are respectively the quantities of the undissociated molecules NaS and NaS'; $(1 - x)a_1$ and xa_2 are respectively the quantities of the $\overset{+}{\text{S}}$ and of the $\overset{-}{\text{S}}'$ ions; and finally $(1 - x)a_1 + xa_2$ is the quantity of the $\overset{+}{\text{Na}}$ ions.

By division of these equations, we obtain

$$\frac{1 - a_1}{1 - a_2} = \frac{a_1}{a_2}, \text{ or } a_1 = a_2;$$

i.e. *both salts are dissociated to the same extent.*

When K_1 and K_2 denote respectively the dissociation constants of the acids, by the application of the law of mass-action to reactions III. and IV., we obtain respectively

$$\text{III. } K_1 x = \frac{\gamma a_1 (1 - x)}{V}.$$

$$\text{IV. } K_2 (1 - x) = \frac{\gamma a_2 x}{V},$$

from which by division, and recollecting the identity of a_1 and a_2, we obtain

$$\frac{K_1}{K_2} = \frac{(1 - x)^2}{x^2}.$$

Here $\frac{1 - x}{x}$ denotes the *ratio of distribution* of the two acids, and we see at once that *it is independent of the nature of the (mon-acid) base.* If $(1 - x) > x$, it denotes that the base claims a larger part of the acid SH than it does of the acid S'H ; and we can express this by saying that the first acid has a greater "*affinity*" for the base, or that the first acid is "*stronger*" ; but we must take care not to include any more in these expressions than is implied by the preceding considerations. The greater "affinity" or "strength" of the first acid consists in this, and in this solely, viz. *that at the same concentration, the former acid is electrolytically dissociated to a greater extent than the second acid is.*

Now, by the use of the proposition, that salts having an analogous constitution are dissociated to the same extent, the state of equilibrium is definitely determined, in that a greater fraction of the more strongly dissociated acid is concerned with the base than of the acid which is dissociated to a less extent ; and *the ratio of distribution* is quantitatively equal to the square root of the ratio of the two dissociation constants.

We may state the result thus. Let us denote the degree of dissociation of the two acids respectively by a_1 and a_2, when each is dissolved alone in volume V ; then we have

$$K_1 V = \frac{a_1^2}{1 - a_1}, \text{ and } K_2 V = \frac{a_2^2}{1 - a_2} ;$$

or, since a_1 and a_2 can be neglected as compared with 1 on account of the slight dissociation of the acids, it follows that

$$\frac{K_1}{K_2} = \frac{(1 - x)^2}{x^2} = \frac{a_1^2}{a_2^2},$$

and, therefore,

$$\frac{1 - x}{x} = \frac{a_1}{a_2}, \text{ and } 1 - x = \frac{a_1}{a_1 + a_2}.$$

That is, the ratio of distribution is accordingly equal to the ratio of the respective degrees of dissociation, at the corresponding dilution.

One method for the experimental determination of the relative distribution of any one base between two acids, was given by Thomsen as early as 1854, long before a clear conception of the process of neutralisation was obtained as a result of the consequences of the theory of dissociation.

If one equivalent of the base is mixed with one equivalent of each of the acids separately, a certain amount of heat is developed, which in the two cases may amount to a and b, respectively. Now, if we mix one equivalent of the base with one equivalent of each of the acids together, a different quantity of heat will be developed, which may be denoted by c.

If the first acid alone unites with the base, and the second acid has nothing to do with the reaction, then $c = a$; and, conversely, if the second acid alone unites with the base, then $c = b$. Now, in fact, both acids participate in the neutralisation, and therefore c must lie between a and b, provided that there are no disturbing side reactions, such as the formation of acid salts, and the like.

The quantity of the first acid concerned in the neutralisation, must amount to

$$\frac{c - b}{a - b} ;$$

the nearer c is to a, the greater the value of this fraction will be ; and the nearer c is to b, the smaller the value of the fraction. Then, according to the method of notation given above, we shall have

$$1 - x = \frac{c - b}{a - b} ; \quad x = \frac{a - c}{a - b} ; \quad \frac{1 - x}{x} = \frac{c - b}{a - c} .$$

This method of proof is free from objection, either from the old or the new standpoint. The change in the views merely concerns *the manner* in which the acid and the base are concerned in neutralising each other. This process consists not only in the formation of a salt from the acid and the base, but also at the same time there occurs, and usually in a preponderating degree, according to the circumstances, the formation of the free ions which constitute the salt.

Instead of using the "heat of reaction" to determine the ratio of distribution, one may employ, with just as good or better results, the changes in the volumes or in the refractive powers of the solutions, on neutralisation, as was shown by Ostwald in 1878 ; and by means of a corresponding method of treatment, one obtains formulæ which are exactly the same in this case as above. In particular, the method of the determination of the changes in volume unites accuracy and simplicity of treatment.

In the following table are given the results of a number of the determinations [1] conducted according to the latter method.

---

[1] Ostwald, *Journ. pr. Chem.* [2], **18.** 328 (1878).

	1 - x Obs.	1 - x Calc.
Nitric acid ; Di-chlor-acetic acid	0·76	0·69
Hydrochloric acid ; Di-chlor-acetic acid	0·74	0·69
Tri-chlor-acetic acid ; Di-chlor-acetic acid	0·71	0·69
Di-chlor-acetic acid ; Lactic acid	0·91	0·95
Tri-chlor-acetic acid ; Mono-chlor-acetic acid	0·92	0·91
,, ,, ; Formic acid	0·97	0·97
Formic acid ; Lactic acid	0·54	0·56
,, ,, ; Acetic acid	0·76	0·75
,, ,, ; Butyric acid	0·80	0·79
,, ,, ; Iso-butyric acid	0·79	0·79
,, ,, ; Propionic acid	0·81	0·80
,, ,, ; Glycolic acid	0·44 (?)	0·53
Acetic acid ; Butyric acid	0·53	0·54
,, ,, ; Iso-butyric acid	0·53	0·54

The significance of the observed value of $1 - x$ may be illustrated most easily in the following way. If four *equivalent solutions* of SNa, S'Na, SH, and S'H, respectively, are mixed, and in the following proportions, viz. : $1 - x$ volume of SNa, x volume of S'Na, x volume of SH, and $1 - x$ volume of S'H,—then there occurs neither contraction nor dilation. It is indifferent whether one uses, instead of sodium, any other mon-acid base (as is also required by theory). We conclude from this *that acids and salts exist together in those relative proportions which correspond to the equilibrium of their mixture.* For if this were not the case a reaction would take place, which would consist in a change of the degree of dissociation of the four electrolytes, and this would be shown by a change of volume. Therefore the value of $1 - x$ must, as determined experimentally, coincide with the formula as developed above.

As a matter of fact this does occur, as was shown by Arrhenius.[1] In the second column of the preceding table are given the values of $1 - x$, calculated by the formula developed above, viz.

$$1 - x = \frac{a_1}{a_1 + a_2},$$

from the ratio of the degrees of dissociation of the two acids at the dilution employed, which amounted to three litres, inasmuch as the solutions which were studied, resulted from the mixture of the three normal solutions, viz. of the base and of the two acids respectively.

With the exception of the first three values,—where the competition [for the base] was between very strong acids, and, therefore, where the proviso of the theoretical formula is not fulfilled,—and, with the exception of one particular value which probably involved some error,—in general a very good coincidence is established between

[1] *Zeitschr. phys. Chem.* **5.** 1 (1890).

the values of $1 - x$, as calculated from the changes of volume on neutralisation and those calculated from the respective conductivities of the pure acids. As the value of $1 - x$ is always greater than 0·5, therefore the acid named first is the stronger in all three cases.[1]

In the competition between any two weak acids, at such dilutions that the salts of the acids may be regarded as completely dissociated, the reaction progresses according to the scheme,

$$\overset{-}{S}H + \overset{-}{S}' + \overset{+}{Na} = \overset{}{S}'H + \overset{-}{S} + \overset{+}{Na},$$

or simply

$$\overset{}{S}H + \overset{-}{S}' = \overset{}{S}'H + \overset{-}{S}.$$

Now the law of mass-action requires that

$$\frac{\text{Acid I.} \times \text{acid-ion II.}}{\text{Acid II.} \times \text{acid-ion I.}} = \text{a constant.}$$

This equation was found to be established by Lellmann and Schliemann.[2] The method employed by them was in principle that of Jellet (p. 462); only instead of using the rotation of light, they used the absorption of light to analyse the state of equilibrium.

The relations involving partition of an acid between two bases are, of course, exactly analogous; if polybasic acids, e.g. sulphuric acid, are used, the theoretical treatment of the conditions of equilibrium is complicated by the formation of acid salts.[3]

The Strength of Acids and Bases.—It is a very common and old experience, that different acids and bases exhibit very different "intensities" or "strengths" in those solutions where their acid or basic nature, as such, comes into play. But in spite of many strenuous endeavours to accomplish it, it is only recently that it has been possible to find a method for expressing their [relative] strengths numerically, i.e. for expressing the numerical coefficient of each particular acid and base, which should make possible the calculation of the degree of their distribution in the reactions which are characteristic of the respective acids and bases.

This problem was first deliberately attacked in a broad way by J. Thomsen (1868); but it was Ostwald (1878-1887) who first succeeded in proving, beyond all doubt, that the property of acids and bases of exerting their action according to the standards of definite coefficients,

[1] See Thiel (*Zeitschr. phys. Chem.* **61.** 114 (1893)) for a theoretical treatment not involving the above simplifying assumptions, and also for an exact experimental proof of the equations involved.

[2] *Leib. Ann.* **270.** 208 (1892). See also Arrhenius, *Zeitschr. phys. Chem.* **10.** 670 (1892).

[3] See A. A. Noyes, "On the Separation of Hydrogen Ions from Acid Salts," *Zeitschr. phys. Chem.* **11.** 495 (1893):

finds its expression not only in the forming of salts, but also in a large number of other and very different reactions.

Ostwald compared the relative order, in which the acids compete for the same base, according to their strength, as obtained by—

(a) Thomsen's thermo-chemical methods, with

(b) His own (Ostwald's) volume-chemical methods, and with the relative order in which the acids arrange themselves,—

(c) Regarding their capacity to bring calcium oxalate into solution; and,—

(d) Regarding the relative velocities with which they convert acetamide into ammonium acetate; and,—

(e) Regarding the relative velocities with which they cleave methyl acetate, catalytically, into methyl alcohol and acetic acid; and,—

(f) Regarding the relative velocities with which they invert cane sugar; and,—

(g) Regarding their relative accelerations of the mutual action of hydriodic acid and bromic acid.

Ostwald showed that in all these widely different cases investigated, one always obtains *the same order for the relative strengths of the different acids,* whichever of the above chemical reactions is chosen as a measure of the strengths.   It should be noticed that all the decompositions enumerated above, were conducted in *dilute water solution,* and therefore the preceding scale refers only to reaction capacities under these conditions.   The order of succession of the acids was shown to be fairly independent of the temperature.

Although Ostwald's investigations clearly indicated *the relative order* of the strength of the particular acids, yet great difficulty was experienced in ascertaining *the quantitative ratios*; and the numerical coefficients, as calculated from the particular reactions, often showed great deviations, although sometimes there were surprising coincidences. In particular the coefficients varied very greatly with the concentration, and in those cases where the concentration of the acid changed considerably in the course of the reaction, the calculation was, of course, entirely untrustworthy.

A similar behaviour was found in the study of bases, though the observations were not so extended.

These seemingly complicated relations were at once cleared up, by the application of the law of chemical mass-action to the exceptional behaviour of substances in aqueous solution—which was first recognised by van't Hoff (1885), and afterwards referred by Arrhenius (1887) to electrolytic dissociation.   The formulæ to be used here in the calculation of the equilibrium ratios, follow naturally from the law of mass-action.

The peculiarities directly presented by the conduct of acids and bases, which must be presented in the sense of the views developed by Arrhenius,—peculiarities, moreover, which are illustrated both in the old-time distinction between *neutral* solutions, on the one hand, and acid and basic solutions on the other, and also in the recognition of a polar contrast between the two latter [viz. acid and alkaline solutions], —all of these peculiarities, in the light of *the theory of electrolytic dissociation*, are now to be conceived of in the following way.

The reactions which are characteristic of acids existing in solution, which are common to all acids, and which can only be effected by acids,—can be all referred to the fact, that the dissociation of these bodies, *as a class*, results in the production of the same molecular species, the positively charged hydrogen ion $\overset{+}{H}$.

Therefore those chemical actions which are characteristic of acids are to be ascribed to the action of the hydrogen ions.

In the same way, *e.g.*, the chemical actions which are common to the chlorides are to be explained by the action of the free chlorine ions.

And in a similar way, *the reactions which are characteristic of bases existing in solution*, justify the view that the dissociation of this class of substances results in the production of negatively charged hydroxyl ions $\left(\overset{-}{HO} \right)$.

Therefore the specific action of bases is due to the hydroxyl ions.

A solution reacts acid when it contains free hydrogen ions; and alkaline when it contains free hydroxyl ions. If we bring together an acid solution and an alkaline solution, *mutual neutralisation* occurs (p. 517), because the positive hydrogen ions and the negative hydroxyl ions are incapable of existing beside each other, but, on account of the extraordinarily weak conductivity, *i.e.* the small dissociation of water, immediately combine to form electrically neutral molecules, in the sense of the equation

$$\overset{+}{H} + \overset{-}{OH} = H_2O.$$

Thus we find a simple explanation of the polar contrast between acid and basic solutions; it consists simply in this, namely, that *the ions which are respectively characteristic of the acid and of the base, together form the two ingredients of the solvent [water], in which we study the reaction capacities.*

The conception of the "strength" of an acid or of a base now explains itself. If we compare equivalent solutions of different acids, each one will exert the actions characteristic of acids the more energetically, the more free hydrogen ions it contains. This follows immediately from the law of chemical mass-action.

The degree of electrolytic dissociation determines the relative strength of the acid; and similar considerations lead to the conclusion that—

The strength of bases depends upon the degree of their electrolytic dissociation.

Now the degree of the electrolytic dissociation varies regularly with the concentration, in the way indicated on p. 508. At very extreme dilution, equivalent solutions of the most various acids contain the same number of hydrogen ions, or, in other words, they are equally strong ; and the same is true of the hydroxyl ions of bases.

The dissociation decreases with increasing concentration, but at a different rate for different substances. Thus the relative strengths of bases and acids must vary with their concentration, as was empirically established by Ostwald.

Now the dissociation constant is the measure of the variation of the degree of dissociation with the concentration ; *i.e. we must regard these magnitudes as the measure of the strengths of acids and bases.* Thus by the consideration of this special case, we again obtain the same result as that previously developed in a general way (p. 511), namely, *the dissociation coefficients are the measures of the reaction capacities of all such substances,* e.g. *both acids and bases.*

The order of succession of the acids, as arranged by Ostwald on the basis of the most various reactions, must coincide with the order of their dissociation constants ; and also, since the depression of the freezing-point increases with the degree of the electrical dissociation, it must coincide with the order of their relative depression of the freezing-point in equivalent solutions. This result is established by experiment.

The degree of dissociation a, of an acid, in a definite concentration at which its molecular conductivity is Λ, is calculated to be (p. 361)

$$a = \frac{\Lambda}{\Lambda_{\infty}}.$$

The conductivity at very great dilution Λ_{∞}, according to the law of Kohlrausch (p. 365), is

$$\Lambda_{\infty} = u + v.$$

Now since u, the ionic mobility of hydrogen, is usually more than ten times as great as v, the ionic mobility of the negative radical of the acid, therefore Λ_{∞} has approximately the same value for the most different acids (usually within less than 10 per cent) ; *and therefore the conductivity of an acid in equivalent concentration corresponds, at least approximately, to the degree of its electrolytic dissociation, i.e. to its strength.*

On the whole, the order of succession as arranged in accordance with the conductivities is identical with the order of succession as shown by their acids in their specific reactions. The recognition by Arrhenius and Ostwald (in 1885) of this remarkable parallelism was an important event, for it amounted to the discovery of electrolytic dissociation.

A detailed discussion of various reactions will now teach us how

2 M

the degree to which acids and bases partake in these reactions, may be calculated *quantitatively* from their dissociation constants.

Hydrolytic Dissociation.—A very important case in which water as a solvent participates in the reaction, is the so-called *hydrolytic dissociation*; or in short "*hydrolysis*," *i.e.* the decomposition of a salt into base and acid by combination with the components of water.

The theory of this, according to what has been explained, is very simple. Let any selected quantities of an acid SH, and a base BOH, be dissolved in a large quantity of water. Then, in general, the five following reactions will occur in one sense or the other by a change in the relative proportions :—

$$\text{I. } SB = \overset{-}{S} + \overset{+}{B}.$$

$$\text{II. } SH = \overset{-}{S} + \overset{+}{H}.$$

$$\text{III. } BOH = \overset{+}{B} + \overset{-}{OH}.$$

$$\text{IV. } H_2O = \overset{+}{H} + \overset{-}{OH}.$$

$$\text{V. } \overset{+}{B} + \overset{-}{S} + H_2O = SH + BOH.$$

Reactions I. to IV. inclusive are cases of electrolytic dissociation; reaction V. is the equation of hydrolytic dissociation. Let K_1 to K_5 inclusive be the respective reaction coefficients, and let the respective concentrations of the reacting molecular species, which are partly electrically neutral molecules, and partly ions, be as follows :—

SB	SH	BOH	$\overset{+}{B}$	$\overset{+}{H}$	$\overset{-}{S}$	$\overset{-}{OH}$
C_1	C_2	C_3	c_1	c_2	c_1'	c_2'.

Now, according to the conditions of the experiment, the total quantity of the radical S, is

$$C_1 + C_2 + c_1' = m ;$$

and that of the radical B, is

$$C_1 + C_3 + c_1 = n ;$$

and also,

$$c_1 + c_2 = c_1' + c_2' ;$$

i.e. the solution contains the same number of positive and of negative ions. The active mass of the solvent, *i.e.* of the molecule H_2O, is very nearly constant (p. 469): it is of course indifferent whether water in the liquid state has this molecular weight or another [polymeric].

The application of the law of mass-action to reactions I. to V. inclusive, gives respectively the following equations :—

$$\text{I. } K_1C_1 = c_1c_1'.$$
$$\text{II. } K_2C_2 = c_1'c_2.$$
$$\text{III. } K_3C_3 = c_1c_2'.$$
$$\text{IV. } K_4 = c_0^2 = c_2c_2'.$$
$$\text{V. } K_5c_1c_1' = C_2C_3.$$

K_1 may, with a satisfactory approach to accuracy, be regarded as the same (p. 510) for all binary electrolytes composed of univalent ions. K_2 and K_3 are the dissociation constants of the acid and base respectively, K_4 is known (p. 519).

By multiplying equations II. and III., we obtain

$$C_2C_3 = \frac{c_1'c_2 \cdot c_1c_2'}{K_2 \cdot K_3},$$

and this, by substitution from IV., becomes

$$C_2C_3 = c_1'c_1 \cdot \frac{K_4}{K_2K_3}.$$

By comparing this with equation V., we get

$$K_5 = \frac{K_4}{K_2K_3}.$$

The reaction constant for hydrolysis can therefore be calculated from the dissociation constant of the reacting molecules, that is, the degree of hydrolysis can be calculated when we know the strength of the acid and base.

In practically applying the above equation we must consider, however, that the value of K is *not* constant (p. 509) for strongly dissociated electrolytes, that is for neutral salts and very strong acids and bases. In this case the above formula may be most practically applied by treating these substances as completely dissociated, and afterwards introducing small corrections on account of the inaccuracy of this assumption.

The strongest hydrolysis is of course to be expected when both the acid and the base are very weak. It may happen in this case that the salt is entirely decomposed, especially when the acid or base is insoluble, and hence the greater part of the substance is precipitated and becomes inactive. Thus white silver borate decomposes on heating, with separation of silver oxide, in the same way ferric acetate decomposes in dilute solution on boiling almost completely into ferric hydroxide and free acid. A case in which the salt decomposes completely in the cold at any attainable dilution is to be found in the behaviour of the salts of the trivalent metals towards carbonates; the hydroxide is here precipitated at once because the hydrolysis of these metals is almost complete.

Walker [1] investigated quantitatively the hydrolysis of the chlorides of some weak bases (such as aniline) by measuring the amount of free hydrogen ions by the velocity of inversion of methyl acetate (see the following chapter). In this case hydrolysis occurs according to the equation

$$\overset{+}{B} + \overset{-}{Cl} + H_2O = BOH + \overset{-}{Cl} + \overset{+}{H},$$

or more simply

$$\overset{+}{B} + H_2O = BOH + \overset{+}{H} ; \cdot$$

as we may here, on account of the strong dissociation of the hydrochloric acid, regard the concentration of the hydrogen ions as very approximately the same as that of the free acid, and, on account of the strong dissociation of the salt, regard the concentration of the $\overset{+}{B}$-ions as being that of the undissociated salt, and finally, on account of the very feeble dissociation of the base, regard the concentration of BOH as equally that of the free base, we get the equation

$$\frac{[BOH]\,[\overset{+}{H}]}{[\overset{+}{B}]} = \frac{Base \times Acid}{Salt} = const.$$

which Walker found to be confirmed by experiment.

In the case stated by Walker the hydrolysis was considerable despite the strength of the acid, because the base was extraordinarily weak; conversely Shields [2] measured the hydrolysis of a number of salts for which the base was strong and the acid very weak. The rate of saponification of methyl acetate was determined, as the amount of free hydroxyl ions is directly proportional to it (see the following chapter), and, on account of the strength of the base used, this is practically identical with the total concentration of the free base. The degree of hydrolytic dissociation at 25° was found for the following salts in $\frac{1}{10}$ normal condition :—

Potassium cyanide . . .	1·12 per cent.
Sodium carbonate . . .	3·17 ,,
Potassium phenolate . .	3·05 ,,
Borax	0·5 ,,
Sodium acetate . . .	0·008 ,,

Since in the above cases the base is very strong and the acid very weak the reaction occurs practically according to the equation

$$\overset{-}{CN} + H_2O = \overset{-}{OH} + HCN,$$

and by using pure salts, that is, by avoiding an excess of acid or base

[1] Zeitschr. phys. Chem. **4**. 319 (1889).
[2] Ibid. **12**. 167 (1893).

the amounts of free acid and base must be equal, so that the law of mass-action gives

$$\frac{\text{Acid} \times \text{Base}}{\text{Salt}} = \text{constant, or the base is proportional to } \sqrt{\text{salt,}}$$

that is, the degree of hydrolysis is proportional to the square root of the concentration of the unhydrolysed salt, and the latter quantity is not very different from the total concentration of the salt when the hydrolysis is small.

We may calculate the dissociation of water from the fact that 0·1 normal sodium acetate is hydrolysed to the extent of 0·008 %. Since acetic acid in presence of its salt is very slightly dissociated, the free base (NaOH) almost completely, we have as the concentrations of the acetic acid and the hydroxyl ions

$$[CH_3COOH] = [\overline{OH}] = 0.000008 \; \frac{\text{mol}}{\text{litre}}.$$

The amount of free hydrogen ions $[\overset{+}{H}]$ is found from the equation

$$K[CH_3COOH] = [\overline{CH_3COO}] \, [\overset{+}{H}],$$

where K, the dissociation constant of acetic acid, is 0·0000178 (p 509), and the concentration of the negative ion of acetic acid is almost precisely that of the salt (0·1). We thus find

$$[\overset{+}{H}] = \frac{0.0000178 \, . \, 0.000008}{0.1} = 1.42 \times 10^{-9},$$

and according to p. 520

$$c_0 = \sqrt{[\overset{+}{H}] \, [\overline{OH}]} = \sqrt{1.42 \, . \, 0.8 \, . \, 10^{-14}} = 1.1 \, . \, 10^{-7},$$

that is, pure water at 25° is 0·11 millionths normal with respect to the hydrogen or hydroxyl ions. Walker (*loc. cit.* p. 514), by means of the values of K given on p. 514, calculated in the same way the hydrolysis of potassium cyanide, potassium phenolate, and borax to be 0·96, 3·0 and 0·3 %, in striking agreement with the experiments of Shields. Compare the work by Kanolt, mentioned on p. 519.

The Theory of Indicators.[1]—Many of the so-called "*colour-reactions*" may be explained by a change in the electrolytic dissociation, whether it is a result of dilution or of the addition of some foreign substance.

We have already seen (p. 389) that each particular ion has its own definite absorption of light, and that in general this changes when the ion unites with another. Thus cupric chloride has a green colour,

---

[1] Ostwald, *Lehrb. d. allg. Chim.* 2nd edit., 1891, Bd. I. p. 799. [See this part translated by P. M. M. Muir, "Solutions," pp. 268-272. London and New York, 1891. —Tr.]; *Grundlagen d. analyt. Chemie,* chap. vi., 4th edit., Leipzig, 1904.

which is occasioned by the undissociated molecules; and it is only at extended dilution that the blue colour of the cupric ions appears, which is exhibited by all cupric salts dissolved in much water. If one adds hydrochloric acid to a dilute solution of cupric chloride, the dissociation retreats, and the solution again becomes a clear green.

The quantitative study of the gradual change in coloration is an elegant method of investigating chemical equilibrium, which was first introduced by Gladstone (1885). It has been used since by Salet (p. 350), Magnanini,[1] Lellmann (p. 526), and others.

Upon phenomena like this depends the common use of *indicators* in volumetric analysis, *i.e.* substances which in acid solutions have colours different from those in alkaline [or neutral] solutions. *Every weak acid or base is suitable for such a purpose when its radical has, as an ion, a colour different from that which it has in an electrically neutral molecule.*

The acid or base must be weak so that a very slight excess of hydrogen or hydroxyl ions may cause a great change in coloration. Thus paranitrophenol is an acid indicator; the undissociated molecule of this acid is colourless, its negative ion is coloured an intense yellow. If acid is present in the solution the already slight dissociation of the indicator is almost entirely destroyed and the solution becomes colourless. If, on the contrary, a base is added, the strongly dissociated solution of paranitrophenol is formed, and the solution becomes yellow. Another acid indicator of similar chemical character is phenolphthalein, which is colourless in the undissociated state, that is, in the presence of a trace of hydrogen ions. But as soon as the solution becomes alkaline the strongly dissociated salt of phenolphthalein is formed, and the intense red of its negative ion appears. Methyl orange is an example of a basic indicator; in acid solutions it is coloured an intense red, in alkaline it is yellowish.[2]

The above considerations show when an indicator is useful, that is, when it gives a sharp change of colour, and when not. If it is a strong or even a moderately strong acid its dissociation would only be destroyed by a considerable excess of hydrogen ions. On the other hand, it must not be too weak an acid, otherwise, with excess of base, the salt formed by the base and the indicator would be hydrolytically decomposed to a considerable extent, and consequently the change of colour would be weakened. The latter circumstance becomes of more importance when the base added is weak. Phenolphthalein, for example, is so weak an acid that its ammonia salt is strongly dissociated hydrolytically, hence when ammonia is titrated with phenolphthalein as indicator the red colour of the ion of phenolphthalein disappears on addition of acid before the ammonia present has been thoroughly

---

[1] *Zeitschr. phys. Chem.* **8**. 1 (1891).
[2] See also on this point F. W. Küster, *Zeitschr. anorg. Chem.* **13**. 136 (1897), who shows convincingly that the acid function of methyl orange is unimportant as regards change of colour (p. 381).

neutralised. Paranitrophenol is a considerably stronger acid, its ammonium salt is less decomposed hydrolytically, but the change of colour remains sharp. Hence weak bases may be titrated with paranitrophenol, but not with phenolphthalein as indicator. In titrating strong bases phenolphthalein gives more exact results than paranitrophenol, because the yellow colour of the negative ion of the more strongly dissociated paranitrophenol appears before the neutralisation is completely effected by the alkali added, whilst the much more weakly dissociated phenolphthalein only shows the red colour of its negative ion when an extremely minute quantity of the strong base is present in excess. The same considerations apply naturally to basic indicators like methyl orange, so that we are led to the following rule as to the use of indicators. *A weak base and a weak acid are not to be used together on account of hydrolysis*; very weak acid indicators are therefore unavailable for titrating weak bases, very weak bases for titrating weak acids. As titrating liquid strong acids and strong bases should always be used (hydrochloric acid, barium hydroxide). If the indicator used is a moderately weak acid or base the change of colour can still be used in titrating weak bases although with a certain loss of sensitiveness.

In multivalent acids it may happen that, on account of the different strengths of its valencies, only one stage of the dissociation may come into evidence on account of the nature of the indicator used. Thus carbonic acid cannot be titrated at all with methyl orange, with phenolphthalein it appears as a univalent acid ; phosphoric acid behaves as a univalent acid on titration with methyl orange, as a divalent acid on titration with phenolphthalein. For further details see the study on indicators by Julius Wagner.[1]

Recent investigations (see J. Stieglitz, *Journ. Amer. Chem. Soc.* **25.** 1112 (1903); further especially Hautzsch, *Ber.* **40.** 3017 (1907); **41.** 1187 (1908)) have shown that the decrease in dissociation of an indicator is accompanied by a change in constitution, and it is this that causes the colour change ; see the paragraph " Tautomerism " in the following chapter. The above considerations are, however, unaffected by this ; but the further condition must be added, that an indicator is only useful when the change in constitution takes place rapidly, which is by no means always the case. But the observation that the colour of some indicators changes with measurable velocity, shows clearly that the change is not only due to a decrease in electrolytic dissociation.

Sensitiveness of Indicators.—According to the preceding paragraph, the sensitiveness of an indicator depends not only on the nature of the colour change, but on the concentration of hydrogen ions in the solution when the change in colour takes place. Every indicator, whether acidic or basic, changes in colour when there is excess of either hydrogen or hydroxyl ions in the solution ; for example, if the indicator is a fairly weak acid, a certain excess of hydrogen ions must be present, before its dissociation is sufficiently depressed ; on the other hand, if it is an extremely weak acid a certain

---

[1] *Zeitschr. anorg. Chem.* **27.** 138 (1901).

excess of hydroxyl ions will be required before hydrolysis is so far prevented that the anion of the acid (*i.e.* the salt of the indicator) can be present in sufficient quantity. It is, of course, best when the change in colour takes place as near as possible to the neutral point —where the concentrations of hydrogen and hydroxyl ions are the same.

These relations have been quantitatively investigated by two methods, under my direction ; Salessky [1] determined the concentration of hydrogen ions at the point where the colour changed by means of a hydrogen electrode (see Book IV. Chap. VIII.); Fels [2] prepared solutions of known (very small) concentration of hydrogen ions by adding acetic acid to sodium acetate, or ammonia to ammonium chloride solutions (the concentration of hydrogen ions can be calculated as in the example on p. 533). The two methods gave concordant results, of which the following table contains the most important :

Indicator.	Colour.		Concentration of Hydrogen Ion corresponding to the different Colours.
	In Alkaline.	In Acid Solution.	
Tropäolin 0·0 .	Red	Orange	$10^{-11\cdot2}$ orange-red
Phenolphthalein	Red	Colourless	$\begin{cases} 10^{-7\cdot8} \text{ red} \\ 10^{-7\cdot5} \text{ colourless} \end{cases}$
Litmus . .	Blue	Red	$10^{-6\cdot97}$ intermediate purple colour
p. Nitrophenol	Yellow	Colourless	$\begin{cases} 10^{-6\cdot7} \text{ yellow} \\ 10^{-6\cdot1} \text{ colourless} \end{cases}$
Methyl orange .	Yellow	Red	$\begin{cases} 10^{-5\cdot2} \text{ yellow} \\ 10^{-4\cdot1} \text{ orange} \\ 10^{-3\cdot3} \text{ red} \end{cases}$
Congo red .	Red	Blue	$\begin{cases} 10^{-4\cdot4} \text{ red intermediate colour} \\ 10^{-3\cdot8} \text{ blue intermediate colour} \end{cases}$
Methyl violet .	Violet	Blue	$\begin{cases} 10^{-2\cdot4} \text{ violet} \\ 10^{-2\cdot05} \text{ blue} \end{cases}$

Rupp and Loose [3] have recently discovered a new indicator (Methyl red), which is apparently very sensitive to alkalies.

The true neutral point is (p. 519) at $10^{-6\cdot9}$; the colour changes of litmus and phenolphthalein take place very close to this. The concentration of hydroxyl ions is of course given by :

$$\left[\overset{-}{OH}\right] = \frac{10^{-13\cdot8}}{\left[\overset{+}{H}\right]}.$$

Formation of Hydrates.—The fact that it is in water especially that dissolved substances dissociate electrolytically, makes it appear probable that the formation of ions is accompanied by chemical com-

[1] *Zeitschr. f. Elektrochemie,* 1904, p. 205.
[2] *Ibid.* p. 208.   [3] *Ber.* **41**. 3905 (1908).

bination with the water. But, as has been already emphasised on p. 271, we can get no evidence of this by determinations of molecular weights in dilute solutions. Further, the applications of the law of mass-action in the preceding paragraphs are independent of any hydration of the ions (see also p. 469). The question is therefore at present perfectly open ; and although there are methods of attacking the problem which are apparently free from objection, yet we are still far from a "hydrate theory" of which many different authors have already spoken

The Mutual Influence of the Solubility of Salts.—We have thus far considered equilibrium in salt solutions, as though these were *homogeneous* systems. We will now consider the case where *solid salts* participate in the equilibrium. The proposition that a solid substance, which dissociates on solution, has a definite solubility at a definite temperature, like every other solid substance (p. 484), holds good of course for the case where the dissociation is electrolytic ; and thus the propositions previously developed may be applied, without further remark, to the case in hand. This statement thus enables us to consider, completely, the case where the solid salt participates in the equilibrium, as will be made plain from the following example.

We will first consider the simple case of *a binary electrolyte*, and we will investigate the change in its solubility caused by the presence of another binary electrolyte which has a common ion. The process can at once be surveyed in a qualitative way.

The saturated solution of the first electrolyte, of course, is never completely dissociated, for some electrically neutral molecules will be present in the solution. The proposition (p. 485) that the concentration remains unchanged by the presence of other substances in the solution may be immediately applied to these neutral molecules. If we add to the saturated water solution of the electrolyte another electrolyte with a common ion, then in exactly the same way that it was found on p. 514, the dissociation of the first electrolyte will retreat, and the quantity of electrically neutral molecules will increase. But this increased quantity prevents the solution pressure of the solid salt from remaining in equilibrium, and therefore a definite part of the dissolved salt will be precipitated from the solution, until the equilibrium is re-established. *Thus the solubility of one salt is depressed in the presence of another having a common ion.*

This proposition may be proved in a *qualitative* way without difficulty. Thus, if one adds to a saturated solution of potassium chlorate a solution of another potassium salt, as *e.g.* potassium chloride, or a solution of another chlorate as *e.g.* sodium chlorate,—and this may be done most easily by adding a few drops of a concentrated solution of the other substance,—a copious separation of solid potassium chlorate takes place after a few moments. A saturated solution of lead chloride gives immediately a white precipitate on addition of a few drops of chloride and so on.

Of course the mutual influence of solubility can also be developed theoretically in a *quantitative* way. Thus let m_0 be the solubility of the solid electrolyte in pure water ; and let a_0 be the degree of dissociation corresponding to this concentration (the latter being expressed, as always, in g-equivalents per litre). Then $m_0(1 - a_0)$ will denote the undissociated, and $m_0 a_0$ the dissociated quantity of the electrolyte. Let its solubility be m, and the corresponding degree of dissociation be a, in the presence of another electrolyte, the free ions of which have the concentration x.

Then the theorem of the constant solubility of the undissociated part, gives

$$m_0(1 - a_0) = m(1 - a),$$

and the application of the isotherm of dissociation, in the two cases, gives

$$Km_0(1 - a_0) = (m_0 a_0)^2,$$
$$Km(1 - a) = ma(ma + x) ;$$

and therefore, there must exist the relation,

$$(m_0 a_0)^2 = ma(ma + x),$$

from which we obtain

$$m = -\frac{x}{2a} + \sqrt{m_0^2 \left(\frac{a_0}{a}\right)^2 + \frac{x^2}{4a^2}} ;$$

this equation enables one to calculate the solubility after the addition, from the solubility of the salt in pure water, and from the quantity of salt added.

This preceding law of solubility, which I developed in 1889, and also experimentally verified (p. 486), was later subjected to a very careful test by A. A. Noyes ;[1] its requirements were established in a striking way. Thus Noyes studied the alteration of the solubility of silver bromate in the presence of silver nitrate and potassium bromate.

I. Addition of $AgNO_3$ or of $KBrO_3$ respectively.	II. Sol. of $AgBrO_3$ on the addition of $AgNO_3$.	III. Sol. of $AgBrO_3$ on the addition of $KBrO_3$.	IV. Calc. sol. of $AgBrO_3$.
0·	0·00810	0·00810	0·00810
0·00850	0·00510	0·00519	0·00504
0·0346	0·00216	0·00227	0·00206

The numbers given under II. are the solubilities on addition of

[1] *Zeitschr. phys. Chem.* **6.** 241 (1890) ; **9.** 603 (1892) ; **26.** 152 (1898).

silver nitrate, under III. those on addition of potassium bromate ; it appears from the table that equivalent mixtures of silver nitrate and potassium bromate displace the solubility of silver bromate equally and by practically the amount that is calculated from the law of mass-action. It also appears that a relatively small addition of a foreign substance is sufficient to reduce the solubility [of the $AgBrO_3$] one-fourth.

Moreover, Noyes also found that the equivalent quantities of chlorides of *univalent* bases depress the solubility of *thallous* chloride to the same degree ; this is a further proof of the proposition (p. 510) that these substances are dissociated to the same extent when in equivalent solutions.

Moreover, the addition of the chlorides of the *divalent* metals, Mg, Ca, Ba, Mn, Zn, and Cu, have the same effect in depressing the solubility ; from which it is to be inferred that these substances, in equivalent solutions, are also dissociated to the same degree. In this way Noyes found the following values for the degree of dissociation of the chlorides just enumerated.

Concentration.	Degree of Dissociation.
0·0344	82·2%
0·05€7	77·6%
0·1045	69·4%
0·2030	61·5%

These values are calculated as though the salt decomposed according to the scheme

$$CaCl_2 = \overset{++}{Ca} + \overset{-}{Cl} + \overset{-}{Cl} \; ;$$

but there is, doubtless, at the same time a decomposition according to the scheme

$$CaCl_2 = \overset{+}{CaCl} + \overset{-}{Cl},$$

although this latter may not amount to very much.

In contrast to the salts just mentioned, $CdCl_2$ is dissociated to a much smaller degree. Thus, in investigating the influence of solubility, we possess, in the suitable choice of substances which are soluble with difficulty, a method, which is applicable to every kind of ion, for the determination of the number of the particular kind of ions contained in a solution.

As an example of the mutual influence of the solubilities of *ternary electrolytes*, Noyes studied the diminution of the solubility of *lead chloride* on the addition of the chlorides of Mg, Ca, Zn, and Mn. As would be expected, these latter substances act with the same strength. The degree of this influence is given by the proposition, that the product of the lead ions and the square of the chlorine ions must be constant.

As before, let m_0 denote the solubility of $PbCl_2$ in pure water, and m its solubility after the addition of x chlorine ions ; and let a_0 denote the original dissociation, and a that after the addition. Then the law of mass-action requires that

$$m_0(1 - a_0) = m(1 - a),$$

and

$$(m_0 a_0)^3 = ma(ma + x)^2.$$

Then, since $PbCl_2$ is dissociated just as strongly as the added chloride, x is equal to the quantity of chloride added multiplied by a. Thus Noyes found the following results :—

Quantity added.	a.	m.	
		Found.	Calc.
0·05	0·697	0·0502	0·0522
0·10	0·661	0·0351	0·0351
0·20	0·605	0·0218	0·0176

$$m_0 = 0·0777 \; ; \; a_0 = 0·7.33.$$

The values of a are taken from the preceding table. The coincidence between calculation and observation is fair.

To precipitate an insoluble salt as far as possible it is therefore convenient to use an excess of the precipitating material in order to displace the solubility of the precipitated salt. It is, however, sufficient, especially in the case of very insoluble substances, to use a quite small excess. For example, the concentration of a saturated solution of silver chloride at atmospheric temperature is about $\frac{1}{100000}$ normal ; if chlorine ions are added, to precipitate silver, only to the extent of $\frac{1}{1000}$ normal in excess, the concentration of the silver ions, as appears from the preceding formulæ, is reduced to a normality of $\frac{1}{100000000}$.[1] Lead sulphate is appreciably soluble, hence the prescription of analytical chemistry to wash this substance with water acidulated with sulphuric acid rather than with pure water, since the acid reduces its solubility to an amount small as regards analysis.

Moreover, Noyes succeeded in proving, both by theory and by experiment, that *conversely the solubility of a salt must increase* on the addition of a second electrolyte containing no ion in common.

[1] See the interesting study by C. Hoitsema, *Zeitschr. phys. Chem.* **20.** 272 (1896).

Thus, to follow out a preceding example, if one adds some KNO_3 to $AgBrO_3$, then a number of molecules of $AgNO_3$ and also of $KBrO_3$ will be formed. This will result in a diminution in the number of the molecules of $AgBrO_3$, which must be replaced from the solid salt. In this and in analogous cases the increase of the solubility is of course very slight; but the increase would be very great if one should add, e.g. HNO_3 to a saturated solution of $CH_3 . CO . OAg$; because here, on account of the small dissociation constant of acetic acid, there will be produced a very considerable quantity of undissociated acetic acid molecules as a result of the addition of the HNO_3; and as the product of the silver ions and the acet-ions must regain its former value, a considerable quantity of solid silver acetate must therefore pass into solution.[1]

A similar explanation may be given of the well-known fact that calcium oxalate is soluble in strong acid, for the product of the concentration of the calcium ions and the oxalic acid ions (the so-called *solubility product*) is much diminished when a strong acid is present, since the hydrogen ions of the latter combine with the oxalic ions and thus diminish their concentration; hence for equilibrium more calcium must go into solution and the amount may become quite large. As another example may be mentioned the solubility of zinc sulphide in strong acids whose hydrogen ions combine with the doubly negative sulphur ions of the zinc sulphide; weak acids do not dissolve it because the concentration of the hydrogen ions is too small. If, therefore, sodium acetate be added to an acid solution of a zinc salt the formation of slightly dissociated acetic acid reduces the concentration of the hydrogen ions to a small amount, and the zinc is satisfactorily precipitated by sulphuretted hydrogen.

Anomalies due to Formation of Complex Ions.—There are cases in which the solubility of a salt is raised by addition of another salt containing the same ion; thus potassium nitrate and lead nitrate raise each other's solubility, mercury chloride is more easily dissolved by water containing hydrochloric acid than by pure water. Closer study of these cases, however, shows that the exception to the general law is only apparent; as has been shown by Le Blanc and Noyes[2] in this and similar cases, new complex molecules are formed, so that the solubility product is not raised by the addition of salt containing the same ion as would otherwise be the case, but reduced.

These anomalous phenomena of solubility are consequently very important for the study of complex salts in solution, a subject which has been very little investigated considering its enormous importance for inorganic chemistry. As an example of the insight to be obtained by means of relatively simple researches we may mention the work of

---

[1] A case of this kind has been exactly worked out by Noyes and D. Schwartz, *Zeitschr. phys. Chem.* **27.** 279 (1898).   [2] *Ibid.* **6.** 385 (1890).

A. A. Noyes and W. R. Whitney.[1] Potassium and sodium hydroxides not only do not reduce the solubility of aluminium hydroxide but take up considerable quantities of this insoluble substance. Yet it was found that the freezing-point of the solutions is *not* altered by addition of aluminium hydroxide. From this it may be concluded that on solution the reaction

$$\overline{OH} + Al(OH)_3 = Al\overline{O}(OH)_2 + H_2O$$

takes place, that is, the addition of aluminium hydroxide does not alter the number of molecules in solution. The potassium aluminate has therefore in solution the formula $KAlO(OH)_2$ or $KAlO_2$ (the methods in use at the present day do not allow of distinguishing between these two formulæ any more than between NH_3 or NH_4OH for ammonia in aqueous solution. See the section on "Normal and Anomalous Reactions.")

The Application of the Law of Mass-action to Strongly Dissociated Electrolytes.—It has already been remarked that the equation of the dissociation isotherm does not hold for strongly dissociated electrolytes such as the neutral salts. Correspondingly, when we calculate, according to the above theory, the influence of other salts on the solubility of these electrolytes, we obtain numbers which show unmistakable, though small, differences, from the values actually observed. It is always found that the solubility is decreased by a less amount than that demanded by theory.[2] This must mean that, besides the normal ions, others, more complex, must be present in the salt solutions.

In any case the deviations from the law of mass-action are relatively small, and may be neglected for most practical purposes, as may be seen from the numerous examples given in this chapter.

The Reaction between any number of Solid Salts and their Solution.—This general case may also be solved simply by the theorem, *that the active mass of the solid substances is a constant.*

An example which belongs here, has been already studied by Guldberg and Waage (1867), namely, the state of equilibrium existing between the difficultly soluble $BaSO_4$ and $BaCO_3$, and K_2SO_4 and K_2CO_3 in solution. Here, in the sense of the old conceptions, we have to deal with the reaction

$$\underset{\text{Solid}}{BaSO_4} + \underset{\text{Dissol.}}{K_2CO_3} \underset{}{\overset{}{\rightleftharpoons}} \underset{\text{Solid.}}{BaCO_3} + \underset{\text{Dissol.}}{K_2SO_4},$$

and therefore the relation obtains that the ratio of the carbonate existing in the solution to the sulphate in solution must be a constant.

---

[1] *Zeitschr. phys. Chem.* **15.** 694 (1894).

[2] See H. Karplus, *Löslichkeitsbeeinflussung.* Dissertation, Berlin, 1907.

Guldberg and Waage allowed a equivalents of K_2CO_3, and b equivalents of K_2SO_4, to react on each other in a water solution in the presence of an excess of solid $BaSO_4$; they determined the quantity x of the $BaCO_3$ formed after a sufficiently long interval, and, as a matter of fact, they found the preceding ratio, namely $\frac{a-x}{b+x}$, to be constant, as shown by the following table:—

b.	a.	x.	$\frac{a-x}{b+x}$.
0	3·5	0·719	3·9
0	?	0·176	4·7
0·25	2	0·200	4·0
0·50	2	0·000	4·0

Now the application of the preceding conception usually leads to results which coincide but poorly with experiment, because electrolytic dissociation must also be taken into account. According to this the reaction occurs in the sense of the equation,

$$BaSO_4 + \overset{=}{CO_3} \underset{\longleftarrow}{\overset{\longrightarrow}{}} BaCO_3 + \overset{=}{SO_4},$$
Solid.   Dissol.   Solid.   Dissol.

and the application of the law of mass-action leads to the result, that in the condition of equilibrium the ratio of the SO_4 ions to the CO_3 ions in the solution must be constant. Moreover, by a displacement of the point of equilibrium in the solution there also occur, in the sense of the preceding reaction, the following side reactions, viz.—

$$K_2SO_4 \underset{\longleftarrow}{\overset{\longrightarrow}{}} 2\overset{+}{K} + \overset{=}{SO_4}, \text{ and } K_2CO_3 \underset{\longleftarrow}{\overset{\longrightarrow}{}} 2\overset{+}{K} + \overset{=}{CO_3},$$

by means of which the calculation of the equation of the isotherm of dissociation may be accomplished.

But now it should be observed that as these two electrolytes have an analogous constitution, and as they are dissociated to the same extent in a common solution (p. 516), therefore it follows that *the total quantity* of the sulphate existing in the solution must stand in a constant ratio to the carbonate.

Thus the older conception here happens to lead to satisfactory results; in other cases—*e.g.* as in the explanation of the measurements given in the preceding paragraph—they fail utterly; and the contradictions can only be explained by the aid of the theory of electrolytic dissociation.

But the newer views lead us a step farther. It follows from the laws of solubility (p. 537) that, in the presence of solid $BaCO_3$ and $BaSO_4$ the products of the Ba ions and the CO_3 ions, and of the Ba ions and the SO_4 ions, must be constant. Now the ratio of these products, in the measurements given above, averages about 4·0.

Moreover, since $BaCO_3$ and $BaSO_4$ are doubtless dissociated to the same extent, therefore the value 4·0 is at the same time the ratio of the undissociated quantities of the carbonate and sulphate in their saturated solution.

Finally, since each of the particular solutions of these two substances, considered by itself, is very highly dissociated on account of its difficult solubility, therefore, according to the rules given on p. 509, the value 4·0 is, at the same time, the ratio of the squares of the total concentrations of the two saturated solutions.[1]

If one pours a solution of KI over solid AgCl, then, as can be proved in a perfectly analogous way, the iodine existing in the solution will be largely replaced by chlorine ; because as AgI *is much less soluble than* AgCl, an equivalent quantity of AgCl will be changed into AgI. This is also established by experiment. If the solubilities of AgCl and AgI are known, then, for a given concentration of KI, we may state the point of equilibrium which the system strives to reach.

The analogous equilibrium between silver oxide and silver chloride in solutions of hydroxides and chlorides has been completely investigated by A. A. Noyes and Kohr.[2]

When a dissolved salt is so strongly *hydrolysed* that the limit of solubility of one of the components (the base or the acid) is exceeded, the solution becomes turbid ; thus iron salts give off ferric hydroxide, silicates give silicic acid. To clear such solutions the hydrolysis must be reduced by an excess of acid or, in the second instance, of base.

If sodium acetate is added to a clear, that is a strongly acid solution of ferric chloride, the concentration of the hydrogen ions is much reduced, the hydrolysis is consequently increased, and colloidal ferric hydroxide is precipitated. In the same way silicic acid may be precipitated from alkaline soluble glass by addition of ammonium chloride which reduces the number of free hydroxyl ions with formation of ammonia.

In conclusion, we will collate the following remarks regarding the theoretical treatment of the equilibrium between a salt solution and any number of solid salts.

For every molecular species which can be formed from the ions, there exists a particular *dissociation constant*, which is the ratio between the concentration of the particular molecular species and the product of the respective concentrations of the ions of which it is composed.

Further, every such molecular species has a *definite solubility* ; *i.e.* there is a definite value of the concentration beyond which it cannot

---

[1] In testing this deduction from the theory, it is to be noted that a saturated solution of barium carbonate in pure water is noticeably hydrolysed.

[2] *Zeitschr. phys. Chem.* **42.** 336 (1902).

pass (excluding supersaturation) ; and this solubility remains unchanged, other things being equal, as long as solid salt remains in contact with the solution.

If one knows the value of the dissociation constants, and also the solubilities of all of the molecular species, then *the equilibrium* in the solution is completely determined, and if the total quantity of each radical is known, one can state *how much of each radical is present as a free ion, and how much of each is combined with other ions, partly in the form of electrically neutral molecules, and partly in the form of solid salt external to the solution.*

Thus the dissociation coefficients determine the number of electrically neutral molecules in the solution, while the solubilities determine the number of those which crystallise out ; and although we may succeed in formulating a number of general empirical rules for the values of the dissociated constants, yet this attempt fails entirely in the case of the solubilities. Thus all binary salts composed of univalent ions, exhibit the same degree of dissociation (p. 510), but they do not exhibit the same degree of solubility [1] ; moreover, the latter property varies with the different polymorphic [allotropic] modifications of the same salt.

Sometimes, as has been already mentioned (p. 500) the salts do not crystallise out from the solution in the pure form, but as isomorphous mixtures. Here the rule holds good that the solubility of each molecular species in a mixture is always smaller than for the particular species when alone. Again, the behaviour of *dilute solid solutions*, when they crystallise out, is very simple. In such cases the principles already developed regarding the equilibrium between phases of variable composition, may be directly applied without further remark. (See the next section.)

Normal and Abnormal Reactions.[2]—The preceding developments now show us, at the same time, the reason for a fact which has long been known, viz., that the [main] reactions of inorganic chemistry, *i.e.* of salt solutions, are characterised by great similarity in classification. Thus, as is well known, we have so-called *typical reactions*, for most radicals : thus all acids colour litmus red ; all bases colour litmus blue ; all chlorides are precipitated by silver salts.[3] These facts are necessary results of the dissociation hypothesis of electrolytes. All acids contain the same hydrogen ion ; all bases the same hydroxyl ion, all chlorides the same chlorine ion, etc. ; and the reactions which are typical for the classes of substances collectively are the specific reactions of the ion common to them. Thus the behaviour of

[1] F. Kohlrausch has published the solubilities of a large number of salts in *Zeitschr. phys. Chem.* **44**. 197 (1903).

[2] Ostwald, *Zeitschr. phys. Chem.* **3**. 596 (1889).

[3] *Ibid.*, see also the work quoted on p. 533 by the same author, written in a more popular form, and more suitable for beginners.

electrolytes regarding their reaction capacity, as also regarding their other properties, is *clearly additive.*

Of course it is not necessary for all electrolytes containing a particular radical to exhibit the reactions which are typical for this radical; they *must* do so only when the radical is contained as *a free ion.* Thus sodium acetate $[CH_3 . CO_2Na]$ does not exhibit the reactions of hydrogen ions, because the hydrogen is not contained as free ions, but exists in the solution, combined with the negative complex of the salt.

Potassium platinic chloride $[K_2PtCl_6]$ and sodium mono-chloracetate $[CH_2Cl . CO_2 . Na]$ do not show the reactions which are typical for chlorine, because the chlorine does not exist there as the free ion, but rather associated with the respective complexes $PtCl_6$ and $CH_2Cl . CO_2$. In this way the contrast between the so-called *normal* and the *abnormal reactions* of certain radicals is explained. The abnormal reactions are those of the new-formed ion complex.

It has already been remarked that potassium bromide can take up bromine forming the salt KBr_3; the solubility of iodine in a solution of potassium iodide is explained in the same way by formation of potassium tri-iodide, that is, the complex ion $\overset{-}{I}_3$ is formed according to the equation

$$\overset{-}{I} + I_3 = \overset{-}{I}_3 ;$$

ammonia forms a new complex with silver ions,[1]

$$\overset{+}{Ag} + 2NH_3 = (NH_3)_2\overset{+}{Ag} ;$$

potassium cyanide can take up silver ions to a large extent; a complex ion is formed according to the equation

$$\overset{+}{Ag} + 2\overset{-}{Cy} = A\overset{-}{g}Cy_2.$$

Naturally these complex ions are more or less dissociated into other components and all possible steps are found. The ion I_3 also is strongly dissociated, the solution of potassium tri-iodide therefore acts like a solution of free iodine. The ion $(NH_3)_2Ag$ is not so strongly dissociated; for a solution of silver nitrate which contains ammonia gives no precipitate of silver chloride on addition of a chloride, that is, the concentration product of the silver ions × chlor-ions remains below the solubility product (10^{-10}). But a precipitate is obtainable on addition of an iodide, that is, the above ion dissociates sufficiently to make the product conc. silver ions × iodine ions exceed the solubility product for silver iodide (about 10^{-16}). In the complex ion $Ag(Cy)_2$ the silver is retained to an extraordinary extent since it is not precipitated even by addition of iodide; sulphuretted hydrogen, however, precipitates it on account of the extreme insolubility of silver sulphide.

[1] Bodländer and Fittig, *Zeitschr. phys. Chem.* **39**. 609 (1902).

In this way we obtain at the same time a strict classification of the *double salts*. The *characteristic double salts* are the isolated points in the series of mixtures, afforded by their components (p. 503). On solution they decompose almost completely into the single salts, and their ions therefore are simply those of. their components. The substances sometimes wrongly called " double salts," such as K_2PtCl_6, K_4FeCy_6 and the like, are to be regarded as entirely different; those in solution conduct themselves as *simple electrolytes*, since they afford *only one electrically neutral molecule, and exhibit only one series of ions*. The substances last referred to are simple salts of hydro-chloro-platinic acid $[H_2PtCl_6]$, and of hydro-ferro-cyanic acid $[H_2FeCy_6]$, etc., and therefore they contain no platinum ions, and no iron ions, etc., respectively.

According to present experience the ions, since they have the character of saturated compounds (p. 395) possess in a high degree the capacity for forming molecular compounds.

The systematic study of complex ions therefore promises to throw new light on the nature of compounds which do not fall under the scheme of valency ; some rules on this subject have already been given on p. 378.

It must by no means therefore be assumed that all chemical reactions are due to ions ; on the contrary every molecular species, ion, or electrically neutral molecule, has its peculiar and typical reaction. Angeli and Boeris [1] have given a striking example of this. It is well known that an aqueous solution of ammonium nitrate decomposes on heating into water and nitrogen and the more readily the more concentrated it is ; in very dilute solutions where only the ions $\overset{+}{N}H_4$ and $\overset{-}{N}O_2$ are present the reaction does not occur ; it must therefore be concluded that it is the undissociated molecule NH_4NO_2 that is capable of the reaction

$$NH_4NO_2 = N_2 + 2H_2O \ ;$$

the chemists mentioned have, in fact, shown that on addition of a salt with a similar ion, for example ammonium chloride or sodium nitrite, the production of nitrogen is increased in consequence of the reduced electrolytic dissociation of the ammonium nitrite, whereas the salts which have no ion in common with ammonium nitrite are inactive. In the same way it seems as if the oxidising action of nitric acid is exclusively or mainly due to the molecular species HNO_3 and depends little or not at all on the ions $\overset{+}{H} + \overset{-}{N}O_3$.

Formation and Solution of Precipitates.—Reactions causing precipitation are of exceptional importance in analytical chemistry ; the theory of the formation and solution of precipitates is indeed contained in the foregoing sections, but certain points of it may be put together here and illustrated by examples.

A precipitate occurs (unless it is prevented by supersaturation) when an electrically neutral species of molecule exceeds the amount of its solubility product (p. 541) ; it goes into solution again when the

[1] *Acad. Linc.* [1892] [5], **1.** II. 70.

product of the ionic concentrations is reduced below the solubility level.

The latter can only occur when other molecular species, either neutral or ionised, are added, causing an increase in one or more of the ions in question. The following cases arise :—

1. The precipitate to be dissolved is an *acid* ; then one of the ions, namely the hydrogen ion, can be removed very completely by addition of a base whose hydroxyl ions combine with it to form water. If the substance to be dissolved is a base it may be similarly dissolved in acid. (For example, benzoic acid dissolves easily in caustic soda, lime in hydrochloric acid, etc.)

If in these cases the acid or the base or both are very weak the solvent action is reduced by hydrolysis ; in this way, as was shown by Löwenherz,[1] the dissociation of extremely weak acids and bases can be measured.

It may be foreseen that in certain cases the water itself, in consequence of its ionisation, will alter the solubility, namely when the substance to be dissolved is hydrolytically dissociated. Thus, if the insoluble barium carbonate is brought into contact with water, the hydrogen ions of the water combine with the CO_3 ions to make the very slightly dissociated compound $\overline{HCO_3}$, and the concentration of the hydroxyl ions is accordingly raised a corresponding amount (see also p. 543).

2. Addition of hydrogen or hydroxyl ions may, however, occur in the two preceding cases by means of the salts of other weak acids (*e.g.* acetic acid) or a very weak base (*e.g.* ammonia). Examples : the equation

$$[Ca]\,[OH]^2 = \text{const.}$$

holds for the solubility of calcium hydroxide, but in presence of ammonium ions a large addition of hydroxyl ions occurs, since the very slightly dissociated ammonium hydroxide is formed.[2] In the same way the relatively large solubility of magnesium hydroxide in ammonium salts is explained, as well as the fact that magnesium salts are either not at all or incompletely precipitated by ammonia.[3]

3. If the precipitate to be dissolved is the salt of a weak acid its anions can be largely combined with hydrogen ions ; example : silver acetate dissolves in acids. In the same way salts of weak bases are dissolved by strong bases.

4. Very often the precipitate dissolves in consequence of the formation of complex ions. Example : silver chloride dissolves in potassium cyanide (p. 546), etc.

It is obvious that the same reagents that dissolve a precipitate prevent its precipitation when they are added before that takes place.

[1] *Zeitschr. phys. Chem.* **25**. 385 (1899).
[2] Investigated by Noyes and Chapin, *ibid.* **28**. 518 (1899).
[3] See also the thorough investigation by J. M. Lovén, *Zeitschr. anorg. Chem.* **11**. 404 (1896).

Distribution of an Electrolyte between Water and a Second Phase.—This is a case of the general law of distribution (p. 491), but it must be noted that the ions cannot be separated in appreciable quantity by partition, any more than in diffusion (p. 369).

The simplest method of treatment is to regard the concentration of the electrically neutral molecules as proportional in the two phases. Since also the concentration of the free ions in the gaseous space or in a solvent that will not mix with water is negligible, it follows that the ions must pass over practically completely into the water.

This may be illustrated by some examples (see also the table on p. 496). The partial pressure of hydrochloric acid over its water solution is simply proportional to the number of its undissociated molecules contained in the solution.

If an electrolyte divides itself between water and ether, there must be a proportionality between the electrically neutral molecules in the water and the concentration in the ether. Now the number of electrically neutral molecules in water decreases with increasing dilution much more quickly than proportionally to the concentration ; and therefore, at slight concentration, both the vapour pressures of electrolytes, and also their solubilities in another solvent, which is in contact with water solution, will be very small.

Thus, e.g., it is possible to distil pure water off from a dilute solution of hydrochloric acid.

If one tries to "shake out" with benzene a sufficiently dilute water solution of an organic acid, then only the slightest traces of the acid will go over to the benzene, even though it is much more soluble in benzene than in water.

Hydrocyanic acid which is very slightly dissociated is much more volatile ; even dilute solutions show its characteristic smell, so do solutions of the salts of this acid, since according to p. 532, they are markedly hydrolysed, i.e. contain free hydrocyanic acid.

The following table given by Kuriloff (p. 506) shows the partition of picric acid (which is strongly dissociated in aqueous solution) between benzene and water ; c_1 and c_2 are the concentrations (normalities) in the two solvents, a the degree of electrolytic dissociation.

c_1.	c_2.	$\dfrac{c_1}{c_2}$.	a.	$\dfrac{c_1}{c_2(1-a)}$.
0·09401	0·02609	3·6	0·9027	38
0·0779	0·02080	3·7	0·9104	41
0·06339	0·01963	3·2	0·9138	37
0·06184	0·01882	3·3	0·9164	39
0·0359	0·01320	2·7	0·9353	42
0·01977	0·00973	2·0	0·9463	38
			Mean .	. 39

Thus, although the undissociated molecules of picric acid are thirty-nine times as soluble in benzene as in water, it would pass over almost completely into water at great dilutions.

The case of partition of ions between a liquid and a *metallic* phase occurs, *e.g.*, on shaking mercury with dilute silver nitrate solution ; mercury ions pass to a certain extent into solution with precipitation of silver. The equilibrium can be treated by means of the law of mass-action (see the interesting study by Ogg, *Dissertation*, Göttingen, 1898 ; *Zeits. phys. Chem.* **27**. 285 (1898)).

The exceptional position of water as a solvent which is shown by its property of dissociating dissolved substances electrolytically, and thus giving them unusual capacity for reaction, appears now in a new light. Closely connected with the above properties is the marked way in which water, in contact with other solvents, retains the last portions of dissolved substances. Of equal importance with the capacity which water possesses to an unusual degree, of dissociating dissolved substances, is the *extraordinarily great solubility of ions in water.*

CHAPTER V

General Observations.—As has been previously emphasised, the hypothesis of Guldberg and Waage is the fundamental law of chemical kinetics. According to this law, the total progress of a reaction occurring *in a homogeneous system*, is determined by the difference between the two velocities with which the decomposition advances from left to right, and conversely from right to left, in the sense of the reaction equation.

Therefore at every instant the velocity of a reaction, *i.e.*, the quantity changed in a moment of time, in the sense of the reaction from left to right, divided by the moment of time, is given by the velocity constant of the change in the sense of the equation from left to right, multiplied by the active masses of the molecular species standing on the left side of the equation, diminished by the velocity constant of the change from right to left in the sense of the equation, multiplied by the active masses of the molecular species standing on the right side of the equation.

Thus, *e.g.*, if a homogeneous reaction takes place according to the simple scheme—

$$A_1 + A_2 = A_1' + A_2',$$

and if c_1, c_2, and c_1', c_2' are respectively the concentrations of the four reacting molecular species A_1, A_2, and A_1', A_2' ; and also if dc_1 denotes the diminution which c_1 will experience in the moment of time dt, where of course the similar diminution of c_2 is of the same amount,—then the reaction velocity at every moment will be

$$-\frac{dc_1}{dt} = kc_1c_2 - k'c_1'c_2',$$

where k and k' respectively are the velocity coefficients of the two opposed reactions. If a substance participates in the reaction with n molecules instead of with one, then of course c^n will appear in the equation instead of c.

Now the velocity coefficients are constant at constant temperature ; but without exception they increase very strongly with rising temperature. Therefore the application of the fundamental equation preceding is permissible *only when the reaction progresses isothermally*, i.e., *only when there is no change of the temperature of the system, as occasioned by heat, developed or absorbed, in the course of the reaction.*

Now for the time when t = 0, let the respective concentrations of the four substances be $a_1, a_2, a_1', $ and a_2' ; and in the time t let the quantity of the substance a_1 decomposed be x g.-mol, and accordingly the same amount of a_2. Thus the preceding equation will be written—

$$\frac{dx}{dt} = k(a_1 - x)(a_2 - x) - k'(a_1' + x)(a_2' + x) ;$$

then by knowing k and k', and remembering the preliminary condition that, when t = 0, then also x = 0, we can, by integration, obtain a complete description of the course of the reaction ; and the result is similar when the course of the reaction is given by an equation involving any arbitrary number of reacting molecular species.

The ascertaining of the concentrations in the state of equilibrium

$$\left(\frac{dx}{dt} = 0\right),$$

as was thoroughly demonstrated in the second chapter of this book, gives *the ratio of the two velocity constants.*

These relations are much simpler when the reaction advances *almost completely* in one direction in the sense of the equation, *e.g.,* from left to right; this is true of most of the reactions thus far investigated. This means that one of the two partial reaction-velocities is very great as compared with the other ; or that k is very large as compared with k'. In this case, the right side of the differential equation reduces to the positive term, and the reaction velocity at every moment is obtained as proportional simply to the product of the active masses of the molecular species standing on the left side of the reaction equation.

In all cases, the integration of the differential equation of the chemical change gives the result that, strictly speaking, the equilibrium would be reached only after an infinitely long time, *i.e.*—

$$\frac{dx}{dt} = 0,$$

only when t = ∞ .

According to this, a chemical system, like a pendulum which is highly damped, tends towards an "*aperiodic*" condition of equilibrium. An "over-shooting of the mark" is incompatible with all our views of chemical processes. This would mean that, under certain circumstances the sense of the reaction would depend upon *the previous history* of the system ; *i.e.* that in two solutions which are *absolutely identical*, the same reaction might progress in opposite directions, the reaction in one solution approaching one state of equilibrium, while the reaction in the other solution would shoot over towards the other state. As a matter of fact, such has certainly never been observed.

The Inversion of Sugar.—Cane sugar in water solution in the presence of acids is practically completely decomposed into dextrose and levulose. The process advances so slowly that it can be followed by easy measurement, as the progress of the reaction can be traced very easily and very sharply by polari-strobometric analysis. The part not inverted turns the plane of polarised light to the right, while the mixture of the products of inversion is laevo-rotatory.

Let a_0 denote the (positive) rotatory angle at the time $t = 0$, which corresponds to an original quantity of sugar a ; let $a_0{}'$ denote the (negative) rotatory angle after complete inversion ; and let a be that actually observed after the time t. Then, since all substances rotate the plane in proportion to their concentration, we have

$$x = a\frac{a_0 - a}{a_0 + a_0{}'}.$$

When the time $t = 0$, then $a = a_0$, *i.e.* $x = 0$. When the time $t = \infty$, after complete inversion, then $a = -a_0{}'$, *i.e.* $x = a$.

The progress of the inversion of sugar has been investigated by a great number of observers, including Wilhelmy (1850), Löwenthal and Lenssen (1862), Fleury (1876), Ostwald (1884), Urech (1884), Spohr (1885, 1886, and 1888), Arrhenius (1889), Trevor (1892), and others. Therefore, as it plays a very important *rôle* in the history of the doctrine of affinity, it demands a thorough description.

Corresponding to its progress according to the equation

$$C_{12}H_{22}O_{11} + H_2O = 2C_6H_{12}O_6,$$

the law of mass-action shows that *the velocity of the inversion at every moment is proportional to the product of the concentrations of the water and of the cane sugar ;* or since the water is usually present in large excess, and suffers only a very slight change in concentration during the course of the reaction, *therefore the velocity must be proportional simply to the concentration of the sugar itself.* That is

$$\frac{dx}{dt} = k(a - x) ;$$

at the start we have $t = 0$, and $x = 0$; k denotes *the coefficient of inversion.* Then by integration, we obtain

$$-\ln(a - x) = kt + \text{const.} ;$$

and as the original condition

$$-\ln a = \text{const.} ;$$

from this we obtain

$$k = \frac{1}{t} \ln \frac{a}{a-x} = \frac{1}{t} \ln \frac{a_0 + a_0'}{a + a_0'}.$$

This equation was discovered, and proved experimentally, by Wilhelmy, before the law of mass-action was advanced. In fact it is an assumption which follows almost directly from the preceding equation, to suppose that *a constant fraction of the sugar is inverted at every moment of time.* The simple meaning of the inversion coefficient is, that its reciprocal value multiplied by ln2 gives the time required for the inversion of half of the total quantity, as is seen at once if we write

$$x = \frac{a}{2}.$$

How well the results of the preceding equation coincide with those of experiment, is shown by the following table for the inversion of a 20 per cent solution of cane sugar in the presence of a 0·5 normal solution of lactic acid, and at a temperature of 25° :—

t (in minutes).		$\frac{1}{t} \log_{10} \frac{a}{a-x}.$
0	34·50°	—
1435	31·10	0·2348
4315	25·00	0·2359
7070	20·16	0·2343
11360	13·98	0·2310
14170	10·61	0·2301
16935	7·57	0·2316
19815	5·08	0·2291
29925	−1·65	0·2330
∞	−10·77	—
		Mean 0·2328

As·we are concerned only with the proof of the *constancy* of the expression given in the third column, we can of course introduce ordinary logarithms instead of natural logarithms.

The Catalytic Action of Hydrogen Ions.—The inversion of sugar proceeds with marked velocity only in the presence of an acid the quantity of which remains unchanged during the reaction ; such reactions as this have been already called " *catalytic.*"

The ultimate explanation of the preceding case is still unknown to us ; but nevertheless some very remarkable results have been obtained regarding the regularity of behaviour which obtains here. Arrhenius [1]

[1] *Zeitschr. phys. Chem.* **4.** 226 (1889).

succeeded in grouping in one simple orderly arrangement all the abundant material observed concerning this reaction.   As the method which is to be pursued here is a typical one, and as it has already led to important results in similar cases, and still promises more, we will give the results observed regarding the dependence of the inversion coefficients upon the nature of the acids and salts which may be present, and we will also give a brief theoretical summary of the same.

The following phenomena were empirically discovered by the study of the question of the variation of the velocity of inversion, with the *concentration*, with the *nature* of the acid, and in the presence of neutral salts.

The more concentrated the acid, the more quickly is the sugar inverted, although this does not take place in an exact proportion.

In the case of *the stronger acids*, the inverting action occurs somewhat *more quickly* than in proportion to the amount contained, and the *converse* of this is true in the case of *the weaker acids*.

The velocity of the inversion varies very greatly with the *nature* of the acid.   Thus the strong *mineral acids* effect the inversion *most quickly*, and with about the same degree of rapidity ; while the *fatty acids*, *e.g.*, exert an inverting action which is much weaker.

In the following table are given some of the results obtained by Ostwald at 25°, with an acid concentration of 0·5 normal.   The figures refer to 1·000 for hydrochloric acid, and are well suited to give a good impression of the variability of the inversion coefficients :—

Hydrochloric acid .	.	. 1·000	Tri-chlor-acetic acid .	. 0·754
Nitric ,, .	.	. 1·000	Di-chlor-acetic ,, .	. 0·271
Chloric ,, .	.	. 1·035	Mono-chlor-acetic ,, .	. 0·0484
Sulphuric ,, .	.	. 0·536	Formic ,, .	. 0·0153
Benzene-sulphonic acid .	.	. 1·044	Acetic ,, .	. 0·0040

The influence of neutral salts is very remarkable.   In the presence of an equivalent quantity of the potassium salt of the respective acid, the inversion velocity is increased about 10 per cent in the case of the stronger acids ; but in the case of acids weaker than tri-chlor-acetic acid, the action is diminished, and that the more as the acid is weaker.

In the case of acetic acid this depressing action is perfectly enormous : thus as a result of the presence of an equivalent quantity of a neutral salt, the inversion velocity sank to $\frac{1}{40}$ of its original value.[1]

The addition of non-electrolytes, in quantities which are not too great, exerts no marked effect.

In order to obtain a general view of the relations aforementioned, which at first sight do not seem to be simple, we will notice at once that it is *all the acids, but only the acids*, which exhibit the characteristic capacity of inverting sugar—*i.e. here we are concerned with a specific action of the free hydrogen ions ;* for it is in water solutions of acids, and

[1] Spohr, *J. pr. Chem.* [2], **32.** 32 (1885).

in these alone, that free hydrogen ions are contained. Now if these hydrogen ions are the actual catalytic agents, then, according to the law of mass-action, it would be expected that the catalytic action of the acids would be respectively proportional to the number of their hydrogen ions, *i.e.* an acid should invert the more strongly accordingly as it is more highly dissociated electrolytically. This anticipation is found to be completely verified in the results of the preceding table, *where the acids are arranged in the same relative order of succession as that required by their respective degrees of electrolytic dissociation.*

But we find only an approximate numerical proportionality between the quantity of the hydrogen ions and the inversion velocity ; this can be seen from the fact that the inversion velocity increases more quickly than in proportion to the acid concentration ; while the reverse is the case with the hydrogen ions, according to the laws of dissociation. Thus a 0·5 normal solution of HCl inverts 6·07 times more quickly than a 0·1 normal, although the former contains only about 4·64 times as many hydrogen ions as the latter.

There is thus a second action of importance : this was formulated by Arrhenius as follows :—

The catalytic activity of hydrogen ions is greatly stimulated by the presence of other ions.

In this way, which, to be sure, is rather puzzling from a theoretical standpoint, we explain the fact that the inversion velocity of the stronger acid increases more quickly than in proportion to their concentration, because the quantity of the free negative ions, which increases with increasing concentration, stimulates the activity of the hydrogen ions : and so we can also explain the observed increase of the inverting action of a strong acid in presence of its neutral salt.

Nevertheless, although this action of the dissociated part of the neutral salt is very interesting, yet it has rather the character of a side reaction of secondary nature. The action of the hydrogen ions is much more distinct, and thus their inverting action on a solution constitutes a very delicate reaction for the presence of hydrogen ions.[1]

Now we have with weak acids a simple means for repressing the dissociation to any desired extent, and thus at the same time for diminishing the quantity of free hydrogen ions to any desired degree. According to the laws of dissociation, which were thoroughly discussed on p. 514, the dissociation retreats on the addition of one of the dissociation products, in a way which can be easily calculated. In fact (see above) the researches have always shown a truly enormous diminution of the inversion velocity of the weaker acids in the presence of their neutral sodium salts ; and Arrhenius, by a consideration of their side reactions, which are not altogether simple, succeeded

---

[1] As shown by Trevor (*Zeitschr. phys. Chem.* **10.** 321, 1892), this reaction can be employed at quite high temperatures (100°), where the inversion velocity is much greater, in order to detect very small quantities of hydrogen ions.

in showing that the *quantitative relations* are, in fact, those required by theory.

Of course dissociation does retrograde also in the case of the stronger acids, as HCl, *e.g.*, on the addition of another chloride ; and although the amount of the diminution of the dissociation may be very slight, yet it does result. The contrary fact, that there is a not inconsiderable increase of reaction velocity is explained by the fact that the retrograde action is more than counterbalanced by the influence of the neutral salt, as mentioned above.

A very exact investigation by W. Palmaer [1] has yielded the important result that in very dilute solutions, in which there is no longer the action of neutral salts referred to above, the rate of inversion is directly proportional to the concentration of the hydrogen ions. If concentrated solutions of cane sugar are used, the velocity coefficient k increases considerably with the concentration of the sugar, though it should remain constant according to the theory. As E. Cohen has shown, this phenomenon indicates that the volume of the reaction is reduced, hence the number of collisions between the molecules of cane sugar and the hydrogen ions is increased, causing an increase in the velocity of reaction. [2]

Again the decrease in the *rotation of the various kinds of sugar with time* proceeds according to the formula for unimolecular reactions ; addition of salts usually accelerates this, hydrogen ions act more strongly, but hydroxyl ions act markedly too. [3]

The Catalysis of Esters.—A phenomenon, which in many respects is very closely related to sugar inversion, is the catalysis of the esters, *i.e.* the accelerating influence of the presence of acids on the decomposition of an ester in dilute water solution, into the corresponding alcohol and the corresponding acid.

According to the discussion on p. 457 *et seq.*, as a result of the mass-action, the cleaving [saponification] will be complete in the presence of a large excess of water ; and therefore we obtain, as the coefficient of the velocity with which the ester and water unite to form alcohol and acid, the same equation as in the case of sugar inversion, viz.

$$k = \frac{1}{t} \log \frac{a}{a - x},$$

provided that in neither case the concentration of the water suffers a marked change ; and also provided that by a we understand the quantity of the substance present when the time $t = 0$; and by x, the quantity of substance changed in the time t.

A simple titration shows the progress of the reaction. The velocity

---

[1] *Zeitschr. phys. Chem.* **22.** 492 (184).   [2] *Ibid.* **23.** 442 (1897).

[3] See the works of P. Th. Muller (1894), Levy (1895), Trey (1895), also the monograph mentioned on p. 334, by Landolt (p. 238 *et seq.*), and especially Osaka, *Zeitschr. phys. Chem.* **35.** 661 (1900). The rotation of milk sugar is discussed below.

of the decomposition at ordinary temperatures is extremely small; but it is very greatly accelerated by the presence of an acid, although this acid may not participate noticeably in the reaction. As was similarly true of sugar inversion, we can arrange the very abundant and also apparently very complicated material here observed, for which we are indebted to Ostwald,[1] in a clear way, under the following simple principles.

1. The velocity with which the ester is saponified is at every moment proportional to its concentration, *i.e.* the velocity coefficient remains constant, in the sense of the Guldberg-Waage theory.

2. The catalytic action of an acid increases with the degree of its dissociation, and the velocity coefficient is approximately proportional to the number of hydrogen ions.

3. In a secondary way the catalytic activity of the hydrogen ions is considerably increased by the presence of neutral salts.

The measurement of the velocity of the decomposition of esters thus furnishes a method for determining the number of hydrogen ions in a solution. This method was applied by Walker (p. 532) in a very ingenious way to investigate the "*hydrolytic dissociation*" of salts: their respective magnitudes could be ascertained by measuring the velocity with which the methyl acetate added to the solution was catalysed; and this formed a measure of the quantity of the free acid separated from the salt, and thus at the same time the strength of the base of the respective salt (a chloride) was estimated at least approximately.

According to the extensive investigations of B. Lowenherz,[2] the rate of saponification of various esters by the hydrogen ions is nearly independent of the nature of the alcohol contained in the ester, but depends largely on the nature of the acid contained. The behaviour of salicine towards acids is similar to that of cane sugar; it decomposes into dextrose and saligenin with separation of a molecule of water.[3]

Formation of Sulphuretted Hydrogen from its Elements.—
There is only a very small number of reactions occurring in the gaseous state which are free from secondary disturbances, such as chemical action or absorption by the walls of the vessel; and their experimental treatment mostly meets with very great difficulties. Bodenstein[4] has recently done a great service in systematically studying gas reactions from the point of view of chemical kinetics, and after discovering a series of sources of error has worked out exact methods for it.

He showed amongst other things that with a sufficient excess of

[1] *J. pr. Chem.* [2], **28.** 449 (1883); see also Trey, *ibid.* [2], **34.** 353 (1886).
[2] *Zeitschr. phys. Chem.* **15.** 389 (1894).
[3] A. A. Noyes and W. J. Hall, *ibid.* **18.** 240 (1895).
[4] Gas reactions in chemical kinetics, *ibid.* **29.** 147, 295, 315, 429, 665; **30.** 113 (1899).

‘sulphur the formation of sulphuretted hydrogen occurs according to the formula

$$\frac{dx}{dt} = k(a - x),$$

where $a - x$ is the amount of hydrogen present at the time t. The sulphur, which occurs as a liquid, evaporates fast enough for its active mass (like that of water in the preceding example) to remain practically constant. The following numbers obtained at 310° indicate the satisfactory constancy of $k(a = 0\cdot9557)$.

t.	x.	k.
720	0·1680	0·000117
1440	0·3049	0·000116
2160	0·4145	0·000114
2880	0·5258	0·000123
4320	0·6610	0·000118
5760	0·7572	0·000118
7200	0·8289	0·000122
8640	0·8494	0·000121
10080	0·9012	0·000123
Mean .		0·000118

It is noteworthy that *catalytic* influences very often occur in gas reactions ; thus the formation of seleniuretted hydrogen, which is also unimolecular, is mainly influenced by the catalytic action of solid selenium.

Unimolecular Reactions.—The same formula for the velocity coefficient, and the same course of the reaction which we met in the case of the inversion of sugar, we find in all cases *where the system suffers an essential change of concentration as a result of the change of only one molecular species.*

Thus, according to researches conducted by Harcourt and Esson as early as 1865, potassium permanganate, by oxidising a large excess of oxalic acid, which is added, disappears according to the logarithmic formula.

According to the researches of van't Hoff,[1] the same is true of the splitting of di-brom-succinic acid into brom-maleic acid and hydrobromic acid ; and also for the decomposition of mono-chlor-acetic acid into glycolic acid and hydrochloric acid, etc.

Following the usage of van't Hoff, we will call reactions of this sort *unimolecular* ; their course always corresponds to the differential equation,

[1] *Études de dynamique chimique* (Amsterdam, 1884), pp. 13 and 113.

$$\frac{dx}{dt} = k(a - x).$$

In an analogous way, we will call those reactions, in the course of which there is a change in the concentration of n molecular species, *n-molecular reactions*.

Bimolecular Reactions — The Saponification of Esters.— The classical example of this case, where the concentrations of two molecular species are considerably changed in the course of the reaction, is the *saponification of esters*. By bringing together a base with an ester in water solution, there are formed gradually the corresponding alcohol, and the salt from the positive ingredient of the base and the negative ingredient of the ester: the reaction takes place according to the scheme—

$$CH_3COOC_2H_5 \quad + \quad NaOH \quad = \quad CH_3COONa \quad + \quad C_2H_5OH$$

Ethyl acetate.   Sodium   Sodium acetate.   Ethyl alcohol.
hydroxide.

Let a and b represent the original concentrations of the base and of the ester respectively; and let x be the quantity of the ester changed after the time t; this can be easily and sharply determined by the titration of the quantity of the base yet remaining. Thus the reaction velocity for every moment is given by the equation,

$$\frac{dx}{dt} = k(a - x)(b - x),$$

or rearranged,

$$\frac{dx}{a - b}\left(\frac{1}{b - x} - \frac{1}{a - x}\right) = kdt.$$

The integral of this equation is

$$-\frac{1}{a - b}\left[\ln(b - x) - \ln(a - x)\right] = kt + \text{const.} ;$$

and, since x = 0 when t = 0, we have

$$-\frac{1}{a - b}\left(\ln b - \ln a\right) = \text{const.} ;$$

from which we finally obtain, by subtraction,

$$k = \frac{1}{(a - b)t}\ln\frac{(a - x)b}{(b - x)a}.$$

Saponification was first studied from the standpoint of the law of mass-action, by Warder;[1] and later and more thoroughly by van't Hoff,[2] Reicher,[3] Ostwald,[4] Arrhenius,[5] Spohr,[6] and others.

[1] *Ber.* **14.** 1361 (1881).   [2] *Études*, p. 107.
[3] *Lieb. Ann.* **128.** 257 (1885).   [4] *J. pr. Chem.* **35.** 112 (1887).
[5] *Zeitschr. phys. Chem.* **1.** 110 (1887).   [6] *Ibid.* **2.** 194 (1888).

It appears that the preceding formula harmonises excellently with the values obtained for the stronger bases.   Thus the following results were obtained for the action of *sodium hydroxide*, which was present in slight excess, on *ethyl acetate* at 10°; the basic [alkaline] titration of the reaction mixture, denoted by c, corresponded as follows to the respective times t, counted in minutes.

t (time).	c (titrat).	k.
0	61·95	...
4·89	50·59	2·36
10·37	42·40	2·38
28·18	29·35	2·33
∞	14·92	...

The figures under c denote the number of c.c. of a $\dfrac{1}{23\cdot26}$ normal acid solution required to neutralise 100 c.c. of the reaction mixture : in order to reduce these figures to our customary standard of concentration, viz. g.-mol per litre, we must multiply them by $\dfrac{1}{23\cdot26 \times 100}$.

Now the quantities a, b, and x in the preceding formula of course correspond : a to the original titration 61·95 ; b to the original titration minus the final one, *i.e.* $61\cdot95 - 14\cdot92 = 47\cdot03$; and x to $61\cdot95 - $ c.   The formula then becomes

$$k = \frac{2\cdot303 \cdot 2326}{14\cdot92 \cdot t} \log^{10} \frac{c \cdot 47\cdot03}{61\cdot95(c - 14\cdot92)}.$$

The factor 2·303 reduces the natural logarithms to ordinary logarithms.   The values for k, given in the third column of the preceding table, vary about a mean value, within the limits of error of experiment.   The significance of k, considering the fact that the time has been estimated in minutes and the concentration in g.-mol per litre, is as follows :—

It denotes the number of g.-mol of the ester which would be saponified in a minute, if 1 g-mol of ester and 1 g.-mol of sodium hydroxide should react on each other in 1 litre, and provided that one had an apparatus which would constantly remove the resulting reaction products from the system, and as constantly renew the corresponding quantities of base and of undecomposed ester.

If one causes equivalent quantities of ester and of base to react on each other, then the reaction velocity at each moment will be simply

$$\frac{dx}{dt} = k(a - x)^2,$$

2 o

which, when integrated, becomes

$$k = \frac{x}{t(a - x)a}.$$

The question regarding *the variation* of the reaction *velocity with the nature of the ester and of the base* has been systematically investigated by Reicher; his results were as follows :—

1. The saponification of methyl acetate at 9·4°, by the various bases.

	k.		k.
Sodium hydroxide . .	2·307	Strontium hydroxide . .	2·204
Potassium ,, . .	2·298	Barium ,, . .	2·144
Calcium ,, . .	2·285	Ammonium ,, . .	0·011

2. The saponification of the acetic acid esters of the various alcohols, by means of sodium hydroxide at 9·4°.

	k.		k.
Methyl alcohol . . .	3·493	Iso-butyl alcohol . .	1·618
Ethyl ,, . . .	2·307	Iso-amyl ,, . .	1·645
Propyl ,, . . .	1·920		

3. The saponification of the ethyl esters of different acids, by means of sodium hydroxide at 14·4°.

	k.		k.
Acetic acid . . .	3·204	Iso-butyric acid . . .	1·731
Propionic acid . . .	2·816	Iso-valeric ,, . . .	0·614
Butyric acid . . .	1·702	Benzoic ,, . . .	0·830

Thus it appears that the strong bases possess a reaction velocity which is about the same; and that as regards the esters, on the whole, their reaction velocity is the smaller, the greater the number of atoms contained.

The numbers also show that the nature of alcohol contained in the ester is of less influence than that of the acid; this result has come out even more strongly in recent researches.[1]

The influence of the nature of the base was afterwards very thoroughly investigated by Ostwald, in all the gradations between sodium and potassium hydroxide (which operate most quickly), and ammonia and allyl-amine (which operate very slowly), and he observed a remarkable phenomenon. In the case of the weak bases the preceding formula fails utterly; thus in *the saponification of ethyl acetate by ammonia*, for the times (t), he found the following corresponding velocity coefficients, which are not directly comparable with the preceding ones.

t	k
0	...
60	1·64
240	1·04
1470	0·484

These values of k are by no means constant. Ostwald found as the reason for this that *the neutral salt produced (ammonium acetate) exerted a very strong effect in hindering the progress of the reaction*, which explains the extreme retardation of the saponification.

Thus in *the saponification of ethyl acetate*, when an equivalent quantity of ammonium acetate was added at the outset in addition to the ammonia, the other conditions of the experiment being unchanged, the following values were found:—

t	k
0	...
994	0·138
6874	0·120
15404	0·119

As a result of the addition of the neutral salt of ammonium, the reaction velocity becomes considerably smaller, but at the same time the velocity coefficient becomes much more constant; the latter fact is explained by the circumstance that the concentration of the ammonium acetate changes, relatively, much less during the course of the reaction.

This remarkable influence, which is exerted by the presence of neutral salts, was afterwards investigated by Arrhenius, who, on the basis of very abundant material of observation, succeeded in establishing the following propositions:—

1. The saponification velocity of the stronger bases in fairly extended dilution is only slightly changed (less than 1 per cent) by the presence of neutral salts.

2. The saponification velocity of ammonia is exceedingly depressed by the presence of ammonium salts; and, moreover, equivalent quantities of the most different salts exert nearly the same effect.

Thus the relation between the velocity coefficient k of the action of a $\frac{1}{40}$ normal solution of ammonia on the equivalent quantity of

[1] Hemptinne, *Zeitschr. phys. Chem.* **13.** 561 (1894); Löwenherz, *ibid.* **15.** 395 (1894).

ethyl acetate, and the quantity S of any selected ammonium salt of a mono-basic acid, may be expressed by means of the following formula, which is purely empirical, and refers to a temperature of 24·7°:—

$$k = \frac{0·1561}{1 + 1241S - 11413S^2}.$$

The Theory of Saponification.—The relations described above, which seemed at first to be very puzzling, are now shown to be *a necessary result of the law of mass-action, on the assumption of the theory of electrolytic dissociation.*

If we consider the process of saponification in the light of this theory, it appears to consist in the action of the hydroxyl ions upon the ester molecule, in the sense of the equation

$$CH_3CO_2C_2H_5 + \overset{+}{Na} + \overset{-}{OH} = \overset{-}{CH_3COO} + \overset{+}{Na} + C_2H_5OH,$$

or more simply,

$$CH_3CO_2C_2H_5 + \overset{-}{OH} = \overset{-}{CH_3COO} + C_2H_5OH.$$

The positive ingredient of the base thus plays a perfectly indifferent *rôle.*[1] Therefore bases dissociated to the same degree must exert effects of the same degree of strength upon the ester; in fact such is the case with sodium and potassium hydroxides. And the less the base is dissociated, the weaker is the action; as, in fact, is shown by ammonia, or ammonium hydroxide rather, which is cleaved into its ions only in the slightest degree, and which accordingly saponifies with a corresponding slowness. Moreover, this is established in a very striking way by the investigations of Ostwald.

As has been already shown to be necessarily true in analogous cases in "Chemical Statics," so here also *the active mass in the mechanism of the reaction corresponds, not to the total quantity of the base introduced, but only to the quantity which is dissociated.*

Thus let us denote the degree of the dissociation by a, then the formula previously used must be corrected to

$$\frac{dx}{dt} = k'a(a - x)(b - x).$$

Now the degree of dissociation of the base is given by its dissociation constant, by its concentration, and by the quantity of neutral salt produced from it. For the stronger bases (which are almost as highly dissociated as the corresponding neutral salts produced from them in the reactions), a remains constant during the progress of the reaction. For in a mixture of any two equally dissociated electrolytes having

---

[1] We find, therefore, that saponification by barium hydroxide is not a trimolecular reaction $(Ba(OH)_2 + 2CH_3CO_2C_2H_5 = \ldots)$, but bimolecular $(\overset{-}{OH} + CH_3CO_2C_2H_5 = \ldots)$ as the above equation requires.

ions in common, *at the same total concentration*, the dissociation is independent of their relative masses (p. 514), and the latter always remains constant during the reaction. Thus if we make

$$k'a = k,$$

then the preceding equation again assumes the original form, which harmonises with experiment.

But the behaviour is quite otherwise in the case of a base, the degree of dissociation of which is very different from that of the resulting salt, *e.g. when the dissociation of the base is much weaker*; this is the case with ammonia and ammonium acetate. Thus it will result that the degree of dissociation of the base will be caused to retreat very much during the progress of the reaction, and also the saponification velocity must diminish much more quickly than it should, if it corresponded to the diminution of the concentration during the reaction; because during the reactions there are produced a relatively large number of ammonium ions. This in fact was found to be true, as above. In this way also the restraining action of the original addition of ammonium acetate is explained.

Now by means of the saponification constants of potassium hydroxide, one may calculate the saponification constant of ammonium hydroxide in the presence of any quantity of ammonium salts, in the following way.[1]

The saponification constant of potassium hydroxide at $24\cdot7°$, and at a concentration of $\frac{1}{40}$ normal, amounts to $6\cdot41$ on the scale previously employed; moreover, as shown by both theory and by experiment, it is almost independent of the concentration. The saponification constant of ammonium hydroxide at the same concentration, and with or without the presence of ammonium salts, according to theory, must be as much smaller as its dissociation under the same circumstances is less than that of potassium hydroxide, which latter substance, according to its conductivity, is dissociated into its ions to the extent of $97\cdot2$ per cent. But now the degree of dissociation of a $\frac{1}{40}$ normal solution of ammonium hydroxide, as calculated on the basis of its conductivity (p. 366), amounts to $2\cdot69$ per cent; and its degree of dissociation in the presence of a quantity S of a binary ammonium salt,—which we may regard as being completely dissociated at large dilution, as is the case here,—may be calculated without noticeable error by means of the following equations;—these equations are obtained by a double application of the isotherm of dissociation, firstly to the pure ammonium hydroxide, and secondly to that containing an ammonium salt, thus—

$$\left(\frac{0\cdot0269}{40}\right)^2 = K\,\frac{1 - 0\cdot0269}{40}$$

$$\frac{a}{40}\left(\frac{a}{40} + S\right) = K\,\frac{1 - a}{40};$$

---

[1] Arrhenius, *Zeitschr. phys. Chem.* **2.** 284 (1888).

here a denotes the degree of dissociation sought, and K denotes the dissociation constant of ammonia. We thus find the saponification velocity k, in the presence of the quantity S of a neutral salt, to be

$$k = \frac{a}{0 \cdot 972} 6 \cdot 41,$$

and similarly for pure ammonia,

$$k = \frac{0 \cdot 0269}{0 \cdot 972} 6 \cdot 41 = 0 \cdot 177.$$

In the following table there are given the values of k, on the one hand the results being calculated in the way just indicated, and on the other hand the results being calculated according to the formula (p. 564), which was *empirically deduced* by Arrhenius ; the latter values of k may therefore be regarded as the immediate expression of a direct observation.

S.	a.	k Calc.	k Obs.
0	2·69%	0·177	0·156
0·00125	1·21	0·080	0·062
0·0050	0·71	0·047	0·039
0·0175	0·118	0·0078	0·0081
0·0250	0·082	0·0054	0·0062
0·0500	0·042	0·0028	0·0033

When one considers that the calculation employs as its basis the very much greater values of the saponification coefficients of potassium hydroxide, the coincidence between the last two columns must be regarded as actually surprising ; and this may be expressed as—

The saponification velocity, under conditions which are similar in other respects, is actually proportional with very close approximation to the quantity of free hydroxyl ions present. In this way we are able to calculate the saponification velocity of any selected base, from its degree of dissociation.

Measurements of the velocity of saponification of dissolved esters is therefore a means for determining the quantity of hydroxyl ions present in a solution. Shields (p. 533) made use of this means in determining the hydrolysis of the salts of strong bases. E. Koelichen showed that the condensation of acetone to di-acetone alcohol in aqueous solution is accelerated by hydroxyl ions and can therefore be used to determine their concentration quantitatively.[1]

Very remarkable results have been found by Wijs[2] in studying the rate of *saponification methyl acetate by pure wate*r. This process clearly occurs in the following way. If the ester is dissolved in pure water the saponifying

---

[1] *Zeitschr. phys. Chem.* **33.** 129 (1900).   [2] *Ibid.* **12.** 514 (1893).

action of its hydroxyl ions yields acetic acid and methyl alcohol according to the equation :—

$$CH_3CO_2CH_3 + \overline{OH} = CH_3\overline{COO} + CH_3OH \; ;$$

hence the number of hydroxyl ions is reduced, and that of the hydrogen ions increased. But the hydrogen ions also possess the power of saponifying (p. 557), although to a much smaller degree than the hydroxyl ions ; the comparison between the rate of saponification by acids and alkalies show that the former occurs about 1400 times as slowly as the latter. These considerations show that at first the rate of saponification in pure water of the dissolved methyl acetate must fall very rapidly on account of the reduction in the number of hydroxyl ions, but later, when much acetic acid has been formed, and the water becomes decidedly acid, it will increase again because the catalytic action of the hydrogen has reached a considerable amount. Hence there must be a minimum of the velocity of saponification whose position can be calculated as follows.

Let us suppose the experiment so carried out that the concentration of the ester is kept constant, then the velocity of reaction is

$$\frac{dx}{dt} = k_1[OH] + k_2[H] \quad . \qquad . \qquad . \qquad . \qquad (1)$$

where k_1 and k_2 are the velocity coefficients for the saponification by hydroxyl and hydrogen ions respectively and for the constant concentration of the ester.

The equation (p. 518),

$$[H][OH] = c_0{}^2$$

differentiated gives the equation

$$[H]\frac{d[OH]}{dt} + [OH]\frac{d[H]}{dt} = 0 \quad . \qquad . \qquad . \qquad (2)$$

To find the position of the minimum we must differentiate equation (1) with respect to t and put it equal to zero,

$$\frac{d^2x}{dt^2} = k_1\frac{d[OH]}{dt} + k_2\frac{d[H]}{dt} = 0 \quad . \qquad . \qquad . \qquad (3)$$

Equation (3), however, is satisfied, as may be seen by comparison with (2), when

$$[H] : [OH] = k_1 : k_2,$$

which determines the position of the minimum ; since hydroxyl ions saponify 1400 times faster than hydrogen ions the time in question must occur when the concentration of the hydrogen ions has become 1400 times as great as that of the hydroxyl ions ; it may also be easily proved that the minimum velocity is 18 times smaller than the initial velocity.

To test these relations experimentally the rate of decomposition of the ester was determined by measuring its electric conductivity ; *it appeared that, in agreement with the theory, the velocity of reaction first fell off, reached a minimum, and then rose again.* To calculate the electrolytic dissociation of water the minimum velocity is the most favourable, so that the values given on p. 519 were determined by calculating the concentration of hydrogen and hydroxyl ions from the observed velocity. The condition that the concentration of the ester should remain constant is easily attained, since the amount of ester decomposed in this early stage of the reaction is only a small fraction of the whole.

Tri- and Multi-Molecular Reactions.—When the three molecular species, which vanish from the system in a tri-molecular reaction, are present in equivalent proportions, then the reaction velocity is

$$\frac{dx}{dt} = k(a - x)^3 \, ;$$

or, considering that x = 0 when t = 0,

$$k = \frac{1}{t} \frac{x(2a - x)}{2a^2(a - x)^2}.$$

Noyes [1] has in recent years found the first case of such a reaction in the action of ferric chloride on stannous chloride

$$2FeCl_3 + SnCl_2 = 2FeCl_2 + SnCl_4.$$

To prevent secondary disturbances it was found useful to add a small amount of the products of reaction.

0·025 norm. $SnCl_2$ 0·025 norm. $FeCl_3$
0·025 norm. $SnCl_4$ 0·025 norm. $FeCl_2$

t	x.	a − x.	k.
2·5	0·00351	0·02149	113
3	0·00388	0·02112	107
6	0·00663	0·01837	114
11	0·00946	0·01554	116
15	0·01106	0·01394	118
18	0·01187	0·01313	117
30	0·01440	0·01060	122
60	0·01716	0·00784	122

In the same way A. A. Noyes and R. S. Wason [2] showed that the reduction of potassium chlorate by ferrous chloride in acid solution is a tri-molecular reaction ; the same is true for the reduction of silver salts by silver formate.[3]

Again W. Judson and J. W. Walker [4] succeeded in finding a good example of a quadri-molecular reaction in the action of bromic acid on hydrobromic acid ; apparently this occurs (see the section below on "Complication of the Course of Reaction") according to the formula

[1] *Zeitschr. phys. Chem.* **16.** 546 (1895).   [2] *Ibid.* **22.** 210 (1897).
[3] A. A. Noyes and G. Cottle, *ibid.* **27.** 579 (1898).
[4] *Journ. Chem. Soc.*, 1898, p. 410.

$$2\overset{+}{H} + \overset{-}{Br} + \overset{-}{BrO_3} = HBrO + HBrO_2.$$

Finally, Donnan and Rossignol[1] have shown that the reaction

$$2KI + 2K_3Fe(CN)_6 = 2K_4Fe(CN)_6 + I_2$$

in neutral solutions is *quinqui-molecular*; the actual process is probably that given by the formula

$$2\overset{-}{Fe(CN)}_6 + 3\overset{-}{I} = 2\overset{-}{Fe(CN)}_6 + \overset{-}{I_3}.$$

That tri-molecular reactions are rare, and those of higher orders still rarer, is evident from the kinetic considerations developed on p. 443; the probability of the simultaneous collision of several molecules is exceedingly small, the velocity of poly-molecular reactions can therefore only be appreciable under quite exceptional conditions.[2] Hence most apparent poly-molecular reactions really take place by means of simpler (uni-, bi- and very rarely tri-molecular) ones, which occur successively. This is confirmed by experience.

· The study by O. Knoblauch[3] on the velocity of saponification of esters of polybasic acids is an excellent example of this. If we indicate by R'' the radical of a dibasic acid, its ethyl ester is saponified by caustic soda according to the equation

$$R''(C_2H_5)_2 + 2NaOH = R''Na_2 + 2C_2H_5OH ;$$

on investigating the course of reaction it appears that this is never a tri-molecular reaction, but that the process occurs in the two stages

1. $R''(C_2H_5)_2 + NaOH = R''(C_2H_5)Na + C_2H_5OH$
2. $R''(C_2H_5)Na + NaOH = R''Na_2 + C_2H_5OH$

consisting therefore of two consecutive bi-molecular reactions. In following the process quantitatively it is therefore necessary to apply the law of mass-action to the two latter equations, that is, a special velocity constant must be introduced for each of the two practically complete reactions.

It may be pointed out here that there is a fundamental difference between the formulæ of chemical statics and chemical dynamics; only the latter can throw any light upon the mechanism of the reaction, while the former are entirely independent of the way by which equilibrium is attained. It can be easily shown, for example, that the equilibrium formulæ of the reaction mentioned above are the same, whether the ester of the polybasic acid is formed directly or indirectly, while the course of the reaction must be entirely different in these two cases.

The Course and the Mechanism of a Reaction.—We have

[1] *Trans. Chem. Soc.* **83.** 703 (1903). [But see *Zeitschr. phys. Chem.* **63.** 513.]
[2] See also Van't Hoff, *Chemische Dynamik*, p. 197, Braunschweig, 1898.
[3] *Zeitschr. phys. Chem.* **26.** 96 (1898).

seen, in the preceding paragraphs, that the course of the reaction always varies in a characteristic way with the number of the molecular species, which experience a considerable change in the course of a reaction in a system considered as homogeneous.   This is clearly shown by the following formulæ, which serve to calculate the velocity coefficients for equivalent quantities of the reacting ingredients.   These, in order, are given, namely,

for uni-molecular reactions, by the expression $\dfrac{1}{t} \ln \dfrac{a}{a - x}$;

for bi-molecular reactions, by the expression $\dfrac{1}{t} \dfrac{x}{(a - x)a}$;

for tri-molecular reactions, by the expression $\dfrac{1}{t} \dfrac{x(2a - x)}{2a^2(a - x^2)}$, etc.

These expressions are so different from each other that, if the course of the reaction exhibits a constant velocity coefficient by applying one of the preceding formulæ, this is never the case in the use of one of the other expressions.   If we make $x = \dfrac{a}{2}$, *i.e.* if we calculate *the time required to change one half of the quantity of the substance capable of change,* we find in the *first* case that the time is independent of the original concentration of " a " employed ; that in the *second* case it is inversely proportional to this ; that in the *third* case it is inversely proportional to the square of this ; and that in general, in an n-molecular reaction, this time is inversely proportional to the $(n - 1)$ power of this original concentration.

Thus one may decide the question, How many molecular species participate in a reaction ?—simply by starting out with equivalent quantities of the reacting substances, and then determining in two experiments (which differ in concentration) the time required to consume *one half* of the substances capable of reaction.

The honour of first showing the possibility of obtaining a glimpse into the mechanism of a reaction from its course belongs to van't Hoff, who has made some applications of it in his classical treatise, *Études de dynamique chimique* (1884), which has been frequently cited in what has preceded.

As van't Hoff showed,[1] the slow course of a uni-molecular reaction in a gaseous system proves that the molecules of a gas are not all in the same condition, otherwise they would either decompose simultaneously or not at all.   The occurrence of all stages of velocity of reaction speak strongly in favour of the kinetic views, and especially of Maxwell's conception (p. 204), that the temperature of a single gas molecule oscillates about a mean.

Very often it happens that a reaction will begin simply and smoothly, and it is not until it has advanced to quite a distance, and

---

[1] *Chem. Dynamik*, p. 187, Braunschweig, 1898.

after the resulting quantity of the reaction products has attained to considerable magnitude, that it is disturbed by side reactions. In these cases one can draw some conclusion regarding the number of molecules of the reacting substances from the dependence of the original velocity upon the original concentration of the reacting substances.

At equivalent concentration c of the reacting ingredients, when n molecules react upon each other, the original velocity is

$$v = kc^n ;$$

now, by observing the original velocities v_1 and v_2 of two different concentrations c_1 and c_2, we have,

$$n = \frac{\ln \frac{v_1}{v_2}}{\ln \frac{c_1}{c_2}}.$$

Although ·it is very difficult to ascertain the original velocity directly, and although the results obtained in this way, at all events, are only approximate, yet they are usually sufficiently accurate to discriminate between the results; for n represents *a whole number* in all cases. Thus van't Hoff[1] found, in studying the action of bromine upon fumaric acid in dilute water solution—a reaction which leads smoothly to the formation of di-brom-succinic acid only in its first stage—the result

$$n = 1 \cdot 87, \text{ instead of } 2 ;$$

this comes sufficiently near to what was expected.

Further applications of this important method are to be found in van't Hoff,[2] Nernst and Hohmann,[3] and A. A. Noyes.[4] In practice it is more accurate, as the author showed in the work with Hohmann mentioned, to determine the expressions

$$\frac{1}{t} \ln \frac{a}{a-x}, \quad \frac{1}{t} \frac{x}{a-x}, \quad \frac{1}{t} \frac{x(2a-x)}{(a-x)^2}, \text{ etc.}$$

in the initial stage, and see whether they are independent of the volume of the reacting mixture or inversely proportional to the first power or inversely proportional to the second power.

After all this repeated and emphatic proof, it hardly needs any other special demonstration to show that one cannot draw any conclusion by any of the methods indicated respecting the question,—Whether a molecular species which is present in great excess (the solvent, . *e.g.*) participates in the reaction or not. The case here resembles that previously encountered (p. 469), where it was shown that the hydration of dissolved substances exerts no influence on the depression of their freezing-point.

[1] *Études*, p. 89.   [2] *Chem. Dynamik*, p. 193.
[3] *Zeitschr. phys. Chem.* **11.** 375 (1893).   [4] *Ibid.* **18.** 118 (1895).

The Reaction-Velocity and the Constitution.—*The principle of intramolecular reactions* (p. 291) depends upon the study of the readiness with which the cleavage products of the compounds in question are formed; this has been repeatedly applied to special questions in stereo-chemistry (pp. 299, 301).

We have now become familiar with the methods by which the conception of "readiness" (which is doubtless somewhat vague) can be replaced by the knowledge of well-defined magnitudes capable of numerical expression, viz. the *reaction-velocities*. The practical application of this information will, to a large extent, still remain a task for the future, but it has already been applied with good results.

It was Evans[1] who saw a connection between the stereo-chemical constitution of chlor-hydrine and the velocity with which it forms hydrochloric acid in the sense of the reaction,

$$R \underset{Cl}{\overset{OH}{<}} + KOH = KCl + H_2O + R : O ;$$

the progress of the reaction as it takes place in dilute solution is ascertained by the titration of the resulting potassium chloride.

In discussing his results, Evans starts out with the view that the distance between the chlorine and the hydroxyl in the molecule conditions the velocity of the formation of the oxide, *i.e.* the velocity will be greater the nearer the two radicals are situated with reference to each other. Space does not allow a thorough discussion of the results obtained regarding the constitution of the seven chlor-hydrines which were investigated.

Application of Chemical Kinetics to determine the Course of Chemical Reactions.—We have already considered one such application (p. 569); this method has been largely used by Heinrich Goldschmidt and his pupils. As an example we will discuss in detail an investigation by Goldschmidt and Merz[2] on the formation of azo-dyes. Diazobenzene sulphonic acid and dimethylaniline hydrochloride unite with measurable velocity to form methyl orange,

$$C_6H_4 \underset{SO_2}{\overset{N=N}{<}} O + C_6H_5N(CH_3)_2HCl = C_6H_4 \underset{SO_3H}{\overset{N=NC_6H_4N(CH_3)_2}{<}} + HCl.$$

The object of the investigation was to determine which of the three possible forms of the dimethylaniline hydrochloride really took part in the reaction. The three forms are

(1) the cation $C_6H_5N(\overset{+}{C}H_3)_2H$;
(2) the undissociated salt $C_6H_5N(CH_3)_2HCl$;
(3) the free amine $C_6H_5N(CH_3)_2$ formed by hydrolysis.

[1] *Zeitschr. phys. Chem.* **7**. 337 (1891).   [2] *Ber.* **30**. 670 (1897).

From the law of mass-action the concentration of each of the forms can be determined as a function of the total quantity of amine present. The velocity of change must be proportional to the concentration of the reacting form, and hence in Case 1 (as electrolytic dissociation is fairly complete) should be nearly proportional to the total concentration, and somewhat diminished by excess of hydrochloric acid, which would tend to diminish dissociation. Case 2 is analogous, but the velocity would be somewhat increased by the presence of excess of acid. Experiment showed that neither condition was satisfied. On the other hand, if the velocity is calculated on the third assumption, we obtain

$$\frac{dx}{dt} = k(a - x)\xi \ .$$

where $(a - x)$ is the concentration of the diazo acid, and ξ that of the amine formed by hydrolysis. But since

$$\frac{\text{free base} \times \text{free acid}}{\text{salt} \times \text{water}} = \text{constant},$$

we get

$$\frac{\xi(\xi + b + x)}{a - \xi - x} = K$$

where b is the excess of hydrochloric acid added, and a the original concentration of the amine. Now ξ is small compared to a and x, and therefore :

$$\frac{\xi(b + x)}{a - x} = K,$$

hence

$$\frac{dx}{dt} = kK\frac{(a - x)^2}{b + x}.$$

This equation was exactly confirmed by experiment : addition of HCl(b) retards the reaction. The percentage change is (as in a reaction of the first order) independent of the concentration, and also the numerical values for kK in different experiments agree satisfactorily with each other, as the following table shows :—

a = 0·0282	b = 0·0282	kK = 0·0056
0·0282	0·0564	0·0058
0·0282	0·0846	0·0055
0·0200	0·0200	0·0050
0·0350	0·0350	0·0058

The Progress of Incomplete Reactions.—Finally, we will devote a few words to the general case where the reaction stops at a point where only a small part of the possible decomposition is effected. This occurs in esterification (p. 457) ; thus, e.g., if one mixes 1 g-mol of alcohol with 1 g.-mol of acetic acid, the mutual action comes to a pause after two-thirds of the maximum possible quantity of ester has been formed.

The reaction velocity for the time t, when the quantity of ester formed is x, is here given by the equation,

$$\frac{dx}{dt} = k(1 - x)^2 - k'x^2,$$

where k and k' denote respectively the velocity constants of the two opposed reactions. If we introduce into the preceding equation the value of the ratio of these two constants, viz.

$$\frac{k}{k'} = 4,$$

as ascertained from the equilibrium of the system, then by integration [1] we obtain

$$\frac{4}{3}\left(k - k'\right) = \frac{1}{t} \log \frac{2 - x}{2 - 3x}.$$

The velocity of esterification, under the preceding conditions, was measured at the temperature of a dwelling-room by Berthelot and Péan de St. Gilles ; their results were as follows :—

Time t.	x Obs.	x Calc.
0 days	0·000	0·000
10 ,,	0·087	0·054
19 ,,	0·121	0·098
41 ,,	0·200	0·190
64 ,,	0·250	0·267
103 ,,	0·345	0·365
137 ,,	0·421	0·429
167 ,,	0·474	0·472
190 ,,	0·496	0·499
∞ ,,	0·677	0·667

The calculated values [2] of x, as given in the third column of the preceding table, are obtained from the theoretical formula, by assuming that

$$\frac{4}{3}\left(k - k'\right) = 0·00575·$$

Moreover, the coincidence between experiment and calculation is good throughout, except at the beginning of the series, where some disturbing side reactions seem to have occurred. We will refer to the calculation again at the close of this chapter.

[1] For the way of carrying out 'such calculations see, for example, Nernst and Schönflies, *Einführung in die math. Behandl. der Naturwissenschaften*, 6th edit. p. 114, München, 1910.

[2] Guldberg and Waage, *J. pr. Chem.* [2], **19.** 69 (1879) ; Ostwald's *Klassiker*, No. 104.

If a small quantity of acid be added to a concentrated solution of water in alcohol, the concentration of the water and the alcohol may be regarded as constant, and we have for the velocity of reaction

$$\frac{dx}{dt} = k_1(a - x) - k_2 x, \qquad . \qquad . \qquad . \qquad (1)$$

where a is the amount of acid added and x is the amount of ester formed in the time t. This equation of course holds also when a small quantity of ester is added to the alcohol-water mixture, and a is the quantity added to the solution, x is the quantity of ester decomposed in the time t ; only that in this case the reaction proceeds in the opposite sense. If in the preceding equation we put the reaction constant

$$K = \frac{k_1}{k_2}.$$

and integrate, we obtain

$$k_1 + k_2 = \frac{1}{t} \ln \frac{Ka}{Ka + (1 + K)x}. \qquad . \qquad . \qquad (2)$$

This equation has been tested in a number of experiments by W. Kistiakowsky ;[1] he has in particular given an important proof that the value $k_1 + k_2$ obtained is the same whether it is derived from the formation or the decomposition of ester.

Another example of the incomplete course of reaction was found by P. Henry [2] in studying the change of *hydroxy-butyric acid into the corresponding lactone.* Here an abundance of free hydrogen ions (in the form of HCl) were added to accelerate the change ; therefore the weaker hydroxy-butyric acid could be regarded as entirely undissociated ; and therefore equations (1) and (2) also apply to this reaction.

In conducting the research, the original concentration of the acid amounted to $\frac{1}{5} \cdot \frac{1}{60}$ g.-equivalent per litre : at the beginning a standard volume, removed by the pipette, consumed 18·23 c.c. of a barium hydroxide solution, excluding the hydrochloric acid present. After a long time the titration remained constant at 13·28 c.c. Therefore we have

$$K = \frac{13 \cdot 28}{18 \cdot 23 - 13 \cdot 28} = 2 \cdot 68.$$

. The series of determinations conducted at 25° were as follows :—

---

[1] *Wied. Beibl.*, 1891, p. 295 ; *Chemische Umwandlung in homogenen Gebilden,* Petersburg, 1895. See also O. Knoblauch, *Zeitschr. phys. Chem.* **22.** 268 (1897).
[2] *Zeitschr. phys. Chem.* **10.** 96 (1892).

t.	x.	$k_1 + k_2$
21	2·39	0·0411
50	4·98	0·0408
80	7·14	0·0444
120	8·88	0·0400
220	11·56	0·0404
320	12·57	0·0398
47 hours.	13·28	...

The values in column t denote minutes ; the values in column x are the quantities of lactone produced, expressed in c.c. of the barium hydroxide solution; on the same scale "a" amounts to 18·23. The constancy of the value of $k_1 + k_2$, as calculated according to the preceding equation, is satisfactory.

The same equation of reaction holds, as Küster[1] has shown, for the mutual conversion of the two hexachlor-keto-R-pentenes ; a mixture of the two isomers tends towards an equilibrium which depends considerably on temperature. It may be noted that the case investigated by Küster was that of a liquid mixture of the two mutually convertible species of molecules without any solvent.

For the process of autoracemisation we have

$$k = k_1 = k_2, \quad K = 1$$

and equation (2) reduces to

$$2k = \frac{1}{t} \ln \frac{a}{a - 2x} = \frac{1}{t} \ln \frac{\dfrac{a}{2}}{\dfrac{a}{2} - x} \qquad . \qquad . \qquad . \qquad (3)$$

Since only half a is transformed, it follows that equation (3) coincides with that of a unimolecular reaction.

According to Walker and Kay[2] the formation of urea from ammonium cyanate takes place in accordance with the equation

$$\overset{+}{N}H_4 + \overset{-}{C}NO = CO(NH_2)_2 ;$$

if a is the quantity of ammonium cyanate present, a the degree of dissociation at the time t, we have

$$\frac{dx}{dt} = k\bar{a}^2(a - x)^2 - k'x.$$

Multirotation of Milk Sugar.—C. S. Hudson[3] has proved that this is also a case of incomplete reaction, and has completely explained

[1] Zeitschr. phys. Chem. **18.** 161 (1895).
[2] Journ. chem. Soc., 1897, p. 489 ; Zeitschr. phys. Chem. **24.** 372 (1897).
[3] Zeitschr. phys. Chem. **44.** 487 (1903).

in this way the process of multirotation mentioned on p. 557.   Both the hydrate and the lactone of milk sugar slowly change their optical rotation in a freshly prepared solution, for in both cases the reaction

$$C_{12}H_{24}O_{12} \underset{\longrightarrow}{\overset{\longleftarrow}{}} C_{12}H_{22}O_{11} + H_2O$$

tends to produce equilibrium; since the rotation of both substances can be determined in a freshly prepared solution, the composition of the solution at any phase of the reaction, and finally the equilibrium can be determined polarimetrically.   If a mols of the hydrate are dissolved in a large quantity of water, the equation

$$\frac{dx}{dt} = k(a - x) - k'x,$$

holds, where x is the amount of lactone produced.   If r_0 is the rotation of a mols of the hydrate we obtain by integration, just as on p. 575

$$k + k' = \frac{1}{t} \ln \frac{r_0 - r_\infty}{r - r_\infty},$$

where r is the variable rotation and r_∞ the rotation in equilibrium. Hudson found this equation confirmed in all cases.

Tautomerism.—Let us consider a mixture of two isomers which are capable of mutual conversion as in the case mentioned above investigated by Küster, and let us assume that the equilibrium between the two isomers establishes itself very quickly; if we attempt to separate the components of such a mixture by any chemical method of separation, the other components will be converted into the first in consequence of the displacement of equilibrium, that is, the whole mixture will react as if it consisted of the first component exclusively. If, on the other hand, we apply a chemical reagent which acts only on the second component, the mixture will conversely behave as if it consisted of the second component only.   Such a mixture can there- fore react according to two constitutional formulæ, that is, we have the phenomenon of *tautomerism* described on p. 294.   Thus it has recently been suggested repeatedly[1] that hydrocyanic acid is a mixture of the molecules NCH and CNH which, however, are mutually converted at ordinary temperatures so quickly that separation of the two is impossible or at least very difficult, just as was the case with the mixture studied by Küster at higher temperatures, because one of the isomers passes into the other too quickly.   According to this view, reduction of temperature would be the means for isolating the two tautomeric forms.

The same view of tautomerism explains why, as Knorr[2] remarked, this phenomenon is *only found in fluids*, whilst for solids we must always assume a definite structure.

---

[1] Similar ideas are to be found in Laar, *Ber. deutsch. chem. Ges.* **18.** 648 (1885).

[2] *Lieb. Ann.* **306.** 345 (1899).

The most thorough test for the accuracy of this view is in separating the isomers and following their mutual conversion. Thus Claisen[1] was able to isolate the enol and keto forms of tribenzoyl methane and similar substances, and Wislicenus[2] those of formyl-phenyl acetic ester. These were distinguished not only by their melting-point but by their chemical behaviour, for example, the acid properties of the enol form and the neutral properties of the keto form. The intensive coloration of the enol form by ferric chloride is especially characteristic, and was used by Wislicenus to follow the course of the inversion and to demonstrate the establishment of equilibrium for both sides. It is to be remarked that the velocity of reaction varies greatly with the nature of the solvent; as in the case of other reactions it is greatest in methyl alcohol, then follow ethyl alcohol and ether, and finally chloroform and benzene.

Hantzsch[3] has made interesting observations on the transformation of tautomeric forms of nitrophenyl-methane and similar bodies, and has shown that the conversion can be followed by measuring the electric conductivity. These substances react sometimes as true nitro bodies, sometimes as isonitro bodies—

$$C_6H_5 - CH_2 - NO_2 \qquad\qquad C_6H_5 - CH - NO - OH$$

Phenylnitromethane. Neutral. Stable in the free state; in alkaline solution changes into the other form.

Isonitrophenylmethane. Acid. Unstable in the free state; stable as salt.

The passage of the second acid substance into the first neutral one is shown by a decrease in conductivity, which finally disappears altogether. The converse reaction takes place when the first form is dissolved in alkali. Here also a slow decrease in conductivity takes place which is due to the formation of the alkali salt of the isonitro-phenyl-methane from the free alkali and the neutral phenyl-nitro-methane, producing the ion of this acid in place of the much more rapid hydroxyl ion. The neutralisation, which in the case of real acids is almost instantaneous, takes place here in a measurable time, that required for the conversion of the neutral substance into the acid. Hantzsch describes such compounds, which are not definite acids, as pseudo-acids. These are also distinguished by an exceptionally large temperature coefficient of conductivity, which increases with rising temperature; also by dissociation constants which change abnormally fast when the temperature increases, and by noticeable colour change on change of temperature.

Hollmann[4] has given another excellent example of the equilibrium between the different modifications of a substance in his study on the modifications of acetaldehyde, while Dimroth[5] has studied the velocity of such changes.

[1] *Lieb. Ann.* **291.** 25 (1896).   [2] *Ibid.* **291.** 147 (1896).
[3] *Ber. deutsch. chem. Ges.* **32.** 575 (1899).
[4] *Zeitschr. phys. Chem.* **43.** 129 (1903).   [5] *Lieb. Ann.* **335.** 1 (1904).

According to these investigations it may be finally assumed that tautomerism is nothing less than a kind of isomerism in which the velocity of mutual conversion is very great.[1]

The Influence of the Medium.—Strictly speaking, we would expect to find a constant velocity coefficient in the course of the reaction, only in the case of those systems where *the nature of the medium* in which the reaction is completed experiences no essential change as a result of the decomposition of the reacting substances.

This condition is certainly only partially fulfilled, in the case of esterification previously considered, in the progress of which the nature of the medium is changed considerably; but the condition is apparently very completely satisfied in the case of reactions occurring in gaseous systems, and doubtless also in reactions occurring in dilute solutions. As a matter of fact, we found in the latter a most excellent demonstration of the law of mass-action in its application to chemical kinetics.

The question how the reaction velocity changes with the nature of the medium in which the reaction occurs has hitherto been attacked only in a desultory way.

But from the fact that the condition of equilibrium of a gaseous system (*e.g.* the dissociation of a gas) is not displaced by intermixture with foreign indifferent gases, it undoubtedly follows that the two opposed reaction velocities (which in equilibrium exactly compensate each other) would be influenced in the same way, if at all; the most probable assumption is *that both of the two reaction velocities remain unchanged,* i.e. *that indifferent gases are without influence on the reaction velocity.* Actually E. Cohen[2] showed that the rate of decomposition of arsine is not altered by the presence of hydrogen or nitrogen.

The problem, very interesting for many reasons, respecting the change in the reaction velocity of a chemical process which occurs in a solution, *with the nature of the solvent,* was first attacked in a thorough way by Menschutkin.[3] For this purpose he selected the reaction leading to the formation of *tetra-ethyl-ammonium iodide, from tri-ethyl-amine and ethyl iodide, thus*—

$$N(C_2H_5)_3 + C_2H_5I = N(C_2H_5)_4I.$$

The procedure consisted in diluting one volume of an [equivalent] mixture of the two substances with 15 volumes of a solvent; this was maintained for a definite time-interval at 100° in a sealed glass tube; thereafter the quantity of the ammonium base produced was determined by titration, so that the progress of the reaction was ascertained. The reaction progressed normally in each one of the

[1] A complete exposition of the views on tautomerism and the experimental material is given by Rabe, *Lieb. Ann.* **313.** 129 (1900).
[2] *Zeitschr. phys. Chem.* **25.** 483 (1898). [3] *Ibid.* **6.** 41 (1890).

twenty-three solvents studied, *i.e.* in accordance with the formula which holds good for bi-molecular reactions; but the value of the velocity coefficient k varied in a very striking way with the nature of the solvent, as is shown by the values given in the following table :—

Solvent.	k.	Solvent.	k.
Hexane . . .	0·000180	Methyl alcohol . . .	0·0516
Heptane . . .	0·000235	Ethyl alcohol . .	0·0366
Xylene . . .	0·00287	Allyl alcohol . .	0·0433
Benzene . . .	0·00584	Benzyl alcohol . .	0·133
Ethyl acetate . .	0·0223	Acetone . . .	0·0608
Ethyl ether . .	0·000757	...	...

The presence of a hydroxyl group, and also of an "unsaturated union" in the molecule, according to this, seems to favour the reaction velocity; and, as a rule, in homologous series, the velocity decreases with increasing molecular weight.

But one circumstance would appear to be very remarkable, viz. that, according to this, those solvents which are endowed with a great "*dissociating force*" towards the dissolved substances (see pp. 270 and 468), are, on the whole, also those which impart the greatest reaction capacity to the dissolved substances. But, as was emphasised by Menschutkin, *the enormous differences between the velocity constants cannot be ascribed to the purely physical action of the solvent*, such as might consist in a difference between the [relative] number of molecular collisions.

Indifferent materials added to the solvent may alter the "nature of the medium," and consequently exercise an appreciable influence on the velocity of reaction; the action of neutral salts referred to on p. 556 is perhaps to be referred in part to such an influence. According to a thorough investigation by Buchböcks,[1] in the action of foreign substances on the decomposition of carbonyl sulphide dissolved in water

$$COS + H_2O = CO_2 + H_2S$$

some connection with the viscosity of the solution is probable.[2]

According to present experience the velocity of reaction in the gaseous state, at least at ordinary temperatures, is with few exceptions vanishingly small; the gaseous state is therefore a medium which, in accordance with its small dissociating power, imparts to the substance present in it very small capacity for reaction. The fact that oxy-hydrogen gas reacts slowly at the walls of the vessel may be

---

[1] *Zeitschr. phys. Chem.* **23**. 123 (1897).

[2] See also C. Tubandt, *Lieb. Ann.* **354**. 259 (1907), who investigated the influence of the medium on the rate of inversion of menthone.

explained by saying that the gas absorbed or dissolved by the walls of the vessel constitutes a medium of greater facility of reaction; it is well known that the facility of reaction is greater still for oxy-hydrogen gas at platinum surfaces. In this way many *catalytic processes* can be, if not explained, at least referred to the apparently less difficult conception of the influence of the medium discussed in this section.

A. Stock and M. Bodenstein [1] have, for example, decisively proved that the decomposition of antimony hydride takes place simply in the layer of gas adsorbed by metallic antimony; as the thickness of this layer increases slower than in proportion to the concentration, we have the equation

$$-\frac{dC}{dt} = kC^\epsilon$$

where C is the concentration of the antimony hydride in the gaseous phase, and ϵ is < 1 (in this case 0·6).

Catalysis.[2]— We have repeatedly noticed in the foregoing, especially in dealing with the decomposition of esters and the inversion of cane sugar, the striking circumstance that many reactions take place with increase of velocity in presence of certain substances, especially acids. Berzelius gave to this phenomenon the name of catalysis; it means *an increase in velocity of reaction caused by the presence of substances which do not take part in it (or only to a secondary extent), although the reaction is capable of taking place without their presence.* Acids and bases seem to exercise a catalytic action on all reactions in which water is affected or split off, and their activity is proportional to the concentration of the hydrogen or hydroxyl ions. Bredig and his pupils have shown that the decomposition of hydrogen peroxide is catalysed by iod-ions,[3] and the condensation of two molecules of benzaldehyde to benzoin by cyan-ions.[4] One of the longest known and most important catalyses is the accelerated oxidation of sulphur dioxide by oxygen in presence of oxides of nitrogen. Another well-known example of catalysis is the extraordinary increase in velocity of combustion of hydrogen and of sulphur dioxide in presence of finely divided platinum. Finally, we may mention the interesting researches of Dixon and Baker,[5] which led to the conclusion that a number of gas reactions, such as the combustion of carbon monoxide, the dissociation of sal-ammoniac vapour, the action of sulphuretted hydrogen on

[1] *Ber. deutsch. chem. Ges.* **40.** 570 (1907).
[2] Ostwald has given a sketch of catalytic phenomena in a lecture to the Hamburger Naturforscherversammlung, *Zeitschr. f. Elektrochemie,* **7.** 995 (1891).
[3] *Zeitschr. phys. Chem.* **47.** 185 (1905).
[4] *Zeitschr. f. Elektrochem.* **10.** 582 (1905).
[5] *Trans. Roy. Soc.* **175.** 617 (1884); *Journ. Chem. Soc.* **49.** 94 and 384 (1886); *ibid.,* 1894, 603-610.

salts of the heavy metals, cease entirely in the absence of water vapour.

" Negative catalysis," that is a retardation of reaction by addition of another substance, has also been occasionally observed, and appears to be due to the destruction of " positive " catalysors by the substance in question.[1]

The catalyser cannot of course affect the affinity of a process. To do so would be in contradiction to the second law of thermo-dynamics, according to which the affinity of an isothermal process, as measured by the maximal work, depends only on the initial and final states. The activity of the catalyser therefore does not touch the driving force of a reaction but only the opposing resistance, as was early[2] recognised.

Since the catalyser takes no part in the reaction the equilibrium constant is not altered by its presence. This was seen (p. 446) to be equal to the ratio between the velocity constants of the two reactions in opposite signs. *A catalyser must therefore always affect the velocity of the reverse reaction.* If, for example, any added substance increases the rate of formation of a body, it must equally increase its velocity of decomposition. We find an example of this in the known fact that the presence of acids causes both the formation and the saponification of esters to take place with increased velocity. The observation of Baker that in absence of water vapour gaseous ammonium chloride does not dissociate, and on the other hand dry ammonia does not combine with hydrochloric acid, may be explained in the same way.

There is no complete theory of catalytic phenomena at the present moment.

Attempts have often been made to explain it by means of inter-mediate products formed by the catalysor and the reacting substance. These intermediate products, whose existence has been proved in many cases, are subsequently decomposed into the catalysor and the product of reaction. Thus in the process of manufacturing of sulphuric acid the action of the oxide of nitrogen has been explained by assuming that in the mixture of sulphur dioxide, nitric peroxide and air, nitro-sulphuric acid, $SO_2 {-OH \atop -NO_2}$, is first formed, and this, by contact with water, is decomposed into sulphuric and nitrous acids. This method of explanation may be employed when the velocities of such inter-mediate reactions are greater than the velocity of the total reaction; this theory of catalysis has only so far been proved in a few cases; in many others it seems plausible.

In cases of catalysis in heterogeneous systems, for example the acceleration of gas reactions by platinum, it is probable that the phenomenon is connected with that of solution of the gases in metal.

---

[1] See Titoff, *Zeitschr. phys. Chem.* **45**. 641 (1903).
[2] See, for example, B. Helmholtz, *Erhaltung der Kraft*, p. 25.

According to the observations of Bredig,[1] colloidal solutions of metals act in the same way as the metals themselves. In the decomposition of hydrogen peroxide a platinum solution containing only $\frac{1}{70000000}$ of a mol per litre produces a measurable action. The catalytic activity of a colloidal platinum solution recalls in many respects that of organic ferments, and for this reason Bredig called it an inorganic ferment. The analogy comes out most strikingly in the change of activity by time, by temperature, and by the power of certain substances, which are poisons towards organisms, to poison, that is to destroy, the activity of inorganic ferments also. Such substances are sulphuretted hydrogen, hydrocyanic acid, etc.

Auto-Catalysis.—Acids produce a catalytic action on the transformation of oxy-acids into lactones; the velocity of this has been measured by Hjelt,[2] and especially with regard to catalysis by Henry (p. 575) and Collan.[3] Thus, for example, γ-oxy-valerianic acid in aqueous solution is changed into valero-lactone with separation of water, and, as usual in such cases, the reaction takes place more quickly in presence of a strange acid ; it is only of course the free hydrogen ions that are catalytically active. Now the acid itself is partly electrolytically dissociated, that is in a solution of oxy-valerianic acid without the addition of any strange acid free hydrogen ions occur; it is therefore natural to suppose that these must produce catalysis, so that the acids *catalyse themselves.* This supposition may be easily tested experimentally. If to the acid be added one of its neutral salts, the dissociation is very much reduced in accordance with well-known rules, that is, the number of free hydrogen ions is diminished. Thus the addition of the sodium salt must greatly hinder the conversion of the acid into lactone. Actually it is found that the strength of the acid in the presence of its sodium salt remains unaltered for days. Another deduction from the theory, which is confirmed by experiment, is that the transformation of acid into lactone does not follow the equation applicable to unimolecular reactions, but that the velocity of reaction at any moment is proportional to the product of the concentrations of the undissociated acid and the hydrogen ions.

Ferment Reactions.—Ferments or enzymes, substances of unknown chemical constitution, which are produced by animal or vegetable organisms, accelerate numerous reactions, which on their side are usually beneficial to the organism ; in other cases, however, they can act as poisons (toxins). These ferment reactions occupy in many respects an exceptional position among catalytic processes : to each process corresponds nearly always a special ferment (while

---

[1] *Anorganische Fermente*, Leipzig, 1900 ; *Zeitschr. phys. Chem.* **31.** 258 (1899).
[2] *Ber. deutsch. chem. Ges.* **24.** 1236 (1891).
[3] *Zeitschr. phys. Chem.* **10.** 130 (1892).

hydrogen ions, for example, catalyse whole categories of chemical processes) ; further, ferments are affected to a considerable degree by outside influences, such as high concentration of the reacting substances or of the products of the reaction, and high temperature. Hence there is often a certain composition of the solutions, and always a temperature, at which the accelerating power of the enzyme is a maximum. These peculiarities are, however, not fundamental, and do not throw doubt on the classification of ferments with catalysers. For ferments also accelerate processes taking place spontaneously, which tend towards an equilibrium depending on the concentration of the reacting substances ; cases have also been observed where the same ferment accelerated the attainment of equilibrium from both sides. Thus E. Pottevin [1] showed that the ferment of the pancreas not only destroyed fat (glycerine esters of the fatty acids) into fatty acid and glycerine, but also built up the fat again from the two components.

Senter [2] has shown that the catalysis of hydrogen peroxide by hamase followed the course of a unimolecular reaction ; in general, however, fairly complicated relations prevail, probably because the enzymes possess variable catalytic power, on account of their great sensitiveness.[3]

The Kinetics of Heterogeneous Systems.—The velocity of reaction in heterogeneous systems does not possess the same theoretical interest as the reaction velocity of homogeneous systems ; because the former is very largely dependent upon the extent and the nature of the separating surface between the reacting phases, and also upon other circumstances of a secondary nature, such as the diffusion capacity and velocity of stirring.

The following may be assumed regarding the solution of metals in acids and analogous processes.

1. The velocity of the decomposition at every instant will be proportional to the extent of the contact surface O between the metal and the acid.

2. It will be proportional to the concentration of the acid.

Thus, let us denote by a the acid titration possessed by the solution at the beginning of the process for the time $t = 0$; and by $a - x$ the acidity after the time t, when x equivalents of the metal shall have gone into solution. Then, according to the assumption made above for the reaction velocity, $i.e.$ for the quantity dx of the metal passing into solution in the time dt, we shall have—

$$\frac{dx}{dt} = kO(a - x) \quad . \quad . \quad . \quad . \quad (1)$$

[1] $C.R.$ **136**. 1152 (1903) ; cf. Bodenstein and Dietz, $Zeitschr.f.\ Elektrochemie,$ **12**. (1906).

[2] $Zeitschr.\ phys.\ Chem.$ **44**. 287 (1903).

[3] See especially the investigations by Henri, $Lois\ générales\ de\ l'action\ des\ diastasés,$ Paris, 1903.

and this, when integrated on the assumption that the surface remains constant during the solution, becomes

$$\ln \frac{a}{a-x} = kOt.$$

Boguski[1] succeeded in verifying the preceding formula fairly well, by a research on the velocity of solubility of Carrara marble in acids. A weighed marble plate was immersed in the acid, and after a measured time was removed, washed, dried, and again weighed. The quantity x dissolved was thus ascertained, corresponding to the time t, by the diminution in weight.

As was to be expected, equivalent solutions of HCl, of HBr, and of HNO_3 acted on the marble with the same velocity.

The *influence of temperature* in particular was later investigated by Spring.[2] He showed that an elevation of the temperature from 15° to 35°, and from 35° to 55°, in each case corresponded to a doubling of the solution velocity; and also that the temperature excites a strong accelerating influence on reactions which occur in *heterogeneous* systems, similarly to what has been regularly proved for *homogeneous* systems.

Iceland spar exhibits a dual solution velocity according as the attack of the acid is directed towards the one or the other of its two principal crystallographic directions.[3] The quotient of the reaction velocities in the direction of the basal section and of the longitudinal section respectively, amounted—

At 15° to 1·13
„ 35° „ 1·15
„ 55° „ 1·14

In order to obtain a better idea of the theoretical treatment of such processes, we will now consider the simplest case, namely the solution of a solid substance by a solvent, *e.g.* benzoic acid by water. If c is the concentration of the acid at time t, and c_0 the saturation concentration, the equation (1) becomes in this case:

$$\frac{dc}{dt} = kO(c_0 - c).$$

This equation has been verified, for the above substances, by Noyes and Whitney.[4] They not only found it to agree very well with observation when the rate of stirring was constant, but also explained it by a simple and very illuminating hypothesis; they assume that at the boundary between the crystals and the solution the solid is at each

[1] *Ber. deutsch. chem. Ges.* **9.** 1646 (1876); see also Boguski and Kajander, *ibid.* **10.** 34 (1877).
[2] *Zeitschr. phys. Chem.* **1.** 209 (1887).   [3] Spring, *ibid.* **2.** 13 (1888).
[4] *Ibid.* **23.** 689 (1897).

moment saturated; the velocity of solution according to this is conditioned only by the rate of diffusion of the saturated solution of the boundary layer into the interior liquid. By stirring the thickness of the liquid layer adhering to the crystal is diminished, and thus the distance through which the diffusion has to take place reduced.

I have shown [1] that this hypothesis can be so generalised as to apply to all reactions in heterogeneous systems. *It is highly probable, namely, that at every boundary between two phases, equilibrium is established with a practically infinite velocity (i.e.* compared with the rate of diffusion).

Slowness of chemical reaction in heterogeneous systems can therefore be explained by means of the above hypothesis, as follows : if no other slow processes in homogeneous systems delay the reaction, its course is simply determined by the diffusion velocities. The rate of solution of solid substances by liquids depends mainly on the velocity of diffusion in the liquid phase, but sometimes also on that in the solid phase.

This hypothesis yields, as was shown by the author and E. Brunner,[2] in a complete experimental study, the means of treating theoretically the velocity of reaction in heterogeneous systems. With sufficiently vigorous stirring, which is kept constant throughout the experiment, it may be assumed that the solution has a homogeneous composition, and that a layer of constant-thickness (δ) adheres to the surface of the solid, and diffusion takes place through this layer. If we consider, for example, the solution of magnesia in acid according to these principles, at the magnesia itself there would be a slight alkalinity, and the concentration of the free acid would therefore be very small ; under these conditions the quantity

$$OD \frac{a-x}{\delta} dt$$

would diffuse to the magnesia in time dt, where D is the diffusion constant of the acid, and the equivalent amount of magnesia would go into solution. The reaction constant k therefore, according to equation (1), becomes

$$k = \frac{D}{\delta} \quad . \qquad . \qquad . \qquad . \qquad (2)$$

If the thickness of the adhering layer δ for a given kind and velocity of stirring can once be determined by experiment, the velocity constant k can be calculated in absolute measure. Thus Brunner, after determining δ as 0·03 mm. from a measurement of the rate of solution of benzoic acid, calculated the rate of solution of magnesia in different acids.

Thus it appears that it is not the strength of the acid which

[1] *Zeitschr. phys. Chem.* **47.** 52 (1904).   [2] *Ibid.* p. 56.

regulates the rate at which it attacks magnesia, but merely its diffusion constant, so that acetic acid, which diffuses rapidly, acts more quickly than benzoic acid, although the latter is much stronger.

Since, according to this, in chemical reactions which occur merely at the boundary between two phases, the phenomenon is essentially one of diffusion, it is useless to try and determine the order of reaction from the rate at which they proceed, as has often been attempted in recent years ; this method of argument is only applicable, according to kinetic considerations, to the probability of collisions in homogeneous systems (p. 443), and loses its meaning when applied to heterogeneous systems.

It has already been pointed out that velocities of diffusion only determine the rate of reaction *when no other processes* (spreading out of thin layers, as when marble is dissolved in sulphuric acid, and so on) *interfere*, and especially when no slow process, taking place in the homogeneous phase, is connected with the progress of the reaction. Thus arsenic trioxide dissolves in water much slower than would be expected from the velocity of diffusion ; this is because the simple solution is accompanied by a slow process of hydration, and it is obviously the latter process that determines the rate of solution.[1]

From an experimental point of view there is the greatest difference between the two cases ; for if the only determining factor is the velocity of diffusion, the influence of the stirring is extremely great, but if slow processes of the second kind also take place, the influence of stirring vanishes, or at any rate is diminished.

With catalysts, which cause reaction between the substances in question to take place with practically infinite velocity, the actual rate of reaction will be determined solely by the velocity with which the reacting substances diffuse to the surface of the catalyst ; whether such a catalyst exists, must of course be determined separately for every case (Nernst, *l.c.*). Well platinised platinum, for example, decomposes hydrogen peroxide practically instantaneously, so that the rate of decomposition of this substance is determined solely by the velocity with which it diffuses to the platinum surface.[2]

The theory developed above has enabled chemical reaction velocities to be calculated for the first time in absolute measure.

[1] The above remarks, which will be found in greater detail in the above-mentioned work of Brunner, probably appear self-evident to the intelligent reader, but I have not been able to omit them, because mistakes on this point have appeared in recent literature. G. N. Lewis goes so far as to say the theory is disproved, because it is inapplicable to cases where the simplest principles of logic show it could not possibly be applicable (see *Journ. Amer. Chem. Soc.* **37.** p. 899, 1906) ; I can discover no reasonable grounds for his conclusions.

[2] Bredig, *Zeitschr. f. Elektrochemie,* **12.** 581 (1906). A few unpublished experiments of the author showed that if the thickness of the adhering layer was determined in special experiments with known rates of stirring, the rate of decomposition of hydrogen peroxide could be calculated.

Bodenstein and Fink (*Zeitschr. phys. Chem.* **60.** 1 (1907)) have success-fully applied similar considerations to the union of sulphur dioxide and oxygen on the surface of heated platinum (*"contact process"*). The rate of reaction on the surface is very great, but the latter gets coated with an adsorbed skin of trioxide, so that the progress of the reaction is delayed since the reacting substances must diffuse through the skin. The *decomposition of antimony hydride* (as already mentioned on p. 581) takes place in the adsorbed skin, which is therefore a medium of great reaction velocity (see Stock and Bodenstein, *Ber.* **40.** 570 (1907)). The adsorption law (p. 498 ff.) is important for the proper understanding of these phenomena.

The linear velocity of crystallisation, i.e. the velocity with which the formation of crystals situated at a point proceeds, *e.g.* in an undercooled liquid contained in a glass tube, has been studied by Gernez (1882), Moore (1893), and in a very complete manner both theoretically and experimentally by G. Tammann.[1] The general behaviour is that it increases at first with the degree of undercooling, reaches a maximum, and, with great undercooling, diminishes; the decrease can go so far that the velocity of crystallisation sinks practically to nothing, so that the undercooled liquid loses its capacity of crystallisation and remains of a glassy character. The maximum rate of crystallisation is, for example, for phosphorus 60,000, azo-benzene 570, benzo-phenone 55, salol 4, betol 1 mm. per minute, it varies therefore in an extreme degree from one substance to another.

According to Tammann, the meaning of this remarkable fact is as follows. In the boundary between the solid and fused substance the temper-ature is that of the freezing-point, so that, when the undercooling is not too great, the velocity of crystallisation measured corresponds to this temperature, although this varies within certain limits with the degree of undercooling. When the undercooling is slight (less than 15°) the velocity is less, partly on account of the impurities always present, and which are very noticeable with slight undercooling, partly because the number of nuclei for crystallisation is too small; this makes the velocity very small if the undercooling is very slight, and causes it at first to increase proportionally to the undercooling till it reaches the maximum. When the undercooling is very great, the heat of fusion does not suffice to bring the boundary of the solid and fused substance to the freezing-point; this reduced temperature is the cause of the decrease in the velocity of crystallisation on great undercooling. These principles have been applied to the process of "*devitrification*" (spontaneous crystallisation of amorphous substances) by Gürtler, *Zeitschr. anorg. Chem.* **40.** 268 (1904).

It was of importance to establish the fact that slight impurities influence the rate of crystallisation very largely;[2] this phenomenon may be used to decide whether a liquid mixture which solidifies to a homogeneous mass, such as $CaCl_2 + 6H_2O$ or $SO_3 + H_2O$ is highly dissociated or not. In the first case, a slight addition of one of the components would alter the velocity of crystallisation very little, in the latter case very much. See the interest-ing study by F. A. Lidbury, *ibid.* **39.** 453 (1902).

---

[1] Friedländer and G. Tammann, *Zeitschr. phys. Chem.* **24.** 152 (1897); Tammann, *ibid.* **25.** 441; **26.** 307 (1898); **29.** 51 (1899).

[2] Bogojawlensky, *ibid.* **27.** 585 (1898).

The Kinetic Nature of Physical and Chemical Equilibrium.

—In concluding this description of the progress of chemical processes, we will turn back again to describe *the condition of equilibrium*.

It has been shown repeatedly that, in the sense of the kinetic molecular theory, *no condition of equilibrium between substances capable of mutual reaction can be regarded as a static, but rather it must be regarded as a dynamic equilibrium*; and this is true whether the action is *physical* or emphatically *chemical*, and also whether the equilibrium is established in a *homogeneous* or in a *heterogeneous* system. According to this view, it is not assumed that the material transformation has entirely ceased in the state of equilibrium ; but only that the reaction progresses with the same velocity in the one direction as in the other, and that therefore for this reason no change can be detected in the system.

In this same way we were able to account for the equilibrium—

(*a*) Between water and water vapour (p. 213).

(*b*) Between alcohol and acetic acid on the one side, and ester and water on the other (p. 444).

(*c*) Between the molecules of the same substance existing in solution, and in the gaseous state ; and

(*d*) Between the different parts of one substance distributed between two solvents (p. 490), etc.

In all of these cases the state of equilibrium was defined by the statement, that at every instant the amount of the decomposition in the sense of the reaction equation in one direction is the same as that in the other direction.

The question now arises, *How great is this decomposition in each particular case ?* It is evident, in any event, that in the sense of the theoretical molecular method of treatment, this question is fully qualified to demand a hearing, although from the nature of the case it may elude a direct experimental decision. It certainly would be very interesting to know how much ester and water are formed in unit time in the state of equilibrium established between these substances on the one hand, and how much alcohol and acetic acid on the other. Of course the same quantity of ester and water must be formed that is decomposed in the same time into alcohol and water.

As a matter of fact, the answer to this question is possible in all cases where we can measure the reaction velocity of a reaction which does not advance to a completion, *e.g.* it is possible in all of the cases enumerated above.

Thus, again, let us denote by k and k' the coefficients respectively corresponding to the partial reaction velocities in the two opposite directions of the reaction equation. Then the measurement of the actual velocity gives the difference

$$k - k',$$

and the measurement of the condition of equilibrium gives the quotient

$$\frac{k}{k'},$$

from which both k and k' can be calculated, and also the opposite [counterbalanced] decomposition in the state of equilibrium.

From the velocity of esterification, which was experimentally measured for equivalent quantities of alcohol and acid, we found that the difference between the coefficients amounted to

$$k - k' = \frac{3}{4}\frac{1}{t}\ \ln\frac{2-x}{2-3x};$$

and, since the undecomposed quantity x was estimated in equivalents, and the time t in days, this becomes

$$\frac{4}{3}(k - k') = 0\cdot00575\cdot$$

Also, according to p. 458,

$$\frac{k}{k'} = 4,$$

from which, by calculation,

$$k = 0\cdot00575.$$

Now since in equilibrium, $\frac{1}{3}$ equivalent of alcohol and of acid are present, therefore it follows that the velocity (previously called "partial") of the change in the state of equilibrium is

$$v = 0\cdot00575\frac{1}{3} \times \frac{1}{3} = 0\cdot00064.$$

Therefore in the system, as it exists in equilibrium, consisting of

$\frac{1}{3}$ g.-mol. alcohol + $\frac{1}{3}$ g.-mol. acetic acid + $\frac{2}{3}$ g.-mol. ester + $\frac{2}{3}$ g.-mol. water

in the course of a day, $0\cdot00064$ g.-mol. of alcohol and acetic acid are transformed ; and of course the same quantity [of ester and water] in the same time is retransformed. From the smallness of this number it is obvious that we are not to conceive of the mutual exchange as always being a very "stormy" one. Of course with increasing temperature (the preceding values refer to the temperature of a dwelling-room), the velocity of exchange will increase in the same proportion as k and k', i.e. very rapidly.

Moreover, particular attention should be called to this, viz. that we must regard the law of mass-action as *an empirical law which is certainly proved*, and therefore one which is independent of every theoretical molecular speculation. If the latter should at some future time come to be regarded as unsatisfactory, and especially if the kinetic conception of physical and chemical equilibrium should have to be relinquished as unreliable,[1] nevertheless the laws developed in this book regarding the decomposition of matter would remain completely undisturbed ; and in addition, it would be the duty of every new theory to give an account in its own way regarding the empirical facts of chemical mass-action.

How far the law of mass-action can be proved in a thermodynamic way, entirely independently of every molecular hypothesis, will be discussed in the last book.

[1] This is all the less likely since chemical kinetics has brought forward a *most striking confirmation* of the kinetic hypothesis.

BOOK IV

THE TRANSFORMATIONS OF ENERGY
(THE DOCTRINE OF AFFINITY, II.)

CHAPTER I

THERMO-CHEMISTRY I

THE APPLICATIONS OF THE FIRST LAW OF HEAT

General Remarks.—In the preceding books we have considered the transformations of matter, in their dependence upon the relative quantities of the reacting substances. Inasmuch as we invariably imagined the displacement of the equilibrium and the progress of the reaction as taking place *isothermally*, variations in temperature were thus excluded, and as we also disregarded the introduction of electrical energy and the action of light, we could consider the chemical changes as being purely *material*, without reference to their associated *changes of energy*.

Now both the state of equilibrium and the reaction velocity are dependent upon a number of other factors besides the relative quantities [of the reacting substances]; the action of these factors collectively may be regarded as being associated with the introduction of energy into, or the abstraction of energy from, the system considered. These factors are especially *temperature, pressure, electrification,* and *illumination*.

And, conversely, *a chemical change* is on its part invariably accompanied by *changes of energy*, which are exhibited by a change in one or more of the factors just enumerated.

By far the most important and universal of these factors are the actions of pressure and temperature upon chemical reaction on the one hand, and the development of heat and the performance of external work by chemical processes on the other.

The description of these relations constitute the subject of *thermo-*

chemistry, to which the first five chapters of this book are devoted. In the following chapters will be presented the outlines of *electro-chemistry* and of *photo-chemistry* respectively.

Heat of Reaction.—As was stated in the introduction, in all processes which occur in nature, we can discriminate the following changes of energy :—

1. The production or absorption of heat.
2. The performance of external work.
3. The variation of the internal energy.

Let us consider a chemical system, and assume for simplicity's sake that after it has experienced some material change, it has returned again to its original temperature, which it had before it had begun to change. Then, according to *the law of the conservation of energy*, the heat q developed in the change, increased by the external work A, performed by the system, is equal to the diminution of the system's internal energy.

Now the heat developed by a reaction can be easily measured, by immersing the flask containing the reaction mixture in the water of a calorimeter, and then conducting the reaction in a suitable way. The amount of the heating of the water in the calorimeter, together with "the water value" of the calorimeter itself, corresponds to the heat developed by the reaction. The amount of work which is associated with the reaction consists almost always in overcoming the atmospheric pressure. It can therefore be estimated in *litre atmospheres*, from the change in volume associated with the reaction given in litres, and by multiplication by 24·19 can be reduced to g.-cal. (p. 13).

The sum of the heat produced in the reaction, and of the external work performed, both of these quantities being expressed in g.-cal. (p. 12), we will call the "heat of reaction" in question : of course this can be either positive or negative, for heat can be either produced or absorbed by the reaction, and external work can be performed either against the external pressure, or by the external pressure upon the system. The heat of reaction represents therefore the change in total energy of the system.

Of course, the heat developed and the work performed are *ceteris paribus* proportional to the quantity of the substance which is changed. Wherever nothing is stated to the contrary, *the heat of reaction will always refer to the change of 1 g. equivalent.*

Thus, *e.g.*, it is observed that in the solution of 1 g.-atom of Zn ($= 65 \cdot 4$ g.) in dilute H_2SO_4, at 20°, there are developed 34,200 g.-cal. At the same time 1 g.-mol. of H ($= 2$ g.) is set free, whereby a certain amount of work is performed against the pressure of the atmosphere. Now since 1 g.-mol. of any gas at 0° occupies 22·41 litres, therefore at the absolute temperature T it occupies

$$22 \cdot 41 \, \frac{T}{273} \text{ litres (p. 40),}$$

and therefore the external work performed by the system amounts to

$$22 \cdot 41 \ \frac{T}{273} = 0 \cdot 0821 \ T \text{ litre atm. ;}$$

and since 1 litre atm. is equal to $24 \cdot 19$ g.-cal., it amounts to $1 \cdot 985$ T, or in round numbers to 2 T g.-cal. ; therefore in the solution of Zn, the work of

$$2(273 + 20) = 586 \text{ g.-cal.}$$

is performed *against the pressure of the atmosphere.*

Thus the heat of reaction, or the difference between the values of the internal energy possessed by the system before and after the solution of the Zn, amounts to

$$34,200 + 586 = 34,786 \text{ g.-cal.}$$

It can be seen from this example that even here, where a gas is developed, and where the change of the volume of the system, as a result of the reaction, is very considerable, the external work performed only plays *the rôle of a correction value* : and that in those cases where the reacting and resulting substances are collectively solid or liquid, and the change of volume is therefore of a much smaller order of value, the external work is infinitesimal in comparison with the unavoidable errors of observation, and can be neglected.

In the case of the combustion of hydrogen and oxygen to form liquid water, for every g. of H there results 68,400 cal. Now in this process there disappears $1 \cdot 5$ g.-mol. of the gases ; and thus the atmospheric pressure, at the same time, performs the work of

$$586 \times 1 \cdot 5 = 880 \text{ cal.,}$$

so that the change in the total energy amounts to

$$68,400 - 880 = 67,520.$$

The Thermo-Chemical Method of Notation.—When a reaction occurs, according to the general scheme,

$$n_1 A_1 + n_2 A_2 + \ldots = n_1' A_1' + n_2' A_2' + \ldots,$$

then there will be associated with it a certain heat of reaction ; let this amount to U when n_1 mols of the substance A_1 unites with n_2 mols of the substance A_2, etc. Then, according to the law of the *conservation of energy* [First Law], this will amount to $- U$ when n_1' mols of the substance A_1' unites with n_2' mols of the substance A_2', etc. The value of U corresponds to *the energy-difference* between the two systems,

$$n_1 A_1 + n_2 A_2 + \ldots, \quad \text{and } n_1' A_1' + n_2' A_2' + \ldots$$

The content of energy of a chemical system is equal to the sum of the contents of energy of the particular components. If we denote the content of energy of 1 mol of a substance A by the symbol

$$(A),$$

then the content of energy of n mols of the substance A will be represented by

$$n(A).$$

The contents of energy of the two systems considered above will be denoted by the symbols

$$n_1(A_1) + n_2(A_2) + \ .\ .\ ., \quad \text{and } n_1'(A_1') + n_2'(A_2') + \ .\ .\ . ;$$

and

$$U = n_1(A_1) + n_2(A_2) + \ .\ .\ . - n_1'(A_1') - n_2'(A_2') - .\ .\ .$$

will denote the heat of the reaction taking place between them, because U corresponds to the difference between the contents of energy of the two systems.

When U is *positive, i.e.* when the progress of the reaction, in the sense of the equation from left to right, is associated with *a development of heat,* then the reaction is called "*exothermic.*" The opposite reaction, therefore, takes place with *absorption of heat,* and is called "*endothermic.*"

Thus, *e.g.,* the symbolic equation

$$(S) + (O_2) - (SO_2) = 71,080$$

denotes that the union of 32 g. of S with 32 g. of O, corresponds to the development of 71,080 cal. The formation of sulphur dioxide from the respective elements is therefore an exothermic reaction.

As a rule the heat of reaction of substances reacting *in dilute water solution* is measured. The energy content of a substance A, *which is dissolved in a large quantity of water,* is denoted by the symbol

$$(A \text{ aq.})$$

(aq. = *aqua*), and therefore the quantity of heat which is developed by the solution of 1 mol of A in a large quantity of water, the so-called "*molecular heat of solution,*" is expressed by

$$U = (A) - (A \text{ aq.}).$$

Thus, *e.g.,* the meaning of the thermo-chemical equation,

$$(HCl \text{ aq.}) + (NaOH \text{ aq.}) - (NaCl \text{ aq.}) = 13,700;$$

is, that by neutralising 1 equivalent of HCl by 1 equivalent of NaOH *in dilute solution,* there are developed 13,700 g.-cal., the so-called "*heat of neutralisation.*"

It is customary to shorten the preceding method of notation in those cases where the resulting condition of the system, after the end of the reaction, can be seen directly from a description of the original condition. In such a case, the difference between the energies contained by the system in its original and in its final condition is denoted by enclosing the formulæ of the reacting substances in a common bracket, the formulæ being separated by commas. Thus, *e.g.*, instead of

$$(S) + (O_2) - (SO_2) = 71,080,$$

we write the shorter form

$$(S, O_2) = 71,080 ;$$

and instead of

$$(HCl \text{ aq.}) + (NaOH \text{ aq.}) - (NaCl \text{ aq.}) = 13,700,$$

the shorter form

$$(HCl \text{ aq.}, NaOH \text{ aq.}) = 13,700 ;$$

and similarly in other cases. Then, of course, *e.g.*, the formula

$$- (HCl \text{ aq.}, NaOH \text{ aq.})$$

will denote the quantity of heat which will be absorbed by the decomposition of a water solution of NaCl to a water solution of NaOH and of HCl, viz. 13,700 cal.

The notation

$$(A) + (B) - (AB) = U,$$

is, of course, identical with

$$(A) + (B) = (AB) + U,$$

because the thermo-chemical equations denote simply the summations of energy magnitudes, and accordingly we may apply the ordinary algebraic transformations to them. Thus, *e.g.*, if, from the preceding equation, we subtract the following one,

$$(A) + (C) = (AC) + U,$$

we obtain as an immediate result from the two preceding formulæ, the equation

$$(B) + (AC) = (AB) + (C) + U - U' ;$$

from this latter equation we deduce the result that the substitution of B in the place of C, in the compound AC, corresponds to a heat of reaction of $U - U'$.

We do not know the value of (A) itself, *i.e.* the absolute content of energy of 1 mol of a substance, although sometimes the kinetic theory of gases leads to a (hypothetical) conception of its magnitude. Thus, according to this theory, the energy content of monatomic mercury vapour consists solely in the translatory energy of its atoms ; and this, at the temperature T (p. 203), amounts in " absolute units " to

$$\frac{M}{2}u^2 = 183,900^2 \frac{T}{273}.$$

But the knowledge of the total energy content of a substance is, for practical purposes, quite unimportant, because we deal only with *the energy differences* of various systems, a knowledge of which is furnished by thermo-chemical measurements.

Finally, it should be noted that, for the sake of brevity, *the atoms* instead of the molecules are often denoted in the thermo-chemical formulæ. Thus, *e.g.*, the equation

$$(H_2, O) = 67,520$$

does *not* denote the entirely unknown heat of reaction consequent upon the union of *atomic oxygen*, but only the union of 1 g.-atom (16 g.) of ordinary oxygen with [the requisite quantity of] hydrogen. Strictly speaking, it would be more correct to write

$$(2H_2, O_2) = 2 \times 67,520,$$

but error is certainly guarded against in such and all similar cases.

The Law of Constant Heat Summation.—If we allow a system to experience various chemical changes, so that it finally returns to its original condition, then the sum of the heats of reaction associated with these processes is equal to zero; for otherwise it would mean a loss or a gain of the total energy, which would contradict the first law of thermodynamics. If we bring the system to the same final condition by means of two different ways, then the heat of reaction must be the same for both methods, *i.e.*—

The energy differences between two identical conditions of the system must be the same, independently of the way by which the system is transferred from one condition to the other.

It is particularly worthy of notice that this theorem, which of course holds good, not only for all chemical processes, but universally, was clearly stated by Hess [1] as " *the law of constant heat summation,*" and experimentally proved by him as early as 1840 ; and this was before "*the law of the conservation of energy* " had emerged from the realm of hazy anticipation, over the threshold of the consciousness of the scientific world.

The following example will illustrate " *the law of constant heat summation.*"

We will consider a system, consisting of 1 mol of ammonia (NH₃), 1 mol of hydrochloric acid (HCl), and a large quantity of water in the two following conditions :—

1. Where the three substances exist separate from each other.

2. Where the three substances form a homogeneous solution of ammonium chloride in a larger quantity of water.

We can pass from the first to the second condition in two different ways : thus, *on the one hand*, the two gases [HCl and NH₃] can unite

[1] Ostwald's *Klassiker*, No. 9.

to form solid ammonium chloride, and then this can be dissolved in water ; or, *on the other hand*, the two gases can be separately absorbed by water, and then the resulting solutions can be caused to neutralise each other. The respective heats of reaction are as follows :—

<table>
<tr><td align="center">The First Way.</td><td align="center">The Second Way.</td></tr>
<tr><td>$(NH_3, HCl) = +42100$ cal.</td><td>$(NH_3, aq.) = + 8400$ cal.</td></tr>
<tr><td>$(NH_4Cl, aq.) = - 3900$,,</td><td>$(HCl, aq.) = +17300$,,</td></tr>
<tr><td></td><td>$(NH_3, aq., HCl aq.) = +12300$,,</td></tr>
<tr><td>$(NH_3, HCl, aq.) = +38200$ cal.</td><td>$(NH_3, HCl, aq.) = +38000$ cal.</td></tr>
</table>

As a matter of fact, the energy difference between the initial and the final states of the system is the same in both cases, within the limits of error.

The theorem of "the constancy of the heat summation" is of the greatest importance and widest application in practical thermo-chemistry. Only very few reactions are suited for a direct investigation in the calorimeter, because it is absolutely necessary for exactness of measurement—

(*a*) That the reaction shall be such as can be easily effected.

(*b*) That it shall take place quickly, in order to avoid a large loss of heat from radiation.

(*c*) That the reaction shall be free from side reactions, which cannot usually be taken into consideration.

But even in those cases, where the conditions of quickness, completeness, and simplicity of reaction are not fulfilled, it is usually possible to accomplish the purpose in indirect ways ; thus, by the assistance of certain suitable intermediate substances, the system can be transferred from the one condition to the other, the energy-difference between which is to be measured. Thus it is not possible to determine directly the energy-difference between charcoal and diamond, because the transformation of one modification into the other cannot be accomplished. But if we can change charcoal and diamond into the same compound by means of an intermediate substance, then the difference between these two quantities of heat gives the heat value for the conversion of one modification into the other.

Such an intermediate substance, and one which is very commonly used, is *oxygen*. Thus, *e.g.*, the different modifications of carbon when burnt in "the calorimetric bomb" (see below), gave the following results :—

<table>
<tr><td></td><td></td><td align="right">Diff.</td></tr>
<tr><td>Amorphous carbon   . :   .   .</td><td>97650</td><td></td></tr>
<tr><td></td><td></td><td>2840</td></tr>
<tr><td>Graphite   .   .   .   .</td><td>94810</td><td></td></tr>
<tr><td></td><td></td><td>500</td></tr>
<tr><td>Diamond   .   .   .   .</td><td>94310</td><td></td></tr>
</table>

This table means that 2840 cal. would be developed by the conversion of 12 g. of charcoal into graphite ; and 500 cal. by the conversion of 12 g. of graphite into diamond.

In a similar way, the "heats of formation" of organic compounds can be ascertained from the respective heats of combustion in oxygen. By this process the compound, whose "heat of formation" is unknown, is changed into compounds (CO_2, H_2O, etc.), the heats of formation of which are known.

The energy-difference between (H_2, I_2) and $2(HI)$ is also not obtainable by a direct measurement, because hydrogen and iodine unite with each other only very slowly.   But suppose—

(a) That we dissolve the hydriodic acid in water.

(b) That we neutralise it with potassium hydroxide.

(c) That we set the iodine free by means of chlorine.

(d) That we decompose the potassium chloride which is formed into potassium hydroxide and hydrochloric acid.

(e) That we decompose the hydrochloric acid which is formed again into chlorine and hydrogen.

Then by means of the intermediate substances H_2O, KOH, and Cl_2, we can proceed from gaseous hydriodic acid to free hydrogen and free iodine; and we can do it by means of reactions which progress *quickly and smoothly, in one sense or in the other*, each one of which therefore has a heat of reaction capable of good measurement.

In fact, the heat of formation of gaseous hydriodic acid has been determined in this way.

The Influence of Temperature upon the Heat of Reaction.—

If we allow the same reaction to occur, once at the temperature t_1 and again at the temperature t_2, then the heat of reaction will be different in the two cases; let it amount to U_1 and U_2 respectively.

Now we can imagine the following cyclic process to be carried out. Let the reaction occur at the temperature t_1, whereby the quantity of heat U_1 will be developed; then we raise the temperature of the system to t_2, whereby there is required the introduction of $(t_2 - t_1)c'$ cal. of heat, where c' denotes the heat capacity of the substances *resulting from the reaction.*

Now let the reaction occur *in the opposite sense* at t_2: this process is associated with the quantity of heat U_2; then let the system be cooled to t_1, whereby the quantity of heat $(t_2 - t_1)c$ will be given off, where c denotes the heat capacity of *the reacting substances*. The system has now returned to its original condition.

Now the law of *the conservation of energy* requires the relation, that the heat absorbed by the system shall be the same as that given out; that is, that

$$U_2 + (t_2 - t_1)c' = U_1 + (t_2 - t_1)c,$$

and hence

$$\frac{U_2 - U_1}{t_2 - t_1} = c - c',$$

that is, the excess of the heat capacity of the reacting substances, over the heat capacity of the resulting substances, gives the increase of the heat of reaction per degree of temperature elevation.

Now the specific heats of the substances taking part in the reaction equation are obtainable by direct measurement; therefore the temperature coefficient of the heat of reaction can be determined much more exactly in this indirect way than is possible by a direct measurement of the heat of reaction at two different temperatures. The preceding equation, moreover, follows directly from the application of the universal theorem developed on p. 9.

On p. 169 we arrived at the result that the specific heats of solid compounds constitute an *additive* property; or, in other words, in the union of solid substances to form solid compounds the heat capacities remain unchanged. Then, according to what has preceded, this law can be extended thus :—

The heat of combination of solid substances is independent of the temperature.

The application of the calculation to special cases shows that the temperature coefficient of the heat of combination of such substances as iodine and silver, in any case, must be smaller than 0·0001.

Thermo-Chemical Methods.—In general, the thermo-chemical methods are those of calorimetry, the fundamentals of which will be found described in every text-book of physics. The *water-calorimeter* is used altogether most frequently; although sometimes, in recent work, use has been made of Bunsen's *ice-calorimeter*, especially when the measurements concern very small quantities of heat. The values obtained by means of this last apparatus of course hold good for 0°, and therefore are not directly comparable with those obtained by means of the water-calorimeter, which usually refer to a temperature somewhere near 18°. In the comparison of different observations, notice should be given to the remarks concerning *the unit of energy* on p. 12.

Here, as in all cases, we assume the calorie referred to water at 18° *as unit.*

Now since, in the case of those chemical reactions which occur very quickly, a certain amount of time elapses before the reaction-heat becomes uniformly distributed through the calorimeter, a correction must be made for the heat absorbed, or that given off by radiation during the reaction. As is well known, this correction is determined by observing· the course of the thermometer from some time before the beginning of the particular experiment till some time after its close.[1] This correction involves a dangerous source of error in thermo-chemical measurements, and therefore the conditions for the investigation must be so arranged that the amount of this correction

[1] For more particulars see the handbooks of physics, or, *e.g.*, Ostwald, *Allg. Chem.*, 2nd edit. p. 572 (1891).

shall be as small as possible. This end will be obtained by paying attention to the following conditions :—

1. The reaction, the heat of which is to be determined, must take place as quickly as possible.

2. ·The heat capacity of the calorimeter must be as great as possible, and thus the change of the temperature of the calorimeter, resulting from the heat developed by the reaction, will be made as small as possible.

The second condition requires the use of a sensitive thermometer in order to determine the changes of temperature very accurately, *e.g.* within $\frac{1}{1000}$th part of its amount. The thermometer described on p. 261, and recommended by Beckmann, is very well suited for this purpose ; by the use of this thermometer differences of $\frac{1}{1000}$th of a degree can be estimated, and exact measurements can therefore be made when the rise in temperature is one degree or even less.

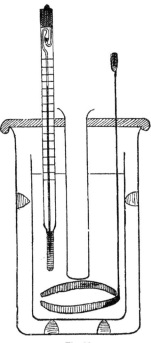

Fig. 35.

The accompanying cut (Fig. 35) shows a model of a calorimeter which can be constructed out of simple material, as recommended by Ostwald. The writer can recommend it from experience.[1]

A narrow beaker glass, which is cut down somewhat at the upper end, rests on cork supports fastened with shellac to a second larger beaker. Through a wooden cover which rests upon the outer beaker there pass a Beckmann thermometer, a thin test-tube in which the reaction is to be effected, and a stirring apparatus made of brass or better of platinum, and provided with a handle of some non-conducting material (as ebonite, wood, or the like).

If it is desired to measure heats of dilution or solution, the substance in question is placed in the test-tube ; then after the temperature equilibrium is established, the bottom of the test-tube is punctured with a glass rod.

An advantage of this apparatus is its transparency. Again, if the capacity of the inner beaker is about a litre, then the "water-value" of the glass, the stirrer, the thermometer, and all, amounts to only a few per cent of the total heat capacity.

[1] *Zeitschr. phys: Chem.* **2**. 53 (1888).

With slight changes, the calorimeter described may be employed also for the measurement of specific heats, of heats of fusion, etc. If one operates with salt solutions, it is important to notice the rule regarding the heat capacity given on p. 101.

Steinwehr has described an apparatus [1] capable of measuring very small quantities of heat for studying the thermo-chemistry of dilute solutions.

Regarding the determination of the heat of combustion, we will say something more later. A method for the theoretical calculation of the reaction-heat from the change of chemical equilibrium will be considered in the second and third chapters of this book.

As a matter of history, it should be noticed that besides Hess, Andrews, Graham, Marignac, Favre, Silbermann, and others, the thermo-chemical investigation of the most varied reactions has been systematically carried out by J. Thomsen in Copenhagen since 1853, and Berthelot in Paris since 1865.[2]

Gases and Solutions.—As the internal energy of gases, as already shown (p. 42), does not change with their volume, the heat of reaction is independent of the density of the reacting gases. Also the inter-mingling of gases is without influence. Of course these laws hold good only when no external work is performed, such as forcing back the atmospheric pressure. When this happens, then the reaction-heat is diminished by an amount which is equal to the work performed against the atmospheric pressure (p. 593). In the case of strongly compressed gases which are cooled by simple expansion (without the performance of external work), the preceding laws no longer hold strictly true.

A complete analogy is found in the conduct of dilute solutions. Since the energy of dissolved substances is independent of the concentration (p. 143), therefore the latter has no influence on the *reaction-heat* of a dissolved substance. The energy of "(A aq.)" is independent of the dilution of the solution, and herein lies the authority for the introduction of this symbol (p. 595).

Thus, *e.g.*, if the *heat of solution* of a substance in a large quantity of water is determined, this heat of solution itself is independent of the quantity of water used; if the *heat of combination* of a metal with

---

[1] *Zeitschr. phys. Chem.* **36**. 185 (1901); cf. also Rumelin, *Dissertation*, Göttingen, 1905.

[2] Thomsen has collected his measurements in the work entitled *Thermo-chemische Untersuchungen*, Leipzig, 1882-86; and Berthelot has collected his in his *Essai de mécanique chimique*, Paris, 1879. See also Naumann, *Thermochemie*, Braunschweig (Brunswick), 1882; and H. Jahn, *Thermochemie*, Wien (Vienna), 1892. Thermo-chemical data collected from different observers will be found in the *Chemiker-kalender*, etc. The figures given in what follows are largely taken from the critical and very complete collection made by Ostwald, *Allg. Chem.* 2. Aufl. (2nd edit.), II. Leipzig, 1893. Berthelot gives a new collection of data in his *Thermochimie*, Paris, 1897, and J. Thomsen in *Thermochemische Untersuchungen* (German by J. Traube), Stuttgart, 1906.

an acid is determined, this heat is independent of the concentration of the acid when the latter is dissolved in a large quantity of water, etc.

But this rule ceases to hold good for concentrated solutions when these exhibit marked heat phenomena on dilution. Thus, *e.g.*, the *heat of solution* of zinc in concentrated sulphuric acid is very different from that in the dilute acid.

The *heat of dilution* has already been discussed (p. 109). We will only recall here that the following equation, viz.—

$$(H_2SO_4 + 3H_2O) + 2(H_2O) - (H_2SO_4 + 5H_2O) = 1970,$$

which states that by the addition of two more mols of H_2O to a solution having the composition $(H_2SO_4 + 3H_2O)$, there will be produced 1970 g.-cal. Moreover, the heat of dilution may be *positive*, as in the case of sulphuric acid ; or *negative*, as in the case of saltpetre.

The Changes of the State of Aggregation.—When a substance changes its state of aggregation, whether the change consists in evaporation, solidification, sublimation, or finally in a change from one modification to another, the changes are always associated with a change in the content of energy ; and therefore the reaction-heat also is changed to the same amount.

In the case of reactions where precipitates are thrown down, the state of the latter must be especially considered. Thus, *e.g.*, if *mercuric iodide* is precipitated from a solution of mercuric chloride by a solution of potassium iodide, the *yellow* modification at first separates, but then quickly changes to the *red* variety, with the accompaniment of an additional heat of reaction.

Thus, *e.g.*, the energy-difference between water at 100°, and water-vapour at the same temperature, is expressed by the equation

$$(H_2O) - (H_2O) = 536 \cdot 4 \times 18 - 2 \times 373 = 8910 ;$$
Liquid   Gas

because the heat of evaporation of 1 g. of water was found to be $536 \cdot 4$, and the external work performed was shown to be $2T = 746$.

The energy-difference between ice and liquid water is

$$(H_2O) - (H_2O) = 79 \times 18 = 1422,$$
Solid   Liquid

because 79 cal. are set free in the freezing of 1 g. of water. On account of the slight change of volume, the external work performed here has only a minimal value.

The energy-difference between 1 g.-atom of the orthorhombic and the monoclinic modification of sulphur amounts to

$$(S_r) - (S_m) = 32 \times 2 \cdot 40 = 76 \cdot 8.$$

Thus in all thermo-chemical statements where a doubt can exist, informa-

tion should be given respecting the state of aggregation, or the modification of the reacting substances, or of those produced.

The Heat of Solution.—By the "*heat of solution*" is meant, as already stated, the quantity of heat produced by the solution of 1 g. of a substance in a large quantity of the solvent. If the heat of dilution of a substance is known, then of course it is possible to calculate the heat evolved on its solution in any quantity of the solvent, however small. The quantity of heat observed when the substance is dissolved to exact saturation is always more or less different from the heat of solution as defined above; and sometimes it has a sign opposite from that of the heat of solution.

In the following tables are given[1] the heat of solution of some substances in a large quantity of water at 18-20° :—

HEAT OF SOLUTION OF GASEOUS SUBSTANCES

Substance.	Formula.	Heat of Solution.
Chlorine	Cl_2	+ 4870
Carbon dioxide	CO_2	+ 5880
Ammonia	NH_3	+ 8430
Hydrofluoric acid . . .	HF	+11800
Hydrochloric ,, . . .	HCl	+17310
Hydrobromic ,, . . .	HBr	+19940
Hydriodic ,, . . .	HI	+19210

HEAT OF SOLUTION OF LIQUID SUBSTANCES

Substance.	Formula.	Heat of Solution.
Methyl alcohol	CH_4O	+ 2000
Ethyl ,, ...	C_2H_6O	+ 2540
Propyl ,, ...	C_3H_8O	+ 3050
Ethyl ether	$C_4H_{10}O$	+ 5940
Acetic acid . . .	$C_2H_4O_2$	+ 420
Sulphuric acid	SO_4H_2	+17850

[1] From Horstmann, *Theoret. Chem.* p. 502, Braunschweig (Brunswick), 1885.

[TABLE

HEAT OF SOLUTION OF SOLID SUBSTANCES

Substance.	Formula.	Heat of Solution.
Potassium hydroxide . .	KOH	+ 12500
,, ,, (cryst. hydrate) . .	$KOH + 2H_2O$	− 30
Lithium chloride	LiCl	+ 8440
Sodium chloride . . .	NaCl	− 1180
Potassium chloride . . .	KCl	− 4440
Sodium bromide . . .	NaBr	− 190
,, ,, (hydrate) .	$NaBr + 2H_2O$	− 4710
Potassium sulphate . . .	K_2SO_4	− 6380
Mercuric chloride . . .	$HgCl_2$	− 3300
Sodium acetate	$NaC_2H_3O_2$	+ 4200
,, benzoate . . .	$NaC_7H_5O_2$	+ 800
Benzoic acid	$C_6H_5CO_2H$	− 6700
Silver chloride	AgCl	− 15800
,, bromide	AgBr	− 20200
,, iodide	AgI	− 26600
Cane sugar	$C_{12}H_{22}O_{11}$	− 800

The figures for gases include the external work : therefore in order to obtain the heat of true solution, the quantity + 580 must be subtracted from the figures given above.

All of the gases thus far examined dissolve with *evolution of heat.* A similar thing is true of liquids, at least as a rule ; while solid substances sometimes dissolve with a development of heat, but more often with absorption of heat.

The explanation of this is simple. Starting with the very probable assumption that a gaseous substance always has a positive solution-heat, then in the liquid state it will dissolve either with absorption or with evolution of heat, according as its heat of vaporisation exceeds the heat of solution, or not. And similarly, the signs for the solution-heat of substances in the solid state are conditioned by the difference between their heat of sublimation and heat of solution in the gaseous state.

The general rules for the solution-heat of the different states of aggregation as just given therefore mean that, as a rule, the heat of solution in the gaseous state is greater than the heat of vaporisation ; but it is usually smaller than the heat of vaporisation plus the heat of fusion, *i.e.* it is smaller than the heat of sublimation.

In general, and especially in comparing substances which are chemically analogous, and difficultly soluble, the heat of precipitation (= the negative value of the heat of solution) is the greater the more insoluble the substance is.[1]

We will consider later a method for the determination of the heat of solution of salts which are soluble with difficulty. The difference between the solution-heats of one substance in two solvents would, of

[1] Thomsen, *Journ. prakt. Chem.* [2], **13.** 241 (1876).

course, allow the calculation of the heat phenomena in the distribution of one substance between two solvents (p. 491).

The Heat of Formation.—*By the " heat of formation " of a chemical compound is meant the quantity of heat which is given off in the formation of the compound from its component elements.*

This is *the thermo-chemical characteristic* of the compound in question. If the "heats of formation" of all the substances which participate in any chemical reaction are known, then the heat of reaction is also known. For we can first imagine the particular substances standing on the left side of the reaction equation to be decomposed into their respective elements; and then imagine the elements to unite to form the substances standing on the right side of the reaction equation. Then in the first of these stages there would be *absorbed* a quantity of heat which would be equal to the sum of the "heats of formation" of all the substances standing on the left side of the equation; and in the second stage there would be *developed* a quantity of heat equal to the sum of the "heats of formation" of all the substances standing on the right side of the equation. It is a matter of indifference whether the chemical process actually takes place in this way or not; because the change in the total energy of any system is independent of the way in which the change is accomplished. We thus obtain the law that—

The heat of reaction is equal to the sum of the heats of formation of the substances formed, minus the sum of the heats of formation of the substances used up.

Here will be given some "*heats of formation*" which will find application in subsequent calculations. The figures refer to constant volumes, *i.e.* they are corrected for the external work performed, whatever it may be. The remarks in the last column refer to the condition of the reacting substances.

Reaction.	Heat of Reaction.	Remarks.
$2H + O = H_2O$	+ 67520	Liquid water.
$C + 2O = CO_2$	+ 94300	Diamond.
$C + O = CO$	+ 26600	,,
$S + 2O = SO_2$	+ 71080	Rhombic sulphur.
$H + F = HF$	+ 38600	Gaseous fluorine.
$H + Cl = HCl$	+ 22000	,, chlorine.
$H + Br = HBr$	+ 8400	Liquid bromine.
$H + I = HI$	− 6100	Solid iodine.
$N + 3H = NH_3$	+ 12000	...
$N + O = NO$	− 21600	...
$N + 2O = NO_2$	− 7700	Dissociated nitrogen dioxide.
$2N + 4O = N_2O_4$	− 2600	Bi-molecular nitrogen dioxide.
$K + F = KF$	+109500	...
$K + Cl = KCl$	+105600	...
$K + Br = KBr$	+ 95300	...
$K + I = KI$	+ 80100	...

The *rise of temperature* due to a reaction (*e.g.* flame temperatures) can be calculated from the heat of reaction and the thermal capacity C of the resulting products ; for

$$\int_{t_0}^{t_1} C dt = q$$

where t_0 is the initial, t the final temperature. The variation of C with temperature must of course be known. See Nernst and Schönflies, *Mathem. Behandl. d. Naturwissensch.* 6th edit. p. 152, Munich, 1910.

The Heats of Combustion of Organic Compounds.—The

work of the investigators previously mentioned enables us to infer the heat of reaction of almost all the more important reactions of inorganic chemistry, directly from the table, or else to calculate them indirectly ; yet, on the other hand, we do not find ourselves so fortunate regarding many reactions of the carbon compounds. The reason for this is that the number of reactions which take place quickly, and without the formation of side products, which conditions are essential for thermo-chemical investigation, is very much smaller in organic than in inorganic chemistry. There is only *one* reaction which occurs quickly and smoothly in all cases, namely, *the combustion of the substance in an excess of oxygen*, whereby all the carbon is oxidised to carbon dioxide, and all the hydrogen to water. Therefore, on the whole, organic thermo-chemistry employs the same reaction which has been long used in analytical chemistry, *i.e.* combustion.

The experimental method followed almost exclusively at present consists in inclosing the substance in a well-enamelled, steel vessel, which is filled with oxygen under a pressure of about 20 atm. ; then the substance is ignited by an iron wire made incandescent by an electric current (Berthelot's calorimetric bomb): the whole apparatus is immersed in *a water calorimeter*, which absorbs the heat developed.[1]

In this way the *heat of combustion at constant volume* is obtained, or simply the heat of combustion which corresponds to the change of total energy. The heat of combustion at constant pressure still includes the, so to speak, accidental amount of external work, and is obtained by subtracting from the former as many times " 2T " as the number of molecules produced exceeds those which disappear.

The *heat of formation* may be calculated from the *heat of combustion* by subtracting the latter from the sum of the heats of formation of the resulting liquid water (67,500 per mol.) and carbon dioxide (94,300 per mol), and of the sulphurous acid formed, if any (71,100 per mol.) ; and thus by the use of these figures we obtain the heat of formation from diamond, gaseous oxygen and hydrogen, and finally, from rhombic sulphur, at the temperature of the experiment.

[1] The recent investigations of E. Fischer and Wrede have shown that extremely accurate measurements can be made with this apparatus (*Sitzungsber. kgl. preuss. Akad. Wiss.*, Berlin, 1908, p. 129).

Now, since the heats of combustion have been determined for the most important organic compoūnds, the heats of formation are also known; and therefore, according to p. 606, the heats of all reactions between these compounds can be calculated. Therefore it is never necessary to calculate the heat of formation, for the *heat* of every reaction can obviously be obtained, *from the sum of the heats of combustion of the substances which have disappeared, minus the sum of the heats of combustion of the substances formed.*

But the results of such calculations are often very inexact, because the heat of reaction is obtained as the difference between magnitudes which differ only slightly; and of course the errors of observation in these cases amount to a very considerable percentage.

Thus, *e.g.*, the heat of combustion of *fumaric acid* was determined to be 320,300, while that of the geometrical isomer, *maleic acid*, is 326,900. Therefore the transformation of maleïc acid to the more stable fumaric acid will develop 6600 calories. But this latter number is extremely uncertain, for if the error of observation in the determination of the heats of combustion amounted to only 0·5 per cent, even then the uncertainty in their difference would amount to nearly 50 per cent.

Reference has been already made (p. 320) to *the relation between constitution and the heat of combustion.* The heats of combustion of some important substances are given below; they are expressed in *large calories* (= 1000 cal.), in order to avoid the repetition of ciphers.

Ethyl alcohol	.	.	.	.	340
Mannite	.	.	.	.	727
Cellulose	.	.	.	.	680
Cane sugar	.	.	.	.	1355
Acetic acid	.	.	.	.	210
Benzoic acid	.	.	.	.	772
Ethyl acetate	.	.	.	.	554
Urea	.	.	.	.	152

The formation of ethyl acetate from the acid and alcohol, according to these figures, would correspond to a heat of reaction of

$$340 + 210 - 554 = -4,$$

which is quite a small amount.

The Thermo-Chemistry of Electrolytes.—The hypothesis of electrolytic dissociation has thrown new light on the meaning of the heat of reactions which take place in salt solutions; and some rules which were previously discovered in an empirical way find a simple explanation as necessary deductions from the theory.

If two solutions of electrolytes, which are completely dissociated, are mixed, there is of course no development of heat, *provided* that the ions of the two electrolytes do not unite to form an electrically neutral molecule nor a new ion complex.   This case is illustrated, *e.g.*, in the mixture of most salt solutions.

Experiment establishes the conclusion.   The so-called *Law of the thermo-neutrality of salt solutions* is nothing else than an expression of the experience that *no heat phenomena result from the mixture of salt solutions (provided that no precipitate is produced)*.

Let AB and A'B' be two salts which obey the "law of thermo-neutrality."   Then no noticeable heat of reaction will result from their mixture, thus

$$(AB \text{ aq.}) + (A'B' \text{ aq.}) = (AB, A'B' \text{ aq.}).$$

A similar thing also holds good for the mixture

$$(AB' \text{ aq.}) + (A'B \text{ aq.}) = (AB', A'B \text{ aq.}).$$

But now the two resulting solutions, which are expressed by the symbols standing on the right sides of the two equations, are identical ; therefore

$$(AB \text{ aq.}) - (AB' \text{ aq.}) = (A'B \text{ aq.}) - (A'B' \text{ aq.}) ;$$

or, in words—

The difference between the heats of formation of any two salt solutions having a common ion is a constant which is characteristic for both of the two other radicals, and is independent of the nature of the common ion.

Thus, *e.g.*,

$$
\begin{aligned}
\text{H} + \text{Cl} + \text{aq.} &= (\text{HCl aq.}) &+ 39320 \\
\text{H} + \text{I} + \text{aq.} &= (\text{HI aq.}) &+ 13170 \\
\hline
\text{Cl} + (\text{HI aq.}) &= \text{I} + (\text{HCl aq.}) + 26150 ;
\end{aligned}
$$

and

$$
\begin{aligned}
\text{K} + \text{Cl} + \text{aq.} &= (\text{KCl aq.}) &+ 101170 \\
\text{K} + \text{I} + \text{aq.} &= (\text{KI aq.}) &+ 75020 \\
\hline
\text{Cl} + (\text{KI aq.}) &= \text{I} + (\text{KCl aq.}) + 26150.
\end{aligned}
$$

As a matter of fact we find that

$$(\text{HI aq.}) - (\text{HCl aq.}) = (\text{KI aq.}) - (\text{KCl aq.}) ;$$

and thus if the iodine in a dilute aqueous solution of an iodide is replaced by chlorine, the same development of heat is always observed, viz. 26,150 cal.   In this case, of course, one is always concerned with the same reaction, viz. the replacing of the iodine ion by the chlorine ion.

But, on the other hand, if the iodine in dissolved *potassium iodate* (KIO_3) is replaced by chlorine, an entirely different heat of reaction is observed, viz.—the *absorption* of 31,700 cal. instead of the development of 26,150 cal. ; for here iodine and chlorine are not ions, and therefore an entirely different reaction occurs.

The case is quite different *where the mixture results in the union of ions to form electrically neutral molecules, which may remain in solution or be removed.*

We have already met the most important example of this case in *the process of neutralisation* on p. 517. If a strong acid is mixed with a strong base, the *hydrogen ions* and the *hydroxyl ions* unite almost completely to form *molecules of water*. *The negative ion of the acid and the positive ion of the base remain free* if the salt produced by their union is highly dissociated (as, *e.g.*, is always the case with univalent bases and acids).

We thus obtain the important result that—

The neutralisation of a strong acid by a strong base must always exhibit the same heat of reaction.

The following table shows how remarkably the theorem is proved by experiment :—

TABLE OF THE HEATS OF NEUTRALISATION OF ACIDS AND BASES

Acid and Base.	Heat of Neutralisation.
Hydrochloric acid and sodium hydrox. . .	13700
Hydrobromic ,, ,, ,, ,, . .	13700
Nitric ,, ,, ,, ,, . .	13700
Iodic ,, ,, ,, ,, . .	13800
Hydrochloric ,, ,, lithium ,, . .	13700
,, ,, ,, potassium ,, . .	13700
,, ,, ,, barium ,, . .	13800
,, ,, ,, calcium ,, . .	13900

In the case of the di-acid bases the figures do not, of course, refer to a molecule, but only to one equivalent of the base. Neglecting the slight correction required by the incomplete dissociation, these figures simply mean that they give the heat developed by the reaction

$$\overset{+}{H} + \overset{-}{OH} = H_2O \ ;$$

or, in the language of thermo-chemistry, we obtain

$$(\overset{+}{H} \text{ aq.}, \overset{-}{OH} \text{ aq.}) = 13,700.$$

When the acid or the base is only partially dissociated electrolytically, then the heat of neutralisation changes by the amount of energy which comes into play in splitting the molecules into the ions. In fact, the following examples show that the *heat of neutralisation* assumes noticeably different values under these circumstances. Thus *the heats of neutralisation* of the following weak acids, by *sodium or potassium hydroxide*, are as follows :—

Acid.	Heat of Neutralisation.	Heat of Dissociation.
Acetic acid	13400	+ 300
Dichloracetic acid . . .	14830	– 1130
Phosphoric ,, ,. .	14830	– 1130
Hydrofluoric ,, . .	16270	– 2570

If these acids were completely dissociated we should obtain a heat development of 13,700 cal. in the neutralisation.   The deviations from this normal value are to be ascribed to the electrolytic dissociation. The *differences* are given in the last column; *these denote the respective quantities of heat which would be required for the electrolytic dissociation of the acids in question.*   These figures only claim to be *approximately* correct, because, on the one hand, the differences between magnitudes which are not very far apart are attended by considerable errors of observation; and on the other hand, the calculation is based on the faulty assumption that the acid is not at all dissociated, and that the base and the neutral salt are completely dissociated.[1]   Nevertheless, these figures, which we shall obtain in a perfectly independent way in the following chapter, are well suited to give us a conception of the amount of *the changes of energy which are associated with the separation into ions.*

Of course it happens in all these changes that sometimes heat will be absorbed, and again it will be set free; and conversely, that in the union of ions to form electrically neutral molecules, sometimes heat will be developed, and again it will be absorbed; and that the final absolute amount is not very great in any case.

On neutralising ammonia, a base which is only slightly dissociated, with a strong acid, there results a heat development of 12,300 cal.; therefore the heat required to ionise ammonium hydroxide is estimated to be

$$13,700 - 12,300 = + 1400 \text{ cal.}$$

The calculation of the most general case, *where neither the base, nor the acid, nor the neutral salt formed is completely dissociated,* is as follows:—

Let the degree of dissociation of the acid SH be a_1, and let that of the base BOH be a_2; now from the mixture of the acid and alkaline solution, each of which contains one equivalent, there results an equivalent of the salt BS; let the degree of dissociation of this salt be a; there also results a molecule of water in the sense of the equation

$$SH + BOH = BS + H_2O.$$

[1] The heat of dilution of some weak acids in dilute solution, from which the heat of dissociation may be calculated, has been measured by E. Petersen (*Zeitschr. phys. Chem.* **11.** 174 (1893); see also v. Steinwehr, *l.c.*, p. 596).

Now the heat of neutralisation is made up as follows :—

1. From the heat of dissociation x of water.

2. From the heats of dissociation W_1 of the acid, and W_2 of the base, which participate to the respective amounts of

$$W_1(1 - a_1), \quad \text{and} \quad W_2(1 - a_2).$$

3. From the heat of dissociation W of the salt, which participates to the extent of

$$W(1 - a).$$

Now by observing that the acid and the base are electrolytically dissociated in the solution, and conversely, that the water and the undissociated salt are formed by the union of ions, we obtain as the expression for "q" the heat of neutralisation,

$$q = x + W(1 - a) - W_1(1 - a_1) - W_2(1 - a_2).$$

If we mix *the highly dissociated salt of a weak acid with a stronger acid*, we have a process which is comparable with the neutralisation of a strong acid by a strong base ; because in both cases, in consequence of the mixture, two ions unite smoothly to form an electrically neutral molecule.

Thus if we mix, *e.g.*, a sodium salt of the weak hydrofluoric acid with hydrochloric acid, then the reaction progresses almost completely in the sense of the reaction

$$\overset{+}{H} + \overset{-}{F} = HF,$$

and the heat of reaction observed is that of this reaction. Thomsen found that 2360 cal. were associated with this mixture, a value which is only slightly different from the value given above for the heat of dissociation of hydrofluoric acid (– 2570).

If *the formation of an insoluble precipitate* results from the union of two electrolytes which are completely dissociated, then the negative value of the observed heat of reaction corresponds, of course, to the *heat of solution of the precipitated substance*. Thus, *e.g.*, if we mix a silver salt and a chloride, solid silver chloride is precipitated, and, according to Thomsen, a heat development of 15,800 cal. is observed, which corresponds to the simple reaction

$$\overset{+}{Ag} + \overset{-}{Cl} = AgCl.$$
$$\text{Dissolved} \qquad \text{Solid}$$

Finally, we would observe that it is possible to calculate the heat of reaction on mixing any solutions, provided that *we know the heats of dissociation, and the heats of solution, of all the molecular species which come into consideration.*

According to the principles developed in Chap. IV. of the preceding book, we can predict the progress of the reaction from the dissociation constants, and from the solubility coefficients, of all the molecular species which are to be considered. But if we know to what extent electrolytic dissociation and the formation of precipitates have taken place, and if we know the heat value of each of these processes, then of course we can state the heat of reaction of the total process.

In thermo-chemical relations the heats of dissociation and of solution go hand in hand with the coefficients of dissociation and of solubility. The following chapter will give us the interesting result that these pairs of magnitudes are closely related.

CHAPTER II

THERMO-CHEMISTRY II

The Application of the Second Law of the Mechanical Theory of Heat: Historical.—The application of the second law of thermodynamics to chemical processes was a step of fundamental significance, because we obtained thereby for the first time an insight into *the relations between chemical energy, heat, and capacity for external work*; and for the first time were enabled to deal with the questions, how far the energy which is set free in chemical processes is convertible without limitation, and whether it is more of the nature of heat or more of the nature of kinetic energy of moving masses; and although it is not possible to give a satisfactory answer to these questions in every special case, yet it is possible to outline clearly the way leading to a systematic mode of attack.

The honour of having first considered chemical processes, and dissociation in particular, from the standpoint of thermodynamics, undoubtedly belongs to A. Horstmann,[1] who demonstrated clearly the fruitfulness of the mechanical theory of heat in this region by the success of his calculations. Almost at the same time there appeared a very remarkable investigation by Loschmidt,[2] who had already recognised that isothermal distillation was a way by which a chemical process could be conducted isothermally and reversibly. He also discussed the process of chemical solution.

Then shortly afterwards the problem was treated very thoroughly, and, from one point of view, finally, by J. W. Gibbs;[3] but, unfortunately, the calculations of this author were much too general in character to be capable of a simple and direct application to special cases of investigation.

---

[1] *Ber. deutsch. chem. Ges.* **2.** 137 (1869); **4.** 635 (1871); *Lieb. Ann.* **170.** 192 (1873).

[2] *Ber. der Wiener Akad.* 59, II. 395 (1869).

[3] *Trans. Conn. Acad.* **3.** 108 and 343 (1874-1878); German translation by W. Ostwald, Leipzig, 1892.

Thus it came about that independently of Gibbs's work, and a little later, there were discovered a large number of theorems which may be deduced directly by specialisation of his formulæ; as for example—the relation between the development of heat and the temperature coefficient in the dissociation of a gas, and the relation between the development of heat and the temperature coefficient of a galvanic element.

The first of these problems in particular has been repeatedly subjected to treatment.[1]

Of the later comprehensive treatises on the application of thermodynamics to chemical processes, reference should be made to the monographs of Le Chatelier,[2] and especially to that of van't Hoff,[3] the study of which cannot be too highly commended, as leading to a more profound knowledge of the important and difficult problems presented here.

Mathematical deduction has gained greatly in clearness and elegance from the more recent methods of treatment of Planck[4] and Riecke;[5] the latter treatise is based entirely on the application of *the thermodynamic potential*, and therefore has unquestioned advantage for all those who are conversant with the potential theory of physics.

Of course the distinctions between the various methods of treatment are *purely conventional*; one method can proceed no farther than another. The author's method is to endeavour to bring all in as close contact as possible with *the results of experiment*, hoping thereby to make the subject in many points more intelligible than it has been made hitherto.

In this and the following chapter we will describe the most important applications made thus far *of the second law of thermodynamics to chemical processes*, considering firstly *complete chemical equilibrium*, which, according to the results obtained on p. 473, is conditioned by the *temperature alone*, and then *incomplete chemical equilibrium*, which is conditioned not only by the *temperature*, but also by *the relative quantities of the reacting substances*.

Gibbs's "Phase Rule."—The "complete chemical equilibrium" (p. 473) had the characteristic that for every temperature there existed only one definite pressure at which the different phases of the system were in equilibrium with each other. If we change this pressure at constant temperature, then the reaction advances to a completion in one sense or the other, *i.e.* until one or more of the phases are

---

[1] van der Waals, *Beibl.* **4.** 749 (1880); Boltzmann, *Wied. Ann.* **22.** 65 (1884); and others.

[2] *Recherches sur les équilibres chimiques.* Paris, 1888.

[3] *Études de dynamique chimique.* Amsterdam, 1884.

[4] *Wied. Ann.* **30.** 562; **31.** 189; **32.** 462 (1887); we may here again refer to the work of Planck quoted on p. 23.

[5] *Zeitschr. phys. Chem.* **6.** 268, 411 (1890); **7.** 97 (1891).

exhausted; if the external pressure is only changed a very little, then each phase maintains its composition unchanged during the reaction.

We have already become acquainted with numerous examples of complete chemical equilibrium. In addition to the simplest case of equilibrium between different states of aggregation, there belong to this category the dissociation of ammonium chloride, excluding an excess of the dissociation products, the dissociation of calcium carbonate, etc.

A very remarkable law regarding *complete heterogeneous equilibrium* was discovered by Gibbs in a theoretical way; it was afterwards thoroughly proved experimentally, and can be used as a safe guide in the investigation of special cases. It may be formulated as follows:—

It is necessary to assemble AT LEAST n *different molecular species, in order to construct a complete heterogeneous equilibrium consisting of* n + 1 *different phases.*

Thus, in order to establish the complete equilibrium,

$$H_2O \rightleftarrows H_2O,$$
Liquid   Vapour

only *one* molecular species (H_2O) is required, because the equilibrium consists of two phases.

In order to establish the complete equilibrium between calcium carbonate and its decomposition products (three phases), we need at least two molecular species, viz. CO_2 and CaO.

By bringing together salt and water, we can establish the three phases of the complete equilibrium between the solid salt, its solution, and the vapour of the solution.

But, on the other hand, if two molecular species, e.g. react upon each other in two phases only, the equilibrium will be incomplete, *i.e.* the progress of the reaction is associated with a change in the equilibrium pressure. Thus if we let any mixture of water and alcohol evaporate, the maximal pressure of the mixture changes with the progress of the reaction in spite of keeping the temperature constant. This reaction would become complete if we should, *e.g.*, allow the water to freeze, and so add a third phase to the system.

Of course we can imagine the heterogeneous system in question to be constructed of *more* than "n" molecular species, as, *e.g.*, in the equilibrium between calcium carbonate and its decomposition products, thus, $CaCO_3$, CaO, Ca, CO_2, etc. But to "n" must be assigned the *minimal value*, and for the preceding system this amounts to 2, whether we imagine the construction of the system to be from CaO and CO_2, or from $CaCO_3$ and CaO, etc. And thus the limitation "at least" is seen to have an essential meaning.[1]

[1] If solid sal-ammoniac be volatilised without excess of its products of dissociation NH_3 and HCl the system can be built up of one kind of molecule (NH_4Cl) only, so that we may put n = 1.

The proof of the "phase rule" can be shown in a simpler way than that given by Gibbs,[1] as follows :[2]—

Let the heterogeneous system considered consist of y phases, for the construction of which we need at least n different molecular species. We will select one phase in which all the molecular species are present, there always being one such phase at least. Thus, *e.g.*, each molecular species must occur in every *liquid* phase, because each molecular species has a definite solubility, though it may be perhaps immeasurably small; and hence each species may be present in quantities which are too small to be weighed. A similar thing holds good for the *gaseous* phase of the system, because every molecular species has a finite vapour pressure.

Let the concentration (*i.e.* the number of mols per litre) of the n molecular species in the selected phase be respectively, $c_1, c_2, \ldots c_n$. The composition of the phase will change in a way which is perfectly definite and unequivocal, if we change the external conditions of the system, viz. the temperature T, and the pressure p; and of course if we also change the concentration of each of the particular molecular species. Therefore an equation must exist which so relates the quantities $c_1, c_2, \ldots c_n$, p, and T, with each other, that a variation in the value of one of their magnitudes necessitates a variation in all the others. We thus obtain the equation

$$F_1(c_1, c_2, \ldots c_n, p, T) = 0,$$

where F_1 is the symbol for any selected function of the variable considered.

The fact that such characteristic equations are only very incompletely known at the present time does not impair the stringency of the proof; it is enough to know that *there is such an equation in each case.* For two molecular species we obtained on p. 244 a characteristic equation of the form

$$f(c_1, c_2, p, T).$$

In the present case the equations must be much more complex, not only because there are more kinds of molecule, but because the relative quantity of each substance may vary with displacement of equilibrium.

Every other phase of the system has its own characteristic equation; but now the composition of one phase unequivocally conditions that of all other phases which may be in equilibrium with it; all phases which are in equilibrium with one phase must be in equilibrium with each other, and this is possible only with perfectly definite ratios of concentration. Thus, *e.g.*, it is evident that from the condition of a

---

[1] *Trans. Conn. Acad.* **3.** 108 and 343 (1874-1878).
[2] Taken mainly from that of Riecke (*Zeitschr. phys. Chem.* **6.** 272), which can be consulted for further details. The new proof by C. H. Wind (*ibid.* **31.** 390, 1899) cannot be regarded as an advance by the author. The investigator mentioned falls into the error of founding his proof on implicit assumptions. See the apt critique of this inadmissible course by A. Byk (*ibid.* **45.** 250, 1906).

liquid phase, the composition of the gaseous phase in contact with it is also given.

Therefore it follows that the compositions of all the other phases are definite and unequivocal functions of the same variables upon which the selected phase depends; and also that for every phase there must exist an equation of condition of the form

$$F(c_1, c_2, \ldots c_n, p, T) = 0.$$

We obtain as many equations of condition of this sort as there are phases in our system, *i.e.* " y " in number.

Now the number of variables, $c_1, c_2, \ldots c_n$, p, T, amounts to n + 2 ; therefore in order that they may be unequivocally determined by the equations of condition, which are " y " in number, it is necessary that there shall be as many equations as there are variables, *i.e.* it follows that

$$y = n + 2.$$

Now this amounts to stating that when n *molecular species react in* n + 2 *phases, an equation of condition is possible between all of them, only when the conditions of temperature and pressure are definite and unequivocal; and also when the ratio of concentration of each of the particular phases is perfectly definite.*

Hence the coexistence of the n + 2 *phases occurs at a point of singularity, the so-called* "**point of transition**" (*Uebergangspunkt*). We shall soon learn something more regarding the peculiarities of this point.

Therefore, in order to have a *complete equilibrium, i.e.* when, during a finite interval, for every value of the temperature T, there corresponds a perfectly definite equilibrium pressure p, and, of course, a perfectly definite composition of each of the particular phases,—we must have *one equation less* than the number of variables, *i.e.* it must follow that

$$y = n + 1.$$

But this is nothing but the phase rule; for this result says that—

The number of phases in a complete equilibrium must be one more than the number of reacting molecular species.

Finally, when

$$y < n + 1,$$

then, with given external conditions of temperature and pressure, $c_1, c_2, \ldots c_n$, remain more or less indefinite, and therefore the composition of all the phases also ; here we are dealing with *an incomplete equilibrium*.[1]

The Point of Transition.—The conditions of complete equi-

---

[1] For apparent exceptions to the phase rule in the case of optically active bodies, cf. the detailed investigation by A. Byk, *Zeitschr. phys. Chem.* **45**. 465 (1903).

librium require that, within a finite temperature interval, to every temperature point there shall correspond a definite pressure value, at which all of the phases of the system may be coexistent. This temperature interval is always limited, as a result of the fact that one of the phases suddenly ceases to be capable of existence, and disappears from the system. Thus, *e.g.*, to take the simplest case imaginable, let us study the equilibrium in the equation

$$H_2O \rightleftarrows H_2O$$
Liquid   Gaseous

at different temperatures. Then, on the one hand, according to what was said above, we can follow the measurements of the vapour pressure of liquid water only up to the critical temperature; and, on the other hand, the investigation will be interrupted at lower temperatures when we arrive at the freezing-point of water (under the vapour pressure itself); beyond this liquid water ceases to be capable of existence, except in the labile condition of an under-cooled liquid. But usually another phase appears to take the place of the one which has disappeared, as in the latter case, where we arrive at the new complete equilibrium

$$H_2O \rightleftarrows H_2O$$
Solid   Gas

(sublimation of ice).

That temperature point, where one phase of a complete heterogeneous equilibrium vanishes, and another takes its place, we call "*the point of transition.*" Thus at the point of transition, and at the corresponding pressure, there are coexistent beside the others, not only the phases which have begun to disappear, but also those which are beginning to appear.

Now, since there were n + 1 phases composed of n molecular species before the point of transition was reached, *therefore, at the point of transition itself there are n + 2 phases, each one of which is, of course, made up of the same n molecular species in a state of singularity.*

In order to obtain a deeper insight into these relations, the universal significance of which is obvious, we will consider some special cases in what follows.

The Equilibrium between the different Phases of Water.— We can easily determine the point of transition at which the *liquid* phase vanishes from the system,—water $\rightleftarrows$ water vapour,—and is replaced by the *solid* phase, ice.

At atmospheric pressure water freezes at $0°$, and under its own vapour pressure, which is very small compared with the atmospheric pressure, at $+ 0.0076°$, because the freezing-point is raised by this amount by diminishing the pressure one atmosphere (p. 68). The *pressure* corresponding to the point of transition, according to Regnault's vapour-pressure tables, is 4·57 mm.

Under these and only these conditions of temperature and pressure are the three phases—ice, liquid water, and water vapour, coexistent.

For a clear consideration of this case, the simplest conceivable, and also for the treatment of more complicated equilibria, we may use with advantage a graphic method, which shows at a glance the dependence of the nature of the equilibrium on the external conditions of temperature and pressure.[1]

In a co-ordinate system where the abscissæ represent the temperature T (properly on the absolute scale), and the ordinates represent the pressure p, are drawn curves along which two different phases of water are coexistent. We will call these "the limiting curves" (*Grenz-kurven*) of the system under consideration.

In general, if we are considering a system composed of a number of phases, and for the construction of which there are requisite n molecular species,—then the meaning of "the limiting curves" is that under the definite and unequivocal conditions of temperature and pressure represented by them, n + 1 different phases are capable of existing beside each other.

These "limiting curves" are well known in the case of water; and it is directly evident that there must be *three*, on each of which can coexist one of the three phase pairs which can be made from the three different states of aggregation of water.

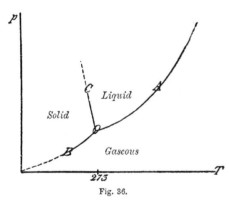

Fig. 36.

Thus we obtain the curve diagram shown in Fig. 36. *Liquid water* and *water vapour* are coexistent along the curve OA. This is the "*vapour-pressure curve*," which is especially well known in the first part, and comes to an end at T = 273° + 364·3°, which is the critical temperature of water.

Under the conditions represented by the point O, and previously determined to be T = 273° + 0·0076°, and p = 4·57 mm., water freezes. Hence the continuation of the curve AO, along the limiting curve OB, represents the conditions under which *ice* and water *vapour* are coexistent; it is the "*vapour-pressure curve*" of ice (p. 71). On account of the smallness of the vapour pressure of solidified water, it has been traced only a short distance downwards from O. But from the kinetic

[1] Roozeboom, *Zeitschr. phys. Chem.* **2.** 474 (1888).

treatment of the properties of matter, we may predict with great certainty that it intersects the point of origin of our system of co-ordinates, and hence that the vapour pressure of ice first becomes zero at the absolute zero-point of temperature, and that at this point water vapour (like every gas) ceases to be capable of existence *as such*.

Finally, the "limiting curve" OC represents the conditions for the coexistence of *water* and *ice*.   Since the freezing of water is accompanied by an increase of volume, the melting-point of ice sinks with increasing pressure, by an amount which is $0.0076°$ per atm., a relatively small amount.   And, moreover, since the depression of the melting-point is proportional to the external pressure, at least at pressures which are not too high, OC is a straight line slightly inclined to the p axis.   Here also the course of the curve OC has only been followed for a slight distance from O.

The point O, in which all the limiting curves are concurrent, and therefore in which all of the three phases are coexistent, is thus a point of singularity in the p, T, plane ; it has been already called *the point of transition*.   According to the number of limiting curves which unite at this point, we may call it "three-fold," "four-fold," etc. ; or "triple," "quadruple," etc.   In the case of water, O is a "triple point."

The limiting curves are, of course, curves of complete equilibrium. If we are considering one point of one of the curves, and if we change the pressure and temperature in a way which is different from what corresponds to the course of the curve, then a complete reaction occurs, and, according to the circumstances, one of the two phases vanishes.

Moreover, the limiting curves divide the plane (p, T) into three fields, each of which corresponds to the existence of one of the three phases.   This does not state that the phases cannot exist beyond the limits of their respective fields.   Thus, *e.g.*, it is known that liquid water may exist at a temperature and pressure which are below the point O.   But in that case the existence of water is a labile one, *i.e.* it is in an "under-cooled" state.

A similar thing is true of water vapour, which we know can exist at temperatures and pressures where it should have become liquefied, according to the course of the limiting curve.   These labile conditions play a much more important *rôle* in nature than has been believed hitherto.   It has been proved repeatedly that some very stable substances, especially those in the solid state of aggregation, are in a state comparable to that of an "under-cooled" liquid ; and thus, according to the laws of chemical equilibrium, have no right of existence.

We should by no means attach the meaning to the term "labile" that the system needs only a slight disturbance in order to change it to the more "stable" form.

In this way we can explain why it is that a well-known *fourth* modification of water, *i.e.* "electrolytic gas," has no place in the (p, T) plane ; at least not in the region thus far considered. "Electrolytic gas" at the ordinary conditions of temperature and pressure is in just as much a labile condition as is under-cooled water, because it can be changed into the stable form of water by several kinds of disturbance ; as, *e.g.*, by a suitable elevation in temperature of one point.

The following circumstance is further very remarkable.

Let us descend along the curve AO at constant volume, by removing heat from the system water and water vapour enclosed in a suitable vessel. At O the water freezes, and it obviously depends upon the *relative quantities of the phases present* as to which of the phases, the liquid or the gaseous, will disappear on further cooling, *i.e.* as to whether, on further removal of heat, the system will progress along the curve OB, or along OC. If the expansion of the gaseous phase is sufficiently great, then all the water will freeze, and we shall advance along the curve OB. If, on the other hand, the volume of the liquid water is sufficiently great in comparison with the gaseous phase, then all the water vapour condenses as a result of the increase of volume resulting from the freezing, and the corresponding increase of pressure ; thus the melting-point will be strongly depressed, and we shall advance along the curve OC.

The Equilibrium between Water and Sulphur Dioxide.—

The system just described could be constructed of *a single molecular species*, (H_2O). We will select as a further and more complicated example of complete heterogeneous equilibrium a system composed of H_2O and SO_2, *i.e. two molecular species*; this has been very thoroughly investigated by Roozeboom.[1]

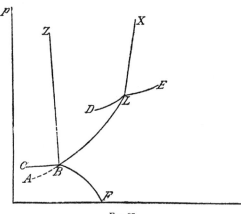

Fig. 37.

We will again plot in a co-ordinate system the curves along which complete equilibrium can exist.

Now, since we allow two molecular species to meet here, then, according to Gibbs's phase rule, *three phases* must be capable of existing beside each other on the limiting curves ; and it is only at singular points that *the coexistence of four phases* is possible.

In the neighbourhood of the point L (Fig. 37) the four following

[1] *Zeitschr. phys. Chem.* **2**. 450 (1888).

homogeneous systems can be prepared by bringing together the requisite SO_2 and H_2O.

1. The *solid hydrate* $SO_2 . 7(H_2O)$: this can easily be caused to separate out by cooling a water solution which is saturated with SO_2.

2. A *solution* of SO_2 in water, which we will designate by the symbol fl.$(H_2O + xSO_2)$. Here x denotes the number of mols which are present in the solution, for 1 mol of H_2O (18 g.); on account of the excess of water in the solution, x is always less than one.

3. A *solution* of water in liquid sulphurous acid, corresponding to the symbol fl.$(SO_2 + yH_2O)$: here, similarly to x, y is always less than one.

4. A *gas mixture*, composed of SO_2 and H_2O, which we will designate by the symbol "gas $(SO_2 + zH_2O)$."

The three phases 2, 3, and 4 are coexistent along the curve LE; the first two are composed of two liquids, water and sulphurous acid, which do not mix with each other in all proportions, but only partially dissolve each other like ether and water, *e.g.*, thus " x " corresponds to the solubility of SO_2 in water, and " y " to the solubility of water in SO_2.   Both of these solubilities vary with the temperature, and of course they must be determined for a number of temperature points, in order to have exact knowledge regarding the aforesaid equilibrium : this has not yet been done.

The *gaseous* phase consists of the vapour emitted by the two liquids ; and the pressure p, which corresponds to any particular point of the curve LE, is the vapour pressure of the two liquids at the corresponding temperature.   The values of " z " were not determined by Roozeboom, but it should be noticed that, by means of the rules already given (p. 491), the pressure p, the composition of the gaseous phase, and therefore the value of z also, may be calculated, at least approximately, from the mutual solubilities, and from the known vapour pressures of the pure solvents.

If we cool the system just described, at constant volume, when the quantities of the particular phases are in suitable proportions, we advance along the curve LD ; the water solution of SO_2 disappears, and there appears instead the solid hydrate No. 1, $(SO_2 . 7H_2O)$; while the two other phases, No. 3, fl.$(SO_2 + yH_2O)$, and No. 4, gas $(SO_2 + zH_2O)$, remain.

The values of y and of z were not measured.

The pressure p of the gaseous phase (the pressure of dissociation of the solid hydrate in the presence of a saturated aqueous solution of sulphur dioxide) which is of course independent of the relative quantities of the solid and liquid phases, has the following values for the corresponding temperatures T :—

T.	p.	T.	p.
$273 + 0.1°$	113.1 cm. Hg.	$273 + 11.0°$	170.1 cm. Hg.
$273 + 3.05$	127.0 ,,	$273 + 11.9$	176.2 ,,
$273 + 6.05$	141.9 ,,	$273 + 12.1$	177.3 ,,
$273 + 9.05$	158.2 ,,	...	...

If we advance along the curve DL, by raising the pressure and the temperature, and by a suitable choice of the relative proportions of the particular phases, we can make the gaseous phase disappear at the point L, and thus cause a water solution of sulphur dioxide to appear. We thus arrive at the system composed of the solid hydrate No. 1, ($SO_2 . 7H_2O$), and of the solutions No. 2 and No. 3, viz. fl.($H_2O + xSO_2$), and fl.($SO_2 + yH_2O$) ; here the hydrate is found in equilibrium with its fusion products, the mutually saturated solutions of water and sulphur dioxide.

At a pressure of 177.3 cm., the melting-point of the hydrate is $T = 273° + 12.1°$. This rises with the pressure ; at 20 atm. it is 12.9°, and at 225 atm. it is 17.1°. Now, since the rise is nearly proportional to the pressure, and only amounts to a few degrees for an enormous change of pressure, the limiting curve LX is a straight line only slightly inclined to the right.

The values of x and y, *i.e.* the mutual solubilities of water and sulphur dioxide in the presence of the solid hydrate, are not known ; they should not differ very much from those corresponding to the curve LE, because the mutual solubilities of two liquids vary only slightly with the pressure.

Advancing down along the system of curves LE or LX, we can, by cooling, proceed either along the curve LD, already described, or, by suitable proportions of the particular phases, along the curve LB. Here the phases solid hydrate ($SO_2 . 7H_2O$), fl.($H_2O + xSO_2$), and gas ($SO_2 + zH_2O$), are in equilibrium ; we are therefore concerned with a system composed of the solid hydrate, its saturated solution in water, and the vapours emitted by them. The concentration of the saturated solution has the following values at the corresponding temperatures :—

T.	$x \frac{6400}{18}.$	T.	$x \frac{6400}{18}.$
$273 + 0°$	10.4	$273 + 7°$	17.4
$273 + 2$	11.8	$273 + 8$	19.1
$273 + 4$	13.5	$273 + 10$	23.6
$273 + 6$	16.1	$273 + 12.1$	31.0

The numbers denote the parts of SO_2 to 100 parts of H_2O. In order to obtain the value of x (*i.e.* the number of molecules of SO_2 to one mol of H_2O), they must be multiplied by

$$\frac{18}{6400} = \frac{1}{355 \cdot 5},$$

where $64 =$ the mol. wt. of SO_2, and $18 =$ the mol. wt. of water.

The vapour pressure p of the saturated solution was as follows at the corresponding temperatures :—

T.	p.	T	.	p.
$273 - 6°$	$13 \cdot 7$ cm. Hg.	$273 + 4 \cdot 45°$		$51 \cdot 9$ cm. Hg.
$273 - 4$	$17 \cdot 65$,,	$273 + 6 \cdot 00$		$66 \cdot 6$,,
$273 - 3$	$20 \cdot 1$,,	$273 + 8 \cdot 40$		$92 \cdot 6$,,
$273 - 2 \cdot 6$	$21 \cdot 15$,,	$273 + 10 \cdot 00$		$117 \cdot 7$,,
$273 - 2$	$23 \cdot 0$,,	$273 + 11 \cdot 30$		$150 \cdot 3$,,
$273 - 1$	$26 \cdot 2$,,	$273 + 11 \cdot 75$		$166 \cdot 6$,,
$273 - 0$	$29 \cdot 7$,,	$273 + 12 \cdot 10$		$177 \cdot 3$,,
$273 + 2 \cdot 8$	$43 \cdot 2$,,	...		...

Thus four limiting curves meet in the point L ; and although only *three phases* are coexistent at every other point of the respective curves, yet at this point L, and only at this point, the four following phases are coexistent :

1. The *solid* hydrate, $SO_2 . 7H_2O$.
2. A *water solution* of SO_2, having the composition ($H_2O + 0 \cdot 087 SO_2$).
3. A *solution* of H_2O in *liquid* SO_2 (*i.e.* $SO_2 + yH_2O$).
4. A *gas mixture* of SO_2 and H_2O (*i.e.* $SO_2 + zH_2O$).

As each one of these systems can be made from the two molecular species, SO_2 and H_2O, therefore, during a *finite* temperature interval, according to the "phase-rule," a complete equilibrium can be established for only *three* of these systems. All four may coexist only at the transition point L, which is in this case a quadruple or fourfold point ; it is situated at

$$T = 273° + 12 \cdot 1°, \quad \text{and } p = 177 \cdot 3 \text{ cm.}$$

Roozeboom did not determine the values of y and z for the point L ; but we may form a conception of their magnitude in the following way :—

The pressure $177 \cdot 3$ cm. in the gas mixture $SO_2 + zH_2O$ is composed of the partial pressures of the particular gases.

Now, since a water solution of SO_2 is present at the transition point, therefore the partial pressure of the water vapour is equal to the partial pressure of pure water at the temperature in question ($12 \cdot 1°$), viz. $1 \cdot 05$ cm., minus the depression caused by the solution of $0 \cdot 087$ mol of SO_2 in 1 mol of H_2O ; and this, according to Raoult's law, is

$$1 \cdot 05 \times 0 \cdot 087 \text{ cm.}$$

2 s

Thus the partial pressure of the water vapour amounts approximately to 0·9 cm., and that of the sulphur dioxide is

$$177\cdot3 - 0\cdot9 = 176\cdot4 \text{ cm.}$$

Hence

$$z = \frac{0\cdot9}{176\cdot4} = 0\cdot0051.$$

The concentration y of water in sulphur dioxide is also found by means of the law for the molecular depression of the vapour pressure. According to Regnault, at 12·1°, pure liquid sulphur dioxide has a vapour pressure of 185 cm. But now, since sulphur dioxide saturated with water is present at the point L, and since the partial pressure of sulphur dioxide so saturated amounts to only 176·4, therefore, in order to occasion the depression of 8·6 cm., ·

$$\frac{8\cdot6}{176\cdot4} = 0\cdot05 \text{ mol of } H_2O$$

must be dissolved in every molecule of SO_2; this corresponds to the value of y.

As stated above, the equilibrium pressures in the system, $SO_2 . 7H_2O$, liq. fl.($H_2O + xSO_2$), and gaseous ($SO_2 + zH_2O$), which are given by the curve LB, have been measured as far down as $-6°$ (Celsius). But the system is in labile equilibrium beyond the point B (which corresponds to the temperature of $-2\cdot6°$ and to the pressure of 21·1 cm.); because the liquid phase vanishes at once on the appearance of ice, and completely solidifies to ice and solid hydrate Thus, instead of advancing along BA, the labile extension of the curve LB (which is figured as a dotted line in Fig. 37), we advance along the curve BC. This curve refers to the system of the three phases :—

1. The solid hydrate.
2. Ice.
3. The gas mixture ($SO_2 + zH_2O$).

The vapour pressures of a mixture of ice and the solid hydrate are as follows :—

T.	p.	T.	p.
$273 - 2\cdot6°$	21·15 cm. Hg.	$273 - 6°$	17·7 cm. Hg.
$273 - 3$	20·65 ,,	$273 - 8$	16·0 ,,
$273 - 4$	19·35 ,,	$273 - 9$	15·0 ,,

They are therefore considerably greater than would be the case if the system were under-cooled, *i.e.* if the solidification of the water solution of SO_2 had not occurred, as can be readily seen from the diagram (Fig. 37). The gas mixture emitted by the ice and the solid hydrate of course consists of H_2O and SO_2. *Now since ice is present, the partial pressures of the water vapour are simply equal to the vapour pressures of ice at the corresponding temperatures*; and these can be taken directly from Regnault's tables, and thus z can be obtained.[1] They are very small in comparison with the total pressures.

Along the curve BF, ice, the water solution of sulphurous acid, and the gaseous mixture ($SO_2 + zH_2O$), are capable of coexistence. The corresponding values of the pressure and temperature are so correlated that the pressure first conditions the concentration of the sulphurous acid, and then this concentration in turn conditions the lowering of the freezing-point of water. For small pressures, *i.e.* at slight concentration of the sulphurous acid, the curve tends to approach the freezing-point F of pure water at T = 273°.

Finally, along the curve BZ, there are capable of coexistence, ice, the solid hydrate, and the melted mixture of the two (*i.e.* a water solution of sulphurous acid). As the melting is attended by a diminution of volume, the curve must bend to the left, *i.e.* the temperature of equilibrium must fall with an elevation of the pressure. But this has not been investigated in detail.

Thus the point B represents a second quadruple point; here there coexist the four following phases :—

1. Ice.
2. The *solid* hydrate, $SO_2 . 7H_2O$.
3. A *water solution* of SO_2, having the composition ($H_2O + 0·024SO_2$).
4. A gas mixture of SO_2 and H_2O (*i.e.* $SO_2 + zH_2O$).

The co-ordinates of this point are

$$T = 273 - 2·6°, \quad \text{and } p = 21·1 \text{ cm.}$$

The vapour pressure of ice at $- 2·6°$ amounts to $0·38$ cm., and hence z must be

$$\frac{0·38}{20·7} = 0·0184.$$

The areas in Figs. 36 and 37, enclosed by the curves, constitute *regions of incomplete equilibrium*.

The Hydrates of Ferric Chloride.—As an example of a more extended investigation of those systems, whose phases can all be formed of *two* molecular species, such as H_2O and Fe_2Cl_6, we will describe Roozeboom's [2] research on the hydrates of ferric chloride. This led to a broadening of our view in several respects.

At the transition points of this system, the four following phases are capable of existing beside each other, viz :—

---

[1] Roozeboom did not draw this conclusion, but its correctness appears to the author to be beyond doubt.

[2] *Zeitschr. phys. Chem.* **10.** 477 (1892).

1. The solid hydrate, $Fe_2Cl_6 . mH_2O$.
2. The solid hydrate, $Fe_2Cl_6 . nH_2O$.
3. The saturated solution.
4. Water vapour.

For the case where the hydrate *ice* occurs, we can make

$$n = \infty \;$$

and for the case where *water-free* ferric chloride separates as a solid phase, we can make

$$n = 0.$$

The four "limiting curves" which meet at the transition point are composed of the vapour-pressure curves of the saturated solutions of the two hydrates, the vapour-pressure curve of a *mixture* of the two solid hydrates, and the solubility curve of a solution which is at the same time saturated with both the hydrates.

Of these numerous curves, Roozeboom investigated *the solubility curves* of the separate hydrates at ordinary pressures; the knowledge of these gives us a fairly complete view of the prevailing relations.

In order to explain these, we will follow the example of Roozeboom and employ a somewhat different graphic delineation than in the preceding cases. As the *concentration* of the solutions here commands our chief interest, the *abscissæ* will represent the *temperature* (on the ordinary scale), and the *ordinates* the composition, expressed in molecules of Fe_2Cl_6 to 100 mols of H_2O.

Fig. 38 gives a good general view of the equilibrium ratios.

If we start out from the equilibrium, water + ice, and add ferric chloride, we obtain the curve AB, *i.e.* the curve of the depression of the freezing-point on addition of the salt. At about $-55°$ we reach the saturation point of the hydrate of $12H_2O$; B therefore represents the point where the so-called "cryo-hydrate," *i.e. a mechanical mixture of ice and solid salt* (p. 502), separates.

Further addition of ferric chloride causes the ice to disappear, and we advance along the curve BC, which is *the solubility curve* of the hydrate with $12H_2O$.

At 37° the concentration of the saturated solution becomes equal to that of the solid hydrate, and at this temperature a solution of the composition $Fe_2Cl_6 + 12H_2O$ solidifies completely to the solid hydrate, or else this solidified hydrate is changed completely to a homogeneous liquid. Thus 37° is the *melting-point* of this hydrate.

If we add anhydrous ferric chloride to this melted hydrate, we advance along the curve CDN. Of the two branches which diverge from C, the one, CB, corresponds to the curve of the depression of the freezing-point occasioned by adding H_2O; the other, CDN, corresponds to the curve of the depression of the freezing-point of the hydrate, occasioned by the addition of Fe_2Cl_6. Thus below the melting-point

[37°] of the pure hydrate [$Fe_2Cl_6 + 12H_2O$] it is possible to prepare *two* saturated solutions, one of which contains more H_2O, and the other less, than the hydrate in equilibrium with the solution. We shall return to this remarkable phenomenon a little later.

The curves for the hydrate with $7H_2O$ (DEF), for the hydrate with $5H_2O$ (FGH), and for the hydrate with $4H_2O$ (HJK), are exactly

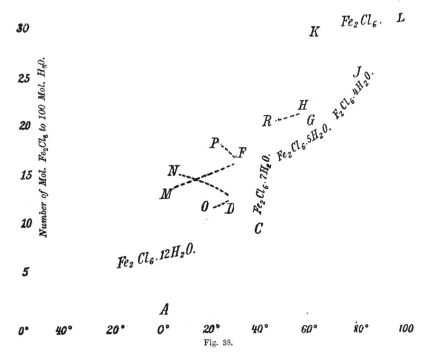

Fig. 38.

similar. At K begins the almost straight solubility curve of *anhydrous* Fe_2Cl_6. The melting-points of these hydrates are at E (32·5°), G (56°), and J (73·5°).

The curve fractions DN, FM, DO, FP, and HR, represent labile conditions. Ice and the hydrate containing most water are in equilibrium at the point B. At the points D, F, and H the respective contiguous hydrates are in equilibrium. And finally, at K, the hydrate containing the least quantity of water is in equilibrium with the anhydrous Fe_2Cl_6.

The *composition* of the respective solutions at each of these points lies between the composition of the two respective solid bodies, because at these points the second branch of the higher hydrate intersects the first branch of the next lower hydrate. The points mentioned lie at $-55°$, $27\cdot4°$, $30°$, $55°$, and $66°$; and these are at the same time the temperatures at which the solutions solidify to mixtures of the two hydrates.

In order to obtain a clear picture of the relations which prevail here, let us imagine the concentration and temperature of a solution of ferric chloride to be given by a point which lies in the right-hand side of the region bounded by the multiple curves ABCDEFGHJKL. On cooling, the solution at first traverses a horizontal line, the composition remaining constant; and at a definite temperature, its path will cut one of the portions of the curve, say FGH. If we suppose supersaturation to be excluded at the moment of the intersection, there will occur the separation of the solid substance to which the portion of curve belongs, e.g. $Fe_2Cl_6 . 5H_2O$. On further cooling the curve would be followed towards lower temperatures until the end point was reached, where another solid substance appears, and complete solidification results.

If the solution had the same composition as one of the hydrates, it would solidify completely at its melting-point. If the solution had a composition corresponding to the intersection of any two of the contiguous curves, then it would solidify completely at the temperature of the point in question.[1]

Most interesting phenomena would be observed on evaporation of a dilute solution of ferric chloride, and the results would be most striking between $30°$ and $32°$. Here, by the removal of water vapour, the dilute solution would first dry down to $Fe_2Cl_6 . 12H_2O$. It would then liquefy, and then dry down to $Fe_2Cl_6 . 7H_2O$. It would then liquefy again, and a third time dry down, this time to $Fe_2Cl_6 . 5H_2O$.

The whole series of these phenomena corresponds to stable conditions. This very remarkable behaviour would be inexplicable were it not a necessary result of the relations which are illustrated in the curves shown in Fig. 38.

Regarding the curve branches, e.g. BCD and DEF, it follows that, within the limits of a certain temperature interval, there are two saturated solutions having a different composition, which are in equilibrium with the respective solid hydrates. One of these always contains more water, the other less, than the solid hydrate.

The second kind of saturated solution was discovered by Roozeboom in an investigation [2] on *the hydrates of calcium chloride.* It should be particularly emphasised that both of these saturated solutions are entirely stable, and nowhere supersaturated.

Supersaturation only occurs in a solution represented by a point on the left of the curve ABCDEFGHJKL; by adding to a solution a

---

[1] These two cases are good examples of the "eutectic and dystectic" mixtures described on p. 121.

[2] *Zeitschr. phys. Chem.* **4.** 31 (1889).

piece of its respective hydrate in the solid state supersaturation will be avoided, when, according to circumstances, the proportion of ferric chloride will be either diminished or increased, according as the saturated solution belongs to the first or the second category.

Before the work of Roozeboom, only the highest hydrate of ferric chloride was known with certainty, a second one being known incompletely. But the investigation of the equilibria led necessarily to the discovery of the others. While Roozeboom was studying the "solubility curve" of the hydrate with $5H_2O$, he found certain irregularities which he suspected to be due to the existence of another hydrate, and thus he was led to the discovery of the hydrate $Fe_2Cl_6 . 7H_2O$. Now the stable part of its solubility curve extends only over the portion DEF, *i.e.* from $27\cdot4°$ to $32\cdot5°$, and from $30°$ to $32\cdot5°$. *This hydrate would hardly have been discovered without a systematic investigation of this sort.*

Detection of Chemical Compounds of two Components by Means of Melting Curves.—A curve of melting-points may always be used to detect chemical compounds of two substances in the same way as for water and ferric chloride in the example given above ; each compound is indicated by a maximum, since an excess of either component lowers the melting-point of the compound; cf. also p. 122. The points C, G, E, J on the curve Fig. 38, are such maximum freezing-points of mixtures of iron chloride and water. They correspond to simple molecular proportions of the two components, according to the law of multiple proportions.

This method is especially useful in studying racemic mixtures ; on account of the exact similarity of the dextro and laevo forms, the melting curve must be symmetrical about the racemic compound. According to the extensive investigations of Adriani,[1] three cases are to be distinguished :—

1. A continuous (convex or concave) curve, indicating mixed crystals.

2. Two curves, cutting at the composition of the racemic mixture, give a eutectic point (no compound).

3. Three curves, the central one with a maximum, indicating a racemic compound ; eutectic points lie symmetrically on each side (mixture of the compound with the dextro or laevo body).[2]

Thermoanalysis.—The practical investigation of melting-point curves presents some difficulties, especially the analysis of the solid phase which often separates from the melt in an impure condition, and commonly so at high temperatures. In these cases a complete

---

[1] *Zeitschr. phys. Chem.* **33.** 453 (1900).
[2] The figures 43, 40, 41 given below, correspond to cases 1, 2, 3 ; except that, according to reasons already given, the curves must be symmetrical about the 50 % mixture.

and clear idea of the prevailing conditions can be obtained by a systematic investigation of the rate of cooling of the fluid mixture prepared from the two components in known proportions. This can also be carried out at high temperature, *e.g.* by using thermo-elements. In recent times, this method of *thermoanalysis* has been extensively used by G. Tammann[1] and his pupils in the investigation of compounds between metals. Following the example of this author we will now describe the application of this method to four principal cases.[2]

Fig. 39 represents the cooling curve of a binary mixture, from which two different kinds of crystals, A and B, separate. Crystallisa-

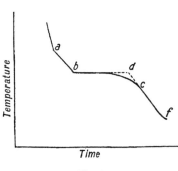

Fig. 39.

tion of A begins at the point a, and lowers the rate of cooling, while at b crystals of B also begin to separate. During the simultaneous crystallisation of A and B, the concentration of the melt is fixed, the equilibrium is therefore complete, and hence the removal of heat does not affect the temperature. We thus obtain an *interval of steady temperature* on the cooling curve. The duration of this is proportional under the same conditions of cooling to the heat set free, *i.e.* to the mass of the eutectically crystallising fluid. As can be seen from Fig. 39 the temperature falls slowly towards the end of the crystallisation, because the melt is no longer in proper contact with the thermometer, which is surrounded to some extent by crystals. In order to determine accurately the duration of crystallisation we must produce fc to cut a horizontal through b. The distance of the point of intersection d from b gives the corrected duration of crystallisation.

The following four principal cases are especially important :—

1. When the two substances A and B are miscible when liquid in every proportion, but form neither a compound nor mixed crystals, then the crystallisation of all possible fluid mixtures of A and B is represented by the diagram in Fig. 40. On the curve ac crystallisation begins with separation of A, on the curve bc with separation of B. When A crystallises from a melt, *e.g.* of the composition m_1, the concentration of B increases till the point c is reached where eutectic crystallisation begins. The mass which crystallises at the temperature of the point c will be different for melts of different composition. If the melt had originally the composition represented by c, the whole of

[1] See the last volume of the *Zeitschr. anorg. Chem.* and the collected results in *Zeitschr. f. Elektrochem.* **14**. 789 (1908).

[2] For further numerous important details see especially the excellent monograph by R. Ruer, *Metallographie*, 1907, Hamburg.

it would crystallise eutectically.   If the melt consisted of pure A or pure B, none of it would crystallise eutectically : between these points the mass of the eutectic mixture obtained is proportional to the concentration.   If the mass of eutectic mixture for the melt m_0 is given by the ordinate pm_0, then the ordinates of the two straight lines Ap and Bp give the mass of eutectic mixture crystallising from melts of various composition.   The time during which the temperature remains steady on cooling will be proportional to these ordinates provided equal masses of the different melts are taken, and the conditions of cooling are the same.

The cooling curves for the compositions o, m_1, m_0, m_2, 100 are shown in Fig. 40.

If these intervals of time, which can be easily determined, are plotted against the concentration, two straight lines Ap and Bp are obtained,

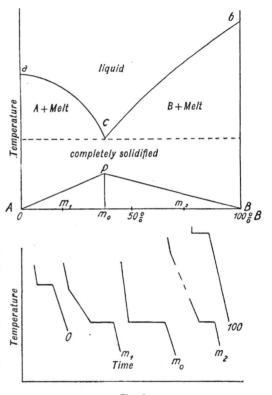

Fig. 40.

which cut at the concentration of the eutectic point c.   If the relations are as described, the two substances form no compound, for in all the mixtures temperature becomes steady at the same point ; the formation of mixed crystals is also out of the question, for if not, the steady point would vanish in the neighbourhood of A or B.

The structure of the conglomerate formed is also closely connected with the behaviour on crystallisation.   In all conglomerates whose composition lies between o and m_0, will be found the primarily formed large crystals of A surrounded by the eutectic mixture c which has a finely grained or granular structure.   The mixtures richer in B will, on the contrary, contain the primarily formed B crystals, surrounded by the eutectic.

2. If the two substances form a compound A_mB_n and are miscible as fluids in all proportions, then if no mixed crystals are formed the diagram Fig. 41 represents the phenomena observed when the molten mass crystallises. The curve dce gives the temperatures at which crystals of the compound A_mB_n are in equilibrium with melts of different composition. This curve is cut by the melting-point curves of A and B, in the points d and e, which are therefore two eutectic points, at the temperatures of which crystallisation of melts of a composition between A and A_mB_n, or B and A_mB_n is complete. The

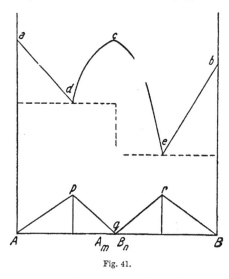

Fig. 41.

mass crystallising at d and e varies as the ordinates of the straight lines Ap, pq, qr, and rB. It is therefore only necessary to determine experimentally the relation between concentration and duration of crystallisation in order to find by extrapolation the point q which gives the composition of the compound. Working with only 20 grams of substance it is easy to find the concentration at q to within a few per thousand. The direct determination of the concentration at the maximum c which corresponds to the point q is much less accurate for the same number of observations.

3. It often happens that a compound A_mB_n does not melt to a homogeneous fluid, but is decomposed to a crystal B and a melt of the composition e according to the equation

$$A_mB_n \xrightleftharpoons{} e + B.$$

Such an example is met with in Glauber salts. The reaction occurs at the point e in the melting-point curve be along which B separates. At this point equilibrium is complete, and hence we obtain intervals of steady temperature on the cooling curves of melts up to the composition represented by the point c (from which B separates). The time during which the temperature remains steady is greatest when the melt is of a composition corresponding to the compound A_mB_n; it will therefore be given by the ordinates of the straight lines tr and rB (Fig. 42).

Further, when melts of a composition between q and p crystallise, we obtain residues which crystallise eutectically at the temperature of the point D—hence the duration of this crystallisation is given by ordinates of the straight line pq. Hence we have two independent ways of determining the composition of A_mB_n ; (a) the length of time during which the temperature remains constant at the point e has its greatest value when the melt has the same composition as the compound, (b) the duration of the crystallisation at the temperature corresponding to the point d is zero when the melt has the composition of the compound. The distance between e and c depends on the amount of melt formed from the compound by overshooting the temperature of the point e. If this mass is very great, and therefore the mass of crystal B small, then c approaches near the point e.

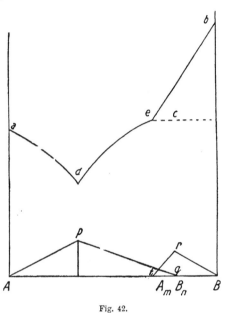

Fig. 42.

4. When the two substances A and B form a continuous series of mixed crystals, we may have either a maximum or a minimum on the freezing-point curve. At such a point the composition of the melt will obviously be the same as that of the mixed crystal in equilibrium with it, just as before. Such a melt will therefore crystallise like a single substance, and the cooling curve will become horizontal to the time axis. We shall confine ourselves to the case where the freezing-point curve rises gradually without maximum or minimum from the melting-point of A to that of B. As both the composition of the mixed crystal and that of the melt alters during crystallisation, we shall not get an interval of steady temperature on cooling, but the beginning and end of the crystallisation will be shown by two well-defined breaks on the curve (Fig. 43), because the heat set free diminishes the rate of cooling. If we plot the temperatures at these breaks, which are shown in Fig. 43 for a few concentrations, against the corresponding concentrations in the temperature-concentration diagram, and join the points which refer to the beginning of crystallisation, we obtain the curve acb, and similarly for the temperature of the end of crystallisation the curve adb. Above the curve acb all mixtures are liquid, under the curve adb only mixed

crystals exist, and in the area between the two curves acb, adb, we have mixtures of melt and mixed crystals. From the diagram Fig. 43 we can read off for every melt the concentration of the mixed crystal in equilibrium with it when crystallisation begins; for example, the melt c is in equilibrium with the mixed crystal d, because at the beginning of crystallisation (*e.g.* in c) the melt, at the end (*e.g.* in d) the solid phase, has the composition which corresponds to the abscissæ in question, and the temperature at c and d is the same.

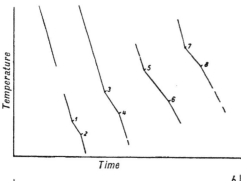

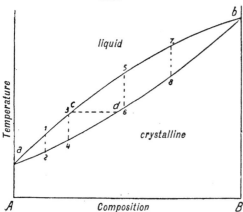

Fig. 43.

Hence, without carrying out analyses which are often made difficult by the separation of mixed crystals from the melt, we can in this case also ascertain by thermo-chemical measurements the composition of mixed crystals deposited from melts of known composition. The condition for the described behaviour is, however, that during cooling the mixed crystals and the melt are in equilibrium at every moment. At first sight it seems improbable that this condition is realised, because equilibrium will not be maintained unless the mixed crystals deposited are continually remelted and redeposited in a form of different composition. Experience teaches, however, that this in fact is very nearly true, especially at high temperatures. Delay in establishment of equilibrium has the effect of lowering the end-point of crystallisation, and therefore the middle part of the curve adb bends downwards towards lower temperatures.

The following remarks may be made on the question whether the maximum of melting-point should be a sharp point, as at c in Fig. 41, or flat, as at the points C, E, etc., in Fig. 38 (cf. also Le Chatelier, *Zeitschr. phys. Chem.* **21.** 557 (1896); van't Hoff, *Vorlesungen*, i. p. 62, ff.). If the compound is practically undissociated in the liquid condition, its melting-point will be lowered by the addition of a component proportionally to the molecular weight of the compound; and a sharp point will be obtained. But if the compound dissociates to a noticeable extent, its dissociation will be diminished by addition of one of the components according to the law of mass-action (just as the electrolytic dissociation of water is diminished by hydrogen or hydroxyl ions). In consequence, the number of molecules is diminished and the freezing-point will not be lowered so much, and therefore the maximum will not be sharp. When dissociation is very great the curve will be so flattened as to form practically a continuous maximum. As long as dissociation remains within reasonable limits, and therefore the laws of dilute solution remain applicable, an exact theoretical discussion seems possible; in the case of very high or practically complete dissociation, we are compelled to use approximation formulæ. A quantitative investigation of this case, if necessary, by the use of the methods for determination of the molecular weight of liquids, appears advisable (Book II. Chap. III.). In the third book we have seen that the relative stability of chemical compounds may be judged from their proportions at equilibrium in a homogeneous system; similarly it is important to notice in this case that the character of the freezing-point curve in the neighbourhood of a maximum gives us a measure of the affinity of components to one another in a homogeneous liquid.

Systems of Three Components.—The investigation of such systems is, of course, much more complicated, since the variety of complete equilibria already reaches an extraordinarily high degree. As, so far as I can see, no new general theoretical considerations are involved, such systems will not be discussed here. Reference may be made to van't Hoff, *Vorlesungen*, i.; Roozeboom, *Heterogene Gleichgewichte vom Standpunkt der Phasenlehre*, Braunschweig, 1904; and further to the publications by Roozeboom, Schreinemakers and their pupils in the *Zeitschr. phys. Chemie*.

General Remarks on Complete Equilibria.—It has already been shown (p. 473) that the so-called complete equilibria possess by no means a special theoretical importance. We have then further seen in the third book that the treatment of *all* heterogeneous equilibria can be referred to chemical equilibria in homogeneous systems, and to the more physical equilibria of evaporation, solubility, and partition of a substance between two phases. From this point of view, which was developed by the author in the first edition of this book, and is at present practically universally adopted, heterogeneous equilibrium assumes quite an arbitrary nature—which perhaps has not been sufficiently emphasised up to now—for it is made up of various phenomena of quite different kinds happening simultaneously. The interest of scientific investigation, which must always, to be of use,—

as the brilliant development of physics has especially shown—be directed to the clear representation of the fundamental phenomena, can therefore only be directed to a deeper investigation of equilibria in homogeneous phases on the one hand, and of the laws of vapour tension, solubility, and partition of a substance between two phases on the other hand—in the last case especially also to the consideration of mixtures of any concentration (not only to dilute solutions, which form the simplest and therefore classical special case). The state of affairs may be shown by an example. The resistance of a spool of wire for alternating currents is of a fairly complicated character; it is made up of the ordinary "ohm" resistance, which can be calculated from the dimensions of the wire and conductivity of the material used, and further of the "impedance," which is a factor depending on the self-induction of the spool and the frequency of the alternating current; finally, rapidly alternating currents give rise to a special phenomenon—the lines of current on the surface of the wire are forced apart, and this tends to increase the resistance.

It is quite clear that in particular cases (e.g. for the needs of electrotechnics) the total resistance of a spool (measured by the potential at its ends for a given intensity of alternating current) is of the greatest importance; but measurements when all the different influences are at work, have no direct interest from the point of view of physics; the object of *scientific investigation* is rather to explain the *separate* phenomena as far as possible. In just the same way the investigation of heterogeneous equilibria may be of the greatest importance in special cases for preparative work, e.g. for the preparation of new compounds, and also for geological and similar questions; yet it is of no direct *theoretical* interest on account of its complicated nature. The objects of scientific investigation lie, in my opinion, in quite another direction, which is perfectly definite, as has been shown above.

It must particularly be noticed that the phase rule is nothing but a scheme into which heterogeneous equilibria fit, and with which, therefore, every investigator of this region must be familiar, just as the analytical chemist must never forget that the law of conservation of mass must remain valid during the carrying out of his operations. But when B. Roozeboom, very naturally overrating the rule that guided him in his fine experimental work, says that there is *no better* point of view in heterogeneous equilibrium [1] than Gibbs' phase rule, he makes a statement as misleading as if an analytical chemist said there was no better point of view for him than the law of conservation of mass. It must not be forgotten that as to the more frequent, and *by far the more important heterogeneous equilibria*, namely, the incomplete, the phase rule has nothing to say. But, apart from this, research must not be too limited in its object, and chemistry would almost be reduced to a triviality if we followed Roozeboom's suggestions. Molecular

---

[1] *Journ. phys. Chem.* **1.** 559 (1897).

theory, thermodynamics of incomplete equilibrium, and especially the law of mass action, are far more important guides, and of deeper meaning, than the scheme of the phase rule, useful and even indispensable as the latter is to chemical research.[1]

The Thermodynamics of Complete Equilibrium.—If we allow a complete equilibrium to pass beyond "the limiting curve" (p. 620), one phase will disappear and a new one will appear; both these phases are coexistent in the limiting curve itself.

If we denote by Q the quantity of heat *absorbed* in the transition, by V_0 the associated increase of volume of the system, and by A the maximal external work performed by the system as a result of the change, then the second law of thermodynamics gives the equation (p. 21),

$$Q = T \frac{dA}{dT}.$$

Both Q and A refer to a *definite* change of volume V_0 of the system, *e.g.* an increase of volume of 1 c.c. If we denote by p the pressure at that point of the limiting curve where the transition occurs, then it follows that

$$A = V_0 p, \quad \text{and} \quad dA = V_0 dp;$$

and we find that

$$Q = T \frac{dp}{dT} V_0 \quad \cdot \quad \cdot \quad \cdot \quad \cdot \quad (\text{I.})$$

This equation contains all that the second law can teach us about a chemical system in complete equilibrium. It is obvious that the thermodynamic formulæ derived for *evaporation* (p. 58), *sublimation* (p. 71), and *fusion* (p. 68), are special cases of equation (I.); because, as is shown on p. 473 and following, equilibrium between different states of aggregation must be included among the cases of complete equilibrium.

Now, as we have already become acquainted with important applications of equation (I.), and as its manipulation in more complicated cases offers no particular difficulties, we may refrain here from a description of any further special applications, and especially so as we shall still frequently make use of this very equation.

Equation (I.) gives simple results when it is applied to *the passage across the limiting curves in the immediate neighbourhood of their points of intersection, i.e. of the transition points.*

---

[1] Thus Van't Hoff remarked, "It is a pity that, valuable as the contents of the phase rule is, there has been a certain exaggeration of its scope" (*Ber. deutsch. chem. Ges.* **35.** 4252 (1892)). Unhappily, the over-estimation which Roozeboom has bestowed upon the phase rule has risen, especially in his monograph mentioned above, to an unjust criticism of those authors who think the continuous development of the phase rule quite unnecessary for their own work.

Let us imagine the system to be conducted around the transition point in a very small circle; then altogether n limiting curves will be crossed, and we shall obtain n equations of the form of (I.), viz.—

$$Q = T \frac{dp}{dT} V_0, \quad \text{or } TV_0 = \frac{dT}{dp} Q.$$

If we add these n equations, it follows that

$$\Sigma Q = \Sigma T \frac{dp}{dT} V_0, \quad \text{and } \Sigma TV_0 = \Sigma \frac{dT}{dp} Q ;$$

now ΣQ is the sum of the heat developed in circling around the transition point, and is accordingly zero, as in every reversible isothermal heat process (p. 19); ΣV_0 is also zero, because the system returns to its original volume; and of course ΣTV_0 is zero, because T changes only to an infinitesimal amount during the passage around the circle. And thus we find that

$$\Sigma \frac{dp}{dT} V_0 = \Sigma \frac{dT}{dp} Q = 0.$$

These are the conditions which arise when one phase is replaced by another, and which must exist between the values of the trigonometrical tangents of the angles at which the limiting curves cut in their common points of intersection; and between the latent heats on the one hand, and the changes of volume on the other.

Reference may be made to the investigations of Riecke [1] for a number of other general relations which are required by thermodynamics for the particular factors of the complete equilibrium.

Tammann (monograph quoted on p. 94) has discovered the following theorem on the position of curves which terminate in a triple point : " *The prolongation of each curve of equilibrium must lie between the other two curves.*" The proof of this theorem rests on the consideration that on a temperature entropy diagram a triangle corresponds to the triple point; a corresponding law necessarily holds for the perpendiculars to the three sides, and this leads to the above theorem on transference to the pressure-temperature diagram.

Condensed Systems.—The complex cases, which van't Hoff [2] calls " *condensed systems*," offer certain peculiarities which justify us in giving them a special description, although, like the cases already considered, they are subject to the general laws of complete chemical equilibria. *Such are the heterogeneous systems, all the reacting components of which are in the solid or liquid state, but not in the gaseous state.*

The simplest type of this sort of reactions is *the melting of a solid body*. The equilibrium with which we are here concerned, which consists in the coexistence of a solid body and its melted product, is "complete," because for any definite temperature there is only one pressure at which both phases of the system are stable beside each other. This pressure changes with the temperature in such a way that it can be calculated from Thomson's formula, when we know the

[1] *Zeitschr. phys. Chem.* **6.** 268, 411 (1890).   [2] *Études de dyn. chim.* p. 139.

change of volume on melting and the associated absorption of heat (p. 68). The temperature at which the two phases can coexist at atmospheric pressure is called the "melting-point" of the solid body.

In contrast to the reactions where a gaseous phase either appears or disappears, the change of volume occasioned by the change of phase in condensed systems is *relatively very small* ; and therefore, according to equation (I.) (p. 639), the influence of the pressure on the equilibrium temperature is only very slight. Thus while the boiling-point varies greatly with the external pressure, the melting-point changes to only a relatively small extent.

This alone must be recognised as the characteristic peculiarity of the reactions of "condensed systems," which places them in an obviously purely quantitative contrast to those reactions where substances volatilise.

Thus for most purposes it is immaterial whether we study the "condensed systems" at atmospheric pressure, or at some other pressure not very far removed from it; and it is still less important to take into account the slight variations of the atmospheric pressure.

That temperature at which all phases of a condensed system can exist beside each other is called the transition temperature. Below this the reaction will advance to a completion (*i.e.* until one phase at least is completely exhausted) *in one direction*, above it, in the *opposite* direction.

The "transition temperatures" of the systems described on pp. 622 and 627 can be found by searching out the temperature points corresponding to atmospheric pressure on the limiting curves which separate the region of liquid and solid phases. They nearly always lie in the immediate vicinity of the intersections of the limiting curves, *i.e.* near the true transition points. This will be more thoroughly explained later.

If we allow the transformation in a condensed system to complete itself in one sense at a temperature only a little below the transformation temperature, and then warm the system to a point a little above the transformation temperature, so that the reaction is reversed —then after cooling down to the original temperature the system is again in its original condition. The two opposite changes complete themselves spontaneously, and are therefore each able to perform a certain amount of external work, although this is usually very slight.

Hence, in this cyclic process, heat must have fallen from a higher to a lower temperature. That is, *the transformation below the temperature of transformation must occur with a development of heat ; and above this temperature with absorption of heat ; or the system which is stable at higher temperatures is formed from the system which is stable at lower temperatures with an absorption of heat.*

As is well known, it always takes an *elevation* of temperature to melt a solid substance ; this fact necessarily requires that to melt a substance heat must be introduced.

2 T

Allotropic Transformation.—An important example of a condensed system is found in the equilibrium between two modifications of the same substance.

The transformation of orthorhombic into monoclinic sulphur has been well studied. At atmospheric pressure these two phases are in equilibrium at $95 \cdot 6°$; if the pressure is kept constant, then above this temperature the orthorhombic sulphur goes over to the monoclinic variety, while, conversely, below this temperature, the monoclinic variety changes to the orthorhombic; in both cases the reaction occurs without change of composition of one of the phases, and therefore it occurs completely, as is the case in all such reactions.

The transformation temperature, which is completely analogous to the melting-point, varies with the external pressure; and it is directly obvious from the considerations of the preceding sections that the variation may be calculated from the same formula (Thomson's) which allows the calculation of the dependence of the melting-point upon the external pressure.

Thus if dT denotes the elevation of the transformation temperature caused by an increase of pressure dp, σ and τ the specific volumes of monoclinic and orthorhombic sulphur respectively at the transformation temperature T on the absolute scale, and r the amount of heat in g.-cal. absorbed when 1 g. of sulphur is transformed, then, according to p. 68, we have

$$r = 24 \cdot 19 . \frac{T (\sigma - \tau)}{1000} . \frac{dp}{dT},$$

and since, according to Tammann,[1]

$$T = 273 + 95 \cdot 4°, \quad \sigma - \tau = 0 \cdot 01395 \text{ ccm.}, \quad \frac{dp}{dT} = \frac{26 \cdot 5}{1 \cdot 0333} \text{ atm. per degree,}$$

therefore

$$r = 3 \cdot 19 \text{ cal.},$$

while Brönsted[2] found the value $r = 2 \cdot 40$ at $T = 273°$, and by using Regnault's values for the specific heats of the two modifications, extrapolated the value $r = 3 \cdot 05$ for the transition temperature.

Although, therefore, the influence of pressure on the temperature of transformation of allotropic modifications is very slight, yet it exists in every case, and may become very considerable when enormous pressures come into play.[3] This point is of great importance in mineralogy; under the enormous pressure of cooling rocks certain modifications may be formed, which have not yet been prepared in the laboratory, because it has not been possible to reproduce the conditions of their formation.

In general, the study of the equilibrium conditions between the

[1] *Schmelzen und Kristallisieren* (Leipzig, 1903), p. 274.
[2] *Zeitschr. phys. Chem.* **55**. 375 (1906).
[3] See especially the researches and calculations in Tammann's work quoted on p. 94.

allotropic forms of a substance is usually rendered impossible by reason of the slowness of the transformation. Thus we do not know for certain which of the modifications of carbon is the more stable, or where the temperature of transformation lies, etc. Moreover, the argument that graphite must be more stable than diamond at high temperatures, because, according to p. 598, it would be formed from diamond with absorption of heat, is not conclusive, for the heat of transformation changes with the temperature on account of the difference between the specific heats of the two modifications, and therefore the heat of transformation at the transition temperature (which is the only determining factor) may be even different in sign to that referred to ordinary temperatures.[1]

As to the velocity of the change there are the greatest differences. In some cases, *e.g.* tetrabrommethane, it is as rapid as the solidification of a liquid ; in others so slow that the two modifications can be kept for years without the transformation taking place. In these cases it is often quite impossible to tell which is the stable form, or where the transition temperature lies, *e.g.* between graphite and diamond, between quartz and tridymite. In fusion, equilibrium can only be overshot in one direction ; a liquid can be cooled far below the melting-point without solidifying, but a solid cannot be heated above the melting-point without fusion. On the other hand, a transition equilibrium can be overshot in both directions, so that a substance can often be heated well above its transition point without being turned into the stable form. The transition is usually hastened by contact with already transformed material, just as an undercooled liquid can be made to freeze by introducing a crystal of the solid. E. Cohen[2] has studied a good instance of this in tin. The white form in which tin is usually known is really only stable above 20°, but can be very much undercooled without conversion into the grey form. In very cold winters spontaneous conversion sometimes takes place, and the mass of tin falls into powder. If the white tin is "infected" with a trace of grey tin, the conversion into the grey form, "the tin disease," goes on at ordinary temperature.[3]

"**Liquid Crystals**."—The fact that certain crystals exist which are flexible and even plastic has been long known ; in recent times it has been brought into parallel with a very remarkable transition point.

For as Reinitzer (1888) first observed,[4] there are substances which are turbid when melted, and then · suddenly become clear at a sharply

---

[1] On the formation of diamond see the very interesting work of Moissan, *The Electric Furnace.*

[2] *Zeitschr. phys. Chem.* **30**. 601 (1899) ; **33**. 57 (1900) ; **35**. 588 (1900).

[3] For applications of Thermodynamics to Metallography see especially *Physikalische Chemie der Metalle*, by R. Schenk (Halle, 1909, published by Knapp).

[4] For details see the monograph by R. Schenk, *Kristallinische Flüssigkeiten*, Leipzig, 1905, bei Engelmann.

defined temperature above the melting-point. On cooling, the phenomena are reversed.

Soon afterwards Gattermann found that these same phenomena were exhibited by a class of chemically well-defined substances, namely, the different derivatives of p-azoxyphenol, and especially by p-azoxyanisol. This last substance melts at 116° to a turbid, bright yellow liquid, which suddenly becomes clear at 135·2°. Hence we have here a transition temperature corresponding to the melting-point, or the equilibrium between two modifications.

O. Lehmann, and later, R. Schenk and others, called the turbid melt "liquid crystals," or more properly, an aggregate of small, very soft crystalline individuals, because when it is placed between crossed Nicol prisms, the field of sight is strongly illuminated.

In the publications of these authors, no difference was made between the phenomenon under consideration and the probably entirely different phenomenon of plasticity of certain crystals, so that there exists at present an obvious confusion which it is decidedly necessary to remove.

The clearing up of the turbid melt doubtless reminds one at first of the critical solution temperature of two liquids which dissolve each other only partially. This idea was put forward and developed by G. Tammann,[1] but yet the questions on the nature of the two partially miscible liquids which must be assumed present in the melt of the single crystallised substance have not yet been answered, although the possibility of the formation of isomers in variable equilibrium with each other cannot be denied beforehand. Further, there is the difficulty that in none of the numerous investigated cases has it been found possible, as with ordinary emulsions, to make a real separation in layers by means of centrifugal stirring and similar methods. All other properties of the turbid liquid, especially the illumination between crossed Nicols, are apparently satisfactorily explained by Tammann's emulsion theory.

On the other hand, there are most decided objections to the view of Lehmann and Schenk. If the faculty of crystallisation is ascribed to the obviously perfectly mobile molecules of the milky fluid, then it is impossible to see why this power of orientation which the molecules possess should not be extended through the whole liquid, and so a clear crystal be formed. If, on the contrary, the milkiness is explained by assuming that crystal aggregates are formed, then these must behave like very large molecules, and, apart from the fact that this makes the mobility of the liquid inexplicable, Schenk himself found, by the method of Eötvös, the normal molecular weight [2] in the classical example of p-oxyanisol.

Moreover, the assumption that the milky fluid consists mainly of

[1] *Annalen der Physik*, **19.** 421 (1906).
[2] *Loc. cit.* p. 111.

molecules of the normal size, but contains also in equilibrium with these a number of highly polymerised, orientated molecules, which would behave therefore like small crystalline individuals, cannot be reconciled with the fact that the clearing up does not take place gradually, but at a temperature which can be sharply determined.

I have found the above considerations neither discussed, nor even put forward, by Lehmann or Schenk, and so it appears to me that their assumptions are in themselves contradictory and therefore cannot be accepted. But Tammann's theory, as shown above, is also without proper foundation.

It is highly probable that the discovery of the true nature of the remarkable transition from milky into clear fluid will lead to important new knowledge. For the closer investigation of the phenomena in question, important material has been put forward in recent times by Schenk from the point of view of physical, and Vorländer [1] from that of pure chemistry. An explanation can obviously only be looked for from a quantitative investigation ; the accumulation of purely qualitative microscopical observations, and the publication of number- less photographic views appear somewhat useless for an extension of our knowledge, in spite of the artistic nature of the pictures.

O. Lehmann (*Physik. Zeitschr.* **7**. 578, 1906) and later Vorländer (*l.c.*) have found substances which pass through two different turbid modifica- tions, and therefore possess two transition points, like that described above. Further, Vorländer made the interesting observation that the turbidity point sometimes lies in the supercooled region ; such substances melt clear, and become turbid when carefully cooled below their melting-points. Finally, Vorländer showed that the appearance of the turbidity point is connected with the existence of certain groups in the molecule, *i.e.* he was able to prove that the property of forming liquid crystals was constitutive (p. 345).

I have taken the above remarks unchanged from the last edition of this book, and it only remains necessary to emphasise again the fact that a satisfactory explanation of the observations mentioned has not yet been arrived at. In particular, it seems to me in no way proved that the new observations of Vorländer [2] on "transparent crystalline liquids" really concern the same range of phenomena ; thus, amongst other things, it is emphasised that the new doubly refractive liquids are very viscous. I found it impossible, however, to obtain a picture of Vorländer's new observations from his description ; the fact that this author thinks that no special hypothesis is necessary to account for the milkiness of the crystalline liquid shows how very hazy his ideas are about the whole phenomenon : " The chemist must often be in a position to notice how a liquid solidifies, and it is nothing out of the ordinary to him when a colourless clear liquid solidifies to a white opaque crystalline mass instead of to a clear crystal. A

[1] *Zeitschr. phys. Chem.* **57**. 357 (1906) ; cf. further *Kristallinisch-flüssige Substanzen*, by the same author. (Stuttgart, 1908, published by Enke.)
[2] *Ber. deutsch. chem. Ges.* **41**. 2033 (1908).

crystalline liquid behaves correspondingly." The author completely overlooks the fact that an opaque crystalline mass is due to flaws or enclosed mother-liquor, and that transparent crystals can always be obtained in these cases by careful working, while in the case of liquid crystals, the milkiness of the substance is inevitably associated with a certain range of temperature. Although I have further above expressly emphasised that "Tammann's theory is without proper foundation," Vorländer, somewhat prematurely, as will be admitted, states that Tammann and Nernst stand on the basis of the emulsion theory. On the contrary, I would repeat that we are still without a hypothesis which is in itself logical, and at the same time enlightening.

Yet it may be finally mentioned that the latest investigations of Boses (*Physik. Zeitschr.* **10.** 32, 1909) probably mark an advance. This author has shown that certain anomalies in the viscosity of the milky fluids vanish entirely, or at any rate, partially diminish, when care is taken to stir thoroughly. In agreement with this, he develops the idea that in the milky condition orientated swarms of molecules are formed under forces of cohesion. These cause the milkiness and anisotropy. At the clearing temperature the intensity of motion due to heat is just enough to destroy the orientating tendency of the anisotropic-fluid condition. I could at first see no decided difference between this and the above shortly mentioned assumption of the formation of highly polymerised orientated molecules, so, according to physico-chemical principles, the milkiness should disappear gradually and not suddenly. But Boses considers that under certain conditions the transition can take place very abruptly.

The Melting of Salts containing Water of Crystallisation.—

Among the other phenomena which belong here, and which are of a chemical nature, in contrast to those preceding, which are more of a physical nature, is the so-called melting of salts containing water of crystallisation. The fact that their fusion is usually accompanied by the separation of a salt containing less water of crystallisation, shows that here we are not dealing with a case of simple fusion, *i.e.* with the smooth change of a solid into a liquid.

Thus from the fusion of Glauber's salt, there results not only a liquid product (a saturated aqueous solution of Glauber's salt, $SO_4Na_2 . 10H_2O$), but also the solid anhydrous salt, SO_4Na_2.

Now it is at once evident that we are dealing here with a "complete equilibrium"; for in the liquefaction of Glauber's salt there are three phases present, namely, $SO_4Na_2 . 10H_2O$ (solid), SO_4Na_2 (solid), and $H_2O + xSO_4Na_2$ (saturated solution), and as we require at least two molecular species, H_2O and Na_2SO_4 to construct all three phases, therefore, according to the phase-rule, for a given pressure there can correspond one, and only one, temperature at which all three phases can coexist beside each other. Below this temperature the reaction,

$$SO_4Na_2 . 10H_2O \rightleftharpoons SO_4Na_2 + 10H_2O,$$

will advance to completion in the direction from right to left; above this temperature, from left to right.

The temperature $(33°)$, which corresponds to atmospheric pressure, is called the "transition temperature." On account of the very slight changes in volume associated with the reaction, this temperature varies to only an inconsiderable degree with the external pressure.

The Formation of Double Salts.—Now there have been found [1] a number of transition temperatures of condensed systems which consist of four phases, and therefore, according to the phase-rule, must be constructed of at least three molecular species.

A reaction of this kind is the formation of *double salts*, such as *blödite* (astrakanite, simonite), $(SO_4)_2Na_2Mg \cdot 4H_2O$, from the sulphates of sodium and magnesium. This reaction is given by the equation

$$SO_4Na_2 \cdot 10H_2O + SO_4Mg \cdot 7H_2O \rightleftarrows (SO_4)_2Na_2Mg \cdot 4H_2O + 13H_2O.$$

The four phases at equilibrium consist of the three solid salts and their saturated solution. The temperature of equilibrium is $21\cdot5°$; above this temperature only the phases occurring on the right side of the reaction equation are coexistent; below it only those on the left. This will appear from the following considerations.

If a mixture of finely pulverised blödite and water, in the proportions given above, is prepared below $21\cdot5°$, the mixture, which at first was a thin paste, hardens in a short interval to a completely dry and solid mixture of the first two sulphates. This does not happen above $21\cdot5°$.

Conversely, if a finely powdered mixture of the two sulphates of sodium and magnesium in molecular proportions is made, then above $21\cdot5°$ blödite is formed after some time, and the water which is set free partially dissolves it; but below $21\cdot5°$ the mixture of the finely powdered sulphates of sodium and magnesium remains unchanged.

This case is further complicated by the liquefaction of the Glauber's salt, which, as mentioned above, occurs at $33°$ in the absence of other salts; but here, as a result of the presence of magnesium sulphate in molecular proportions, the melting-point experiences a depression of $7°$, just as the melting-point of water is depressed by the presence of dissolved salts.

The conditions for the formation of *sodium-ammonium-racemate* are completely analogous. Above $27°$ the double salt can be obtained by rubbing together a dry mixture of dextro and laevo sodium-ammonium-tartrates; but below this temperature it cannot be formed.

At the transition temperature four phases, namely, the three solid salts and their saturated solution, are coexistent.

At every other temperature the reaction

$$2C_4O_6H_4NaNH_4 \cdot 4H_2O \rightleftarrows (C_4O_6H_4NaNH_4)_2 \cdot 2H_2O + 6H_2O$$

advances to completion either in one sense or the other. If therefore we wish to separate from an optically inactive mixture dextro and

---

[1] Van't Hoff and van Deventer, *Zeitschr. phys. Chem.* **1.** 170 (1887).

laevo modifications by the method described on p. 337, we must carry out the experiment on the right side of the transition temperature (in this case, *e.g.*, below it).

The formation of *calcium-copper-acetate* $(CaCu(Ac)_4 . 8H_2O)$ from the two salts $(Ca(Ac)_2 . H_2O$ and $Cu(Ac)_2 . H_2O)$, and the corresponding quantity of water $6H_2O$ is peculiar,[1] for it takes place easily at lower temperatures, but not above $76°$, and hence, above this temperature, the double salt is decomposed, which is just the opposite to the cases already described. Further, the decomposition of the double salt on raising the temperature is accompanied by a very considerable contraction and by a very apparent change in colour, the double salt being blue, the copper acetate green, and the calcium acetate colourless.

The formation of *cupric-potassium-chloride* $(CuCl_2KCl)$, and also that of *cupric-di-potassium-chloride* $(CuCl_22KCl . 2H_2O)$, has been thoroughly investigated by Meyerhoffer.[2] The transition temperatures of the two reactions

$$CuCl_2 . 2KCl . 2H_2O \rightleftarrows CuCl_2 . KCl + KCl + 2H_2O ;$$

$$CuCl_2 . 2KCl . 2H_2O + CuCl_2 . 2H_2O \rightleftarrows 2CuCl_2 . KCl + 4H_2O ;$$

are at $92°$ and $55°$ respectively; below these temperatures, only the systems on the left side are capable of existence; above them, only those on the right side. At the transition temperatures *four* different phases are coexistent, and for their construction we need in both cases *three* molecular species $(H_2O, KCl, and CuCl_2)$.

The systems standing on the left differ by the presence of a molecule of cupric chloride; the fact that this molecule occasions a depression of about $37°$ in the transformation of the cupric-potassium-chloride, reminds us again of the depression of the freezing-point of a solvent by the addition of a foreign substance.[3]

The Double Decomposition of Solid Salts.—Finally, some condensed systems are known where *five* phases are coexistent in the equilibrium, and hence where *four* molecular species are required to construct the phases. This is the case in the *double decomposition of solid salts*; as, *e.g.*, of magnesium sulphate and sodium chloride to form the double salt blödite (a sodium-magnesium-sulphate) and magnesium chloride. This occurs according to the equation

$$2NaCl + 2SO_4Mg . 7H_2O \rightleftarrows (SO_4)_2MgNa_2 . 4H_2O +$$
$$MgCl_2 . 6H_2O + 4H_2O.$$

The transition temperature is $31°$; if finely pulverised blödite is mixed below this temperature with magnesium chloride and water in the

---

[1] Reicher, *Zeitschr. phys. Chem.* **1.** 221 (1887).
[2] *Ibid.* **3.** 336 (1889), and **5.** 97 (1890).
[3] For further examples, see Van't Hoff, *Bildung und Spaltung von Doppelsalzen*, Leipzig, 1897.

above proportions, the thin paste at once solidifies to a completely dry solid mass, which consists of sodium chloride and magnesium sulphate; above 31° the mixture remains unchanged. Conversely, an equimolecular mixture of NaCl and $MgSO_4 . 7H_2O$ changes above, but not below, 31°, into blödite and $MgCl_2$, and the water which is eliminated partially dissolves the mass.

At the transition temperature there are five phases coexistent, namely, the four solid salts and their saturated solution.

The relations are precisely analogous in the reaction

$$SO_4Na_2 . 10H_2O + 2KCl \rightleftarrows SO_4K_2 + 2NaCl + 10H_2O,$$

the transition temperature of which [1] is 3·7°.

Vapour Pressure and Solubility at the Transition Temperature.

—In all the condensed systems mentioned above, the case has arisen where n molecular species reacted in n + 1 phases, and hence were in complete equilibrium.

But in every case we can imagine a *new phase* added to the system, namely, the gaseous phase; because we can think of the system under its own vapour pressure instead of atmospheric pressure. This change in pressure will cause a displacement of the transition temperature, but only a relatively small one, and rarely as much as a few tenths of a degree; for we have just recognised that the chief peculiarity of a condensed system is the small dependence of the transition temperature on the external pressure.

Under these conditions we have a system of n + 2 phases, for the construction of which we need only n molecular species. That point at which the n + 2 phases coexist is therefore a "transition point" in the sense defined on p. 618, and, moreover, it is an (n + 2)-fold point.

The space above the n-systems will be filled by the vapours emitted by each of the solid or liquid phases; and although the vapour pressure of any single one (as of the water-free salts, *e.g.*) may be extremely small, nevertheless it is not absolutely zero, but is a definite although perhaps minute fraction of the total vapour pressure.

Now under the conditions of temperature and pressure at the transition-point, the phases standing on the left-hand side of the reaction-equation exist side by side in stable equilibrium with those standing on the right-hand side; hence it necessarily follows that at the equilibrium temperature the vapours sent out by each group of phases *have the same composition and density*.

Therefore *the vapour-pressure curves* of two mutually convertible systems, *e.g.* of ice and water, rhombic and monoclinic sulphur, Glauber's salt and the saturated aqueous solution of Na_2SO_4, etc., must cut each other at the transition point, and also approximately at the

---

[1] Van't Hoff and Reicher, *Zeitschr. phys. Chem.* **3.** 482 (1889).

adjacent temperature of transformation—a conclusion which has been most thoroughly justified in all cases thus far investigated.

Now it is frequently possible to measure the vapour pressures of each system both above and below the transition temperature, where in the first case one system, in the second the other system, is in a *labile* condition. Then, obviously, the vapour pressure of the stable system will be the smaller, and that of the labile system the greater. Measurements have, in fact, shown that below the transformation temperature the stable system does show the smaller vapour pressure, but that above this point the same system, which has now become labile, has the greater vapour pressure.

An analogous conclusion is arrived at for the solubility of two groups of phases which are convertible into each other in the sense of the reaction equation concerned.

Thus if we treat the two systems with any (chemically indifferent) solvent at the temperature of transformation, the two solutions obtained must have the same composition and concentration; for if this were not the case and the two solutions were placed in communication with each other, then the equalisation of differences in composition would cause diffusion to take place, while at the points where the two groups of phases were in contact with their two (communicating) solutions, the concentration would be kept constant by continuous solution or crystallisation, and such a process would necessarily lead to the disappearance of one or several phases, which is impossible as they are actually in equilibrium.

This conclusion has been experimentally verified in a great number of cases by van't Hoff and his students.

Thus, *e.g.*, a saturated water solution of blödite at the transformation temperature, $21 \cdot 5°$, had the same concentration as a saturated solution of sodium and magnesium sulphates; under this temperature the mixture of the two sulphates, as the more stable system, had the lesser solubility, and the solution of blödite, as the labile system, the greater solubility.

Thus the solution of the less stable system has the character of a supersaturated solution, and, in fact, crystallisation follows on contact with the ingredients of the other systems.

Above the transition point the behaviours of the two systems are reversed, and at the transition point itself the solubility curves intersect.

The amorphous condensation products of a substance (p. 94) must, since they are in an unstable state, have a greater vapour pressure and solubility than the crystalline variety.

The Determination of the Temperature of Transformation.— In most cases it is easy to obtain an upper and a lower limit for the temperature of transformation by finding two temperatures, at one of which the reaction takes place in one way, and at the other in the opposite way. But it is only very rarely that an exact determination can be made in this way, because the reaction is frequently retarded.

The following methods, however, which were devised by van't Hoff, and remind us partly of the melting-point determinations (p. 329) are almost always applicable :—

1. The fact that the change of one group of condensed systems into the other is almost always associated with more or less large change in volume can be made use of in the following way. The ingredients of one group, intimately mixed, are placed in a dilatometer, which must be filled with an indifferent liquid, as oil. If the temperature of the water bath in which the bulb of the dilatometer is placed is then altered very gradually, the level of the oil in the projecting capillary tube changes steadily; but in the immediate neighbourhood of the transformation temperature a sudden displacement of the oil level takes place caused by the transformation, and very different to the otherwise steady change.

It is advisable, as a rule, in order to promote the occurrence of the reaction, and prevent the system persisting in the labile condition, to mix beforehand with the substances a little of the ultimate products of decomposition.

2. The fact that the change is almost always accompanied by either a development or an absorption of heat can be used to determine the transformation temperature in a way similar to that in which the development of heat in freezing allows an exact determination of the freezing-point. That system which is converted into the other with a development of heat is under-cooled ; then when the reaction occurs, the temperature rises to the transformation temperature, which may be read off from a thermometer dipping into the mixture.

3. The vapour pressure, or solubility curves of the two systems are determined, and then the respective points of intersection correspond to the temperature desired.

In order to measure the very slight differences of vapour pressures which are met with here, it is advantageous to use the differential tensimeter.[1]

Thus, in determining the temperature of transformation of the systems

$$SO_4Na_2 . 10H_2O \underset{\longleftarrow}{\overset{\longrightarrow}{}} SO_4Na_2 + 10H_2O,$$

the vapour tensions were found to be equal at $32\cdot5° - 32\cdot6°$; while the interpolation of Loewel's determination of the solubilities of the two solid salts, showed an identity of solubility at $32\cdot65°$.

---

[1] Bremer, *Zeitschr. phys. Chem.* **1.** 424 ; Frowein, *ibid.*, **1.** 10 (1887).

Temperature.	Solutions of	
	SO_4Na_2	$SO_4Na_2 . 10H_2O$
31·84°	40	50·37
32·78°	50·76	49·71

The two determinations of the temperature agree excell
also sufficiently well with the so-called melting-point, 33°,
directly determined.

The Thermodynamics of Incomplete Equilibrium.—Although the influence of temperature on *a complete equilibrium* is always such that, at constant pressure, the slightest change of temperature is sufficient to cause one of the phases to vanish completely, thus occasioning an entire rearrangement of the system, yet a similar change of the temperature has an entirely different effect in the case of an *incomplete equilibrium*. Here a slight change in the temperature never occasions more than a very slight change in the equilibrium ; because the relative proportions of the reacting ingredients are always so changed by a displacement of the equilibrium in one sense or the other, that the slight change in the reaction coefficient caused by a slight change in the temperature is exactly compensated.

The results of a variation in the external pressure, at constant temperature, are exactly similar ; in the first case [that of complete equilibrium], complete elimination of one of the phases takes place ; in the second case [that of incomplete equilibrium], there is only a very slight displacement of the equilibrium.

If we denote by

$$\frac{\partial p}{\partial T}\, dT,$$

the change in the pressure of a reaction mixture, caused by a rise of temperature dT at constant volume, and by

$$\frac{\partial Q}{\partial V}\, dV,$$

the heat absorption which takes place if we increase the volume of the reaction mixture by dV at constant temperature, then, according to p. 24, we have

$$\frac{\partial Q}{\partial V} = T\frac{\partial p}{\partial T} \qquad . \qquad . \qquad . \qquad . \qquad \text{(II.)}$$

The equation (I.) on p. 639 is a special case of (II.) and is obtained when Q and V are proportional to each other.

Equation (II.) is applicable both to *gaseous* systems and also to solutions, provided that in the former cases the equilibrium pressure p is measured by means of an ordinary manometer, and in the latter case by means of an osmotic apparatus. It is also applicable even when the gases or the dissolved substances react in a high state of concentration,[1] or when various solid substances take part in the equilibrium.

It is easy to see that when this formula is applied to the equilibrium between a solution and its vapour, we obtain Kirchhoff's equation, which we have already arrived at in a way (p. 113) identical in principle with the preceding.

But equation (II.) is too general to be really useful, and we must look for a more convenient form. This can be obtained if we again confine ourselves—as in the treatment of complete equilibrium in the preceding book—to the case when *the phases of systems of variable composition are either gases at not too high pressure, or else solutions at not too high concentration.*

The Reaction Isotherm, and the Reaction Isochore.

—It was van't Hoff who succeeded in reducing to a very simple form, the equations which are obtained by the application of the second law of thermodynamics to the special chemical processes described above.

Consider a chemical system consisting of one phase which has a variable composition (as a gas mixture or a dilute solution), and of any number of phases of constant composition, and suppose a reaction to take place according to the scheme :—

$$\nu_1 a_1 + \nu_2 a_2 + \ldots + n_1 A_1 + n_2 A_2 + \ldots \underset{\longleftarrow}{\overset{\longrightarrow}{}} \nu_1' a_1' + \nu_2' a_2' + \ldots$$
$$+ n_1' A_1' + n_2' A_2' + \ldots$$

where $\nu_1, \nu_2 \ldots \nu_1', \nu_2' \ldots$ denote the numbers of molecules of the reacting solid substances $a_1, a_2 \ldots a_1', a_2' \ldots$ respectively. Then application of the law of mass-action gives us the equation

$$K = \frac{c_1'^{n_1'} c_2'^{n_2'} \cdots}{c_1^{n_1} c_2^{n_2} \cdots} \qquad . \qquad . \qquad . \qquad \text{(III.)}$$

where $c_1, c_2, \ldots c_1', c_2' \ldots$ denote the concentrations of the molecular species, $A_1, A_2, \ldots A_1', A_2' \ldots$

The equilibrium coefficient K is constant at a given temperature ; i.e. it is independent of the relative proportions of the reacting substances : its change with the temperature is given by the following equation deduced by van't Hoff :

---

[1] Compare, *e.g.*, van Deventer and van der Stadt, *Zeitschr. phys. Chem.* **9.** 43 (1891).

$$\frac{d \ln K}{dT} = -\frac{U}{RT^2};$$

here, as always, ln denotes the natural logarithm, U the heat of reaction measured at the abs. temp. T, and R the gas constant.

This equation is of the highest importance and widest application, as will appear in the following sections; he who would penetrate deeper into the relations between heat and chemical energy, must be familiar with its meaning and manipulation.

While the equation of Guldberg and Waage,

$$K = \frac{c_1'^{n_1'} c_2'^{n_2'} \dots}{c_1^{n_1} c_2^{n_2} \dots},$$

enables us to calculate the influence of changes in concentration *at constant temperature*, the van't Hoff equation

$$\frac{d \ln K}{dT} = -\frac{U}{RT^2},$$

instructs us regarding the influence of temperature upon the equilibrium of a system *at constant volume*. Therefore I suggest that the former be called *the equation of the reaction isotherm*, and the latter *the equation of the reaction isochore*.

The latter is a differential equation; its integral is

$$\ln K = \frac{U}{RT} + B,$$

where B is an integration constant. ·

If the value of K is K_1 and K_2 at the temperatures T_1 and T_2 respectively, then we obtain

$$\ln K_1 = \frac{U}{RT_1} + B,$$

and

$$\ln K_2 = \frac{U}{RT_2} + B;$$

and by subtraction

$$\ln K_2 - \ln K_1 = \frac{U}{R}\left(\frac{1}{T_2} - \frac{1}{T_1}\right).$$

In this integration, it was assumed that U does not change with the temperature, which is, in fact, only approximately true. But, if the changes are but slight, and the temperatures T_1 and T_2 are not too far removed from each other, then the preceding equation will be strictly applicable, and will give a value of U corresponding to the temperature

$$\frac{T_1 + T_2}{2}.$$

The Derivation of the Reaction Isotherm.—The equation of the reaction isotherm, which must be considered the general expression of the law of chemical mass-action, can be made to appear correct, at least in all probability, by means of kinetic considerations, as we have already seen on p. 443. Moreover, as we have already thoroughly shown in the third book, a wide experience has shown us that the law of mass-action is well founded on experiment.

In spite of this, this chemical law is of such fundamental importance, that a closer investigation of the question from the point of view of thermodynamics will not be superfluous.

Following the example of van't Hoff we will consider the following process. Let a system be given which is either gaseous, or a dilute solution; and moreover, let it be in contact with various solid substances.

Now suppose equilibrium to be established by the reaction,

$$\nu_1 a_1 + \nu_2 a_2 + \ldots + n_1 A_1 + n_2 A_2 \ldots \underset{\longleftarrow}{\overset{\longrightarrow}{}} \nu_1' a_1' + \nu_2' a_2' + \ldots + n_1' A_1' + n_2' A_2' + \ldots$$

which takes place according to the scheme on p. 654, the concentration of the molecular species A being denoted by c (of course adding the corresponding indices). Also, let all the molecular species be in the free state, $a_1, a_2 \ldots a_1', a_2'$ being in the solid state, in which state they participate in the equilibrium, and $A_1, A_2 \ldots A_1', A_2'$ being present, either as gases if the phase of variable composition of the system considered is gaseous, or else dissolved in the respective solvent if the variable phase is a solution. These take part in the equilibrium according to their concentrations $C \ldots$ (again taking into account the proper indices).

We will suppose $\nu_1, \nu_2 \ldots$ and $n_1, n_2 \ldots$ molecules of the substances occurring on the left side of the equation, to be introduced into the mixture, and at the same time $\nu_1', \nu_2' \ldots$ and $n_1', n_2' \ldots$ molecules of the substances on the right side of the equation, to be removed from the reaction mixture.

We will also imagine the process so conducted that the reaction mixture preserves its composition unchanged, so that at every moment the quantity of A molecules introduced is equivalent to that of A' molecules taken out, and hence in the reaction mixture the change from left to right continually completes itself, without causing any perceptible alteration in the concentration ratios.

In this way it is clearly possible to conduct the reaction isothermally and reversibly; the only question is whether we can calculate the work so performed.

It will be simpler first to take a particular case, *e.g.* the formation of water vapour according to the equation

$$2H_2 + O_2 = 2H_2O.$$

Let c_1, c_2, c_1' be the concentrations of the reacting molecular species at equilibrium, and suppose the substances originally in the free state with concentrations C_1, C_2, C_1'.

We will first deal with the problem of calculating the work involved in transferring a mol of gas from a space where its concentration is C to one where it is c, and for simplicity we will assume that both spaces are so large that the addition or withdrawal of a mol makes no appreciable difference to the concentration. If the pressure and volume in the two spaces are PV and pv respectively, the mol must first be withdrawn from space I, by which the amount of work PV is gained, then expanded to volume v, yielding work $= RT \ln \dfrac{v}{V}$ (see p. 51) and finally introduced under the constant pressure p into space II, which requires work pv; hence the work gained is

$$PV + RT \ln \frac{v}{V} - pv$$

or since

$$PV = pv,$$

simply

$$RT \ln \frac{v}{V} = RT \ln \frac{C}{c},$$

since

$$V : v = c : C.$$

In conveying n mols the work is, of course,

$$nRT \ln \frac{C}{c}.$$

We can now calculate the maximum work done when hydrogen and oxygen of concentration C_1, C_2 are converted isothermally and reversibly into water vapour of concentration C_1'. If two mols of hydrogen are taken from a space of concentration C_1 into a space where the concentration is c_1, and there is equilibrium with the other molecular species, we gain work $2RT \ln \dfrac{C_1}{c_1}$; for a mol of oxygen $RT \ln \dfrac{C_2}{c_2}$; and to remove the water vapour formed requires the work $2RT \ln \dfrac{C_1'}{c_1'}$. Hence the work gained is

$$A = 2RT \ln \frac{C_1}{c_1} + RT \ln \frac{C_2}{c_2} - 2RT \ln \frac{C_1'}{c_1'},$$

or

$$A = RT \ln \frac{C_1^{2} C_2}{C_1'^{2}} + RT \ln \frac{c_1'^{2}}{c_1^{2} c_2}.$$

The maximal work must, however, be independent of the nature

2 U

of the reaction mixture, which only plays the part of an intermediary which suffers no appreciable change during the process. This is only possible if, at constant temperature, the expression $RT \ln \dfrac{c_1'^2}{c_1^2 c_2}$, and therefore $\dfrac{c_1'^2}{c_1^2 c_2}$ remains constant; *this is, however, nothing else than the law of mass-action.*

There is now no difficulty in dealing with the most general case. We have only to calculate, as in the special case above, the work done in introducing into the mixture the substances on the left of the equation, and removing those on the right, the process being, of course, isothermal and reversible.

The work done in introducing or removing the molecular species a and a' which are solid, is, of course, nothing; the work gained in introducing the molecules on the left-hand side of the equation is

$$n_1 \, RT \ln \frac{C_1}{c_1} + n_2 \, RT \ln \frac{C_2}{c_2} \dots$$

and the work done in taking out the equivalent molecules on the right-hand side of the equation

$$- \left(n_1' RT \ln \frac{C_1'}{c_1'} + n_2' RT \ln \frac{C_2'}{c_2'} \dots \right).$$

Hence altogether we find

$$A = RT \ln \frac{C_1^{n_1} C_2^{n_2} \dots}{C_1'^{n_1'} C_2'^{n_2'} \dots} + RT \ln \frac{c_1'^{n_1'} c_2'^{n_2'} \dots}{c_1^{n_1} c_2^{n_2} \dots}.$$

Since A cannot depend on the nature of the reaction mixture

$$K = \frac{c_1'^{n_1'} c_2'^{n_2'} \dots}{c_1^{n_1} c_2^{n_2} \dots}$$

is constant; *i.e. we have the law of mass-action in its most general form.*

If the concentrations $C_1, C_2, \dots C_1', C_2'$ are all unity we have simply

$$A = RT \ln K;$$

the maximal work of a chemical process can be therefore very simply derived from the constant K.

Assuming that the process described is realisable in all cases, then the proof given above is strictly valid, *i.e.* the law of chemical mass-action is a necessary conclusion from thermodynamics. We can hardly doubt the possibility of its realisation in those cases where there are several molecular species both on the left and on the right sides of the equation.

But when this is not the case, when for example we are given a case of dissociation to consider, the doubt arises that the respective molecular species cannot be removed from the reaction mixture in a pure state, but at once dissociate—that is, that if *e.g.* we wished to remove phosphorus pentachloride from a mixture of this with phosphorus trichloride and free chlorine, it would at once dissociate.

This doubt may· be removed by remembering that we only have to remove the molecular species in question quickly enough and bring it into such a state that dissociation cannot take place ; *e.g.* it may be brought to a state of strong condensation, or into a solvent which does not cause dissociation ; in this way the process described above can be modified in a way which is perfectly immaterial for the final result. If we assume the possibility of working *with sufficient rapidity*, then the process described is realisable *in all cases, and we find that the law of mass-action is a strict postulate of thermodynamics.*

Now, the maximal work A is not only independent of the relative concentrations, but is also independent of the whole nature of the reaction mixture, *e.g.* it is independent of the nature of the solvent in which the equilibrium of the reaction considered is established.

Hence it is easy to see that *if we know the equilibrium constant K for any particular phase, and if we also know the distribution coefficients of the reacting molecular species as compared with any other phase, then we are also able to state the condition of equilibrium in this phase.* This result has been already obtained in an entirely different way (p. 505).

If the *solvent* is one of the reacting molecular species, then it follows (p. 111) that for the transference of n molecules there is required the work

$$n \ln \frac{c}{c_0} RT,$$

where c and c_0 denote respectively the concentrations of the saturated vapour at the temperature in question, of the solution containing the reacting substances and of the pure solvent. Now, c_0 is constant at a given temperature ; whence it follows that the solvent has the active mass c ; *i.e. we may regard the active mass of a solvent as proportional to the concentration of the vapour emitted by it*, which proves the proposition given on p. 469. ´ This result could not be deduced from kinetic considerations, and was first discovered by me in this way. Thermodynamics in such cases can lead us further than kinetic considerations, and it should be emphasised that, *when we deal with concentrated reaction mixtures*, theoretical treatment is entirely dependent on thermodynamics. If we were in the possession of rules for the vapour pressure of mixtures of any degree of concentration, then we should be able to treat the reactions of such systems with the same completeness as in the case of the reactions of dilute solutions.

Finally, in order to consider briefly the case of *electrolytic dissociation* from the standpoint of thermodynamics, the application of the law of mass-action to electrolytes, which has been discussed in Chap. IV. of the preceding book, necessarily follows from the purely experimental result that for the compression of an electrolyte which is dissociated into n ions, n times as much work is required as in the case of the undissociated substance.

The Derivation of the Reaction Isochore.—*The equation of the reaction isochore* is at once given by the application of the fundamental equation (p. 23) :

$$A - U = T \frac{dA}{dT}$$

to the process considered on page 656. We found the maximal work A to be

$$A = RT \ln \frac{C_1^{n_1} C_2^{n_2} \cdots}{C_1'^{n_1'} C_2'^{n_2'} \cdots} + RT \ln K \; ;$$

$$\therefore \frac{dA}{dT} = R \ln \frac{C_1^{n_1} C_2^{n_2} \cdots}{C_1'^{n_1'} C_2'^{n_2'} \cdots} + R \ln K + RT \frac{d \ln K}{dT}.$$

The decrease in total energy U is, however, nothing else but the latent heat of the chemical process, *i.e.* the heat which is given out when the process takes place *without performance of external work*.

It follows on introducing the value of A and $\frac{dA}{dT}$
that

$$U = - RT^2 \frac{d \ln K}{dT}.$$

This is *the equation of the reaction isochore.*

Now it should be expressly emphasised, that, as also doubtless follows from the derivation of the equation of the reaction isochore, we are dealing *with the concentrations and not with the partial pressures* of the particular molecular species. It was immaterial in the application of the equation of the reaction isotherm whether we worked with one or with the other of these magnitudes ; but this is not the case with the reaction isochore, since if the temperature is changed at constant volume the concentration of a substance remains constant but not its pressure.

In what follows we shall make several applications of the integrated form of the preceding equation, obtained on p. 655 :

$$\ln K_2 - \ln K_1 = \frac{U}{R}\left(\frac{1}{T_2} - \frac{1}{T_1}\right).$$

If we express as usual the heat of reaction U, in calories, then R amounts to 1·985 (p. 48). If we work with *ordinary logarithms* instead of natural, then we get finally

$$U = - \frac{4·571(\log K_2 - \log K_1)T_1 T_2}{T_2 - T_1} \text{ cal.}$$

Vaporisation.—We have found for the equilibrium between a simple liquid and its saturated vapour, the relation

$$K = c = \frac{p}{RT} \; ;$$

i.e. for every temperature there corresponds a definite concentration of the saturated vapour. Now if we denote, by p_1 and p_2 respectively, the values of the vapour pressure corresponding to the temperatures T_1 and T_2 (which are only slightly different from each other), then we obtain from the preceding equations

$$\ln \frac{p_2}{T_2} - \ln \frac{p_1}{T_1} = -\frac{U}{R}\left(\frac{1}{T_1} - \frac{1}{T_2}\right).$$

From the figures which Regnault obtained for water, viz.

$$T_1 = 273°, \qquad\qquad p_1 = 4\cdot54 \text{ mm.,}$$
$$T_2 = 273° + 11\cdot54°, \qquad p_2 = 10\cdot02 \text{ mm.,}$$

it follows that $U = -10,030$. Now the molecular heat of evaporation λ, at $5\cdot77°$, was found to be $10,854$; and if we subtract from this latter value the external work, $2T = 558$, then it follows that

$$U = -10,296,$$

a value which is in satisfactory agreement with the preceding. Later measurements by Henning [1] give for U the value

$$U = -10,663 + 558 = -10,105,$$

which agrees still better with the calculated value.

We have previously (p. 59) found that

$$\lambda = RT^2 \frac{d \ln p}{dT}.$$

Now if we compare this equation with that obtained by the application of the reaction isochore, viz.

$$-U = RT^2 \frac{d \ln \frac{p}{T}}{dT},$$

we obtain, in agreement with what precedes, the equation

$$\lambda + U = RT^2 \frac{d \ln T}{dT} = RT.$$

The Dissociation of Solid Substances.—The *heat of sublimation of a solid substance* can be calculated from its vapour pressure at two different temperatures, in exactly the same way that the heat of vaporisation is calculated for a liquid. Therefore here we will consider only the case where *the sublimation is attended with dissociation.*

Let us suppose that the solid substance is broken up into n_1 mols of the substance A_1, and n_2 mols of the substance A_2, and that the partial pressures of the particular molecular species amount respectively to p_1, p_2, etc. Then, according to p. 482 :

[1] *Ann. d. Physik* [4], **21**. 849 (1906).

$$K = c_1{}^{n_1} c_2{}^{n_2} \ldots = \frac{p_1{}^{n_1} p_2{}^{n_2} \ldots}{T^{n_1 + n_2 + \ldots}}.$$

If the decomposition products in the vapour space in contact with the solid bodies are present in the same proportion in which they are produced by the reaction, then we have

$$p_1 = P \frac{n_1}{n_1 + n_2 + \ldots}, \qquad p_2 = P \frac{n_2}{n_1 + n_2 + \ldots},$$

where P denotes the total pressure (dissociation pressure) of the gases. If this amounts to P_1 and P_2 for the two temperatures T_1 and T_2 respectively, then it follows that

$$\ln K_1 - \ln K_2 = (n_1 + n_2 + \ldots)\left(\ln \frac{P_2}{T_2} - \ln \frac{P_1}{T_1} \right) = \frac{U}{R}\left(\frac{1}{T_1} - \frac{1}{T_2} \right).$$

In the *dissociation of ammonium hydrosulphide*,

$$NH_5S = NH_3 + H_2S \, ;$$

$n_1 = 1$ and $n_2 = 1$. Hence

$$\ln \frac{P_1}{T_1} - \ln \frac{P_2}{T_2} = \frac{U}{2R}\left(\frac{1}{T_1} - \frac{1}{T_2} \right).$$

And from the figures

$$T_1 = 273 + 9 \cdot 5°, \quad P_1 = 175 \text{ mm.,}$$
$$T_2 = 273 + 25 \cdot 1°, \quad P_2 = 501 \text{ mm.,}$$

it follows that $U = -21,410$ g.-cal.

Now the thermo-chemical measurements give 22,800 as the molecular heat of sublimation of NH_4SH; and if we subtract from this value the amount of the external work, *i.e.*

$$4T = 1160,$$

we obtain as the value of U observed, $= -21,640$ g.-cal.[1]

It is of some historical interest to point out that, by a calculation which is completely analogous to the preceding, Horstmann[2] in 1869 ascertained theoretically the heat of sublimation of *ammonium chloride*, and thus for the first time applied the second law of the mechanical theory of heat to chemical processes ; the great fruitfulness of the law, when applied in this direction, has been clearly brought out by the investigations of Horstmann and his successors.

Of course a similar calculation can be made for the *dissociation of compounds containing water-of-crystallisation* ; and thus the combining heat of water-of-crystallisation can be theoretically calculated from the change of the dissociation pressure with the temperature. Horstmann called attention to this, and later on Frowein[3] investigated it thoroughly.

[1] Van't Hoff, *Études*, p. 139.
[2] *Ber.* **2**. 137 (1869); more thoroughly **14**. 1242 (1881).
[3] *Zeits. phys. Chem.* **1**. 5 (1887).

Moreover, *the curve of the dissociation pressure of calcium carbonate*[1] has made possible the calculation of the heat of formation of this substance from CO_2 and CaO.

The Dissolving of Solid Substances.—The analogy between the processes of dissolving in any solvent, and of evaporation, is also shown by the fact that the same formula which allows us to find the heat of vaporisation from the change of the density of the ·saturated vapour with the temperature, allows the calculation of *the heat of solution from the change of solubility with the temperature.* Thus, since every substance has a definite solubility in a definite solvent at a definite temperature, we have simply

$$K = c \; ;$$

here c denotes the concentration of the saturated solution at the temperature T.   Let us suppose that c has the respective values c_1 and c_2, at the temperatures T_1 and T_2 ; then for the heat U absorbed during solution, *i.e.* the negative value of the heat of solution (p. 602) of 1 mol of the dissolved substance, we obtain

$$. \quad \ln c_1 - \ln c_2 = \frac{U}{R}\left(\frac{1}{T_1} - \frac{1}{T_2}\right).$$

From the solubility of succinic acid in water

$$c_1 = 2 \cdot 88, \quad T_1 = 273°,$$

$$c_2 = 4 \cdot 22, \quad T_2 = 273° + 8 \cdot 5°,$$

van't Hoff[2] calculated the value of U to be $- 6900$, while direct measurement by Berthelot gave $- 6700$.

The values of the solubility denote the weight per cent.   By the term mol is meant of course that quantity of the dissolved substance which exerts, at the same volume and temperature, the same [osmotic] pressure as 1 mol of an ideal gas, and therefore the applicability of the preceding formula involves a knowledge of the molecular condition in the solvent used.   In the special case just considered, succinic acid is dissociated electrolytically to only a slight extent, and therefore has the normal molecular weight.

Conversely, from the comparison of the observed heat of solution with that calculated, it is, of course, possible to draw an inference as to the size of the molecule in the respective solvent.

The correction for the external work performed, which was of importance in the case of the heat λ of vaporisation (see above), can be neglected in the case of the heat of solution, because no perceptible external work is associated with the solution of a solid substance.   (See also p. 141, where Q denotes the heat of solution under the osmotic

---

[1] Le Chatelier, *l.c.* 98.   [2] *Lois de l'équilibre*, etc., p. 37 (1885).

pressure of the saturated solution, and differs from U by the amount of the external work, viz. 2T.)

The Dissociation of Solid Substances on Solution.—This case is, of course, treated in a way exactly similar to that for the dissociation of solid substances on vaporisation (p. 661).

As an example we will consider the solution of silver chloride ; thus,

$$AgCl = \overset{+}{Ag} + \overset{-}{Cl}.$$

If the solubility of this substance at T_1 and T_2 is c_1 and c_2 respectively, then it follows that

$$\ln c_1 - \ln c_2 = \frac{U}{2R}\left(\frac{1}{T_1} - \frac{1}{T_2}\right).$$

F. Kohlrausch and F. Rose [1] have measured the conductivity of saturated silver chloride solutions at a number of different temperatures, and give for the solubility c_t at $t°$ the formula

$$c_t = c_{18}[1 + 0·049(t - 18) + 0·00089(t - 18)^2]$$

which agrees well with their observations above 18°.

It is more convenient here to apply the unintegrated equation

$$U = -2RT^2\frac{d\ln c}{dT},$$

from which we get

$$\frac{d\ln c}{dT} = \frac{0·049 + 2 \cdot 0·00089(t - 18)}{1 + 0·049(t - 18) + 0·00089(t - 18)^2}.$$

From this may be calculated that at 22° U = − 16,000, whilst on p. 612 we found − 15,800. The agreement is remarkable,—c_{18} is $1·05 \times 10^{-5}$ g. equiv. per litre.

The Solution of Gases.—For gases we have

$$K = \frac{c'}{c},$$

where c denotes the concentration in the gaseous state, and c′ that in solution (Law of Henry). Let us denote the Bunsen coefficient by a ; then, according to p. 490,

$$K = a\frac{T}{273} ;$$

and therefore

$$U = RT^2\frac{d\ln K}{dT} = \frac{RT^2}{a} \cdot \frac{da}{dT} + RT.$$

---

[1] *Wied. Ann.* **50.** 136 (1893) ; see also F. Kohlrausch, *Zeits. phys. Chem.* **44.** 197 (1903).

The heat of solution Q amounts to

$$Q = RT - U ;$$

and therefore, according to Kirchhoff (1858),

$$Q = -\frac{RT^2}{a} \cdot \frac{da}{dT}.$$

Thus Naccari and Pagliani [1] found for carbonic acid, that

$$a = 1\cdot5062 - 0\cdot03651\, t + 0\cdot000292\, t^2 ;$$

from which, for $t = 20$ (*i.e.* $T = 273° + 20°$), Q is calculated to be 4820; while Thomsen by a direct measurement found 5880. It is probable that the measurements of the absorption coefficients are not accurate enough for this calculation; thus, for instance, the older measurements of Bunsen are entirely unsuited for this purpose.

The Dissociation of Gaseous Substances.—If a molecular species A, whether it exists as a gas or in dilute solutions, decomposes according to the general equation of dissociation,

$$A = n_1 A_1 + n_2 A_2 + \ldots ;$$

then at equilibrium we have

$$Kc = c_1^{n_1} c_2^{n_2} \ldots ;$$

where $c, c_1, c_2 \ldots$ are respectively the concentrations of $A, A_1, A_2 \ldots$

If the dissociation products are present in equivalent proportions, and if x denotes the dissociation coefficient, then, if 1 mol occupies the volume v, we have

$$c = \frac{1 - x}{v}, \quad c_1 = \frac{n_1 x}{v}, \quad c_2 = \frac{n_2 x}{v}, \ldots$$

and therefore

$$K = \frac{n_1^{n_1} n_2^{n_2} \ldots x^{n_1 + n_2 + \cdots}}{(1 - x) v^{n_1 + n_2 + \cdots - 1}}.$$

Let us suppose that the mol considered occupies the volumes v_1 and v_2 at the temperatures T_1 and T_2, and that it is dissociated to the fractional extent of x_1 and x_2 respectively. Then the equation of the reaction isochore gives, for the calculation of the heat of dissociation, the relation

$$\ln \frac{x_2^{n_1 + n_2 + \cdots}}{(1 - x_2) v_2^{n_1 + n_2 + \cdots - 1}} - \ln \frac{x_1^{n_1 + n_2 + \cdots}}{(1 - x_1) v_1^{n_1 + n_2 + \cdots - 1}} = -\frac{U}{R}\left(\frac{1}{T_1} - \frac{1}{T_2}\right).$$

Let us apply this equation to the dissociation of nitrogen dioxide,

$$N_2O_4 = 2NO_2 ;$$

[1] *N. Cim.* [3], **7**. 71 (1880).

then
$$n_1 = 2, \quad n_2 \ldots = 0,$$
and we obtain
$$\ln \frac{x_2^2}{(1 - x_2)v_2} - \ln \frac{x_1^2}{(1 - x_1)v_1} = -\frac{U}{R}\left(\frac{1}{T_1} - \frac{1}{T_2}\right).$$

Let the vapour density, at the temperatures T_1 and T_2, and at atmospheric pressure, be Δ_1 and Δ_2 respectively; then, according to p. 349, we shall have
$$x_1 = \frac{3 \cdot 179 - \Delta_1}{\Delta_1}, \quad \text{and} \quad x_2 = \frac{3 \cdot 179 - \Delta_2}{x_2};$$
where $3 \cdot 179$ is the vapour density without dissociation, as calculated from its molecular weight, $N_2O_4 = 92$.

Now the volumes occupied by 1 mol of N_2O_4, in the two cases, are respectively
$$v_1 = 0 \cdot 0821 T_1 \frac{3 \cdot 179}{\Delta_1}, \quad \text{and} \quad v_2 = 0 \cdot 0821 T_2 \frac{3 \cdot 179}{\Delta_2};$$
because the mol of an ideal gas at T, and at atmospheric pressure, occupies the volume, $0 \cdot 0821 T$ litre, and the volume of 1 mol of N_2O_4, as a result of the partial decomposition, is increased in the ratio $\dfrac{3 \cdot 179}{\Delta}$. Observing, moreover, that
$$1 + x = \frac{3 \cdot 179}{\Delta},$$
we finally obtain
$$\ln \frac{x_2^2}{T_2(1 - x_2^2)} - \ln \frac{x_1^2}{T_1(1 - x_1^2)} = -\frac{U}{R}\left(\frac{1}{T_1} - \frac{1}{T_2}\right).$$
From the values
$$T_1 = 273 + 26 \cdot 7^\circ, \ \Delta_1 = 2 \cdot 65, \ x_1 = 0 \cdot 1996,$$
$$T_2 = 273 + 111 \cdot 3^\circ, \ \Delta_2 = 1 \cdot 65, \ x_2 = 0 \cdot 9267,$$
it follows that
$$U = -12,900.$$

The dissociation of 96 g. of N_2O_4 then requires the very considerable quantity of heat of 12,900 g.-cal., provided that it occurs without the performance of external work; as, *e.g.*, by connecting a vessel filled with nitrogen dioxide with another which is exhausted; during the equalisation of the pressure, the volume of the enclosed gas is increased, and therefore a certain fraction of it, which can be calculated from the equation of the isotherm of dissociation, is dissociated into the single molecules.

Such an experiment, which would lead to a direct determination of U, has not yet been carried out; but by means of the measurements by Berthelot and Ogier (p. 350) of the mean specific heat of nitrogen dioxide between 27° and 150° under atmospheric pressure, van't Hoff[1] calculated the heat of dissociation by subtracting from the quantity of heat required for this rise of temperature, the energy required for the simple warming of the gas, and also the energy consumed in the performance of the external work, thus obtaining the energy used up in the dissociation.   It coincides well with the calculated value [2]

$$U = -12,500.$$

Swart[3] has recently shown that all the vapour-density determinations of nitrogen dioxide are in harmony with the preceding formula, and that, moreover, the variation of the specific heat of this gas, as observed by Berthelot and Ogier, can be calculated in a completely theoretical way.

Now if we substitute in the integrated equation of the reaction isochore (cf. also p. 453)

$$K = \frac{4x^2}{(1-x)v} = \frac{4x^2P}{(1-x^2)RT}$$

(where P = the total pressure of the gas), we obtain

$$\ln \frac{(1-x^2)T}{x^2P} = -\frac{U}{RT} + a \text{ const } ;$$

or after introducing the theoretical vapour density δ, and that observed Δ, we obtain

$$\ln \frac{(2\Delta - \delta)}{(\delta - \Delta)^2} \frac{T}{P} = -\frac{U}{RT} + a \text{ const.}$$

This is a general equation of condition for gases existing in the state of binary dissociation.

In order to determine U and the integration constant, measurements of the vapour density at two different temperatures must be made ; and then by means of the two preceding formulæ we can calculate the degree of dissociation, and also the vapour density, for any conditions of temperature and pressure (U being assumed independent of T).

It should be observed, in making calculations of this kind, that the constants in the two equations have different values, as is apparent from the derivation.   The first form is more convenient to work with, especially when a table is calculated for $\ln \frac{1-x^2}{x^2}$ in every case.

It was shown by Gibbs[4] (1879) that all the observations on the vapour densities of formic acid, acetic acid, and phosphorus pentachloride, can be satisfactorily represented by means of the preceding equations.

[1] *Études*, p. 133.   [2] See also Boltzmann, *Wied. Ann.* **22.** 68 (1884).
[3] *Zeits. phys. Chem.* **7.** 120 (1891).   See also Schreber, *ibid.* **24.** 651 (1897).
[4] *Sill. Journ.* **18.** 277 (1879) ; see also p. 493.

The Dissociation of Dissolved Substances.—The formulæ developed in the preceding section can be applied to this case without alteration; v_1 and v_2 denote respectively the volumes at T_1 and T_2 of solutions containing 1 g.-mol, and x_1 and x_2 the respective degrees of dissociation under these conditions. For the special case of a binary electrolyte, we have

$$\ln \frac{K_2}{K_1} = \ln \frac{x_2^2(1-x_1)\,v_1}{x_1^2(1-x_2)\,v_2} = -\frac{U}{R}\left(\frac{1}{T_1}-\frac{1}{T_2}\right);$$

on account of the very slight expansion of water solutions from heat one may, without hesitation, make $v_1 = v_2$, if the same solution is investigated at two temperatures.

We have only a few data at hand for the calculation of the *heat of ordinary dissociation in solution.*[1] As, however, the measurement of electrical conductivity leads to an exact determination of the degree of electrolytic dissociation, data for the calculation of the heat of dissociation can be obtained by the very simple and exact *measurement of the temperature coefficients of the conductivity.*

In this way Arrhenius[2] ascertained the heats of dissociation for

Electrolyte.	U
Acetic acid	− 28
Propionic acid	183
Butyric acid	427
Phosphoric acid	2103
Hydrofluoric acid	3200

the electrolytes given in the preceding table : the figures refer to a temp. of $21\cdot5°$.

At higher temperatures U increases, *i.e.* the specific heat of the electrically neutral molecules is greater than that of the free ions ; the heat of dissociation of acetic acid at higher temperatures is positive.

In this way, therefore, it is also found that *the dissociation of a substance into its ions is usually attended with a development of heat.*

The value for hydrofluoric acid agrees well with the value 2570, found on p. 611, especially when we consider that the latter value could only be roughly estimated.

A stricter calculation shows that the coincidence between the heats of dissociation calculated from the conductivities, with the thermochemical measurements of Thomsen, is excellent ; this is shown by the following results, which are calculated according to the more

[1] From the results of experiments on the partition of benzoic acid between two solvents, Hendrixson (p. 496) calculates the heat of dissociation of this substance in benzene to be 8710 cal.—a relatively high value.
[2] *Zeits. phys. Chem.* **4.** 96 (1889), **9.** 339 (1892) ; see also Petersen, *ibid.* **11.** 174 (1893).

exact formula of Arrhenius (p. 612) ; here x, the dissociation heat of water, is put at 13,210, and the values of W, W_1, and W_2 are ascertained from the conductivities.

Acid.	Obs.	Calc.
HCl	13,700	13,740
HBr	13,760	13,750
HNO_3	13,810	13,680
C_2H_5COOH	13,400	13,450
HF	16,120	16,270

The figures refer to the heat developed on neutralising the acid with sodium hydroxide, the concentration of acid and base being $\dfrac{1}{3 \cdot 6}$ normal.

Attention should be especially directed to the fact that *the value of the heat of neutralisation does not stand in any direct relation to the strength of the acid.* Thus propionic and hydrofluoric acid are both weak acids; yet the neutralisation heat of the former is smaller than, and that of the latter is greater than, the heat of neutralisation of either of the three strong acids, HCl, HBr, or HNO_3. This shows, therefore, that we cannot detect any simple relation between the heat of dissociation of acids and their strength. Hence we cannot measure the affinity between an acid and a base by the quantity of heat developed when they neutralise each other, as has been so often wrongly proposed.

If an electrolyte develops heat on ionisation, then its dissociation must diminish with rising temperature. If a solution of such an electrolyte is warmed, the number of conducting molecules is diminished, which tends to make its *conductivity decrease.* But, on the other hand, the conductivity increases considerably on account of the diminished ion friction, and as the latter influence preponderates, an increase of the conductivity of aqueous solutions with rising temperature is almost always observed.

It was Arrhenius who, guided by these considerations, first discovered those electrolytes, where, conversely, the restraining influence of the diminishing ionisation preponderates. Thus phosphoric and hypophosphorous acid, at the respective temperatures of $54°$ and $75°$, show *maxima of conductivity,* and above these respective temperatures have negative temperature coefficients. No one before this had suspected the existence of such electrolytes.

Electrolytic Dissociation of the Solvent.—We found on p. 518, for the dissociation of water,

$$K = c_0{}^2 ;$$

whence the heat of dissociation is

$$U = - RT^2 \frac{2}{c_0} \frac{dc_0}{dT}.$$

In this equation U is known (p. 610), so that the temperature coefficient of the dissociation can be calculated. Since the temperature coefficient of the ionic friction is also known, that of the conductivity may be arrived at theoretically, and Kohlrausch and Heydweiller[1] calculated it as $5\cdot81\%$ at $18°$; this is unusually large, because in this case increase in ionic mobility is associated with a rapid rise of dissociation with temperature. These observers found that with increased purity the temperature coefficient increased from $2\cdot4\%$, as shown by ordinarily "pure water," to a maximum of $5\cdot32\%$. The theoretical temperature coefficient is thus nearly, but not quite reached, so that the most completely purified water is probably not quite pure. The authors mentioned estimated the remaining trace of impurity from the difference between the observed and theoretical temperature coefficient, and in this way obtained a fairly accurate value for the dissociation of water. They found at

$$t = \quad 0° \quad 10° \quad 18° \quad 34° \quad 50°,$$
$$c_0 = 0\cdot35 \quad 0\cdot56 \quad 0\cdot80 \quad 1\cdot47 \quad 2\cdot48;$$

where c_0 is the amount in mols dissociated in 10,000,000 litres.

Production of Endothermic Compounds at High Temperatures.—The equation of the reaction isochore teaches us that the dissociation of a compound increases with rising temperature when it takes place with absorption of heat, or, which is the same thing, when the compound is *exothermic, i.e.* is formed from its components with formation of heat. Conversely, an *endothermic* compound becomes more stable as the temperature rises, and when, like hydrogen peroxide, the substance in question is practically completely dissociated into its components (water and oxygen) at ordinary temperatures, it becomes the more stable the higher the temperature (provided, of course, that the heat of reaction does not change its sign at high temperatures). This explains why noticeable quantities of hydrogen peroxide are present in the oxyhydrogen flame, as M. Traube (1885) showed; it also explains the formation of nitric oxide in air heated to a high temperature, and of ozone in strongly heated oxygen, etc.

The equation of the reaction isochore may be applied in the most complete manner to the case of nitric oxide;[2] the following table gives the percentage (by volume) x of nitric oxide formed in air at the corresponding absolute temperatures. The values given in the

[1] *Wied. Ann.* **53.** 209 (1894).

[2] Nernst, *Zeitschr. anorg. Chem.* **49.** 213 (1906).

third column are calculated thermodynamically from the assumption that the reaction

$$N_2 + O_2 = 2NO$$

takes place with the (constant) absorption of heat of 43,200 cal.

T.	x (obs.).	x (calc.).
1811	0·37	0·35
1877	0·42	0·43
2023	Between 0·52 and 0·80	0·64
2033	0·64	0·67
2195	0·97	0·98
2580	2·05	2·02
2675	2·23	2·35

Cases like these are examples of the phenomenon of *apparent* stability at low temperatures, because the substance in question only decomposes very slowly.   Thus nitric oxide can be kept for any length of time at room temperature, although at equilibrium it would be practically completely decomposed.   At very high temperatures, on the other hand, where equilibrium is attained very rapidly, we enter on a range of true stability.

General Integration of the Reaction Isochore.—Experience shows that specific heats only alter very slowly with the temperature, so that we can express them accurately by a formula such as

$$c = c_0 + aT + bT^2 + \dots$$

c_0 is therefore the specific heat at very low temperatures.   Now as (p. 599) the alteration of the heat of reaction with the temperature is determined by the specific heats of the substances taking part in the reaction, we can also assume

$$U = U_0 + \alpha T + \beta T^2 + \gamma T^3 + \dots$$

where U_0 is the heat of reaction near absolute zero.   By substituting in the equation of the reaction isochore $U = - RT^2 \dfrac{d \ln K}{dT}$ and integrating, we find

$$\ln K = \frac{U_0}{RT} - \frac{\alpha}{R} \ln T - \frac{\beta}{R} T - \frac{\gamma}{2R} T^2 - \dots + I$$

where I is the integration constant.

The right-hand side of this equation contains—beside the integration constant—only purely thermal magnitudes (heat of reaction, specific heats and their temperature coefficients).

We shall make frequent application of the above equation further on ; it may be pointed out here that Gibbs, Le Chatelier, and in more recent times, especially Haber in his excellent work *Thermodynamik technischer Gasreaktionen* (München, 1905), have made frequent use of the general form of the integrated equation of the reaction isochore.

The Law of the Mutuality (*Vertretbarkeit*) **of Phases.**—*If two phases, respecting a certain definite reaction, at a certain temperature, are in equilibrium with a third phase, then at the same temperature and respecting the same reaction, they are in equilibrium with each other.*

This law, which explains itself, is an immediate conclusion from the considerations advanced on p. 618. It also follows necessarily from the law (p. 16) that it is not possible to construct an apparatus which can yield continuous external work when kept at a constant temperature.

For if two phases, A and B, were in equilibrium with a third, C, but not with each other, then in a combination arranged as follows,

$$C$$
$$A \quad B,$$

there would occur at first a displacement between A and B, which would disturb the equilibrium with C. Hence at constant temperature the respective reactions between A and B, B and C, and C and A, would take place continuously, without ever establishing an equilibrium.

We have already made repeated applications of this law (pp. 132, 137, 495) which clearly illustrate its fruitfulness.

If we consider, *e.g.*, a reaction such as the removal of water from different phases, then the preceding law teaches that two liquid or solid phases which are in equilibrium with water-vapour of the same pressure, must also be in equilibrium with each other.

If we treat a liquid with a solid salt, then the latter will absorb more water the smaller the dissociation pressure of its water-of-crystallisation (p. 478). This observation gives us the theory of the method of drying.

If we have once investigated the equilibrium between water vapour and ether containing water, then conversely the determination of the quantity of water taken up by shaking a salt hydrate with ether will give the dissociation pressure of the salt, as was shown by Linebarger.[1]

The identity of the law of the relative depression of the solubility (p. 145), with the law of the relative depression of the vapour pressure, is also an immediate deduction from the preceding principle.

According to p. 479, the product of the partial pressures of ammonia and hydrochloric acid over sal-ammoniac is constant ; according to the above law the product must be the same over a saturated solution of sal-ammoniac. Since, however, free ammonia is present in the solution, in consequence of hydrolysis, but hardly any free undissociated hydrochloric acid, the partial pressure of the ammonia is greater than that of the hydrochloric acid, so that on evaporation the distillate is alkaline, the residue acid.

---

[1] *Zeits. phys. Chem.* **13.** 500 (1894).

Influence of the Extent of a Phase.—A general law was stated on p. 472, and has been applied since, that equilibrium in heterogeneous systems is independent of the extent of the phases, e.g. the vapour pressure of a liquid is independent of the amount of liquid, the solubility of a solid independent of the amount of solid. A simple thermodynamic consideration shows, however, that this is only true when the extent of the phase does not fall below a certain minimum.

If from a given heterogeneous system we allow unit mass of a phase to disappear, by means of a change in pressure, a certain amount of work A_0 can be performed by the system. If now we first suppose this unit mass divided into n equal parts, separate in space, and that to perform this separation requires A_n of work, then we must have

$$A = A' - A_n,$$

where A' is the work done when the unit of mass disappears in n portions.

So long as the subdivision is not carried too far, A_n remains infinitesimal, so that the law as originally stated is true; but as soon as the work of subdivision becomes appreciable, A' differs from A, and therefore the active mass of the phase is changed; for the modified equilibrium we have simply

$$A = RT \ln K = RT \ln K' - A_n,$$

where K' is the new reaction constant; the latter may be calculated when A_n is known.

This can easily be found for a liquid from the surface tension; in this case the equation becomes identical with the formula given by Lord Kelvin in 1870 for the increase of the vapour pressure of very small drops.

The work of subdivision for solids is unknown; but G. A. Hulett [1] showed experimentally that very fine powder is more soluble than large crystals; e.g. barium sulphate, ground into powder of about 10^{-5} cm. diameter, is nearly twice as soluble as larger crystals of the same salt. This is a fact of the highest importance for the theory of spontaneous crystallisation (p. 243).

The Influence of the Temperature, and of the Pressure, upon the State of Chemical Equilibrium.—1. Up to now we have only employed our fundamental thermo-chemical formula,

$$\frac{d \ln K}{dT} = - \frac{U}{RT^2},$$

to calculate, from the displacement of a chemical equilibrium, the heat of reaction which is associated with the reaction, the equilibrium of which we are investigating. Conversely, we can, of course, estimate

[1] *Zeitschr. phys. Chem.* **37**. 385 (1901).

the influence of temperature from the heat of reaction, and thus obtain the following law :—

If we heat a chemical system, at constant volume, a displacement of equilibrium occurs in the direction in which the reaction takes place with absorption of heat.

For if $U > 0$, K decreases with increase of temperature, *i.e.* the equilibrium is displaced on increase of temperature in the sense of the chemical equation from right to left, *i.e.* in the sense in which the reaction proceeds with absorption of heat.

Of course, the preceding formula really only proves this ·law for those systems for which it is strictly valid, namely for equilibria in gases or dilute solutions.   But we have already seen that the law can be applied to condensed systems (p. 641).   *Thus it is universally valid.*

Those chemical forces which cause a development of heat, will always be weakened by an increase of temperature ; and conversely, those which cause an absorption of heat will be strengthened by a rise in temperature ; and it is this fact which makes the above law universally valid.

This law, which van't Hoff called the "*principle of mobile equilibrium*" (*principe de l'équilibre mobile*), is of the greatest assistance. Thus it shows us at once that, *e.g.*, the pressure of a gas, the vapour pressure, the degree of dissociation, etc., must each and all increase with the temperature ; because the expansion of gases, evaporation, · and the decomposition of complex molecules into more simple ones, all take place with absorption of heat.

The transformation of acetic acid and alcohol into water and ester is unaccompanied by any noticeable evolution of heat (p. 608), and therefore the state of equilibrium between these substances is independent of the temperature (p. 457).

Substances formed with absorption of heat, such as ozone, acetylene, hydrogen peroxide, which are unstable in high concentration at ordinary temperature, must become more stable at high temperatures.

2. Completely parallel with the preceding law is one which concerns the influence of *pressure* upon a chemical equilibrium :—

If we compress a chemical system at constant temperature, a displacement of equilibrium takes place in the direction which is associated with a diminution of volume.

This proposition can be easily derived for gaseous systems, from the law of mass-action (see p. 450).   It holds good, however, universally.

The solubility of a salt in water, *e.g.*, will increase with the pressure, when it takes place with a contraction *of the solution plus the salt* ; and conversely, the solubility will decrease if the separation of the salt is associated with a diminution of the volume of the system.[1]

Those chemical forces, in fact, which cause a diminution in volume

[1] F. Braun, *Wied. Ann.* **30**. 250 (1887) ; *Zeitschr. phys. Chem.* **1**. 259 (1887).

are strengthened by compression; and those which cause an increase in volume are weakened by compression.

The influence of pressure on equilibrium in dilute solution is obtained as follows. If $d\nu$ mols of a reaction mixture are converted, the work $d\nu \, RT \ln K$ is done (p. 657); if the mixture is at pressure p, and suffers a change in volume dv, the work pdv is performed. Hence

$$dA = RT \ln K \, . \, d\nu + pdv \, ;$$

but this equation is of the form

$$dA = \mathfrak{K}_1 d\mathfrak{w}_1 + \mathfrak{K}_2 d\mathfrak{w}_2 \; [\text{T const.}],$$

so that, according to p. 26,

$$\frac{\partial \mathfrak{K}_1}{\partial \mathfrak{w}_2} = \frac{\partial \mathfrak{K}_2}{\partial \mathfrak{w}_1},$$

or in the special case considered,

$$-\frac{\partial RT \ln K}{\partial v} = \frac{\partial p}{\partial \nu},$$

or

$$RT \frac{\partial \ln K}{\partial p} = -\frac{\partial v}{\partial \nu} = -V_0,$$

whence V_0 is the change in volume due to conversion of one mol.

This equation, in a slightly different form, was first obtained by Planck (*Wied. Ann.* **32.** 491, 1887).

Fanjung[1] applied this equation to the influence of pressure on the dissociation of weak acids. He found the dissociation constant under different pressures by means of the conductivity, and found, *e.g.*, for acetic acid,

$$p_1 = \quad 1 \text{ atm.} \quad \log^{10} K_1 = 0.254 - 5,$$

$$p_2 = 260 \text{ atm.} \quad \log^{10} K_2 = 0.305 - 5.$$

Since K and p vary proportionally within wide limits we have

$$\frac{d \ln K}{dp} = 2.302 \frac{\log^{10} K_2 - \log^{10} K_1}{p_2 - p_1},$$

and

$$V_0 = -0.0821 \, (273 + 18) \, 2.302 \frac{0.305 - 0.254}{259} = -0.0108.$$

Since p is expressed in atmos. and R ($= 0.0821$) in litre-atmospheres, we get V_0 in litres; *i.e.* when the ions of acetic acid combine to form undissociated molecules there is a decrease in volume of 10.8 c.c. per mol; according to p. 385, the molecular volume of acetic acid when ionised is 40.5, and when undissociated 51.1, an increase of 10.6 c.c. This is as good an agreement as could possibly be expected; Fanjung found equally good results for the other acids studied.

As electrolytic dissociation always, so far as known, involves contraction,

---

[1] *Zeitschr. phys. Chem.* **14.** 673 (1894).

the dissociation must, as with acetic acid, always be favoured by increase of pressure.

The formula

$$RT \frac{\partial \ln K}{\partial p} = -V_0$$

can be more simply derived by first investigating the influence of pressure on the partition coefficient between compressed and uncompressed solvents, and then arriving at the influence of pressure on the chemical equilibrium by means of the theorem developed on p. 503.

If the solution of the substance in question is unaccompanied by any alteration in volume, the above considerations show that the partition between compressed and uncompressed solvents would not alter.

3. It is possible, following Le Chatelier,[1] to unite the two preceding laws in the following principle :—

Every change of one of the factors of an equilibrium occasions a rearrangement of the system in such a direction that the factor in question experiences a change in a sense opposite to the original change..

This reminds us of the mechanical principle of ACTION and REACTION.

Effect of non-uniform Pressure.—So far we have always assumed that the external pressure (as measured by a manometer) is the same in all parts of the chemical system. Le Chatelier[2] has considered the interesting case of a fluid or a solid compressed by a piston that is not gas tight, so that one phase of the system may have quite a different pressure to a second phase in contact and equilibrium with it. The thermodynamic treatment of this case also can be carried out exactly.

If $d\nu$ mols of a solid or liquid of vapour pressure π are distilled isothermally into a phase of pressure π_0, the work

$$RT \ln \frac{\pi}{\pi_0} . d\nu$$

is gained ; if at the same time the system which is under pressure p contracts by dv, the external work pdv is done ; so that

$$dA = RT \ln \frac{\pi}{\pi_0} d\nu - pdv ;$$

and as on p. 675 we find

$$\frac{\partial RT \ln \pi}{\partial v} = -\frac{\partial p}{\partial \nu},$$

or

$$\frac{RT}{\pi} . \frac{\partial \pi}{\partial p} = -\frac{\partial v}{\partial \nu},$$

---

[1] *Équilibres*, p. 210.
[2] *Zeitschr. phys. Chem.* **9.** 335 (1892). See also the more complete treatment by E. Riecke, *Gött. Nachr.* (1894), No. 4.

the percentage change which the vapour pressure suffers as a consequence of the external pressure is therefore

$$- \frac{100}{RT} V_0,$$

where by $\frac{\partial v}{\partial \nu} = V_0$ is meant the increase in volume of the solid or liquid on evaporation of one mol, and is naturally always negative.   Thus for ice $V_0 = -19 \cdot 65$ c.c. ; $RT = 22{,}420$ c.c. if ‘ p is reckoned in atmospheres. Hence $\frac{d\pi}{\pi}$ for an increase of pressure of one atmosphere is $0 \cdot 00088$, *i.e.* the vapour pressure of ice is increased by pressure to the extent of $0 \cdot 088$ % per atm.   This is, moreover, equal to the fall in vapour pressure produced by an equal osmotic pressure in the interior of a liquid.   Similar considerations show that the solubility of solid is increased if whilst it is in contact with the solvent it is compressed by a sieve-like arrangement.   Also a consideration of the diagram Fig. 15 (p. 137) shows at once that compression of ice (or other solid) must lower its melting-point by an easily calculable amount if it is in contact with the uncompressed liquid ; for the melting-point under these conditions is obviously the point at which solid and liquid have the same vapour pressure.

It is well known that ice can be cut by pressing a wire through it. The solidification of moist precipitated powders by pressure is another phenomenon that falls into this category.

Thermodynamic Potential.—If we consider two phases in contact, work can be performed if one increases at the cost of the other ; if the volume increases by dv, work is done to the extent pdv where p is the pressure on both phases.   On the other hand, components of the one phase may pass over into the other, and the transference of $d\nu$ mols of a component of the first phase involves an amount of work $(\mu_1 - \mu_2)$ $d\nu$, where μ_1 and μ_2 are proportional factors peculiar to the phases and components in question.   We find therefore that

$$dA = pdv - \Sigma(\mu_1 - \mu_2)d\nu \text{ (T const.)} . \qquad . \qquad . \quad (1)$$

where the sum is to be taken for all the components.   The reason for the negative sign of $d\nu$ is that we understand by ν the amount of the given component in the first phase, and this, after the reaction, becomes $\nu - d\nu$.

$(\mu_1 - \mu_2)$ is called, after Gibbs, the difference in thermodynamic potential for the given component ; μ_1 and μ_2 are therefore the *thermodynamic potentials* of the component in the two phases.

For equilibrium according to p. 28,

$$\delta A = 0 \qquad . \qquad . \qquad . \qquad . \qquad . \quad (2)$$

for all possible isothermal changes consistent with the conditions of the system.   If the system is kept at constant volume

$$\delta A = \Sigma(\mu_1 - \mu_2)\delta \nu,$$

and since this relation must hold for all the (infinitesimal) varia $\delta\nu$, it follows that

$$\mu'_1 = \mu'_2, \ \mu''_1 = \mu''_2, \text{ etc. .} \qquad . \qquad . \qquad .$$

i.e. *if two phases maintained at constant temperature and volume are in equilibrium, the thermodynamic potential of each component mu identical in the two phases.*

Example.—If a molecular species in the gaseous state or in solution changes in concentration from c to c_0, the work done is RT l hence

$$\mu d\nu = (RT \ln c - A)d\nu,$$

where

$$A = RT \ln c_0.$$

Hence the thermodynamic potential of this molecular species is

$$\mu = RT \ln c - A.$$

For two coexistent phases in equilibrium, the equation

$$RT \ln c' - A' = RT \ln c'' - A'',$$

or

$$\frac{c'}{c''} = e^{\frac{A' - A''}{RT}}$$

must hold good for every molecular species. Since, however, the expr on the right is constant for any given molecular species, at a given perature, it follows that at equilibrium there must be a constant rat partition between the two phases ; this is the *partition law* (p. 491).

In equilibrium the different states of aggregation have, accor to the above, equal thermodynamic potentials (but not equal energy). For further applications of the thermodynamic potentia the references on p. 615 ; it should be remarked, however, that theory of thermodynamic potential is essentially equivalent to thermodynamic treatment adopted in this book.

TEMPERATURE AND THE REACTION VELOCITY

The Acceleration of Chemical Reactions by Means of an Elevation of the Temperature.—In the last two chapters we have sought to formulate the influence of the *temperature upon chemical equilibrium*, but in this chapter we return again to *chemical kinetics*.

In the last chapter of the preceding book, we became acquainted with the equations which enable us to calculate the course of reactions which occur at constant temperature, and the influence of temperature must therefore be capable of expression in the *numerical values of the velocity-coefficients*.

The problem we have to solve is the discovery of the nature of these temperature functions.

The following result has been empirically obtained :—

All experimental measurement has shown that the velocity with which a chemical system strives to reach its state of equilibrium, increases enormously with the temperature.

This appears to be a universal phenomenon ; its importance for the course of chemical change, and its significance for the so-called "stormy reactions" (detonations, explosions, etc.) is at once evident.

As an example of the law we will give the figures obtained for the *velocities with which cane-sugar is inverted* (p. 553) at the temperatures t, the other conditions being unchanged :—

t.	Inversion Coefficient.
25°	9·67
40	73·4
45	139
50	268
55	491

A rise in temperature of only 30° is sufficient to increase the reaction velocity fifty-fold ; and the increase is similarly rapid in many other cases which have been investigated.[1]

It is very easy, from the standpoint of the molecular theory, to account for the fact that substances react much more quickly in homogeneous, gaseous, or liquid systems, the higher the temperature rises, because the activity of the heat movement, and therefore also the relative number of the collisions of the reacting substances, increases with the temperature. But when we consider that the velocity of the molecular movement in gases—and in all probability in liquids also—is proportional to the square root of the absolute temperature, and also that at room temperature it increases by only about $\frac{1}{6}$ of one per cent per degree, a difficulty at once arises. But if it is assumed, as H. Goldschmidt[2] has shown, that only those molecules react whose velocity exceeds a certain high value, then the very great influence of temperature can be explained kinetically.

When we consider various systems at the same temperature we find the greatest conceivable divergences of reaction velocity.

Thus, e.g., while on the neutralisation of a base by an acid the reacting ingredients unite so quickly that we have not yet been able to estimate the reaction velocity, yet, on the other hand, hydrogen and oxygen react so extraordinarily slowly at ordinary temperatures, that for this reason it has thus far been impossible to measure the velocity. It is only by a depression of the temperature in the former case, and an elevation of temperature in the latter case, that it is sometimes possible to change the experimental conditions in a way favourable for observation.

Non-reversible Decomposition.—The relations prevailing here are of the greatest importance for the problem of the determination of chemical equilibrium. Such a problem can of course be studied only when the progress of the reaction in question is sufficiently rapid to allow the equilibrium to be established in observable time. When this is not the case, then we must work at higher temperatures ; and when we have carried out the measurement at two different temperatures, we can calculate the equilibrium for those lower temperatures for which a direct observation is impossible by means of the thermodynamic principles given in the two preceding chapters.

Sometimes even this method is debarred ; as, e.g., when the reaction velocity does not become sufficiently great until such temperatures are reached that the equilibrium has already been displaced so very much towards one side or the other, as to make measurement impossible.

An example of this is *the direct formation of ammonia from nitrogen*

---

[1] A rise of 10° usually doubles or trebles the velocity of reaction ; see the collection of data in van't Hoff, *Chem. Dynamik*, p. 225.

[2] *Physik. Zeitschr.* **10.** 206 (1909).

and hydrogen. At lower temperatures neither do hydrogen and nitrogen react upon each other, nor does ammonia decompose into nitrogen and hydrogen, at least in observable intervals of time. At high temperatures, such as those produced by the electric spark, ammonia decomposes practically completely ; and a determination of the real equilibrium between ammonia and its decomposition products has only been possible in recent times, at a mean temperature of about 1000°.

The fact that the reaction velocity in chemical systems is usually extraordinarily small, no matter how far removed the system is from equilibrium, is of the very greatest importance for our knowledge of chemical compounds. The greater part of all organic compounds would never have seen the light of day, if they had changed over to their stable conditions with great velocity. The many polymeric hydro-carbons of the formula C_nH_n could not all exist at the same time if they all tended to go at once to the system of greatest stability corresponding to the formula C_nH_n. The fact that, in the sense of the preceding, *organic chemistry is peculiarly the region of unstable compounds*, which change over into more stable forms either extraordinarily slowly or not at all in measurable time, finds its explanation in *the inertia* of the carbon union (p. 289).

Those chemical systems which are far removed from the stable form usually change with an increase of temperature, when this sufficiently increases the velocity with which they tend to reach equilibrium. Thus consider the innumerable decompositions, char-rings, detonations, etc., of organic compounds on heating, or consider the combustibility of many compounds in oxygen, etc. In most of these cases heat only accelerates a reaction—whether a decomposition or a union—which would really take place spontaneously, though perhaps only after thousands of years.

When the change is once completed by heating, then, of course, it cannot be made reversible by cooling, because the system is in a more stable condition after cooling than before.

In this way we can explain the existence of the many non-reversible reactions : *these, and also many of the reactions which take place in only one direction, are essentially different from the real dissociation phenomena.*

This accounts for the fact that until very recently the real nature of chemical equilibria escaped the attention of the chemist, and that in his estimation of the nature of chemical processes he was too largely guided by the phenomena of non-reversible processes. Just as the physicist could not have studied successfully the laws of the so-called " physical reactions " of changes of state by means of under-cooled vapours or liquids, so it is impossible to study the laws of chemical processes by starting out with the investigation of non-reversible decompositions, and *e.g.* to obtain an insight into dissociation phenomena by the investigation of explosives.

The Application of Thermodynamics.—Strictly speaking, the doctrines of thermodynamics have nothing to teach regarding the *velocity* of a process ; because the velocity always depends, not only upon the driving force, but also upon the magnitude and *the nature of the friction,* which lie wholly beyond the domain of thermodynamics. Nevertheless, a few theoretical conclusions on the dependence of reaction velocity on temperature may be drawn from the much-discussed formula which has already done such good service :—

$$\frac{d \ln K}{dT} = -\frac{U}{RT^2}.$$

When we recall the meaning of K in the sense of the theory of Guldberg and Waage (p. 446), namely that it is the ratio of the velocity coefficients of the mutually opposed reactions, the difference between which conditions the total reaction velocity,

$$K = \frac{k}{k'},$$

we arrive, in the first place, at the result that when $U = 0$, then K is independent of the temperature, and *k and k′ represent the same temperature function.* Thus, *e.g.*, the velocity with which alcohol and acetic acid unite to form water and an ester increases in exactly the same way as the velocity with which the ester and water unite to form acetic acid and an alcohol.

The equation

$$\frac{d \ln \frac{k}{k'}}{dT} = -\frac{U}{RT^2},$$

can be expressed in the two more general forms

$$\frac{d \ln k}{dT} = \frac{A}{T^2} + B,$$

and

$$\frac{d \ln k'}{dT} = \frac{A'}{T^2} + B.$$

Here

$$A' - A = \frac{U}{R};$$

and B may be an arbitrary temperature function. But van't Hoff[1] finds that in many cases

$$B = 0,$$

because usually the coefficient k of the reaction velocity can be expressed by the equation

$$\frac{d \ln k}{dT} = \frac{A}{T^2},$$

[1] *Études,* p. 114.

which, on integration, becomes

$$\ln k = -\frac{A}{T} + C,$$

where C is a constant (not a temperature function). From this equation k can be calculated with excellent results, by a suitable choice of the values for A and C. The expression resembles the interpolation formula, which was used to represent the vapour pressure curve, and altogether the enormous increase of reaction velocity reminds us of the increase of vapour pressure with the temperature.

If U is not assumed constant, but changes with the temperature, the above expression can be extended to

$$\ln k = -\frac{A}{T} + C + DT.$$

At high temperatures the influence of the first member on the right-hand side gradually vanishes, while that of the last becomes greater and greater.

Since chemical equilibrium is established aperiodically, we are concerned with a process of the same kind as the movement of a particle under great friction (p. 14), the displacement of ions in a solvent (p. 363), or the diffusion of dissolved substances (p. 368). In all these cases the velocity of the process is at each instant directly proportional to the driving forces, and inversely to the frictional resistance ; so that we conclude that an equation of the form

$$\text{velocity of reaction} = \frac{\text{chemical force}}{\text{chemical resistance}}$$

similar to Ohm's law must hold. The "chemical force" at any moment may be derived from the change in free energy ; of the chemical resistance we know little, but it is not impossible that it may be measured directly. In that case the problem of calculating absolute chemical velocities of reaction would be solved in a similar way to that of calculating the rate of diffusion of electrolytes in absolute measure (p. 370).

According to all experience the chemical resistance increases rapidly with fall of temperature, and becomes infinitely great at the absolute zero (in accordance with kinetic views). At the absolute zero, therefore, all chemical reaction would cease, since the denominator of the above fraction is infinite.

The velocity of reaction in heterogeneous systems is zero at the transition point, because then the chemical force is nil. With fall of temperature it must first increase because the numerator of the above fraction (chemical force) increases with the distance from the temperature of equilibrium. When the temperature is sufficiently lowered, however, it decreases on account of the enormous increase in the denominator of the above fraction. Examples of such behaviour are to be found in the researches on velocity of crystallisation (p. 588) and those of E. Cohen on velocity of transition.[1]

---

[1] *Zeitschr. f. Elektrochemie*, **6.** 85 (1899).

Explosions and Combustions.—The great influence of temperature upon the velocity of a chemical change, teaches us, in the first place, that care must be taken in measuring the course of a reaction to maintain the system at a constant temperature, which can be accurately measured. This can be most easily accomplished by putting the system in a thermostat.

But it is not usually possible to avoid heating or cooling taking place, on account of the heat of reaction associated with the chemical change ; as when the change takes place with a velocity too great for an equalisation of the temperature of its surroundings to follow. The quantitative investigation of such a process offers very considerable difficulties.

Reactions with Development of Heat.—Let us first consider the case where the reaction progresses in the sense which is associated with the *development of heat.* The progress of the reaction causes an elevation of temperature, which accelerates the velocity. But this accelerated velocity means a quicker decomposition, and therefore in turn causes an increased development of heat, which again reacts to hasten the decomposition. Thus it is evident how a very extraordinary acceleration of the reaction velocity may take place under favourable circumstances. In this way we can explain the "stormy reactions." It will be found that these are invariably associated with a development of heat.

The reaction velocity in many systems at the ordinary temperature is very slight, and perhaps may have no appreciable value. In such cases the mutual acceleration of the reaction velocity and the development of heat does not come into play, because the slight amount of heat developed is conducted away to the environment before any perceptible rise in temperature occurs.

Thus, *e.g.*, this is the case with *electrolytic gas* ; doubtless a mutual reaction and a corresponding development of heat takes place between oxygen and hydrogen at all times, but as this occurs extraordinarily slowly at ordinary temperatures, it reaches no appreciable amount, and in consequence the temperature of the electrolytic gas mixture does not rise perceptibly above its surroundings. But it is quite otherwise at 530° to 600° ; here the reaction velocity reaches a magnitude sufficient to cause such a lively development of heat that the union of the two gases is enormously accelerated, and this results in a combustion or explosion of the system.

Now, it is by no means necessary to bring the *whole* system to a temperature at which the reaction velocity is sufficiently great ; to ignite the gases it is only necessary to heat them locally to a certain extent, as can be done by means of the electric spark.

Let us consider again for the sake of simplicity a homogeneous system, such as an electrolytic gas mixture ; then in every case, at that point where the temperature reaches a sufficient limit, the reaction between the two gases will progress more quickly, and therefore the temperature of the point will rise. One of two events will then happen :

Either, the heat developed will be taken away from the environment of the point by radiation and conduction more quickly than it can be generated anew, and therefore after a short time the temperature will sink, and the reaction velocity will again return to a minimal value ;

Or, the heat developed at the point considered will be sufficiently great to heat the surroundings to a temperature of lively activity ; in this case the high temperature causes the rapid reaction between the gases to spread over the whole system, and a combustion takes place, resulting in the almost complete union of all the gases in the system which are capable of reaction.

That temperature, to which a point of the system must be heated in order to cause combustion, is called the "ignition temperature.' It is obvious from the preceding considerations that its value depends on a large number of factors, such as the heat of the reaction, the thermal conductivity, the capacity for diffusion possessed by the gas, and the dependence of the reaction velocity upon the temperature ; it will also vary, especially with the temperature of the surroundings, and with the pressure of the system.[1]

Thus, the ignition temperature has quite a secondary nature ; it is clear that it cannot be described as the point where the mutual action of the gases *begins*. This would be as absurd as to say that the boiling-point of a liquid was the point where vaporisation begins.

All of these considerations may be applied to explosions in heterogeneous systems, as the ignition of gunpowder and the like.

Reactions with Absorption of Heat.—But the relations are entirely different in those cases where the progress of the reaction is associated with an *absorption of heat*, *i.e.* with a cooling down. Here the temperature sinks during the course of the reaction, and the chemical change is the more retarded the quicker it takes place.

The phenomenon of a retardation occasioned by the chemical change itself may be observed in the process of *evaporation*, which process is associated with a strong absorption of heat ; the cooling thus brought about causes the vapour pressure to fall very rapidly.

The reason why gunpowder is an explosive substance, while solid carbon dioxide is not, in spite of the fact that both are capable of the same reaction, viz. conversion into gaseous products, is that *in the first case*, when the reaction has once been started, it spreads and accelerates itself on account of the lively development of heat ; but in the second

---

[1] Actually V. Meyer and Freyer found that an exact determination of the temperature of ignition is not possible (*Ber. deutsch. chem. Ges.* **25.** 622, 1892). Another way, which is free from these sources of error, will be described below.

case, on the other hand, the cooling which takes place brings the action to a standstill almost immediately.

The Reaction Capacity of Gases.—The considerations advanced in the preceding section will be applied to gaseous systems in some further respects. It is a striking fact that many gases which are able to combine with each other with a lively development of heat—as oxygen and hydrogen, carbon monoxide and chlorine—do nevertheless approach so slowly to the state of equilibrium (which involves almost complete combination), that they may be regarded as chemically indifferent towards each other at ordinary temperatures. Yet, as has been repeatedly emphasised, there can be no doubt that a reaction *does* take place at ordinary temperatures, but the reaction velocity is so extremely slow that the amount changed in the lapse of years would be smaller than that produced in a fraction of a second by an elevation of a few hundred degrees. We can regard this as only another example of the enormous influence of temperature upon the reaction velocity.

Now the phenomenon that the mutual action of gases can be brought to an almost complete standstill by cooling can be made use of to obtain an insight into the condition of equilibrium at higher temperatures.

This fact was first applied by Deville (1863) in the construction of his " cold-hot tubes " (*kalt-warmen Rohre*) ; by means of this apparatus he succeeded in showing the decomposition of CO_2, of SO_2, and of HCl. The gases were conducted through an incandescent porcelain tube, through the axis of which passed a silver tube conducting a stream of cold water. As soon as the decomposition products produced at the high temperatures diffused from the hot wall towards the middle of the porcelain tube, they were suddenly cooled by the silver tube, and thus a reunion to form the original compound was at any rate partially hindered.

We can consider the dissociating action of strong electric sparks in a similar way. A part of the gas is raised to a very high temperature, and thus is decomposed to a greater or less extent ; then the decomposed products are partially separated from each other by diffusion, and are cooled before they can reunite with each other completely.

In this way it is possible, as A. W. Hofmann[1] found, to demonstrate easily the dissociation of CO_2, or of water vapour, by passing the gases through a glass-tube in which sparks are produced from a strong induction apparatus, strengthened by connection with the poles of a Leyden jar. Of course the decomposition cannot pass beyond a certain limit, for there would then occur the explosive

[1] *Sitzungsber, der Berl. Akad.*, 1889, p. 183 ; *Ber. deutsch. chem. Ges.* **23.** 3303 (1890).

reunion of the gaseous products of decomposition. Thus Hofmann and Buff (1860) observed that under suitably chosen conditions carbon dioxide, enclosed in a eudiometer, could be alternately decomposed partially into carbon monoxide and oxygen, and again united with a weak explosion by means of a constant stream of sparks. Here the decomposition only goes on till the mixture becomes explosive, and then the decomposition products again unite by ignition, and the cycle begins afresh.

Determination of Chemical Equilibrium in Gaseous Systems at High Temperatures.—The fact that in gaseous systems equilibrium is generally attained very slowly at low temperatures, and also usually lies so very much to one side (as in the case of the dissociation of water vapour) that even when it is reached its determination is impracticable, forces the experimenter to carry out his investigations at high temperatures. The method described on p. 253 for the determination of molecular weight at high temperatures is often sufficient for a rough estimation of equilibrium; for more exact measurements the author has worked out in the last few years in conjunction with his pupils a number of methods which will now be described :—

1. **The Streaming Method.**—Deville's method, mentioned above, can be easily brought into a form suitable for quantitative investigations by passing the gaseous mixture to be studied through a space kept at a constant high temperature and then analysing it. Certain precautions, however, must be taken. It will be most simple to consider the scheme shown in Fig. 44. The gas mixture is allowed to flow through a long tube. Between the points a and b the tube is kept at the temperature t, at which equilibrium is to be studied; from b to c the temperature is made to fall as quickly as possible, so that at the point c the temperature t is so low that the velocity of reaction

Fig. 44.

has practically vanished. Now, in order that the gas leaving the tube shall have a composition corresponding to the equilibrium temperature, the two following conditions must obviously be fulfilled: firstly, the distance ab must be long enough to give the gas time to reach equilibrium; and secondly, the time cooling from b to c must be short enough to prevent any disturbance of this equilibrium. The first condition may be always theoretically fulfilled by making the length ab sufficiently great; practically it is realised best by widening the tube between a and b. Another plan is to fill the space between a and b with a catalysing agent, as Kinetsch [1] did in his investigation on the formation of sulphur trioxide. The question whether the velocity of reaction is really high enough at the temperature t can always be solved by passing through the tube mixtures of compositions which first lie on one side and then on the other of the composition of the equilibrium mixture. The second condition can be best fulfilled by making bc a narrow capillary in order to give the gas as high a velocity as possible, and to make the drop in temperature as sudden as possible. Of course the conductivity for heat of the material of the tube interferes with this, and it can be by no means concluded that this source of error is eliminated when the composition of the mixture leaving the apparatus is independent of the velocity of streaming.

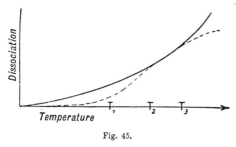

Fig. 45.

This follows from the fact that an infinitely high velocity of streaming by no means necessitates an infinitely rapid fall in temperature. Of course, catalysing agents must be excluded as far as possible from bc.

It is especially important to notice that at high temperatures, and correspondingly great reaction velocities, equilibrium is certainly reached in ab, and no less certainly disturbed in bc. The gases leaving the tube have then the same composition whether the original mixture differed in one direction or the other from the equilibrium mixture, but at the same time the composition may be far from that at equilibrium. The above curve (Fig. 45) will illustrate this clearly; the unbroken curve is the curve of equilibrium (for instance, the amount of knall gas formed by dissociation of water vapour), while the dotted curve represents experimental values. In general the effect of the above sources of error is to make the yield too small. If, however, ab is large compared to bc, there will always be a region where correct values can be obtained. To the experimenter falls the task of finding this temperature interval T_2 to T_3, which will evidently extend more to the left the greater ab is, and more to the right the quicker the cooling takes place. An extremely important indication that the right temperature interval has been found lies in the fact that in this region the *tangents of the observed curve must coincide with those of the equilibrium curve*, and, as the latter can be nearly always theoretically calculated from the heat of reaction of the process, we have a safe criterion for judging whether the observed values within a certain interval agree with the true values for the equilibrium. At lower temperatures, where the velocity of reaction is measurable, but too

[1] *Ber. deutsch. chem. Ges.* **34**. 4069 (1901).

small for equilibrium to be attained (*i.e.* somewhere in the region of T_1), we can calculate the equilibrium by measuring the velocities of the two opposing reactions, and then interpolating, graphically or otherwise, the concentrations at which the total velocity would be zero.   (J. Sand.[1])

2. **Explosion Method.**— Exactly the same considerations apply to an apparently quite different kind of experiment.   In an explosion, a gaseous mixture is really under the same conditions as in the streaming method; it is brought to a high temperature and then quickly cooled.   But it is only at the high temperature for a very short time, so the method is only applicable when the velocity of reaction is very high—that is, at such high temperatures that the preceding method fails.   As a matter of fact, equilibrium is usually disturbed during the cooling; for instance, water is formed quantitatively when knall gas is exploded in a eudiometer, although at the maximal temperature of the explosion water vapour is fairly strongly dissociated; for the same reasons the experiments of different authors[2] on the distribution of oxygen between hydrogen and carbon monoxide, or of hydrogen between oxygen and chlorine, are useless for the calculation of equilibria, because we do not know to what temperature correspond the concentration ratios which are found in the eudiometer after combustion.   From the amount of nitric oxide formed by explosion of knall gas in the presence of air at the absolute temperatures 2600 to 2700° the equilibrium of the reaction (cf. p. 671)

$$N_2 + O_2 = 2NO$$

can be calculated with apparent accuracy by application of the above principles.   These are the highest temperatures at which equilibria have been satisfactorily measured.

3. **Calculation of Chemical Equilibria from the Maximal Pressure of Explosions.**—The maximal pressure of an explosion can be very accurately determined (p. 43), and as the attainment of equilibrium alters the evolution of heat and therefore indirectly the maximal pressure, observation of the latter allows the calculation of equilibrium.   The maximal pressure is also directly influenced by an alteration of equilibrium when this causes a change in the number of molecules.   The extension of this method, which has only been applied to isolated cases hitherto,[3] would be of great value.

---

[1] *Zeitschr. phys. Chem.* **50.** 465 (1904).   For applications of these principles see Nernst, "Bildung von Stickoxyd" (*Zeitschr. anorg. Chem.* **49.** 213, 1906); Nernst and v. Wartenberg, "Dissoziation von Wasserdampf und Kohlensäure" (*Zeitschr. anorg. Chem.* **56.** 513, 1906).

[2] See for example Bunsen, *Lieb. Ann.* **85.** 137 (1853); Horstmann, *ibid.* **190.** 228 (1878); Botsch, *ibid.* **210.** 207 (1881); Schlegel, *ibid.* **226.** 133 (1884); Hautefeuille and Margottet, *Ann. chim. phys.* [6] **20.** 416 (1890).

[3] Nernst, *Zeitschr. anorg. Chem.* **45.** 130 (1905).

4. Method of the heated Catalysing Agent.—At temperatures at which the velocity of reaction is still small in the space occupied by the gas, but large on the surface of a catalysing agent, it is obviously sufficient simply to heat the catalyst to a high temperature. This method, which was proposed by the author and worked out by Langmuir [1] is very simple when the catalysing agent, *e.g.* a platinum wire, is electrically heated. In an atmosphere of water vapour a short time suffices to establish the concentration of knall gas, which corresponds to the temperature of the glowing platinum wire. The temperature is most simply calculated from the electrical resistance of the wire.

5. Method of the Semipermeable Membrane.—A very exact method, first described by Löwenstein,[2] consists in using a membrane which is permeable only to one component of the equilibrium mixture. At present we only possess such membranes for hydrogen, which diffuses through palladium, platinum, and iridium. The kind of apparatus used for determining the dissociation of water vapour will

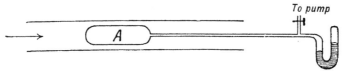

Fig. 46.

be made clear by the sketch, Fig. 46 : A is a vessel made of palladium, platinum, or iridium—according to the temperature of the experiment, and is placed inside an electric furnace. A capillary tube connects the vessel with a mercury pump, and a manometer. After it is evacuated and closed by a stopcock, water vapour is passed over it, and after a short time the pressure of hydrogen within the vessel corresponds to the dissociation of the water vapour at the temperature of the furnace.

Dissociation of Water Vapour and Carbon Dioxide.—The methods which have just been described have been used among others for determining the dissociations of water vapour and carbon dioxide, which are of great importance from many points of view.

The following table contains the results obtained : x is the degree of dissociation of water vapour at atmospheric pressure; the fourth column shows which method was used. The last column contains the name of the author and the place where the reference can be found.

[1] *Journ. Amer. Chem. Soc.* **28.** 1357 (1906).
[2] *Zeitschr. phys. Chem.* **54.** 707 (1906).

DISSOCIATION OF WATER VAPOUR.

T	100 x obs.	100 x calc.	Method.	Observer.
1300	0·0027	0·0029	4	Langmuir (p. 690)
1397	0·0078	0·0084	1	Nernst and v. Wartenberg (p. 689)
1480	0·0189	0·0185	1	,, ,, ,, ,,
1500	0·0197	0·0221	4	Langmuir
1561	0·034	0·0368	1	Nernst and v. Wartenberg
1705	0·102	0·108	5	Löwenstein (p. 690)
2155	1·18	1·18	5	v. Wartenberg (p. 691);
2257	1·77	1·79	5	,, ,, ,,
2300	2·6	2·08	3	Nernst (p. 689)

The application of the law of mass-action to the equation

$$2H_2O = O_2 + 2H_2$$

gives the relation

$$Kc_1^2 = c_2c_3^2$$

where c_1, c_2, c_3, are the concentrations of H_2O, O_2, H_2, respectively. If there is no excess of any of the products of dissociation, and P is the total pressure, then

$$c_1 = \frac{P\frac{2-2x}{2+x}}{RT}, \quad c_2 = \frac{P\frac{x}{2+x}}{RT}, \quad c_3 = \frac{P\frac{2x}{2+x}}{RT},$$

where x is the degree of dissociation corresponding to the pressure P and the temperature T.

Hence

$$K = \frac{p}{RT} \cdot \frac{x^3}{(2+x)(1-x)^2}.$$

If we take for the specific heat of water [1]

$$C_v = 5·61 + 0·000717T + 3·12 . 10^{-7}T^2$$

and for H_2 and O_2

$$C_v = 4·68 + 0·00026T$$

then, according to p. 599,

$$-U = 114400 + 2·74T - 0·000637^2 - 6·24 . 10^{-7}T^3$$

(taking − U as 115300 cal at T = 373).

If we take $100x = 3·02 \times 10^{-5}$ at T = 1000°, then from the equation of the integrated reaction isochore (p. 671) we obtain easily

$$\log \frac{2P(100x)^3}{(2+x)(1-x)^2} = 11·46 - \frac{25030}{T} + 2·38 \log \frac{T}{1000}$$
$$- 1·38 . 10^{-4}(T-1000) - 0·685 . 10^{-7}(T^2 - 1000^2).$$

[1] v. Wartenberg, Verhandl. d. d. physik. Ges. **8**. 97 (1906).

The numbers calculated from this equation agree as well as could be expected with the observed values, as the above table shows ; *i.e.* the degrees of dissociation found by very different methods are in excellent thermodynamical agreement.

In a similar way the dissociation of carbon dioxide was determined. For this we have

$$- U = 135400 + 3\cdot83T - 0\cdot00588T^2 + 1\cdot47 \times 10^{-6}\ T^3$$

and further

$$\log \frac{2P\ (100x)^3}{(2 + x)\ (1 - \dfrac{x}{100})^2} = 15\cdot48 - \frac{29600}{T} + 2\cdot93 \log \frac{T}{1000}$$

$$- 0\cdot001286\ (T - 1000) + 1\cdot61 \cdot 10^{-7}\ (T^2 - 1000^2)$$

In the following tables the degrees of dissociation (in percentages) of water vapour and carbon dioxide are calculated for a series of (absolute) temperatures and pressures.

WATER VAPOUR.

T	P=10 Atm.	P=1 Atm.	P=0·1 Atm.	P=0·01 Atm.
1000	$1\cdot39 \cdot 10^{-5}$	$3\cdot00 \cdot 10^{-5}$	$6\cdot46 \cdot 10^{-5}$	$1\cdot39 \cdot 10^{-4}$
1500	$1\cdot03 \cdot 10^{-2}$	$2\cdot21 \cdot 10^{-2}$	$4\cdot76 \cdot 10^{-2}$	$0\cdot103$
2000	$0\cdot273$	$0\cdot588$	$1\cdot26$	$2\cdot70$
2500	$1\cdot98$	$3\cdot98$	$8\cdot16$	$16\cdot6$

CARBON DIOXIDE.

T	P=10 Atm.	P=1 Atm.	P=0·1 Atm.	P=0·01 Atm.
1000	$7\cdot31 \cdot 10^{-6}$	$1\cdot58 \cdot 10^{-5}$	$3\cdot40 \cdot 10^{-5}$	$7\cdot31 \cdot 10^{-5}$
1500	$1\cdot88 \cdot 10^{-2}$	$4\cdot06 \cdot 10^{-2}$	$8\cdot72 \cdot 10^{-2}$	$0\cdot188$
2000	$0\cdot818$	$1\cdot77$	$3\cdot73$	$7\cdot88$
2500	$7\cdot08$	$15\cdot8$	$30\cdot7$	53

The following is a further control of these values :

The equilibrium of the reaction

$$CO + H_2O = CO_2 + H_2$$

has been measured by Boudouard [1] and more exactly by Hahn.[2]

The equilibrium constant [3]

$$K = \frac{[CO]\ [H_2O]}{[CO_2]\ [H_2]}, \quad \cdot \quad \cdot \quad \cdot \quad \cdot \quad (1)$$

was found, *e.g.*, to be 1·6 at 1000°.

---

[1] Theses, Paris, 1901.   [2] *Zeitschr. phys. Chem.* **44.** 513 (1903).

[3] Here, as elsewhere, square brackets denote concentrations.

If the dissociation constants of water vapour and carbon dioxide are K_1 and K_2 respectively at the same temperature, and the degrees of dissociation x and y, then

$$K_1 = \frac{[H_2]^2 [O_2]}{[H_2O]^2} = \frac{x^3}{2v (1-x)^2} \quad . \quad . \quad . \quad (2)$$

where v is the volume containing one mol of H_2O, and accordingly

$$[O_2] = \frac{x}{2v}, \quad [H_2] = \frac{x}{v}, \quad [H_2O] = \frac{1-x}{v}.$$

Similarly for carbon dioxide we have

$$K_2 = \frac{[CO]^2 [O_2]}{[CO_2]^2} = \frac{y^3}{2v (1-y)^2} \quad . \quad . \quad . \quad (3)$$

In the equilibrium denoted by equation (1), there must always be a small amount of free O_2 present, which must be in equilibrium both with water vapour in the sense of equation (2), and with carbon dioxide in the sense of equation (3). If we refer equations (2) and (3) to the system (1), and divide one into the other, then the oxygen concentrations, being equal, cancel out, and we obtain

$$K^2 = \frac{K_2}{K_1} = \frac{y^3 (1-x)^2}{x^3 (1-y)^2}.$$

From the value of K at 1000°, (T = 1273) given above, we may calculate that at this temperature the dissociation of water vapour must be 0·73 times that of carbon dioxide, which is in agreement with the above tables and formulæ.

In practice, nearly all combustions result in the formation of water vapour and carbon dioxide as end products ; the knowledge of the dissociation of these substances has therefore also great practical importance. As Le Chatelier[1] has already shown, the influence of the dissociation of carbon dioxide is vanishingly small in the case of explosives and only perceptible in melting furnaces and in ordinary flames. We may add that the same is true of the explosion chamber of petrol engines, and further, that similar considerations apply to the dissociation of water vapour. Moreover, at fairly high temperatures and not too small pressures, the disturbing influence of the dissociation may be entirely eliminated by the presence of a small excess of oxygen, according to the law of mass-action.

Ignition of an Inflammable Mixture of Gases by Adiabatic Compression.—If we compress an inflammable mixture of gases, its temperature rises, according to the gas laws (p. 47) ; the velocity of reaction is thereby increased, and ignition ensues at the moment when the heat evolved by the reaction exceeds that lost by radiation.

[1] *Zeitschr. phys. Chem.* **2.** 782 (1888).

If the compression takes place very quickly, *i.e.* nearly adiabatically, the temperature can be calculated from the magnitude of compression, and hence we can arrive at the ignition temperature of the mixture by measuring the compression necessary for ignition. As catalytic action of the walls of the vessel, etc., is prevented by this method, it is to be expected that exact values of the ignition temperature can be thus obtained. An investigation by G. Falk[1] at the suggestion of the author, has confirmed this expectation. The values obtained for mixtures of different composition are given in the following table :—

Mixture.	T.	Ignition Pressure in Atmosphere.
$4H_2 + O_2$	893,	48·2
$2H_2 + O_2$	819	36·9
$H_2 + O_2$	796	31·8
$H_2 + 2O_2$	808	33·5
$H_2 + 4O_2$	849	39·8

The pressures are referred to the original pressure of 1 atmosphere; the influence of the latter is only small. The fact that the mixture $H_2 + O_2$, (not $2H_2 + O_2$) is most easily ignited is obviously explained by the primary formation of hydrogen peroxide. Emich[2] had already established that this mixture needed the smallest electric spark to ignite it.

Propagation of Combustion in an Inflammable Gaseous Mixture.—Recent investigations have shown that when the combustion of a gaseous mixture is started at one point, as by an electric spark, it can be continued in two very different ways.

Slow combustion consists in the layer of gas first ignited passing on its heat by conduction to the next layer, and thus bringing the latter to the point of ignition; the rate of propagation depends, therefore, firstly on the amount of heat conducted, and secondly, on the velocity with which a moderately heated layer begins to react chemically, and so to bring itself to a high temperature, *i.e.* the rate depends in general on the change of reaction velocity with temperature.[3]

Combustion may also be propagated in a second, entirely different way, depending on the phenomenon we have just discussed, that an

---

[1] *Journ. Amer. Chem. Soc.* **28**. 1517 (1906). [These experiments have, however, been repeated by H. B. Dixon, who obtained no indication of a minimum ignition temperature for the mixture $H_2 + O_2$.]

[2] *Monatshefte f. Chemie,* **18**. 6 (1897).

[3] A constant slow combustion takes place in the middle of a Bunsen flame ; for the theory of the latter see Haber, *Techn. Gasreaktionen,* p. 282 ff.

explosive mixture of gases can be ignited by strong compression, or—more correctly—by the resulting rise in temperature. The increase of pressure causes an increase in concentration, and therefore, according to the law of mass action, also an increase in reaction velocity. Hence it is extraordinarily favourable to the rate at which the heat of combustion is developed. We see, therefore, that a very powerful wave of compression produced in a gas can start as well as propagate the combustion, and moreover, with extraordinary great velocity.

A compression wave of this kind is produced in a gaseous mixture brought to a very high temperature by combustion; it must travel considerably faster than the ordinary compression wave, because in the compressed (still unburnt) layer, ignition causes a very strong development of pressure, which, according to the theory of waves, must increase the rate of propagation.

On the basis of these considerations can be calculated the absolute velocity of the explosion wave, but this will not be entered into more closely here. It is clear, however, that it must be considerably greater than the velocity of sound in the mass of gas (heated to a high temperature by the explosion). The measurements given below confirm this; they show that the velocity of the explosion wave is one and a half to two times the velocity of sound at the temperature of combustion. The processes taking place after ignition in a combustible gas contained in a long tube, can now be presented as follows : the first condition is that of slow combustion ; the heat is conducted to the next layer of gas, and thus combustion is propagated at the rate of but a few metres a second. As, however, a strong increase of pressure is produced by the combustion, so at the same time the neighbouring, still unburnt, layers are compressed ; this causes an increase in the reaction velocity, as has been already shown, and ignition takes place more rapidly. But the result of this is to cause the next layers to be still more strongly compressed, and in this way we can see that, provided we have a mixture which burns sufficiently fast, the rate of combustion must constantly be increased. As soon as the compression in the unburnt layers becomes so great that self-ignition follows, the resulting extraordinarily powerful compression wave is propagated with very great velocity and with simultaneous ignition, i.e. we have the spontaneous development of the " explosion wave."

Berthelot,[1] who discovered the formation of an explosion wave, showed that its rate of propagation was independent of the pressure, of the diameter of the tube which contained the "knall gas," and of the material from which the tube was made, and hence that it represented a constant characteristic for each mixture, the determination of which was of great interest.

The following table contains some of the results of Berthelot side

[1] Compt. rend. 93. 18 (1881).

by side with those of Dixon[1] of later date (1891). The numbers, which agree very well, refer to metres per second.

	Berthelot.	Dixon.
$H_2 + O_2$	2810	2821
$H_2 + N_2O$	2284	2305
$CH_4 + 4O$	2287	2322
$C_2H_4 + 6O$	2210	2364
$C_2H_2 + 5O$	2482	2391
$C_2N_2 + 4O$	2195	2321
$H_2 + Cl_2$		1730
$2H_2 + Cl_2$		1849

The maximal pressure of the explosion wave is very great; according to the experiments described on page 694, mixtures of hydrogen and oxygen at the original pressure of one atmosphere must be compressed up to 30-40 atmospheres to produce self-ignition. Now, as the heat developed on explosion causes a rise in temperature of about 2-3000°, that is to say, an increase in absolute temperature to about four times the value it has on compression, we are concerned with pressures considerably above 100 atmospheres. Not only the magnitude of this pressure, but also the fact that it is produced so suddenly, causes the extraordinary destructive force which distinguishes the explosion wave from slow combustion.

The above considerations on the propagation of combustion were brought forward by Mallard and Le Chatelier, "Recherches expérimentales et théoriques sur la combustion des mélanges gazeux explosives," *Annales des mines,* September to December 1883; (also in a separate pamphlet, Paris, 1883, published by Dunod). In this work the experimental methods are brilliantly worked out, and at the same time, the theory is developed in the clearest manner. It must be considered a classical treatise on this branch of chemistry.

The above considerations show that the theory of the propagation of combustion could be completely developed as a pure hydrodynamical problem; the rate of propagation has been discussed in excellent investigations by E. Jouguet, *Journ. mathémat.,* 1905, p. 347, and 1906, p. 6; and L. Crussard (*Bull. Société de l'industrie minérale,* **6.** 1907); these authors calculated the velocity of the explosion wave for a number of cases—the results being in close agreement with observed values.

Molecular theoretical considerations, such as those by which Berthelot and Dixon explained the phenomena in question, seem as unnecessary in this case as they are for the treatment of acoustics. The author has shown in a small pamphlet, *Physikalisch-chemische Betrachtungen über den*

---

[1] For the literature see the comprehensive report by Dixon, *Ber. deutsch. chem. Ges.* **38.** 2419 (1905).

Verbrennungsprozess (Berlin, 1905, published by Springer), that the many phenomena which Dixon discovered in a very fine experimental research, in which he continued the older researches of Mallard and Le Chatelier, and succeeded in photographing the combustion processes, may be simply and clearly explained by purely hydrodynamical considerations.

Finally, it may be mentioned that also single gases, such as acetylene, and even elements such as oxygen in the form of ozone, are explosive; the decomposition, or transformation into a stable form, is accompanied in this case also by a strong development of heat.

Liquid and Solid Explosives.—It has thus been fairly established by experiment, that the velocity of explosion of gaseous systems is a characteristic of the system, in the same way as, and in fact in close relation to, the velocity of sound in a gas. In the case of explosives in other states of aggregation, however, the question still remains open; in recent times Berthelot [1] endeavoured to determine *whether liquid and solid explosives* show a similar behaviour to explosive mixtures of gases. It can be easily imagined that even the boldest experimenter would find nothing very attractive in the quantitative investigation of modern practical explosives; it is not without astonishment that we learn of the researches of this French investigator.

Development of heat and change in volume are the chief characteristics of an explosion. The following table contains these values for various explosives; the volume refers to that of the decomposition products of one gramme of explosive at 0°; the corresponding development of heat is given in the last column.

Explosive.	Volume.	Heat produced.
Methylnitrate . . .	870 cm.	1431 cal.
Nitroglycerine . . .	713 ,,	1459 ,,
Nitromannite . . .	692 ,,	1427 ,,
Guncotton . . .	859 ,,	1010 ,,

When these substances explode in their own volume, the pressure rises approximately to 10,000 kg. per square centimetre.

The rate of explosion of methylnitrate in long tubes of a few millimetres inside diameter was measured by Berthelot's chronographic method, which had already been widely employed. In tubes of caoutchouc the rate was 1616 metres per second, in glass tubes 1890-2482, in Britannia metal 1230, and in steel 2100.

The tubes were always burst by the explosion, usually being torn into long strips; those of glass were naturally reduced to powder. The stronger the tube, the greater on the whole is the rate of

[1] *Compt. rend.* **112.** 16 ; more fully in *Ann. chim. phys.* [6] **23.** 485 (1891).

explosion ; whether constant values could be obtained if the tubes did not burst could not be determined, because such tubes were impossible to make. Berthelot supposes that in such cases the rate of explosion would be approximately equal to the velocity of sound in liquids, that is about 5000 metres a second. The rate of explosion of nitro-glycerine in lead tubes was 1300 metres, of dynamite 2500 m. ; the physical condition of the explosive is thus of the greatest importance. The results show that the greatest velocity is attained in solid explosives as nitromannite (7700), picric acid (6500), or guncotton (5400 when closely packed). (For an account of the determination of explosive action, see the lecture by Will,[1] which also contains references to this literature.)

The theory of solid and liquid explosives will probably progress along the same lines as that of gaseous explosives ; in particular, the pressure necessary to produce the explosion will be of fundamental importance for the theory of the development of the explosion wave.

Reactivity of Oxygen.[2]—Oxygen, at high temperatures an extremely reactive element, is strikingly inert at ordinary temperature, not because its affinity, but because its reactivity, is small. Only a few bodies—the spontaneously oxidisable or "autoxidisable" bodies—are capable of combining more or less energetically with oxygen at the ordinary temperature. To this class belong the alkaline metals, especially those of high atomic weight, as rubidium and caesium ; also the compounds of sulphurous acid and sulphuretted hydrogen, finely divided metals, and such metallic oxides as are capable of higher states of oxidation ; but, most of all, certain organic bodies, e.g. alkyl compounds of phosphorus, arsenic, antimony, zinc ; the aldehydes ; many ethereal oils like turpentine, etc. In the spontaneous oxidation of these substances it is observed that they induce oxidation of other substances not spontaneously oxidisable. We may therefore attribute to them the power of putting oxygen in a more active state. This fact has received practical applications, e.g., in the bleaching of textiles and paper by turpentine.

These processes have been specially studied by Schönbein, and later by Engler and Weissberg, Brodie,[3] Clausius,[4] Löw,[5] Hoppe-Seyler,[6] Baumann,[7] M. Traube,[8] and in more recent times by van't Hoff,[9]

[1] Zeitschr. f. Elektrochem. **12.** 558 (1906).
[2] See Bodländer, Langsame Verbrennung, Stuttgart, 1899 ; and especially the excellent monograph by Engler and Weissberg, Vorgänge der Autoxydation, Brunswick, 1904.
[3] Phil. Trans., 1850, p. 759 ; Jahresber. f. Chem., 1850, p. 248.
[4] Pogg. Ann. **103.** 644 (1858) ; **121.** 256 (1864).
[5] Zeitschr. f. Chem. N.F. **6.** 610.
[6] Zeitschr. physiol. Chem. **2.** 24 : Ber. deutsch. chem. Ges. **12.** 1551 (1879).
[7] Zeitschr. physiol. Chem. **5.** 244.
[8] Ber. deutsch. chem. Ges. **15.** 2434 (1882).
[9] Zeitschr. phys. Chem. **16.** 411 (1895) ; Chem. Ztg., 1896, 807.

Jorissen,[1] and especially by Engler and Wild.[2] Most early writers thought the activation was due to conversion of the oxygen molecule into ozone and a hypothetical "antozone," or decomposition into free atoms. M. Traube[3] showed that in such processes of oxidation, especially of finely divided metals, in presence of water, hydrogen peroxide is formed, and this causes further oxidation. Van't Hoff and Jorissen investigated the facts quantitatively, and found, as Schönbein and Traube[4] had partly done before, that the autoxidisable substance renders as much oxygen active as it requires for its own oxidation ; in other words, that the autoxidisable and the other substance take up equal amounts of oxygen. They tried to explain this by a decomposition of oxygen into opposite electrically charged atoms. According to the important investigations of Engler and Wild, the phenomena attending autoxidation are to be explained by combination not with single atoms but with half-broken oxygen molecules —O—O—, forming peroxides of the type of hydrogen peroxide, *i.e.* of constitution

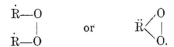

These peroxides, like hydrogen peroxide, can give up an atom of oxygen to other oxidisable substances, being converted themselves into the simple oxides $\ddot{R}_2O$ and $\ddot{R}O$. The active oxygen is therefore not in the form of free atoms, but it is combined oxygen which is easily removable. The stability of the peroxides varies according to the nature of the radicle R. Some are easily isolated, such as the peroxides of alkali metals (sodium, rubidium, etc.), that of hydrogen (in palladium hydride) and further those of aldehydes (acetyl peroxide, propionyl peroxide, benzoyl peroxide) ; others are less stable. Probably too the autoxidation of phosphorus yields a very easily decomposed peroxide, which gives off spontaneously an atom of oxygen, which combines with a molecule of oxygen to form ozone.

The action of light on autoxidation is very important ; it causes an extraordinary acceleration, as may be observed especially in the oxidation of organic bodies such as aldehyde, turpentine, etc. The bleaching of dyes may very probably be due to the formation of oxidising peroxides, accelerated by illumination. It may be imagined that light dissociates the closed oxygen molecules O = O into reactive complexes —O—O—, an hypothesis, however, that has not yet been verified.

Van't Hoff and Jorissen's rule as to the quantities of oxygen taken up by the autoxidisable and other substance holds only when the

[1] *Zeitschr. phys. Chem.* **22.** 34-59 (1897).
[2] *Ber. deutsch. chem. Ges.* **30.** 1669 (1897) ; see also Engler, *ibid.* **33.** 1109 (1900), also the monograph mentioned on page 698.
[3] *Journ. prakt. Chem.* **93.** 25 (1864).
[4] *Ber. deutsch. chem. Ges.* **26.** 1471 (1893).

lower oxide formed from the peroxide is stable, and does not oxidise further itself. If the lower oxide can give up its oxygen the original autoxidisable body is reformed, and by a kind of catalytic action is capable of oxidising an indefinite quantity of the other substance. Oxidation in the animal body very likely takes place in this way. Hæmoglobin has two stages of oxidation, oxyhæmoglobin and metoxyhæmoglobin, and the investigations of Schützenberger and others show that in oxyhæmoglobin half the oxygen is more easily split off than the other half. The first is to be regarded as peroxide oxygen, the second as oxide oxygen.

According to Haber [1] the best idea of autoxidation occurring in aqueous solution can be obtained by comparing it to the process in a voltaic cell ; at the anode a mol of oxide of the substance in question is formed, and, simultaneously, but at a separate place, a mol of hydrogen peroxide is found at the cathode, which must be charged with oxygen.

The Catalytic Action of Water Vapour.—Another very striking phenomenon is that the presence of *the very slightest traces of water vapour* are of the utmost importance for the ignition of certain explosive gas mixtures. Thus Dixon [2] discovered that a *completely dry mixture of carbon monoxide and oxygen* cannot be made to explode by means of the electric spark, or at most only with the greatest difficulty, but that the mixture is made capable of explosion by the introduction of the very slightest traces of water vapour.

When *other foreign gases* were mixed instead of water vapour with the carbon monoxide mixture $[2CO + O_2]$, it was found that explosion occurred on passing the electric spark in all cases where the foreign gas contained hydrogen, e.g. H_2S, C_2H_4, H_2CO_2, NH_3, C_5H_{12}, or HCl— but not when traces of SO_2, CS_2, CO_2, N_2O, C_2N_2, or CCl_4 (none of which contain hydrogen) were introduced.

It is the view both of Dixon and of L. Meyer [3] that the action of the water vapour necessary for the combustion of the carbon monoxide mixture $[2CO + O_2]$, consists in the water vapour being reduced by the carbon monoxide, and then the mixture of hydrogen and oxygen burning with a velocity sufficient for explosion, and at much lower temperatures than those at which the combustion of carbon monoxide occurs ; according to this, the water vapour acts as a carrier of oxygen, according to the two equations :—

(1) $\quad CO + H_2O = CO_2 + H_2,$

and

(2) $\quad 2H_2 + O_2 = 2H_2O,$

[1] *Zeitschr. phys. Chem.* **35.** 81 (1900).
[2] *Trans. Roy. Soc.* **175.** 617 (1884) ; *Journ. Chem. Soc.* **49.** 94 and 384 (1886).
[3] *Ber. deutsch. chem. Ges.* **19.** 1099 (1884).

which together lead to the result

(3) $2CO + O_2 = 2CO_2$;

only a much higher temperature is needed for the velocity of reaction (3) to be great enough to produce an explosion, than for the velocities of reactions (1) and (2).

It is possible that the action of water vapour may be referred to the fact that the equilibrium

(4) $H_2O + O_2 = 2H_2O_2$

is almost simultaneously established at high temperatures, and that hydrogen peroxide oxidises carbon monoxide—

$$H_2O_2 + CO = CO_2 + H_2O$$

quicker than oxygen itself does at the same temperature (see also p. 694).

In other cases this explanation fails, as has been shown by Baker,[1] in numerous examples ; hydrochloric acid and ammonia form no ammonium chloride, and vapour of ammonium chloride does not dissociate, when they are made very thoroughly dry. The peculiar catalytic action of water in these instances is suggestive of the high dissociating power of liquid water.[2]

Chemical Equilibrium and Temperature Gradient. — A temperature gradient can also alter the chemical equilibrium, *i.e.* if a system is in a stationary condition, but has not the same temperature at every point, then equilibrium can be different at every point to that which would correspond to the temperature, pressure, and proportions of the reacting substances. For in such a system the partial pressures of the separate components is different from point to point, and hence diffusion occurs, which causes more or less disturbance of equilibrium. The disturbance will be greater the more the rate of diffusion exceeds the reaction velocity. An extreme case has already been mentioned on p. 690 ; the equilibrium between water, hydrogen and oxygen in the neighbourhood of a glowing platinum wire is spread through the whole system by diffusion, for the velocity of reaction in the space apart from the wire is extraordinarily small. For the general formulæ applying to this case see the paper [3] in which the theory was first developed.

---

[1] *Journ. Chem. Soc.*, 1894, p. 611 ; *Chem. News*, **69.** 270 (1894).

[2] For further literature see the paper by Dixon, mentioned on p. 696.

[3] Nernst, *Festschrift Ludwig Boltzmann*, p. 904 (Leipzig, 1904). It is also possible that the equilibrium in an incandescent gas mixture (*e.g.* in a flame) is disturbed by radiation of heat to the cooler surroundings which contain the components as a rule in different proportions. For this means that the temperature of the separate components differs more or less from the mean value.

CHAPTER V

HEAT AND CHEMICAL ENERGY

The "Principle of Maximal Work," an Erroneous Interpretation of Heat of Reaction.—In what precedes we have described the most important laws which have been developed regarding *the application of the doctrine of energy to chemical change.*

In the *law of the constancy of the heat summation* (the expression of the first law of thermodynamics), and in *the equation of the reaction isochore* (the simplest expression of the second law of thermodynamics) we possess results of investigation which, on the one hand, rest on the firmest theoretical foundations, and, on the other, have been completely confirmed by experiment, and thus may be regarded as among the safest possessions of natural science.

The history of theoretical chemistry in the last forty years shows how a faulty consideration of these principles has led to persistent error.

This error owes its origin to a mistaken notion which has in many ways invaded the most different regions, and which has been conquered at the cost of much trouble ; the notion, namely, that the *heat of reaction* (*i.e.* the development of heat plus the external work), *associated with the completion of a natural process, must be regarded as the measure of the force which urges the system in question into its new condition.*

From this point of view we should have to regard the heat of reaction as the measure of the mutual affinity which exists between reacting substances ; and therefore we should have to conclude that "*every chemical change gives rise to the production of those substances which occasion the greatest development of heat.*" This theorem was advanced in 1867 by that highly-gifted experimenter, Berthelot, after Thomsen had previously, 1854, expressed a similar opinion. Berthelot later [1] claimed that this was not only the guiding principle of thermochemistry, but even of all chemical mechanics.

[1] *Essai de mécanique chimique,* Paris, 1878.

For a long time this theorem found unquestioning recognition, although it was shown in the most different ways, by Horstmann, Rathke, Helmholtz, Boltzmann, and others, that the theorem was untenable, both from a theoretical and an experimental standpoint.

Measure of Chemical Affinity.—Before we criticise Berthelot's principle, we shall have to consider what we are to regard as the measure of affinity. That the *velocity* of a reaction is not such a measure, needs no special proof after what we have already learnt ; it depends too much upon the, so to speak, accidental resistance opposing the course of the reaction. The assumption that at 400° iodine has a greater affinity for hydrogen than oxygen has, is as inadmissible as if we were to measure the capacity for work of two motors by the number of their revolutions. Again, we cannot conclude from the interesting researches of Raoul Pictet [1] that sodium has a *very much weaker* affinity for water at − 80° than at the ordinary temperature, because it will not act on aqueous alcohol at that temperature ; this conclusion would only be valid if it were shown that metallic sodium was precipitated when hydrogen was passed through a solution of sodium in aqueous alcohol (which is certainly *not* true). The obvious interpretation [2] of this experiment is that the velocity of reaction is greatly diminished by the large fall in temperature, so that water and sodium show a similar (*apparent*) indifference to each other at − 80°, as hydrogen and oxygen do at the ordinary temperature. Since every chemical process—in fact, every process occurring in nature (p. 16)—can advance without the introduction of external energy only in that direction in which it can perform work, and since a measure of chemical affinity must satisfy the invariable condition that every process completes itself in the sense of its affinity, we may without doubt regard *the maximal external work of a chemical process* (i.e. " *the change in free energy* ") *as the measure of affinity.*

The object of thermo-chemistry is thus clearly defined ; it is to measure with the greatest possible accuracy the changes in free energy associated with chemical processes, the extent of the measurement being as far as possible equal to that of the measurements of changes in total energy, *i.e.* heats of reaction. When this problem is solved, we shall be able to predict whether a reaction can complete itself or not under given conditions. All reactions advance only in the sense of a diminution of free energy, *i.e.* only in the sense of affinity, as defined above.

In order to ascertain the change in free energy associated with a chemical reaction, the reaction must be conducted *isothermally and*

---

[1] *Chem. Zentralbl.*, 1893, I. p. 458.

[2] This explanation of Pictet's experiments was published by me in *Jahrbuch der Chemie*, ii. p. 41 (1893), and was soon after completely confirmed by Dora and Vollner (*Wied. Ann.* **60.** 468, 1897).

reversibly ; we can then directly ascertain the maximal work which the process can yield. If the process can take place in several ways under the given conditions, the change in free energy must be the same for each way. For if not, we could complete the change in one way and reverse it in another, thus establishing a reversible isothermal chemical process, by means of which an unlimited amount of work could be performed at the expense of the heat of the environment. This is contrary to the second law of thermodynamics. Hence we arrive at the result that : *the change in free energy of a chemical process is independent of the way in which the process is completed, and is determined solely by the initial and final states of the system.* This is analogous to the law of constant heat summation (p. 597).

It follows directly that changes in free energy may be employed in calculations in the same way as changes in total energy. For example, the change in free energy of a chemical process is equal to the sum of the free energies of formation of the newly formed molecules, minus the sum of the free energies of formation of the decomposed molecules. By "*free energy of formation*" of a compound, we mean the maximal work which can be obtained by the union of the elements contained in the compound. In the chemistry of changes in free energy, therefore, the "free energy of formation" corresponds to the "heat of formation" in thermo-chemistry, and its determination is particularly important.

Comparison of Free and Total Energy.—According to the above considerations, Berthelot's theorem, that the course of chemical processes is determined by the heat of reaction, *i.e.* by the change in total energy, requires the relation that

$$A = U \qquad . \qquad . \qquad . \qquad . \qquad (1)$$

It can easily be shown that this relation cannot hold good in general ; in chemical processes between gases or in dilute solutions, for example, U is independent of the concentration (p. 602), but A is not so by any means, as is shown by the equation (p. 658)

$$A = RT \ln \frac{C_1{}^{n_1} C_2{}^{n_2} \cdots}{C'_1{}^{n'_1} \cdot C'_2{}^{n'_2} \cdots} + RT \ln K \qquad . \qquad . \qquad (2)$$

An equality of the two magnitudes is therefore at once excluded. Compare further equation (1) with our fundamental equation

$$A - U = T \frac{dA}{dT} \qquad . \qquad . \qquad . \qquad . \qquad (3)$$

Then if $A = U$, $\frac{dA}{dT} = 0$, and therefore also

$$\frac{dU}{dT} = 0.$$

We thus obtain the necessary (but not sufficient) condition for the truth of Berthelot's theorem, *that the heat of reaction U is independent of the temperature.*

Now this law is by no means established by experiment; on the contrary, in all those cases where *liquids* and *gases* take part in the reaction, the heat developed varies with the temperature; this is on account of the considerable difference between the specific heats of the reacting substances and of those produced. Thus we conclude that the heat of reaction which is associated with a chemical change does not at all correspond to the maximal external work to be obtained by the isothermal progress of a reaction.

We get a different behaviour when *solid* substances unite to form new complexes which also exist in the *solid* state; here the heat of reaction is found to be practically independent of the temperature, and in such cases it is possible, but by no means necessary, that the energy set free in the form of heat under ordinary conditions, might be entirely converted into mechanical energy by a suitable arrangement of the reaction process.

If A, the maximal work, is independent of the temperature, then we must necessarily have

$$A = U.$$

This latter condition is identical with the principle of the greatest work, but is also not fulfilled. When the temperature coefficient of A, namely $\dfrac{dA}{dT}$, is not zero, then of course the maximal work A and the heat of reaction U become equal when the other factor of the member on the right hand side of the equation, namely T, vanishes.

At absolute zero,[1] *i.e.* at $-273°$, the maximal work and the heat of reaction are therefore identical. At this temperature the theorem of Berthelot holds good absolutely, because here only *complete and exothermic reactions* are possible; the farther we are removed from this the more probable is the occurrence of endothermic reactions.

As a matter of fact, the preponderating chemical reactions at lower temperatures are, on the whole, the association phenomena taking place with a development of heat; while the reactions preponderating at higher temperatures are the dissociation phenomena which take place with the absorption of heat.[2]

The Results of Experiments.—Now as a matter of fact, a critical and careful comparison of the thermo-chemical data with the course of the reaction has shown that the direction of the chemical change does not necessarily coincide with the direction in which the reaction progresses exothermally.[3]

---

[1] That U should become equal to zero (and A also) at about the same limit is usually quite excluded.   [2] See Van't Hoff, *Études*, p. 174.

[3] See especially Rathke, *Abhandl. der naturforschenden Gesellschaft zu Halle*, **15.** (1881); also *Beibl. z. Wied. Ann.* **5.** 183.

If we bring equivalent quantities of gaseous HCl and of gaseous NH_3 into a given space, a part of the gases will unite to form solid NH_4Cl, and the formation of this salt will be carried to the point corresponding to the dissociation pressure at the temperature in question. On the other hand, if we bring the NH_3 and HCl, united in the form of solid NH_4Cl, into a sufficiently large space at the same temperature, then the same substance which was formed in the first case is decomposed into its products of dissociation. In the first case the reaction is exothermic,—in the second endothermic.

In general we may say that every single one of the numerous examples of reversible reactions is enough to disprove the universal validity of Berthelot's principle. For if a reaction is exothermic in one direction, it must be endothermic in the opposite direction; and if only the former were possible, then all reactions would advance to a completion, and there would be no such thing as a chemical equilibrium. And after what we have learnt about this in Book III., we must absolutely agree with Ostwald [1] when he characterises the advancement of Berthelot's principle as a return to Bergmann's doctrine of affinity (p. 446).

Berthelot himself soon noticed the inadmissibility of his principle in this connection. He therefore limited his law that a chemical system strives towards that final condition which has the greatest diminution of total energy compared with the original state, to those cases only where the interference of foreign energy does not form a disturbing factor. We shall not consider here all the unsuccessful attempts which have been made to explain every process which occurs with an absorption of heat, by the interference of some foreign (not chemical) force.

It must not be forgotten, however, that the defence of the universal truth of Berthelot's principle is due to the fact that on the whole, the occurrence of those reactions which develop heat, is more probable than that of endothermic reactions ; *and also that very frequently the sense of the chemical forces coincides with that in which a chemical process takes place with a development of heat.*

The claim of this principle to be an absolute law of nature must be rejected; and yet it is too often true for us to ignore it entirely. It would be as absurd to give it complete neglect, as to give it absolute recognition.

Now it is never to be doubted in the investigation of nature, that a rule which holds good in many cases, but which fails in a few cases, contains a genuine kernel of truth,—a kernel which has not as yet been "shelled" from its enclosing hull. And so in this case, as I have emphasised in the earlier editions of this book, it seems to me possible that, in a clearer form, Berthelot's principle may some day regain its importance. Inasmuch as we are dealing here with a

[1] *Allg. Chem.* ii. 614 (1887).

question of great significance—a significance which is rarely met in chemical investigation—we will try to specialise the somewhat too general form of Berthelot's rule, and apply it to some simple cases.

We must, however, always be on our guard against a confusion which is liable to arise in this kind of reasoning. Since development of heat causes an elevation of temperature and therefore always increases the reaction velocity, while, conversely, heat absorption decreases it, therefore exothermic reactions must always be self-stimulating, and endothermic reactions self-restraining, unless the reaction mixture is artificially maintained at constant temperature.

It must not be forgotten that *velocity of reaction* is of the highest importance for the question what particular compound of all those possible will result from a reacting system. It often happens that relatively unstable substances are first formed, and then change over to the more stable substances after a lapse of time which may be immeasurably great. We meet with many such examples in organic chemistry (cf. page 681). It can even be said that the attainment of definite equilibrium is almost always preceded by the formation of such unstable intermediate products; Horstmann [1] cleverly referred this phenomenon to the fact that, as a rule, *the rate of formation of a compound is smaller, the greater the accompanying development of heat.* But these relations have not yet been cleared up, and it is in any case premature to put forward a "law of successive reactions," as has recently been done.

Methods for the Determination of Affinity.—We have already found, *in the determination of the equilibrium between the reacting substances*, a method of very general applicability for the determination of the affinity of reactions; the change of free energy A referred to unit concentration was found to be (p. 658)

$$A = RT \ln K.$$

If this refers to a dissociation, then K denotes the dissociation constant, and the negative value of A denotes the "free energy of formation" of the compound. If all the dissociation constants of all of the reacting compounds are known, then we know the affinities of all the reactions; this theorem finds an excellent illustration [2] in the treatment of reactions between electrolytes, as given in Chapter IV. of Book III.

Another method for the measurement of affinity, which is very simple and exact, will be given in the following chapter: it depends on the *determination of the electromotive force of galvanic combinations.*[3]

The great importance of affinity determinations as those just described, may be illustrated by the following example among many.

---

[1] *Theoret. Chem.*, Brunswick, 1885.
[2] Compare Van't Hoff, *Zeitschr phys. Chem.* **3.** 608 (1889).
[3] *Zeitschr anorg. Chem.* **14.** 145 (1897).

As is well known, the combustion of carbon is the reaction whose capacity for work provides the driving power of most of our engines. The affinity of this reaction, *i.e.* the maximal external work which can be obtained by the combustion of 1 g. atom of carbon (= 12 g.) to carbon dioxide was previously unknown; and therefore we did not know the capacity for work of an ideal machine working at its maximum efficiency, when it is fed with coal.

The following method leads to a solution of this problem. We know the equilibrium between carbon dioxide, carbon monoxide, and oxygen (p. 692), *i.e.* we know the affinity A_1, of the reaction

$$2CO + O_2 = 2CO_2 + A_1,$$

and, moreover, at all temperatures. On the other hand, Rathke (p. 705) has observed that it is not possible to reduce carbon dioxide completely to carbon monoxide by the action of glowing coal. Thus a single quantitative experiment on the equilibrium between carbon monoxide, carbon dioxide, and carbon, would give us for all temperatures, exactly as in the preceding case, the affinity A_2, of the reaction

$$C + CO_2 = 2CO + A_2.$$

Then the addition of these two energy equations gives indirectly,

$$C + O_2 = CO_2 + A_1 + A_2 ;$$

that is, the required affinity of the combustion of carbon: this cannot be directly determined owing to the extremely minute dissociation of carbon dioxide into oxygen and carbon.

By means of the recent investigations of Boudouard,[1] who found that at 1000° and atmospheric pressure 99·3% CO and 0·7% CO_2 can exist in presence of solid (amorphous) carbon, we can determine the affinity of carbon and oxygen in the way I have proposed above. According to p. 692 carbon dioxide is dissociated to the extent of 0·0027% at 1000° and under atmospheric pressure. The quantity of oxygen x which coexists with carbon monoxide at 0·993 and carbon dioxide at 0·007 atmospheres can be found by the law of mass action, which gives

$$K \cdot (1)^2 = (0 \cdot 000027)^2 (0 \cdot 0000135)$$
$$K \cdot (0 \cdot 007)^2 = (0 \cdot 993)^2 \cdot x,$$

whence $x = 4 \cdot 9 \times 10^{-19}$ atmospheres. In order to combine carbon and oxygen at atmospheric pressure we may suppose, according to the cyclic process on p. 656, oxygen introduced into the system investigated by Boudouard and carbon dioxide removed. This gives as the affinity in question

$$A = A_1 + A_2 = RT \ln\frac{1}{x} - RT \ln\frac{1}{0 \cdot 007} .$$

---

[1] *Compt. rend.* **128.** 842 ; *Bull. soc. chim.* of the 5th August 1899 and 5th March 1900.

or (p. 660)

$$A = 4 \cdot 571 \cdot 1273 \cdot \log \frac{0 \cdot 007}{x} = 94,000 \text{ cal.}$$

The heat of reaction at atmospheric temperature is, according to p. 598, 97,650, and therefore is little different to the above value ; but as A and Q become more nearly equal in any case at lower temperatures (p. 705), we obtain the result that the *heat of combustion of coal at atmospheric tempera-ture is almost completely convertible into external work.* This result will be verified further on in an entirely different way.

Further calculations and considerations of this kind are to be found in Bodländer (*Zeitschr. f. Elektrochemie*, **8**. 833 (1902)) and Nernst, *Betrachtungen über den Verbrennungsprozess in den Gasmotoren*, Berlin, 1905 (Springer).

A New Theorem of Thermodynamics. — We have seen above (p. 705) that the comparison of total and free energy in reactions in which gases or solutions take part, has, strictly speaking, no meaning. On the other hand, when a reaction takes place between perfectly pure substances, entirely in solid or liquid form, the differences between A and U are usually found to be small. I have been led to the con-clusion that not only do A and U become equal at the absolute zero of temperature, but that their *curves touch asymptotically at this point.* That is to say

$$\lim \frac{dA}{dT} = \lim \frac{dU}{dT} \text{ (for T = 0)} . \quad . \quad . \quad (4)$$

It is to be remembered that this equation is only strictly applicable to pure solid or liquid substances ; gases are incapable of existence at absolute zero, while the behaviour of solutions needs closer study.

This simple theorem leads to a number of results which in my opinion have been completely confirmed by experience. From the standpoint of molecular theory, also, the new theorem seems not improbable. The second law of thermodynamics teaches us that at absolute zero itself A and U are equal, *i.e.* that the decrease in potential energy caused by the process under consideration is equal to the heat developed. If we allow the reaction to take place slightly above the absolute zero, the atoms of solid and liquid substances have still very small kinetic energy, and therefore oscillate only slightly about their positions of rest. Hence we can assume that the relative distances between the centres of attraction, and consequently the potential energy, is only altered to an infinitesimal extent, *i.e.*

$$\lim \frac{dA}{dT} = 0 \ (T = 0).$$

Substituting this in equation (3) p. 704, we obtain also

$$\lim \frac{dU}{dT} = 0 \ (T = 0).$$

It is very striking that from this hypothesis we can obtain relations between chemical affinity and heat of reaction which enable the calculation of chemical equilibria from thermal data —*i.e.* that the same problem is solved which Berthelot's principle was meant to solve.[1]

The recent considerations by A. Einstein (*Ann. d. Phys.* (4) 22, pp. 184 and 800, 1907) and M. Thiesen (*Verh. d. d. Physik. Ges.*, 18 Dec. 1908) agree in principle with my own theorem. For, according to these authors, the specific heats of solid bodies practically vanish in the neighbourhood of absolute zero, and then increase at first rapidly with rising temperature and afterwards slowly. It follows that the change in energy U associated with a chemical change must in fact obey the equation [2]

$$\lim \frac{dU}{dT} = 0 \quad (T = 0).$$

Einstein assumes further that the molecules of a crystallised body at absolute zero are kept in place by elastic forces, like the cross points of a latticed frame work. At higher temperatures the molecules oscillate isochronously about their positions of equilibrium, the impulse for these oscillations being given by the dark rays which fill the bodies.

Obviously the same assumptions must be made for isotropic solid substances (undercooled liquids), and when we observe that the energy of radiation, and therefore the amplitude of the above oscillations, increases in any case with a considerably higher power than the first with the temperature, it follows that also

$$\frac{dA}{dT} = 0 \quad (T = 0),$$

which is in agreement with my own considerations.

Relation between Affinity and Development of Heat in Condensed Systems.—If we assume, as we are entitled to do by experience, that the specific heats of solid and liquid bodies can be expressed in whole powers of the temperature, then it follows that the development of heat U can also be expressed in the same form :

$$U = U_0 + aT + \beta T^2 + \gamma T^3 \qquad . \qquad . \qquad . \qquad (5)$$

Substituting in the equation

$$A - U = T\frac{dA}{dT} \qquad . \qquad . \qquad . \qquad (3)$$

---

[1] The above thermodynamical theorem is developed in the following papers : Nernst, " Berechnung chemischer Gleichgewichte aus thermischer Messungen," *Nachr. d. Ges. d. Wissensch. zu Göttingen, Math-phys. Kl.*, 1906, Heft I. ; Nernst, *Sitzungsber. Preuss. Akad. d. Wissenschaft.*, 20 Dec. 1906. A detailed account, and calculation of numerous examples, will be found in the Silliman Lectures by Nernst, *Applications of Thermodynamics to Chemistry* (Scribner & Sons, New York, 1907) ; see further the list of references at the end of this chapter.

[2] [Einstein's theory has been to a large extent confirmed by the recent work of Nernst and his collaborators on specific heats at low temperatures. See p. 171, also *Sitzungsb. d. K. Akad. d. Wiss.*, Berlin, 3rd March 1910.]

and integrating, we obtain

$$A = U_0 + aT - aT \ln T - \beta T^2 - \frac{\gamma}{2}T^3 + \quad . \quad . \quad (6)$$

where a is an unknown integration constant.

The correctness of this integration may be easily seen by substitution in (3).

Differentiation gives us

$$\frac{dU}{dT} = a + 2\beta T + 3\gamma T^2 + \ldots ;$$

$$\frac{dA}{dT} = a + a - d \ln T - 2\beta T - \frac{3}{2}\gamma T^2 - \ldots$$

From our theorem

$$\lim \frac{dA}{dT} = \lim \frac{dU}{dT} \quad (T = 0)$$

it follows at once that

$$a = 0 \text{ and } a = 0 \quad . \quad . \quad . \quad . \quad (7)$$

and hence that

$$U = U_0 + \beta T^2 + \gamma T^3 + \quad . \quad . \quad . \quad (8)$$

$$A = U_0 - \beta T^2 - \frac{\gamma}{2}T^3 - \quad . \quad . \quad . \quad (9)$$

We see therefore that A can be calculated from purely thermal data, which was impossible by the application of the laws of thermodynamics known hitherto.

The relation

$$a = \lim \cdot \frac{dU}{dT} = 0$$

signifies moreover that in the neighbourhood of absolute zero molecular heats must be purely additive, and equal to the sum of the atomic heats. This holds for solid as well as liquid (amorphous) bodies.

The calculation of numerous examples shows that the coefficients β and γ, which can be obtained from the specific heats, are not very large, and this explains why the difference (per cent) between A and U is very small when the heat of reaction is considerable. This fact has been confirmed in recent times by different investigators, especially for the changes of solid substances ; it also explains at the same time the regularities put forward by Berthelot in support of his principle.

The accompanying diagrams may finally help to elucidate the position. If we omit all but the first member of the series representing U as a temperature function, then Fig. 47 gives the curves for U and A which would be obtained from equations (5) and (6), i.e. simply with the help of the two laws of thermodynamics known up to the present time.

Curves of this kind have been briefly discussed by van't Hoff[1] and by Broensted.[2]

The course of the curves is distinctly different when we combine the new hypothesis (4) with the familiar laws of thermodynamics. Taking into account only one term involving T in the series for U we must put

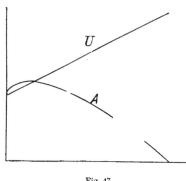

$$U = U_0 + \beta T^2 \quad A = U_0 - \beta T^2$$

and we thus obtain the curves shown in Fig. 48. The advance due to our new hypothesis is that the integration constant a, which would have to be determined separately for each reaction, cancels out, and therefore a calculation of A from thermal data becomes possible for condensed systems.

The relation

$$a = 0$$

further enables certain conclusions to be drawn on the change of specific heats with temperature.

Transition Point.—When applied to reactions in condensed systems which take place with considerable changes in affinity, the new theorem only explains the regularities which have already been empirically observed (and of course allows us to calculate the small difference between A and U quantitatively from the specific heats). But when A is small in comparison with U, and therefore Berthelot's principle is absolutely invalid, application of the new theorem leads to quite new results.

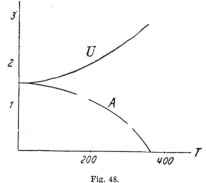

Fig. 48.

Transition points are an instance of this (p. 641); from the theorem, which permits the calculation of A from purely thermal data, we can evidently obtain the temperature at which

$$A = 0,$$

[1] *Boltzmann Festschrift*, 1904, p. 233.
[2] *Zeitschr. phys. Chem.* **56.** 645 (1906).

i.e. the transition temperature.   We can use the formula

$$A = U_0 - \beta T^2$$

thus limiting ourselves to two terms in the series for U, or in other words assuming that the difference between the capacities for heat of the disappearing and resulting substance is proportional to the absolute temperature.   As an example, let us consider the *change of monoclinic into rhombic sulphur.*   Broensted[1] studied this change in a brilliant investigation, obtaining the values for both U and A at different temperatures.   If we assume that the difference between the specific heats c_2 and c_1 of the two modifications rises proportionally[2] to the temperature, then we obtain

$$2\beta T = c_2 - c_1$$

$$= \frac{dU}{dT} \text{ (from the first law of thermodynamics)},$$

and hence by integration

$$U = U_0 + \beta T^2,$$

where U is the heat developed by the change of 1 g. sulphur.
   Numerically we find

$$U = 1\cdot57 + 1\cdot15 \times 10^{-5} . T^2$$

T.	U (obs.).	U (calc.).	Observer.
273	2·40	2·43	Broensted (*l.c.*)
368	3·19	3·13	Tammann (p. 642)

A is therefore given at the same time by the equation

$$A = 1\cdot57 - 1\cdot15 . 10^{-5} T^2.$$

(Fig. 48, p. 712, represents the change in U and A according to these formulæ.)
   If we calculate the transition temperature T_0 (under the pressure of saturated sulphur vapour), at which A = 0 (neglecting the vanishingly small external work caused by the difference in volume between the two modifications), we obtain

$$T_0 = \sqrt{\frac{1\cdot57}{1\cdot15 \times 10^{-5}}} = 369\cdot5 \text{ (instead of } 273 + 95\cdot4 = 368\cdot4).$$

Broensted further determined the values of A (in g. cal) for a series of temperatures by means of solubility determinations (cf. pp. 141 and 663).—

[1] *Zeitschr. phys. Chem.* **55.** 371 (1906).
[2] At absolute zero c_2 and c_1 must be equal, according to (7).

T.	A obs.	A calc.
273	0·72	0·71
288·5	0·64	0·61
291·6	0·63	0·59
298·3	0·57	0·55

The values agree to within a few per cent, to which extent Broensted states the observed values are uncertain.

It is therefore established that the maximal work of the above reaction can actually be calculated from purely thermal data.[1]

[Since $\beta = 1·15 \times 10^{-5}$, the difference between the specific heats is given by

$$c_2 - c_1 = \frac{dU}{dT} = 2·30 \times 10^{-5}T.$$

The following table shows the observed and calculated values of this difference at various temperatures.

T.	$\dfrac{dU}{dT}$	$2·30\,T \cdot 10^{5}$.	Observer.
83	$0·0854 - 0·0843 = 0·0011$	0·0019	Nernst
93	$0·0925 - 0·0915 = 0·0010$	0·0021	,,
138	$0·1185 - 0·1131 = 0·0054$	0·0032	Koref
198	$0·1529 - 0·1473 = 0·0056$	0·0046	Nernst
235	$0·1612 - 0·1537 = 0·0075$	0·0054	Koref
290	$0·1774 - 0·1720 = 0·0054$	0·0067	Wigand[2]
293	$0·1794 - 0·1705 = 0·0089$	0·0067	Koref
299	$0·1809 - 0·1727 = 0·0082$	0·0069	Wigand
329	$0·1844 - 0·1764 = 0·0080$	0·0076	Regnault

It will be seen that, in accordance with theory, the difference between the specific heats tends to decrease at low temperatures. The observed values for $\dfrac{dU}{dT}$ are of the same order of magnitude as those calculated; the actual differences between corresponding values in the two series of numbers being irregular, although sometimes apparently exceeding the error of observation.[3]]

If $c_1°$ and $c_2°$ are the specific heats, and $U°$ the heat of transformation at the transition point T_0, then it is easy to show that

[1] The calculation carried out by Broensted (l.c.) with the help of much more complicated formulæ founded on the second law of thermodynamics is not of the same importance, for T_0 was assumed known.

[2] *Ann. der Physik* [4], **22**. 79.

[3] [These additions to the text (of the sixth German edition) have been mainly taken from the latest exposition of the new theorem. Nernst, *Journ. de chim. phys.*, June (1910), p. 228.—TR.]

$$T_0 = \frac{U^\circ}{c_2{}^\circ - c_1{}^\circ}.$$

A corresponding equation is also true for melting points, but only when the difference between the specific heats of solid and supercooled liquid rises proportionally with the temperature. This seems actually approximately true in many cases, for Tammann[1] found the same relation empirically, e.g. for naphthalene,

$$U^\circ = 34\cdot7 \quad c_1{}^\circ = 0\cdot332 \quad c_2{}^\circ = 0\cdot442$$

and

$$\therefore T_0 = \frac{34\cdot7}{0\cdot11} = 315 \text{ (instead of 353)}.$$

As is well known, the specific heat of water in the liquid condition exhibits great anomalies, obviously on account of strong association. The series for U must therefore be carried further than the second term, and consequently we find that the above relation does not even hold good approximately in this case :

$$T_0 = \frac{80}{1\cdot00 - 0\cdot51} = 163 \text{ (instead of 273)}.$$

For a complete calculation in this case we should have to know the specific heats of supercooled water at low temperatures; direct measurement is impracticable, but it will probably be possible on theoretical grounds to obtain some insight into the phenomena in question.

[Other substances, however, such as betol and benzophenone, can be supercooled to a high degree. In these cases it is interesting to compare the specific heats of the crystal and of the supercooled liquid forms at different temperatures. Koref has obtained the following values :

Benzophenone.

T	$\dfrac{dU}{dT}$
137	$0\cdot1526 - 0\cdot1514 = 0\cdot0012$
295	$0\cdot3825 - 0\cdot3051 = 0\cdot0074$

Betol.

130	$0\cdot148 - 0\cdot144 = 0\cdot004$
240	$0\cdot256 - 0\cdot2205 = 0\cdot0355$
320	$0\cdot362 - 0\cdot295 = 0\cdot067$

Here we see plainly how the specific heats of the two forms tend to become equal at low temperatures, and how therefore $\dfrac{dU}{dT}$ converges towards zero.

[1] *Kristallisieren und Schmelzen*, p. 42 ff. (Leipzig, 1903).

In the case of salts containing water of crystallisation the affinity of the reaction (combination of one molecule of water with the salt) can be calculated by the formula

$$A' = RT \ln \frac{\pi}{p}$$

p being the vapour tension of water, and π the dissociation pressure of the hydrated salt. The heats of hydration of some salts have been measured with great accuracy; measurements of the specific heats of the hydrated and anhydrous salts at low temperatures puts us therefore in the possession of a complete set of data for testing the theorem. Some interesting examples will be found worked out in the paper mentioned above.]

It must be expressly emphasised that our knowledge of the variation of specific heats must be further extended before the problems put forward in this chapter can be solved with greater accuracy. The fact that the new theorem of thermodynamics developed above requires that molecular heats of solid and liquid substances should be exactly additive at low temperatures is an important basis for investigations of specific heats (cf. also p. 711).

We may complete this paragraph with the following general remarks : strictly speaking, the use of equation (8) requires the knowledge of specific heats down to absolute zero, and so an impression could easily arise that the application of the new theorem was extremely hypothetical. But in reality the conditions,

$$\frac{dA}{dT} = \frac{dU}{dT} = 0$$

or, in other words, the equality of A and U is fulfilled at easily attainable temperatures. Calculation of numerous examples has shown that even at absolute temperatures of $100°$, at which exact measurements can be conveniently carried out, the difference between A and U is only a few hundred cals. at the most, and usually very much less. At the boiling-point of hydrogen, where also exact investigation can be made, as the recent researches of Dewar and Kamerlingh Onnes have especially shown, the difference in question is almost always completely negligible.

Chemical Equilibrium in Homogeneous Gaseous Systems.—

It can now be easily shown that the equilibrium in homogeneous gaseous systems can also be calculated when we know, as above, the heat of reaction, and besides this, the integration constants of the vapour pressure curves of the reacting substances.

If the heat of reaction is given by the expression

$$U = U_0 + aT + \beta T^2 + \gamma T^3 + . \qquad . \qquad . \qquad (10)$$

then the second law of thermodynamics gives the relation (p. 671)

$$\ln K = \frac{U_0}{RT} - \frac{\alpha}{R} \ln T - \frac{\beta}{R}T - \frac{\gamma}{2R} T^2 - \ldots + I \quad . \quad (11)$$

In order to make use of our theorem, we consider the equilibrium in question at a temperature low enough for all the reacting molecular species to be either in the liquid or solid state; we can then consider the reaction as taking place between simply solid and liquid (pure) substances, according to the scheme

$$\nu_1 a_1 + \nu_2 a_2 + \ldots = \nu_1' a_1' + \qquad . \qquad . \qquad (12)$$

For each of these substances we can obtain from the second law of thermodynamics a vapour pressure formula which we can express as a special form of equation (11); if ξ is the concentration of the saturated vapour, then,

$$K = \frac{1}{\xi}$$

and hence

$$- \ln \xi = \frac{\lambda_0}{RT} - \frac{a_0}{R} \ln T - \frac{\beta_0}{R}T - \frac{\gamma_0}{2R} T^2 \ldots - i. \quad . \quad (13)$$

where

$$\lambda = \lambda_0 + a_0 T + \beta_0 T^2 + \gamma_0 T^3 + \qquad . \qquad . \qquad (14)$$

λ is the heat of condensation and i the integration constant.

In order to calculate the affinity of reaction (12), we conduct the process isothermally and reversibly, exactly as described on p. 656, thus finding that

$$A = RT (\ln K - \Sigma\nu\ln \xi) \qquad . \qquad . \qquad . \qquad (15)$$

where $\Sigma\nu\ln \xi$ is the summation

$$+ \nu_1 \ln \xi_1 + \nu_2 \ln \xi_2 + \ldots - \nu_1' \ln \xi_1' - \quad .$$

But now our theorem requires (p. 711) that for a reaction taking place according to the scheme (12), the coefficients of the terms T and T ln T in equation (15) must vanish; combining this equation with (11) and (13) we see at once that the term containing the factor T is [1]

$$RT (I - \Sigma\nu i)$$

and therefore

$$I = \Sigma\nu i \qquad . \qquad . \qquad . \qquad (16)$$

This equation is a very remarkable consequence of the new theorem; equation (11) contains besides thermal magnitudes only the integration constant I; this is now referred to a sum of integration constants which can be determined once and for all for every molecular species, most directly from the vapour pressure curves of the substance

---

[1] The condition that the factor of T ln T vanishes is satisfied by the additivity of atomic heats of solid substances at very low temperatures. It presents therefore nothing new.

in question in the liquid or solid condition. The above calculations show at the same time that the *integration constant i is independent of the nature of condensation product, e.g.*, it is the same for ice as for water; the two known laws of thermodynamics teach us nothing about this.

Heterogeneous Equilibrium.—We will now assume that in a homogeneous gaseous system for which the relation (according to the preceding paragraph)

$$\ln K = \frac{U_0}{RT} - \frac{a}{R} \ln T - \frac{\beta}{R}T - \frac{\gamma}{2R} T^2 + \Sigma \nu i \qquad . \qquad (17)$$

holds good, one molecular species is present as solid or liquid. Then, subtracting from the above equation the expression

$$- \nu \ln \xi = \left(\frac{\lambda_0}{RT} - \frac{a_0}{R} \ln T - \frac{\beta_0}{R} T - \frac{\gamma_0}{2R} T^2 - i\right)\nu$$

referring to the molecular species in question, we arrive at the result that the equilibrium constant K goes over to the value which, according to the earlier rules (p. 482), corresponds to the heterogeneous equilibrium in question. The value of i for the solid or liquid molecular species cancels out of the last term, and the remaining terms, which contain only thermal data, go over analogously to those values which refer to the heterogeneous system.

When several molecular species are present in the solid or liquid state, the above operation must be repeated for each species, and we thus arrive at the simple result that equation (17) can also be applied to heterogeneous systems in which any number of solid bodies coexist with a gaseous phase. The thermal magnitudes are connected with the heat developed by the reaction; the value of K is determined only by those molecular species *which do not coexist at the same time in the solid state*, and consequently we have only to sum the values of "i" for these molecular species in order to obtain the integration constant I.

Numerical Calculation of Chemical Equilibria from Heats of Reaction.—For an exact proof of the above formulæ the knowledge of specific heats of gaseous and condensed substances down to very low temperatures is necessary. Unluckily, such knowledge is only incomplete; it is, however, certain that the specific heats of condensed substances diminish very rapidly with the temperature (pp. 171 and 710), and for the present I have assumed that the atomic heats of the element approach the value $1\cdot5$ at very low temperatures; it fortunately makes very little difference what value we assume between 0 and 2. As the molecular heats of monatomic gases are constant at $3\cdot0$ (for constant volume, p. 203), the atomic heats of monatomic substances would be 1·5 greater in the gaseous than in the condensed condition at low temperatures. I have therefore made the assumption that at such temperatures the molecular heats of all gases are 1·5 greater at constant volume, and correspondingly 3·5 greater at constant pressure than the molecular heats of the corresponding condensation products.

These assumptions lead us to the vapour pressure formula, which has already been put forward on p. 235, and takes the following form on introducing ordinary logarithms :

$$\log p = -\frac{\lambda_0}{4\cdot571\mathrm{T}} + 1\cdot75 \log \mathrm{T} - \frac{\epsilon}{4\cdot571}\mathrm{T} + \mathrm{C} \quad . \quad (18)$$

where

$$\mathrm{C} = \frac{i + \ln\mathrm{R}}{2\cdot3023}$$

If we calculate with partial pressures instead of with concentrations—which is more convenient in dealing with gaseous systems—our new constant

$$\mathrm{K'} = \frac{p_1{}^{\nu_1} p_2{}^{\nu_2} \cdot \cdot \cdot}{p_1{}^{\nu_1'} \cdot \cdot \cdot} = \frac{1}{\mathrm{K}} \cdot (\mathrm{RT})^{\nu_1 + \nu_2 + \cdot\cdot\cdot -\nu_1' \cdot\cdot\cdot},$$

and hence, as can be easily shown,[1]

$$\log \mathrm{K'} = -\frac{\mathrm{Q}_0}{4\cdot571\mathrm{T}} + \Sigma\nu\, 1\cdot75 \log \mathrm{T} + \frac{\beta}{4\cdot571}\mathrm{T} + \frac{\gamma}{2\mathrm{R}}\mathrm{T}^2 + \Sigma\nu\mathrm{C} \quad (19)$$

Q, the heat developed at constant pressure, is correspondingly given by the expression

$$\mathrm{Q} = \mathrm{Q}_0 + \Sigma\nu\, 3\cdot5\mathrm{T} + \beta\mathrm{T} + \gamma\mathrm{T}^2 \quad . \quad . \quad (20)$$

[The following examples will serve to show how equation (18) may be used to obtain values of the constant C :

Hydrogen.

$$\log p_{mm.} = -\frac{55\cdot82}{\mathrm{T}} + 1\cdot75 \log \mathrm{T} - 0\cdot0535\ \mathrm{T} + 4\cdot4154$$

T =	20·60	20·41	19·61	19·03	18·35	17·57	16·58	15·13	14·11
p (calc.) =	799·7	759·8	604·9	504·7	401·0	299·7	197·4	95·8	52
p (obs.)[2] =	800	760	600	500	400	300	200	100	50

Toluene.

$$\log p_{mm.} = \frac{2202\cdot0}{\mathrm{T}} + 1\cdot75 \log \mathrm{T} - 0\cdot004884\ \mathrm{T} + 5\cdot9700$$

T = 195	252	273	298·8	324·8	362·7	372·3	383·4
p (calc.) = 0·0054	1·598	6·826	28·73	99·86	404·2	546·4	750
p (obs.)[3] = 0·0054	1·607	6·86	28·75	100	400	550	750

For T = 384°, λ is calculated to be 7922 cal. instead of 7866 (obs.).

[1] See p. 717 for the carrying out of this summation.
[2] Travers, *Experimental Study of Gases.*
[3] Barker, *Zeitschr phys. Chem.* **71.** 235.

In the last case, the vapour pressures vary in the ratio 1 : 100,000 over the range of temperature investigated, and yet the observed values agree very well with those calculated by means of the relatively simple formula given above. If we express p in atmospheres we must subtract log 760 from both sides of the equation, thus obtaining for hydrogen $C = 1\cdot54$, and for toluene $C = 3\cdot09$.]

The values of C can be called "chemical constants," for, with the thermal coefficients, they are characteristic for the chemical behaviour of the substances to which they refer. Their determination was attended at first with great difficulties; there are only a few substances of which we have accurate vapour pressure measurements extending over a wide range of temperature, which enables us to calculate with certainty the three constants λ_0, ϵ, and C of equation (18). But after the calculations had been carried out in a number of cases, it became obvious that there was a distinct parallelism between the values for a in the equation on p. 234 on the one hand, and the so-called "Trouton constants" (p. 274) on the other. If the vapour pressure in equation (19) is expressed in atmospheres, we obtain the formulæ

$$C = 1\cdot1 \quad a = 0\cdot14 \frac{\lambda_0}{T_0} \text{ (approximately)}.$$

In this way finally the following table could be constructed :—

CHEMICAL CONSTANTS.

H_2	. 1·6	HCl .	. 3·0	CS_2 .	. 3·1
CH_4 .	. 2·5	NO .	. 3·5	NH_3 .	. 3·3
N_2 .	. 2·6	N_2O .	. 3·3	H_2O .	. 3·6
O_2 .	. 2·8	H_2S .	. 3·0	CCl_4 .	. 3·1
CO .	. 3·5	SO_2 .	. 3·3	$CHCl_3$	. 3·2
Cl_2 .	. 3·1	CO_2 .	. 3·2	C_6H_6 .	. 3·0

We see that the value of C for the majority of these substances is about 3·1; the low boiling substances, especially hydrogen, have smaller, and the associated substances greater, values, i.e., C behaves exactly the same as the quotient $\frac{\lambda}{T_0}$ (p. 274); the parallelism between the two magnitudes should not, however, be carried further.

Example.—We will illustrate the practical application of equation (19) by calculating the dissociation of water vapour.

In this case we have

$$U = 113880 + 3\cdot5T + 0\cdot0035T^2 - \frac{4}{3}\frac{T^3}{10^6} - 0\cdot4\frac{T^4}{10^9}.$$

When $T = 290$ this expression gives a value for $U = 115160 = 2(68200 - 18\ 590)$: (68200 = heat of formation of 1 molecule liquid water, 590 = heat of evaporation per gram).

By differentiating we obtain for the difference of the molecular heats the expression

$$2H_2 + O_2 - 2H_2O = 3\cdot5 + 0\cdot007T - 4\frac{T^2}{10^6} - 1\cdot6\frac{T^3}{10^9},$$

which agrees satisfactorily up to fairly high temperatures with the recent measurements of Holborn (*Annalen der Physik*, 23, p. 809, 1907).

It follows further that

$$\log K' = -\frac{113,880}{4\cdot571T} + 1\cdot75 \log T + \frac{0\cdot0035}{4\cdot6}T - \frac{0\cdot67}{4\cdot6}\frac{T^2}{10^6} - \frac{0\cdot13}{4\cdot6}\frac{T^3}{10^9} - 1\cdot2$$

$$(\Sigma\nu C = 2 \cdot 1\cdot6 + 2\cdot8 - 2 \cdot 3\cdot6 = -1\cdot2).$$

According to p. 691 the degree of dissociation x under atmospheric pressure at T = 1300 is $0\cdot29 \cdot 10^{-4}$ and hence

$$\log K' = \log \frac{x^3}{2} = -13\cdot90\cdot$$

The temperature which corresponds to this value for K is given by the above equation as

$$T = \frac{113,880}{4\cdot571\left(13\cdot90 + 1\cdot75 \log T + \frac{0\cdot0035}{4\cdot6}T - \frac{0\cdot67}{4\cdot6}\frac{T^2}{10^6} - \frac{0\cdot13}{4\cdot6}\frac{T^3}{10^9} - 1\cdot2\right)}$$

As the terms of this denominator which contain T are only correction terms, we can calculate T easily by approximation. The value thus found is

T = 1320 (calc.) instead of 1300 (obs.).

Differences as great and even greater than this are obviously to be attributed to the uncertainty of the thermal data, especially of specific heats; the degree of dissociation varies very greatly with the temperature, and it is therefore evident that the differences between the calculated and observed results can be large. But it obviously shows a want of critical capacity to make such unavoidable differences the basis of an attack against the principles of the theory; this would only be admissible if the differences were certainly greater than could be explained by the uncertainty of the thermal data.[1]

Derivation of an Approximation Formula.—As the coefficients β and γ in equations (19) and (20) can only be calculated at present for isolated cases, we may for the time make use of the approximation formula

$$\log K' = -\frac{Q'}{4\cdot571T} + \Sigma\nu \, 1\cdot75 \log T + \Sigma\nu C \quad . \quad (21)$$

Q' is the heat developed at ordinary temperatures and under constant pressure, and can be taken directly from thermochemical tables. Of course the equations (8), (9), and (16) must be always used when it is

[1 The specific heats of hydrogen, oxygen, and water vapour have been recently redetermined by Pier (*Zeitschr. f. Electr.* **15.** 536); this has necessitated slight alterations in the above calculation.—TR.]

3 A

a question of testing the theorem we have developed, but the calculation of numerous examples has shown that the above approximation
formula is very well suited to obtain with the help of thermochemical
tables a *fairly accurate* idea of the state of equilibrium in a system. In
the following paragraph a few examples of this kind will be discussed.

Discussion of a few Examples.—Let us first consider the case
when $\Sigma \nu = 0$, *i.e.* when as many gaseous molecules disappear in the
reaction as are formed. Then we have

$$\Sigma \nu \cdot 1 \cdot 75 \log T = 0,$$

and it is also to be noticed that the expression $\Sigma \nu C$ is not very considerable because of the approximate equality of the values for C. If
the heat of reaction is also small in this case, as, *e.g.*, in the reaction

$$H_2 + I_2 = 2HI,$$

or even exactly zero, as in the passage of one optical isomer into its
antipode, then K′ will be nearly or exactly = 1. This means that the
components in equilibrium have approximately (or exactly) equal
partial pressures. This is entirely confirmed by experiment; besides
the examples already given may be mentioned the formation of esters,
the classical case of chemical equilibrium. As the formation of gaseous
ethyl acetate and water from the vapours of alcohol and acetic acid
takes place with an inconsiderable heat of reaction, it follows that, as
in the case of hydriodic acid, an equilibrium is established in which all
the components take part in appreciable concentrations, and as the
vapour tensions of the four substances are not very different, such an
equilibrium must also occur in the liquid mixture. .

If, on the other hand, a considerable development of heat takes
place, as in the reaction

$$H_2 + Cl_2 = 2HCl,$$

then the right-hand side of equation (21) is strongly negative at low
temperatures, *i.e.* there is practically no free hydrogen and chlorine
at equilibrium; it is only at high temperatures that the right side
approaches the value zero or at any rate becomes small, and we come
into a range of perceptible dissociation. The reaction

$$2NO = N_2 + O_2$$

also takes place from left to right with considerable evolution of
heat, and consequently nitric oxide only becomes comparatively stable
at high temperatures. The formation of acetylene from hydrogen and
solid carbon

$$H_2 + 2C = C_2H_2$$

is similar to the last case. Like the formation of nitric oxide, it is
attended with strong absorption of heat; acetylene can therefore be

formed from its components only at very high temperatures, and even then only in minute quantities.[1]

Let us now consider the case when the reaction is accompanied by a change in the number of molecules of the gaseous components ; the phenomenon of dissociation is the classical example of this. In these cases the sum of the two last terms of equation (21) is positive and may be not inconsiderable at fairly high temperatures. It follows that, e.g., although the reaction

$$2NO_2 = N_2O_4$$

takes place according to p. 667 with the fairly large development of 12,500 calories, a pronounced dissociation equilibrium is established in the neighbourhood of $T = 300$, and that N_2O_4 is almost quantitatively decomposed at slightly higher temperatures.

In the dissociation of many solid bodies, e.g. calcium carbonate, there are also more gaseous molecules on the right than on the left side of the equation ; this is still more pronounced in reactions like the dissociation of solid ammonium hydrosulphide (p. 662)

$$NH_4SH = NH_3 + H_2S.$$

For the same reason we observe in these cases a distinct dissociation pressure even at moderately low temperatures, although the heat of formation from the components may be considerable, as in the case of ammonium hydrosulphide (22,800 cal.), or even very great, as in the case of calcium carbonate (42,520 cal.).

Applying the above equation to the dissociation of calcium carbonate and similar processes, we obtain

$$\log p = -\frac{Q'}{4\cdot571T} + 1\cdot75 \log T + 3\cdot2,$$

where the chemical constant of CO_2 is 3·2. The temperature T_1 at which the dissociation pressure is one atmosphere is therefore given by

$$\frac{Q'}{4\cdot571T_1} = 1\cdot75 \log T_1 + 3\cdot2.$$

When T_1 is somewhere in the neighbourhood of $250 - 350$, $\log T_1$ alters only slightly with the temperature, and hence

$$4\cdot571\,(1\cdot75 \log T_1 + 3\cdot2) = 34 \text{ approximately,}$$

and therefore

$$T_1 = \frac{Q'}{34}.$$

This result has been actually empirically established by Le

[1] See v. Wartenberg, Zeitschr. anorg. Chem. 50. (1907) and Zeitschr. phys. Chem. 61. 366, and 63. 269 (1908), for a quantitative application of the theory to these and a few similar cases.

Chatelier and Forcrand; the new theorem not only explains in a simple manner the number found empirically (mean about 32), but also indicates the limits within which the law is true. It must fail at very low temperatures (at which, however, no examples have yet been found) and also at very high temperatures. The following table contains heats of dissociation of a number of carbonates, the observed temperatures at which the dissociation pressure is one atmosphere, and also the temperatures calculated according to Le Chatelier, Forcrand (T_1 calc. I), and according to the new theorem (T_1 calc. II). Only the latter agree satisfactorily with observations.[1]

Substance.	Q'.	T_1 (calc. I).	T_1 (calc. II).	T_1 (obs.).
$AgCO_3$	20060	627	548	498
$PbCO_3$	22580	706	610	575
$MnCO_3$	23500	741	632	about 600
$CaCO_3$	42520	1329	1091	1098
$SrCO_3$	55770	1743	1403	1428

It may finally be pointed out that the chemical affinity of a process can now of course be calculated by means of equation (2), p. 704, from thermal data and the chemical constants. For example, the maximal work which can be obtained by the combustion of carbon can be easily determined with the help of the above approximation formula. We have

$$A = -RT \ln K' = Q + (3 \cdot 2 - 2 \cdot 8) \, 4 \cdot 6 T,$$

when the resulting carbon dioxide has the same partial pressure as the disappearing oxygen. As the value of the second term is not 1 per cent of the heat of combustion Q at fairly low temperatures (e.g. at room temperature), we obtain in this simple way the same result already arrived at on p. 709, that A and Q are practically equal.

It must be noticed that at higher temperatures the change of Q with the temperature materially influences the value of A. In a similar manner we can of course calculate easily the maximal work to be obtained by the combustion of petroleum, etc.; this is only possible at present with the help of the above formula, for measurements of equilibria have not been carried out, and, ndeed, would be scarcely practicable.

It is clear that there lies before us the task of determining more accurately the values of C and the higher terms of equations (8), (9), and (15), by means of investigations of vapour pressures and specific heats, and then of working over afresh the whole of chemistry from the standpoint of Thermochemistry. But it may be already said that

[1] Brill, *Zeitschr. phys. Chem.* **57.** 736 (1907).

the relations between heat and chemical energy, for the discovery of which Berthelot's principle was a temporary guide, have now been firmly established in their proper lights.

Besides the literature already mentioned the following researches within the range of the new theorem may be referred to : E. Falck, *Physik. Zeitschr.* **9.** p. 433, 1908 ; R. Naumann, *Diss.*, Berlin, 1907 ; Barker, *Diss.*, Berlin, 1909 ; H. Schottky, *Zeitschr. phys. Chem.* **64.** p. 415, 1908 ; M. Trautz, *Zeitschr. für Elektrochemie*, 1908, p. 534. Chapter VII. of this book contains further applications.

CHAPTER VI

ELECTRO-CHEMISTRY I

Electrolytic Conduction.—The transport of electricity in conducting substances may happen in two different ways, *with or without* simultaneous transport of matter. The latter happens in the case of *metallic* conductors, and the former in *electrolytic* conductors ; these are also called conductors of the *"first"* and *"second"* classes, respectively.

The nature of metallic conduction is little known. On the other hand, we have very detailed conceptions of the nature of electrolysis, which has so often been a common link in the histories of physics and chemistry. It consists in a chemical decomposition which overcomes the strongest affinities by means of the electric force, the study of which has long been the favourite occupation of students of physics.

In considering the theory of electrolytic dissociation (p. 353), we saw how the process of the conduction of the current was caused by the displacement of the *free* ions (*i.e.* ions which are not united with each other to form electrically neutral molecules) in the solution under the influence of electric force ; the positive ions migrating from anode to cathode, and the negative ions in the opposite direction.

Hence a solution conducts electricity better, the more numerous the ions, and the smaller the friction which the ions encounter in their migration.

This conception may now be applied, unchanged, to every substance which conducts electrolytically,—whether gaseous, liquid, or solid,—whether simple or a mixture.

The electric charge of the ions is equally great whether they occur in solution, or in a substance of simple composition ; this follows from the fact that the fundamental electrolytic laws of Faraday hold good for fused salts as well as for aqueous solutions.

The most important features of electrolytic conductivity *in solution*, and in particular in aqueous solution, have been already discussed with the theory of electrolytic dissociation, and the doctrine of affinity.

The conductivity of simple substances, as, *e.g.*, of fused salts, like that of solutions, is obviously directly proportional to the degree of dissociation, and inversely to the friction of the ions. But it has not yet been possible to reduce the observed conductivities to these two factors; because here, of course, there can be no occurrence of a phenomenon, analogous to the changes of concentration near the electrodes, due to the Hittorf transportation in solutions. And thus we cannot state how large a fraction of the total molecules present in a fused salt is decomposed into ions, although an indirect solution of the question may be possible.[1]

Electrolysis.—When a system composed of conductors of the *first class* is traversed by a galvanic current, *thermal* action (Peltier's effect) takes place on the surface between different conductors; and also heat (Joule's heat) is developed in the whole circuit; but there is no migration of matter associated with the passage of the electricity.

But, on the other hand, when the galvanic current passes through conductors of the *second class*, then, *in addition to the above phenomena, there occurs a transportation of matter* (migration of the ions); and also on the boundaries between the conductors of the first and second classes, there occur peculiar chemical processes, which consist primarily in the solution of the electrodes or in the separation of the ions from the electrolytes, but are usually complicated by secondary reactions between the electrolyte and the separated products.

If two similar metallic electrodes dip into an electrolyte (a solution, or a fused, or a solid, salt), then the current J in a circuit formed by the electrolytic cell of resistance w and a source of electricity of electromotive force E, and resistance W, is, according to Ohm's law,

$$J = \frac{E}{W + w}.$$

This assumes that there are no changes produced by the current in the electrolytic cell, of such a nature as to make it a source of E.M.F. But it usually happens in the process of electrolysis, that either the nature of the surface of one electrode is changed, whether by having another metal precipitated upon it or by dissolving (occluding) the separated gases, or else the composition of the electrolyte bathing the electrode is modified in some way.

In all such cases a resistant electromotive force is produced in the cell, the so-called *galvanic polarisation*; if we denote the value of this by ϵ, then the strength of the current falls to

$$J = \frac{E - \epsilon}{W + w}.$$

[1] For water, which is at ordinary temperature an electrolyte, though a very poor one, the problem has actually been solved indirectly; see p. 519. The monograph by R. Lorenz, *Elektrolyse geschmolzener Salze* I. and II. (1905, W. Knapp), contains our present knowledge on conduction in fused salts.

The quantity of ions separated by the current may be ascertained by means of the law discovered by Faraday in 1833; according to this, the quantity of the ion separated in unit time upon the electrode, is proportional to the intensity [strength] of the current; and the same quantity of electricity will, in the most different electrolytes, electrolyse chemically equivalent quantities of ions.

When the chemical value of the ions is capable of changing, of course the meaning of *chemical equivalence* changes; thus the same current which separates 200 g. of mercury from a solution of mercurous nitrate $HgNO_3$, will separate 100 g. of mercury from a solution of $Hg(CN)_2$.

The quantity of electricity that suffices to deposit one electrochemical gram equivalent is

$$\frac{1}{1\cdot035} \cdot 10^5 = 96{,}540 \text{ coulombs (ampere seconds)}$$

and will be expressed by F (*Faraday*).

The Development of Electrical Energy by Chemical Systems.—Several different forms of apparatus are known which are capable of developing the galvanic current, and of transforming into electrical energy heat (thermopiles), mechanical energy (dynamos), or chemical energy (galvanic cell). We shall consider only apparatus of the last-named category.

A chemical system in which the changes of energy, associated with the changes of matter, succeed in producing electromotive activity, is called a *galvanic element.* As the galvanic current is associated with changes of matter only in conductors of the second .class—electrolytes—and as, on the other hand, it is only in electrolytes that changes of matter tend to produce galvanic currents, therefore the galvanic elements must contain substances which conduct electrolytically. Hitherto these have been almost exclusively aqueous solutions, and in isolated cases molten salts.

Galvanic elements can be constructed either only by means of substances which conduct electrolytically, or else with the help of conductors of the first class (*i.e.* electrodes of metal or carbon). In the first category are included the so-called "*liquid cells,*" which are formed by arranging in series, water solutions of electrolytes (acids, bases, and salts); by such means the electromotive forces developed on the contact surfaces between the metals and liquids, are completely eliminated. These liquid circuits have been the subject of repeated investigation, by du Bois-Reymond (1867), Worm-Müller (1870), Paalzow (1874), and others.

These circuits have recently increased in interest because an insight into the manner in which they develop their current has been obtained by means of the modern theory of solution (Chap. VIII.);

the electromotive force is produced simply by the mingling of the various solutions.

The process by which current is produced in other galvanic elements is also in most instances simple and clear. The current brings about certain changes in the element producing it, which changes can almost always be predicted from a knowledge of the nature of the electrode, and of the liquid which bathes it.

Thus in the cell of Volta, *e.g.*,

$$\text{Zn} \mid \text{H}_2\text{SO}_4\text{aq.} \mid \text{Cu,}$$

the metal of the negative electrode, zinc, goes into solution and hydrogen is developed on the positive copper pole.

In the Daniell element,

$$\text{Zn} \mid \text{ZnSO}_4\text{aq.} \mid \text{CuSO}_4\text{aq.} \mid \text{Cu,}$$

the process which develops the current can be expressed by the equation,

$$\text{Zn} + \text{CuSO}_4 = \text{Cu} + \text{ZnSO}_4.$$

In the Clark element,

$$\text{Zn} \mid \text{ZnSO}_4\text{aq.} \mid \text{Hg}_2\text{SO}_4 \mid \text{Hg,}$$

which consists of mercury covered with mercurous sulphate, a saturated solution of zinc sulphate, and metallic zinc, zinc goes into solution at the negative pole and separates out on the positive pole; but instead of forming an amalgam with the mercury, the solid mercurous sulphate is reduced according to the equation

$$\text{Zn} + \text{Hg}_2\text{SO}_4 = \text{ZnSO}_4 + 2\text{Hg.}$$

All of these chemical processes occur in accordance with Faraday's law.

If the same quantity of electricity passes through the most different galvanic elements, the decompositions are all (electrically) equivalent.

The experimental determination of electromotive forces is most easily carried out by comparison with a standard cell, such as the Clark element, which has a potential reliable to within one part in a thousand; its value in international volts according to Jäger and Kahle is [1]

$$E_t = 1 \cdot 4292 - 0 \cdot 0012 \,(t - 18).$$

Recently the Weston cell has been preferred; this is constructed in the same way as the Clark cell, but instead of zinc and zinc sulphate cadmium and cadmium sulphate are used. The electromotive force of this cell (see the preceding references) is

$$E_t = 1 \cdot 0187 - 0 \cdot 000035 \,(t - 18),$$

that is, for most purposes may be regarded as independent of temperature. For very exact measurements of electromotive force it is desirable to use

---

[1] *Zeitschr. f. Instrumentenkunde*, 1898, Heft 6, p. 161; *Wied. Ann.* **65**. 926 (1898).

both cells, as they can be constructed without difficulty. For details of the measurements see Kohlrausch, *Leitf. d. Phys.* 9th edit., and especially W. Jäger, *Normalelemente*, Halle, 1902.

Special Electrochemical Reactions.—In the electrolysis of, *e.g.*, hydrochloric acid, the ions are directly deposited in a neutral condition as gaseous hydrogen and gaseous chlorine, but more often this is not the case, but complications occur from the action of the ions on each other, on the metal of the electrode, or on the solvent, or, finally, on other dissolved substances. The following reactions which are intelligible without further explanations may be taken as examples :—

$$2\overset{-}{OH} + 2 \oplus = H_2O + \frac{1}{2}O_2$$

$$2C\overset{-}{H_3COO} + 2 \oplus = C_2H_6 + 2CO_2$$

$$\overset{-}{Cl} + \oplus + Ag = AgCl$$

$$\overset{++}{Zn} + 2 \ominus + 2H_2O = Zn(OH)_2 + H_2$$

$$\overset{-}{Cl} + \oplus + FeCl_2 = FeCl_3$$

$$2\overset{+}{H} + 2 \ominus + H_2O_2 = 2H_2O.$$

All these reactions may be regarded as due to the action of positive and negative *electrons* on the electrolyte, p. 395 ; the introduction of negative electrons into the reaction indicates that the reaction takes place at the cathode, where the positive ions (cations) are deposited, and similarly the occurrence of positive electrons indicates that the reaction takes place at the anode. The number of electrons occurring in the reaction gives at the same time the number of F's which are required for the electrochemical reaction in question.

For more precise knowledge of the nature of electrochemical principles it is indispensable to know the most important electrochemical reactions ; for this we may refer to the excellent work of W. Borchers, *Elektrometallurgie*, 3rd edit. (Leipzig, 1903, Hirzel), F. Haber, *Grundriss der technischen Elektrochemie auf theoretischer Grundlage* (R. Oldenbourg, München-Leipzig, 1904), and B. Neumann, *Theorie und Praxis der analytischen Elektrolyse der Metalle* (W. Knapp, Halle, 1897). For the experimental study we may note as introductions to practical electrochemical work the writings of W. Loeb (Leipzig, 1899), R. Lorenz (Göttingen, 1901), and K. Elbs (Halle, 1902). Le Blanc gives a short account of theoretical electrochemistry in his *Lehrbuch der Elektrochemie*, 4th edit. (Leipzig, 1906) ; while F. Foerster has published an excellent book on *Elektrochemie wässriger Lösungen* (Leipzig, 1905, A. Barth).

CHAPTER VII

ELECTRO-CHEMISTRY II

THERMODYNAMIC THEORY

Electrical Work.—Electrical work is given by the product of the potential (volts) and the quantity of electricity (coulombs); the unit of electric work is the volt-ampere-second, or, more briefly, the watt second, and is performed when a current of one ampere flows under a difference of potential of one volt for one second. In absolute measurement the volt is 10^8, the ampere 10^{-1}, so that the watt second is

$$10^7 \text{ absolute units (cm}^2 \text{ g sec}^{-2}),$$

or according to p. 12

$$\frac{10^7}{41,890,000} = 0 \cdot 2387 \text{ cal.}$$

This amount of heat is evolved, for example, when a current of 1 ampere flows for one second through a resistance of 1 ohm.

To deposit one electrochemical gram equivalent is needed 96,540 coulombs, which number we have already designated F. When a galvanic cell of electromotive force E yields so much current as suffices for the chemical conversion of one gram equivalent the work done is

$$\text{EF watt seconds} = 96,540 \times 0 \cdot 2387 \times \text{E} = 23,046 \text{ E cal.}$$

If an electrolytic cell has a back electromotive force ϵ the work needed to decompose one gram equivalent of the electrolyte is ϵF.

Application of the First Law of Thermodynamics.—If a galvanic cell of electromotive force E and internal resistance W is closed by a resistance w, then, according to Ohm's law, the current is

$$i = \frac{E}{W + w}$$

and the heat evolved in the external circuit is

$$i^2 wt = E^2 \frac{w}{(W + w)^2} t.$$

If W is very small compared with w all the electrical energy given out by the cell is spent on the external circuit and we have

$$i^2wt = \frac{E^2}{w} t = \nu FE,$$

where the number of F's yielded by the element is given by

$$it = \nu F.$$

If U is the heat of reaction of the process that yields the current per gram equivalent of chemical conversion, a cell which is short circuited and enclosed in a calorimeter will give the thermal effect νU, when ν gram equivalents are converted; for, according to the law of conservation of energy, the thermal effect is the same in whatever way the chemical transformation may take place. But if the electrical circuit is placed outside the calorimeter, the heat developed in the calorimeter will be less by the amount i^2wt, and if w is great compared with W the conversion of ν equivalents will yield in the calorimeter the quantity of heat

$$\nu U - i^2wt = \nu(U - FE)$$

or per gram equivalent in the cell the heat

$$H = FE - U$$

will be *absorbed*. H may conveniently be described as the latent heat of the cell.

If we may make the supposition that H is negligible, it follows that

$$E = \frac{U}{F},$$

that is, the electromotive force of the cell can be directly calculated from the heat of reaction. Experience shows that in many cases, especially in those in which U is large, this assumption holds; it is not permissible, however, to make the assumption tacitly.

In the following we will describe the heat of reaction in electrochemical processes by U, bearing in mind that in practical applications the systems of units in which E and U are respectively expressed, must be taken into consideration.

It was long believed and is still occasionally stated that in a galvanic cell the decrease in total energy which is associated with the chemical change, that is the heat of reaction, is the direct measure of the electromotive force, or, in other words, that the chemical energy is simply converted into electrical; this assumption would involve the equation

$$FE = U,$$

as has already been remarked above; if U is measured in calories and E in volts we should have, according to the above,

$$E = \frac{U}{23,046} \text{ volt.}$$

This relation was put forward tentatively by v. Helmholtz (1847) and W. Thomson (1851), and is commonly known as Thomson's law; *it would follow from the law of conservation of energy if a galvanic cell neither rose nor fell in temperature when yielding current*, that is, if it neither gave heat to its surroundings nor withdrew heat from them, but though this is often approximately the case it is not accurately true. It was long considered that the difference between calculation and observation was due to errors of experiment, but this view was completely disproved by the experimental investigations of Thomson,[1] and especially Braun,[2] and by the thermodynamic treatment of v. Helmholtz given below, which led to new and very careful measurements, and finally controverted Thomson's rule both experimentally and theoretically.

The unqualified recognition which this rule long enjoyed was largely due to the circumstance that in the first case to which it was applied it agreed very well with observation; in the Daniell cell, namely, the electromotive force has almost precisely the value which was calculated from the heat of reaction. The heat of formation of one equivalent of zinc sulphate from metal, oxygen and very dilute sulphuric acid is

$$\frac{1}{2} (\text{Zn, O, SO}_3, \text{aq.}) = 53,045,$$

and for copper sulphate the corresponding amount is

$$\frac{1}{2} (\text{Cu, O, SO}_3, \text{aq.}) = 27,980.$$

The difference between these two values,

$$53,045 - 27,980 = 25,065,$$

gives the change of energy associated with the transport of unit amount of electricity from the cell and consequently with the deposition of 1 gram equivalent of copper from the solution of its sulphate by zinc; according to Thomson's rule, therefore, the electromotive force of the Daniell cell should be

$$E = \frac{25,065}{23,046} = 1 \cdot 088 \text{ volt,}$$

whilst direct measurement gives 1·09 to 1·10. Similarly good agreement is found for combinations of the type of the Daniell cell in which silver replaces copper and cadmium replaces zinc in the solutions of their salts.

Thomson's rule, however, fails altogether in liquid cells and concentration cells; here the current-yielding process consists simply in

[1] *Wied. Ann.* **11.** 246 (1880).   [2] *Wied. Ann.* **17.** 593 (1882).

the mixing of solutions of different concentrations, and if the solutions are sufficiently dilute the heat of reaction is nothing, whilst the electromotive force can reach a considerable amount. We shall subsequently become acquainted with a whole series of a galvanic combinations in which there are large differences between the observed electromotive force and that calculated thermochemically.

Just the same considerations apply to electrolytic processes, where instead of electromotive force E of the galvanic combination we have the opposing electromotive force of polarisation ϵ (p. 727). Here also only approximate agreement is to be found ; for example, to electrolyse dilute hydrochloric acid requires about 1·3 volt, whilst the heat of reaction is, according to the equation,

$$\frac{1}{2}(H_2, Cl_2) = 22,000$$
$$(HCl, aq.) = 17,310$$
$$\overline{\text{Total} = 39,310}$$

and therefore we have

$$\epsilon = \frac{39,310}{23,046} = 1\cdot71 ;$$

it must also be remarked that U is independent of the concentration of the hydrochloric acid, whereas ϵ is not so (see Chap. VIII.). The galvanic polarisation of a common salt solution calculated from the thermodynamic equations

$$\frac{1}{2}(H_2, Cl_2) = 22,000$$
$$(HCl, aq.) = 17,310$$
$$(HCl \ aq., NaOH \ aq.) = 13,700$$
$$\overline{\text{Total} = 53,010}$$

gives

$$\epsilon = \frac{53,010}{23,046} = 2\cdot30,$$

whereas experiment shows it to be about 2·0 volt.

Reversible Elements.—When we send the same quantity of electricity through a galvanic cell, first in one direction, and then in the opposite, we must distinguish between two cases. The element may return to the original state or not. An example of the first case is given by the Daniell cell,

$$Zn \mid ZnSO_4 \mid CuSO_4 \mid Cu.$$

If unit quantity of electricity (measured electrochemically) is sent through this cell in the direction from left to right, then an equivalent of zinc goes into solution at one pole, and an equivalent of copper is precipitated upon the other pole. Then if the same quantity of electricity is sent through the cell from right to left, an equivalent of copper goes into solution, and an equivalent of zinc separates out. Thus the system returns again to its original condition.

An example of the second case is given by Volta's cell, combined according to the scheme,

$$Zn \mid H_2SO_4 \mid Cu.$$

If unit quantity of electricity pass through this cell from left to right, an equivalent of zinc goes into solution at the zinc pole, and an equivalent of hydrogen is set free at the copper pole. Then when the same quantity of electricity passes back from right to left, an equivalent of copper passes into solution at the copper pole, and at the zinc pole an equivalent of hydrogen is set free. Thus, at the end of the experiment, an equivalent of copper and an equivalent of zinc have passed into the solution, and two equivalents of hydrogen have been set free from the system.

In the first case, the heat developed during the cyclic process, and also the external work performed, are both equal to zero. Therefore the element must possess the same electromotive force, whether the current flows in one direction or the opposite.

But, in the second case, there must be compensation for the chemical changes produced in the course of the experiment; this can only be found in the fact that the sum of the work performed in the passage of unit quantity of electricity first in one direction and then in the other through the cell, has a certain definite value; *i.e.* that *the element has a different electromotive force* in the two cases. This is possible only when an opposite electromotive force is developed by the passage of electricity, that is when the element is polarised.

We therefore call these two classes of cells *non-polarisable* and *polarisable*, or *non-reversible* and *reversible*, respectively. A kind of intermediate link between these two groups is found in such elements as Grove's cell (platinum, nitric acid, sulphuric acid, and zinc); these are non-polarisable in one direction, namely in that in which they produce current; but they become polarised by leading the current through in the opposite direction.

Strictly speaking, all reversible batteries can be used as *accumulators*, and, conversely, all good accumulators must act reversibly. Only the reversible elements work rationally, *i.e.* with the maximum efficiency; the cells which are non-reversible are comparable to badly built steam-engines, which work with leaky pistons and valves. This fact justifies our dealing mainly with cells which work ideally, *i.e.* with those which are reversible.

In the first place, it is indispensable, for the reversibility, that the *processes taking place at the electrodes shall be reversible.* A metal plate which dips into a solution of one of its salts *is a "reversible electrode"* of this sort; because, by the passage of the current from the electrode into the solution, metal only passes into the solution, and when the current passes in the opposite direction the metal passes back from the solution to the metal plate. Thus the change is reversible. Such electrodes may be called " *reversible electrodes of the first class.*"

These electrodes can also be suitably called " *electrodes which are reversible as regards the cation,*" because the transfer of electricity is limited exclusively to the *cation.*

Similarly,' " *reversible electrodes of the second class* " may also be called " *electrodes which are reversible with reference to the anion.*"

Thus, *e.g.*, if we cover a piece of silver with a layer of AgCl, and then dip the electrode so prepared into a solution of a chloride, as KCl, the conditions required for an electrode of the second class are fulfilled. The passage of electricity from the electrode to the electrolyte can only take place by chlorine ions (obtained by the reduction of the AgCl) going into solution; or, when the current is in the opposite direction, the chlorine ions will be precipitated upon the electrode, uniting with the silver to form AgCl. In both cases the electronegative ions accomplish the transport of the electricity from the electrode to the solution, *i.e.* the electrode described behaves as though it were a modification of chlorine, which conducts like a metal, and, therefore, it completely satisfies the condition of reversibility.

In general, every metal covered with one of its insoluble salts, in which it forms the basic ingredient, and placed in a solution of another salt containing the same electronegative ingredient as the first salt, is an " *electrode which is reversible as regards the anion.*"

It is preferable to use *mercury* as the metal, because, being a liquid, its surface remains in the same condition ; and also, because it forms a large number of insoluble compounds with negative radicals.

Since such insoluble compounds render the electrode unpolarisable they are called *depolarisators.*

Reversible galvanic elements may therefore be divided into the three following classes—

1. Those composed of two reversible electrodes of the first class, as, *e.g.*, the Daniell element.

2. Those composed of one reversible electrode of the first class, and of one reversible electrode of the second class, as, *e.g.*, the Clark " normal " element.

3. Those composed of two reversible electrodes of the second class; no use has thus far been made of any element of this last type.

The Conversion of Chemical Energy into Electrical Energy.—The relations between *the heat development* of the current-generating process of a reversible galvanic cell, and the external work performed by this element, *i.e. its electromotive force*, can be arrived at by means of a cyclic process.

We will allow the galvanic element having the electromotive force E to perform the work E, at the temperature T, whereby an equivalent of the positive metal is precipitated upon the positive pole, and an equivalent of the metal of the negative pole goes into solution. Let U denote the heat of reaction associated with these chemical processes. It can be calculated from the thermochemical data ; in the Daniell element, *e.g.*, it corresponds to the difference between the heats of formation

$$(Zn, SO_4, aq.) - (Cu, SO_4, aq.).$$

The heat developed in the element is equal to the heat of reaction minus the external work, *i.e.*

$$= U - E = - H.$$

We will now bring the element from the temperature T to T + dT, whereby the electromotive force will change from E to E + dE; and reverse the chemical change in the element by sending in unit quantity of electricity in the opposite direction. This requires expenditure of the work E + dE, and there occurs an absorption of heat amounting to

$$U + dU - E - dE.$$

After cooling to T the system comes again to its original condition.

Now, during this reversible cyclic process, the work dE is performed from without; and at the same time the quantity of heat, E − U, is taken from T + dT to T.

But now, according to the law regarding the conversion of heat into external work, it follows that

$$dE = (E - U)\frac{dT}{T},$$

or

$$E - U = T\frac{dE}{dT}. \qquad . \qquad . \qquad . \qquad (1)$$

According as the electromotive force of the element increases or decreases with the temperature,

$$E > U, \text{ or } E < U.$$

That is, the electromotive force will, respectively, be greater or smaller than the heat of reaction of the chemical processes which produce the galvanic current.

The preceding equation, which may be obtained directly from the fundamental equation on p. 23, by setting the change of the free energy A equal to E, was first derived by H. v. Helmholtz,[1] and was soon after subjected to an experimental test by Czapski ;[2] its correct-

---

[1] *Sitzungsber. der Berl. Akad.* for Feb. 2 and July 7, 1882 ; *Ges. Abh.* Bd. II.
[2] *Wied. Ann.* **21.** 203 (1884) ; see also Gockel, *ibid.* **24.** 618 (1885).

ness was thus shown by these experimental results, together with those of Jahn.[1]

Experience teaches that there are reversible galvanic elements with positive temperature coefficients, as well as with negative ; and therefore sometimes a greater and sometimes a smaller amount of external work can be obtained than is equivalent to the heats of reaction of the chemical processes producing the current.

The recent and very exact researches of Jahn (l.c.), who determined directly by means of a Bunsen ice calorimeter the amount of heat (U) developed in the whole closed circuit of a galvanic element, clearly proved that the difference $E - U$ is by no means always equal to zero, and can only be neglected in comparison with the total change of energy.

The following table contains the values of the electromotive force E, for a number of combinations, expressed both in volts and also in cal.; and also the heat of reaction of the chemical changes referred to 1 g. equivalent. An example may serve to show how the calculation is carried out.

It was found for the Daniell cell at 0°

$$E = 25,263, \quad U = 25,055, \quad E - U = 208 \text{ cal.} ;$$

on the other hand, its temperature coefficient is

$$\frac{dE}{dT} = + 0 \cdot 00034,$$

from which, according to Helmholtz's formula,

$$E - U = 0 \cdot 00034 \cdot 23,046 \cdot 273 = 213 \text{ cal.}$$

The agreement is amply sufficient, considering the uncertainty of the slight difference between $E - U$.

Combination.	E expressed in		U.	E - U.	
	Volts.	g.-cal.		Obs.	Cal.
Cu, Cu(C₂H₃O₂)₂aq. Pb, Pb(C₂H₃O₂)₂ + 100 H₂O	0·470	10,842	8,766	+ 2076	+ 2392
Ag, AgCl Zn, ZnCl₂ + 100 H₂O	1·015	23,453	26,023	− 2570	− 2541
Ag, AgCl Zn, ZnCl₂ + 50 H₂O	1·001	23,146	24,456	− 1310	− 1305
Ag, AgCl Zn, ZnCl₂ + 25 H₂O	0·960	22,166	23,493	− 1327	− 1255
Ag, AgBr Zn, ZnBr₂ + 25 H₂O	0·828	19,138	19,882	− 644	− 663

[1] Wied. Ann. **28.** 21 and 491 (1886) ; see also Jahn, Elektrochemie, Wien, 1895.

A combination found by Bugarszky,[1]

$$\text{Hg} \mid \text{HgCl} - \text{KCl} - \text{KOH} - \text{Hg}_2\text{O} \mid \text{Hg},$$

is especially interesting. This cell yields an electromotive force of 7566 cal., and the current given by it is from right to left, so that the current-producing process is—

$$\text{HgCl} + \text{KOH} = \frac{1}{2}\text{Hg}_2\text{O} + \frac{1}{2}\text{H}_2\text{O} + \text{KCl}.$$

This process, however, occurs with *absorption of heat* ($U = -3280$), that is an endothermic reaction is here electromotively active. $T\dfrac{dE}{dT}$ according to Bugarszky $= +11,276$, which is very considerable, and according to Helmholtz's theory $U = E - T\dfrac{dE}{dT} = -3710$.

Galvanic Polarisation.—If we electrolyse a system in equilibrium the decomposition caused by electrolysis produces a displacement of equilibrium. This of course needs the application of a certain amount of external work which is performed by the galvanic current. It follows necessarily from this, *that the current which is transmitted through the system has to overcome an opposing electromotive force.* And from this there follows this theorem : *if we electrolyse a chemical system, which is kept at constant temperature, a reaction takes place in such a way as to oppose, in an electromotive way, the passage of the current through the system.* This principle is included under the more general one of *action and reaction*, stated on p. 676.

As remarked on p. 727, the intensity of the current in a circuit which contains the electromotive force E and an electrolytic cell is given by the expression

$$i = \frac{E - \epsilon}{W + w} ;$$

if the polarising force is equal to the back electromotive force we shall get equilibrium, that is the electrolytic cell forms a galvanic element of electromotive force $E = \epsilon$. Hence the formula

$$\epsilon - U = T\frac{d\epsilon}{dT}$$

will, according to p. 737, apply to it. It is to be remarked, however, that U, the heat of reaction of the process yielding the current, can rarely be determined with certainty, because polarisation is commonly due to extremely small quantities of substances occluded by the electrodes or by changes of concentration in the immediate neighbourhood of the electrodes, which are difficult to define. For these reasons the above formula has only been applied in a few cases.

Moreover, ϵ is usually considerably less than E on account of certain

[1] *Zeitschr. anorg. Chem.* **14.** 145 (1897).

irreversible processes, such as convection, diffusion, and the like; see especially von Helmholtz (*Sitzungsberichte der Berliner Akademie*, 1883, p. 660; *Ges. Abh.* vol. iii.).

The thermal effects which accompany polarisation have been very thoroughly studied by H. Jahn.[1]

Thermodynamic Calculation of Electromotive Forces from Vapour Pressures.—Since the electromotive force of a reversible galvanic cell measures the maximal work which the current-yielding process can give, and since at any given temperature this amount of work is perfectly defined, *we can calculate the electromotive force of any combination if we know the affinity of the current-yielding reaction.* This has been done, in the first place, with so-called concentration cells in which the current-yielding process consists simply in the mixing of solutions of different concentrations. The calculation was first carried out in 1877 by Helmholtz;[2] if two copper electrodes are dipped into two communicating cells of a copper salt, copper is dissolved in the dilute solution and precipitated from the more concentrated; the process which yields the current is therefore the equalisation of concentration of the solutions round the two electrodes. The maximal work to be obtained in this case can be calculated in various ways, most simply by means of isothermal distillation, as shown on p. 110, and it follows that this work must be equal to the electromotive force, as is confirmed by experiment.[3] In more recent times I have considerably simplified the theory of Helmholtz for dilute solutions by application of van't Hoff's law, and by making use of reversible electrodes of the second kind (see the following chapter) subjected it to a relatively exact experimental proof.[4]

A different kind of concentration cell was subsequently studied by G. Meyer,[5] after Türin[6] had given a theoretical discussion of it. In an element which follows the scheme

| Concentrated amalgam | Solution of a salt of the metal dissolved in the amalgam | Dilute amalgam |

the current which it yields transfers metal from the more concentrated to the dilute amalgam; and since the process is reversible, the electromotive force of the cell is again the measure of the maximal work which can be obtained from the current-yielding process. On the other hand, the osmotic pressure of the metal dissolved in the mercury measures the same quantity, and hence by determining the electromotive force of cells constructed according to the above type the osmotic pressure of the dissolved metal may be obtained. In all the cases experimented on (Zn, Cd, Pb, Sn, Cu, Na) it

---

[1] *Zeitschr. phys. Chem.* **18.** 399 (1895); **26.** 385 (1898); **29.** 77 (1899).
[2] *Wied. Ann.* **3.** 201 (1877); *Ges. Abhandl.* i. p. 840.
[3] J. Moser, *Wied. Ann.* **14.** 61 (1881).
[4] *Zeitschr. phys. Chem.* **4.** 129 (1889).
[5] *Ibid.* **7.** 477 (1891).   [6] *Ibid.* **5.** 340 (1890).

appeared that (1) the osmotic pressure is proportional to the concentration of the metal dissolved in mercury, and (2) that its value (to within a small percentage) is that calculated from the temperature (mostly 18-20°) and concentration of the amalgam on the assumption *that the molecular weight of the dissolved metal is identical with its atomic weight*; the latter result is in complete agreement with other determinations of the osmotic pressure of metals dissolved in mercury (see p. 406).

The preceding considerations applied to the equilibrium between solid and liquid states of aggregation show that at the melting-point of a metal, electrodes in the *solid and liquid states* must possess *the same electromotive activity*; the force of an element therefore suffers no change when the electrode melts, which is in agreement with the experiments of Miller.[1]

Application of Thermodynamics to the Lead Accumulator.

—The thermodynamic treatment given above has been applied to the lead accumulator in a very interesting paper by F. Dolezalek.[2] If we assume that the current-yielding process is, as suggested by Planté, expressed by the equation

$$PbO_2 + Pb + 2H_2SO_4 = 2PbSO_4 + 2H_2O,$$

the electromotive force must clearly increase when the concentration of the sulphuric acid is increased and that of the water decreased. If two lead accumulators filled with acid of different concentrations are opposed to one another, the current-yielding process of the combination is simply that for two Fs two mols of sulphuric acid are transported from the first accumulator to the second, and at the same time two mols of water from the second accumulator to the first. If p_1 and p_2 are the vapour pressures of the sulphuric acid, P_1 and P_2 those of the water in the two accumulators, the work done per F, which is accordingly the electromotive force ΔE of the combined cell, is

$$\Delta E = RT\left(\ln \frac{p_1}{p_2} + \ln \frac{P_2}{P_1}\right) \quad \cdot \quad \cdot \quad \cdot \quad \cdot \quad (1)$$

The vapour pressures of water over aqueous sulphuric acid are known (p. 160); those of sulphuric acid are impossible to measure on account of their smallness. According to the considerations on p. 112 we can calculate the vapour pressure of one of the components of a mixture when we know that of the other as a function of the composition. We may therefore express $\ln \dfrac{p_1}{p_2}$ in equation (1) by means of the vapour pressure P of water; we found (p. 113)

$$\ln \frac{p_0}{p} + x \ln \frac{P_0}{P} = \int_0^x \ln \frac{P_0}{P}\, dx,$$

[1] *Zeitschr. phys. Chem.* **10**. 459 (1892).
[2] *Zeitschr. f. Elektrochemie*, **4**. 349 (1898); *Wied. Ann.* **65**. 894 (1898); see also especially the monograph by the same author, *Theorie des Bleiakkumulators*, Halle, 1901, Knapp.

and this may be applied to the two solutions, of which one contains x_1 and the other x_2 mols of water for one mol of sulphuric acid, and yields

$$\ln \frac{p_1}{p_2} = x_2 \ln P_2 - x_1 \ln P_1 - \int_{x_1}^{x_2} \ln P \, dx,$$

hence

$$\Delta E = RT\left(x_2 \ln P_2 - x_1 \ln P_1 - \int_{x_1}^{x_2} \ln P \, dx + \ln \frac{P_2}{P_1}\right).$$

In order to obtain ΔE in volts we must set

$$R = 0 \cdot 861 \, . \, 10^{-4}.$$

Dolezalek calculated the electromotive force of two accumulators opposed to one another also from the formula

$$\Delta E = U + T \frac{\partial \Delta E}{\partial T};$$

where U can be calculated from the heat of dilution of sulphuric acid, and $\frac{\partial \Delta E}{\partial T}$ is given by the measurements of Streintz[1] on the variation of the temperature coefficient of the accumulator with the concentration of the acid. Moreover $T \frac{\partial \Delta E}{\partial T}$ is very small (0·02 volt as the maximum), which is in complete agreement with the considerations on p. 160, according to which the heat of dilution of a sulphuric acid mixture is almost the same as the maximal work done in dilution. The following table contains the results of calculation, and shows the striking agreement between the electromotive force calculated in different ways and measured by different observers.

ELECTROMOTIVE FORCE OF ACCUMULATORS OF DIFFERENT
DENSITIES OF ACID

No.	Density of Acid.	% H_2SO_4.	x.	Vapour Pressure P mm. Hg.	Electromotive force E in volts (0°).			
					Calculated		Measured	
					from P.	from U.	Dolezalek.	Streintz.
1	1·553	64·5	3	0·431	2·383	2·39	2·355	...
2	1·420	52·15	5	1·297	2·257	2·25	2·253	2·268
3	1·266	35·26	10	2·975	(2·103)	(2·10)	2·103	(2·103)
4	1·154	21·40	20	4·027	2·000	2·06	2·008	1·992
5	1·035	5·16	100	4·540	1·892	1·85	1·887	1·891

[1] *Wied. Ann.* **46**. 454 (1892).

During the charge of an accumulator the acid becomes, according to the above equation, more concentrated, during discharge more dilute ; accordingly during charge the electromotive force of the accumulator must rise, during discharge it must fall.   If the charge and discharge are carried out with considerable current density, relatively large changes of concentration will occur at the plates, and accordingly the accumulator will show a noticeably higher electromotive force during charge and a noticeably smaller during discharge than corresponds to the normal value of 1·95 volt ; this is confirmed by experiment.   Accordingly we have in the accumulator a polarisation of a peculiar kind, namely a change in the concentration of acid which takes place in the same sense at both the positive and negative plates, although to a greater extent at the positive.   The accumulator, which of all galvanic cells is by far the most important, is also, as Dolezalek has shown in the monograph mentioned above, one of the most interesting combinations from the thermodynamic point of view ; the thermodynamic treatment has yielded the important result that *the accumulator works reversibly in the sense of the above reaction.*

Electromotive Force and Chemical Equilibrium.—The maximal work that a chemical process can yield is, according to p. 658,

$$A = RT \ln \frac{C_1{}^{n_1} C_2{}^{n_2} \cdots}{C_1{}'^{n_1'} C_2{}'^{n_2'} \cdots} + RT \ln K ; \qquad . \qquad (1)$$

if E is the electromotive force of a galvanic combination, in which the current-yielding process is given by a reaction to which equation (1) refers, we have

$$E = A . \qquad . \qquad . \qquad . \qquad (2)$$

These equations were developed in a somewhat different form, but in principle the same, by Helmholtz (1889).[1]

To express E in volts it is necessary, according to p. 731, to put

$$R = \frac{1·985}{23,046} = 0·861 \times 10^{-4}.$$

These equations have recently been confirmed experimentally for the reaction

$$TlCl + KSCN \ aq. = TlSCN + KCl \ aq.,$$

by C. Knüpffer,[2] who, at the suggestion of Bredig, measured both the chemical equilibrium in the above reaction, and the electromotive force of the combination

$$Tl\text{-amalg.} \ | \ TlCl - KCl - KSCN - TlSCN \ | \ Tl\text{-amalg.}$$

Especially striking results were obtained by the application of the formulæ (1) and (2) to the " knall-gas " cell :

$$Pt \ | \ H_2 \ | \ H_2O \ | \ O_2 \ | \ Pt.$$

[1] *Ges. Abh.* iii. p. 108.
[2] *Zeitschr. phys. Chem.* **26.** 255 (1898).

Assuming that hydrogen and oxygen are present under unit pressure, we have

$$E = \frac{RT}{4} \cdot \ln\frac{1}{\pi_1{}^2\pi_2},$$

where π_1 and π_2 are the partial pressures of hydrogen and oxygen in saturated aqueous vapour. At $T = 290$ ($t = 17°$) for example,

$$x = 0{\cdot}48 \times 10^{-25}\%,$$

and reduced to the vapour pressure of water $= 0{\cdot}0191$ atm. at this temperature

$$x = \frac{0{\cdot}48 \times 10^{-25}}{0{\cdot}0191^3} = 1{\cdot}80 \times 10^{-25}\%.$$

Hence $\pi_1 = 0{\cdot}0191 \cdot 1{\cdot}80 \cdot 10^{-27}$ atm. and

$$\pi_2 = \frac{0{\cdot}0191 \cdot 1{\cdot}80 \cdot 10^{-27} \text{ atm.}}{2}$$

and we obtain :

$$E = 0{\cdot}01438 \log^{10} 4{\cdot}92 \cdot 10^{85} = 1{\cdot}2322 \text{ volt at } 17°.$$

This value, calculated by Wartenberg and myself,[1] appeared at first sight improbable, as direct measurements—employing weakly acidic or alkaline solutions instead of pure water to avoid polarisation—had given the considerably lower value of $1{\cdot}15$. This difference, however, may be obviously explained by the fact that the oxygen electrode does not attain its full potential, so that we are probably dealing with the lower potential of an oxide of platinum. If the heat of formation of this oxide is low (which is extremely probable), we can easily understand why the temperature coefficient of the "knall-gas" cell obeys equation (1), p. 737.

Broensted[2] has calculated indirectly the value $1{\cdot}238$ volt which is practically identical with the above; in the following paragraph we shall again arrive at the same result in a totally independent way.

Finally it may be pointed out that we can calculate with partial pressures instead of concentrations in equation (1); the equilibrium constant K must then, of course, be calculated in the same way.

Calculation of Electromotive Force from Thermal Data.
Historical.—As has been already explained on p. 733, Helmholtz in 1847 and later W. Thomson in 1851 brought forward the theorem that in a galvanic element chemical energy is completely transformed into electrical energy; if we express the chemical energy U (taken from the thermochemical tables) in gram-calories per gram equivalent,

[1] *Gött. Nachr.* Heft 1 (1905) ; *Zeitschr. phys. Chem.* **56.** 544 (1906).
[2] *Ibid.* **62.** 385 (1908).

then the electromotive force could be calculated from the simple formula

$$E = \frac{\cdot U}{23046} \text{ volt} \quad . \quad . \quad . \quad . \quad (1)$$

It is obvious (cf. pages 705 and 732) that, the above equation is identical in principle with the so-called Berthelot's law of maximal work, which supposes that the course of a chemical process is determined solely by the heat developed. Both laws are often approximately true, but internal reasons alone show that they cannot be true laws of nature.

The application of the second law of thermodynamics to the galvanic element was an important advance, for which we must thank Gibbs and Helmholtz (p. 737). Putting $23,046\,E = A$, we find the relation

$$A - U = T\frac{dA}{dT} \quad . \quad . \quad . \quad . \quad (2)$$

But this equation gives no real solution of the problem, for integration is necessary before the electromotive force can be calculated from the thermal data, and this involves the appearance of a completely undetermined integration constant.

As the temperature coefficient of the electromotive force is usually low, equation (2) explains why A and U are so often nearly equal to one another, especially when the absolute temperature T is not high. But why the temperature coefficient is often so small remains unexplained, and it is also not possible by means of equation (2) to calculate electromotive force from heats of reaction.

Application of the New Theorem of Thermodynamics.—The

theorem developed on p. 709 ff. yields the solution of the problem under discussion. If we construct a galvanic element from absolutely pure substances in the liquid or solid state, then the theorem gives us the relations :

$$U = U_0 + \beta T^2 + \gamma T^3 + \quad . \quad . \quad . \quad (3)$$

$$A = U_0 - \beta T^2 - \frac{\gamma}{2}T^3 - \quad . \quad . \quad . \quad (4)$$

The meaning of the coefficients β, γ, . . . is found as before by differentiating U with regard to T :

$$\frac{dU}{dT} = C_1 - C_2 = 2\beta T + 3\gamma T^2 + \quad . \quad . \quad (5)$$

$C_1 - C_2$ is here the difference between the capacities for heat before and after the transformation of one gram equivalent ; equation (5) is therefore fulfilled when the molecular heat C of the reacting components can be expressed by the relation

$$C = C_0 + 2\beta'T + 3\gamma'T^2 + \ldots$$

It will be useful to explain the above relations a little more fully.

I. The equations (3) and (4) must be at first confined to *pure* solid and liquid substances, because it is highly probable that the phases of a heterogeneous system at absolute zero can only be formed from substances containing molecules of only one kind. As a matter of fact it is not difficult in most cases to carry out the calculation for galvanic combinations which do not satisfy these conditions. Let us consider, *e.g.*, the element

Pb/ saturated aqueous solution of $PbBr_2$/ Br_2/ Pt.

The process which yields the current is given by the equation :

$$Pb + Br_2 = PbBr_2.$$

The substances Pb, $PbBr_2$, are in a pure condition, but the liquid bromine dissolves some water. Now, according to the law of the relative lowering of solubility (p. 145), the taking up of water lowers the solubility of the bromine, and correspondingly the electromotive force is somewhat decreased ; by means of the law just mentioned we can calculate what the solubility of the bromine would be if it took up no water, and hence arrive at the true electromotive force of the pure combination.

II. Equations (3) and (4) cannot strictly be applied when gases are included in the process which yields the current, because gases are incapable of existence at absolute zero ; but, as we have already seen on p. 716, the theory can also be extended to this case. (See below.)

III. See the remarks (p. 716) on specific heats, a knowledge of which is, in principle, necessary. At the boiling point of hydrogen the difference between thermal and chemical energy in equation (1) hardly ever exceeds 0·001 volt.

Hence we obtain, in general, the following rules for the calculation of electromotive force from heats of reaction : by means of the first law of thermodynamics we extrapolate the thermochemical data obtained at ordinary temperatures to as low temperatures as possible, and then put

$$E = \frac{U}{23046}.$$

We can then calculate the electromotive force at the temperature required by means of the second law of thermodynamics (equation (2)), or, more simply, by means of equation (4). The galvanic combination under consideration must, of course, satisfy the conditions enumerated under I., or be such that its departure from these conditions can be suitably allowed for.

As an example we will take the Clark cell. It has already been explained that equations (3) and (4) are only applicable to galvanic combinations which are composed of absolutely pure substances; we must therefore often make use of a suitable artifice to reduce the combination under consideration to the required form. In the special case of the Clark element this is easily done by lowering the temperature to such a point that ice is present in the solid state. The process yielding the current is then expressed by the equation:

$$Zn + Hg_2SO_4 + 7H_2O \text{ (ice)} = ZnSO_4 . 7H_2O + 2Hg.$$

The heat developed by this reaction can be calculated from the data:

$$(Zn, S, 2O_2) = 230,090, (2Hg, S, 2O_2) = 175,000,$$

$(ZnSO_4, 7H_2O) = 22,690$, latent heat of ice per mol at $17° = 1580$. .

Hence

$$2U = 66,720 \text{ at } T = 290°.$$

The molecular heats are

$$Zn = 6·0 \ (10°), \ Hg_2SO_4 = 31·0 \ (50°), \ 7H_2O = 63·7 \ (10°),$$
$$ZnSO_4 . 7H_2O = 89·4 \ (10°), \ 2Hg = 13·2 \ (10°).$$

The values for Hg_2SO_4 and $ZnSO_4$, $7H_2O$ have been recently determined by Schottky (p. 725); the value for ice is the most uncertain, as it had to be extrapolated for $+10°$ from the measurements of Person, Regnault, and Dewar. From the above numbers we obtain

$$2\frac{dU}{dT} = 4\beta T = -1·9 \text{ for } T = 283 ;$$

this value is of course not very accurate, especially as the specific heats do not all refer to the same temperature. But, on the other hand, it is only a matter of a small correction, and even an uncertainty of $0·8$ cal. in $\frac{dU}{dT}$ only represents a difference of $0·005$ volt.

It follows that

$$U = 38,505 - 0·0017T^2 ;$$
$$A = 38,505 + 0·0017T^2.$$

The electromotive force of the Clark element at $T = 266$ where ice is present is

$$E = 1·4624 \text{ volt. (obs.)} ;$$

from the above formula we obtain for this temperature

$$E = \frac{A}{23026} = 1·4592 \text{ volt. (calc.).}$$

It is also obvious that at $T = 100$, A and U only differ by a few parts in a thousand. The difference between A and U is considerable in the ordinary Clark element, where the behaviour of the solution comes into play $(A = 32,937, U = 40,565 \text{ at } T = 291)$.

For further applications see W. Nernst, *Sitzungsber. Berl. Akad.*, 21st January 1909.

The new theorem enables us to calculate the E.M.F. of *gas cells* most simply by means of formula (2), p. 704, where we substitute for log K, or, if we calculate with partial pressures instead of concentrations, for log K', the equations (17), p. 718, or (19), p. 719.

It can be at once seen that the E.M.F. of a gas element can also be calculated from the thermal data of the current-yielding process and the chemical constants of the gases in question (which are not present in the solid or liquid state).

As an example we will deduce the E.M.F. of the " knall-gas " element. If hydrogen and oxygen are present under the pressure of one atmosphere it follows that (see also p. 744)

$$E = \frac{0 \cdot 0001983 \; T}{4} \log \frac{1}{K' \pi^2},$$

where π is the value of the vapour pressures of water in atmospheres ($= 0 \cdot 0191$ at $T = 290$) and K' can be calculated according to p. 719. We obtain therefore

$$E = 1 \cdot 237 \text{ volt at } T = 290$$

in agreement with the result on p. 744.

If we make use of the approximation formula (21), p. 721, we have

$$\log K' = -\frac{115160}{4 \cdot 571 \; T} + 1 \cdot 75 \log T - 1 \cdot 2,$$

and from this we find

$$E = 1 \cdot 25 \text{ volt,}$$

i.e. a fairly accurate value. At higher temperatures where the influence of the specific heats is greater, the approximation formula would of course give considerably inaccurate results.

It appears that a first approximation to the calculation of E.M.F. at ordinary temperatures may be very easily obtained by the use of the above approximation formula, which is exceedingly easy to manipulate. Bodländer[1] compared the heats of formation of numerous iodides and chlorides with the electromotive forces of the corresponding elements. He found that the difference between the two magnitudes was only small in the case of the iodides ; in the light of our formulæ

$$23,046 \, E = U_0 - \beta T^2, \quad U = U_0 + \beta T^2 ;$$

this means that the influence of the coefficient β is small, and of different sign for different combinations. In the case of the chlorides, on the other hand, Bodländer obtained a good agreement by subtracting from the heats of formation the value

$$5060 \text{ cal.} = 0 \cdot 22 \text{ volt}$$

per gram equivalent. The above consideration shows that if we again neglect the small coefficient β, the difference between the two magnitudes is

[1] *Zeitschr. phys. Chem.* **27.** 55 (1898).

$$\frac{4\cdot571 \cdot 290 \ (1\cdot75 \ \log \ T + 3\cdot2)}{2} = 4971 \text{ cal.} = 0\cdot217 \text{ volt.}$$

Bodländer's empirical conclusion is therefore quantitatively explained by our theory.

The electromotive forces calculated up to the present time with the help of the new theorem of thermodynamics (Nernst, *l.c.* p. 747) are collected in the following table:

Chemical Process.	T.	E obs.	E calc.
$Pb + 2AgCl = 2Ag + PbCl_2$	290	0·4891	0·4890
$Hg + AgCl = HgCl + Ag$	288	0·0439	0·0437
$Zn + Hg_2SO_4 + 7H_2O \text{ (ice)} = ZnSO_4\cdot7H_2O + 2Hg$	266	1·4624	1·4592
$Pb + I_2 = PbI_2$	291	0·863	0·863
$2Ag + I_2 = 2AgI$	291	0·678	0·618
$H_2 + HgO = Hg + H_2O$	273	0·934	0·880
$2Ag + Cl_2 = 2AgCl$	290	1·157	1·092
$Pb + Cl_2 = PbCl_2$	290	1·612	1·594
$2H_2 + O_2 = 2H_2O$	290	1·231	1·237
$H_2 + Cl_2 = 2HCl \text{ (6n)}$	303	1·160	1·170
$H_2 + Cl_2 = 2HCl \text{ (1n)}$	298	1·366	1·365

The difference between the observed and calculated values is in most cases only a few millivolts, and therefore lies within the error of thermochemical measurements. It rises to a few centivolts only in three cases; it will be necessary to show whether this is due to irregularities in the specific heats at low temperatures. In any case it is perfectly evident that electromotive forces can be calculated with far greater accuracy and certainty by means of the new theorem than according to the rule of Helmholtz and W. Thomson.

The Galvanic Element considered as a Chemical System.—
A galvanic element represents a heterogeneous chemical system, and has certain peculiarities; but, on the whole, the influence of mass ratios and temperature on the system follows the laws which have already been developed for ordinary heterogeneous chemical systems.

The peculiarity which characterises galvanic batteries above other chemical systems is this, that the two metals must be connected by a conductor before the reaction can take place. We may have a Clark cell in open circuit for an indefinite length of time without observing a chemical change; but we cannot conclude from this that the system is in equilibrium, any more than we were at liberty to draw a similar conclusion regarding a "knall-gas" mixture (p. 681).

The reaction velocity in an "open" element, if not absolutely *nil*, is at least practically so, and it does not attain a measurable value until the two poles are electrically connected. This reaction velocity can be made to vary as desired, by changing the resistance in the circuit, and corresponds directly to the intensity of the current ; [1] for according to Faraday's law, the intensity of the current and the chemical change are directly proportional to each other.

. Thus we can speak of having an equilibrium, only when the two poles are connected by a conductor, and when also we compensate the potential difference in some way by means of an opposing electromotive force. This opposing electromotive force is completely analogous to the opposing pressure which we found necessary to apply in the case of solid NH_4Cl, *e.g.* in order to prevent its complete sublimation and consequent separation into its two dissociation products.

---

[1] Closing the circuit of a galvanic element may be considered the simplest and most illuminating case of chemical catalysis.

The Mechanism of Current-Production in Solutions. — The considerations thus far advanced rest essentially upon a thermodynamic basis. It is in the nature of this method of investigation, when properly applied, to give results which are undoubtedly correct, but not particularly illuminating. In particular, the mechanism of galvanic-current production has remained, for the present, entirely outside our considerations. But it now appears that the recent views of the ionic theory enable us to take an important step forward. This chapter is therefore devoted to *a special theory regarding the electromotive activity of ions*, which I developed in 1888 and 1889, and which is now generally accepted.

We have already developed the view, p. 369, that in the contact between two solutions of an electrolyte of different concentrations, there is developed an electromotive force which so acts between them, that the one ion strives to pass by the other. In this way we obtained for the first time a mechanical explanation of the potential difference between any two substances, and it became possible to calculate this value in absolute measure.

If we solve the differential equation on p. 370,

$$dS = - Uqdz \left(\frac{dp}{dx} + \eta\frac{dP}{dx}\right) = - Vqdz \left(\frac{dp}{dx} - \eta\frac{dP}{dx}\right),$$

for $\frac{dP}{dx}$ we find

$$\frac{dP}{dx} = - \frac{U - V}{U + V} \frac{1}{\eta} \frac{dp}{dx},$$

or, bearing in mind equation (2), p. 371,

$$\frac{dP}{dx} = - \frac{u - v}{u + v} \frac{1}{\eta} \frac{dp}{dx}.$$

Inserting the value of the osmotic pressure,

$$p = \eta RT,$$

and integrating, we have

$$P_1 - P_2 = \frac{u - v}{u + v} RT \ln \frac{\eta_2}{\eta_1} \qquad . \qquad . \qquad . \qquad (1)$$

where $P_1 - P_2$ is the potential difference between two solutions of the same kind, consisting of two univalent ions and assumed to be completely dissociated; η_1 and η_2 are the concentrations of the two solutions.

The preceding formula may also be deduced thermodynamically in the following way, as was shown by the author.[1] Suppose the quantity of electricity F to pass across the surface of contact of the two solutions in the direction from the concentrated to the dilute solution, $\frac{u}{u + v}$ equivalents of cations will migrate in the same direction, $\frac{v}{u + v}$ anions in the opposite. Since the cations pass from the concentration η_1 to the concentration η_2, they are capable, according to p. 52, of doing the work of expansion $\frac{u}{u + v} RT \ln \frac{\eta_1}{\eta_2}$, whilst conversely the anions need an amount of work $\frac{v}{u + v} RT \ln \frac{\eta_1}{\eta_2}$; the total work performed by the process is, therefore,

$$A = \frac{u - v}{u + v} RT \ln \frac{\eta_1}{\eta_2},$$

and thus the expression is equal to the electromotive force $P_2 - P_1$. If $\eta_1 > \eta_2$ and $u > v$, we have $A > 0$, i.e. there is an electromotive force tending to produce a current from the concentrated to the dilute solution. In the case of incompletely dissociated solutions the ionic concentrations must be used instead of η.

We can explain mechanically in an entirely similar way,[2] the potential difference occasioned by *the contact of the solutions of any two different electrolytes.*

Thus let us bring into contact with each other a solution of HCl and of LiBr; then, on the one hand, more hydrogen ions than chlorine ions will diffuse from the first solution into the second, and therefore the second solution will receive a positive charge; and, on the other hand, more bromine ions than lithium ions will diffuse from the second solution into the first, because of the greater mobility of the bromine ions; and thus the positive charge of the second solution will be increased.

Moreover, these electromotive forces can be calculated in absolute

[1] *Zeitschr. physik. Chem.* **4.** 129 (1889).
[2] Nernst, *ibid.* **2.** 613 (1888); **4.** 129 (1889); *Wied. Ann.* **45.** 360 (1892).

units of measurements, from the gas laws and the ion mobilities, for which purpose Planck,[1] has developed, by integration, the general equations given by me.

In this way we have arrived at a general method for calculating theoretically the electromotive forces of any liquid cells, provided that only dilute solutions are used, by means of the gas laws and the ionic mobilities; and, moreover, the details of mechanism by which these batteries produce the current, are now perfectly clear.

The electromotive forces between different solutions are nearly always small and usually counted only by hundredths or thousandths of a volt, but of course they must not be neglected in exact calculations, the more so as in most cases they can be estimated with sufficient accuracy. In dealing with dilute solutions there is a very simple means to reduce them almost to the vanishing point; this is to use as solvent, not pure water, but solution of a suitable indifferent electrolyte (see p. 758). Under these circumstances the current flows almost entirely through the indifferent electrolyte and consequently no appreciable osmotic work is done, and there is no appreciable potential difference between the solutions.

The gas constant R may be expressed in the electrochemical system of units as follows. We have

$$p = \eta RT = \eta \frac{p_0}{273} T,$$

where p_0 is the osmotic pressure in a space of unit concentration. Expressing the concentration in mols per c.cm. we have

$$p_0 = 22412 \text{ atm.} = 22412 \cdot 1033 \cdot 3 \cdot 981 \text{ abs. units.}$$

Now unit quantity of electricity in absolute measure is associated with $1 \cdot 035 \cdot 10^{-4}$ mols of a univalent ion; accordingly if we take as the unit of concentration the corresponding number $1 \cdot 035 \cdot 10^{-4}$,

$$p_0 = 22412 \cdot 1033 \cdot 3 \cdot 981 \cdot 1 \cdot 035 \cdot 10^{-4},$$

we find, as on p. 743,

$$R = 0 \cdot 861 \cdot 10^4 \text{ abs. units;}$$

but in order to express potential differences in volts the preceding number must be multiplied by 10^{-8}.

Hence

$$R = 0 \cdot 861 \cdot 10^{-4}.$$

We have therefore

$$RT \ln \frac{p_1}{p_2} = 0 \cdot 861 \cdot 10^{-4} T \ln \frac{p_1}{p_2} = 0 \cdot 0001983 \ T \log^{10} \frac{p_1}{p_2} \text{ volt.}$$

Or, putting $T = 273 + 18$, we get

$$RT \ln \frac{p_1}{p_2} = 0 \cdot 0577 \log^{10} \frac{p_1}{p_2} \text{ volt.}$$

[1] *Wied. Ann.* **40.** 561 (1890).

3 C

The Solution of Metals.—In order to account for the activity of galvanic elements, we will subject the current-producing process to a closer examination; the most important feature of this process is obviously the solution and precipitation of the metals of the electrode. And this at once leads us to the following observation.

Metals are characterised by only being able to go into solution positively charged, i.e. *in the form of positive ions.*

Thus, whether, in the electrolysis of a solution of a nitrate, we convert the silver serving as the anode into silver nitrate, or whether we change zinc into zinc sulphate by simply dipping it into sulphuric acid, the ions of the metals appear in solution under all circumstances, and then either remain free, or else unite with the negative ion of the salt contained in the solution, to form electrically neutral molecules.

Thus the process of the solution of metals appears in a very peculiar light. We see that *forces of an electrical nature* play a very prominent part in these chemical processes. And, in fact, if we accept the conceptions which we have already developed (pp. 141 and 485) on the general process of solution, we can, by means of the views advanced above, explain simply and easily the electromotive activity of the metals.

Let us, therefore, ascribe to each metal a *certain solution pressure towards the water*; for every substance must have such a pressure towards any selected solvent; and, as before, we understand by this the expansive force, which tends to drive the molecule of the substance into the solution. In the case of electrically neutral molecules, this expansive force is held in equilibrium by the osmotic pressure of the saturated solution.

But it is characteristic of the metals *that those molecules which the solution pressure tends to drive into solution, are positively charged.* Therefore their solution pressure may be suitably called "*electrolytic.*"

It is now easy to examine the processes which will take place on dipping a metal into pure water or into any solution.

We will first consider the case when the ions of the metal in question, are either not at all present in the solution, or, at most, to only a very slight extent. It will happen that a number of ions, driven by the solution pressure of the metal, will pass into solution, with the immediate result that the solution becomes positively charged and the metal negatively. But these electric charges (just as we saw in considering the diffusion of electrolytes, p. 369), give rise to a force, which, on the one hand, opposes the further passage of the metallic ions into the solution; and, on the other hand, seeks to drive the metallic ions already in the solution back on to the metal.

On account of the enormous electrostatic capacities of the ions, this force attains an extremely high value long before a weighable quantity has passed into solution. One of two events will now happen:

1. Either the action of the solution pressure of the metal will be

exactly compensated by the electrostatic charges, and a state of equilibrium will be established ; in this case no more of the metal will pass into the solution, neither will any more positive ions be driven out of the solution. This happens, *e.g.*, when silver is dipped into a solution of NaCl. We should not conclude that the solution pressure of this metal is very small, just because the silver is not dissolved under these circumstances. It is much more conceivable that it is to be estimated in thousands of atmospheres, and that it is compensated in its action by the electrostatic charge of the solution as it comes into contact with the metal.

2. Or the electrostatic charges may reach such an amount, as a result of the magnitude of the solution pressure, that the positive ions which are contained in solution are driven out on to the metal. We observe an illustration of this case, *in the precipitation of one metal by another*; thus, *e.g.*, when iron is dipped into a solution of a copper salt, the iron ions go into the solution and the electrically equivalent quantity of copper ions is driven out of the solution, by electrostatic repulsion of the solution, and by the electrostatic attraction of the metal ; and thus the copper ions are precipitated upon the iron.

Another illustration is the *evolution of hydrogen* (see below).

The foregoing considerations have received a striking confirmation by the researches of W. Palmaer.[1] If, as shown by Fig. 49, mercury is dropped into a solution which contains only a few mercury ions, some of these ions will be deposited on each drop, because mercury, being a noble metal, possesses an extremely small solution pressure. If the drops fall into a mass of mercury below, their charge disappears, that is, they give the mercury ions back to the solution. We see then that where the new mercury surface is formed, that is, at the opening of the mercury funnel, the solution becomes poorer in mercury salt, whilst where the drops unite and there is a diminution of surface between mercury and electrolyte the solution must become richer in salt. It has long been noticed that a potential difference arises between dropping mercury and still mercury ; I showed (see my note on contact electricity)[2] that this arrangement may be regarded as a concentration cell, and Palmaer proved experimentally that changes of concentration do occur in the sense expected ; this he demonstrated first by measurements of potential difference as compared with small inserted mercury electrodes, and afterwards[3] by purely chemical means.

Fig. 49.

The Theory of the Production of the Galvanic Current.—

The considerations advanced in the preceding section, lead directly to

[1] *Zeitschr. physik. Chem.* **25.** 265 (1898).
[2] Supplement to *Wied. Ann.*, 1896, Heft Nr. 8.   [3] *Ibid.* **28.** 257 (1899).

an insight into the production of galvanic currents from electrically active systems which depend on the use of metals. To fix our ideas, we will consider a particular example, namely the Daniell cell.

Let a zinc rod be dipped in a solution of zinc salt (for example, $ZnSO_4$), as in Fig. 50, and a copper rod in a solution of copper salt ($CuSO_4$); then the zinc, in consequence of its greater solution pressure,

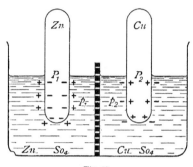

will send out a quantity of positive ions into the solution, whilst conversely, if the osmotic pressure p_2 of the copper ions is sufficiently great, copper ions will be deposited on the copper rod and the copper will thus receive a positive charge.

As long as the circuit is *open*, neither zinc ions nor copper ions will go over into the solution, because the electrolytic solution pressures of these metals are held in equilibrium by the opposing

Fig. 50.

charges, which both the metals and the solutions have received from the (inappreciable) passage of ions; and therefore no chemical change takes place in the cell.

But it is different when the circuit between the two poles of the element is *closed* by a conducting union; then the reaction can advance, because it is possible to equalise the electric charges associated with the solution and the precipitation respectively, of the two metals; and thus the reaction takes place in such a way, that that metal having the greater solution pressure drives its ions into the solution; and conversely, that metal having the smaller solution pressure is precipitated from the solution.

In the Daniell element the zinc is dissolved, and the correspondingly equivalent quantity of copper is driven out of the solution, because the force tending to bring the zinc ions into solution is greater than that tending to bring the copper ions into solution.

The passage of the zinc into the solution and of the copper out of the solution, necessarily results in a movement of positive electricity in the external circuit, from copper to zinc; i.e. *the production of a galvanic current* ensues in the direction indicated.

We have already seen that the osmotic pressure of the ions of a metal tends to oppose its solution pressure. Thus the force which brings the zinc ions into solution will be the smaller, the greater the concentration of the zinc sulphate solution; and likewise the force tending to separate the copper ions will be the greater, the stronger the concentration of the copper sulphate. Thus the electromotive force of the Daniell element will increase by diluting the zinc sulphate solution ; and it will diminish by diluting the copper sulphate solution ; and both of these statements are completely verified by experiment.

The electromotive force of a Daniell cell may be expressed by means of the formula given below—

$$E = \frac{RT}{2} \left(\ln \frac{P_1}{p_1} - \ln \frac{P_2}{p_2} \right) ;$$

here the small potential difference at the contact of the two electrolytes is neglected.

Concentration Cells.—The above considerations lead at once to a very simple expression for the potential difference between the metal and the solution which contains a larger or a smaller amount of ions in question. If A is the work that can be performed by the solution of one electro-chemical gram equivalent of the electrode metal in the electrolyte considered, when the osmotic pressure of the univalent ions of the metal amounts to p; then clearly,

$$A = E, \qquad . \qquad . \qquad . \qquad (I.)$$

where E is the potential difference required. If p becomes p + dp, A becomes A + dA, and accordingly E becomes E + dE. Let us now dissolve one electro-chemical gram equivalent ; then dA is equal to the work that must be spent if the electro-chemical equivalent is to be brought from pressure p + dp to pressure p. This amounts, therefore, to p . dv (where v is the volume which one electro-chemical equivalent assumes in the solution), hence we have

$$dE = dA = p . dv = - RT \frac{dp}{p}$$

or, integrating,

$$E = - RT \ln p + \text{const.}$$

that is

$$E = RT \ln \frac{P}{p} .$$

In this equation clearly E = 0, when P = p, hence P indicates the electrolytic solution pressure of the metal in question. Instead of using the pressure p we may use the ionic concentration c, which is proportional to it, and obtain

$$E = RT \ln \frac{C}{c} \qquad . \qquad . \qquad . \qquad . \qquad (II.)$$

where c is the concentration corresponding to the osmotic pressure p. In what follows we shall describe c loosely as the solution pressure.

The equation

$$A = E = \text{const.} - RT \ln c$$

may also be derived immediately from the theory of the thermodynamic potential given on p. 677.

If the ion whose solution is considered is n-valent, we have

$$dA = -\frac{RT}{n} \cdot \frac{dp}{p},$$

and accordingly

$$E = \frac{RT}{n} \cdot \ln \frac{C}{c}.$$

These equations, developed by me in the year 1889, contain both the theory of galvanic current production and that of galvanic polarisation.

We will first consider the case of two electrodes of a univalent metal dipping in two solutions of a salt of that metal of different concentrations ; we then have a concentration cell, for example

$$Ag \left| \begin{array}{c} AgNO_3 \\ c_1 \end{array} \right| \begin{array}{c} AgNO_3 \\ c_2 \end{array} \right| Ag.$$

In these galvanic combinations we have three contacts of dissimilar conductors, and accordingly three potential differences, which may be separately calculated and whose sum gives the electromotive force of the combination. At one of the metal-electrolyte contacts we have the force $RT \ln \frac{C}{c_1}$, at the contact of the two solutions, according to p. 752, $\frac{u-v}{u+v} RT \ln \frac{C_1}{c_2}$, at the other contact between metal and electrolyte the force $RT \ln \frac{C}{c_2}$; hence the total electromotive force of the cell will be

$$E = RT \ln \frac{C}{c_1} + \frac{u-v}{u+v} RT \ln \frac{C_1}{c_2} - RT \ln \frac{C}{c_2} = -\frac{2v}{u+v} RT \ln \frac{c_1}{c_2}.$$

Assuming, for example, $c_1 = 0\cdot1$; $c_2 = 0\cdot01$ mols per litre, we get, at room temperature, according to p. 753,

$$E = 2 \cdot 0\cdot522 \cdot 0\cdot0577 = 0\cdot0604 \text{ volt}$$

$\left(\frac{v}{u+v} = 0\cdot522, \text{ according to p. 366} \right)$; experiment gave $0\cdot055$ volt,

i.e. a somewhat smaller value. Bearing in mind, however, that the electrolytic dissociation in the solutions used was incomplete, the theory gives $0\cdot057$, which is in complete agreement with the experiment. If two metal electrodes dip into the same solution of an indifferent electrolyte, and a small quantity of the ions of the electrode metal are added to produce concentration c_1 in the first solution and c_2 in the second, where c_1 and c_2 are small in comparison with the concentration of the indifferent electrolyte, the electromotive force of contact between the two electrolytes vanishes ; then under these circumstances the current is conducted almost entirely by the indifferent electrolyte, so that practically no osmotic work is spent in the electrolyte, and for concentration cells of this type we have the simple formula

$$E = \frac{RT}{n} \ln \frac{c_2}{c_1}.$$

The electromotive force of such cells can occasionally become very large, viz. when one of the concentrations (c_1 or c_2) becomes extraordinarily small; thus the electromotive force of the cell

$$Ag \mid 0\cdot1\ AgNO_3 \mid 1\cdot0\ KCl \mid AgCl \mid Ag$$

has been found $0\cdot51$ of a volt; this relatively large electromotive force of a cell with two identical electrodes is due to the fact that the osmotic pressure of the silver ions in the solution of silver nitrate is considerable, but in the potassium chloride solution surrounding the silver chloride is excessively small; not only on account of the very small solubility of silver chloride but because it is further reduced by the presence of chlorine ions. We can confirm this quantitatively; c_1 is about $0\cdot1$ gram-ion per litre, since the solution of silver nitrate was deci-normal; c_2, according to p. 664, would be $1\cdot1 \times 10^{-5}$ at 20°, if there were no potassium chloride present; and, as the latter forms a normal solution, the solubility sinks, according to p. 537, to $(1\cdot1 \times 10^{-5})^2 = 1\cdot21 \times 10^{-10}$. Hence the electromotive force of the cell becomes

$$0\cdot058\ (9 - \log_{10} 1\cdot21) = 0\cdot52 \text{ volt,}$$

which is in very good agreement with the direct measurements ($0\cdot51$); bearing in mind that the electrolytic dissociation of the KCl and AgNO$_3$ is not complete, the calculated value should be a trifle reduced.[1]

In the case of negative ions, such, for example, as a platinum electrode charged with chlorine, the potential difference is of the opposite sign, and in this case

$$E = - RT \ln \frac{C_1}{c_1} = RT \ln \frac{c_1}{C_1} \qquad \cdot \qquad \cdot \qquad \cdot \qquad \text{(III.)}$$

If mercury is covered with the very slightly soluble mercurous chloride the passage of a current through the electrode either forms or reduces calomel according to its direction, in other words, ions either come out from the solution or enter it. Such an electrode behaves therefore electrolytically, as if it were made of a metallically conducting modification of chlorine, and equation III. is applicable to it. Such electrodes, which consist of a metal covered with one of its insoluble salts and a solution which contains the same anion at a concentration C_1, are known as *reversible electrodes of the second kind* (p. 736), while electrodes to which equation II. is applicable are called *reversible electrodes of the first kind*. Electrodes of the second kind may be reduced to the first kind, as may be seen from the foregoing calculation with the electrode Ag(AgCl).

---

[1] See Goodwin, *Zeitschr. physik. Chem.* **13**. 577 (1894).

In a concentration cell such as

$$\text{Hg} \mid \text{HgCl} \mid \text{chloride } c_1 \mid \text{chloride } c_2 \mid \text{HgCl} \mid \text{Hg,}$$

the electromotive force may be determined by means of equations I. and III. exactly in the same way as on p. 759 for concentration cells with electrodes of the first kind. We find in this way

$$E = \frac{2u}{u + v} RT \ln \frac{c_1}{c_2}.$$

For example the author found :—[1]

Chloride.	c_1.	c_2.	E.	
			Obs.	Cal.
HCl	0·1	0·01	0·0926	0·0939
KCl	0·1	0·01	0·0532	0·0542
LiCl	0·1	0·01	0·0354	0·0336

In the first of these three combinations the electromotive force at the contact of the two electrolytes adds to the total effect, in the third it reduces it, in the second it is almost nothing.

Normal and Abnormal Potentials. — According to the equation

$$E = \frac{RT}{n} \ln \frac{C}{c}$$

the potential difference between the metal and electrolyte varies at room temperature by $\frac{0·058}{1}$ volt when the concentration of the n-valent ions of the metal is altered tenfold; the change of electromotive force is consequently small when dealing with moderate concentrations, and even if the ionic concentration varies by a large amount the electromotive force of the combination suffers, as a rule, only a small percentage modification. It is otherwise of course when the ionic concentration is reduced by several times tenfold : then there are very considerable alterations in electromotive force.

Thus, for example, silver in solutions of a silver salt of moderate concentration has always approximately the same potential ; if by any means silver ions are very completely removed from the solution the potential is considerably altered. This can be done in two different ways ; either by adding a reagent (for example a chloride) to precipitate the silver ions, or by adding a reagent such as potassium cyanide,

[1] *Zeitschr. physik. Chem.* **4**. 161 (1889).

which forms a complex salt with the silver ions and so equally removes them from the solution.   By these two ways it is possible to reduce the concentration of the silver ions enormously ; accordingly it is found that metals in such solutions give quite different, so-called "anomalous" potentials, in opposition to the "normal" potentials observed in solutions containing larger quantities of their ions.

If a metal is dipped in a solution which originally contains no ions of it, the potential observed is, unlike that in the preceding cases, variable and uncertain ; traces of the metal in larger or smaller quantity, according to the circumstances (for example under the action of the atmospheric oxygen), pass into solution, and these accidental quantities of course give accidental potential differences.

As an example of the great change in potential of a metal against an electrolyte that can be produced by precipitation, we have already mentioned the concentration cell with silver electrodes, which has an unusually large electromotive force (p. 759).   If to the copper of a Daniell cell a sufficiently concentrated potassium cyanide solution is added, the copper ions are so completely taken up by it that the electromotive force of the combination even changes its sign, i.e. in such a combination copper goes into solution and reduces the zinc.   A series of further examples are given by Hittorf,[1] who first carefully studied cases of this kind, and by Ostwald,[2] who qualitatively explained those anomalies on the basis of my formula, while the theoretical calculation was first given by me in the first edition of this book (1893).

Gas Batteries. — Platinum charged with hydrogen behaves electrolytically like the electrode of a metallically conducting variety of hydrogen ; charged with oxygen as if it were a metallically conducting form of oxygen.   If these electrodes are immersed in a solution of an electrolyte we have a galvanic combination of an electromotive force

$$E = RT \ln \frac{C}{c} + \frac{RT}{2} \ln \frac{C_1}{c_1} = \frac{RT}{2} \ln \frac{C^2 . C_1}{c^2 . c_1} ;$$

here C and C_1 are the solution pressures of the two electrodes, c and c_1 the concentrations of the hydrogen ions and the doubly charged oxygen ions.   Since in dilute aqueous solutions

$$c^2 . c_1 = \text{const.}$$

it follows that E is independent of the nature of the dissolved substances ; at atmospheric temperature it amounts to $1 \cdot 23$ volt, a value which is of much importance in electro-chemical calculations (p. 744).

The potential of a hydrogen electrode is very different in acid and alkaline solutions (about $0 \cdot 8$ volt), because the concentration of the hydrogen ions in the two cases is, according to p. 518, enormously

[1] *Zeitschr. physik. Chem.* **10**. 593 (1892).
[2] *Lehrbuch der allg. Chem.* 2nd edit. vol. ii.

different, and the same is of course true of the oxygen electrode. The above formulæ allow us to foretell quantitatively these relations.

In a similar way the theory of all gas batteries which contain dilute solutions of an electrolyte may be studied by means of the osmotic theory. It must be noted, however, that the solution pressure of an electrode charged with gas depends on the degree of saturation of the gas in the electrode, and naturally increases with the concentration of the dissolved gas.

Oxidation and Reduction Cells. — Chemically an oxidising material is characterised by its power of giving off oxygen, a reducing material by its power of giving off hydrogen. In some cases this power extends to the visible evolution of gas; thus hydrogen peroxide gives off oxygen violently on a platinum surface, chromous solutions give off hydrogen, etc. Clearly the oxidising or reducing power is the greater the higher the pressure the evolution of gas can reach. If thus we bring platinum electrodes into solutions which contain an oxidising or reducing agent they will be charged with oxygen or hydrogen; by combination we get a cell according to the scheme

Pt | oxidising medium | indifferent solution | reducing medium | Pt,

we have, therefore, an *oxyhydrogen cell*, but with this difference, that the oxygen or hydrogen charge can be, according to the nature of the oxidising or reducing medium, greater or smaller than if the charge were immediately produced by oxygen or hydrogen at atmospheric pressure, as in the ordinary gas cell. In other words, the values C_1 and C in the formula of the previous section depend upon the nature of the reagents used.

Hence it follows that (for constant charge of the platinum) the potential difference between each electrode and the solution depends on the concentration of the hydrogen or hydroxyl ions, and that if several oxidising agents are present at once in the solution the strongest determines the potential difference, that is the one which charges the electrode with oxygen most strongly. The same of course is true for the reducing materials.

If an oxidising and a reducing material are present simultaneously in the solution it often, but not always, happens that chemical action will take place; this must, however, happen as soon as platinum is brought into the solution and the charge of gas reaches sufficient magnitude, because oxygen and hydrogen occluded by platinum react violently.

In order to calculate the dependence of the potential difference on the concentration of the various reagents we must write the reaction for the evolution of oxygen and hydrogen in each case. Thus, ferrous sulphate charges platinum according to the equation

$$\overset{++}{Fe} + \overset{+}{H} = \overset{+++}{Fe} + \frac{1}{2}H_2 \,;$$

hence the hydrogen charge is proportional to the concentration of the ferrous and hydrogen ions directly, and inversely to that of the ferric ions. See on this point the work by Peters,[1] which is full of interesting observations. That a palladium electrode becomes charged with hydrogen when dipped into the solution of a reducing agent could be shown by the diffusion of hydrogen through the electrode.[2] Ostwald has pointed out that measurements of electromotive force determine the oxidising or reducing action of a reagent.[3]

Theory of Electrolysis.—If we consider an electrolytic cell with two unalterable electrodes, on electrolysis the cations must be deposited at the cathode, the anions at the anode ; if the electromotive force necessary for the first of these processes be called ϵ_1, for the second ϵ_2, we have for the back electromotive force of polarisation

$$E = \epsilon_1 + \epsilon_2.$$

Now the cation is the more easily deposited at the cathode the higher its concentration and the more difficultly the more dilute it is ; by considerations exactly similar to those on p. 757 we find that

$$\epsilon_1 = \frac{RT}{n} \ln \frac{C_1}{c_1}$$

and

$$\epsilon_2 = -\frac{RT}{n} \ln \frac{C_2}{c_2}.$$

If we have several kinds of cations and anions present *together* in the solution, which always happens when we are dealing with aqueous solutions, in which besides the ions of the dissolved substance there is water present, *the electrolysis will begin when the electromotive force E, conveniently known as the decomposition potential, is large enough to discharge one of the cations present and one of the anions.*

The great service involved in bringing out clearly this point, following on the earlier researches of Helmholtz, Berthelot, and others, is due to Le Blanc,[4] who investigated electrolytic decomposition in a very thorough manner. Le Blanc showed that the conceptions and formulæ deduced by the author for galvanic production of current can be applied without change to electrolysis, and so laid the foundation for the osmotic theory of electrolysis. This investigator has also made many important applications of his law.

Thus it became possible,[5] by applying different potentials, to arrive

---

[1] *Zeitschr. physik. Chem.* **26.** 193 (1898).
[2] Nernst and Lessing, *Gött. Nachr.*, 22 Feb. 1902.
[3] See *Allg. Chem.* 2nd edit. p. 883, etc., Leipzig, 1893.
[4] *Zeitschr. physik. Chem.* **8.** 299 (1891) ; **12.** 333 (1892).
[5] This was first shown by M. Kiliani (1883) ; the further working out of it is due to H. Freudenberg, *Zeitschr. physik. Chem.* **12.** 97 (1893), on the suggestion of Le Blanc.

at a method for separating electrolytically the various metals; it is clearly not the current density which primarily determines the electrolytic process, but the *potential difference between the electrodes*.

In the following table Wilsmore [1] has collected the potential differences of the most important electrodes from a critical summary of the measurements so far obtained :—

DECOMPOSITION POTENTIALS

For Normal Concentrations

ϵ_1 (Cations)		ϵ_2 (Anions)
Mg + 1·482		J − 0·520
Al + 1·276	H = ± 0	Br − 0·993
Mn + 1·075		O − 1·23*
Zn + 0·770		Cl − 1·353
Cd + 0·420		OH − 1·68*
Fe + 0·344		SO_4 − 1·9
Co + 0·232		HSO_4 − 2·6
Ni +0·228	0.228	CH_3COO − 2·5
Pb + 0·151		
Cu − 0·329		
Hg − 0·753		
Ag − 0·771		

These numbers, in accordance with the preceding formulæ, refer to normal concentrations of the ions; a reduction of tenfold in the concentration increases the numbers by $\dfrac{0\cdot058}{n}$ volt (where n = the number of charges or the chemical valency of the ion). The potential of hydrogen is taken at zero; for there are always both anode and cathode, and therefore an arbitrary term to be added to all the above numbers, that is, it is necessary to make an arbitrary standard of some one of them. The value of O and OH (distinguished by a star) refer to a *concentration which is normal with respect to the hydrogen ions*. In order to discharge O or OH from normal concentration of OH the voltage needed is less by 0·8, in order to set free hydrogen from the same solution 0·8 volt more is required than in acid solution, as may be calculated from the concentration of the ions of water.

A number of important conclusions may be drawn from the above numbers. In the first place, they yield the decomposition potentials of all ionic combinations. For example, zinc bromide requires for decomposition $0\cdot99 + 0\cdot77 = 1\cdot76$ volt, if its ions are present in normal solution. The decomposition of hydrochloric acid requires 1·353 + 0 = 1·353 volt, and so on. We saw that it is easy to separate silver from copper electrolytically, because the difference between their solution pressures is almost half a volt; but similarly the electrolytic separation of iodine from bromine and bromine from chlorine can be carried out satisfactorily.[2] The electrolytic decomposition of silver

---

[1] *Zeitschr. physik. Chem.* **35**. 291 (1900).
[2] See Specketer, *Zeitschr. f. Elektrochem.* **4**. 539 (1898).

iodide in normal solution would, according to the above figures, not only require no force but should, on the contrary, yield 0·26 of a volt $(0·52 - 0·78 = -0·26)$. Silver iodide itself, however, cannot be obtained in such concentrations on account of its extreme insolubility in water, and indeed we may conclude from the above numbers that at usual temperatures silver iodide to be *stable* must be very insoluble, a conclusion which of course can very easily be generalised.

Naturally also the above numbers give at the same time the electromotive force of cells combined with the electrodes in question ; thus the Daniell cell gives $0·770 + 0·329 = 1·099$ volt.

As a further example which gives rise to interesting speculations we may take the electrolysis of sulphuric acid. It is well known that in this case we get hydrogen at the cathode and oxygen at the anode, assuming of course that the electrodes are unalterable. We conclude from the above table that electrolysis will only take place if the potential difference is greater than 1·23 volt ; with this potential difference hydrogen ions can be discharged at the cathode and doubly charged oxygen ions at the anode ; it is actually found that if a small platinum point be used as cathode and a large platinised plate as anode at this potential, hydrogen is evolved violently at the point, and the electrolysis can be kept up indefinitely by means of this electromotive force. We have here the reverse of the gas battery on p. 761. But if a large platinum plate charged with hydrogen is used as cathode and opposite it a small platinum point as anode, oxygen bubbles do not form until the potential has reached 1·66 volt, that is when the decomposition potential of hydroxyl ions is exceeded and the electrolysis only takes place freely with still higher electromotive force, by means of which the SO_4 ions are discharged. The doubly charged oxygen atoms are present in such small quantity that it is not possible to keep up any considerable electrolysis by their means, whereas hydrogen ions are abundant and consequently can be discharged in large quantities as soon as the potential rises sufficiently high. The circumstances are more favourable in the case of the hydroxyl ions, whose concentration is much greater than that of the doubly charged oxygen ions, but in order to electrolyse freely the potential must be raised till both at the cathode and anode ions present in large quantities can be discharged.

Preuner[1] has shown that when acetates are electrolysed, oxygen is evolved as long as the anode potential is kept under 2·5 volts ; when this potential is exceeded considerable quantities of ethane and carbon dioxide are evolved, resulting from the discharge of the acetions (p. 764).

In electrolysing *lead salts* it was observed that at the cathode lead is precipitated, at the anode lead peroxide. According to the views of Liebenow[2]

[1] *Zeitschr. physik. Chem.* **57.** 72 (1907).
[2] *Zeitschr. f. Elektrochem.* **2.** 420 (1895-96).

this is a case of primary electrolysis, since he supposes lead salt to be hydrolytically dissociated according to the equation

$$\overset{++}{Pb} + 2H_2O = \overset{--}{PbO_2} + 4\overset{+}{H}.$$

As a matter of fact compounds like PbO_2Na_2, PbO_2Ca, and so on, are known. If a solution of lead salt is electrolysed in presence of a copper salt, copper comes down on the cathode instead of lead, because copper has a much smaller decomposition potential; all lead finally appears at the anode in the form of peroxide (Luckow's process for the electrolytic determination of lead). If, on the other hand, oxalic acid is added to lead salt, its negative ions are more easily discharged at the anode than the lead peroxide ions, so that all the lead appears in metallic form on the cathode.

In the *accumulator* on charge, according to Liebenow's view, $\overset{++}{Pb}$ ions are deposited primarily on the cathode, $\overset{--}{PbO_2}$ ions on the anode. Although on account of the small solubility of lead sulphate very little of these ionic species are present in solution, they are continuously replaced by means of the lead sulphate on the electrode. It is only when the lead sulphate is used up that the sulphuric acid is electrolysed, and hydrogen appears at the cathode and oxygen at the anode.

A very noticeable phenomenon was investigated by Caspari,[1] who found that visible electrolytic separation of hydrogen at a platinised plate takes place at a potential of practically zero (0·005 volt), but with other metals requires a special excess-potential. He found the values

Au 0·02, Pt (blank) 0·09, Ag 0·15, Cu 0·23, Pd 0·48, Sn 0·53, Pb 0·64, Zn 0·70, Hg 0·78 volts.

In consequence of this excess-potential, hydrogen does not appear on the cathode of an accumulator during charge, but lead is separated, and it is only when the lead sulphate is reduced and the potential consequently raised that gaseous hydrogen is evolved. It can therefore be shown[2] that with small currents lead sulphate is much more easily reduced at a lead electrode than at a platinum electrode, and also that by means of electrodes with high excess-potentials (especially mercury and zinc) it is possible to obtain reduction products that would otherwise be very difficult to prepare.[3] Apparently hydrogen can only give off bubbles when the electrodes have occluded an appreciable amount; in metals which occlude very little hydrogen, considerable quantities of gas must first be generated by the potential before any formation of bubbles can take place. A similar phenomenon may be expected in the case of other gases which can be produced electrolytically; oxygen has been investigated by Coehn and Osaka[4] in this respect. Nickel behaves in a remarkable manner in this respect, since oxygen can be evolved from alkaline solution in gaseous form at about 1·3 volt against hydrogen, whilst on platinum 1·7 is required.

[1] *Zeitschr. physik. Chem.* **30.** 89 (1899).
[2] Nernst and Dolezalek, *Zeitschr. f. Elektrochemie*, **6.** 549 (1899-1900).
[3] See Tafel, *Ber. deutsch. chem. Ges.* **33.** 2209 (1900).
[4] *Zeitschr. anorgan. Chem.* **34.** 68 (1903).

For the theory of excess-potential see the interesting study by G. Möller (*Ann. d. Phys.* [4.] 27, p. 566, 1908).

Chemical Application of the Osmotic Theory.—It has long been customary to draw chemical deductions from the galvanic potential series of the metals, which is given in the table (p. 764), and which is now seen to find quantitative expression in the solution pressures or the decomposition pressure so determined; it must not, however, be assumed that copper is always precipitated by zinc. On the contrary, the ionic concentration is a second important factor, and the above (p. 761) experiment with the Daniell cell shows that under suitable conditions zinc can be reduced by copper.

Similar conclusions may be drawn as to the decomposition potential of the anions; thus it is known that bromine throws out iodine from solution of iodide, and the chlorine similarly precipitates bromine quickly and very completely (how complete the precipitation is may be easily calculated from the solution pressure according to principles already given). We have, in fact, the well-known simple reactions—

$$Br_2 + 2\overline{J} = J_2 + 2\overline{Br};$$

$$Cl_2 + 2\overline{Br} = Br_2 + 2\overline{Cl}.$$

We see further, that chlorine must be capable of evolving oxygen from acid solution, but not so bromine or iodine. It is known, however, that the evolution of oxygen by chlorine takes place very slowly, unlike the rapid deposition of bromine by chlorine. This need not surprise us in view of what has gone before; for the chlorine, in order to pass to the ionic state, must replace the $\overline{\overline{O}}$ ions that are present in excessively small quantities, since the $\overline{OH}$ ions, which are more abundant, do not give up their negative charge except by means of a potential 0.3 volt higher than that of chlorine.

One of the most interesting reactions is the *decomposition of water by metals with formation of hydrogen*; the conditions for this process can easily be deduced from the foregoing considerations (p. 754). The electrical forces in question act not only on the ions of the metals in question, but also on all the positive ions present; for example, on the hydrogen ions which always exist in aqueous solution. The separation of hydrogen ions must occur as soon as *the osmotic pressure of the hydrogen ions and the electrostatic attraction are sufficient to overcome the electrolytic solution pressure of hydrogen at atmospheric pressure*, that is, we must have $\epsilon_1 > \epsilon_2$ or $\sqrt[n_1]{\dfrac{C_1}{c_1}} > \dfrac{C_2}{c_2}$, where the index 1 refers to the metal and 2 to the hydrogen, and n_1 is the chemical valency of the metal in question.

We see, therefore, that the favourable conditions for decomposition of water are :—

1. Large osmotic pressure of the hydrogen ions.

2. Large electrostatic force, that is great solution pressure of the metal and small opposition pressure of the ions of this metal.

Potassium decomposes water violently under all circumstances on account of its enormously great electrolytic solution pressure, for we can neither make the osmotic pressure of the hydrogen ions small enough, nor that of the potassium ions large enough to hinder the solution. *Zinc* possesses large enough solution pressure to decompose water in acid solution, but it is incapable of doing so when the concentration of the zinc ions is sufficiently great, or that of the hydrogen ions sufficiently small; for example, when zinc is dipped into a neutral solution of zinc sulphate. In strongly alkaline solutions it is again capable of decomposing water rapidly, although the concentration of the hydrogen ions is exceedingly small, because in this case, through formation of zincates, the concentration of the zinc ions is very greatly reduced. *Mercury*, in spite of its small solution pressure, evolves hydrogen from strong hydrochloric acid because the concentration of the hydrogen ions is large, and that of the mercury ions very small, owing to the insolubility of mercurous chloride which is increased by the presence of considerable quantities of chlorine ions. *Copper*, whose ions, as we have already seen, are eagerly taken up by potassium cyanide, gives off hydrogen violently in such solution, despite its alkalinity.

The preceding considerations apply, of course, only to reversible formation of hydrogen, which, however, we can always produce when the metal in question is surrounded with platinum wire (best platinised); otherwise formation of hydrogen only takes place when

$$\epsilon_1 > \epsilon_2 + \eta,$$

where η is the excess-potential given on p. 766. The sponge-like electrode of an accumulator in moderately concentrated sulphuric acid gives off no hydrogen, although here $\epsilon_1 > \epsilon_2$; it does so as soon as it is touched with a platinum wire. In very concentrated acid gas is given off spontaneously, because the above inequality is satisfied.

These considerations for the formation of hydrogen by metals can be at once applied to the *electrolytic separation* of metals. If $\sqrt[n_1]{\dfrac{C_1}{c_1}} < \dfrac{C_2}{c_2}$, the metal will be deposited, if $\sqrt[n_1]{\dfrac{C_1}{c_1}} > \dfrac{C_2}{c_2}$, hydrogen is more easily evolved electrolytically. Hence for galvanic separation of metals it is necessary to make first the concentration of the metallic ions as large as possible, second, that of the hydrogen ions as small as possible. Now in aqueous solution the concentration of the hydrogen ions is inversely proportional to that of the hydroxyl ions; hence the product of the concentration of the metallic and hydroxyl ions must be made as large as possible. But, according to the laws of solubility, a limit is set to this product by the solubility of the hydroxide of the metal; hence the impossibility, for example, of separating aluminium or magnesium from aqueous solution is due, not only to the great solution pressures of those metals, but to the insolubility of their *hydroxides*.[1]

Metals of too great solution pressure, as, *e.g.*, the alkali metals, act spontaneously on water and hence cannot be deposited in the pure form, although they may be obtained as amalgams with mercury. A strongly negative element behaves similarly; fluorine, for example, causes spontaneous evolution of oxygen from water, and can only be obtained pure when perfectly dry hydrofluoric acid, which is made a conductor by means of potassium fluoride, is electrolysed (Moissan, 1887).

At the electrodes the elements or radicals appear deprived of their electric charges, and their affinities, which in the ionic state are saturated by the electric charges, and in the undissociated state by the other constituent, are now unsatisfied. This leads most frequently to the combination of two similar ions: $2Cl$ gives Cl_2, $2H$ gives H_2, $2HSO_4$ gives persulphuric acid $H_2S_2O_8$ (according to F. W. Küster's views), a case which has recently been investigated very thoroughly by Elbs, $2KCO_3$ gives, according to Hansen and Constam,[2] potassium percarbonate $K_2C_2O_6$. Many other so-called secondary reactions, that is, chemical actions between ions deprived of their electrical charges, are known. The application of electrolysis to oxidation, reduction, chlorination, and so on, depends on these actions, and has recently been investigated with many important results by Gattermann, Elbs, Loeb, and others.[3]

The fact that no compounds such as S_2O_8, N_2O_6, etc., have been isolated may be perhaps explained in the same way as the non-isolation of fluorine in aqueous solutions; these substances might possibly be obtained by working with a more stable solvent than water.

The pressure under which the ion is given off in the gaseous form, or the concentration to which it dissolves, depends essentially on the potential with which it is electrolysed; in other words, *the active mass can be varied arbitrarily by applying varying electromotive force of polarisation.* We can thus cause chlorine to appear at the anode in a state of more than homœopathic dilution, or under pressures which are to be reckoned by millions of atmospheres, and employ it *chemically.* It cannot be doubted, therefore, that, *e.g.*, in organic preparations, all possible stages of chlorination may be reached by changes of potential. It is true that the current density, to which attention was formerly paid, changes with the potential, and is closely related to that

---

[1] See also Glaser, *Zeitschr. f. Elektrochemie*, **4.** 355 (1898).
[2] *Ibid.* **3.** 137, 445 (1897).
[3] See also especially the collection of Loeb, *ibid.* **2.** 293.

quantity, but it depends also upon the form of the electrodes and the specific resistance of the electrolyte, and can therefore not be regarded as a measure of the capacity of a current to chlorinate, oxidise, reduce, etc.

The principles given above have found important applications in the work of Haber ;[1] he showed that the reducing action of electrolytic hydrogen on nitrobenzene depends solely on the potential at the cathode. Thus he was able to stop the reduction at the stage of azoxybenzene by keeping the cathode potential constantly under a certain fixed value. Another application is to be found in a paper by Dony Hénault,[2] who oxidised alcohol to aldehyde quantitatively, that is, according to Faraday's law, by keeping the anode potential during electrolysis under a certain critical value ; otherwise acetic acid and higher products of oxidation appear.

The Rate of Electrochemical Reaction.—Chemical decomposition is under all circumstances proportional to the strength of current (Faraday's law) ; it is often observed, however, that under certain conditions an electrochemical process will not proceed farther than a certain point, although we may try to increase the strength of the current by raising the potential.

If we apply the hypothesis brought forward on p. 586 to this case, i.e. assume that at the electrode itself attainment of equilibrium is practically instantaneous, then the electrochemical process can only be delayed during electrolysis in two ways :

I. The substance to be acted upon (e.g. reduced, oxidised, chlorinated, etc.) takes time to diffuse through to the electrode.

II. The substance to be acted upon is only an intermediate product of a slow chemical process (taking place in a homogeneous phase).

Which of these reasons is correct in any given case can be generally very easily decided by stirring, which will greatly increase the reaction velocity (strength of current) in the first case, and hardly at all in the second (p. 587). Temperature will also have a much greater influence in the second than in the first case.

The rate of reduction at the cathode of the halides, for example, depends on their diffusion velocities, but potassium chlorate, which only gives up its oxygen with great difficulty at ordinary temperatures, is reduced at a much slower rate.

For further examples and a quantitative treatment, see Nernst and Merriam,[3] where references to the literature will also be found.

Solution of Metals.—Similar considerations obviously apply to the solution of metals, which is evidently an electrochemical process. Consider, e.g., the solution of a metal of high solution pressure in acid solutions. The equilibrium of hydrogen evolution (p. 767) must be

[1] *Zeitschr. f. Elektrochemie.* **4.** 506 (1898).   [2] *Ibid.* **6.** 533 (1900).
[3] *Zeitschr. phys. Chem.* **53.** 235 (1905).

at once reached on the surface between metal and solution, *i.e.* the solution of the metal and the consequent liberation of hydrogen must proceed at the same rate as the diffusion of the dissolved acid to the boundary surface.

Experience teaches, however, that, *e.g.*, pure zinc dissolves at a much slower rate in acids than corresponds to the mass of diffusing acid.[1] It has been supposed that the reaction

$$2H = H_2$$

takes place slowly in the metallic phase,[2] so that although zinc, *e.g.*, contains at any moment that concentration of hydrogen atoms which corresponds to the electromotive force, yet the formation of ordinary hydrogen only takes place slowly. In any case there is a close connection between these phenomena and the excess-potential (p. 766).

Passivity.—The ignoble metals, in a state of anodic polarisation, often offer a much greater resistance to their solution than would be expected from their position in the decomposition potential series ; this is usually known as the " passive state."

Sometimes this phenomenon occurs without polarisation, *e.g.*, iron behaves towards nitric acid as if it were a noble metal, that is to say, is in the passive state. The reason why some metals become passive under certain conditions is, as has been shown with certainty in a few cases, that the metal becomes covered during electrolysis with a *difficultly soluble* compound which obviously prevents the passage of the metallic ions. An example which has been especially well worked out[3] is the anodic solution of gold in potassium cyanide. When sodium is present, even in small traces, the gold becomes passive ; when sodium is completely absent it remains active. The cause of this behaviour was traced to the formation of a difficultly soluble sodium-gold cyanide. Whether the formation of a difficultly soluble protecting skin may be taken as the cause of passivity in every case is not yet certain. For instance, the formation of a skin of oxide when iron becomes passive has been doubted on the grounds that the reflective power of the metal is not altered. On the other hand, a good argument in favour of the formation of a protecting skin of oxide in this case, is that the passivity vanishes on cathodic polarisation, or by treatment with reducing agents.[4]

Theory of Galvanic Polarisation.—A quantity of electricity passed through a voltameter gives changes of concentration in all

[1] See especially the investigations of Ericson, Auren, and W. Palmaer, *Zeitschr. phys. Chem.* **39.** 1 (1901) ; **45.** 182 (1903) ; **56.** 689 (1906).

[2] Tafel, *Zeitschr. phys. Chem.* **34.** 200 (1900) ; E. Brunner, *ibid.* **58.** 41 (1907).·

[3] Coehn and C. L. Jacobsen, *Zeitschr. anorg. Chem.* **55.** 321 (1907).

[4] See the chapter on " Elektrochemie " by A. Coehn in Müller-Pouillet's *Lehrbuch der Physik*, IV. Paragraph, " Passivität," p. 611, for further details and the literature of the subject.

cases ; the theory of galvanic polarisation is therefore simply that of concentration cells.[1]

The changes of concentration producing electromotive force can consist either in a change in the concentration of the ions of the electrode metal or in a change in the substance occluded by the electrodes. We have an instance of the former in the electrolysis of sulphuric acid with mercury electrodes. If a quantity of electricity is passed through this voltameter the concentration of the mercuro-ions at the cathode is reduced, at the anode increased, hence we have a potential difference amounting to (p. 759)

$$E = \frac{RT}{n} \ln \frac{c_1}{c_2}.$$

Since $\frac{c_1}{c_2}$ can be made extremely large, considerable back electromotive force may be produced in such cases, and for a given quantity of electricity the change of concentration produced will be greater the smaller the concentration of the ions of the electrode metal in the first place. We have an instance of the second case in the electrolysis of sulphuric acid between platinum plates ; since these are charged with oxygen through the air they may be regarded as (approximately) reversible with respect to oxygen ; and since the concentration of the oxygen ions in the electrolyte is not appreciably altered by small quantities of electricity, the most important concentration change is that in the occluded oxygen. The back electromotive force is therefore

$$E = \frac{RT}{4} \ln \frac{c_1}{c_2},$$

where c_1 and c_2 are the concentrations (active masses) of oxygen in the electrodes ; the factor $\frac{1}{4}$ depends upon the fact that the oxygen molecule is electrochemically quadrivalent.

Further details on this subject belong to the region of pure physics.

Calculation of the Electrode Potentials from Thermal Data.—This calculation is a combination of the results obtained by applying the new theorem of thermodynamics to electromotive forces (see the preceding chapter) with the formulæ obtained in this chapter by means of the osmotic theory. It will be most simple to consider a particular example, say the element Ag/I_2 ; if P_1 and P_2 are the solution pressures of the two electrodes and p_0 the osmotic pressure of an aqueous solution saturated with silver iodide, then the electromotive force is given both by the osmotic theory and by the thermodynamical theory developed on p. 745 ff. :

[1] See also Warburg, *Wied. Ann.* **38.** 321 (1889).

$$RT \ln \frac{P_1}{p_0} + RT \ln \frac{P_2}{p_0} = \epsilon_1 - \epsilon_2 - RT \ln p_0{}^2 = \frac{U_0 - \beta T^2 - \frac{\gamma}{2} T^3}{23046}.$$

It is therefore possible to calculate the characteristic solution tension of each electrode (to a common factor), or the electrode potential E when we know an additive constant; the latter of course cancels out in the practical use of the numbers, because the electrode potentials are referred to that of one electrode; for example, the potential of the hydrogen electrode is taken as zero. As the osmotic theory allows us to calculate the E.M.F. of any galvanic combination which contains only dilute aqueous solutions, we can see that this theory is extended by the thermodynamical considerations given above, because the electrode potentials which could be obtained by the osmotic theory at any given temperature by one measurement with the electrode in question, are now capable of a simple theoretical calculation; they can, namely, be calculated from thermal and solubility data (see the paper by Bodländer referred to on p. 748).

For the calculation of each electrode potential we only need to know the solubility of one difficultly soluble salt; the solubilities of all other difficultly soluble salts can then be calculated.

General Theory of Contact Electricity.[1]—The general principle by means of which, as we have shown in this chapter, we have calculated the potential differences between substances may be formulated as follows. We attribute to the ions the same properties as to electrically neutral molecules; if we now consider any phenomenon which involves a change of place of molecules (*molecular phenomenon*), then the same process applied to free ions will usually have the consequence of separating anions and cations; this causes a potential difference. We may of course calculate the latter if we know the laws of the molecular phenomenon in question. On account of the enormous electrostatic capacity of the ions the quantities that are actually separated are too small to weigh.

Thus, for example, the theory of diffusion of non-electrolytes (a molecular phenomenon) leads to the theory of potential difference between dilute solutions, since the general laws of diffusion are applied to the diffusion of electrolytes (an ionic phenomenon). The comparison of the solubility of ordinary substances with the solubility of metals leads to the much used formula for the potential difference between metal and electrolyte.

A few further examples may be briefly noted. If a solution has different temperature in different parts the dissolved substance will travel along the temperature gradient, a phenomenon observed by

---

[1] See my report "*Über Berührungselektrizität,*" supplement to *Wied. Ann.*, 1896, vol. 8, where a collection of literature is to be found.

Soret.[1] If this molecular phenomenon be applied to the solution of electrolytes, and we suppose that Soret's formula is different for the different ions as it is for the different species of molecules, we arrive at the result that there must be potential differences in a solution of varying temperature.

It may easily be shown, as on p. 751, that in order that equal masses of positive and negative ions should move along the temperature gradient the equation

$$U\left(\frac{dp}{dx} + c\frac{dP}{dx} + ck'\frac{dT}{dx}\right) = V\left(\frac{dp}{dx} - c\frac{dP}{dx} + ck''\frac{dT}{dx}\right)$$

must be satisfied, where T is the variable temperature and k' and k'' the forces which, apart from osmotic action, drive the ions along the temperature gradient. The theory which van't Hoff[2] gave for Soret's phenomenon puts k' = k'' = 0, which, however, is not always true. The above equation can of course be utilised for the case of any number of dissolved substances. (See the thorough investigation of electrolytic thermo-elements, by W. Duane.[3])

If we consider further the division of a substance between two solvents (p. 495), and attribute, as we may according to all analogies, to each of the ions a *specific coefficient of distribution between two solvents,* it follows that the ions will not be divided between the phases in electrically equivalent quantities, if no other force is added to that arising from the existence of coefficients of distribution. But ions in the interior of a homogeneous phase must be present in electrically equivalent quantities ; if this is to be so some other force must exist, and it is easily seen that it is again of an electrostatic character, that is, there must be in general a potential difference between two homogeneous phases. Such phenomena must be found in the *occlusion of gases* by electrodes, and in the *precipitation of one metal on another,* and may help to explain the phenomena of polarisation as well as the behaviour of inconstant cells.

The above theory of contact electricity may be applied without change to non-conductors (for example, to the frictional electricity between glass and silk and the like), since, according to our present knowledge, these substances are merely bad electrolytes ; there is, however, the difficulty that we know nothing of the ions in such cases. From the observations so far given, however, Coehn[4] has arrived at an important conclusion, *that substances of high dielectric constant become positive by contact with substances of lower dielectric constant.*

It is only a short step to apply the same treatment to the *electrons* which we assume on p. 410 in the explanation of metallic conduc-

[1] This was observed before Soret (1881) by Ludwig, as early as 1856.
[2] *Zeitschr. phys. Chem.* **1.** 487 (1887).
[3] *Wied. Ann.* **65.** 374 (1898).
[4] *Ibid.* **64.** 217 (1898).

tion.   If the metals are regarded as solvents containing positive and negative electrons in varying concentration, then a consideration of the changes of position which they undergo in various circumstances would, like the ionic theories already developed, lead to a theory of potential difference in different metals or metals of differing temperature.

Conclusion.—Looking back finally on the electrochemical theories developed in this chapter, we may well say that the osmotic theory has enabled us to give in many cases a thorough explanation of the mechanism by which current is produced, and that we have reached a general solution of the problem of calculating electromotive forces from other phenomena which are easily observed.   Assuming also the correctness of the thermodynamical theory developed in Chapter V., we can calculate from specific heats and heats of reaction the electromotive force of those galvanic cells where only pure liquid or solid substances take part in the process which yields the current (p. 745 ff.). If we now imagine any solvent brought into contact with the substances in question, which does not alter the E.M.F., then we also know the electromotive force of the galvanic cell made up of saturated solutions.   The thermodynamical relations discussed in the preceding chapter, and the osmotic theory developed in this, enable us therefore to calculate the E.M.F. for any concentration, so that we have arrived in fact at a general solution of the problem.

CHAPTER IX

The Action of Light.—When ether vibrations pass through a material system, they are capable of affecting it in two essentially different ways. On the one hand, they raise the temperature of the system, their energy being partially converted into heat; on the other hand, they give rise to changes of a chemical nature.

We have already considered the first class of phenomena (p. 339), under the subject of the *absorption of light*.

The description of the second class of phenomena will form the subject of this chapter.

The ordinary absorption of light is a very general phenomenon. Every substance, in a way which varies largely of course with its own particular nature, and with the wave-length of light, can change the energy of the ether vibrations partially into heat; and this can be done completely if the layer permeated has a sufficient thickness.

But the *chemical action of light*, so called, takes place only in exceptional cases, since it is only rarely that illumination is able to exert an influence on the reaction velocity of a system in process of change, or on the state of equilibrium of a system which is in chemical repose. Of course it is not impossible that photo-chemical action may be very general; and that it may usually be too slight to be noticed under the ordinary conditions of research.

The chemical action of sunlight, such, *e.g.*, as that shown in the bleaching process, in the production of the green colour of plants, in its destructive effect on certain colours of the artist, has been recognised from time immemorial. But only recent investigation has taught us that numerous compounds are sensitive to light, and has convinced us that in these cases we have to do with a remarkable conversion of ether vibrations into chemical forces, which is deserving of the greatest interest.

It would take too much space to enter into the detailed enumera-

---

[1] See the comprehensive lectures by Luther, Trautz, Byk, Stobbe, Schaum, Scheffer, v. Hübl and Wiesner, and the resulting discussions at the 15th anniversary meeting of the Deutsche Bunsengesellschaft (*Zeitschr. f. Elektrochemie*, 1908, p. 445 ff.).

tion and description of the particular phenomena belonging here, and therefore we will only refer to the very complete bibliography prepared by Eder.[1] But it should be emphasised that *gases* (as, *e.g.*, the explosive mixture of hydrogen and chlorine), *liquids* (as, *e.g.*, chlorine water, which gives up oxygen, under the influence of light), and *solids* (as, *e.g.*, white phosphorus, which changes to the red modification in the light ; or cinnabar, which turns black), all respond to the ether vibrations.

Also the photo-chemical process may consist both in the *production* of a compound, as is the case with hydrochloric acid gas, and in the *decomposition* of a compound, as is seen in the decomposition of hydrogen phosphide, with the separation of phosphorus.

Trautz[2] has recently shown that light sometimes acts as an anticatalyst, and that in the same reaction (*e.g.* oxidation of pyrogallol by oxygen) one kind of light (*e.g.* violet light) accelerates, and another (*e.g.* red light) delays the reaction.

The sensitiveness to light of organic compounds has been systematically worked out by Ciamician and his colleagues. In a review of the whole material (*Bull. de la Soc. Chem.* iii., iv., No. 15, p. 1) he considers the influence of light on oxidations and reductions. A whole series of bodies with alkoxyl groups react on substances containing carbonyl, the alcohol group being oxidised by the carbonyl oxygen. For instance, ethyl alcohol reacts on quinone to give aldehyde and hydroquinone besides some quinhydrone. Especially interesting are the mutual internal oxidations and reductions of bodies containing nitrogen : *e.g.* o-nitrobenzaldehyde goes over to o-nitrosobenzoic acid. Other classes of reactions which are especially influenced by light are enumerated by Ciamician as follows : autoxidations, polymerisations, and condensations, the change from the fumaric to the maleic type, and hydrolysis (*e.g.* splitting up of cyclic ketones). In this way many reactions can be carried out which take place with difficulty, or not at all, in the dark. Organic photo-reactions are catalysed to a large extent by uranium salts. (Seekamp, *Ann. d. Chem.* **122.** 113 [1862] and **133.** 253 [1865].)

Although, on the one hand, this kind of light action in photo-chemical processes varies greatly according to the nature of the system illuminated, in contrast to ordinary absorption which always develops heat, yet like ordinary absorption it is highly dependent upon the wave-length of the light used. Thus we know photo-chemical reactions which are mainly caused by ultra-violet rays, or by the visible rays, or by the ultra-red rays of the spectrum, respectively ; and in all cases the intensity of the photo-chemical action depends in the highest degree upon the wave-length of light,

---

[1] *Handbuch der Photochemie*, Halle, 1906 ; Fehling's *Handwörterbuch*, under *Chemische Wirkungen des Lichtes.* See further M. Roloff, *Zeitschr. phys. Chem.* **26.** 337 (1898).

[2] *Physik. Zeitschr.* **7.** 899 (1906).

a fact which should be given proper attention in researches of this kind.

After a discussion of all the material up to date, Eder [1] comes to some general empirical laws, which are essentially contained in the following statements.

1. Light of every wave-length, from the infra-red to the ultra-violet, can exert photo-chemical action.

2. Only those rays are effective which are absorbed by the system; so that the chemical action of the light is closely associated with the optical absorption; but conversely, optical absorption does not always necessitate chemical action.

3. According to the nature of the substance absorbing the light, every kind of light may act as an oxidising or a reducing agent; but it may be said, in general, that *red* light has usually an *oxidising* effect, and *violet* light a *reducing* effect, on metallic compounds. The case where red light may also exert a reducing effect occurs in the *latent light action* [2] of silver salts. So far no oxidising action of violet rays on metallic compounds has been observed with certainty.

Violet and blue light usually act most strongly on the compounds of the metalloids with each other : as, *e.g.*, on " chlorine knall-gas," on nitrous acid, on sulphurous acid, and on hydriodic acid; yet hydrogen sulphide solution is decomposed more quickly by red light.

The light action is partly oxidising and partly reducing according to the nature of the substance. In most cases, violet light exerts the strongest oxidising action on organic compounds, especially the colourless ones. Coloured substances are oxidised most strongly by those light rays which they absorb.

4. Not only does the absorption of the light rays, by the illuminated substance itself, play an important part, but also the absorption of light by *foreign* substances mixed with the principal substance, is important; for the sensitiveness of the main substance can be stimulated for those rays which are absorbed by the admixed substance (*optical sensitisation*).

While this phenomenon was originally only known for sensitive solid substances, it has recently been shown by F. Weigert that gas reactions may also be optically sensitised (*Ann. d. Physik.* **24.** p. 243, 1907). If chlorine is added to a mixture of hydrogen and oxygen the union of these two gases is perceptibly accelerated by rays which the chlorine absorbs; the same holds good for the oxidation of sulphurous acid by oxygen gas, and the catalytic decomposition of ozone. The last reaction has been more exactly worked out by F. Weigert, *Zeitschr. f. Elektrochemie,* **14.** p. 591, 1908.

If we mix the optically sensitive body with a substance which

---

[1] *l.c.* p. 28 ; and *Beibl. zu Wied. Ann.* **4.** 472 (1880).

[2] For the various applications of the sensitiveness of silver salts, see especially the text-books of photography by Eder (Halle, 1906), and by H. W. Vogel (Berlin, 1878), Supp., 1883.

unites with one of the products resulting from the photo-chemical reaction (as oxygen, bromine, and iodine), the reaction velocity is accelerated because the reverse action is impossible. This may be also regarded as a consequence of the law of mass-action (chemical sensitisation).

In many cases, as Roloff observed (*Zeitschr. phys. Chem.* **13**. 327, 1894) the action of light consists in the transport of ionic charges : see the paper of the same author quoted on p. 777.

Actinometry.—The action of the light upon a chemical system is the greater, the more intensive the ether vibrations are, upon which it depends. In the quantitative investigation of any selected photo-chemical process, we possess a means for measuring the intensity of the chemically active rays.

All pieces of apparatus designed to measure the photo-chemical intensity of light, and depending on the observation of the changes which are experienced by substances sensitive to light, when under the influence of the ether vibrations, are called *actinometers*. As all the empirical laws of photo-chemistry thus far discovered have been ascertained by the aid of actinometers, the most important of these will be enumerated in the pages immediately following.

But first we may make a general remark on the value to be placed upon conclusions as to the intensity of light which are drawn from actinometric experiments.

The data obtained from all kinds of actinometers are of a purely individual nature.

Thus it may be shown in two ways that they serve to give only a *relative* measurement of the intensity of light; for, on the one hand, even when using the same kind of light, the nature and reaction velocity of the chemical process occasioned in each particular case, will vary according to the varying behaviour of the system which is subjected to the action of light, and, on the other hand, when light is used which consists of rays of very different wave-lengths, the data of the same actinometer will by no means be proportional to the intensity of light; because the action of different kinds of light varies greatly according to the wave-length.

The eye is also an actinometer, having an individual nature; because apparently its sensitiveness to the ether vibrations depends upon certain photo-chemical processes which are occasioned thereby.

The photometric measurement of light, and the actinometric methods to be described below give results which are neither parallel with each other, nor with the results obtained by the thermometric measurements, which used to be regarded as the absolute measure of radiation.

It has been proved, however, that the results obtained by several actinometers are at least approximately proportional to each other.

Although we are not justified in drawing even an approximate conclusion regarding the photo-chemical activity of two light sources which have been studied only in an optical-physiological [visual] way, yet, on the whole, the "chlorine knall-gas" actinometer and the "silver chloride" actinometer, for example, give results which correspond with each other.

The Chlorine "Knall-gas" Actinometer.—This depends upon the discovery of Gay-Lussac and Thénard in 1809, of the action of light on the combination of chlorine and hydrogen; in strong light this action advances with a velocity which results in an explosion, but in weak light it progresses gradually and steadily. This actinometer was first constructed by Draper in 1843, but it was brought by Bunsen and Roscoe [1] to an improved form suited for exact measurement. The method consists in measuring the diminution of a volume of "chlorine knall-gas" (standing over water and kept at constant pressure), as a result of the formation of hydrochloric acid which is absorbed by the water. As the manipulation of this apparatus requires unusual patience and skill on the part of the observer, Bunsen and Roscoe later turned their attention to—

The Silver-Chloride Actinometer.[2]—In this the *time* required to darken photographic paper until a definite "normal" shade is reached, serves as a measure of the light intensity.

The Mercury-Oxalate Actinometer.—A solution of mercuric chloride and ammonium oxalate will remain unchanged an indefinitely long time in the dark; but in the light, CO_2 and mercurous chloride are developed in the sense of the equation,

$$2HgCl_2 + C_2O_4 (NH_4)_2 = Hg_2Cl_2 + 2CO_2 + 2NH_4Cl.$$

Either the quantity of CO_2 set free, or else the amount of mercurous chloride precipitated, may serve as a measure of the intensity of light; the latter gives much more exact results.

According to Eder,[3] it is best to mix two litres of water containing 80 g. of ammonium oxalate, with 1 litre of water containing 50 g. of mercuric chloride; some of this is then poured into a beaker glass of about 100 c.c. capacity, which is "light tight" on all sides, but which has an opening in its cover. As the concentration of the sensitive solution changes during the illumination, the separation of the mercurous chloride takes place with an increasing slowness, and thus does not directly correspond to the light energy introduced; it is therefore necessary to apply a correction, the amount of which can be taken from the table furnished by Eder. Elevation of the temperature

---

[1] *Pogg. Ann.* **96**. 96 and 373 ; **100**. 43 and 481 ; **101**. 255 ; **108**. 193 (1855-1859).

[2] *Ibid.* **117**. 529 ; **124**. 353 ; **132**. 404. For the numerous modifications which this has experienced in order to adapt it to the needs of practical photography, see Eder, *Handbuch der Photographie*, **1**. 174 ff.

[3] *Wiener Sitzungsber.* **80**, 1897 ; *Handbuch*, **1**. 169.

is favourable to the action of light, and this must be considered in quantitative research.

This apparatus is chiefly sensitive to the ultra-violet rays.

Instead of mercuric oxalate, we may make use of the oxalate of iron or uranium in a similar way.

The Electro-Chemical Antinometer.—If two silver electrodes which have been chlorinised or iodised, are dipped into dilute sulphuric acid, then, as observed by Becquerel in 1839, an electromotive force will be established between them, as long as *one* electrode is illuminated ; *the current will flow in the solution from the unlighted to the lighted pole.*

The strength of a current, as read by means of a sensitive galvanometer, will serve to determine the intensity of light. The results obtained by this actinometer are approximately parallel with those obtained in photometric ways. The most useful form is that of Rigollet,[1] which consists simply of two copper plates, slightly oxidised in the Bunsen flame, and immersed in 1 per cent solution of an alkaline halide, only one plate being exposed to the light.

Photo-Chemical Extinction.—As light which is chemically active performs a certain amount of work, it is to be expected—other conditions being the same—that the light will be absorbed to a greater degree when it occasions or accelerates a chemical process, than when it does not.

In fact, Bunsen and Roscoe[2] found that light which had passed through a layer of chlorine knall-gas was much more weakened in its chemical activity (as measured by the chlorine knall-gas photometer) than when it had only passed through a layer of pure chlorine of the same thickness, and thus had had no opportunity to form hydrochloric acid. In both cases the light is weakened by absorption by the chlorine ; the absorption occasioned by the hydrogen can be neglected. In the second case the weakening is due purely to optical absorption ; and therefore the loss of energy of the light reappears in the heat which is developed. But in the first case, an additional fraction of the light-energy is consumed in performing chemical work, which thus occasions a stronger absorption.

This phenomenon was called by Bunsen and Roscoe, "*photo-chemical extinction*" ; it is apparently very common, and it has surpassing interest for our conceptions regarding the mechanism of the chemical action of light. Further experimental investigation on this point is greatly needed, especially as recent research has failed to confirm the observations of Bunsen and Roscoe.[3]

Photo-Chemical Induction.—Another very remarkable fact, for the discovery of which we are likewise indebted to the classical

---

[1] *Journ. de Phys.* [3], **6.** 520 (1897).   [2] *Pogg. Ann.* **101.** 254 (1857).
[3] Burgess and Chapman, *Journ. Chem. Soc.* **89.** 1399 (1906) ; see also Weigert, *Zeitschr. f. Elektrochemie*, 1908, p. 596.

investigations of Bunsen and Roscoe, is the so-called "*photo-chemical induction*"; by this is meant the phenomenon when light usually acts very slowly at first, and attains its full activity only after a lapse of some time.

Thus, with the steady illumination of a kerosene lamp, the quantities (S) of hydrochloric acid produced in every minute (as measured by the displacement of the water filament in the scale tube of the chlorine knall-gas actinometer), are given in the following table; the time t denotes the minutes in order.

t.	S.	t.	S.
1	0·0	7	14·6
2	1·6	8	29·2
3	0·5	9	31·1
4	0·0	10	30·4
5	0·5	11	32·4
6	2·1	...	...

As is obvious, the action [which at first is very slow] begins to be constant only after about nine minutes; after this the hydrochloric acid produced is proportional to the product of the time and the light intensity; and only then does the actinometer become suitable for measurements. But if the actinometer is afterwards allowed to remain some time in the dark, then it requires a renewed illumination, although a shorter one, in order to bring it again to the condition where it gives results which are proportional to the product of the intensity of the light and the duration of the illumination. If the apparatus stands as long as half an hour in the dark, then the influence of the preceding illumination vanishes completely.

It is now certain that photo-chemical induction is a secondary phenomenon (see below); Pringsheim,[1] Dixon,[2] and others, showed that in the preceding case it depended on the formation of intermediate compounds, and afterwards Luther and Goldberg[3] proved that the addition of oxygen delayed all photo-chemical reactions of chlorine—the oxygen being used up first, and chlorine monoxide being probably formed. Induction is therefore essentially due to the impurification of the hydrogen-chlorine mixture by ·oxygen. Burgess and Chapman (*l.c.*) have discussed the influence of other impurities.

That the induction cannot be due to the formation of HClO or ClO_2 was shown by Mellor,[4] who tried without success to shorten the induction period by adding these substances to the mixture.

Moreover, there is the well-known fact, that a very slight preliminary exposure of photographic plates makes their sensitiveness

[1] *Wied. Ann.* **32.** 384 (1887).
[2] *Zeitschr. phys. Chem.* **42.** 318 (1903).   [3] *Ibid.* **56.** 43 (1906).
[4] *Trans. Chem. Soc.* **81.** 1292 (1902).

much greater ; and also, in harmony with this, that " under-exposed " plates can be strengthened by a slight subsequent exposure. It is highly probable that these facts must be regarded as analogous to the photo-chemical induction of chlorine knall-gas. Both of the facts just mentioned indicate that the photographic action of light is relatively slow in the first moments of exposure ; and that it is some time before the state of maximum sensitiveness is reached.[1]

The precipitation of calomel in Eder's photometer also suffers an initial retardation ; the cause of this photo-chemical induction is, however, of a secondary nature, as Eder showed ; enough calomel must be formed for saturation before any is precipitated.

The Latent Light-Action of Silver Salts.[2]—The so-called " *latent light action* " of silver salts (p. 778) has both great theoretical and also great practical interest ; it offers, in particular, much that is puzzling, but it has long found practical application in photography.

All of the photographic methods, from the " positives " of Daguerre to the " collodion emulsion " and the " dry-plate " methods (which are almost exclusively used at present) depend on the principle that light is not allowed to act upon the plate until a visible picture is formed, but that the light action is interrupted long before this ; the image is then " developed " by suitable treatment of the plate in the dark.

The photographic action of the light does not consist in a marked material change of the exposed plate, but only to such an extent that the different parts of the plate, having met more or less light respectively, react with correspondingly greater or lesser velocity in the subsequent treatment.

The action of the developer produces visible changes ; a picture appears, and the chief art of the photographer consists in the proper choice of the time of " exposure," and in interrupting the process of development at the right moment.

In order to preserve the picture, the remaining substance, which is sensitive to light, and which has not been fixed by the developer, must be removed (" fixing "). For this purpose use is commonly made of some suitable solvent which removes the undecomposed silver salt.

A distinction must be made between *physical* and *chemical development*.

The first found application, *e.g.* in the daguerreotype ; this physical development consists in the fact that mercury vapour is most quickly precipitated upon those portions of a silver plate which have been exposed to the light, the plate having been previously slightly iodised on the surface.

The image is formed in the same way in the collodion process, as

[1] See the researches of Abney, Eder's *Jahrbuch*, 1895, pp. 123 and 149 ; Englisch, *Arch. wiss. Phot.* **1.** 117 (1899).

[2] See, in connection with this section, the attractively written monograph, " Chem. Vorgänge in der Photographie," by R. Luther, Halle (Knapp), 1899.

silver is separated from a solution of a silver salt containing reducing agents on to those parts which have been exposed to light. Chemical development is applied in the modern negative process, in which a gelatine film impregnated with silver bromide is illuminated and is then treated with reducing agents (aqueous solution of potassium ferro-oxalate, alkaline salts of amido- or polyphenols, hydroquinone, pyrogallol, p-amidophenol, etc.); the silver halide in the plate is then reduced to silver most quickly at the illuminated spots. The distinction between the two methods is a purely external one, for in all cases the precipitation of the solid produced by developing (mercury, silver) takes place more rapidly in the places where the product of reaction of light exists, and about proportionally to the amount of this product.[1] Only the material for depositing silver is taken from the photographic layer in the "chemical" process, and is added from outside in the "physical."

Many views have been put forward as to the chemical nature of the latent action of light. There is no doubt that the changes that silver halides undergo on illumination is a reduction with formation of free halogen; but the nature of the reduction product is not in all cases known. Direct chemical investigation and isolation of the reduced substance has not been accomplished, and is not promising, on account of the minute quantity formed. Further, the nature of the binding material—collodion, gelatine, albumen, etc.—in which the silver halide is embedded, seems to affect the reduction. It has recently been shown by Luther,[2] for films of silver chloride and bromide without any binding material, that the products of reduction are the subchloride Ag_2Cl and subbromide Ag_2Br.

Under ordinary conditions of illumination of silver halide the photochemical reaction is indefinite, as the halogen set free is at an arbitrary potential, which depends on thickness, resistance to diffusion, moisture, and especially the chemical nature of the film. Luther showed first that sufficient exposure, with any intensity of illumination, produces a definite equilibrium, that can be reached from either side, involving, besides the solid phases of unchanged and reduced silver salt, a definite halogen potential, increasing with the illumination. This shows that the action of light on the silver halides is reversible. Further, Luther showed that both the *latent* developable image produced by short illumination and the *visible* image that takes longer to produce are permanent in solutions of a certain halogen potential, and are destroyed in one of a higher potential, so that they apparently consist of the same substance. Finally, this halogen potential of the reduction product agrees nearly with that which exists over silver subchloride and subbromide, so that these substances must be regarded as the latent and visible products of reaction of light when no binding material is used.

---

[1] Abegg, *Arch. wiss. Phot.* **1.** 109 (1899).

[2] *Zeitschr. phys. Chem.* **30.** 628 (1899); and *Arch. wiss. Phot.* **2.** 35, 59 (1900).

The following view has long been taken of the process of development. On the illuminated spots of the plates small particles of metallic silver are deposited by reduction, with a density increasing with the intensity of the light; but always in such small quantity that no visible change occurs in the substance of the plate. When the plate is put in the developer those invisible silver particles act as nuclei for precipitation of silver, just as a small crystal brings about crystallisation in a supersaturated solution. The denser the silver particles at any spot the denser will be the deposit of silver during development.

This theory requires slight modification, on the view that the latent image does not consist of metallic silver. It may be supposed that the silver sub-halide is easily reduced by the developer, and the silver nuclei thus produced serve for further deposit.

There is much uncertainty in the chemical theory of ordinary photographic preparations, which contain the silver halide in various binding materials, although steps towards an explanation have been made by Luggin.[1]

Moreover, a further very remarkable discovery was made by H. W. Vogel (1878). According to this, photographic plates may be made much more sensitive by intermixture with slight traces of organic colouring substances, and the plates are usually especially sensitive for the kinds of light absorbed by the particular colouring substances (*optical sensitisation*). And thus, as desired, plates may be prepared sensitive to yellow or red light, etc.

Thus far, no theoretical explanation has been given for this phenomenon. A thorough investigation of this subject by E. Vogel[2] has led to the result that, of the eosin colours, erythrosin and di-iodofluorescein work best; and that, in general, these substances "sensitise" best, which are themselves most sensitive to light. The sensitising action increases in a striking way with the diminution of *fluorescence*.

Action of the Silent Discharge.—Chemical action takes place in many gaseous mixtures under the influence of rapidly alternating electrification, the so-called "*silent discharge*"; for example, ammonia is decomposed into nitrogen and hydrogen, nitrogen and water vapour combine to form ammonium nitrite, acetylene is polymerised,[3] etc.

The best known of these phenomena is the *ozonising* of oxygen, which has been carefully investigated by Warburg[4] in recent times. He showed that to every particular kind and strength of silent discharge, there corresponded a definite proportion of ozone in the

[1] *Zeitschr. phys. Chem.* **14**. 385 (1894) ; **23**. 577 (1897).
[2] *Wied. Ann.* **43**. 449 (1891).
[3] Berthelot, *C.R.* **131**. 772 (1900).
[4] *Ann. d. phys.* **9**. 781 (1902) ; **13**. 464 (1904).

mixture, and that this equilibrium could be reached from both sides. That the phenomenon was not due to electrolysis produced by the current, was convincingly shown by the fact that the production of ozone could rise to 1000 times the amount corresponding to the quantity of electricity sent through. The action of the silent discharge is probably somewhat complicated; it is certainly partly of a photo-chemical nature, as Warburg showed for the special case of ozone formation, for chemically active ultra-violet rays are produced by the silent discharge in the gas. But besides this, "*cathodochemical action*" certainly comes into force, for, just as cathode rays can bring about many reactions, so under the influence of the silent discharge, collisions take place between electrons and gaseous ions, and thus lead to chemical decompositions and combinations.

The decompositions brought about by strong radium preparations belong to the same category; their further examination will probably open up an entirely new chapter in the investigation of the transformations of chemical energy.

The Laws of Photo-Chemical Reaction.—As there is no difference but the difference in wave-length between the visible rays and those which are chemically active, and probably also the waves of great wave-length (such as those produced by electrical agitation of the ether, Maxwell and Hertz); and as all these rays must be regarded as caused by the transmission of disturbances developed in the luminiferous ether, there can be no doubt that the chemically active rays should be refracted, reflected, and polarised, like all other rays; that their intensity should diminish as the reciprocal of the square of the distance from the point of origin (*i.e.* the source of light); and that if an absorbing substance is placed in the path of the rays, their photo-chemical action should be weakened according to the same laws as those for optical rays, etc. etc. The test of these laws has, in fact, given the anticipated results.[1]

Moreover, abundant research has led to the result, that when a photo-chemical system is illuminated, the resulting action depends solely on the amount of the impinging light,[2] and is independent of the time taken to introduce the same number of similar vibrations into the system. This law is usually stated in the following way:

When light of the same kind is used, the photo-chemical action depends solely on the product of the intensity and the duration of exposure.

Thus Bunsen and Roscoe[3] proved in the very sharpest way that the time required for the development of the normal colour on their sensitive paper was proportional to the number of light waves which

---

[1] See especially the investigations of Bunsen and Roscoe.
[2] The phenomenon of photo-chemical induction, described on p. 781, is probably only an apparent exception.
[3] *Pogg. Ann.* **117**. 536 (1862).

struck the paper in a second; by changing the cross section of the aperture through which the sunlight entered, it varied precisely according to the way indicated. A corresponding proof was given by Goldberg[1] for the oxidation of quinine by chromic acid.

Chemiluminescence.—It has long been known that many chemical and physico-chemical processes are accompanied by an emission of light which is far greater than that which should correspond to the temperature of the system, and therefore does not obey Kirchhoff's law. The crystallisation of potassium sulphate and many other substances is accompanied by flashes of light; phosphorus becomes luminous when slowly oxidised; many organic substances also become luminous when treated with oxidising agents. The luminescence which accompanies the simultaneous oxidation of pyrogallol and formaldehyde by hydrogen peroxide is especially fine, and very suitable for a lecture demonstration. This phenomenon has been recently systematically investigated by Trautz,[2] and shown to be of a very general character. Trautz collected all the existing observations, and also described a number of new reactions which cause luminescence. His proof that the intensity of the light emitted is proportional to the velocity of reaction is very noteworthy; in accordance with this it is found that many reactions are accompanied by distinct light phenomena, if care is taken to ensure a high velocity of reaction.

Especially important from a theoretical point of view is the proof that in many cases reactions which are sensitive to light, emit light rays of the same wave-length as those towards which they are most sensitive.

Theory of Photo-Chemical Action.—The theories on the mechanism by which the energy of the vibrations of the luminiferous ether is applied to the performance of chemical work are at present only vague. When we, however, consider that, in the light of recent views, light vibrations are produced by electric agitations, it is probable that the chemical action of light corresponds to the formation and decomposition of chemical compounds under the influence of the galvanic current. In this connection it is important to notice O. Wiener's proof that when stationary light waves act on silver chloride-collodion, it is only the electric and not the magnetic vector in the light which causes the photo-chemical process.[3] But the principles on which the mathematical description of the course of a photo-chemical reaction depends, appear to have been discovered. They differ considerably in the most important cases from those which apply to reactions taking place in the dark. In order to get a useful working

[1] *Zeitschr. phys. Chem.* **41**. 1 (1902).
[2] *Ibid.* **53**. 1 (1905); *Jahrbuch der Radioaktivität,* **4**. vol. 2 (1907).
[3] *Wied. Ann.* **40**. 203 (1890).

hypothesis, we must suppose that light action is of two kinds. In the so-called catalytic photo-reactions, as, for instance, the decomposition of hydrogen iodide, investigated thoroughly by M. Bodenstein,[1] light accelerates a reaction which may also take place in the dark, though at a much slower rate, or only at high temperatures. Light has here a loosening effect. The second kind of action is reversible, and consists in the alteration of a state of equilibrium by light, which therefore performs work against the chemical forces. Often both effects are produced at once, as in the mutual transformation of oxygen and ozone, where rays of a certain wave-length perform work by changing oxygen into ozone, while at the same time rays of another wave-length change the resulting ozone back into oxygen, thus working in the same direction as the chemical forces. Regener[2] has shown that in the neighbourhood of a quartz glass mercury vapour lamp, which is extremely rich in ultra-violet rays, a considerable quantity of ozone is present at equilibrium, while at the ordinary temperature in the dark, the amount of ozone present at equilibrium is immeasurably small. An especially good example of the displacement of an equilibrium by light, which is quite free from catalytic disturbances, was discovered by Luther and Weigert.[3] Anthracene changes under the influence of light into a bimolecular dianthracene, which changes back into anthracene in the dark very slowly at the ordinary temperature, but with measurable velocity at about 160°—the change being practically complete. W. Marckwald[4] and H. Stobbe[5] have described reversible transformations of solid substances under the influence of light.

Catalytic light reactions obey the formulæ of ordinary chemical dynamics. Experience has shown, however, that a reaction which takes place in certain ways in the dark can also go on in other ways in the light, so that although the same end products are reached in both cases, the reaction in light may be of a different order. An excellent example of this is found in the decomposition of hydrogen iodide, which has already been mentioned above. In the light this reaction is of the first order, and takes place according to the equation

$$HI = H + I,$$

while in the dark it is of the second order, and is represented thus :

$$2HI = H_2 + I_2.$$

We must assume, however, that the bimolecular reaction also takes place in light, besides the monomolecular, although its importance is insignificant.

We arrive, therefore, at a general formulation for the reaction

[1] Zeitschr. phys. Chem. **22.** 23 (1897).
[2] Ann. d. phys. **20.** 1033 (1906).
[3] Zeitschr. phys. Chem. **51.** 297 ; **53.** 385 (1905).
[4] Ibid. **30.** 140 (1899).
[5] Liebig's Ann. **359.** 1 (1908).

velocity by putting V equal to a sum of expressions of the kind given on p. 445. The velocity coefficients of all these reactions and reverse reactions will depend more or less on the intensity of illumination, and it is the fact that the degree of this dependence is different for the different reactions that often cause the reaction as a whole to be of a different order in the light. Experimental evidence supports the obvious inference that the change caused by light of a certain kind in the velocity coefficients of the reactions taking place in the dark, is proportional to the intensity of the light. But apart from the different ways in which the reaction takes place, it is to be expected for purely optical reasons that the reaction in light can be of a different order to that in the dark ; for the optical and photo-chemical absorption of the light causes a variation in light-intensity from point to point in the system, so that the different velocity coefficients become functions of position. But the varying reaction velocities involve the further complication that differences in concentration are set up in the system, which tend to equalise themselves by diffusion—a point which is especially to be remembered when dealing with the theory of liquid actinometers.

The relations are very simple when the light intensity in the system can be regarded as constant ; when the reaction advances almost to completion, so that $k' = 0$; and when, finally, the reaction can only take place in one way. These conditions are fulfilled in Wittwer's[1] researches, who investigated the velocity of the action of dissolved chlorine upon water, under the influence of light. In this special case, the above general equation reduces simply to

$$V = -\frac{dc}{dt} = kc$$

where c is the concentration of the chlorine. This agrees very well with the observations.

But although catalytic light reactions can be included in the general scheme of chemical dynamics, yet they really occupy a peculiar position. This is shown in the influence of temperature upon them. The velocity of photo-chemical reactions, even when they are reversible, rises only slightly with the temperature, whereas that of reactions taking place in the dark is very highly increased.[2] We cannot, there-fore, suppose that the action of light in a photo-chemical process is to loosen the combination of the atoms in the molecule, nor, in other words, that illumination has a similar influence to a rise in temperature on the reaction capacity ; rather must the primary effect be an action on the light ether, and it seems probable that the ionisation phenomena described in the ninth chapter of the second book play a part in photo-chemical processes.

[1] *Pogg. Ann.* **94.** 598 (1855).
[2] See the paper by Goldberg, referred to on p. 787.

Byk[1] has developed a mathematical theory of reversible light reactions with the help of thermodynamics, starting from the hypothesis "that no transformation of *material*, but only of *energy*, is caused by the intensity of the incident light (its energy), and that the work performed against chemical forces is proportional to the incident light energy." Byk arrived at the following formula for the velocity of formation of dianthracene from anthracene : —

$$\frac{dD}{dt} = \frac{aE_a}{V\left(e + RT \ln \dfrac{D}{A^2}\right)} - kD,$$

where D and A are the concentrations of dianthracene and anthracene respectively, aE_a the quantity of light energy made chemically useful in one second, e the work of transformation for certain normal concentrations, V the total volume, k the velocity constant of the reaction in the dark. From this equation a series of further peculiarities of the process besides those already mentioned can be deduced, as, for example, the influence of the strength of light upon the concentration of dianthracene at equilibrium. To obtain a better quantitative agreement, Byk has made the further assumption that a certain fraction of the radiation energy is converted into heat—an assumption which is perfectly legitimate from the electromagnetic standpoint.

Resonance phenomena probably have a good deal to do with the special kind of electromagnetic process taking place here. As the amount of accumulated energy of resonance is determined in the first place by the refractive indices, it can be understood that the strongly refractive rays of short wave length are the most photo-chemically active.[2]

In agreement with this it is found that photographic plates can only be made sensitive for light rays of long wave-length by means of dyes which cause anomalous dispersion, *i.e.* which have abnormally high refractive power for the long rays.

Warburg (*Ber. d. D. Physik. Ges.* **5**. 753 (1907)) and Trautz (*Zeitschr. f. wissenschaftl. Photographie*, **6**. 169 (1908)) have pointed out the necessary deduction from the second law of thermodynamics that the work available for chemical purposes is to a certain extent limited even in the most favourable case. If T' is the temperature of radiation, T the temperature of substance, then according to the Carnot-Clausius principle only the fraction $\dfrac{T' - T}{T'}$ of the energy of radiation can in any case be available for chemical work. With the sources of light generally used, however, the difference of this factor from unity has only the nature of a small correction. There can be no doubt that the second law of thermodynamics is applicable to photo-chemical processes, and yet it seems that difficulties of a peculiar

---

[1] *Zeitschr. phys. Chem.* **62**. 454 (1908).   [2] Byk. *l.c.* p. 486.

kind are met with. ' If we make the assumption (which can scarcely be disputed) that it is possible to fill a chemical system with any (mono-chromatic) radiation, and that photo-chemical equilibrium is attained before this radiation is destroyed or transformed by absorption, then by considera-tions exactly analogous to those on p. 675 we arrive at the relation

$$RT \frac{\delta \ln K}{\delta \pi} = - V_0,$$

where π is the radiation pressure of the (monochromatic) relation in question, and V_0 the increase in volume which is produced at the radiation pressure π, by the luminescence radiation caused by the transformation of one mol.

This equation contains the thermodynamical foundation of Trautz's theorem mentioned on p. 787 ; an experimental proof of it would be of the greatest interest. It is not to be supposed, however, that this equation covers all photo-chemical processes.

The problem to what degree in any single case light acts with or against the chemical affinity still lacks a complete solution ; its importance is best made clear by pointing out that *photo-chemical processes* are practically the only means by which we can store up the energy of the sun's radiation [1] in the form of useful work, and their products are the greatest objects of the "struggle for existence."

The struggle for existence is therefore, as Boltzmann [2] emphasised, not a struggle for fundamental material—the fundamental material of all organisms is present in excess in earth, air, and water : it is not even a struggle for energy itself, for quantities of energy fill our environment in the inconvertible form of heat ; it is a struggle *for the free energy available for work*, which the plant world stores up from the sunlight, like electrical energy is stored in an accumulator.

In the preceding chapters of this book we have been able to develop the relations between heat, electrical and chemical energy, and there can be no doubt that a similar thorough explanation of the *transformation of radiant energy into chemical* would be a success of the highest importance, and a further step towards the goal which theoretical chemistry even now makes possible, of placing side by side and in perfect equality with the doctrine of the *material* changes of nature, so long the chief interest and incentive of the chemist, a *doctrine of the transformations of energy.*

[1] The enormous economic value of the sun's radiation, the greater part of which is still turned to no account, has been recently pointed out by R. Luther in a lecture on the *Problems of Photo-chemistry* (Leipzig, 1905, A. Barth). The earth receives from the sun constantly some 200 billion horse-power, while the horse-power of all steam and other engines collectively is some two million times smaller. Only about three-millionths of the above amount of energy is utilised photo-chemically by the plant world, the remainder leaves the earth without performing any useful work. "In face of this enormous amount of energy it needs no prophetic power to foretell an age of technical photo-mechanics and technical photo-chemistry."

[2] *Der zweite Hauptsatz der mech. Wärme*, Wien (Gerold), 1886, p. 21. *Populäre Schriften*, No. 3 (Leipzig, 1905).

INDEX OF SUBJECTS

793

INDEX OF AUTHORS

THE END

Printed by R. & R. CLARK, LIMITED, *Edinburgh.*

MACMILLAN AND CO.'S
STANDARD WORKS ON CHEMISTRY

CHEMICAL TECHNOLOGY AND ANALYSIS OF OILS, FATS, AND WAXES. By Dr. J. LEWKOWITSCH. Fourth Edition, entirely rewritten and enlarged. In three volumes. With Illustrations. Medium 8vo. 50s. net.

LABORATORY COMPANION TO FATS AND OILS INDUSTRIES. By Dr. J. LEWKOWITSCH. 8vo. 6s. net.

CHEMISTRY OF THE PROTEIDS. By Dr. GUSTAV MANN. Based on Prof. Cohnheim's "Chemie der Eiweiss-Korper." 8vo. 15s. net.

ANALYTICAL CHEMISTRY. By Prof. A. MENSCHUTKIN. Translated by J. LOCKE. 8vo. 17s. net.

HISTORY OF CHEMISTRY FROM THE EARLIEST TIMES TO THE PRESENT DAY. By ERNST VON MEYER, Ph.D. Third Edition. Translated by G. McGOWAN, Ph.D. 8vo. 17s. net.

THEORETICAL CHEMISTRY. By Prof. WALTER NERNST, Ph.D. Revised in accordance with the sixth German edition by H. T. TIZARD, Magdalen College, Oxford. 8vo.

QUALITATIVE CHEMICAL ANALYSIS OF INORGANIC SUBSTANCES. By A. A. NOYES, Ph.D. 8vo. 6s. 6d. net.

SCIENTIFIC FOUNDATIONS OF ANALYTICAL CHEMISTRY. By Prof. W. OSTWALD. Translated by G. McGOWAN, Ph.D. Crown 8vo. 6s. net.

PRINCIPLES OF INORGANIC CHEMISTRY. By Prof. W. OSTWALD. Translated by Dr. A. FINDLAY. Third Edition. 8vo. 18s. net.

EXPERIMENTAL PROOFS OF CHEMICAL THEORY FOR BEGINNERS. By Sir WILLIAM RAMSAY, K.C.B., F.R.S. Pott 8vo. 2s. 6d.

GASES OF THE ATMOSPHERE: THE HISTORY OF THEIR DISCOVERY. By Sir WILLIAM RAMSAY, K.C.B., F.R.S. Third Edition. Extra Crown 8vo. 6s. net.

A TEXT-BOOK OF INORGANIC CHEMISTRY. By Prof. IRA REMSEN. 8vo. 16s.

COMPOUNDS OF CARBON; OR, AN INTRODUCTION TO THE STUDY OF ORGANIC CHEMISTRY. By Prof. IRA REMSEN. Crown 8vo. 6s. 6d.

COLLEGE TEXT-BOOK OF CHEMISTRY. By Prof. IRA REMSEN. Second Edition. 8vo. 10s. net.

A NEW VIEW OF THE ORIGIN OF DALTON'S ATOMIC THEORY. By Sir H. E. ROSCOE, F.R.S., and A. HARDEN, F.R.S. 8vo. 6s. net.

OUTLINES OF INDUSTRIAL CHEMISTRY. A Text-Book for Students. By FRANK HALL THORP, Ph.D. 8vo. 16s. net.

ESSAYS IN HISTORICAL CHEMISTRY. By Sir EDWARD THORPE, C.B., LL.D., F.R.S. Third Edition. 8vo. 12s. net.

THE EXPERIMENTAL STUDY OF GASES. By Dr. MORRIS W. TRAVERS, F.R.S. With Introduction by Sir W. RAMSAY, K.C.B. 8vo. 10s. net.

INTRODUCTION TO PHYSICAL CHEMISTRY. By Prof. JAMES WALKER, F.R.S. Sixth Edition. 8vo. 10s. net.

FRACTIONAL DISTILLATION. By Prof. SYDNEY YOUNG, D.Sc., F.R.S. Crown 8vo. 8s. 6d.

MACMILLAN AND CO., LTD., LONDON.

CPSIA information can be obtained
at www.ICGtesting.com
Printed in the USA
LVOW05s0040070817
544067LV00016B/748/P